Designing, engineering, and constructing with masonry products

Designing Engineering and Constructing with

Edited by
Dr. Franklin B. Johnson
Chairman
Architectural Engineering Department
The University of Texas at Austin
Austin, Texas

Masonry Products

Taken from the proceedings of
The International Conference on Masonry Structural Systems
College of Engineering
The University of Texas at Austin

Gulf Publishing Company
Houston, Texas

Library of Congress Catalog Card Number 72-86856

Acknowledgements

The International Conference on Masonry Structural Systems required the time, cooperation, and financial support of many indivduals and organizations. The College of Engineering at The University of Texas at Austin and the conference cochairmen gratefully acknowledge the enthusiasm, the time, the dedication, and the support of the many people and organizations contributing to the conference. Among those who deserve special consideration for their contribution is the National Science Foundation, which served as a sponsor and aided the conference financially. The Clay Products Association of the Southwest and The Structural Clay Products Institute also served as sponsors and contributed heavily to the financial support of the conference.

Gratitude is expressed for the cooperation of the following organizations: The American Institute of Architects, The American Society of Testing and Materials, The American Society of Civil Engineers, and The Building Research Advisory Board–The National Academy of Sciences.

Clayford T. Grimm, the Conference Secretary and Executive Director of the Clay Products Association of the Southwest, deserves special praise for the organizational talents and zeal that he gave to the conference. The devotion of his personal time and that of his staff were truly indispensable to the success of the conference.

Other individuals who contributed heavily of their time and were instrumental to the success of the conference were: Donald Foster of the Structural Clay Products Ltd., England; Jack Cutler, director of Canadian Structural Clay Assn., Canada; Jørgen Bryrup, Teglindustriens Tekniske Tjeneste, Denmark; and James G. Gross of Structural Clay Products Institute, U.S.

Appreciation is also expressed for the inspiration and humor of the conference keynote speaker, George Vernon Russell, F.A.I.A.

J. Neils Thompson
Franklin B. Johnson
Cochairmen

Foreword

For 7,000 years, masonry construction has been a system commonly used to house and serve man. Over this time a considerable amount of knowledge about this technology should have been recorded. Unfortunately, this was not done. For example brick has been used as a compression material, yet there is no internationally recognized column formula which adequately describes the buckling characteristics of a brick wall or column. The same is true for other masonry materials. The lack of a structural design consensus regarding masonry cannot be attributed to a dearth of research. On the contrary, there is a wealth of excellent research data in existence throughout the world.

Compression testing of masonry began in this country with the work done at Watertown Arsenal in 1882. But the fact remains that, although the world's literature is replete with individual research papers, there are only two books in English which describe the structural properties of masonry. Although much research and testing had been done on shear, flexure, compression and tension, there was no recognized worldwide engineering criteria for considering these phenomena at the time the International Conference on Masonry Structural Systems was held.

The lack of accepted universal design procedures in these areas can be explained by the nearly complete absence of communication among the world's engineers in this field. There is no periodical devoted to the exchange of scientific information relating to the structural technology of masonry such as is provided by the American Concrete Institute for Portland Cement products and the Forest Products Laboratory publications on wood technology. The scarcity of literature in English on masonry structural systems can be partly attributed to the fact that until only recently unit masonry was considered an architectural material rather than an engineering structural system. However, especially since World War II, a number of multi-story, load-bearing masonry buildings have been built in Europe and the U.S.

Another deterrent to the development of literature in this field has been the lack of opportunity to examine the technological interfaces which are the architect's and the engineer's concern as well as that of the manufacturer. Innovation has been stifled by the lack of communication between engineers, scientists, and architects in research, industry, and practice.

There are many benefits to be achieved through greater dissemination of existing information. The economy of masonry structural systems used in Switzerland, if understood in the U.S., could add significantly to U.S. building efficiency. The manufacturing know-how for the production of high strength masonry units which exists in the U.S. could affect the economy of construction in other areas of the world. The International Conference on Masonry Structural Systems was organized to fill the obvious need for an international exchange of information.

This collection of papers comprises the proceedings of the International Conference on Masonry Structural Systems, which was held at the University of Texas at Austin, November 30–December 2, 1967. It was a meeting of some of the world's most knowledgeable authorities on every aspect of masonry materials, design construction and function. Sixty-nine authors from 14 nations presented 58 significant papers in seven conference sessions.

The International Conference on Masonry Structural Systems was organized and conducted by the College of Engineering at The University of Texas at Austin. Dr. John J. McKetta, Dean of Engineering, appointed the conference cochairmen and the conference secretary. The cochairmen then appointed a committee whose members planned the conference and, for the most part, also acted as session chairmen.

The conference co-chairmen were: Professor J. Neils Thompson, P.E., Civil Engineering Department, and Director of the Balcones Research Center at The University of Texas at Austin; and Dr. Franklin B. Johnson, P.E., and Chairman of the Department of Architectural Engineering at The University of Texas at Austin.

The conference secretary was Clayford T. Grimm, P.E., Executive Director of Clay Products Association of the Southwest in Austin, Texas.

Papers were summarized by a panel member, and after comments by the panel members, the author answered questions from the floor.

The session chairmen and panelists for "The Creative Challenge Of Masonry," were: D. K. Sargent, F.A.I.A., U.S., Chairman; Alan Y. Taniguchi, A.I.A., U.S.; and Charles E. Croom, A.I.A., U.S.

The chairman of "Materials Science Relevant To Structure," was Albert G. H. Dietz of the U.S., and panelists were: R. E. Bradshaw, Scotland; Jørgen Bryrup, Denmark; and D. Lenczner, England.

The chairman and panelists for "Structural Performance," were: Clarence B. Monk, P.E., U.S., Chairman; W. S. Kinne, P.E., U.S.; Nat W. Krahl, P.E., U.S.; Edward O. Pfrang, P.E., U.S.; and Kenneth Thomas, England.

William J. Lemessurier, P.E., U.S., was Chairman of "Structural Interaction," and panelists were: Richard Gensert, P.E., U.S.; A. W. Hendry, Scotland; and David Watstein, P.E., U.S.

The chairman and panelists for "Design Methodology," were: P. E. Mikluchin, P.E., Canada, Chairman; Clark Craig, P.E., U.S.; Donald Foster, England; and Sven Sahlin, Sweden.

The Chairman of "Case Studies," was Harold Hauf, A.I.A., U.S., and panelists were: Walter Dickey, U.S.; George C. Hanson, U.S.; George Vernon Russell, F.A.I.A., U.S.; A. J. M. Soane, England; Barry A. Haseltine, England; and Thomas Woodward, A.I.A., U.S.

The Chairman and panelists for "Construction," were: Harry B. Zackrison, Sr., P.E., U.S., Chairman; George Miller, U.S.; James G. Gross, P.E., U.S.; and Robert Taylor, U.S.

Sponsors for the conference were The National Science Foundation, Clay Products Association of the Southwest, and The Structural Clay Products Institute. Cooperating organizations were the American Institute of Architects, The American Society of Testing and Materials, American Society of Civil Engineers, and the Building Research Advisory Board–The National Academy of Science.

Special conference advisory organizations were: Structural Clay Products Ltd., of Potters Bar, Herts, England; Canadian Structural Clay Assn., of Willowdale, Ontario, Canada; Portland Cement Association, of Chicago, Illinois U.S.; Teglindustriens Tekniske Tjeneste, of Kobenhavn, Denmark; Mason Contractors Association of America, of Chicago, Illinois, U.S.; and The Facing Tile Institute, of Chicago, Illinois, U.S.

Franklin B. Johnson

Austin, Texas
May, 1969

Contents

Part 4 : Structural interaction.

Part 5 : Design methodology.

Part 6 : Case studies.

Part 7 : Construction.

Contributors

Anderson, Donald E.
Chapter 14

Donald E. Anderson is a principal of the Engineers Collaborative, Chicago, Illinois, and is co-author of "Design of Brick Masonry Columns." He is a graduate of the University of Illinois and has been a practicing engineer for many years. He is Assistant Chief Engineer for Skidmore, Owings, and Merrill, and also works with an independent consultant organization.

Anderson, Orville G.
Chapter 45

The author of "Hemispheric Brick Planetarium," Orville G. Anderson, Jr., received both his bachelor's degree in Architectural Engineering and his graduate degree in Architecture from the University of Colorado. He is licensed to practice architecture in Colorado and has been with the firm of Wheeler and Lewis, Architects, Denver, Colorado, since 1961.

Angerer, E. W.
Chapter 1

Edward W. Angerer, author of "Appeal and Potential of the Polyfunctional Characteristics of Engineered Brickwork," was graduated from Iowa State University in 1952 and opened his own office in 1958 in Rock Island, Illinois. He is president of the Western Illinois Chapter of the American Institute of Architects, Chairman of the Judiciary Committee of the Illinois Council of the AIA, and past chairman of the Beautification Committee of Rock Island. He has designed varied projects, including an 11-story high-rise, load-bearing masonry apartment building for the elderly in Rock Island.

Astbury, Dr. N. F.
Chapter 26

The co-author of "Tests on Storey-Height Brickwork Panels and Development of Site Control Test for Brickwork," Dr. N. F. Astbury, was graduated from St. John's College, Cambridge, where he was a Scholar and Prizeman. He was Professor of Applied Physics at the N.S.W. University of Technology until 1951, when he became Professor of Physics at the University of Khartoum until 1956. Dr. Astbury has been the Director of the British Ceramic Research Association since 1960. He is Honorary General Secretary of the British Ceramic Society and Deputy Chairman (formerly Chairman) of the Committee of Director of Research Associations. Dr. Astbury is a member of the Governing Body of the North Staffordshire College of Technology, is a Vice-President of the Parliamentary and Scientific Committee, belongs to the newly-formed Construction Research Advisory Council of the Ministry of Public Building and Works, and is Vice-Chairman of the Harwell Ceramics Centre Advisory Committee.

Bradshaw, R. E.
Chapters 15 and 37

R. E. Bradshaw is co-author of "Preliminary Crushing Tests on Storey Height Cavity Walls," Chapter 15, and "Assessment of British Design Methods of Calculated Brickwork," Chapter 37. He was graduated from Westminister Technical College and received a Master of Science degree of Edinburgh University in 1966. Bradshaw is a senior lecturer in Structures at Leeds School of Architecture in Leeds, England. He is an Associate Member of the Institution of Civil Engineers, and an Associate Member of the Institution of Structural Engineering. Bradshaw has been in private practice for the last five years as a Structural Consultant specializing in loadbearing brickwork.

Bryrup, Jørgen
Chapter 53

Jørgen Bryrup, author of Chapter 53, "Development of Structural Clay Facing Wall Panels in Denmark," was graduated from the Danish Technical University in 1951. He has been the Head of the Technical Information Service of the Danish Brick and Tile Industry (Teglindustriens Tekniske Tjeneste) since June, 1960.

C. Carter
Chapter 27

C. Carter, Co-author of "Structural Behavior of Masonry Infilled Frames Subjected to Racking Loads," is a teacher at the College of Technology in Southhampton, England. He has been collaborating with Dr. B. Stafford Smith for three years on a research project concerning the behavior of infilled frames as part of a wider investigation into shear-wall structures conducted at Southampton University. The investigation is sponsored by the British Science Research Council.

Cattaneo, Louis E.
Chapter 17

Louis E. Cattaneo, Structural Research Engineer, National Bureau of Standards, Washington, D.C., is a co-author of "Effect of Edge Load on Flexural Strength of Clay Masonry Systems Utilizing Improved Mortars." His research has been in the areas of flexure and racking of masonry, and dimensional stability of reinforced concrete. Recently, he has worked to develop test methods and acquire data for establishing better design criteria. Cattaneo is a graduate of the Catholic University of America where he became Assistant Professor of Civil Engineering before joining NBS.

Cochran, M. R.
Chapter 46

M. R. Cochran, author of "Retaining Wall for North Carolina's Death Valley," was graduated from North Carolina State University with a Bachelor of Civil Engineering degree. Cochran worked with the North Carolina State Highway Commission, High Point, N.C., as City Engineer and currently is an Engineering Consultant for Brick and Tile Service, Inc.

Curtin, W. G.
Chapter 38

W. G. Curtin, co-author of "Design and Construction of Slender Wall Brickwork Buildings," has worked with numerous contractors as structural detailer and designer, and as Site Engineer. He was Assistant Engineer to Sir Frederick Snow and Partners, Consulting Engineers, and later worked as assistant in the building research section of the London County Council. Curtin began lecturing in Structural Engineering at the Brixton School of Building and was later appointed senior lecturer in structural engineering at the Liverpool College of Building. He established private practice as a consulting engineer in 1960 and is a member of the Structural Ceramics Advisory Group and the Building Science Committee of the British Ceramic Research Association.

Dickey, Walter L.
Chapters 16 and 47

Walter L. Dickey, author of Chapter 16, "Reinforced Masonry Revisited, Ten Years Later," and Chapter 47, "Seismic Resistant Reinforced Masonry Naval Barracks," is a consulting structural engineer in Los Angeles, California. Dickey, a registered professional engineer, received his undergraduate and graduate degrees from the University of Southern California and the California Institute of Technology. He belongs to numerous engineering and concrete groups including the Consulting Engineers Association of California (Consulting Engineers Council) and is past President of the Northern California Structural Engineers Association.

Dikkers, Robert D.
Chapter 41

Robert D. Dikkers, a co-author of "Building Code Requirements Relating to Loadbearing Brick Masonry," is Chief Engineer of the Structural Clay Products Institute and has been with the SCPI Department of Engineering and Technology since January, 1964. Dikkers received his B.S. degree in Civil Engineering from Northwestern University and a M.S. degree from the California Institute of Technology. He is a member of the American Society of Civil Engineers, American Concrete Institute, and the National Society of Professional Engineers.

Firestone, Charles E.
Chapter 2

Charles Essig Firestone, a practicing architect for the last 56 years and author "Structural Glazed Masonry Units," received a Bachelor of Architecture degree from Middlebranch, Ohio, and then a Bachelor of Architectural Engineering degree from the University of Michigan in 1914. He is a partner in the firm, Firestone and Motter, Architects, in Canton, Ohio, and has been a member of the American Institute of Architects since 1921. He advanced to Fellowship in the Institute in 1947. He is also a charter member and past president of the Eastern Ohio Chapter of the A.I.A.; past president of both The Architects Society of Ohio, 1935-1938, and the National Council of Architectural Registration Boards, 1953-1954; and for 20 years, a member of the Ohio State Board of Examiners of Architects, until 1962.

Foster, D.
Chapter 37

D. Foster, lecturer and member of British Standard Committees dealing with ceramic products and their use and, now, in private practice, is the co-author of "Assignment of British Design Methods of Calculated Brickwork." Foster was graduated from the University of Durham School of Architecture in 1941. In 1964, he became a consultant architect with Structural Clay Products Ltd., Potters Bar, Herts.

Foster, P. K.
Chapter 13

P. K. Foster, Director of the New Zealand Pottery and Ceramics Research Association, Inc., is co-author of "Miniature Tensile and Panel Flexure Properties of Brickwork." Foster received his Master of Science degree in Physical Chemistry from the University of Canterbury, New Zealand, in 1949. He received his Ph.D. and D.I.C. degrees from the

Imperial College of Science and Technology, London, where he studied high temperature equilibria. After three years in the welding industry in England and New Zealand, he was appointed to the Chemistry Division of the New Zealand Department of Scientific and Industrial Research where his research concerned corrosion.

Gensert, R. M.
Chapter 39

R. M. Gensert, co-author of "Engineering Evaluation for East Liberty Plaza," received his Bachelor of Science degree in Civil Engineering from Case Institute of Technology. He received his Master of Science in Civil Engineering from Ohio State University and is a principal in the R. M. Gensert Associates firm with offices in Cleveland, Ohio, and Pittsburgh, Pennsylvania. He also lectures at Western Reserve University, Department of Architecture in Cleveland.

Gero, John S.
Chapter 25

John S. Gero, author of "Prestressed Masonry Reinforced Concrete Space Structure," is lecturer in Architectural Science at the University of Sydney, Australia. He received a Bachelor of Science degree with honors from the University of New South Wales, and a Master of Building Science degree from the University of Sydney. Gero has written a number of research publications and co-authored the book, *Models in Architecture.* He is an Associate Member of the American Society of Civil Engineers and belongs to the Institution of Engineers, Australia. He has acted as consultant for a number of building projects in both Sydney and Melbourne.

Grenley, Dallas G.
Chapters 5 and 17

Dallas G. Grenley, University of Michigan graduate, is the author of "Study of the Effect of Certain Modified Mortars on Compressive and Flexural Strength of Masonry," and co-author of Chapter 17, "Effect of Edge Load on Flexural Strength of Clay Masonry Systems Utilizing Improved Mortars." Grenley was a research chemist with Dow Chemical Company for a number of years where his work centered on developing thermoplastic polymers and processes for a variety of coating and extrusion applications. As a result he holds several patents in these areas. He has just completed a year as a Research Associate at the National Bureau of Standards.

Gross, James G.
Chapter 41

James G. Gross, Director of Engineering and Technology for the Structural Clay Products Institute and co-author of "Building Code Requirements Relating to Loadbearing Brick Masonry," has been in the Washington SCIP headquarters since October 1957. As a graduate of North Dakota State University with an Architectural Engineering degree, Gross worked for three years as a field and staff engineer for The Clay Products Association of the Southwest before joining the national office as a staff engineer. In 1960, he was named Assistant Director of Engineering and Technology, in 1961, Association Director, and in 1963, he became Director. Gross is a member of the American Society for Testing and Materials, the American Society of Engineering and Education, the Association of Collegiate Schools of Architecture, the Construction's Specifications Institute and is an Associate of the Building Research Advisory Board.

Haller, P.
Chapter 18

Professor P. Haller, the author "Load Capacity of Brick Masonry," received a diploma as Technician in Structural Engineering from Technikum Winterthur and a diploma in Civil Engineering from the Swiss Federal Institute of Technology, Bern, where he is now a professor. He is also section head for the building materials section of the Swiss Federal Institute for Testing Materials and Research. Haller has published articles concerning mortars, concrete, masonry, roof tiles, floor covering, road gravel, buckling problems in masonry, influence of frost on masonry, drying of building materials, and building acoustics.

Halsell, Don
Chapter 54

Don Halsell, Director of Training, Clay Products Association of the Southwest, Austin, Texas, is a co-author of "Bricklayer Training in the U.S." He was graduated from Central State College of Edmond, Oklahoma, in 1963 with a Bachelor of Science degree and received his Master of Education degree in Trade and Industrial Education from Colorado State University in Fort Collins, Colorado, in 1965. Halsell formerly served as Vocational Training Field Representative for Structural Clay Products Institute in Washington, D.C.

Hanson, George C.
Chapter 48

George C. Hanson, author of "Park Mayfair East," is a graduate of South Dakota School of Mines and Technology with a Bachelor of Science in Civil Engineering and a professional Civil Engineering degree. He is a member of the National Society of Professional Engineers, the Colorado Society of Engineers, the American Concrete Institute, and the Prestressed Concrete Institute. Hanson is a Fellow of the American Society of Civil Engineers and is a registered Professional Engineer in nine states.

Haseltine, Barry
Chapter 49

Barry Haseltine, author of "Some Loadbearing Brick Buildings in England," was educated at Collyer's School in Horsham, Sussex, England, and received a Civil Engineering degree with honors at the City and Guilds College, Imperial College of Science and Technology, London, where he won the Unwin Medal in 1954. He is a partner in the firm of Jenkins and Potter, Consulting Engineers of London, England.

Hendry, A. W.
Chapters 15, 23, 38, and 51

Prof. A. W. Hendry, a graduate in Civil Engineering from the University of Aberdeen, is the co-author of Chapter 15, "Preliminary Crushing Tests on Storey Height Cavity Walls," Chapter 23, "Racking Tests on Storey Height Shear-Wall Structures with Openings Subjected to Precompression," Chapter 38, "Design and Construction of Slender Wall Brickwork Buildings," and Chapter 51, "Case Studies and Critical Evaluation of High-Rise Load-Bearing Brickwork in Britain." He worked for Sir William Arrol and Company Ltd., Bridge Builders and Engineers, Glasgow, before he took appointments in the Universities of Aberdeen, London, Khartoum, and Liverpool. He is presently Professor of Civil Engineering at the University of Edinburgh and an associate of W. G. Curtin and Partners, Consulting Engineers, Liverpool.

Hilsdorf, Hubert
Chapter 6

Hubert Hilsdorf, Associate Professor of Civil Engineering at The University of Illinois, wrote "Investigation into the Failure Mechanism of Brick Masonry Loaded in Axial Compression." A native of Munich, Germany, he received a Civil Engineering degree in 1953 and a Doctor of Engineering degree in 1964 from the Technical University of Munich. He was a Research Engineer at the Laboratory for Building Materials of the Technical University of Munich under Hubert Rusch's direction and has authored numerous papers on behavior of plain concrete and reinforced and plain masonry units.

Hockaday, R. B.
Chapter 36

R. B. Hockaday received a Bachelor of Science degree in Ceramic Engineering from North Carolina State University. Hockaday is co-author of "Effect of Manufacturing and Construction Variables on Durability and Compressive Strength of Brick Masonry." He is Manager of Clay Exploration and Research, Acme Brick Company, Denton, Texas, and is a member of the American Ceramic Society and The National Institute of Ceramic Engineers.

Hoffman, Edward S.
Chapter 14

Edward S. Hoffman, co-author of "Design of Brick Masonry Columns," is a partner of The Engineers Collaborative, Chicago, Illinois. He was graduated from Iowa State University and, prior to his present position, Hoffman was Chief Structural Engineer for Childs and Smith, Chicago.

Holmes, I. L.
Chapter 40

I. L. Holmes, author of "Masonry Building in High Intensity Seismic Zones," is a consulting engineer and partner in the firm, Holmes and Wood, Christchurch, New Zealand. This firm has recently concentrated on masonry structural systems, particularly those using concrete block, and has designed masonry buildings for seismic conditions in New Zealand, and in the New Hebrides and British Solomon Islands. Holmes is a member of the New Zealand Standards Association Committees for Masonry and for Loadings, the New Zealand National Committee on Earthquake Engineering, and the Council of the New Zealand Prestressed Concrete Institute.

Howard, James W.
Chapter 36

James W. Howard, co-author of "Effect of Manufacturing and Construction Variables on Durability and Compressive Strength of Brick Masonry," received his Bachelor of Science degree in Architectural Engineering from The University of Texas at Austin in 1958. He is Staff Engineer with Clay Products Association of the Southwest in Amarillo, Texas, and is a member of the Texas Society of Professional Engineers.

Isberner, Albert W.
Chapter 7

"Properties of Masonry Cement Mortars" was written by Albert W. Isberner, Research Engineer, Applied Research Section, Portland Cement Association, Skokie, Illinois. He received a Bachelor of Science degree in Civil Engineering from the University of Wisconsin in 1953. Isberner is a member of the ASTM and is Chairman of ASTM C 12.2–Mortars for Unit Masonry–Research and Methods of Test. He is also Chairman of American Concrete Institute, ACI 524–Portland Cement Plastering.

Johnson, Dr. Franklin B.
Chapters 8 and 19

Dr. Frank B. Johnson is co-author of both Chapter 8, "Development of Diametral Testing Procedures to Provide a Measure of Strength Characteristics of Masonry Assemblages," and Chapter 19, "Correlation of Tests of Masonry Assemblages with Strength Characteristics of Reinforced Masonry Beams." He is Chairman and Graduate Advisor of the Architectural Engineering Department at The University of Texas at Austin, where he received his B.S. and M.S. degrees in Architectural Engineering, and His Ph.D. in Civil Engineering. Dr. Johnson is a registered professional engineer, and is a member of the American Society of Civil Engineers, American Society of Testing Materials, American Concrete Institute, National Society of Professional Engineers, and the Texas Society of Professional Engineers.

Johnson, Paul V.
Chapter 35

Paul V. Johnson received a B.S. degree in 1924 from the State University of New York, and the professional degree of Ceramic Engineer in 1950 from the College of Ceramics at Alfred University. He has worked for the Structural Clay Products Institute since 1946. Johnson is a member of numerous technical societies and past president of the American Ceramic Society.

Kirsis, Uldis
Chapter 39

Uldis Kirsis, co-author of "Engineering Evaluation for East Liberty Plazà," received his Bachelor of Science degree in Civil Engineering at Northeastern University and a Master of Science in Civil Engineering from Case Institute of Technology. Kirsis is a principal in the R. M. Gensert Associates firm and is a lecturer at Western Reserve University, Department of Architecture, Cleveland, Ohio.

Krahl, Nat W.
Chapter 28

Nat Wetzel Krahl is Associate Professor of Structural Engineering at Rice University in Houston, Texas, with a joint appointment in the School of Architecture and the Department of Civil Engineering. He is co-author of "Case Study of Brick Used as Floor and Roof Structure." A registered professional engineer, he received his B.A. and B.S. degrees at Rice University and his M.S. and Ph.D. at the University of Illinois.

Lechner, H.
Chapter 50

H. Lechner, author of "Special Quality Brick Masonry Multistory Apartment Houses Built in Switzerland," was graduated from Charlottenburg Institute of Technology in Structural Engineering in 1937. Since 1939, Lechner has had his own structural engineering practice in Zurich, and has specialized in multistory building of brick masonry since 1955.

Lenczner, Dr. D.
Chapter 9

Dr. D. Lenczner, author of "Creep in Model Brickwork," was born in Czestochowa, Poland, but moved to Britain in 1945. A 1954 honor graduate in Civil Engineering at Glasgow University, Lenczner lectured at the University of Strathclyde, Glasgow, then at Nottingham University. He became a corporate member of the Institution of Civil Engineers in 1957 and obtained his Doctorate in 1962 for his research on the interactions of footings and soil. Dr. Lenczner is a senior lecturer in Building Technology at the University of Wales, Institute of Science and Technology, Cathays Park, Cardiff, Wales.

Malchev, Rocen
Chapter 55

Rocen Malchev, co-author of "Some Investigations Concerning Design, Technology, and Test of Cored Brick Panels," was graduated from the Higher Building Institute in Sofia, Bulgaria, in 1959. He is with the Building Research Institute in Sofia, where he is studying the use of ceramic products as structural elements in floor and roof construction.

McDonald, Alex
Chapter 12

Alex McDonald, co-author of "High Strength Adhesive Mortar in Concrete Masonry Structural Systems," is a partner in the firm of Schupack and Associates of Stamford, Connecticut. He has been associated with Mr. Schupack since 1955. After graduation from Cornell University in 1950, he joined the firm of E. Lionel Pavlo and later, the firm of Severud-Elstad and Krueger. McDonald is a member of the American Concrete Institute and the American Society of Civil Engineers.

Mikluchin, Plato Theodore
Chapters 3, 10, and 42

Plato Theodore Mikluchin, who has written several books in the structural engineering field, is the author of Chapter 3, "Morphotectonics of Masonry Structures," Chapter 10, "Rheological Behavior of Masonry Structures," and Chapter 42, "Design of Tall Masonry Buildings with Complex Layout." He received his Civil Engineering and Doctor of Engineering degrees from the University of St. Petersburg where he became Professor of Structural Engineering and Director of the Laboratory for Testing Materials. In 1956 he established P. T. Mikluchin and Associates Ltd., Consulting Engineers, Toronto, Ontario, Canada. He is also a member of the Structural Advisory Committee, NBC/National Research Council, Ottawa, Ontario, and the Engineering Advisory Committee, SCPI, in Washington, D.C.

Mitev, Ilia
Chapter 55

Ilia Mitev was graduated from the Higher Building Institute in Sofia, Bulgaria, in 1957. He co-authored "Some Investigations Concerning Design, Technology, and Test of Cored Brick Panels." He is associated with the Building Research Institute in Sofia. Mitev is mainly concerned with the application of ceramic products as structural elements of precast construction.

Monk, Clarence B., Jr.
Chapter 20

Clarence B. Monk, Jr., author of "Column Action of Clay Masonry Walls," received his Bachelor of Science degree in Architectural Engineering from Pennsylvania State University in 1942 and his Master of Science degree in Civil Engineering from the University of Illinois in 1948. He is an Associate Professor of Construction Engineering at the School of Civil Engineering, Purdue University, Lafayette, Indiana. Monk was Manager of Engineering Research, Structural Clay Products Research Foundation, Geneva, Illinois, for 12 years. He is a member of the American Society of Civil Engineers, the American Society for Testing and Materials, Building Research Institute, and the National Society of Professional Engineers.

Motteu, Henri
Chapter 21

"Research on Load Bearing Masonry in Belgium Since 1963" was written by Henri Motteu. Motteu received the Association of Engineers degree from the University of Brussels. Since 1960, he has been Chief Engineer with the Division "Main Structures" at the Scientific and Technical Center of Construction in Brussels, Belgium.

Pfrang, Edward O.
Chapter 17

Edward O. Pfrang, co-author of "Effect of Edge Load on Flexural Strength of Clay Masonry Systems Utilizing Improved Mortars," is Chief of the Structures Section, Building Research Division, National Bureau of Standards, Washington, D.C. Prior to joining NBS, Dr. Pfrang was a member of the Civil Engineering staff of the University of Nevada and the University of Delaware. He has also authored numerous papers on the behavior of reinforced concrete and steel structures. Dr. Pfrang is a member of fifteen technical committees, and was recently appointed Chairman of a U.S.-Japan Panel on Cooperation in the Design of Structural Systems to Resist Wind and Seismic Loads. He received his undergraduate degree from the University of Connecticut and degrees from Yale University and the University of Illinois.

Plummer, Harry Custer
Chapter 43

Harry Custer Plummer, author of "Modular Coordination in the U.S.," is Dean of Engineering at the Structural Clay Products Institute. He was graduated from Ohio University in 1918 with a Bachelor of Arts degree, and received a Bachelor of Science degree in 1923, and a Civil Engineering degree in 1940 from the Case Institute of Technology. Plummer was formerly Director of Engineering and Technology at SCPI, Chief Engineer at the Brick Manufacturers Association, and President and General Manager of Sterling Engineering Company, Cleveland, Ohio. He is a member of the American Society for Testing Materials, American Society of Civil Engineers, American Ceramic Society, Building Research Advisory Board, Building Research Institute, Construction Specifications Institute, and the U.S. Standards Institute.

Pume, Dr. Dimitrij
Chapter 29

Dr. Dimitrij Pume, author of "Structural Performance of Clay Tile Wall Panels," was graduated from the Civil Engineering Faculty of the Technical University, Prague, in 1953. In 1958, he received a C.Sc. degree. For the last 12 years, he has been employed by the State Building Research Institute in Prague, Czechoslovakia. He is one of the two authors of *State Recommendations for Design of Multistory Buildings.*

Ramaswamy, G. S.
Chapter 30

Professor G. S. Ramaswamy is the author of "Funicular Brick Shell Roofs for Industrial Buildings." He received his Bachelor of Engineering in Civil Engineering with honors from Madras University and his M.S. and C.E. degrees from the California Institute of Technology. Professor Ramaswamy is the Chairman of Shell Structures Group of the Institution of Engineers in Roorkee, India. He is a member of the American Concrete Institute, Committee 115 on Concrete Research, and is Chairman of the Committee set up by the Indian Standards Institution which drafted its "Criteria for the Design of Reinforced Concrete Shell Structures and Folded Plates." Ramaswamy is Director of the National Building Construction Corporation in New Delhi, India.

Ransom, Harry S.
Chapter 28

Harry S. Ransom is co-author of "Case Study of Brick Used as Floor and Roof Structure." An architect and educator, he is Professor in charge of Architectural Design, senior level, and Architectural Management, graduate class, at Rice University. Currently, he is a consultant in the fields of campus and regional planning in Mexico, the Dominican Republic, and Brazil.

Rao, Dr. R. N. S.
Chapter 11

Dr. R. N. S. Rao, the Head of the Civil Engineering Department of Prairie View Agriculture and Mechanical College in Prairie View, Texas, wrote "Experimental Investigation on Structural Performance of Brick Masonry Prisms." A native of India, Rao received his Bachelor of Civil Engineering from the University of Mysore in India, his M.S. degree in Soil Mechanics and Hydraulics from the University of Connecticut, and his Ph.D. from Rutgers. He is a member of the American Society of Civil Engineers, American Society of Engineering Education, American Association of University Professors, American Society for Testing Material and Highway Research Board, American Concrete Institute, Texas Society of Professional Engineers, and the National Society of Professional Engineers. A registered professional engineer, his honors include Chi Epsilon, Phi Kappa Phi, and Sigma Xi.

Risager, Svenn
Chapter 31

The author of "Structural Behavior of Linear Elastic Walls Having No Tensile Strength," is Svenn Risager. He received a M.S. in Civil Engineering and is an Assistant Professor of Theoretical and Applied Mechanics, Civil Engineering Department, Technical University of Denmark. Risager worked for Christiani and Nielsen from 1957-62.

Sahlin, Sven
Chapter 32

Sven Sahlin, author of "Interaction of Brick Masonry Walls and Concrete Slabs," was graduated from the Royal Institute of Technology in Stockholm in Civil Engineering in 1953, received his Doctor of Technology degree in 1959, and became Docent in 1960. He has held a position of Laborator at the Royal Institute of Technology since 1960 and is a visiting Professor of Civil Engineering at the University of Illinois.

Schupack, M.
Chapter 12

M. Schupack, co-author of "High Strength Adhesive Mortar in Concrete Masonry Structural Systems," graduated from Ohio

State University in 1947. From 1957-66 he was partner in the firm of Schupack and Zollman and is now senior partner of Schupack and Associates, Stamford, Connecticut. Schupack is a member of the American Concrete Institute and Chairman of the subcommittee on Precast Concrete. He is also a member of the Reinforced Concrete Research Council, The Prestressed Concrete Institute, and the American Society of Civil Engineers.

Scrivener, Dr. J. C.
Chapter 22

"Static Racking Tests on Concrete Masonry Walls" was written by Dr. J. C. Scrivener, senior lecturer at The University of Canterbury and a visiting Associate Professor at Massachusetts Institute of Technology, Cambridge. Scrivener received his Bachelor of Science in Physics and Mathematics from Otago University, New Zealand, in 1954; his Master of Science degree from the University of Canterbury in 1958; and his Ph.D., D.I.C. from Imperial College, University of London, England, in 1962. He is a member of the New Zealand Institution of Engineers, Christchurch Test Walls Committee.

Sinha, B. P.
Chapter 23

B. P. Sinha, author of "Racking Tests on Storey Height Shear-Wall Structures With Openings, Subjected to Precompression," is a graduate of Bihar College of Engineering, Patna University, India. He received his advanced degrees at the Universities of Liverpool and Edinburgh. Presently, he is working as a Research Assistant to Professor A. W. Hendry in the Department of Civil Engineering and Building Science, Edinburgh University, Scotland, and is conducting research on the strength and rigidity of ceramic and concrete panel structures.

Smith, Dr. B. Stafford
Chapter 27

Dr. B. Stafford Smith, co-author of "Structural Behavior of Masonry Infilled Frames Subjected to Racking Loads," is a member of the teaching staff of Southampton University, England. For the past three years, he has collaborated with C. Carter on a research project concerning the behavior of infilled frames as part of a wider investigation into shear-wall structures conducted at Southampton University. The investigation is sponsored by the British Science Research Council.

Soane, Alastair, J. M.
Chapter 33

Alastair J. M. Soane, author of "Interaction of Brickwork Walls and Concrete Floors Under Lateral Load," received a Civil Engineering degree and a Ph.D. from the University of Edinburgh. He is an associate partner of Bingham Blades and Partners, Consulting Structural Engineers, Liverpool, England. Soane developed a technique for the solution of interconnected shear wall problems and won an Institution of Civil Engineers medal for portions of this work.

Soderstrum, William K.
Chapter 36

William K. Soderstrum, co-author of "Effect of Manufacturing and Construction Variables on Durability and Compressive Strength of Brick Masonry," received a Ceramic Engineering degree from the University of Illinois in 1952. He was Ceramic Engineer with Structural Clay Products Research Foundation in Geneva, Illinois until his death in 1967. He was a member of the American Ceramic Society and the National Institute of Ceramic Engineers. Soderstrum's work with the Foundation earned him recognition as an authority on the properties of structural clay materials and their use.

Stockbridge, Jerry G.
Chapter 51

Jerry G. Stockbridge, Project Engineer with Skidmore, Owings, and Merrill, Architects and Engineers, Chicago, wrote "Case Studies and Critical Evaluation of High-Rise Load-bearing Brickwork in Britain." He was graduated from the University of Edinburgh, Scotland, in 1967 with his Master of Architecture degree.

Sutherland, R. J. M.
Chapter 44

R. J. M. Sutherland, author of "Design Engineer's Approach to Masonry Construction," is a partner in Harris and Sutherland, Consulting Engineers, London, England. He is a member of the Code of Practice Committee for Load-bearing Walls and of the Structural Ceramics Advisory Group to the British Ceramic Research Association. Before joining Harris and Sutherland, he spent 10 years on heavy civil engineering (hydro-electricity and steam power plants) both in the field and in the design office.

Szerdahelyi, Dénes
Chapter 56

Dénes Szerdahelyi, co-author of "14-Storey Buildings in Switzerland with Brick Wall Elements Prefabricated by Preton Process," is a Civil Engineering graduate of the Swiss Federal Institute of Technology. Szerdahelyi worked as Senior Designer with a consulting engineer in Geneva, Switzerland, on the design and construction of industrial and housing projects. Since 1962, he has worked with Emch & Berger, Consulting Engineers, Berne Switzerland, where he is now Head of the Department for Building Research.

Thomas, Kenneth
Chapter 34

Kenneth Thomas, Author of "Current Post-Tensioned and Prestressed Brickwork in Britain," studied Structural Engineering at the Royal Technical College (now the University of Salford), Salford, England. In 1959, Thomas lectured in Civil and Structural Engineering at Belfast College of Technology. For the last three years, Thomas has been Principal of the Clay Products Technical Bureau of Great Britain. He represents the brick industry on numerous B.S.I. committees and offers a consultant service to members of the construction industry.

Thompson, J. Neils
Chapters 8 and 19

Professor J. Neils Thompson is co-author of both Chapter 8, "Development of Diametral Testing Procedures to Provide a Measure of Strength Characteristics of Masonry Assemblages," and Chapter 19, "Correlation of Tests of Masonry Assemblages with Strength Characteristics of Reinforced Masonry Beams." He received his B.S. and M.S. degrees in Civil Engineering at The University of Texas at Austin where he is now a Professor of Civil Engineering and Director of the Balcones Research Center. Professor Thompson is a registered professional engineer, past President of the Texas Society of Professional Engineers and has been Director, President, and Vice President of the National Society of Professional Engineers. He is also a member of other state and national engineering societies and has received the American Concrete Institute's Wason Medal for Noteworthy Research.

Turner, D. J.
Chapter 24

D. J. Turner, co-author of "A Prestressed Clay Masonry Floor," was graduated from the University of Canterbury, New Zealand, with a Bachelor of Engineering degree in 1962. He was employed for three years by a firm of consulting engineers before taking his present position as Design and Development Engineer, Amalgamated Brick and Pipe Company Limited, Auckland, New Zealand.

Wakefield, Donald A.
Chapter 57

Donald A. Wakefield, author of "Prefabricated Brick Panels in Colorado," has been Regional Director of Structural Clay Products Institute, servicing Colorado, Wyoming, and New Mexico for the past 10 years, and has been involved in the innovative use of brick and tile. He was Regional Engineer in St. Louis, Missouri, for SCPI and worked in an architectural-engineering office following graduation from Washington University in St. Louis in 1950 with a Bachelor's degree in Architectural Engineering.

Wass, R. J.
Chapter 24

R. J. Wass, co-author of "A Prestressed Clay Masonry Floor," is a Design and Development Engineer with the Amalgamated Brick and Pipe Company, Limited in Auckland, New Zealand. He received his Bachelor of Engineering degree in 1957 from Auckland University, New Zealand. Wass worked for 3 years with a firm of Consulting Engineers before moving to England where he spent 2 years with the Research and Development Division of Costain Concrete Company Limited, developing design methods for Stahlton Flooring and lightweight concrete. He returned to New Zealand four years ago as Manager of a new branch of Amalgamated Brick and Pipe Co. Limited manufacturing Stahlton Flooring.

Watstein, David
Chapter 35

David Watstein, co-author of "Experimental Determination of Eccentricity of Floor Loads Applied to a Bearing Wall," received his B.S. in Civil Engineering from the University of California in 1930, and his M.A. degree in physics from George Washington University in 1940. From 1956 to 1966, he was Chief of the Structural Engineering section, Building Research Division, National Bureau of Standards Institute, McLean, Virginia.

West, H. W. H.
Chapter 26

H. W. H. West, co-author of "Tests on Storey-Height Brickwork Panels and Development of Site Control Test for Brickwork," received his degree in Geology with honors from the University of Southampton. He is Head and Officer in Charge of Mellor-Green Laboratories, Heavy Clay Division, British Ceramic Research Association, Penkhull, Stone-on-Trent, England. Since 1961, he has been a member of the General Ceramic Society and Honorary Secretary of the Building Materials Section.

Woodward, Thomas E.
Chapters 4 and 52

Thomas E. Woodward is the author of Chapter 4, "Design Potential of Masonry Bearing Walls," and Chapter 52, "Jayhawker Apartment Towers." He received a Civil Engineering degree with honors from Yale University in 1954 and in 1959, was graduated from Yale University Graduate School of Design, in architecture. Before establishing Woodward, Cape and Associates of Dallas, Texas, in 1962, he worked with Gamble and Partners and then with Broad and Nelson. He is a registered professional engineer and a registered architect and has received the National Council of Architectural Registration Boards Certificate.

Youl, V. A.
Chapter 13

V. A. Youl, co-author of "Miniature Tensile and Panel Flexure Properties of Brickwork," was graduated from the School of Architecture, Auckland University, New Zealand, in 1949. He was elected Associate of the New Zealand Institute of Architects in 1953 and Fellow in 1967. Youl joined the staff of the New Zealand Pottery and Ceramics Research Association in 1953 and, until 1959, carried out research in brickwork and brick structures. He returned to practicing architecture in Wellington in 1959. Youl established a practice in Auckland in 1961 and accepted an appointment as Technical Consultant to Amalgamated Brick and Pipe Company Limited. He is also post graduate lecturer at the School of Architecture at Auckland University.

Zenobi, George V.

Chapter 56

George V. Zenobi, co-author of "14-Storey Buildings in Switzerland with Brick Wall Elements Prefabricated by Preton Process," is a Civil Engineering graduate of the Swiss Federal Institute of Technology. He is Assistant General Manager of the Bureau BBR for prefabrication in Zurich, Switzerland. Zenobi has been a Professor's Assistant at the Swiss Federal Institute of Technology, Senior Designer with a consulting engineer in Montreal, Canada, Field Engineer for a cableway in Venezuela, and has worked in the Department of Planning and Development of Stahlton Ltd.

Designing, engineering, and constructing with masonry products

Part 1: The creative challenge of masonry

1. Appeal and potential of the poly-functional characteristics of engineered brickwork.

Edward W. Angerer, AIA, Rock Island, Illinois

When operating under the relatively esoteric title "Masonry Structural Systems" we must maintain perspective lest we become enthralled by what happens in the joints to the neglect of the most vital consideration: What relevance does structural masonry have to the process of building man's environment? Not only must these systems follow sound engineering principles, but their application must result in architecturally usable spaces.

A few comments from Dr. Arthur Clarke's speech at the recent AIA convention may be helpful in broadening our view of structural masonry's applicability to man's environmental needs. Predicting that improved communications will enable man to work at home, Dr. Clarke concludes that "vast uninhabited areas of the earth could be opened up because people will have far greater freedom to choose where they will live. These trends will inevitably accelerate the disintegration of cities, whose historical function is now passing . . . . . ." He then describes a mobile town. "When you take one of Bucky's famous geodesic domes and make it very large—a mile or so in diameter—the air inside weighs so much more than the dome and its contents that a rise in temperature of a few degrees could make the whole thing take off like a hot air balloon. So why not go south in the winter and north in the summer—without leaving home."[1]

If, in addition, one meanders vertically there would be the "elevator to the stars". Last year Professor John Isaacs at La Jolla pointed out that if one starts from the synchronous orbit 22,000 miles up, one could lower cables all the way to the earth's surface and use them to send payloads into space. Now where do you stack your bricks in a world like that?

Although Dr. Clarke speculates about an increment of the future not contiguous with ours, it would be risky to take his predictions lightly, since we have all witnessed how Utopian aspirations have a way of becoming reality—and with a steadily diminishing time gap between the two.

Furthermore, Mies Van Der Rohe feels that architecture is not bound to the day nor to eternity, but to the epoch. "It is absurd," he states, "to invent arbitrary forms, historical and modernistic forms, which are not determined by construction, the true guardian of the spirit of our times."[2] Although Mies is identified with another structural technique, his words are still applicable to our subject.

Potential of Structural Brickwork

How then to assess the potential of structural brickwork in our epoch? The very word *potential* is loaded with suggestions. As defined by Random House potential is a "latent excellence which may or may not be developed." In the context of our subject this means that structural brickwork must not only possess this excellence, but that this excellence depends on outside forces. The degree to which this potential is realized depends on the balance between those conditions which make structural brickwork usable and those forces which render it obsolete.

Passing the test for "latent excellence" should not be difficult. A simple semantic reexamination of structural brickwork reveals much. For example, if we refer to the basic unit in the system as a handsize, prefabricated building component which is fireproof, insoluble in most liquids, highly resistant to abrasion and compressive forces, universally available, finished or unfinished, in a variety of colors, textures, and shapes, many more circuits are triggered in our brain than if we simply refer to the thing as a brick. This brick has a number of qualities, any one of which makes it a highly desirable building material. And, indeed, while often used for only one or a few of these properties, the optimum utilization of brick occurs when all these qualities are exploited.

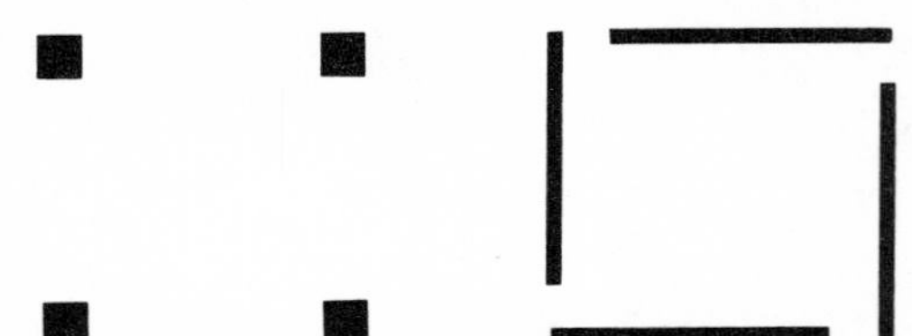

Figure 1-1.

As Mies Van Der Rohe points out, "Architecture begins when two bricks are placed together—carefully."[3] It also marks the beginning of a structural system. Thanks to research conducted by the *Structural Clay Products Institute* and other research agencies and to refinement of the ingredients themselves, brickwork can now reliably respond to engineering analysis. Brick, previously used in intuitively designed structures, now can function as an element in a significantly stressed, precisely engineered building system. We call it *engineered brick masonry* and the English call it *calculated brickwork.* However, structural brickwork has no more in common with ordinary brickwork, though the ingredients are the same than structural concrete has with a sidewalk.

Because of brickwork's compressive strength it could, theoretically, be used in a variety of compression members. However, the most efficient use of brickwork's structural qualities occurs in membrane structures; that is, structures in which the space defining elements (walls, partitions, screens, etc.) also resist superimposed loads. A comparison between a membrane structure and the commonly used skeletal system illustrates this. For example, to enclose a space with skeletal techniques, four piers might be positioned to receive a floor or roof frame as shown in Figure 1-1. If the material is redistributed we have not only superimposed the load, but we have also gained a room and stabilized the structure against horizontal forces.[4]

This single material satisfies many construction needs, structural system, weathertight enclosure, fireproofing, acoustical insulation and finished surfaces. And this is engineered brickwork's latent excellence: its polyfunctional nature.

But, as noted earlier, these inherent merits will remain latent until building successfully utilizes brickwork. Through recognition of brickwork's versatility the designer reduces the materials used and thus also the number of problems. He no longer needs to connect materials with dissimilar characteristics, such as expansion rates and chemical incompatibility.

Design Flexibility of Brickwork

Moreover, the brick module allows design flexibility which is particularly appealing to the architect as it allows freedom for plastic expression. Coming within 4" of absolute plasticity is not a serious tradeoff for its other advantages. It compares favorably with that other well known, higher priced product, whose plasticity is no greater than that from which it is made.

This flexibility frees the architect so that he may address directly the ultimate problem of architecture: the spatial considerations. Ideally, architectural form must be ordered by the parameters of human usefulness, not by accretion of th details.

Aesthetically, the disciplines imposed by brickwork resu in visual unity, a unity not easily achieved by other techniqu which must manipulate several different materials. Th harmony elicits a favorable response from even the most naiv observer. The suggestion of how a thing was put together characteristically found in all great architecture. Moreove brick is large enough, when viewed from close up, to form reference pattern against which other objects in the enviro ment can be measured; yet small enough that it does not tak charge. Viewed from afar, brick graciously yields its ind viduality to the larger element in which it is placed, thereb releasing the newly-formed element to set still anoth cadence.

Applying Brick to Environmental Needs

But neither structural brickwork's appeal to the archite nor his recognition of its merits implement its full potentia The system must be applied to the environmental needs of i era.

Historically, brickwork has demonstrated this suitabilit Whether the problem was to provide a simple hut for shelter to create a monumental space membrane structures a especially appropriate. These introverted environments requi ever increasing space to conduct the air, electricity and liqui in and out of them. Incorporating these "servant spaces" ca be turned to an advantage with structural masonry. Instead the normal procedure of building additional housings aroun the mechanical devices, the structural walls could be tubula thereby, achieving greater stability with minimum material an creating a usable void—structural ductwork so to spea Because of this mechanical domination, it would be adva tageous in some instances to place these buildings undergroun to avoid the cyclical stresses due to temperature changes an wind. Here, the compressive qualities of structural mason could be exploited in the form of retaining walls, buttresse etc.

Economic competitiveness also influences the shape of ou buildings. The current building examples noted earlier for the structural competitiveness have also been economical. Th economy resulted from simplified logistics because with fewe materials to handle and schedule, there were fewer trades t co-ordinate. Simple, universally recognized constructio techniques can aid in cost control. But, the greatest econom results when walls, partition, and other special barriers w need anyway are put to work.

The Future of Structural Brickwork

Where do we go from here? While we can predict with fair degree of certainty the forces of wind and gravity; this not so with the other determinants of architectural form. In a era of technological expansion and economic competitivenes pointing to historic continuity is an extremely shaky basis o which to extrapolate any significant predictions. Therefor any suggested immortalizing an individual or an institution brick was the medium. True, until a hundred years or so ago, if one wanted to build a durable structure there were not many alternatives. But, brickwork still maintained its historical continuity by being used for one or another of its qualities, if not always as a structural material.

This lull in brickwork's development was not without merit. New materials enable the architect to exploit the best qualities of each in composite structures.

Many current examples in this country and in Europe testify to the structural feasibility and architectural suitability of the system.[5] But, while their numbers are significant, the breadth of application is not. With few exceptions most current projects call for small repetitious space modules such as apartments. The peculiar applicability to this type building results from the limited need for interior planning flexibility and the stringent demands for acoustical insulation between dwelling units.

As the designer's confidence increases the applications will vary more, particularly those relating to many current environmental trends.[6] One tendency is to build closed spaces in which ventilation, light and sound are mechanically controlled such as: laboratory buildings, electronically oriented teaching spaces, and automated factories. With fewer openings for windows and such, application for structural brickwork should be directed toward environmental, technological and economic conditions we can reasonably foresee.

According to the environmental planners, our future cities will consist of a comprehensively coordinated continuous matrix of spaces of variable but modest height. Such a complex would accommodate a multitude of activities with diverse space requirements. Noted earlier was structural brickwork's particular applicability to dwellings and to the inward oriented spaces for teaching and working. Another required type of space in the matrix is the anonymous one designed to allow periodic interior rearrangement. This flexible space is really larger space. Cellular or tubular walls accommodate the mechanical devices and furnish a stable base to bear long span members.

Although the technological means exist for constructing such cities, the coordinating bodies capable of building on such a comprehensive scale are lacking. This lack is alluring to such giants of industry as Westinghouse, General Electric and others, who, armed with their computers, are eyeing the

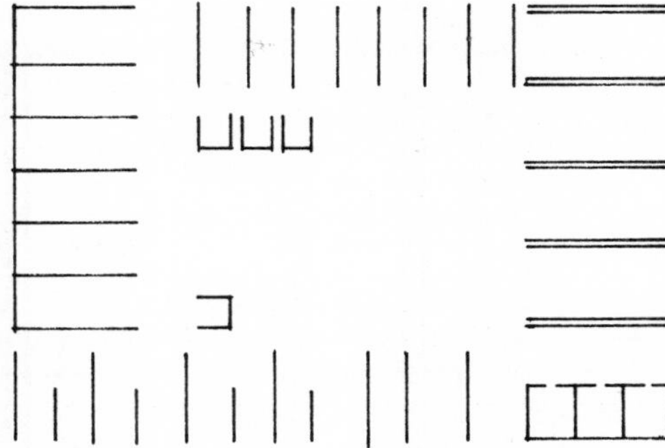

Figure 1-2.

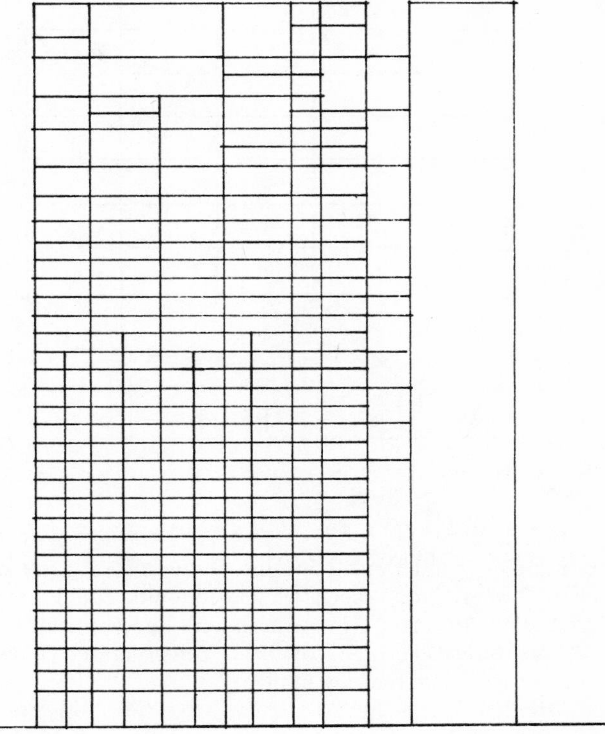

Figure 1-3.

building industry as potential hunting ground and have already experimented with building entire towns.[7] But, the entry of these corporations into the building industry does not, ipso facto, signal the demise of structural masonry. The forte of these giants lies primarily in their managerial skills and authoritarian chain of command throughout the building process. It is likely that the very stuff of construction will continue to be those materials of tested merit. The greatest cause for concern would be whether or not brickwork could adapt to the automated and large scale prefabrication techniques these companies use. Consequently, the aspect of structural brickwork most vulnerable to obsolescence is the handcraft technology used for placing bricks. This should be of no great consequence to the building industry itself, although it would have passing significance to those perpetuating the outmoded techniques. The merit of brickwork is primarily in the brick, not in the work. Since it is in the joints where the inherent qualities of the system are diluted, improvements in placing techniques would be most welcome. Attempts have already been made to factory assemble the conventional units into large panels.[8] But this idea has all the drawbacks of other large factory-spawned building systems: difficulty in connecting the units to one another and to the other elements of the structure and the loss of design flexibility characteristic of the smaller module. Maybe the conventional brick could be placed by machine using a fast setting bonding agent comparable in quality to the brick itself.

If machines take over the validity of the hand-size unit might be questioned. Perhaps we should drop the brick

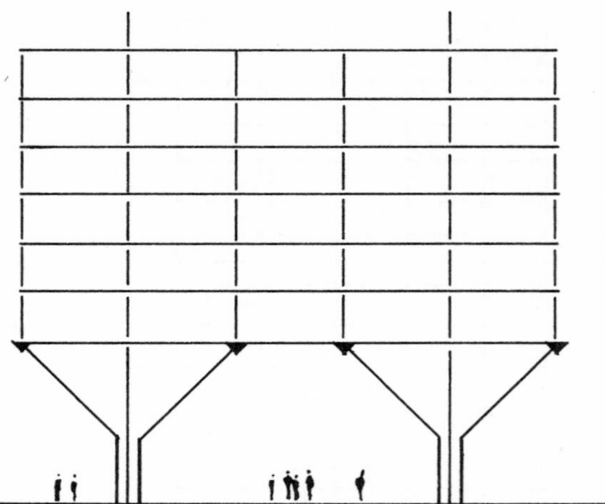

Figure 1-4.

terminology and think in terms of the entire genre of fired clay. Several large specially shaped units could be factory assembled to create a room—a much more applicable module for prefabrication than panelized construction. Or why not extrude and bake the clay in place!

Whether or not these particular suggestions prove feasible is irrelevant. What is important, however, is that the degree to which the potential of structural masonry is realized will depend on the ability of the craft to adapt. Not only to the predictable laws of nature, but to the less precise tenets of economics and technology as well as the vicissitudes of environmental planning. For ideas and technologies respond to Darwinian principles, though in a different context, just a surely as do biological organisms.

Will this resurgent interest in masonry structures b identified in years to come as the final lurch of a flounderin craft lost in a flood of technological plethora? I think not. Th very technological boom that may tend to render masonr structural systems obsolete may also devise ways of expandin its use. It is unlikely that a system with such latent excellenc will be abandoned through technological default.

I believe that the historic continuity of brickwork wi remain intact—a continuity which began when that geniu many years ago discovered that rectilinear lumps of clay f together better than the random shaped objects he found i nature. Until we hang from cables to the stars it will b necessary for us to continue the struggle to pry ourselves awa from the earth. What better prop than bricks!

Hypothetical Examples

Hypothetical examples should remain fairly abstract. Sinc development of masonry structural systems is far from ende present limiting dimensions will be surpassed with improve materials and methods. Therefore no dimensions or details ar given.

1. The simplest form for a tall structure is vertic development of a constant plan—a vertical extrusion so t speak. This is not only the most direct response to gravit loads, but results in their visual expression. The shape of th plan would be determined by its use: a room, air shaf plumbing stack, etc. Vertical development would be partic larly suited to a self climbing device for placing the bricks. S as not to interrupt its operation, pockets could be left in th

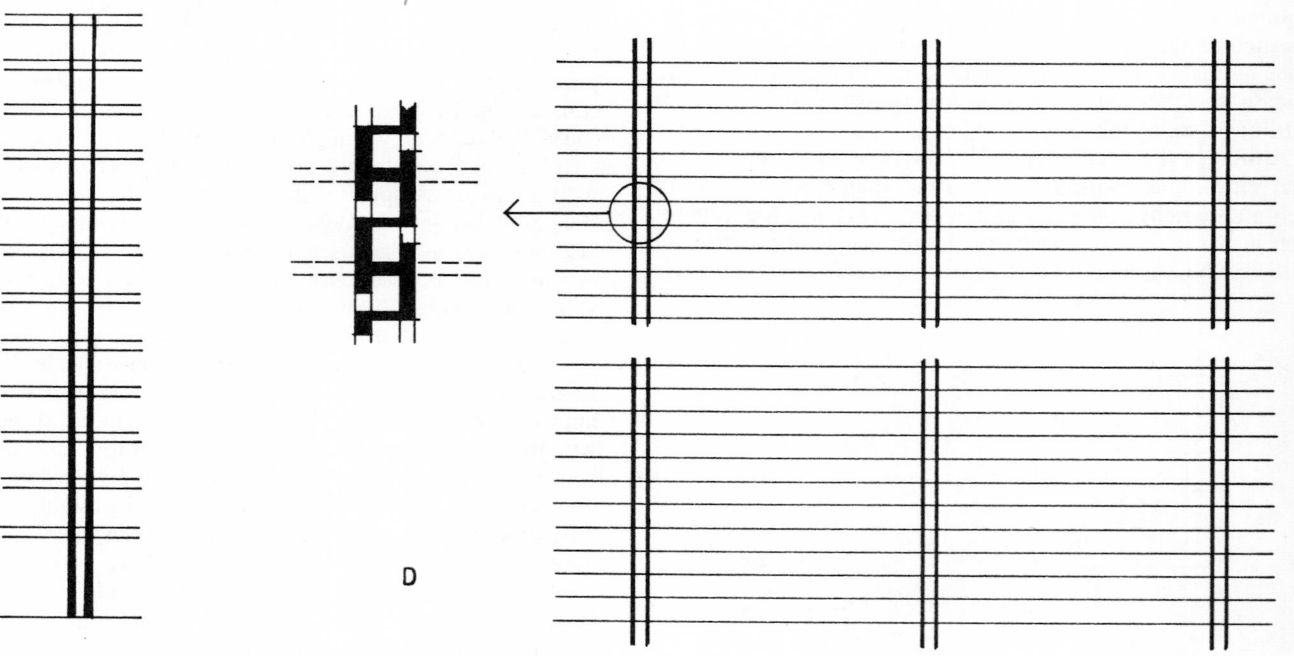

Figure 1-5.

Figure 1-6.

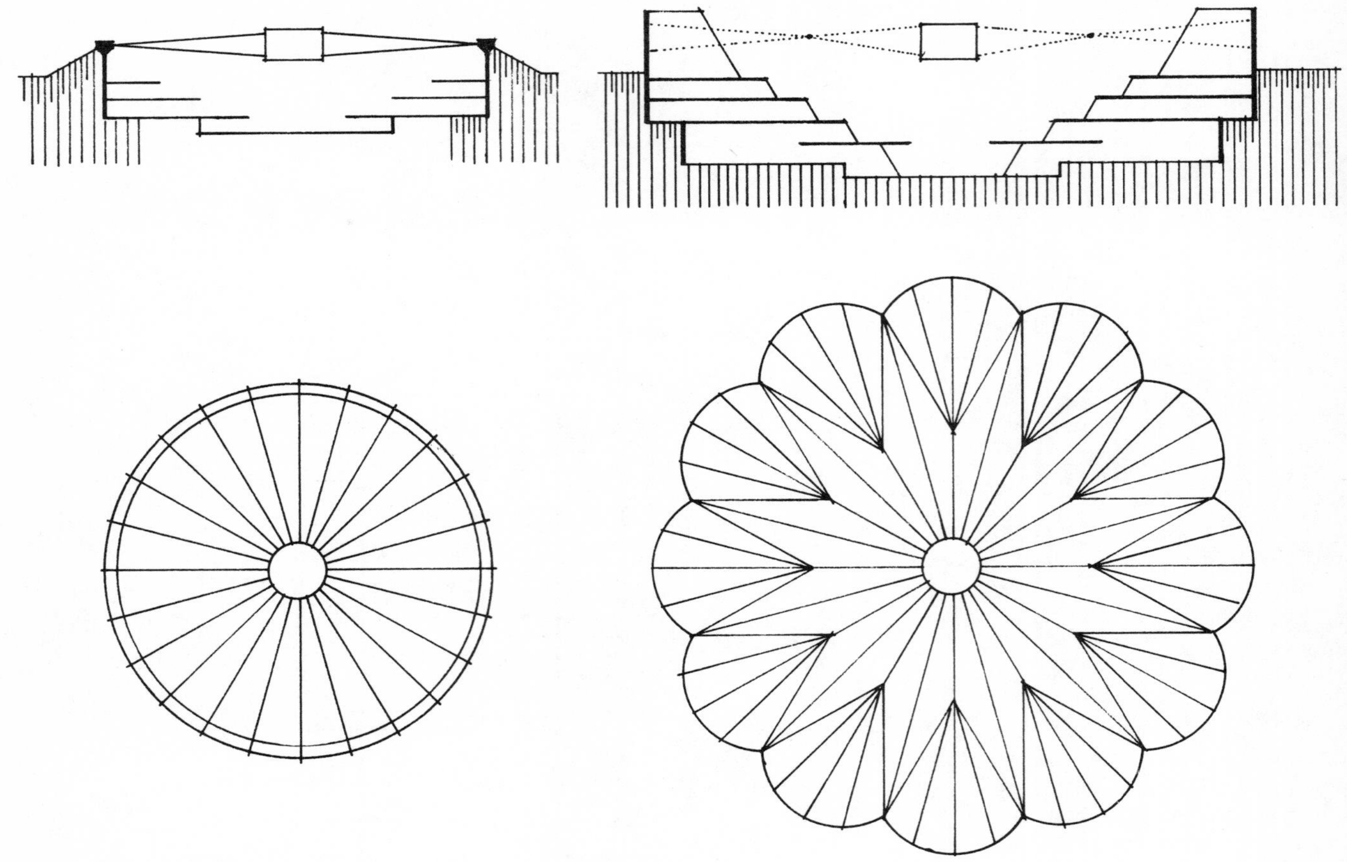

Figure 1-7.

walls to receive floor members. Conceivably, taking advantage of our computerized automated age, this machine could extrude curved shapes as economically as straight lines, relieving us of the tyranny of the taut string. Combinations of various shapes could solve unlimited spacial requirements (Figure 1-2).

2. Dropping out walls as gravity loads diminish permits increasingly larger spaces as height increases (Figure 1-3).

3. To create a large space at the bottom canted diaphragms could receive intermediate walls above (Figure 1-4).

4. Long Span spaces for periodic interior rearrangement, consisting of tubular walls housing the mechanical devices, could achieve stability with minimum material. As the walls thicken with the accumulation of loads decreasing, ductwork merges into a structure of constant exterior dimensions (Figure 1-5).

5. The circular form is extremely stable and is adaptable to many building types, for example: hospitals, dwellings, and car parks; and it is efficient for underground application where the horizontal forces are constant in all directions (Figure 1-6).

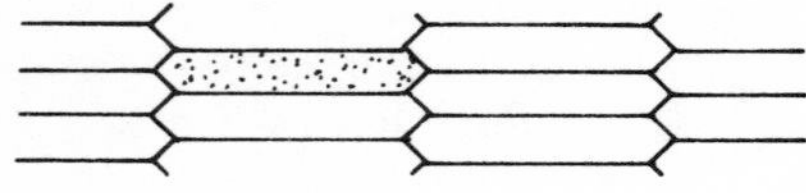

Figure 1-8.

6. Combining the tensile qualities of steel with the compressive qualities of brick results in a suspension roof system (Figure 1-7).

7. Suggested brick shape would eliminate the awkward header joint and give greater lateral shear strength (Figure 1-8).

References

1. Clarke, Arthur B., "A Glimpse of the Future–Near and Otherwise," *AIA Journal,* XLVIII, No. 4, October 1967, p. 52-56.
2. Blaser, Werner, Mies Van Der Rohe, *U.S.A., Frederick A. Praeger, Inc.,* 1965, p. 10.
3. Ibid.
4. Angerer, Fred, *Surface Structures In Building* Reinhold Publishing Corporation, 1961.
5. Monk, Clarence B., Jr., Gross, James G., "European Clay Masonry Loadbearing Buildings," *Structural Clay Products Institute,* pp. 1-91.
6. Angerer, Edward W., "Bearing Walls That Express and Exploit," *AIA Journal,* XLVIII, No. 3, September 1967.
7. Progressive Architecture, "Performance Design," *Progressive Architecture,* August, 1967, p. 126-32.
8. Taylor, Robert B., Gross, James G., "Structural Clay Report," *Progressive Architecture,* April, 1962, p. 136.

2. Structural glazed masonry units.

Charles E. Firestone, Firestone & Motter Canton, Ohio

History of Structural Glazed Tile

The story of a new product is always exciting. The glazed tile structural masonry unit is this type of product.

Incised painted figures on the walls in the tombs and temples, depicting the life of the ancient Egyptians, were the beginning of the useful and decorative structural wall.

Our concern with history is what enamellers did and how they did it. Technically, enamel is a coating of color on glass, pottery, metal, or whatever mineral substances will stand enough heat to fuse it. There are no records of Egyptians using enamel until the Roman Egyptian period. Greeks used enamel in their jewelry and western Europeans, during the Celtic period, also enameled articles. In the first few centuries A. D., enamel was used mostly for jewelry. From the Byzantine period through the Gothic period, enamel served only for decorative motifs and jewelry. In the Orient and Far East enamel was utilized for ornaments and decoration but not for integral building parts. Bright colorful porcelain panels lend an interesting decorative motif to the gabled walls of Thailand buildings (Figure 2-1). The balustrade or handrail of the stairs at the approach to the temple is the body of a snake which terminates at the newel post with a glazed, red, seven-headed serpent. The surface of the Temple of the Dawn (Wat Arun Rajarararam), almost completely covered with porcelain, made a most striking and imposing decorative exterior.[1]

Figure 2-1. Colored gables, Bangkok, Thailand.

Figure 2-2. Semiglazed structural building.

Throughout the world are examples of enameled or glazed decorative units as part of buildings but not as structural bearing material. Ornaments, decorations, and motifs flourish in many countries, particularily in Western Europe and the Far East. The Aztec Indians and most Indian cultures applied color to gargoyles, ornaments, and figures, and perhaps to some of the sun-baked building units used in their temples and shrines.

We leave the past and approach modern development of glazed-structural-facing tile units. In the late 1800's or early 1900's in northern Ohio, structural tile units 8″ x 8″ x 16″ and 8″ x 12″ x 16″ with a shell about 1″ in thickness were manufactured. Burning the clay with its various ingredients produced this reddish-brown or purple tile with a semiglossy surface. According to information available, no ingredient was added to the clay itself or to the coal fired units in beehive kilns to produce this particular color or semiglaze. In some instances these units had one face pressed in a mold to imitate a rock face surface in low relief.

Schools, factories, silos, even residences and other small buildings made use of this semiglazed structural building units. Some of the buildings were two and three stories high (Figure 2-2).

In the late 1890's or early 1900's in some areas of northern Ohio, salt was added to the beehive kiln at fire box presumably to prevent a scum forming on the brick. Although it did not accomplish its purpose, this application of salt in the fire box produced salt-glazed brick. Its color varied from light yellow to dark brown with a glossy surface, depending on the location of the unit in the kiln and intensity of the heat produced by the kiln. Neither barium nor any other foreign agent was added to the salt to give other colors. This scum cover, or salt-glazed brick, immediately became a popular and economical facing unit because it was impervious to moisture, and easy to clean, and resistant to fire. After this development, manfacturers of (3½″ x 5″ x 8″ and 12″ and 3½″ x 8″ x 8″ and 12″) structural back-up tile began to make a salt-glazed structural tile unit, thus the glazed structural facing tile industry. (Figure 2-3) This popular facing unit was used mostly on interiors.

Manufacturers of glazed enamel household articles, particularily kitchen utensils, dipped treated metal into a liquid glaze material, allowed this to dry, and then baked it in a furnace under uniformly controlled intense heat which formed an impervious glazed coating. If an enamel could be fused to clay surfaces, manufacturers of structural building units saw an opportunity for various colored facing units. Experiments resulted in the fusion of enamel and clay into one unit, and so the structural glazed facing-tile industry began. The dipping process developed various colors for structural glazed facing tile. Now, this tedious task demanded time and individual effort and depended entirely on the ability and agility of the person who dipped the product. Too, there was much waste due to human error as the process included handling the clay biscuit, dipping and drying, burning, and taking the finished product from the kiln to storage or transportation vehicles.

Figure 2-3. Examples of salt-glazed structural units.

Terra cotta preceded the technical application of glazed material on a clay or shale biscuit or clay form.

Manufacturers discussed ways and means to eliminate the waste. A spraying process used such products as paint and germicides, so why not coat the tile by spraying the liquid glaze? In the late 1920's spraying of glaze on clay units began; thus, a new technique was brought into practical use. The development of spray glaze allowed economical production of a multiplicity of colors. It is possible now to achieve any hue, value and intensity in the color spectrum together with various textures of the surface. The surface texture is formed by pressing the clay biscuit into a mold or by scratching and rolling to produce a rug finish on the clay surface before the glaze is applied. The manufacturers of these units in northern Ohio were the first in the country to produce glazed, structural facing-tile building units as a part of the structural bearing wall. Modern gas-fired tunnel kilns produce a more uniform color, size, and texture of this type tile; and when fired at approximately 2100° F., the units are highly fire resistant.

Structural Glazed Tile Today

It remained for the structural glazed tile industry to develop the final structural, aesthetic, and load-bearing unit. Some glazed tile units are made with a continuous horizontal void and a shell of about 1/2″ to 3/4 ″. Other manufacturers use vertical voids varying from 1/4″ to 2″ in diameter. Test results of structural qualities of the units are available with respect to the allowable bearing load of the structural glazed masonry unit as part of a wall.[3]

The following example (Table 2-1) of a masonry wall with structural glazed tile was taken from "Technical Notes on Brick and Tile Construction 22", May – June 1965.

Table 2-1

A 12″ wall	Laid with	Allowable load lbs. per sq. ft.
Brick one side	type M mortar (85 psi)	12,000
Glazed tile one side	type S mortar (75 psi)	10,580
Masonry Bonded	type N mortar (75 psi)	9,860
Other thicknesses of wall construction, pages 10 – 11		

The use of these structural glazed tile units is universal however, in northern states because of climatic conditions, the glazed units are recommended only as part of the interior surface of masonry walls. Glazed units are particularly desirable where vehicular and human traffic is heavy and where moisture and dirt are always present.

Figure 2-4. Structural glazed tile used for wall surface designs.

Because structural glazed masonry units have hard reflective surfaces, the industry developed an acoustical tile to reduce noises where necessary.[4]

With structural glazed facing tile the wall and finish can be erected in one operation, thus saving the increased cost of labor for finished wall coatings and applications. The permanent color, durable surface, fire resistance, non toxic, acoustical, load bearing qualities make structural glazed facing tile an exceptional value for the construction dollar. Very few new products offered as substitutes for the wall area can match this above mentioned list of product values. Laying masonry walls unit by unit continues to be a very economical and satisfactory method of building a wall.[5] Epoxy type wall coatings offering glazed like surfaces are no better than the units to which they are applied, and time has not proven the durability of these surface finishes.

The uses of structural glazed facing tile have included many walls designed to relieve the surface appearance of one color facing tile walls. Murals and geometric designs give relief to the walls. The relief available is limited only by the creative ability of architects and engineers.

The elimination of the mortar joint has not been essential in the design and applications of facing tile. The availability of dirt resistant mortars increases the use of facing tile to areas where cleanliness is a must. The value of the glazed surface with small dirt resistant joints compares favorably to substitute products with less durable finishes and little or no joints. However, the application of mortar joints make them impervious to penetration of moisture and dirt for an unlimited time.

Conclusion

In conclusion structural glazed masonry units become a primary consideration of any building, because:

1. It is economical in the ultimate building cost as it is an integral part of the structural wall.
2. Its glazed surface provides a sanitary finish.
3. Its glazed surface is highly resistant to abrasions; therefore long life is assured.
4. It is highly fire resistant, has zero flame spread, no toxic fumes, and does not contribute fuel to burning.
5. Its aesthetic value is pleasing, many colors and textures are available on the market.
6. Its density provides high sound transmission loss through the wall.
7. Glazed acoustical tile absorbs sound.
8. Surface maintenance is minimal.

The Future of Structural Glazed Tile

Structural glazed tile will soon be produced on an assembly line operated by electronics. Because clay deposits are widely distributed, the same technique will probably be required as the present day strip mining. These techniques include excavating the clay, placing it in small carrier cars operated electronically which will take it to the assembly line where the clay will be dumped into a pulverizer, and moisture eliminated. The dry clay then enters a pug mill; water and other ingredients are added for the right consistency to be extruded with pressure to the various shapes of the tile. It is then glazed by a spray, dried at a regulated temperature, carried on into the kiln, and burned at temperatures now 2100° F. Finally it passes out at the kiln, is then sorted, graded, and packaged for stock or shipment. All the above operations, except for excavating and placing in stock, are assembly line techniques operated by remote control electronics and the only hand operation is the preparation of the various glaze colors.

The future of structural glazed tile is unpredictable because today glazed color units have been worked in the wall surfaces in various designs and patterns and depicting men, animals, birds and others (Figure 2-4). Glazed color tile walls will probably depict life of the people today in wall panels in low relief, as have the stone carvings in the Far East and throughout Europe. Science and the ingenuity of man will overcome todays limitations and soon represent the most fantastic colorful walls that will last throughout the life of the building.

References

1. King Phra Chao and four succeeding kings made additions to this beautiful structure 243 feet high.
2. *Technical Notes*, No. 16 (revised) Structural Clay Products Institute.
3. "Wall Sections," *Technical Notes*, No. 22, Structural Clay Products Institute, p. 10.
4. *Technical Notes*, No. 5 (Sc. R. Acoustile), Structural Clay Products Institute. "A Review of Sound in Schools," *American School Board Journal*, Nov. 1963, p. 40.
5. Grimm, Clayford T., P. E., Tables 3, 4, 5, 6, *Ultimate Cost of Wainscot Material Used in Public Elementary School Buildings*, Structural Clay Products Association of the Southwest, October, 1965.

3. Morphotectonics of masonry structures.

Dr. P. T. Mikluchin, P. E., P. T. Mikluchin & Associates, Toronto, Ontario, Canada

Latest developments in building science and technology impose greater and more complex demands on a designer and require a deeper insight into the essence of modern architectural and engineering design of buildings and structures. Such insight can be achieved with the help of the ideas contained in a fast growning design philosophy of morphotectonics.

The term "morphotectonics," derived from Greek words "morphe" - form, and "tektonikos" - constructive, can be defined as the art and science of formation and construction of buildings and structures. Morphotectonics deals with creation and unity of architectural and structural forms, influence of physical aspects of building materials and methods of construction on these forms, and aesthetic expression of strength and stability, inherent in such forms.

In the hands of creative designers, morphotectonics can be one of the most powerful tools for achieving the high degree of perfection in overall architectural design.

Naturally, the solution of morphotectonic problems must be coordinated with the solution of the general architectural problems.

Often designers consider the problem of architectural design as purely aesthetic problem. In reality, this problem is organically and uniquely connected with the construction technology and material.

Morphotectonics is more than a formal art concerned with concepts such as organization of abstract forms in space and relationships of different parts to each other and to the whole. It deals with the realities of the physical world, not with the fictions of the abstract world.

The end result of morphotectonic design is a material construct which we will define as a morphotectonic continuum.

Such continuum is a three-dimensional continuous space construct whose elements are integral, indivisible parts of the whole. These elements are not isolated or independent parts, but inseparable elements, structurally and aesthetically, of the total structure. Morphotectonic continuum is an integral part of the overall architectural complex.

A creative designer must try to reveal the latent kinship between material and its morphotectonic use. Proper use of the material is the quintessence of the sound design philosophy. The choice of materials should be inherent in the design concept. The problem is to express and use materials so as to achieve the best possible morphotectonic effect.

Great variety of forms can be created from any building material, if a sensitive designer allows the morphotectonic nature of the material to generate its own latent morphogenetic or form-creating forces.

Expressiveness of Structure

Modern architecture is the expressive in structure. If the designer utilizes all fundamental principles of building materials properly, then the architectural and structural concepts will fuse together into an integrated whole.

If, after masterful application of morphotectonic principles, nothing can be added or taken away from the building, the structure transcends into the work of art. Structure and architecture become one indivisible whole.

Indeed, creations of great pottery makers and goldsmiths are excellent illustrations of complete fusion of structure and form. In such creations, morphotectonic principles reign supreme.

All great art aspires to perfect harmony and identity of form and structure.

In many cases, a modern designer should act as a sculptor when he creates a form from an amorphous mass of material. He would do well to follow the example of Michelangelo, who was always speaking of necessity of "liberating forms from the marble blocks."

It is axiomatic that the problem of design of morphotectonic forms is inseparable from the problem of choice and treatment of building materials.

Every building material is a medium through which the design concept, created in the mind of the designer, is expressed. All materials possess certain physical and aesthetic characteristics. These characteristics greatly affect the final choice of morphotectonic forms.

It is easy to see the importance of the statement made, although in somewhat different context, by Frank Lloyd Wright, who said, "Each material has its own message to the creative artist."[7]

A creative designer must study thoroughly all intrinsic characteristics of building materials. Without knowing the material medium, it is impossible to communicate the intended message, because every medium determines and expresses the aesthetic reality in its own unique way.

There is a great deal of good, common sense in the famous dictum of Marshall McLuhan, who said, "the medium is the message."

Modern morphotectonic development is characterized by the fusion of various concepts of rigorous science, aesthetic intuitions, and powerful modern technology.

Morphotectonics is a synthesis of art, science, and technology applied to the design and construction of buildings and structures.

Principles of Morphotectonic Design

Morphotectonic design involves, among other things, concepts of formal organization of space, utilization of intrinsic qualities of building materials and judicious choice of constructional techniques.

The creative design cannot be put into Procrustean bed of rigid, formalized rules. A designer cannot arrive at the final solution of a given problem solely by pure rationalization. He creates forms intuitively and tries to justify them rationally.

It is impossible to devise any definite rules or formulas which would guide the designer effortlessly to the final solution, but certain precepts and principles can be established.

As a guide, the following principles could be used:

Compatibility

This principle states that the form of a morphotectonic continuum and building material, which is chosen for realization of this continuum, must be compatible. The designer must be familiar with the unique physical, geometrical and constructional characteristics of the chosen building material to create forms which would correspond to these characteristics.

Simplicity

Simplicity of morphotectonic concept results in an aesthetically satisfying form of a structure and, as a rule, in the most favorable and efficient flow of internal stresses in the body of the structure.

Integral Action

Each element must perform its own function and at the same time, due to the organic unity existing among all elements of such continuum, every element must take part in assisting all other elements. In truly morphotectonic structures there are no redundant members. All members are of equal importance. Perfect structure can be defined as the morphotectonic logic made visible.

Minimization of Strain-Stress Energy

Properly designed morphotectonic continuum characteristically has a specific stress and strain distribution within the body which produces the required stability and equilibbrium with the minimum expenditure of stress-strain energy.

These principles are not dogmatic, rigid formulations ready for use in the design, but flexible, interdependant, helpful concepts, serving only as guides.

It is now possible to use mathematical models for morphological studies of structures in general and masonry structures in particular, especially with the help of electronic computers.

Certain forms are geometrically possible but morphotectonically unrealizable.

A clear, logical rapport between science, building technology and morphotectonic aesthetics can be and must be established.

Morphotectonics of Masonry

Essentially, masonry is a result of the geometry of one unit extended, according to a certain method, in a given direction in three-dimensional space.

Such a form is a logical consequence of the inner arrangements of masonry units. There is no limit to the complex forms which could be created from these masonry units.

In nature, form and structure are one. In morphotectonic design this unity of form and structure should be the ultimate goal of the designer.

In buildings, generally, realization of the balance between gravity, lateral forces, and reactive inner forces dictates the geometry of the structural form.

In masonry structures, physical properties and geometrical characteristics of masonry units impose additional requirements on the final form.

Certain forms, because of adherence to well defined physical and geometric laws, produce organic shapes. Such forms are natural, logical, and immediately convincing.

Morphotectonic design of masonry structures is a search for simplicity, logic and order. A guide in this search is the discipline which strives to eliminate the arbitrary, erratic elements in design.

In this connection L. Mies van der Rohe said, "Take a brick . . . how sensible is its small, handy shape, so useful for every purpose. What logic in its bonding, pattern and texture. What richness in the simplest wall surface, but what discipline this material imposes!"[2]

Today, as in the past, understanding the possibilities and limitations of building materials is the source of many morphotectonic masterpieces.

Final building form results from the creative synthesis of structural, geometrical and aesthetic nature of basic elementary units themselves, the methods of their assembly and aesthetic philosophy of the designer.

One must always remember that the choice and treatment of building materials is inseparable from the problem of morphology of structure.

In morphotectonics the bearing and the borne are one.

The goal of the morphotectonic design, as applied to masonry buildings, is to produce continuous, expansible systems which could be terminated at certain chosen boundaries without destroying inner morphological order characteristic for the given material. It is analogous to crystal forming process and, in certain aspects, to the biological growth.

Such boundary systems must be used for the construction of a desirable space. Such space can be created by certain combination of two-dimensional boundary elements (walls, floors).

Planar structures fulfill two most important functions: load-bearing and space-defining.

The load-bearing masonry structures, in particular, serve several functions of paramount importance; such structures support all loads acting on them, define geometric space, provide architectural finish with the wide choice of textures, patterns and colors, and, finally, give a scale.

Space, generally speaking, has no scale and requires an appropriate yardstick to define it.

In masonry morphotectonics, scale is established through the relationship between the dimensions of basic building unit, man, and structure.

Structurally, masonry is highly resistant to compressive forces. However, resistance to tension, bending, shear, and torsion, unless it is reinforced is relatively low. It logically follows that specialized structural shapes must be used.

Any masonry structure must grow organically and logically from a basic material unit used in a given building.

Such basic masonry building unit is the brick, which is the first modular and first prefabricated unit produced by the genius of man at the dawn of our civilization. Its importance to mankind's progress could be compared to the invention of the wheel, pottery, or textile.

Out of these units, bonded together with mortar, man created one of the best known building materials—masonry.

Hierarchy of Masonry

Masonry unit is a basic manufactured unit component with fixed dimensions, used for construction of buildings and structures.

Masonry is a special building material, either structural or architectural, which consists of masonry units and cementitious materials bonded together into one continuous whole.

Figure 3-1. Example of linear and planar type systems used in masonry structures (I. W. Colburn).

Masonry component is a portion of a masonry structure, erected on a site or manufactured in the shop (lintel, wall, shell).

Masonry structure is a three-dimensional space system consisting of a complex of masonry elements, and it is built in accordance with the morphotectonic principles.

A masonry building unit must be considered as a fundamental morphogenetic or form-producing building component.

Generally, masonry wall form is controlled by its own internal logic of construction, derived from the shape of the unit and technique of assembly of these units. As it was pointed out, a form of masonry structure is a consequence of its inner arrangement.

The nature of this arrangement gives us the basis for the classification of masonry systems.

Classification of Morphotectonic Systems of Masonry

The morphotectonic growth of masonry is accomplished by the process of repetitive superposition of one building unit on the other. There are, essentially, three principal types of this process: When the successive superposition takes place along a single axis, it is called uniaxial process. When such superposition takes place along two axes simultaneously, it is called biaxial process. Triaxial process is when the process of superposition progresses along three axes.

This process of repetitive superposition creates an infinite number of various spatial configurations of masonry structures.

Naturally it results in a series of structural elements which can be classified as follows:

1. Linear structural elements, which could be subdivided into rectilinear elements (columns, spandrels, beams), and curvilinear elements (arches).
2. Planar structural elements, which could be subdivided into continuous plane surfaces (walls, slabs, diaphragms), and continuous curved surfaces (shells, vaults, domes).
3. Stereo structural elements or structures. Such structures are represented by three-dimensional bodies (cubes, prisms).

These well-known structural elements, produced from various building materials, possess their own morphotectonic characteristics.

Figure 3-2. Planar structure in form of continuous curved surface.

Figure 3-3. Another example of planar structure used in continuous curved surfaces.

On the basis of this classification of various elements, three main morphotectonic systems can be established.

1. *Linear* morphotectonic systems. These systems consist of the spatial framework of linear elements arranged in accordance with the general requirements of a particular design problem (e.g. space frames).

2. *Planar* morphotectonic systems. Such systems consist of three-dimensional compositions of plane or curved surfaces, combined into one integral structure (e.g. integral shell structures).

3. *Stereo* morphotectonic systems. These systems consist of spatial solid bodies (e.g. pyramids).

Among these three systems of masonry structures, mainly linear and planar systems are used. Very often various combinations of these systems can be found. An example of the use of linear and planar type is shown in Figure 3-1. Several examples of buildings belonging to planar structures in form of continuous curved surfaces are shown in Figures 3-2 and 3-3.

Unfortunately many superb building designs expressed through brick masonry contain different, and very often incompatible, structural materials hidden inside of these walls.

Some Design Considerations

It is impossible to give an exhaustive list of practical considerations which could be used during the process of design. The following is a very brief list of useful design recommendations:

The middle surface of two-dimensional planar elements must be either plane or continuously curved, without any abrupt changes in the curvature.

Thickness of two-dimensional elements should be either constant or changing in certain strategic points (e.g. at the levels of horizontal diaphragms). Sudden changes in thicknesses are highly undesirable because they intensify local stresses.

Large openings inevitably introduce very high concentration of stresses at the reentrant corners of such openings.

Unless special provisions are made, an opening in the bearing wall creates unfavourable distribution of internal stresses. Visually such a wall is unsatisfactory as well. In connection with this Frank Lloyd Wright said, "Often I used to gloat over the beautiful buildings I could build if only it were unnecessary to cut windows in them".[3] Illuminating example of one of his solutions of this problem is shown in Figure 3-4.

Any opening (e.g. a door) should not give an impression of a hole, but it must be arranged as logical and consistent interspace.

Any discontinuity in bearing walls should be treated as a definite, clear division of overall space, aesthetically justified, and not as an unwanted disturbance.

In general, the designer must consider the physical behavior of the building in its totality, affected by volumetric changes due to thermal stresses, differential shrinkage, creep phenomena and absorption of moisture. This behaviour will determine the location of expansion and contraction joints

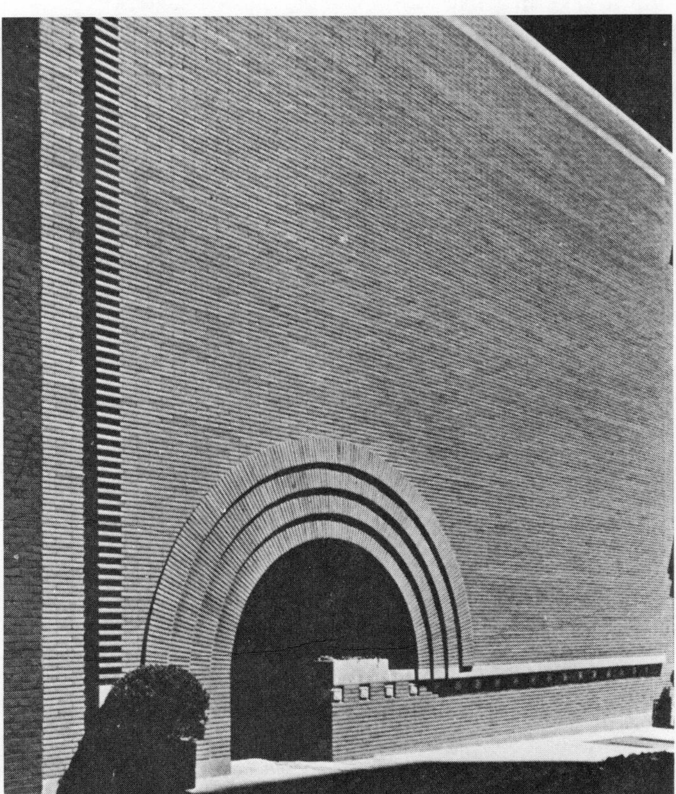

Figure 3-4. Frank Lloyd Wright, Morris Store, San Francisco, California.

which could affect the aesthetics of the building. He must try to establish definite constructional procedures.

Properly designed masonry buildings have excellent performance. This is due to small coefficients of expansion and contraction, low degree of shrinkage and creep and the absence of flexible structural frameworks within the building, which, in many instances, cause highly undesirable excessive movements.

Challenge of Modern Morphotectonics of Masonry

Modern morphotectonics is in a state of transition. It is constantly changing and evolving.

Modern technology coupled with the latest achievements in morphotectonic design, structural engineering and construction techniques opens up new vistas for the creative designer.

Buildings and structures resulting from new design approaches will be different from previous buildings.

These changes will be intensified by the rapid progress of building science, modern technology and ever-changing aesthetic sensibilities and philosophies of creative designers.

The problem is not whether these changes will affect the morphotectonic concepts or not, but how.

Our task is not to wait for these changes to come to pass but to take an active role in making these changes.

In order to face this challenge, in the realm of morphotectonics of modern masonry, we should understand structural and form producing potentials of modern masonry, try to see this material in the light of new discoveries and find new ways of using innumerable potential forms that lie hidden in this material. We should exploit the morphotectonic qualities of this material to the greatest possible degree, study the problems of joining basic masonry units, creating an array of new units and new patterns. Such new units shall consist of structurally efficient and visually well defined basic elements which could be used successfully in the context of the overall architectural design.

We should study colour, tone and textural relationships of these materials.

Changes in structural make-up of the basic units and in the methods of assembly and in the constructional techniques will play the deciding role in the continuous evolution of morphotectonic forms. Such changes must be furthered by the creative designers.

The latest progress in prefabrication of masonry components will greatly affect the philosophy of modern morphotectonics of masonry.

Recent developments in reinforced masonry have definitely widened the possibilities of creating new, exciting forms as it has already been proven in some of the projects built in South America.

In the conclusion we would like to reiterate that modern masonry has the unique ability to produce strong and beautiful building material with the infinite variety of textures and patterns, to offer a wide choice of integral colours, to provide all important scale and to contribute greatly to the creation of new modern buildings and structures.

References

1. Wright, Frank Lloyd, "On Architecture," *Selected Writings*, Edited by F. Gutheim, New York, 1960.
2. Van der Rohe, L. Mies, "Inaugural Address", Illinois Institute of Technology, Chicago, 1938.
3. Collins, P., "Changing Ideals in Modern Architecture," McGill University Press, Montreal, 1965.

4. Design potential of masonry bearing walls.

Thomas E. Woodward, AIA, Woodward, Cape & Associates, Dallas, Texas

Many projects produced in our office during the past five years utilize masonry or masonry load-bearing construction because this type of construction offers a structural vocabulary for economical design execution.

Building should provide a physical structure which will accommodate the functional requirements of a particular activity; but most important, and herein lies the real challenge, it should create an appropriate physiological environment which contributes to the success of the activity. For example, a classroom may provide all the physical requirements for teaching and learning, but if it does not also stimulate the teaching and learning processes, then it is falling short of its purpose.

While the designer must offer as a minimum an acceptable solution to the functional requirements, he is primarily preoccupied with creating the appropriate environment. In considering a construction type or material the design motivations of the Architect are very important as are the creative possibilities of the material he uses.

Masonry load-bearing construction provides a variety of functions which other systems have to provide separately. It provides structural support, division of space, finished wall surfaces, fire and weather protection, and thermal and acoustical insulation. But the greatest advantage, and in my opinion the principal reason for its resurgence, is that it is a plastic material—that is, it is flexible and versatile in the hands of the designer and can be shaped to fulfill his design concept.

Architects are reacting to the manufactured slickness of steel and glass curtain walls, and are weary of the design process as an attempt to assemble catalog products. We want to shape and create totally individual designs. Structural brickwork is a wonderful medium with which to fulfill these aspirations.

Examples of Existing Masonry Structures

Office Building

Our initial experience with masonry was as brick in-filling walls in a seven-story office building in downtown Dallas. This concrete frame building has 8-inch brick walls forming the exterior enclosure. Brick met the design critera by providing the required enclosure with an interesting form, and also adding warmth in texture and color. These walls provide a maintenance free interior and exterior finish as well as thermal insulation and weather protection.

Using brick as the primary building material enabled us to design a building which would seem to have been there always, and hopefully, will age gracefully (See Figure 4-1).

Townhouse Development

This project is a 20-unit, three-story townhouse in Oklahoma City. The choice of brick was for structural, acoustical and aesthetic reasons. The use of masonry as the party walls between all units provides an excellent sound barrier, and by carrying these through the roof to form parapets, fire insurance costs were reduced. They extend beyond the exterior and exterior wall line to give a visual separation of the individual townhouse units. Each unit has a fireplace, and the chimneys add interest to the skyline (See Figure 4-2).

The Leaves Sanatorium

The nursing sanitorium in Richardson, Texas is a one-story bearing wall structure. Brick in the finish walls gives acoustical separation for privacy between individual patient rooms and provides relatively maintenance free walls. The arches use brick as a structural material to span the opening in the small-individual courtyards. This form contributes a sense of individuality in the rooms and is the primary aesthetic factor in the visual identity of the structure (See Figures 4-3, 4-4).

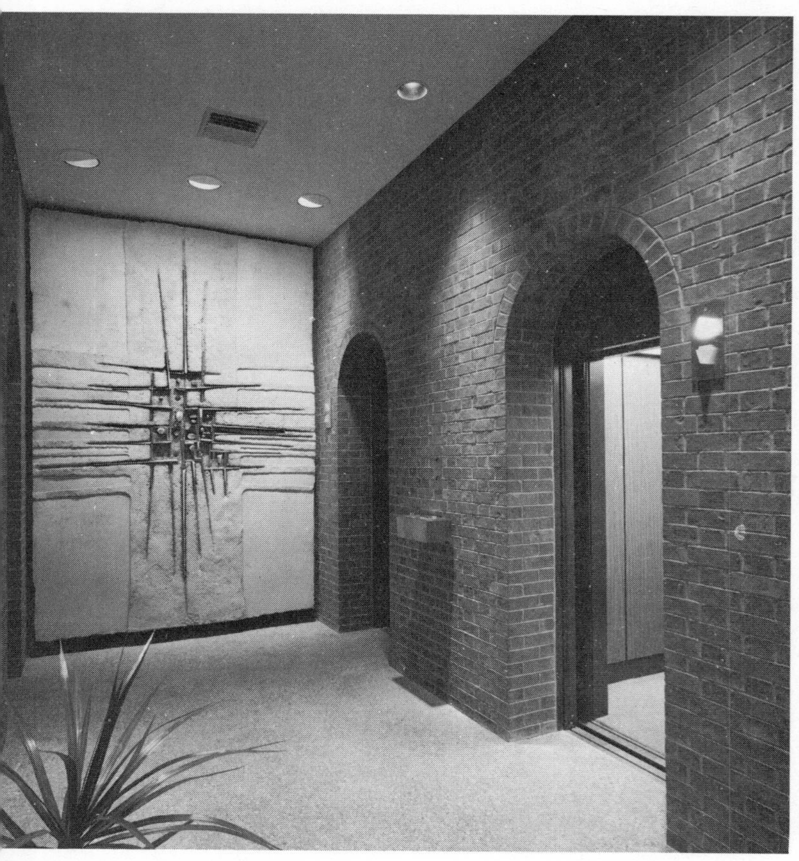

Figure 4-1. Brick used as a primary building material (Southwest Title Building).

Hahn-Cook Street and Draper Funeral Home

A funeral home in Oklahoma City uses masonry load-bearing walls throughout. These brick walls and piers, especially on the interior of the chapel and courtyard, illustrate some design opportunities in using masonry as a construction vocabulary. This technique has a geometry of its own which seems to inject into the design distinctive interest in detail, human scale and warmth (See Figure 4-5).

Office Building

The design of a two-story office building on a major expressway in Dallas was our first use of reinforced masonry load-bearing construction. This building is basically reinforced masonry piers at right angles to the exterior walls which support concrete spandrel beams carrying the floor and roof construction. A cost analysis run on the reinforced masonry versus rubbed concrete found the masonry to be somewhat cheaper.

These piers also form an arcaded two-story landscaped mall through the center of the building which becomes the building's main lobby. The brick piers give a depth to the exterior facade and create a strong visual image for a Mortgage and Investment Company's home office (See Figure 4-6).

Figure 4-2. Example of brick used for aesthetic, structural and acoustical purposes (Aberdeen Townhouses).

Figures 4-3 and 4-4. Brick arches contribute to individuality of rooms (Leaves Sanatorium).

Figure 4-5. Hahn-Cook Funeral Home uses masonry load-bearing walls throughout.

Jayhawker Apartment Towers*

The project is a privately owned apartment complex located in Lawrence, Kansas. The owners, who are University alumni, wanted an income-producing property which would also contribute significantly to the campus. They envisioned an environment oriented to student living which would accommodate approximately 1200 single and married residents in 300 apartment areas and include laundry facilities, vending machine areas, administrative offices, swimming pool, and common areas. The project was constructed in two phases; the first phase consisted of 150 apartments, related offices, and common areas, was ready for occupancy in September 1968.

The project site is on the brow of a hill overlooking the campus. It is bounded on three sides by University owned property and by a major street on the north. The site is in close proximity to all classrooms and existing University student housing. A large open field which bounds the site to the south affords a view to the distant plains. The site slopes sharply from west to east, with a grade variation of approximately 66 feet.

*Also see Chapter 52.

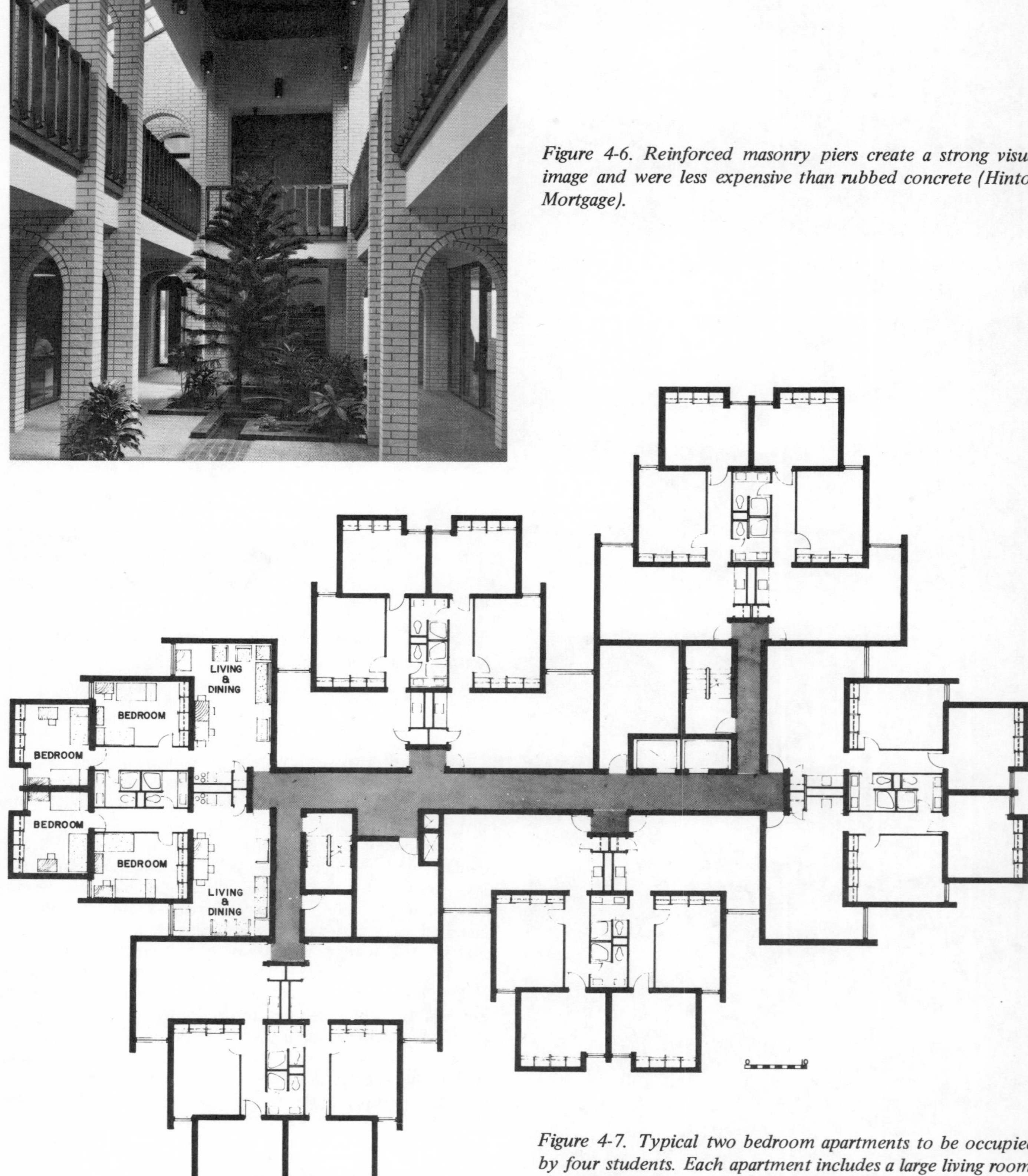

Figure 4-6. Reinforced masonry piers create a strong visual image and were less expensive than rubbed concrete (Hinton Mortgage).

Figure 4-7. Typical two bedroom apartments to be occupied by four students. Each apartment includes a large living room, a kitchenette, and a bath (Jayhawker Apartment Towers).

The solution to the problem was influenced largely by the sloping site, which required phasing, and the surrounding campus. Four six-story towers are clustered in a semi-circle around a large plaza facing south. The towers become walls which create outdoor spaces or rooms leading from this central plaza. These spaces step up and down the sloping site with the buildings forming an ever-changing spatial sequence for the pedestrian.

The courts formed by these spaces serve as multi-purpose activity areas for the apartment dwellers. The towers, designed to appear as one building to the passerby, blend with the scale of the existing campus buildings. They form a larger scale orientation of the project to the campus on the south and help define the campus from the residential area to the north. The pool is integrated into the main public space adjacent to the central plaza at an intermediate level. Landscaping, paving patterns, concrete retaining wall textures, and exterior lighting are all designed as an integral part of the project. A two-story administration building nestled between two of the towers serves as the main street side entrance of the project. An open arcade through the building forms a gateway for the major pedestrian movement.

Each tower contains six floors of apartments, plus a partial lower floor containing meeting rooms, laundry rooms, and mechanical rooms. A typical apartment tower floor has six apartment clusters with two apartments forming a cluster. Each cluster is terminated by a foyer. A typical two bedroom apartment with a large living room, kitchenette, and bath are occupied by four students. (See Figure 4-7.) The parking is distributed at opposite ends of the site in parking structures tucked into the slopes and conforming to the existing grades. The grouping of the buildings, with the parking, also facilitates the phasing of the project. (See Figure 4-8.)

Future Masonry Load-Bearing Structures

Recently, we have had an opportunity to develop some ideas using masonry load-bearing construction. This has provided the opportunity for a limited amount of research, giving us a glimpse of design possibilities with this construction technique.

We chose three building types which lend themselves to masonry load-bearing construction due to their program requirements. The case studies, a doctor's clinic (Figure 4-9), a hospital (Figure 4-10), and a senior citizens home (Figure 4-11), are all inherently cellular in nature. Although the projects are hypothetical, we made the design solutions real

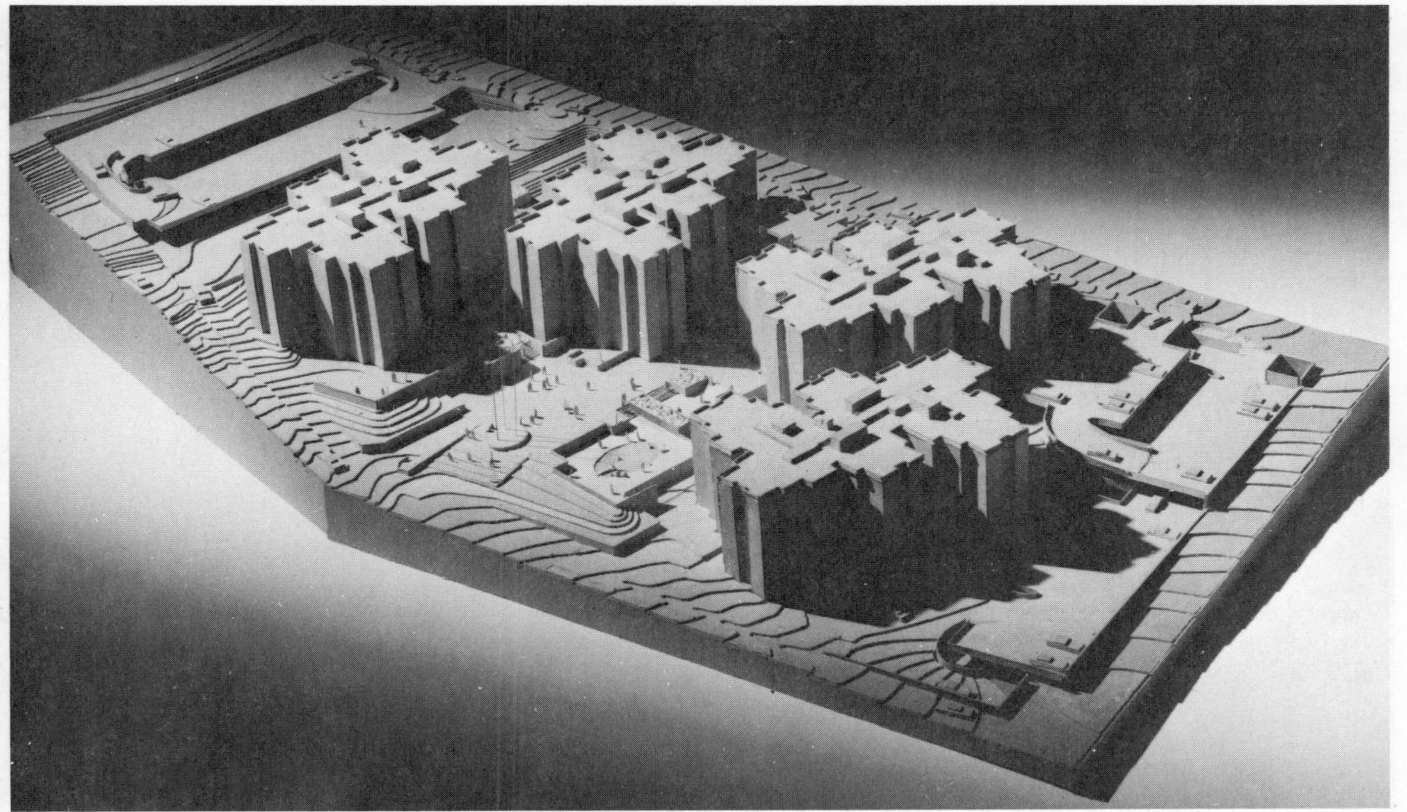

Figure 4-8. Jayhawker Apartment Towers consist of four six-story towers clustered in a semi-circle around a large plaza.

enough to satisfy anyone interested in a particular project, so they can be real solutions to real problems.

Our thinking has developed to a point where we now are investigating the use of masonry bearing wall construction in projects other than those which are cellular in nature. For example, we now have in the design stage an eight-story office building. The site is on a major expressway leading to the Dallas Central Business District. The client desires a building distinctive in design which will offer lease space to compete with existing speculative type office building. We feel it is feasible to design a masonry load-bearing structure at a cost competitive with the typical curtain wall type structure. Our past experience and preliminary estimates on this project bear this out.

In conclusion, I feel the importance of structural brickwork is in the possibilities it offers the designer for executing his design concepts and ideas. If he has conceived of a project as

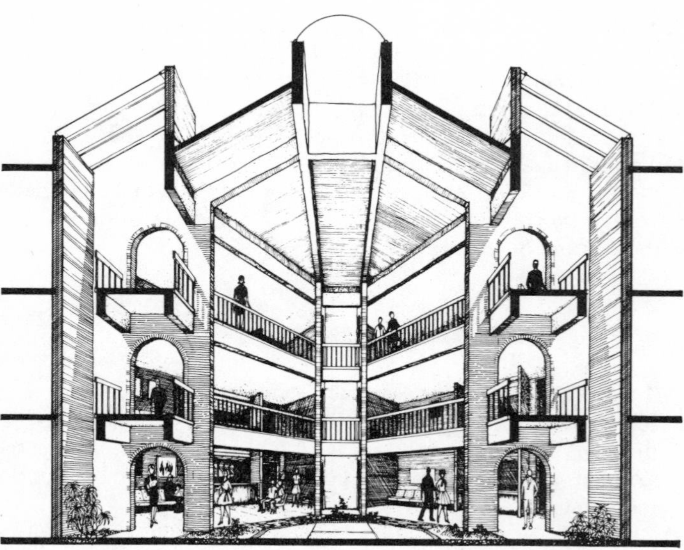

Figure 4-9. Courtyard section of a hypothetical doctors' clinic which lends itself to masonry load-bearing construction.

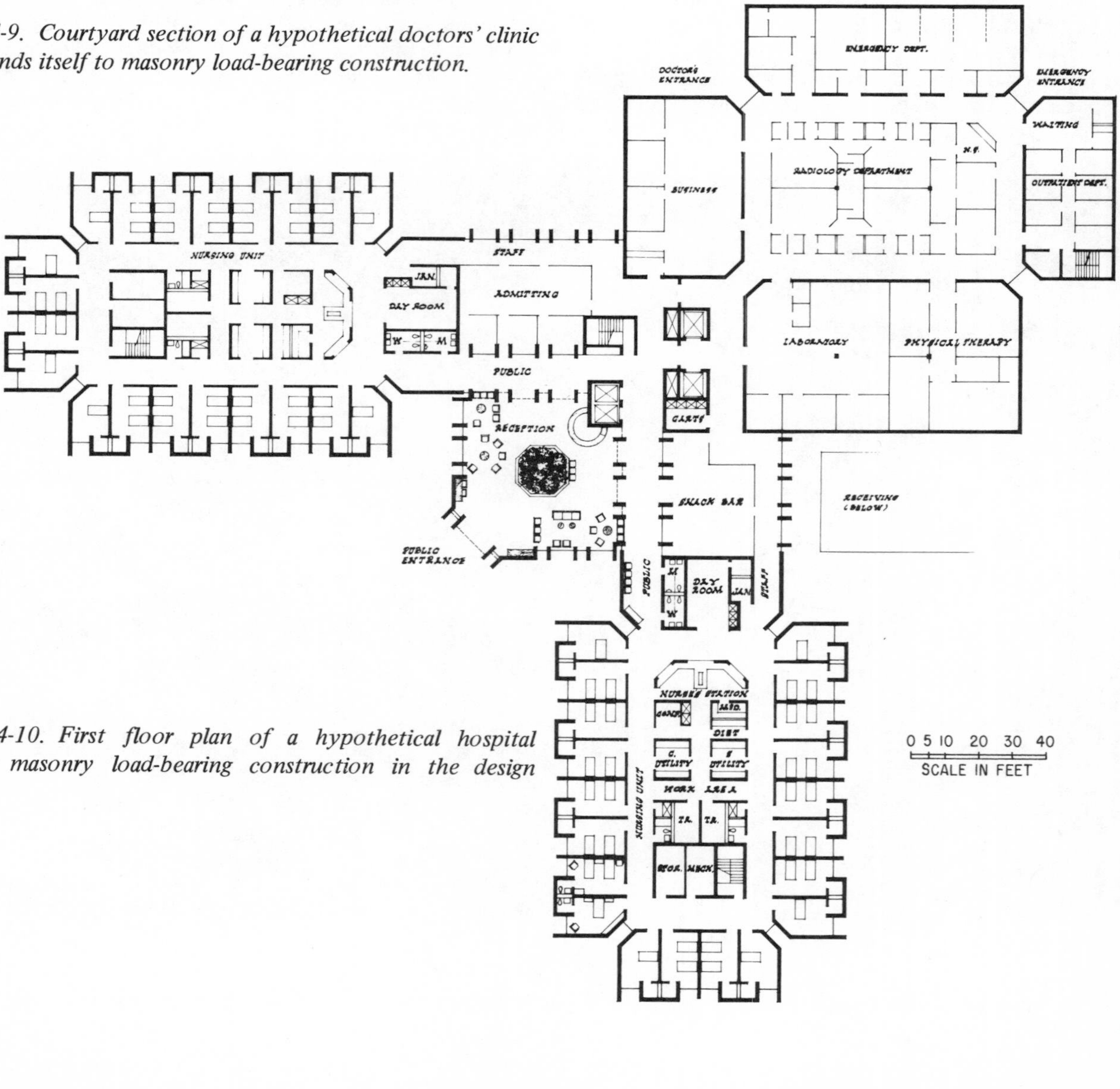

Figure 4-10. First floor plan of a hypothetical hospital utilizing masonry load-bearing construction in the design solution.

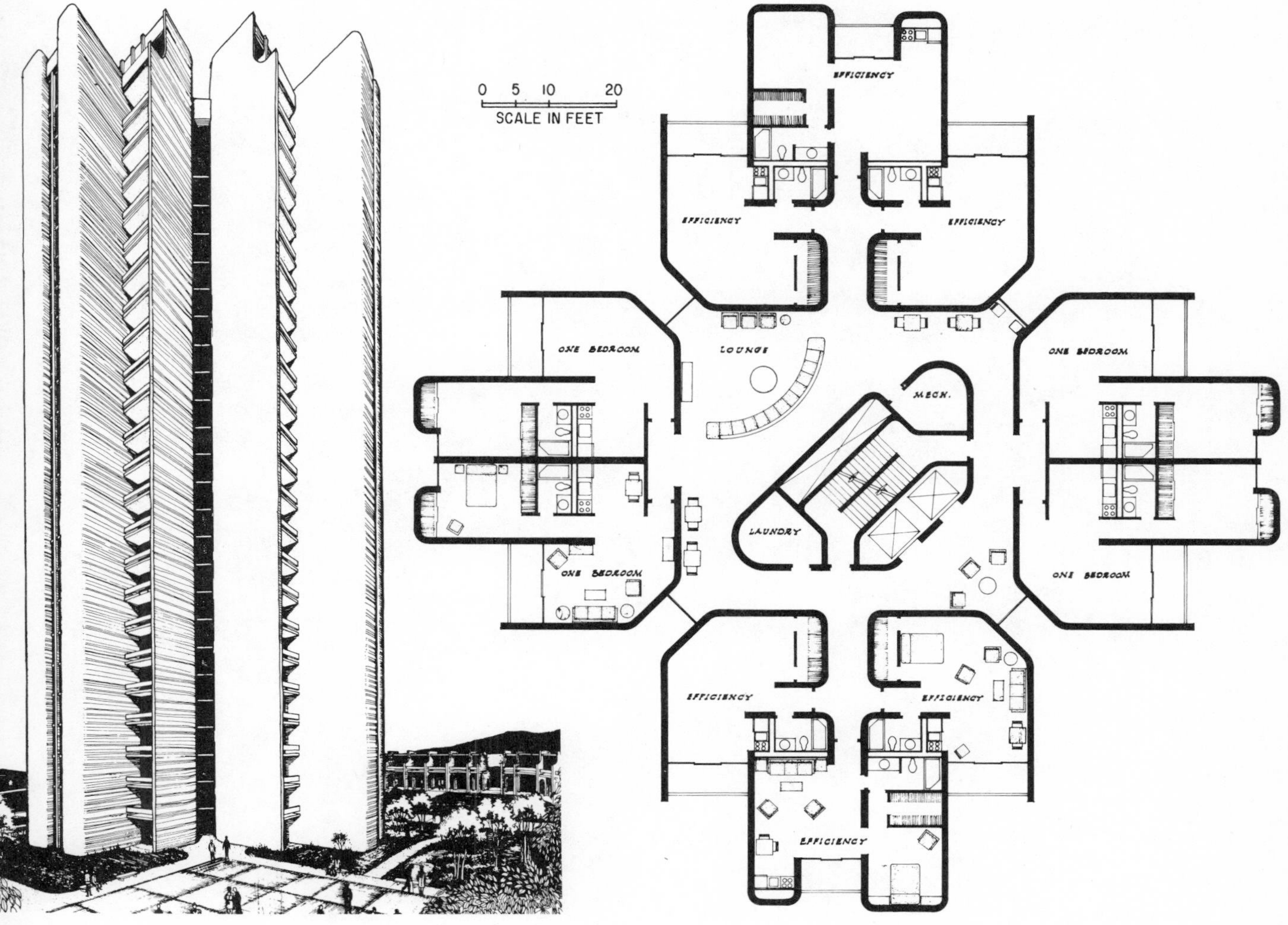

Figure 4-11. Design solution to a hypothetical senior citizens' home with self care living units.

executed by another construction technique, such as a structural frame of steel or concrete, then it is going to be very difficult for masonry bearing wall construction to compare favorably. So what is important is the Architect's concept of the structural material he wants as he is conceiving and sketching in the very preliminary stages. Thus will evolve structures fully utilizing the bearing type of construction which could not be economically executed in any other manner, and which visually, totally express the way they are built.

Part 2: Materials science relevant to structure

5. Study of the effect of certain modified mortars on compressive and flexural strength of masonry.*

Dallas G. Grenley, Dow Chemical Co., Midland, Michigan

Organic additives enhance the strength of mortars and concretes made from hydraulic cements. Commonly used entraining agents are perhaps best described as agents which extend the conditions under which cement products are useful rather than as agents which increase strength.

Next to this type of compound, polymeric additives, specifically snythetic latexes, have wider commercial acceptance than other types of organic materials suggested for strengthening cement products. Their use, however, has been generally restricted to mortars for resurfacing, patching, or grouting applications.

Yet, there is a distinct need for improved mortars in structural situations. As a structural system, masonry is almost always limited by strength of the mortar or the strength of the bond between the mortar and the brick. Nonetheless, with but one recent exception, latex modified cement mortars have not been suggested as structural materials.

This exception is a commercial polyvinylidene chloride latex designed to improve the performance of masonry mortars. Walls utilizing these mortars have been structurally tested, and uses based on their high strength have found a place in masonry design. The latex is used as an admixture to a mortar that is otherwise conventional in that it contains portland cement, sand, and limestone in typical ratios. Applied by masons using customary tools and techniques, it yields a bond strength and tensile strength almost an order of magnitude greater than that of conventional mortars. Its compressive strength is in the range of that of many brick.

Thus, while the effect of mortar properties on the strength of masonry has been extensively studied[1] this mortar suggests a new investigation as it extends ranges over which mortar properties may be investigated. More important, the mortar strength is such that the masonry frequently behaves as a monolithic unit. Thus, the natural sequence is new design concepts with improved masonry systems.

This question was investigated by measuring the behavior of full scale masonry walls under racking, flexural, and compressive loads as well as under combinations of these loads.

Before initiating a full scale testing program, however, it seemed advisable to study the relationships between brick and mortar properties and structure performance on a smaller scale to see what correlations might be evident. This could be readily accomplished since a wide variety of brick is available; changing the level of latex additive under controlled laboratory conditions offered a way to vary the strength of the mortar. Since the importance of this phase is in relative strengths of structures and not in values upon which structural design might be based, small scale masonry assemblages were adequate.

This paper reports and discusses the results of this small scale study. The concern here is not the mode of increasing the mortar strength nor the chemical or physical reactions within the mortar or between the brick and mortar. Rather, this is an attempt to measure the relative performance of masonry specimens using either high strength or conventional mortars.

Experimental Methods

Five different measurements were carried out. They were: 1) *Compressive strength of mortar*—Each batch of mortar

Figure 5-1. Compressive strength test specimens.

used was sampled and tested in accordance with ASTM C-91. Is this term clear to everyone?

2) *Brick physical properties*—ASTM C-67 techniques were used for compressive strengths, flexural strength, and absorption data. In addition an "unrestrained" compressive strength test suggested by Watstein was determined.[2]

3) *Compressive strength of masonry assemblies* was measured utilizing piers illustrated in Figure 5-1. They were constructed by an experienced mason on a level table using a level to insure that vertical surfaces were plumb. Joints were

Figure 5-2. Flexural test in progress.

3/8" thick, determined during construction by mason's eye; subsequent measurements indicated a very close tolerance. Full bed joints and head joints were used. Mortar beds were not furrowed. The selected structure pattern subjected head joints as well as bed joints and bricks to compressive stress. Piers were capped with plaster prior to testing to insure uniform loading.

4) *Flexural strength of masonry* was determined by utilizing test specimens, tested as shown in Figure 5-2. End supports were 16" apart, the load applied was 5-3/8" from either end support, and each was measured horizontally. The testing machine load was applied through devices having biaxial freedom of rotation which provided adjustment for complete load bearing and support bearing of the specimens. The load was transmitted through a small piece of fiber board to avoid localized bearing stresses during testing.

Figure 5-3. Flexural failure of brick experienced using conventional crossed-brick test with high bond mortar.

5) *Bond adhesion in tension* was measured by a cross-brick technique. The high bond strength of some mortars required a departure from customary techniques. If a crossed-brick adhesion test was run using the normal bed joint surface of the brick a premature shear failure of the brick occurred as illustrated in Figure 5-3. Brick were used edgewise; this presented a different surface to the mortar than the normal bed joint. Some thought was given to limiting the bonded area while retaining the customary orientation of the two brick; this, however, would prevent mortar flow as the upper brick was tamped onto the lower unit. Since a special technique was required for some mortars, it was used for all since the need was for relative rather than absolute data. The samples were prepared by laying one brick on a level surface between two jigs 3/8" higher than the brick. An excess of mortar was

Table 5-1

Brick Designation	Compressive Strength		Modulus of Rupture (MOR), psi	Absorption Data		
	Restrained psi	Unrestrained psi		Initial, grams in 1-min.	24 hr.	5 hr. boil
A	14,480	5470	848	6.2	3.3%	5.1%
B	20,660	5000	761	2.6	2.7%	3.3%
C	8,100	4680	676	2.5	8.7%	12%
S	17,560	6870	741	19.8	7.6%	10%

applied to the edge of the brick and another brick placed on the mortar at right angles to the lower brick. The upper unit was then tamped gently until barely contacting the jigs. Excess mortar was raked away and the sample allowed to cure. The test load was transmitted through supports having biaxial freedom of rotation to insure uniform loading.

Materials

While the interest here was in mortars, the nature of the brick also affects structure performance. Thus, a range of brick properties was desired. Table 5-1 describes the brick selected. They cover a wide range of compressive strengths, yet the highest and lowest have almost identical initial absorption rates. Two bricks are intermediate in compressive strength, one with a moderately higher absorption and another with a much higher absorption.

For both properties there is a reasonable range over which correlation studies might be made.

The brick are illustrated in Figure 5-4. Brick A is a cream colored, extruded, wire cut brick with 3 cores; B is grey, extruded, wire cut with 5 oval cores; C is a red, sand struck pressed brick with a 1/4" deep frog on one bedding surface; S is a red, solid, extruded and wire cut brick. Brick C was brushed throughly before use to remove loose sand. Brick dimensions are given in Table 5-2.

Figure 5-4. Brick specimens left to right C, A, S, B.

Mortars of five strength levels were used in this work. Fou contained the same inorganic mix:

94 lb Type I portland cement
50 lb fine limestone
3.5 cu ft masonry sand

The cement and sand met ASTM Specifications C-150 and C-144 respectively. The limestone passed a number 200 sieve The mason selected, according to his preferences, the amount of sand from within reasonable limits offered him. He then added water to get the consistency he preferred.

The mortar strength was varied by the amount of latex added. The latex used was a commercially available poly

Table 5-2
Brick Dimensions (inches)

Brick	Length	Width	Depth
A	7.97	3.63	2.35
B	8.08	3.75	2.25
C	8.15	3.64	2.24
S	8.00	3.62	2.26

Table 5-3
Mortar Compressive Strength, f'_c, psi

Mortar	f'_c	Average
1	3050 3000 3350 3360 3005	3150
2	4060 4125 3900 3620 3700	3825
3	4500 5125 5500 4750 4850	4945
4	6275 5500 5875 5860 5610	5825
5	500 485 515	500

Table 5-4
Test Results on Piers

Brick	Mortar	Compressive Strength f'c psi	Average	Flexural MOR psi	Average	Crossed-Brick Bond Adhesion f'c psi	Average
A	1	5857		52		52	
		5594	5448	57	57	62	55
		4895		59		60	
	2	5294		43		50	
		4983	5115	45	46	55	56
		5069		51		62	
	3	5872		138		120	
		6309	5985	147	145	128	113
		5774		149		90	
	4	6241		378		220	
		6223	6240	346	368	205	215
		6259		382		219	
	5	2899		39		28	
		2861	2880	35	35	30	29
				31			
B	1	5937		51		20	
		4980	5485	54	54	31	28
		5540		56		33	
	2	6497		57		88	
		6481	6315	58	59	66	76
		5969		63		74	
	3	7818		122		163	
		6942	7380	128	124	181	180
						196	
	4	7686		428		220	
		7591	7650	436	434	231	230
		7673		439		240	
	5	3532		42		10	
		3367	3450	45	46	12	11
				52			

Brick	Mortar	Compressive Strength f'c psi	Average	Flexural MOR psi	Average	Crossed-Brick Bond Adhesion f'c psi	Average
C	1	3223		10*	*	**	
		3206	3215	8	9		
				7			
	2	3161		8*	*	**	
		3101	3160	14	9		
		3218		6			
	3	3038		90		**	
		3427	3140		90		
		2954					
	4	3437		200		**	
		3083	3260	215	207		
				205			
	5	2714		**		**	
		2687	2700				
S	1	5105		10*			
		5416	5260	18	14*	<10	<10
	2	5086		16*		11	
		5447	5275	15	14*	15	14
		5292		11		15	
	3	6868		180		160	
		7515	6906	190	195	169	164
		6336		215		163	
	4	7494		214		>200	
		6940	7320	228	222	Brick	>200
		7529		224		Broke	>200
	5	3063		27		12	
		3298	3200	23	28	30	27
		3239		34		42	

* Values not accurate in ⩽20 range ** Values not determined ∮ Based on gross area

vinylidene chloride[3]. Mix number 1 contained none; number 2 contained 9.4 pounds; number 3 had 18.8 pounds; number 4 had 37.6 pounds. The fifth mortar was made from a proprietary masonry cement containing approximately equal volumes of cement and lime which was mixed with masonry sand in the ratio of 1 to 3 by volume.

All mortars were mixed in a barrel mixer with rotating blades—the usual commercial mixer used by masons on construction sites. An experienced mason constructed all specimens on a level table using conventional tools and techniques. The finish in all cases was a "struck joint," that is, the excess mortar extruded from the joint during construction was simply raked off by the mason's trowel.

All specimens were aged 35 days under ambient conditions in an air-conditioned laboratory.

All strength tests were performed on a 300,000 pound capacity hydraulic testing machine at the National Bureau of Standards. Loading was always applied through mechanical links that permitted biaxial rotation of the loading head to conform to the plane surface of the test specimen. Rates of loading were selected to cause specimen failure in from four to five minutes.

As is evident from the photographs, some exploratory strain gage work was done. This was done to develop techniques for future work and to obtain modulus data needed for calculations in work to be reported later.

Data from this series of tests are presented in Tables 5-3 and 5-4.

Discussion

Data from Tables 5-3 and 5-4 are presented in a series of graphs at the end of the chapter. Figure 5-7 is a graph for compressive strength, f'_c, relating values for the pier to those

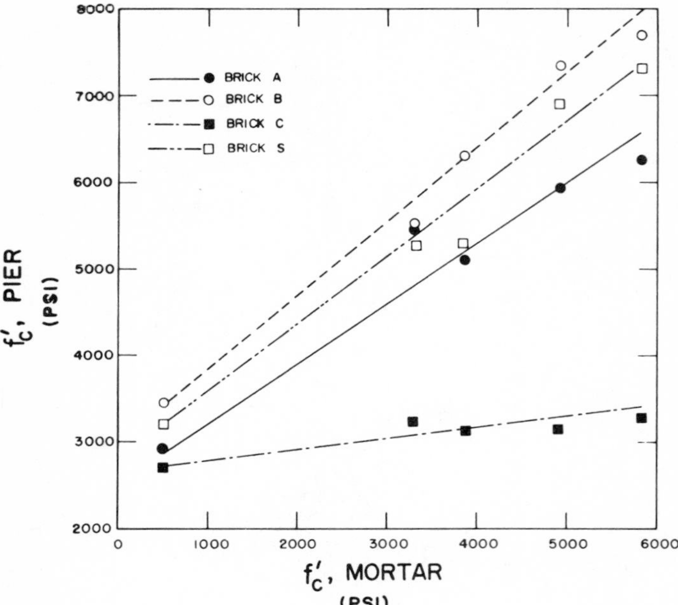

Figure 5-5. Pier Compressive strength vs mortar compressive strength.

of the mortar with the brick type shown as a parameter. The lines of Figure 5-5 were drawn in by eye to assist the readers's observation of the general relationships between variables. With three of the brick, the increase in pier strength as mortar strength increases is quite substantial. The fourth brick, designated C, yields piers of about 3200 psi regardless of the mortar type used. An explanation of this anomalous behavior may be that piers of this relatively weak brick fail explosively under compression as if there were a concentric delamination. Specimens built with brick A, B, or S exhibit the pyramidal fracture associated with compressive failure. The compressive strength of brick C is well above 3200 psi, yet this appears to be the maximum stress it can endure in a structural system. Figure 5-6 exhibits the same data as Figure 5-5, but uses the restrained brick compressive strength as one variable, with the mortar strength a parameter. There is indication that increasing the brick strength increases the pier strength when the piers are built with other than low compressive strength mortars. However, the weaker mortars produce piers whose strength approaches a limit with medium strength brick which is not increased by the use of higher strength brick.

No attempt has been made to fit curves to the experimental points shown in Figure 5-6, since each point represents a discrete combination of a number of parameters. Thus, it should not be expected that a smooth curve could be used to

Figure 5-6. Pier compressive strength vs brick compressive strength.

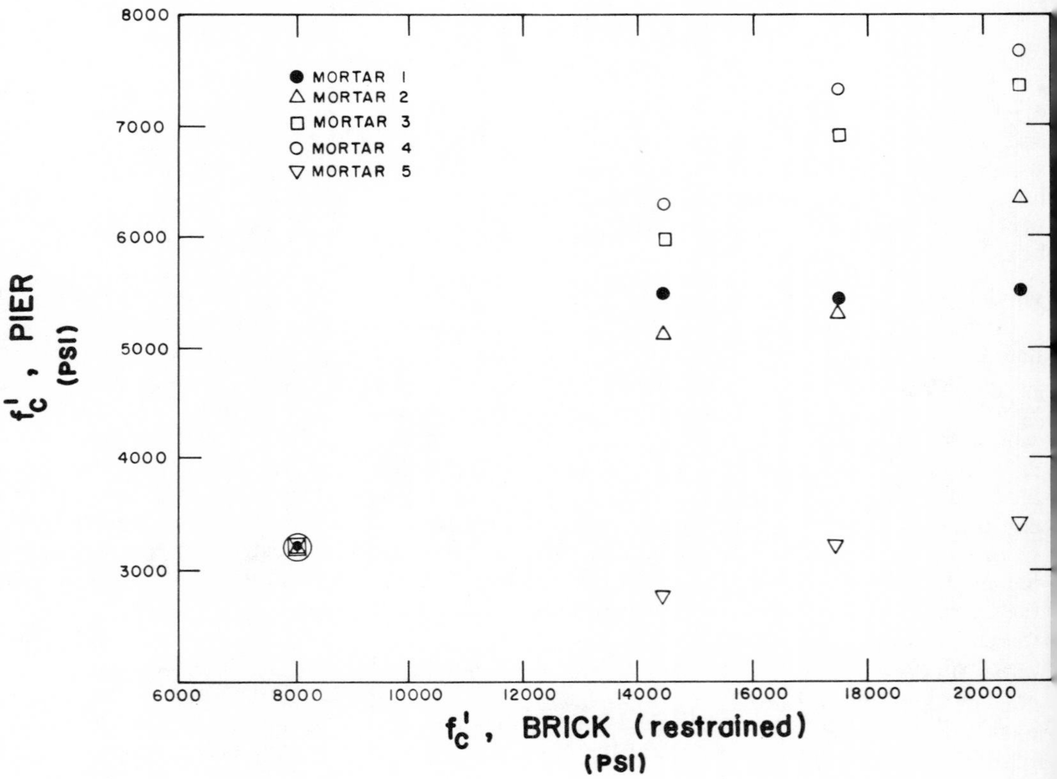

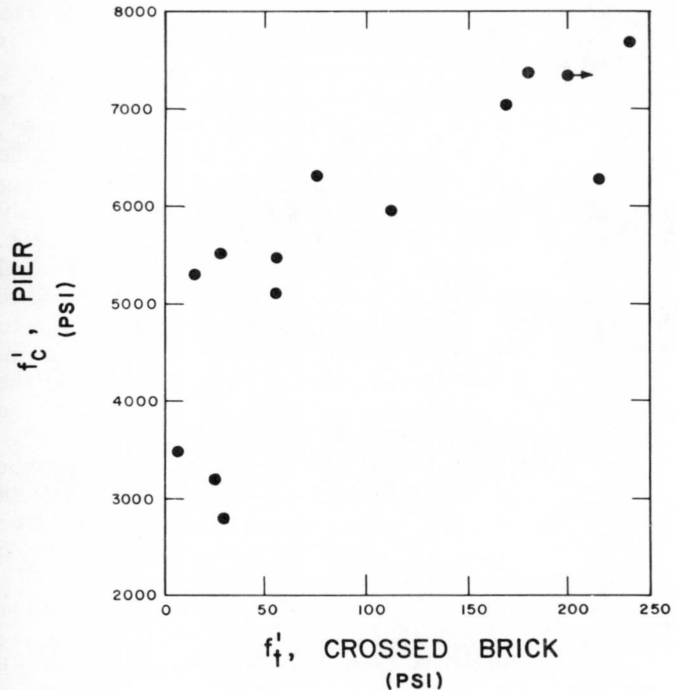

Figure 5-7. Pier compressive strength vs bond adhesion of crossed-brick.

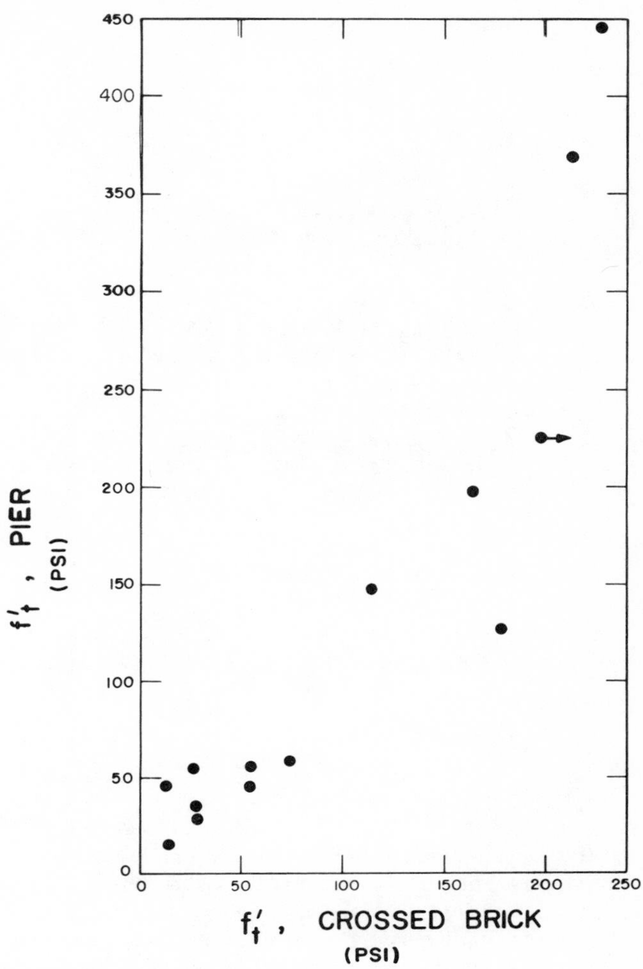

Figure 5-8. Pier flexural strength vs bond adhesion of crossed-brick.

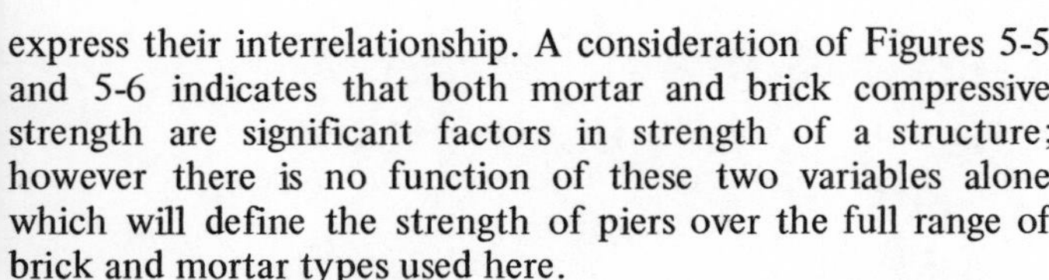

express their interrelationship. A consideration of Figures 5-5 and 5-6 indicates that both mortar and brick compressive strength are significant factors in strength of a structure; however there is no function of these two variables alone which will define the strength of piers over the full range of brick and mortar types used here.

Figures 5-7, which shows bond adhesion of crossed-brick couplets to compressive strength of the piers, suggests that the adhesion of mortar to brick plays a significant role in pier compressive strength. However, those mortars which are high in adhesion are also high in compressive strength; hence the contribution of each phenomenon is not clearly delineated.

Figure 5-8 illustrates the increase in pier flexural strength experienced by increasing the bond between the mortar and the brick. In some cases of very high bond strength, failure was tensile failure in the mortar or delamination of the brick.

Conclusion

Clearly, the structural strength of masonry can be markedly improved by increasing the strength of the mortars and the strength of the bond between the mortar and the brick. The inherent high strengths of clay masonry units can be more fully utilized in structures as better mortars are developed.

Acknowledgement

The author is indebted to Mr. R. E. Butler and Mr. Harvey Shirley of the National Bureau of Standards for their skilled assistance; to all the members of the Structures Section, Building Research Division, IAT, at the Bureau for their advice, help, and many courtesies during his too-brief time with them.

References

1. Fishburn, C. C., National Bureau of Standards, Monograph 36, November, 1961.
2. Watstein, Mr. David, NBS, private communication. The "unrestrained" compressive strength of a brick is measured between 1/8" thick teflon gasket-sheets rather than polished steel. Values reflect more nearly the performance of the brick in a structure under compressive stress.
3. Known as Sarabond [R], manufactured and supplied for these tests by the Dow Chemical Company.

6. Investigation into the failure mechanism of brick masonry loaded in axial compression.

Prof. Hubert K. Hilsdorf, Civil Engineering Dept., University of Illinois

Introduction

Structural engineers often hesitate to employ reinforced or unreinforced brick masonry as a structural material. This is not surprising. Despite the use of masonry over thousands of years, its potentials hardly have been utilized and our knowledge of its structural behavior is still quite limited. The prediction of masonry strength from known characteristics of bricks and mortar used in a masonry unit is rather unreliable. Therefore, acceptance of brick masonry units often require experimental determination of the compressive strength of a particular type of masonry rather than to predict it from known properties of its constituents. Because of these uncertainties, the allowable stresses for masonry are rather conservative; thus, the use of brick masonry as a load-bearing material may then become uneconomical.

In previous investigations[1,2], for a given slenderness ratio of the test piece and given coring pattern of the bricks, the masonry strength increased as the standard compressive strength of bricks and mortar increased. However, even if the strengths of mortar and bricks are approximately equal, the strength of the masonry is smaller than the strength of its constituents. Poor workmanship and low workability of the mortar generally result in masonry strength reduction. Furthermore, thick mortar joints reduce the masonry strength, and masonry strength is influenced by the water absorption of the bricks. However, these relationships exhibit unusually larger scatter.

From observations of brick failure mode, it was concluded that the failure of masonry loaded in compression is initiated by vertical cracking or splitting of the bricks. Therefore, various attempts have been made to relate the compressiv strength of masonry to the tensile strength of the bricks.[3]

Since a multitude of parameters govern the compressiv strength of brick masonry, a reasonably accurate estimate (the masonry compressive strength is possible only if thes parameters are considered simultaneously, and if the failu mechanism of masonry is taken into account. In the followin this failure mechanism will be studied and, based upon th discussion, a procedure will be developed which may enable t to predict strength and behavior of masonry units fro characteristic properties of its constituents which can b determined in simple tests.

The Stress State in Brick Masonry Subjected to Uniaxial Compression

Brick masonry is a two-phase material, both phases nc only have different strengths but also different deformatio characteristics. In general, the uniaxial compressive strengt and the modulus of elasticity of the mortar are considerabl lower than the corresponding values of the bricks. Therefor if the mortar could deform freely, its lateral strains would b larger than the strains in the bricks. This is especially true i the external load approaches the uniaxial compressive strengt of the mortar. However, because of bond and friction betwee brick and mortar, the mortar is confined. Thus, an interna state of stress is developed which consists of axial compressio and lateral tension in the brick and triaxial compression in th mortar (Figure 6-1). It is only because of this triaxial state o compression that a masonry unit can be subjected to externa stresses which exceed the uniaxial compressive strength of th mortar.

Even if care is taken in laying bricks, not all bricks will b evenly supported by their mortar bed. Then, in addition to th external load and the internal stress state described above, th bricks are subjected to flexural and shear stresses. Insufficient filling of the mortar joints or varying thickness of bricks and joints give rise not only to these flexural stresses, but they also result in an uneven distribution of the external load. Then, stress concentrations are developed in the bricks which may be considerably larger than the nominal average stress on which all calculations of masonry strength are generally based.

Results from an Experimental Investigation

With this concept in mind, the author has investigated the failure mechanism of clay brick masonry units while working at the Laboratory for Building Materials at the Technical University of Munich. A detailed description of this investigation is reported in Reference 4.

Most of the masonry specimens tested in this investigation consisted of five layers of bricks (Specimen Type B in Figure 6-2). The thickness of the mortar joints was 0.47 inches and 0.24 inches, respectively. The bricks, 9.2 by 4.2 by 2.7 inches, had a standard compressive strength of 5300 psi according to the German Specification DIN 105. The flexural strength of the bricks was 780 psi, their tensile splitting strength amounted to 410 psi. The major parameters in this study were type and strength of the joint mortar. Either lime mortars, lime-cement mortars or cement mortars were used. Their compressive strength was determined from prismatic specimens 1.6 by 1.6 by 4.1 in. and ranged from 21 psi for the lime mortar to 3500 psi for the high strength cement mortars. Additional data are summarized in Table 6-1.

Numerous strain measurements over a gage length of 2 in. at the surfaces of several bricks were carried out to study the state of stress acting in the bricks if the masonry unit was subjected to an axial load (Figure 6-2).

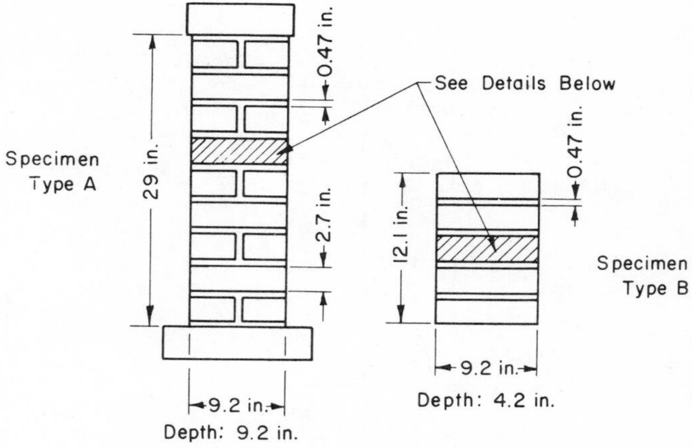

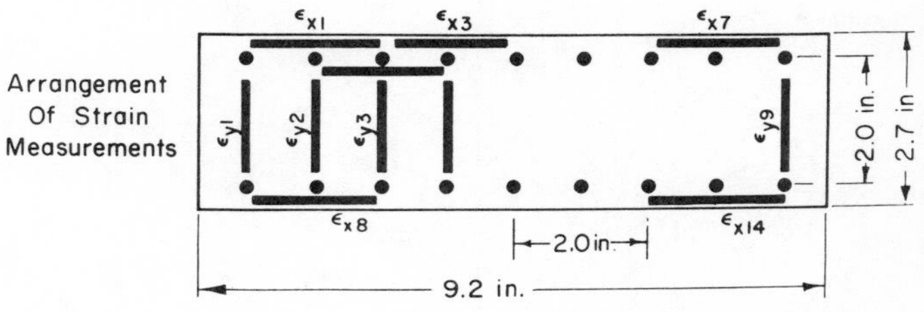

Figure 6-2. Types of specimens and arrangement of strain measurements.

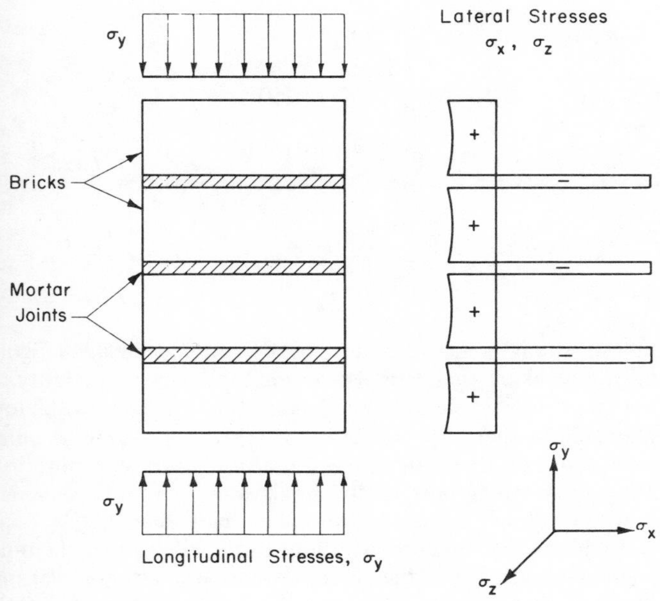

Figure 6-1. Idealized stress distribution in a masonry unit subjected to concentric compression.

In evaluating the strain measurements it was assumed that the stresses in the bricks acting in the horizontal x-direction are linearly distributed over the height of the brick. Then the stress σ_x can be separated into two components: (a) the flexural stresses σ_{xM} and the normal stresses σ_{xN} which are constant over the height of a brick. The stresses σ_{xN} can be attributed to differences in lateral strains between the mortar and the bricks. The flexural stresses may be caused by an uneven support of the bricks as described earlier.

For two specimens the distribution of lateral stresses σ_{xN} and σ_{xM} and of the longitudinal stresses σ_y across the width of a brick is given in Figures 6-3 and 6-4. These results confirm the original concept of the stress state in masonry. Lateral tension, whose magnitude increases as the external load is increased, was observed in the bricks. Despite the extreme care taken in manufacturing the masonry samples, the flexural stresses and an almost random distribution of the stresses in the direction of the external load could not be avoided.

Vertical cracking was observed in the bricks at loads considerably below the failure load. In most cases initial cracking occurred in sections in which the sum of the stresses $\sigma_x = \sigma_{xM} + \sigma_{xN}$ reached a maximum.

Table 6-1
Summary of Test Results

Specimen		Mortar			Bricks			Masonry Unit		
Nr.	Type	Type	f'_j	E_j	f'_b	f'_{bt}	E_b	f'_m	$f'_{m\ Calc.}$	U_u
–	–	–	psi	psi	psi	psi	psi	psi	psi	
1/1	A	lime cement	410	5.1×10^5	5300	450	2.2×10^6	2210	–	–
1/2								2370	2250	1.63
2	B	lime cement	410	5.1×10^5	5300	450	2.2×10^6	2930	2760	1.58
3/1								3460	–	–
3/2	B	cement	2550	3.1×10^6	5300	450	2.2×10^6	3100	2860	1.53
3/3								3290	2650	1.66
4/1								3600	–	–
4/2	B	cement	3500	3.5×10^6	5300	450	2.2×10^6	4850	3480	1.35
4/3								3320	3300	1.43
5/1								1060	–	–
5/2	B	lime	21	9.4×10^4	5300	450	2.2×10^6	1370	1610	2.18
5/3								1830	1870	1.88
6/1								1570	–	–
6/2	B'	lime	21	9.4×10^4	5300	450	2.2×10^6	1490	1910	1.85
6/3								1530	1790	1.95

joint thickness: specimens A, B: 0.47 in.
specimens B' : 0.24 in.

To express analytically the nonuniformity of the stresses in the direction of the external load σ_y, the nonuniformity coefficient, U, was introduced. This coefficient is the ratio between the maximum normal stress observed within one brick to the average normal stress acting on the masonry. The coefficient of nonuniformity is a function of the applied load. At low stresses, U decreases as the external load increases: local "yielding" or crushing of the mortar at points of high stress concentration results in a more even distribution of stresses. As failure approaches, the nonuniformity coefficient rapidly increases (Figure 6-5).

The coefficient of nonuniformity at failure is also a function of strength and workability of the mortar. As the mortar strength increases the coefficient U decreases (Figure 6-6). It is likely that U is also a function of the workability of the mortar. It should be larger for mortars with low workability than for mortars with high workability, since workable mortars result in more uniform joints and, thus, in more uniform support of the brick. However, this tendency cannot be clearly deduced from the available data.

If the local stress concentrations in the bricks were the only parameter affecting the compressive strength of various masonry units made from the same types of bricks, then failure should occur as soon as the maximum local stress $\sigma_y = U \cdot \sigma_{ym}$ exceeds the compressive strength of the brick, where U is the nonuniformity coefficient and σ_{ym} is the applied ıverage stress. In Figure 6-7 this maximum stress observed in nasonry units made of different types of mortar is given as a unction of the compressive strength of the mortar. Figure 6-7 hows, however, that as the compressive strength of the mortar ncreases, the maximum local stress in the brick at failure also ncreases. On a phenomenological basis this tendency can be xplained as follows: low strength mortars develop larger ateral tensile stresses in the bricks than do the high-strength nortars. In general, the compressive strength of brittle naterials in a given longitudinal direction decreases as imultaneously acting tensile stresses in lateral directions ncrease. Consequently, the maximum stress which the brick an sustain decreases as the mortar strength decreases.

An Analytical Procedure to Predict the Strength of Clay Brick Masonry Loaded in Compression

Figure 6-8 shows the development of stresses as they may ccur in a single brick within a masonry unit subjected to axial ompression. It is assumed that the lateral tensile stresses in he x and z directions, σ_x and σ_z, are equal. In Figure 6-8 hese stresses are given as a function of the local maximum tresses, σ_y, which act in the direction of the external load. The stresses σ_y can be computed from the average masonry

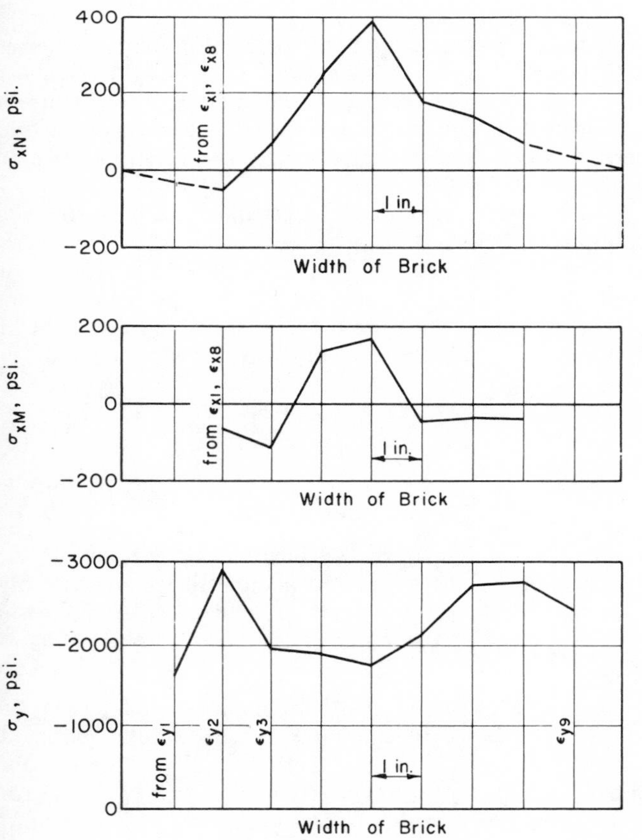

Figure 6-3. Distribution of stresses in a brick within specimen no. 2. Joints are lime-cement mortar. $\sigma_{ym} = 2400$ *psi.*

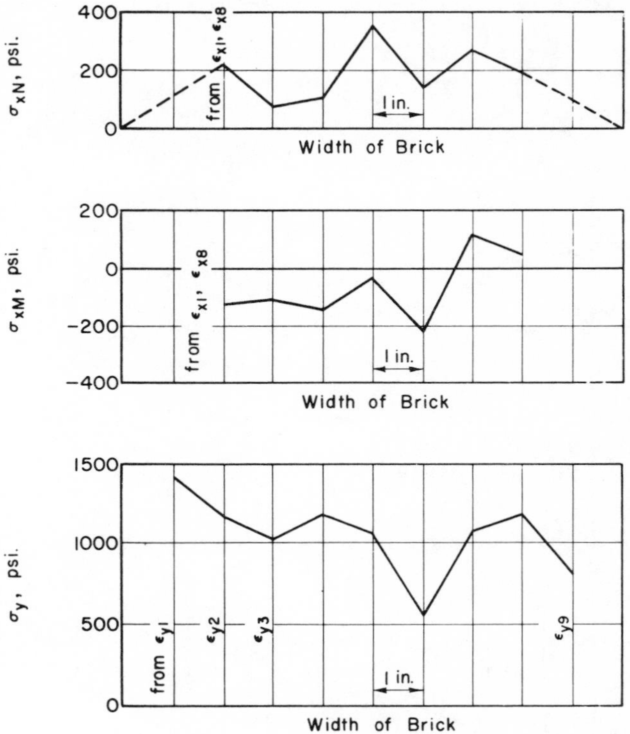

Figure 6-4. Distribution of stresses in a brick within specimen no. 5/3. Joints are lime mortar. $\sigma_{ym} = 1220$ *psi.*

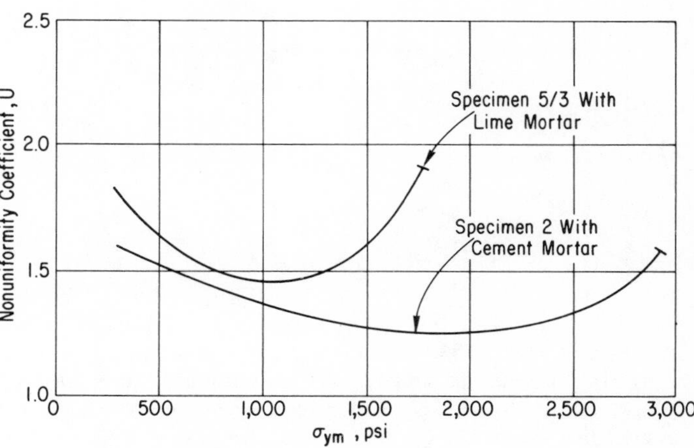

Figure 6-5. Nonuniformity coefficient as function of applied average masonry stress, σ_{ym}.

stresses, σ_{ym}, and the coefficient of nonuniformity U. Line A in Figure 6-8 represents the failure criterion for the triaxial strength of bricks and indicates the combinations of compressive stresses σ_y and lateral tensile stresses σ_x and σ_z which will cause local failure or cracking of the brick. For $\sigma_x = \sigma_z = 0$, σ_y is equal to the uniaxial compressive strength of the

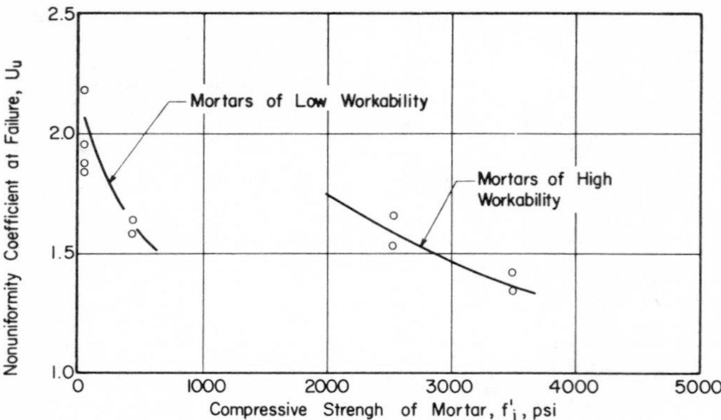

Figure 6-6. Variation of nonuniformity coefficient with type of mortar.

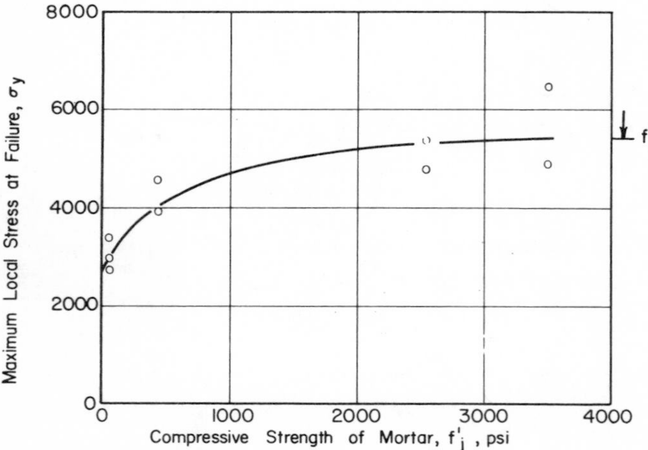

Figure 6-7. Maximum local stress in brick at failure.

brick. The exact shape of this failure criterion is presently unknown. If bricks follow Mohr's theory of failure assuming a straight line envelope, then this failure criterion would correspond to a straight line as shown in Figure 6-8.

If the masonry is subjected to external compression σ_{ym}, lateral tensile stresses σ_x and σ_z are developed following the dashed line B_1 in Figure 6-8. If this line intersects the failure criterion line A, local failure occurs; i.e., a crack is formed in the brick in a direction parallel to the direction of the external load. This, however, does not correspond to complete failure of the masonry unit. At the cracked section the lateral stresses diminish, and part of the flexural stresses in the uncracked sections of the bricks are relieved. If the external load is already larger than the uniaxial compressive strength, then the mortar has to be laterally confined. Therefore, a certain minimum lateral compressive stress has to act upon the mortar. This stress is counterbalanced by tensile stresses in the uncracked sections of the bricks. These minimum tensile stresses are represented by Line C in Figure 6-8. Wit increasing external load or increasing local stress, the minimur lateral tensile stress increases.

If the external load is increased beyond the load at firs cracking, then stresses in an uncracked section of the bric may develop along Line B_2. As soon as line B_2 intersects th failure criterion Line A, the second crack is formed. Thi process of cracking continues, and the brick may be split int small elements. Excessive cracking also results in an increase c the coefficient of nonuniformity (see test results in Figure 6-5

Under the best conditions, failure of the masonry occu when the lateral tensile strength of the brick is smaller tha the stress which is necessary to sufficiently confine the morta Therefore, the intersection of the failure criterion Line A an the minimum lateral stress Line C corresponds to the ultimat load of the masonry unit.

In Figure 6-8 the parameters which are known to affect th compressive strength of brick masonry are considered:

1. The uniaxial compressive strength of the brick.
2. The biaxial tensile strength of the brick.
3. The failure criterion for bricks under a triaxial state o stresses as represented by Line A.
4. The uniaxial compressive strength of the mortar whic corresponds to the onset of Line C in Figure 6-8.
5. The behavior of the mortar under a state of triaxi compression, determining the shape and inclination of Line C
6. The coefficient of nonuniformity.

Failure of the masonry may occur before Line A intersect with Line C: the stress state at the surface of the brick and th mortar joints is only biaxial, so the mortar is not sufficientl confined; therefore, spalling of the surface layers of the brick may occur at lower stresses and may result in a rapidl progressing failure.

The following equation is an attempt to express the failur criterion described above in an analytical form. No informa tion on the behavior of bricks under triaxial stresses wa available. Therefore, it was assumed that the failure criterio Line A as shown in Figure 6-8 corresponds to a straight line Then, Line A can be expressed by the following equation:

$$\sigma_x = \sigma_z = f'_{bt}\left[1 - \frac{\sigma_y}{f'_b}\right] \quad (6\text{-}1$$

in which $\sigma_x, \sigma_z, \sigma_y$ = stresses in x, y or z-direction
f'_b = uniaxial compressive strength of bric
f'_{bt} = strength of brick under biaxial tensio $\sigma_x = \sigma_z$

Line C corresponds to the minimum lateral tensile stres which has to act in the brick to sufficiently confine th mortar. It depends on the behavior of the mortar unde triaxial compression. No corresponding tests have been carrie out in this investigation. Therefore, it was assumed that th strength of the mortar under triaxial compression is similar t the strength of concrete under triaxial compression. Richart Brandtzaeg and Brown in their investigation of the triaxi strength of concrete[5] found that the triaxial strength of concrete can be approximated by the following expression:

$$f_1' = f_c' + 4.1\sigma_2 \qquad (6\text{-}2a)$$

In which f_1' = compressive strength of a laterally confined concrete cylinder
f_c' = uniaxial compressive strength of concrete cylinder
σ_2 = lateral confinement of cylinder

If Equation 6-2 is valid for mortars, then the minimum lateral confinement of the mortar joint is:

$$\sigma_{xj} = \frac{1}{4.1}(\sigma_y - f_j') \qquad (6\text{-}2b)$$

In which σ_{xj} = lateral compressive stress in mortar joint
σ_y = local stress in y-direction
f_j' = uniaxial compressive strength of mortar

For simplicity let us assume that the lateral stresses σ_x in bricks and mortar joints are uniformly distributed over the height of bricks and mortar. Then from the equilibrium condition it follows that

$$\sigma_{xb} \cdot b = \sigma_{xj} \cdot j \qquad (6\text{-}3)$$

In which σ_{xb} = lateral tensile stress in bricks
σ_{xj} = lateral compressive stress in mortar joint
b = height of brick
j = thickness of joint

Substituting Equation 6-3 in Equation 6-2a we obtain an expression for Line C in Figure 6-8

$$\sigma_x = \frac{j}{4.1_b}(\sigma_y - f_j') \qquad (6\text{-}4)$$

From Equation 6-1 and 6-4 the magnitude of the maximum local stress at failure, σ_y, can be determined. It corresponds to the point of intersection of lines A and C:

$$\sigma_y = f_b' \cdot \frac{f_{bt}' + a \cdot f_j'}{f_{bt}' + a \cdot f_b'}$$

where $a = \dfrac{j}{4.1b}$

Using the nonuniformity coefficient at failure U_u, the average masonry stress at failure can be expressed as

$$\sigma_{ym} = f_m' = \frac{\sigma_y}{U_u}$$

Then we obtain as a general expression for the axial compressive strength of masonry:

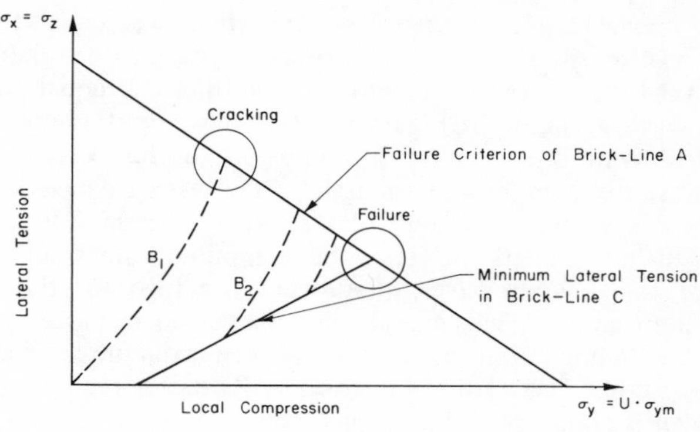

Figure 6-8. Failure criterion of brick masonry.

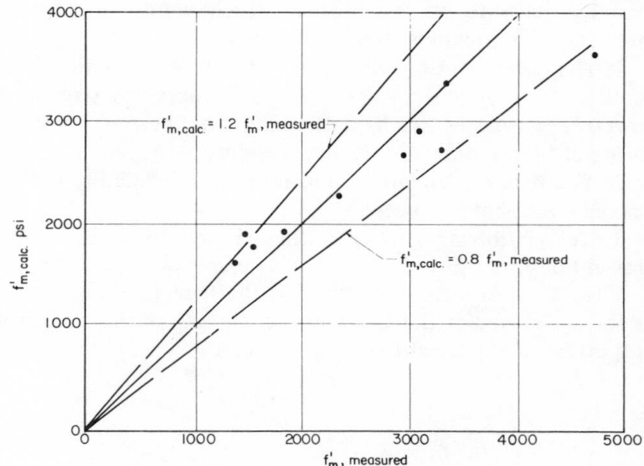

Figure 6-9. Comparison of measured and computed values of masonry strength.

$$f_m' = \frac{f_b'}{U_u} \cdot \frac{f_{bt}' + a \cdot f_j'}{f_{bt}' + a \cdot f_b'} \qquad (6\text{-}5)$$

This expression depicts the known relationships between the compressive strength of masonry and various parameters: masonry strength increases with increasing compressive strength of bricks and mortar, with increasing tensile strength of bricks, and with decreasing ratio of joint thickness to height of brick. It should be realized, however, that U_u is not a constant but depends on a number of parameters including the joint thickness and the mortar strength.

Conclusions

Equation 6-5 was used to evaluate the results of this investigation. The biaxial tensile strength of the bricks or the relationship between uniaxial tensile strength and biaxial tensile strength were unknown. Therefore, it was assumed that the biaxial tensile strength of the brick was equal to its uniaxial tensile strength. Furthermore, it was assumed that the uniaxial compressive strength of the bricks is equal to its standard strength. In Figure 6-9 the masonry strength computed from Equation 6-5 is compared to the experimental results: the compressive strength of the test specimens could be predicted within a range of ± 20% of the actual values. For the higher strength mortars, the computed values generally were too low; however, they were too high for the low-strength mortars. This may be due to an erroneous assumption of the failure criterion for bricks and mortar under triaxial stress states. The relationship given by Richart, Brandtzaeg and Brown is empirical and is not necessarily the same for all types of mortars. Nevertheless, this rational approach in the prediction of the compressive strength of masonry units appears to be promising. Before a general applicability of Equation 6-5 could be recommended, various characteristic properties of masonry have to be established which were normally not investigated in previous studies. These are:

1. The coefficient of non-uniformity, U, as a function of (a) quality of workmanship, (b) type and compressive strength of mortar, (c) type of bricks, (d) pattern of masonry unit and coring of bricks, and (e) thickness of joints.

2. The behavior of bricks and mortars subjected to defined triaxial stress states.

3. A relationship between the strength of bricks under biaxial tension, uniaxial tension and flexure.

Then an approach as outlined in the foregoing may enable us to safely predict the compressive strength of masonry from properties of its constituents which can be easily determined in standard tests.

Notations

a	Coefficient to evaluate Equation 6-5
b	Height of brick
E	Modulus of elasticity
f_c'	Uniaxial compressive strength of brick
f_{bt}'	Biaxial tensile strength of brick
f_c'	Compressive strength of standard concrete cylinder
f_j'	Uniaxial compressive strength of joint mortar
f_m'	Compressive strength of masonry unit
f_l'	Compressive strength of standard concrete cylinder which is confined by a stress σ_2
j	Thickness of mortar joint
$\sigma_x, \sigma_y, \sigma_z$	Stresses in x, y and z-direction
σ_{xb}	Stress in brick acting in x-direction
σ_{xj}	Stress in mortar joint acting in x-direction
σ_{ym}	Average masonry stress in y-direction
σ_2	Confining pressure of a concrete cylinder
U	Nonuniformity coefficient
U_u	Nonuniformity coefficient at failure

References

1. Monk, C. B., "A Historical Survey and Analysis of the Compressive Strength of Brick Masonry," Structural Clay Products Research Foundation, Geneva, Illinois, Research Report No. 12, 1967.
2. Graf, O., "The Load Carrying Capacity of Masonry, especially of One-Story High Walls," Fortschritte und Forschungen im Bauwesen, Reihe D, No. 8, Stuttgart, 1952.
3. McBurney, J. H., "The Effect of Strength of Brick on Compressive Strength of Brick Masonry," Proceedings, American Society for Testing and Materials, Vol. 28, Part II, 1928, pp. 605-634.
4. Hilsdorf, H., "Investigation into the Failure Mechanism of Brick Masonry," Material prufungsamt f.d. Bauwesen, Technische Hochschule, Munich, Report Nr. 40, 1965.
5. Richart, F. E., Brandtzaeg, A., Brown, R. L., "A study of the Failure of Concrete under Combined Compressive Stresses," Bulletin 185, University of Illinois Engineering Experiment Station, 1928.

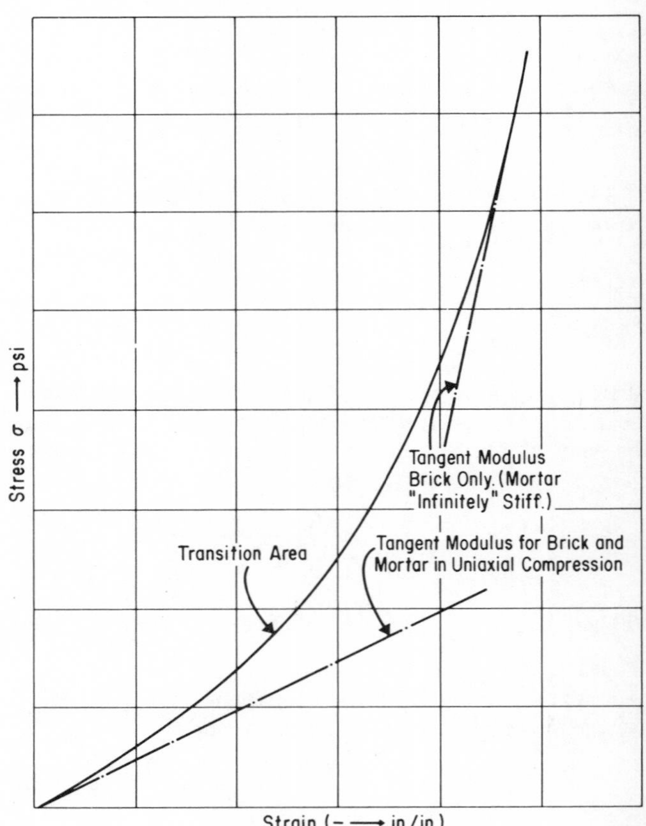

Figure 6-A. Stress strain curve.

Remarks

By Bob D. Campbell
Bob D. Campbell & Company, Structural Engineers

I was impressed by the mutual support of papers 2 and 7 of the third session (chapters 6 and 11). Professor Hilsdorf's paper, "An Investigation Into the Failure Mechanism of Brick Masonry Loaded in Axial Compression" clearly answered the question of "Why" the tangent modulus of elasticity increased with load on the stress-strain curve of "Experimental Investigation on the Structural Performance of Brick Masonry Prisms" by Dr. Rao. This increase was not necessarily slackness of experimental set up, nor was it densification of mortar, per se, as Dr. Rao proposes. It more likely is a picture of the mortar shifting from uniaxial compression to the triaxial compression condition reported by Professor Hilsdorf.

At the start of the loading it appears the tangent modulus is the result of the combination of the shortening of the brick plus that of the mortar in uniaxial compression. The final Tangent modulus is more nearly that of the brick alone. That is, with a true triaxial compression condition Poisson's ratio is zero, and the mortar, so confined, is infinitely stiff. See Figure 6-A herewith.

The curved transition between the two end conditions is the interesting part of the graph. It appears to be a "picture" of that which is taking place, and I feel it should be closely analysed as future research in the interaction of brick and mortar.

I would like to commend the whole conference and these two authors in particular for the contribution to a more complete understanding by the practicing professions in masonry construction of many of the actions of brick, mortar, concrete, etc. when combined.

7. Properties of masonry cement mortars.

Albert W. Isberner Portland Cement Assoc., Skokie, Illinois

Introduction

Since the late 1920's when masonry cements first entered the construction materials market, their acceptance by the masonry industry has increased production to 23 million barrels in 1966[1]. The marketing of a "one-bag" cementitious material which balances the economic selection of cementitious material with plasticizer has been most successful. This material provides the desired characteristics of masonry mortars in the plastic and hardened state.

Historically, masonry mortars have progressed from the sand-lime mortars early in the century to the present cement-plasticizer-sand mixtures. Sand-lime mortars, which depend on carbon dioxide for carbonation and strength development, were adequate for the massive construction then built using relatively slow-paced construction procedures. However, when natural and portland cement were introduced they proved to be compatible with limes and produced a desirable early setting, thus permitting more rapid construction. As the masonry construction rate increased, the acceptance of portland cement additions increased until, at the present time, sand-lime mortars are seldom used.

The first masonry cements combined portland cement and lime. These blends eased the construction site mixing operation and increased the quality control.

Plasticizers other than lime were interground with portland cement to cut the cost and to provide a more desirable cement for masonry construction. Plasticizers, such as clay and limestone, and air-entraining agents provide mortars with increased workability. These plasticizers improved workability without sacrificing setting and hardening properties. As the new formulations entered the construction market, they were field tested to check performance of the mortar and to ascertain the acceptance by the mason.

Present-day masonry cements are considered custom cementitious materials for masonry construction. Their wide acceptance and the paucity of complaints or failures supports their present use for general masonry work. The gro interest in engineered masonry may require modificatio the formulations.

This report reviews specifications related to mas mortars and summarizes the writer's opinion regarding ification of present-day formulations for engineered masc

Mortar Types in Current Use

The current specifications for mortars for unit mason the American Society for Testing and Materials[2], Table recognizes five mortar types: M, S, N, O and K. Mortar are further identified by proportion, property specifica and cementitious combination. Portland-masonry cement tars and masonry cement mortars are identified as Type M S, and N mortars, respectively, in the proportion specific Their mortar type classification under the property ification is dependent solely on their combined str characteristics determined using standard laboratory tests

The proportion specification identifies mortar type th mix proportions, by volume, of combinations of po cement with masonry cement, masonry cement singly combinations of portland cement and lime. The aggreg cementitious material ratio of the mixture is cont between 2¼ and 3 times the sum of the individual volun cementitious materials.

The property specification identifies mortar type wi average cube compressive strength of mortar mixtures days. This specification allows combination of po cement, masonry cement, and lime to attain the d strengths. The aggregate to cementitious material ratio mixture is controlled at 2¼ to 3½ times the sum individual volumes of cementitious materials.

Another physical requirement of both specifications water-retention limit. The flow after suction of m possessing an initial flow of 100 to 115 percent must 70 percent.

Lime is normally proportioned in the field using 50 lb of lime with 94 lb. bags of portland cement. In p

Table 7-1
Mortars for Unit Masonry
ASTM Designation: C 270-64T

Proportions Specification*					Property Specification	
Water Retention					Water Retention	
Flow after suction of mortar with an initial flow of 100 to 115%, min				70%	Flow after suction of mortar with an initial flow of 100 to 115%, min	70%
Proportions by Volume					Aggregate Ratio	
Mortar Proportions, by Volume					Damp loose volume of aggregate to volumes of cementitious materials	2¼ to 3½
Mortar Type	Portland Cement	Masonry Cement	Lime	Aggregate	Compressive Strength	
Portland Cement–Masonry Cement Mortars					Average compressive strength of three 2-in. cubes, initial flow 100 to 115%	
M	1	1	–	2¼ to 3 times the sum of the cements	Mortar Type	Average Comp. Str. at 28 days, psi
S	½	1	–			
N	0	1	–			
O	0	1**	–			
Portland Cement–Lime Mortars						
M	1	–	¼	2¼ to 3 times the sum of cement plus lime	M	2500
S	1	–	¼-½		S	1800
N	1	–	½-1¼		N	750
O	1	–	1¼-2½		O	350
K	1	–	2½-4		K	75

*Unless data are presented to show that the mortar meets the requirements of the property specifications, the proportion specifications shall govern. Mortar shall be accepted under only one set of specifications.

**Type I or Type II masonry cement. (ASTM C 91-66 no longer identifies masonry cement by types.)

laboratory testing of portland lime mixes, the blending of portland and lime is in the proportion of 94 lbs. of portland cement to 40 lbs. of lime. Currently ASTM is attempting to modify the laboratory testing specification to require the blending of 94 lbs. portland cement to 50 lbs. lime. This requirement as well as an increase in minimum water retention from 70 percent to 75 percent, applies to mortar Types M, S, N, and O. Type K mortar will be deleted.

The individual materials of masonry construction are further controlled by product specification to insure their desired performance. Individual specifications in masonry cement mortar materials are described below.

Masonry Cement

The current specification for masonry cements of ASTM[3] is a property specification governing masonry cements for general masonry use. The 1965 version of this specification was approved as USASI standard A1.3-1965. Physical requirements are imposed on fineness, soundness, time of setting, compressive strength, air content, and water retention. An optional staining requirement, limiting the maximum water soluble alkali content, may be imposed where deemed essential. The physical requirements of ASTM C 91-66 are shown in Table 7-2.

Presently, this specification is being revised to include a maximum air content limit of 24 percent and to replace hand mixing with mechanical mixing of pastes for normal consistency, soundness, and time of setting tests.

Aggregates for Masonry Mortars

The current specification for aggregates for masonry mortars of ASTM[4] is a major revision of previous specifications. This specification applies to natural and manufactured sand. The specification imposes grading, composition, and soundness limits on the masonry aggregates. The specified requirements are shown in Table 7-3.

Table 7-2
Standard Specification for Masonry Cement
ASTM Designation: C 91-66

Physical Requirements	
Fineness, residue on a 325 sieve, max., %	15
Soundness	
Autoclave expansion, max., %	1.0
Time of Setting, Gillmore Method	
Initial Set, min. hr.	2
Final Set, min. hr.	24
Compressive Strength, 2-in. Cubes	
7 days, min., psi (kg/cm^2)	500 (35)
28 days, min., psi (kg/cm^2)	900 (63)
Air Content, min., %	12
Water Retention, flow after suction, min. % of original flow	70
Optional	
Water soluble alkali, max., %	0.03

Table 7-3
Aggregates for Masonry Mortars
ASTM Designation: C 144-66T

Materials	
Natural Sand and Manufactured Sand	
Grading	
Item	Limit
Percent Passing Sieve	
No. 4 (4.76 min.)	100
No. 8 (2.38 min.)	95 to 100
No. 100 (149 – μ)	25 max.
No. 200 (74 – μ)	10 max.
Percent Modulus	1.6 to 2.5
Water Demand, ratio by weight	0.65 max.
Composition	
Deleterious Substances	
Friable particles, max., % by wt.	1.0%
Lightweight particles with specific gravity of 2.0 or less, max., % by wt.	0.5%
Organic Impurities	
Color standard	
Petrographic analysis	
Cube strength, ratio of unwashed to washed sand mortars, %, min.	95%
Soundness	
Weight loss after 5 cycles, max.	
Sodium sulfate solution	10%
Magnesium sulfate solution	15%

Masonry Cement Manufacture

Masonry cements are manufactured by intergrinding, blending, or combining these two processes. The three processes allow proportioning clinker, gypsum, supplemental materials, and additives to yield a product meeting existing specifications.

Properties of Masonry Cement Mortars

Portland cement is the major constituent of masonry cement, and the performance of cement mortars is largely dependent on the amount of cement in it. Tricalcium silicate and tricalcium aluminate are the two chemical compounds in portland cement that contribute to early strength development.

The portland cement fraction of a masonry cement requires water to initiate and continue the hydration for setting and hardening. Thus, the availability of water for hydration is of prime importance. When mortars are mixed, water is added until the mortar attains the proper workability. This mix water is readily available for cement hydration which begins with hydration of the tricalcium aluminate. After mixing, when the mortar is either on the mason's board or in the masonry, hydration of the tricalcium aluminate continues and the hydration of the tricalcium silicate becomes important. As hydration continues, along with absorption by the masonry unit and evaporation, the water available for hydration may decrease until the hydration process is slowed and finally stopped.

Proper curing of mixtures containing portland cement is recommended to prolong this hydration process. Application of water or maintenance of moist environments greatly prolongs the hydration period and increases the cementing characteristics of the portland cement component. Although curing during the early periods after placement is most effective, the application of water at later ages will reactivate the hydration process. These principles of curing have been well documented and practiced for concrete construction, but curing of masonry is seldom practiced. Laboratory tests to determine the hydration period in masonry, relying only on the water initially in the mortar and no addition or prevention of evaporation, showed that less than 3 days of hydration are available for the mortar immediately adjacent the mortar joint surface.

The performance characteristics of mortars, i.e., their properties, are evaluated by laboratory tests. A discussion of mortar properties, their significance, and means of attaining or altering the properties follows.

Workability. The workability of a masonry mortar is difficult to define and equally difficult to measure. The mason's appraisal of workability of plastic mortars depends on its ability to be spread easily, its ability to cling to vertical surfaces, and its resistance to flow during placement of a masonry unit. In laboratory tests, workability is recognized as a complex rheological property which includes adhesion, cohesion, density, flow-ability, plasticity, and viscosity. Although research continues to measure these individual properties, no one test method, per se, measures workability. In performing his task, the mason integrates these influences and arrives at a subjective determination of the mortar's workability.

In the laboratory, the evaluation of mortar properties is made using mortars having the same flow. They may or may not have comparable workabilities, as judged by a mason. In the flow test, a truncated cone of mortar is subjected to twenty-five 1/2-in. drops of a standard flow table, (Figure 7-1). The diameter of the disturbed sample is equated to the original diameter of the conical mortar sample. Mortar mixtures with water additions gaged to this standard mortar flow are then used in evaluating other properties.

Water Retention. The water retention characteristics of plastic mortar reflects the mortar's ability to retain its mix water when subjected to an absorptive force. Water retention as measured in the laboratory compares the flow of a mortar sample after being subjected to a vacuum (2-inches of mercury for 1 minute) to the original flow of the mortar.

Water retention in the field is evidenced by the mortar's ability to remain workable after contacting an absorptive masonry unit. Mortars with low water retention lose water rapidly from the mortar bed, making placement of the units difficult, whereas mortars with high water retention retain the water and allow easy unit placement. Water retention and masonry unit absorption should be balanced to prevent the units from "floating" and thus causing unnecessary delays in construction.

The mortar's retention can be increased by additions of water, air-entraining agents, and finely ground plasticizers such as limestone, clay and lime.

Compressive Strength. The mortar's compressive strength is a measure of its ability to support an imposed compression force. Compressive strength is the mortar property normally specified to show early age and continued strength development. Because strength reflects the degree of hydration which also influences other performance characteristics, it serves as an indicator of other physical properties.

Compressive strength as measured in the laboratory involves casting, curing, and testing 2-in. cubes in compression (Figure 7-2).

Tensile Bond. The tensile bond strength is the adhesive strength developed between mortar and masonry unit. The tensile bond developed is influenced by the masonry unit and the mortar. The mortar must possess the ability to flow and

Figure 7-1. Flow test.

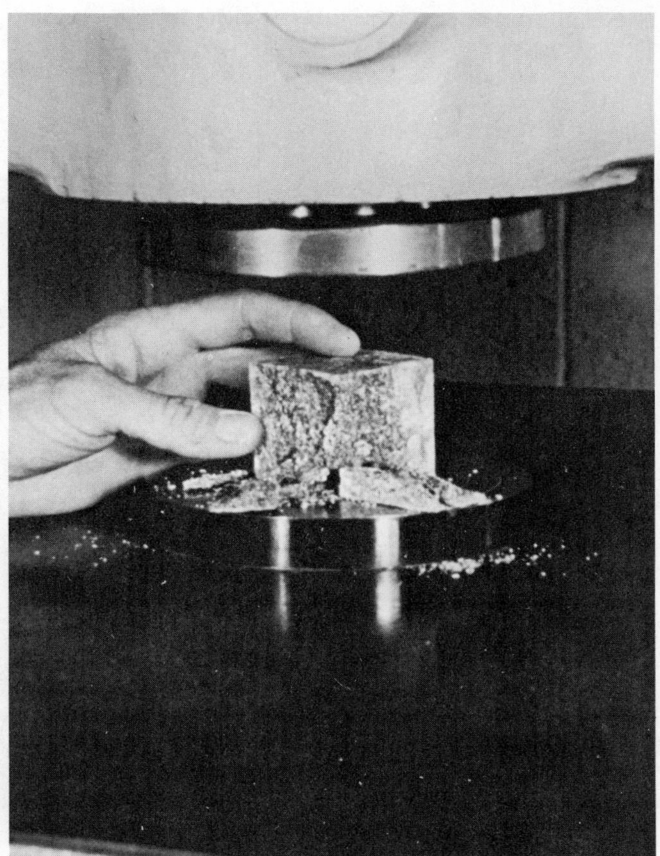

Figure 7-2. Cube compressive strength test.

fill bed and head joints and wet the to-be-bonded surface of the masonry units. The masonry unit must possess sufficient surface irregularities to provide mechanical bond, and sufficient absorption to draw the mortar into these surface irregularities.

Although some tensile bond strength develops immediately after brick and mortar contact, bond continues to increase as the cement hydrates. Tensile bond is important not only from a strength or load standpoint, but also with regard to forces generated by volume changes and temperature changes.

In the laboratory, tensile bond strength is measured by determining the tensile force required to separate masonry assemblages (Figure 7-3). Although the test method has varied over the years, the majority of test methods duplicate the mason's operation during bedding of a unit, using either a constant applied pressure during placement or sufficient pressure to obtain a constant mortar joint thickness.

Durability. The durability of a masonry mortar is its ability to endure the exposure conditions to which it is subjected. Cyclic freezing and thawing of masonry is considered the primary deteriorating effect, but chemical attack from atmospheric contamination and sulfate soils may also affect masonry's durability.

The **durability** characteristics of individual construction materials and of masonry assemblages are evaluated in the laboratory or under natural exposure. Mortar prisms subjected to severe freeze and thaw tests show that the portland cement content and the air content are the most significant factors affecting mortar durability. Through hydration portland cement produces a mortar of greater density with lower absorption characteristics and greater strength capabilities to resist the expansion forces of freezing water. Air entrainment through inclusion and dispersion of minute air bubbles throughout the mortar absorbs the expansive forces of freezing

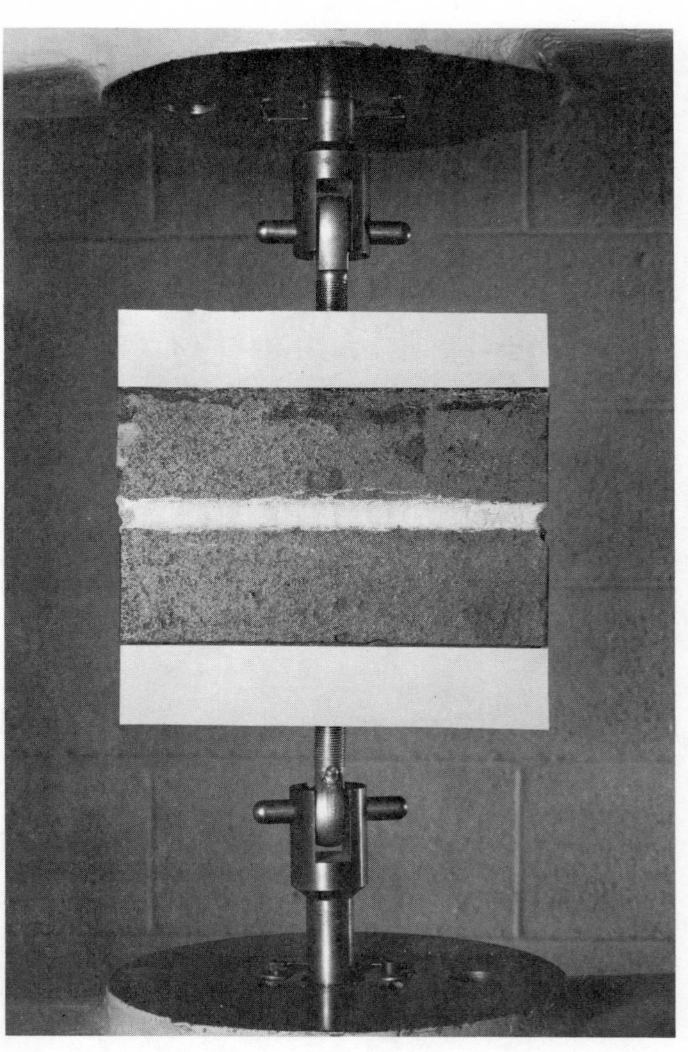

Figure 7-3. Tensile bond test.

Figure 7-4. Volume change test.

water. Durability tests of masonry assemblages in accelerated laboratory tests, and under natural weathering show that masonry's durability depends on the combination of construction materials and the degree of saturation of the masonry.

Volume Change. The free shrinkage characteristics of mortar are measured in the laboratory using 1 × 1 × 11¼-in. prisms, (Figure 7-4). The specimens are measured for length as a function of time during air storage. As the specimens lose moisture through evaporation, shrinkage occurs. Such volume change information provides a relative indicator of the shrinkage characteristics of mortars in masonry, and is useful in analysis of wall movements and the distribution of strains in masonry.

Factors Influencing Properties

The quality control tests of construction materials, previously mentioned, are performed in the laboratory under ideal conditions. Cement mortars receive curing to develop maximum hydration, and lime mortars are stored in air to develop maximum carbonation. At the construction site, however, ideal conditions for attaining optimum physical properties do not always prevail. To show the influences of certain factors on the physical properties of mortars, the effect of water additions to mortar, curing, and air content are described below.

Water. In the current specification for mortars for unit masonry[2] ". . . the maximum amount of water to produce a workable consistency . . . ." is specified as a mixing requirement. Producing mortars with high water contents improves workability and tensile bond at the expense of compressive strength, durability, and volume change. High water content mortars flow more readily, and more water is available for the absorptive masonry and the hydrating cement.

Tests showing the effect of water additions on tensile bond and compressive strength illustrate that such water additions result in lower compressive strengths but higher tensile bond strengths, (Figure 7-5). The water additions caused the flow of these mortars to increase progressively from 100 to 135 percent and the air content to increase from 11.8 to 13.5 percent. Because the specimens were moist cured until tested, the increased tensile bond can be attributed to more intimate contact between plastic mortar and masonry unit.

Curing. As previously indicated, the portland cement in mortars requires water to hydrate. Although complete hydration is never realized, the degree of hydration greatly influences the physical properties. The degree of hydration cannot be directly measured, but it can be indirectly approximated. Hydration continues only during the period when the relative humidity of the mortar exceeds about 85 percent[5], and the rate of hydration decreases as the relative humidity of the mortar approaches this value[6].

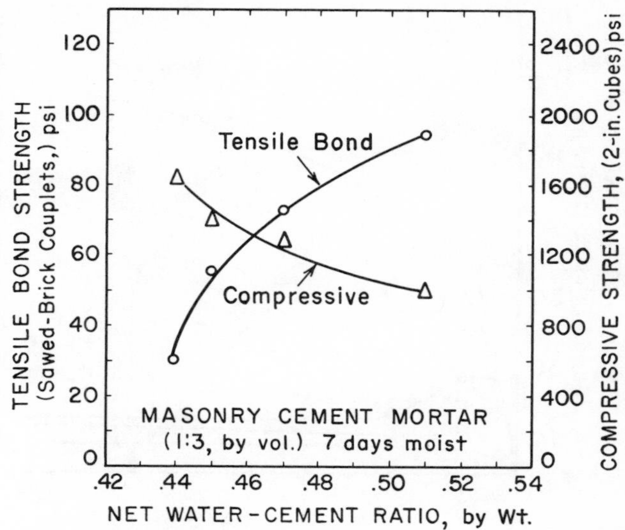

Figure 7-5. Effect of water-cement ratio of masonry cement mortars on tensile bond and compressive strength.

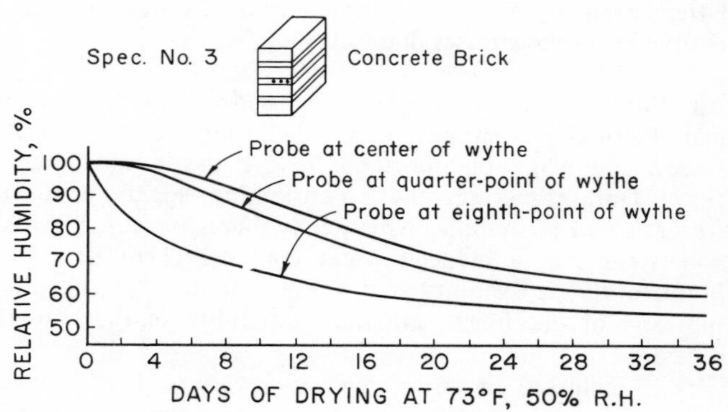

Figure 7-6. Relative humidity of masonry cement mortar as a function of drying time.

Relative humidity measurements immediately behind the exposed joint surface show that the mortar can lose enough water in 3 days to reduce the relative humidity to 80 percent, (Figure 7-6). Other measurements show that the humidity at 1/4 to 1/2 depth may undergo 12 to 15 days of hydration, respectively. Tensile strengths of masonry walls probably reflect an averaging of these times, whereas flexural strength of walls reflect only the 3-day hydration.

Moist curing of tensile bond masonry assemblages further show the advantages of adequate curing (Figure 7-7). Moist cured couplets developed considerably higher bond strengths than did their stored-in-air counterparts. Applications of curing compounds, typical of those used in the concrete industry, immediately after fabrication were only partially effective in increasing the bond. The retrogression for these

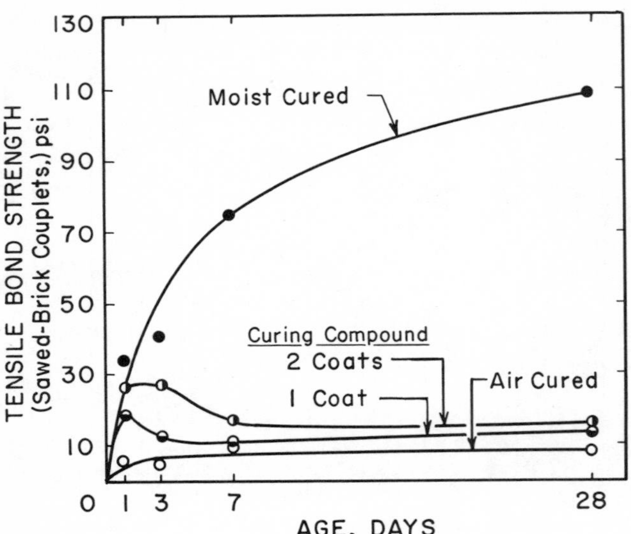

Figure 7-7. Effect of curing on tensile bond of mortars to masonry units.

latter specimens probably resulted from the development of perimeter tensile stresses due to drying.

Air Content. Air-entraining agents added by the cement manufacturer play an important role during the mortar mixing period and when the mortar is in the plastic and hardened state. During mixing, the air-entraining agents cause the formation of air bubbles which contribute to workability and cohesiveness at a reduced water content. These air bubbles improve the workability and water retention of the plastic mortar and the freeze and thaw durability of the hardened mortar.

The inclusion of air in masonry mortars does, however, reduce the compressive strength of the mortar. Tests by Fishburn[7] indicate that a 1 percent increase in air content causes about a 2 percent decrease in the compressive strength of Type S portland masonry cement mortars. He also found that ". . . the effects of the two variables (air and water) on compressive strengths (of Type N masonry cement mortars) so masked each other that the individual relationships were not significant."

Other influences of air content on mortar properties, such as the amount of air required for durability, are presently being studied at the PCA Laboratories. Studies are also being directed at determining the effect of mixer type and mixing period on the air content and other properties of masonry mortars.

Interaction Between Mortar and Unit

When the individual construction materials are combined in masonry, masonry's performance depends on the physical characteristics of the individual materials, the design of the wall, the workmanship during fabrication, and the ambient conditions. Therefore, prediction of wall performance is difficult. To show some of the interactions between mortar and unit on the performance of masonry, the compressive strength and flexural strength of masonry walls are discussed below.

Compressive Strength. The principal factors affecting the compressive strength of masonry walls are the strength properties of the masonry unit and the mortar, the design of the wall, the workmanship, and the degree of curing. Although the strength of a wall may be increased through material selection, the strength increase is not proportionate to the material's strength.

Wall tests by Fishburn[8] using two cements and two mortar types showed that concrete masonry wall strengths increased only about 10 percent when mortar cube strength increased 130 percent. Composite wall strengths increased 25 percent when mortar cube strength increased 160 percent.

Inequalities between cube test and wall test include curing and size factor. Non-curing of mortar would result in lower compressive strengths, however shorter heights of mortar (joint vs cube) would result in appreciably higher compressive strengths.

Flexural Strength. The principal factors affecting the flexural strength of masonry include type of masonry unit, the mortar's tensile bond strength, the workmanship, and ambient conditions.

Wall tests by Fishburn[8] showed that flexural strength of walls was a function of mortar bond strength. His test data showed that changing mortar type from N to S increased wall flexural strength from 13.2 to 17.4 psi, respectively. Bond test specimens cast using the same mortar had "stored-in-air" bond strength of 9 and 18 psi. Their self-cured (curing in container) counterparts possessed bond strengths of 17 and 24 psi, respectively.

These data show that flexural wall strength is a function of the portland cement content of the mortar. Additionally, the effect of curing bond test specimens suggests that if bond strength improvement in the wall had been obtained through some curing system the flexural wall strength may have been improved.

Copeland and Saxer[9] attained an appreciable increase in flexural tensile bond by curing the test specimens under plastic for 7 days, during which the specimens were rewetted with fine water spray the first 4 days after fabrication. Stored-in-air specimens developed 86 psi flexural tensile bond strengths whereas their spray-cured counterparts averaged 156 psi, for a portland cement-lime mortar. Spray-cured values ranging from 157 to 175 psi were measured for three portland-masonry cement mortar types included in this same study.

Volume Change. Although compressive and tensile bond strength are of primary importance in masonry structures, too much strength may adversely affect the masonry's performance.

Hedstrom, Litvin and Hanson10 concluded from their study of the effects of longitudinal forces in concrete masonry walls that weaker mortars accommodated greater block shrinkage than stronger mortars through longer time lapse (greater creep effects) prior to failure. They further found that walls containing the weaker ASTM mortar types when subjected to full shrinkage restraint provided the higher tensile strengths.

These findings further support the need for a proper balance of physical properties of mortars for engineered masonry.

Role of Masonry Mortar in Engineered Masonry

The present-day masonry mortar types, especially Types M, S and N, provide a sufficiently high portland cement content that will, if utilized, develop the compressive, tensile, and shear bond strengths deemed essential for engineered masonry. This is particularly true if the masonry is adequately cured to develop the hydration characteristics of the portland cement component in these mortars.

Options available if present-day formulations used under present construction conditions fail to provide the desired performance characteristics include:

1. Devote more attention toward curing the structure by reducing the rate of moisture loss by units or by supplementing the water through intermittent fog spraying during the early period after construction.
2. Increase the portland cement content of present day mortars.
3. Intergrind organic compounds which will act as self-curing agents and retain the moisture, thus providing a higher level of tensile bond strength.
4. Utilize organic modified mortars which combine two compatible cement agents.

Necessity for Quality Control at the Construction Site

In reviewing specifications for construction materials and mortars and the performance of masonry walls, it was noted that one factor contributed significantly to the strength of masonry. This was workmanship. Laboratory tests conducted in strict accordance with specifications which stipulate test methods detailing the workmanship quality. Quality control at the construction site, however, is seldom practiced.

The need for quality control at the construction site is further supported by Stang, Parsons and McBurney[11] who found that commercial workmanship produced walls having compressive strengths approximately 70 percent of the compressive strength of similar walls in which inspected workmanship was used.

As presently envisioned, quality control at the construction site could best be directed at obtaining better control of mortar mixtures and better supervision of construction. Control of mortar mixtures through batching by weight and by testing the mortar would upgrade the batch to batch uniformity. Construction could best be controlled by supervising construction details and periodic fabrication of brick beams which would be cast using the materials and masons doing the construction. The rheological properties of the mortar could be checked during the construction process, using a flow test or slump test; for example, overshadowing effects of workmanship and curing are such that rheological tests are considered secondary importance.

Summary

In summary, the production of a quality controlled masonry cement and the testing cement and mortar in accordance with existing specifications provides the construction specifier with materials of known performance characteristics. Combining masonry cements with additional portland cement for producing Type M and S mortars will provide additional versatility where higher strength is required.

Present-day specifications for materials and mortar shows their performance limits provide adequate coverage of masonry requirements except for tests for workability, tensile bond, and durability.

Maximum water additions to mortars at the mixer improve the tensile bond characteristics while reducing compressive strength, durability, and volume change.

Curing of masonry prolongs the hydration period and appreciably increases the tensile bond of mortars to masonry units. Non-cured mortars subjected to flexural loads may receive as few as 3 days of hydration at the critical section, and non-cured mortars subjected to direct tensile loads may receive as few as 12 to 15 days of curing as an average.

Compressive strength tests of walls show that only a relatively small improvement of wall strength is realized by substantial increases in the compressive strengths of mortars.

Wall flexural strength tests show that wall strength is dependent on tensile bond strength of mortars. The single most important influence contributing to increase tensile bond strength of mortars containing portland cement is moist curing.

Options available for upgrading the performance characteristics of masonry mortars in construction include: curing of structure, increasing portland cement content, intergrinding organic "self-curing agents", and utilizing organic modified mortars.

Quality control at the construction site is the most fertile area for masonry improvement. More precise batching and testing of mortars and closer supervision of construction and testing of masonry assemblages is recommended.

References

1. Allsman, P. L., "Cement in 1966," U. S. Department of Interior, Bureau of Mines, *Mineral Industry Surveys,* Annual, Preliminary, Dec. 19, 1966.
2. ASTM Designation: C 270-64T "Tentative Specifications for Mortars for Unit Masonry" *Book of ASTM Standards,* Part 12, 1967, American Society for Testing and Materials, Philadelphia, pp. 190-193.
3. ASTM Designation: C 91-66 "Standard Specifications for Masonry Cement" *Book of ASTM Standards,* Part 9, 1967, American Society for Testing and Materials, Philadelphia, pp. 66-72.

4. ASTM Designation: C 144-66T "Tentative Specifications for Aggregate for Masonry Mortar" *Book of ASTM Standards,* Part 12, 1967, American Society for Testing and Materials, Philadelphia, pp. 127-129.
5. Powers, T. C. and Brownyard, T. L., "Studies of the Physical Properties of Hardened Portland Cement Paste," *Journal American Concrete Institute, Proceedings* V. 43, 1947, pp. 989.
6. Copeland, L. E., Kantro, D. L., and Verbeck, G. J., "Chemistry of Hydration of Portland Cement," Chemistry of Cement, *Proceedings of the Fourth International Symposium,* Washington, D. C., held at the National Bureau of Standards (U. S. Department of Commerce), Monograph 43, Vol. 1, Session 1, Paper IV-3, pp. 429-465.
7. Fishburn, C. C., "Properties of Cement Mortars" *Building Research,* Mar.-Apr. 1964, pp. 19-22.
8. Fishburn, C. C., "Effect of Mortar Properties on Strength of Masonry," National Bureau of Standards (U. S. Department of Commerce), Monograph 36, November 1961, pp. 45.
9. Copeland, R. E. and Saxer, E. L., "Tests of Structural Bond of Masonry Mortars to Concrete Block," *Journal* American Concrete Institute, *Proceedings* V. 61, No. 11, November 1964, pp. 1411-1452.
10. Hedstrom, R. O., Litvin, A. and Hanson, J. A., "Influence of Mortar and Block Properties on Shrinkage Cracking of Masonry Walls." *Journal of the PCA Research and Development Laboratories,* January 1968.
11. Stang, A. H., Parsons, D. E. and McBurney, J. W., "Compressive Strength of Clay Brick Walls," *Journal of Research* Bureau of Standards (Department of Commerce) Vol. 3, No. 4, Research Paper 108, October 1929.

8. Development of diametral testing procedures to provide a measure of strength characteristics of masonry assemblages.

Dr. Frank B. Johnson, Prof. J. Neils Thompson, College of Engineering, The University of Texas

This chapter presents research performed in 1963 which resulted in the diametral testing procedure for brick masonry assemblages. Insofar as is known, this was the first time this type of test had been used to evaluate the strength of a composite masonry unit. Because brick masonry is a brittle material and the failure mode is normally that of tension, an investigation of the tensile properties of plain brick masonry was undertaken. Several testing procedures were available for evaluating the overall strength of a masonry assemblage, but these testing procedures had proven to be either impractical from the standpoint of reliability or not feasible because of the prohibitive cost. These conditions provided the impetus for developing diametral testing procedures of masonry discs for evaluating tensile strength of masonry assemblages.

The objective was to establish comparative basic strength relationships between standard portland cement-lime mortars and latex high-bond mortars, utilizing a new testing technique with some development and adaption. The two techniques include the diametral testing of 15-inch diameter masonry discs and the diametral testing of 3-inch diameter by 2-inch thick mortar discs. These results were related to the results of compression test of 2-inch mortar cubes.

General

The loading rate of the various specimens was relatively slow to avoid the dynamic effects of rapid loading rates. The rate of loading was reasonably constant.

All specimens were tested as near to 28 days after their construction as was possible. The large number of specimens tested prevented a rigid adherence to the 28-day schedule. In some cases, 30 days elapsed between construction of the specimen and the actual testing. It is believed that this time difference of two days did not significantly affect the results.

The various components tested were constructed and aged indoors, thereby providing some uniformity in curing conditions. During the construction and aging stages the weather was very mild and uniform. A low temperature of 50° occurred within the building during two of the nights. These relatively uniform conditions minimized temperature as a variable.

Preparation and Testing of Specimens

Masonry Discs

Fifteen-inch diameter masonry discs were formed from 16-inch square masonry panels of one brick wythe. The masons, using mortar prepared for them by research assistants working on this project laid up the square panels. All of the panels were constructed identically, using 3/8-inch bed joints and 1/2-inch head joints. All joints were full and their surfaces were tooled slightly. Upon completion of a panel, four bricks were placed on top of the panel to provide some weight on the bed joints of the upper courses. The panels were not disturbed for 14 days to permit the mortar to gain sufficient strength for handling. At the end of this period, the panels were trucked to a monument company where a 15-inch diameter circle was inscribed on the panel and the corners were removed with a diamond saw. These cuts were made quickly. This equipment easily approximated the shape of the circle. The final shaping was done with a large grinder using an abrasive disc.

To obtain the desired stress distribution the masonry discs tested with the bed joints in the normal horizontal position required the filling of extrusion holes in the bearing brick with sulphur compound. Strips of 1/2-inch plywood provided the bearing surface, utilizing a technique developed for the split cylinder tests. The strips were 1 1/4-inch in width and 5-inches in length.

Each masonry disc was carefully aligned in the universal testing machine by centering and plumbing the points of bearing with the vertical axis of the machine head (Figure 8-1). The load was slowly applied until failure occurred by a sudden splitting of the disc. The ultimate load was recorded along with the measured dimension of the disc for the determination of the ultimate tensile unit stress of the specimen. A sketch of the failure pattern was drawn for further study.

Mortar Cubes

The preparation for testing the 2-inch mortar cubes varied according to the type of mortar. Cubes made of Type M regular cement-lime mortar were treated according to ASTM Specification C-270-61T.

This specification requires curing of the cubes by submergence in water during the entire curing period and testing them in compression immediately after removal from the water.

The high-bond mortar cubes were not cured in the manner of the Type M mortar because the latex polymer additive is affected by water. The manufacturer of the additive indicated that high-bond mortars must be air cured to attain proper strength. These high-bond mortar cubes did not receive special attention and were allowed to cure in the same environment as the corresponding masonry assemblages.

Mortar Discs

The treatment and handling of the mortar discs, 3 inches in diameter by 2 inches thick, prior to testing were identical to that of the companion mortar cubes. These discs, prepared from high-bond mortar, were air cured under the same conditions as the companion masonry assemblages. Discs prepared from regular cement-lime mortar were moist-cured in a similar manner to that used in curing the corresponding mortar cubes.

The actual testing utilized methods similar to those used in the split-cylinder testing of concrete.

The disc was placed on edge and carefully aligned in the testing machine. Strips of 1/4-inch plywood 3/8-inch wide were used to distribute the load more uniformly. When the specimen was properly aligned in the testing machine, the load was slowly applied until the cylinder suddenly failed. (Figure 8-2.) This failure load was used to determine the ultimate tensile stress that occurred in the disc, using the previously recorded disc dimensions in each case.

Results

Failure Patterns of Mortar Disc in Diametral Test

Because mortar has essentially the same property characteristics as has concrete, the authors assumed that the failure mode in the mortar cylinders would be similar to the mode of failures in concrete cylinders. The failure patterns showed that most of the cylinders failed in some form of cleft mode. The deformable bearing plates used for this test were plywood strips, 3/16-inch thick, 3/8-inch wide, and 2 1/2-inches long. This provided a plate to mortar cylinder diameter ratio of 1/8. A smaller plate width would probably have produced a mode of failure more nearly conforming to the ideal pattern.

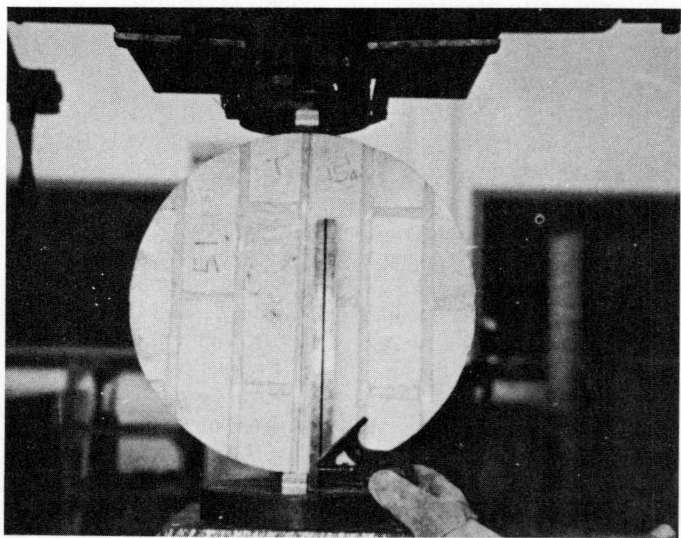

Figure 8-1. Alignment of masonry disc prior to loading.

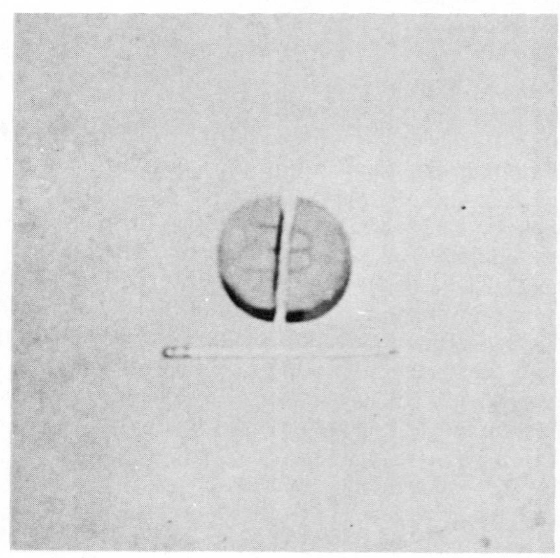

Figure 8-2. Diametral test of mortar disc.

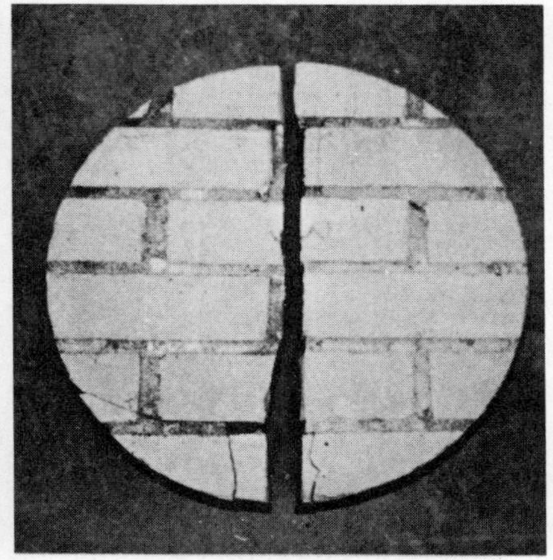

Figure 8-3. Masonry disc failure pattern θ = 0°.

Figure 8-4. Masonry disc failure pattern θ = 22.5°.

Figure 8-5. Masonry disc failure pattern θ = 45°.

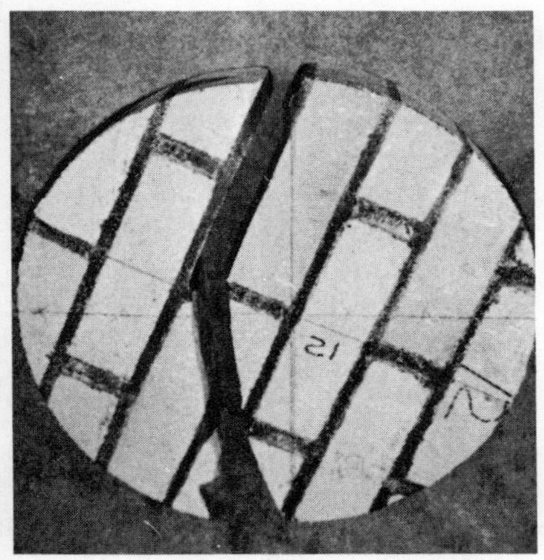

Figure 8-6. Masonry disc failure pattern θ = 67.5°.

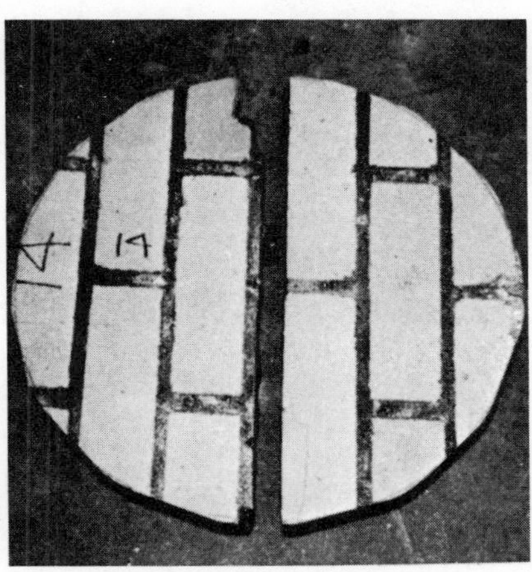

Figure 8-7. Masonry disc failure pattern θ = 90°.

Figure 8-8. Masonry disc (θ = 90°) failure through part of brick surface.

The effect of plate size on the mode of failure was considered. Since the characteristics and behavior of the high-bond mortar were not known, and because of the need for usable values of ultimate tensile strength, it was decided to use a slightly larger plate-disc diameter ratio than that ordinarily used on a concrete cylinder test. In view of the relatively small scatter of results obtained from the diameteral test of the mortar discs from each sample, it is believed that this testing method provides a reliable measure of the ultimate tensile strength of the mortar.

The modes of failure of the masonry discs were very consistant, particularly in the angle between the principal tensile stress and the bed joint of the disc. Figures 8-3 through 8-8 illustrate the typical failure pattern of masonry discs. All discs with the bed joint of the brick perpendicular to the loaded diameter failed in the same ideal tension mode, with the failure line passing through the intercepted brick and along the mortar brick interface, in the most direct line between load points. A somewhat similar mode of failure occurred in the masonry discs where the loaded diameter was parallel to the brick bed joint. In these cases, the failure line was along the brick-mortar interface. In this group the failure mode was the typical ideal tension failure.

Differences in failure patterns of tests with the discs bed joints at intermediate angles were evident. In high strength mortar, the failure mode approached the ideal tension failure with the fracture crack extending through the brick and the mortar joints directly to the load points. In lower strength mortar, the fracture cracks followed the mortar-brick interface and rarely cut through a brick unit. Although the failure crack did not always follow the most direct path, the patterns were still those of a tension failure.

Here, as in the mortar discs, a relatively small scatter of ultimate tensile strength existed within each group. Thus, the results may be accepted with a high degree of confidence.

Correlation of Numerical Results

The testing program was designed to provide information on the behavior and the tensile strength of masonry assemblages under load and to determine, if possible, the interrelationships that exist between the components of the masonry assemblages. The numerical results, along with the diagrams of the failure pattern previously discussed, are presented in graphical form.

Mortar Water-Cement Ratio vs Compressive Strength Relationships. Figure 8-9 is a plot of the ultimate compressive strength of the mortar cubes tested versus the corresponding water-cement ratio of the mortar batch from which the specimens were made. The compressive strength relationship with water-cement ratio is immediately evident and closely corresponds to the compressive strength-w/c ratio relationship of concrete.

Mortar Water-Cement Ratio vs Disc Tensile Strength. Figure 8-10 is a plot of the ultimate tensile strengths as determined from diametral compression tests of the mortar discs versus

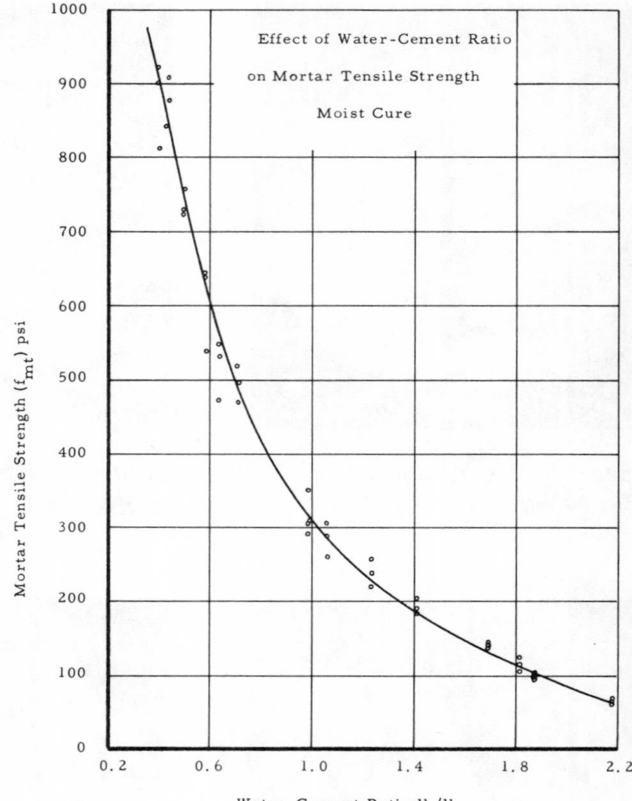

Figure 8-10. Effect of water-cement ratio on mortar tensile strength moist cure.

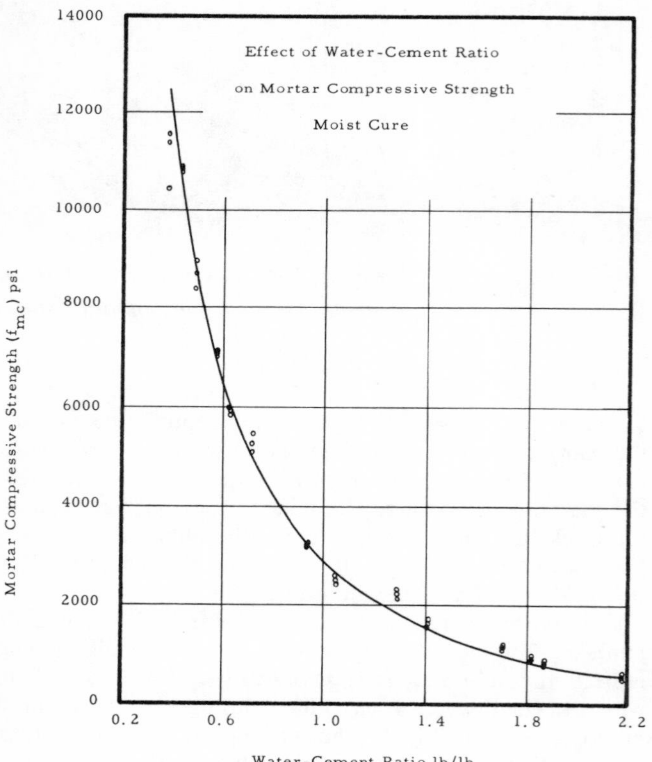

Figure 8-9. Effect of water-cement ratio on mortar compressive strength moist cure.

the corresponding water-cement ratio of the mortar. The tensile strength of mortar discs were obtained by using the theoretical equation for maximum tensile unit stress as developed from diametral compression testing of cylinders. The equation expressed in symbols specifically for the mortar discs was as follows:

where:

$$f_t = \frac{2P}{\pi D_t}$$

f_t = mortar ultimate unit tensile strength, psi
P = applied load, lb
D = measured diameter (approximately 3 in.), in
t = measured thickness (approximately 2in.), in

The values shown in Figure 8-10 exhibit a relationship very similar to the water-cement ratio-compressive strength relationship shown in Figure 8-9. Thus, the low water-cement ratio in the mortar produces high ultimate tensile strength and, conversely, a high water-cement ratio in mortar produces low ultimate tensile strength. Both of these relationships bear approximately the same degree of nonlinearity, thus indicating that a close relationship exists between ultimate compression strength and ultimate tensile strength of the mortars.

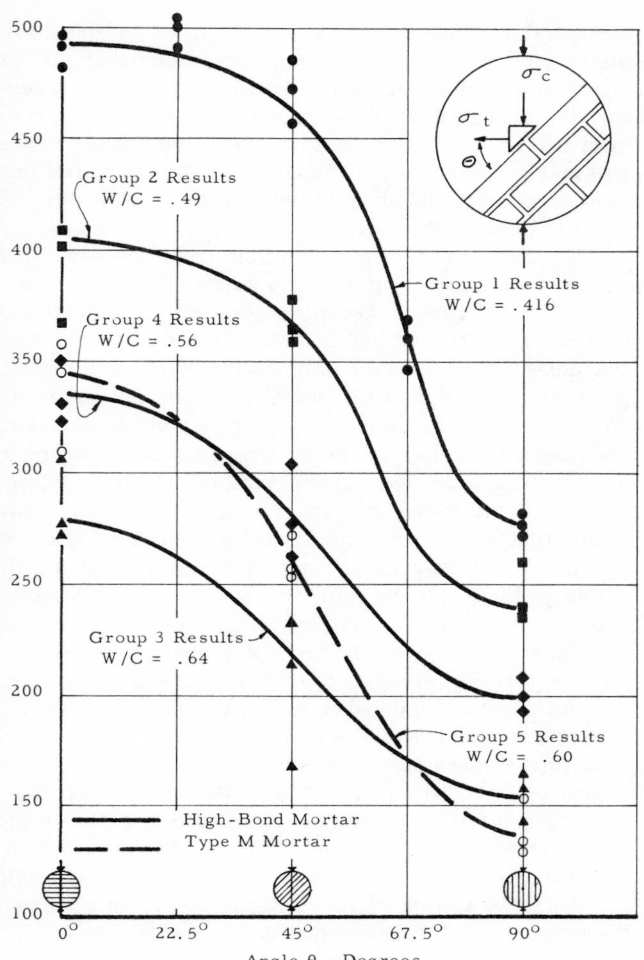

Figure 8-11. Effect of direction of principal tensile stress bed joint angle on masonry disc tensile strength.

Tensile Strength of Masonry Disc

Orientation of Bed Joint. Figure 8-11 is a plot of the masonry disc tensile strength as related to the angle between the load and the bed joint. The tensile strength of the five groups provided a family of curves with the water-cement ratio as the variable. High-bond mortar groups 1 through 4 exhibit the same general behavior while group 5, the cement-line Type M mortar, behaved somewhat differently.

The general shape of the curves indicates that the highest disc tensile strength of the masonry assemblages occurred when the compressive load was perpendicular to the bed joint or when the principal tensile stress was parallel to the bed joint. The lowest resistance to tensile stresses occurred when the compressive load was parallel to the bed joint or when the principal tensile stress was perpendicular to the bed joint. In the discs with the load parallel to the bed joint where the fracture occurred along the interface of brick and bed joint, this condition provides a measure of the bond strength between the mortar and the brick.

At the opposite end of the angular scale where the principal tensile stress was parallel to the bed joint, the failure patterns indicate that the cracks occur along the mortar-brick interface of every other brick course and intercept and proceed through the brick in the alternate course. Evidently, the stress component normal to the bed joint influences the failure behavior of the masonry discs. Figure 8-12 shows the variation of the stress component normal to the bed joint, through an angular rotation of 90°, for the stress condition that exists at the center of the disc. For angles of 60° to 90° the bed joint is in tension where the weak plane of bond between masonry and mortar effectively reduces the strength of the masonry disc tensile strength. This behavior is evident when the curves of Figure 8-11 are compared with Figure 8-12.

Other less important factors unquestionably influence the strength of the masonry discs in that the stresses normal to the head joint, which are 90° out of phase with the bed joint, will effectively reduce the tensile strength of the masonry disc in

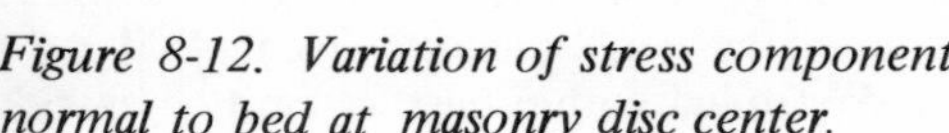

Figure 8-12. Variation of stress component normal to bed at masonry disc center.

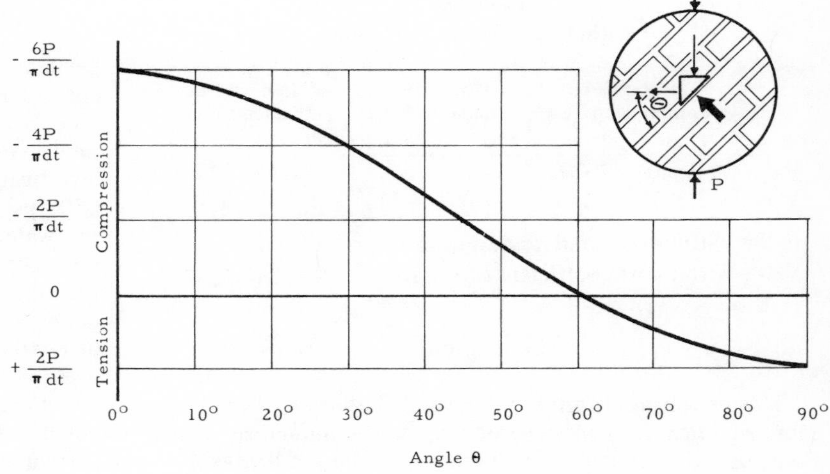

the vicinity of bed joint angles of 0° to 30°. In addition, the shearing stress that corresponds to the stress normal to the bed and head joints is particularly effective in the bed joint angular range of 45°. This behavior is further established by the failure pattern exhibited by the masonry discs. Masonry discs loaded with the bed joint angle of 67.5° all failed along the bed joint that most nearly intercepted the loading point. In all cases, the failure pattern followed nearly the same line of least resistance. In masonry discs loaded with a bed joint angle of 45° and where the mortar strengths were relatively low, the path of least resistance was the interface of masonry and mortar rather than through the brick unit. This behavior was particularly true of the masonry discs in group 5 which were made with Type M cement-lime mortar.

Statistical Evaluation of Results

Within-test standard deviations and coefficients of variation were determined for the results of the mortar cube, the mortar disc, and the masonry disc tests using the A.C.I. Standard 214 are shown in Table 8-1. The values presented represent all tests irrespective of the variations of mortar properties and type.

The within-test coefficients of variations are unusually low considering the types of materials being tested and generally reflect the high degree of overall control exercised over the construction and testing of specimens. Comparing within-test coefficients of variation reveals that the masonry disc diametral tests have higher values than the mortar cube compression test or mortar cylinder diametral test. This is to be expected in that variations in the brick and in the workmanship were factors in the composite masonry assemblages, but not in the homogeneous mortar specimens.

An important point drawn from these findings is that a high degree of control can be exercised over masonry construction and testing in the laboratory. Also, the difference in the coefficient of variation between the composite masonry disc diametral tests and the homogeneous mortar specimens tests indicates the importance of the variations of the brick and the workmanship which can be reflected only in the composite masonry disc.

Table 8-1
Within-Test Group Variations

	Mortar Cube Compression Test		Mortar Disc Diametral Test		Masonry Disc Diametral Test	
	Phase 1	Phase 2	Phase 1	Phase 2	Phase 1	Phase 2
σ 1	198.0	262.0	34.2	35.9	16.7	27.3
V 1	3.60%	4.17%	4.46%	4.51%	5.3%	7.10%

σ 1 = Within-test standard deviation
V 1 = Within-test coefficient of variation

Conclusions

This investigation produced general findings that may have more significance than some of the specific numerical results. Some of the more important factors are discussed below:

Diametral Testing. The diametral testing of mortar discs and masonry discs proved to be a simple, feasible procedure for the measurement of the respective tensile properties. It is believed that the diametral testing of mortar discs is far superior to the briquette method of determining tensile strength. The low within-test coefficients of variation for the diametral tests of mortar discs (as shown in Table 8-I) are an indication of the uniformity of results that can be obtained.

The diametral testing of mortar discs can only provide information concerning the properties of the mortar as a monolithic specimen. The properties and behavioral characteristics of mortar acting as a component part of a masonry assemblage depended not only on the batch proportions and properties of the mortar, but also on the properties of the individual masonry units and the workmanship exercised by the mason on individual units. Diametral testing of masonry discs provides an inexpensive method of determining the behavioral properties of masonry assemblages and provides results that include all of the variables mentioned. Rectangular test panels can be easily constructed and converted into the masonry discs, and the actual testing is no more complicated than the procedure for testing the standard concrete cylinder in compression. The within-test coefficient of variation (Table 8-I) for the masonry disc testing was unusually low for this type of material and indicates the reliability of results that may be obtained with the composite unit.

A further advantage of masonry disc diametral testing is the variety of information that can be obtained by the rotation of the bed joint with respect to the direction of the principal tensile stress. When the angle between the direction of the principal tensile stress and the bed joint is 90°, the results of the diametral testing of the masonry discs give a measure of the bond strength between the mortar and the brick. This can have an extremely valuable application in the correlation of lateral strength of masonry walls with such variable as mortar strength, brick properties, wall and cavity width, percentage of headers, and masonry workmanship. When the angle between the direction of the principal tensile stress and the bed joint is 45°, the results of the diametral testing of the masonry disc becomes a measure of the shear strength of a masonry assemblage which is applicable to masonry beams and shear walls.

Quality Control. At present quality control in masonry construction on the job is nearly absent. Mortar performance is normally specified by mortar type, but the specification is rarely enforced effectively. The type M mortars used in this investigation had strengths which ranged from 4000 psi to 6500 psi and were controlled within narrow limits by varying the water-cement ratio. Even though a large range of properties may occur with a particular mortar type on construction, the authors believe that control over the mortar quality can be obtained through control of the water-cement ratio and material proportioning.

Although the degree of rigid control exercised in this investigation cannot be obtained in a field operation, it is possible to exercise some degree of control in the field, particularly by using the diametral testing of masonry discs.

The masonry disc provides not only a measure of the composite properties of the mortar and the masonry units, but also a measure of the mason's workmanship and skill in constructing the assemblage. The testing of the masonry disc from a construction job could provide an index of construction quality similar to the testing of the concrete cylinder in concrete construction. Further, the masonry disc could be used to "qualify" a brick-mason in the same manner that a welder must "qualify" by demonstrating his individual skill through test weld samples.

Acknowledgement

The authors express their gratitude to the Dow Chemical Company and the Structural Clay Products Research Foundation for their support of this project.

References

1. Monk, C. B., Jr., "Testing of High-Bond Clay Masonry Assemblages," Paper presented at the Symposium on Masonry Testing held in conjunction with the Annual Meeting of the American Society for Testing and Materials, New York, New York, June 28, 1962.
2. ACI Committee 214, Wm. A. Cordon, Chairman, "Recommended Practice for Evaluation of Compression Test Results of Field Concrete (ACI 214-57)," *Journal of the American Concrete Institute,* Vol. 29, July 1957, p.1.
3. Den Hartog, J. P., *Advanced Strength of Materials,* New York, Toronto, London, McGraw-Hill Book Company, Inc., 1952, p. 200.
4. Carneiro, F. L. L. B., and A. Barcellos, "Concrete Tensile Strength," Union of Testing and Research Laboratories for Materials and Structures, No. 13, March 1953.
5. Mitchell, Neal B., Jr., "The Indirect Tension Test for Concrete," *Materials Research and Standards,* Vol. 1, No. 10, October 1961, pp. 780-788.
6. Rudnick, A., A. R. Hunter, and F. C. Holden, "An Analysis of the Diametral-Compression Test," *Materials Research and Standards,* Vol. 3, No. 4, April 1963, pp. 283-289.
7. Frocht, Max Mark, *Photoelasticity,* Vol. 1, New York, John Wiley and Sons, Inc., 1941, p. 43.
8. Worthing, Archie G., and Joseph Geffner, *Treatment of Experimental Data,* New York, John Wiley and Sons, Inc., 1943.

9. Creep in model brickwork.

Dr. D. Lenczner, Building Technology, University of Wales Institute of Science and Technology, Cardiff Wales

Introduction

At present there is an urgent need to know more about the creep in brickwork. Lack of knowledge in this field has seriously hindered the proper development of brickwork as a major structural material. The need for this knowledge is particularly pressing today with new trends toward more slender calculated brickwork construction and prefabricated wall panels. For a more economic composite construction, with brickwork as one of the load-bearing constituents, data on creep behaviour of the latter becomes imperative. A fuller knowledge of this behaviour would also enable us to use more realistic values of the Young's modulus of brickwork and make its analysis more accurate with respect to stability, buckling, and deformation problems.

Toward this aim the author, under the sponsorship of the Brick Development Association of Great Britain, undertook an investigation to determine the fundamental factors which affect the creep in brickwork. The factors investigated were: strength of brick, strength of mortar, stress level, humidity, temperature, and age at loading. It was thought essential for this type of investigation to carry out the creep tests under controlled conditions of temperature and humidity, and as the available controlled temperature and humidity room was of a limited size, it was decided that as far as the initial investigation was concerned the tests could be carried out on half-scale model brickwork with the intention of correlating the results at some future date with the creep behaviour of full-size brickwork. Preliminary tests had shown that, so far as elastic deformations were concerned, there was good agreement between model and full-size brickwork.

This chapter describes the initial creep tests on half-scale model brickwork. Three types of model brick were used. One was of medium strength extruded in the direction of its length. This is not the usual direction of extrusion, but it was the only type which the British Ceramic Research Association who supplied the bricks could provide at the time. The second type of brick was of high strength and again extruded in the direction of its length. The third type was a medium strength brick extruded normal to its length. In all tests a 1:1:6 cement-lime-mortar mix was used.

This chapter describes briefly the creep machines used in this investigation, and specifies properties of model bricks and mortar, experimental procedure, results, and conclusions.

Description of Creep Machines

The creep machines' design and their description have been published elsewhere, and so they will only be briefly mentioned here. The machine for testing model panel walls was designed to give a maximum compressive stress in brickwork of 600 p.s.i. The load, which was applied by hand through a worm shaft operating two counter-rotating gears, was measured by demec gauges on previously calibrated steel rods screwed at both ends to the machine columns.

The other two creep machines were for testing brickwork piers. To simplify the construction of the machines, hollow piers were used so that a central column was sufficient to apply the load to the brickwork. The load was measured by a load-cell with a central hole which allowed the central column to pass through it. Two machines, with a capacity of 20 tons each, were built, giving a maximum stress in brickwork of 1000 p.s.i. Occasionally there was a drift in the load-cells after a sustained load of six weeks or more. This amounted usually to some 3 percent of the applied load, but, in one case, it was as high as 10 percent, and the load-cell had to be replaced. New creep machines which the author is building for testing full-size brickwork piers have proving rings in place of the load-cells to improve long-term stability under load.

Experimental Procedure

The hollow brickwork piers used in the creep tests consisted of 12 courses of half-scale bricks with four bricks in each course and 3/16 ins. horizontal joints. The one leaf panel walls were approximately 50 ins. high and 28 ins. wide. The model bricks were immersed in water for 24 hours and then dried to saturated surface dry condition prior to laying. Three identical piers were cast on the same day. One was for the creep test; another was a companion specimen to measure moisture movements which were deducted from total combined strains; the third was to measure the strength of brickwork at 28 days when the load was applied. To ensure a perfect fit in the creep machine, the pier was placed in position; a layer of high strength cement mortar was laid on top; the top plate was lowered to rest on the pier; and the layer was then allowed to set. Sensitive dial gauges measured the vertical and horizontal strains of the piers over the full height of the pier and, in some cases, over the middle two-thirds of the pier to check any discrepancies caused by end effects. A similar testing method was used to test the panel walls, except that no special walls were cast to measure moisture movements or brickwork strength.

All creep tests were carried out in a temperature and humidity control room with the temperature set at 70° ± 1°F and relative humidity at 50 ± 2 percent. The factors which were varied were the type of brick and stress level which varied from approximately 200 p.s.i. by 200 p.s.i. increments to 800 p.s.i. for the piers and from approximately 400 p.s.i. to 500 p.s.i. for the panel walls. The appropriate moisture movements were deducted from the combined strains to give the total mechanical strain caused by loading (subsequently referred to as total strains). The creep strains were obtained by deducting the instantaneous strains from the total strains. The instantaneous strains were obtained by extrapolating the strain-time curve over the first few minutes to cut the strain axis at zero time. As already stated, the load was applied 28 days after casting. Details of specimens tested are given in Table 9-1.

Properties of Model Bricks

The model bricks were of three types. Types A and B were extruded along their length, and type C was extruded normal to its length. The dimensions of the model bricks were approximately 4 5/16 ins. by 2 1/16 ins. by 1 5/16 ins. The properties of the bricks are set out in Table 9-2.

Properties of Mortar

In all tests a 1:1:6 cement, lime sand mortar mix by volumes was used. The sand was a local (Trent River Valley) building sand. Although its grading satisfied the requirements laid down in B.S. 1200:1955, it had a fairly high proportion of fines. This accounted for the comparatively low strength of the mortar because a higher water cement ratio than is normal had to be used to give the mix a workable consistency. The 28 days 3 ins. mortar cube strength of 520 – 550 p.s.i. was lower than that obtained by Skeen[2] (650 – 750 p.s.i.) and considerably lower than the values obtained by Davey and Thomas[3] (1,000 – 1,200 p.s.i.) and Stedham[4] (1,260 – 1,820 p.s.i.). A full description of the mortar properties used by the author is given in reference 5. The author has recently carried out some tests on a 1:1:6 mortar mix using a standard washed Leighton Buzzard sand. These gave 28 day strength ranging from 800 – 1,150 p.s.i. These results show considerable variations can be obtained in the strength of nominally the same mortar mixes. The author intends to use the standard Leighton Buzzard sand in all future investigations.

Creep and Moisture Movements in Model Brickwork Piers and Walls

The creep of visco-elastic materials is obtained by deducting the instantaneous strains from the total strains. Theoretically, the instantaneous strain is that strain which takes place immediately after the load has been applied and can be obtained only by extrapolating the initial strain-time curve to cut the strain axis at zero time. Since the creep rate is highest in the initial stages of loading, a delay of even a few seconds in recording the first reading can easily produce an error of ± 10 percent in the instantaneous strain. The resultant creep values are consequently affected by the accuracy to which one can

Table 9-1
Details of Creep Tests on Model Brickwork Piers and Walls

$$SR = \frac{\text{Applied stress}}{\text{Brickwork strength}}$$

1:1:6 mortar used throughout

Specimen	Type of Brick	Average Mortar Strength @ 28 days psi	Average Brick Strength psi	Average Brickwork Strength @ 28 days psi	S.R.	Total strain less shrinkage × 10^4 (in/in) Time after application of load (weeks)											Shrinkage × 10^4 (in/in) Time after application of load (weeks)										
						0	1	2	3	4	5	6	7	8	9	10	0	1	2	3	4	5	6	7	8	9	10
Pier No 1	A	540	4,214	1,117	.18	6.29	10.31	11.17	12.23	12.90	13.25	13.40	13.40	13.45	13.57	13.60	0	.60	.84	.88	.88	.88	.88	.88	.88	.88	.88
Pier No 2	A	540	4,214	1,117	.36	14.09	18.25	19.31	20.42	21.29	21.89	22.21	22.26	22.31	22.34	22.36	0	.60	.84	.88	.88	.88	.88	.88	.88	.88	.88
Pier No 3	A	515	4,004	997	.60	26.30	44.67	46.58	48.26	49.48	50.28	50.47	50.48	50.48	50.52	50.55	0	.76	1.12	1.21	1.24	1.26	1.27	1.27	1.26	1.23	1.22
Pier No 4	A	515	4,004	997	.80	35.00	71.21	74.15	76.31	78.27	79.85	80.70	81.10	81.33	81.63	81.77	0	.76	1.12	1.21	1.24	1.26	1.27	1.27	1.26	1.23	1.22
Pier No 5	B	515	14,206	3,400	.06	0.88	2.30	2.40	2.40	2.40							0	.15	.33	.59	.91	1.05	1.18	1.23	1.23	1.21	1.20
Pier No 6	B	515	14,206	3,400	.13	1.74	6.35	6.50	6.65	6.70	6.75	6.80	6.95	7.10	7.20	7.30	0	.15	.33	.59	.91	1.05	1.18	1.23	1.23	1.21	1.20
Pier No 7	C	522	5,355	1,770	.12	3.50	8.76	9.29	9.66	10.12	10.60	10.94	10.97	11.32	11.51	11.70	0	1.19	1.75	2.06	2.27	2.38	2.52	2.55	2.57	2.57	2.57
Pier No 8	C	522	5,355	1,770	.24	7.50	13.89	14.96	15.76	16.51	17.15	17.80	18.05	18.25	18.55	18.85	0	1.19	1.75	2.06	2.27	2.38	2.52	2.55	2.57	2.57	2.57
Pier No 9	C	522	6,250	1,915	.32	9.50	16.70	17.70	18.45	18.65	18.75	18.90	20.40	20.45	20.80	21.10	0	.70	1.30	1.80	2.10	2.30	2.40	2.30	2.60	2.50	2.50
Pier No 10	C	522	6,250	1,915	.43	11.40	25.90	27.95	30.30	30.80	31.55	31.55	32.10	31.90	32.20	32.45	0	.70	1.30	1.18	2.10	2.30	2.40	2.30	2.60	2.50	2.50
Wall No 1	A	540	4,214	1,117	.34	9.08	13.94	15.63	16.10	16.26	16.44	16.46	16.47	16.51	16.52	16.52	0	.60	.84	.88	.88	.88	.88	.88	.88	.88	.88
Wall No 2	A	515	4,004	997	.50	20.20	28.54	30.28	30.79	31.06	31.13	31.14	31.14	31.23	31.30	31.33	0	.76	1.12	1.21	1.24	1.26	1.27	1.27	1.26	1.23	1.22
Wall No 3	C	522	5,355	1,770	.23	7.30	12.53	12.66	12.75	12.75	12.79	12.85	12.93	12.98	13.13	13.18	0	1.19	1.75	2.06	2.27	2.38	2.52	2.55	2.57	2.57	2.57

Table 9-2
Properties of Model Bricks

Type of Brick	Direction of Extrusion	Batch No.	No. of bricks tested	Average Crushing strength psi	Range psi	Standard deviation S	Coef-ficient of Variation %	Absorption %
A	in direction of length	1	18	4214	4040-4478	126	3.0	11.9
A	”	2	16	4004	3784 4527	212	5.3	11.9
B	”	1	23	14206	9946 17017	1648	11.9	10.7
C	normal to length	1	22	5355	4389 6455	505	9.7	11.4
C	”	2	12	6250	4722 7050	418	6.7	11.4

determine the instantaneous strains. In view of the practical difficulty which exists in such situations, the author now feels that the definition of the instantaneous strain ought to be altered to make it compatible with the speed with which loads can be applied and recorded. A reasonable definition of instantaneous strain would be that strain which took place within one minute of the initial application of load.

Because the initial purpose of the investigation was to study the different factors influencing the creep in model brick work, the loading time had to be limited. The standard time chosen was 70 days, although in some cases the load was sustained for approximately six months. Figure 9-1a shows the creep and shrinkage strains for Piers 1 and 2 and Wall No. 1 where medium strength model brick A was used. Figure 9-1 shows creep and shrinkage strains for Piers 3 and 4 and Wa No. 2 where bricks A were again used. Figure 9-1c shows th creep and shrinkage strains for Piers 5 and 6 where hig strength model brick B was used. In case of Pier No. 5 th load-cell ceased to function properly after 30 days and the tes had to be discontinued. Finally Figures 9-1d and 9-1e sho the creep and shrinkage strains for Piers 7, 8 and Wall No. and Piers 9 and 10 respectively. A summary of these results i given in Table 9-1.

Due to the limited space, the comments on this work ar confined to the bare essentials. It must be emphasized tha they apply only to the model brickwork under the condition

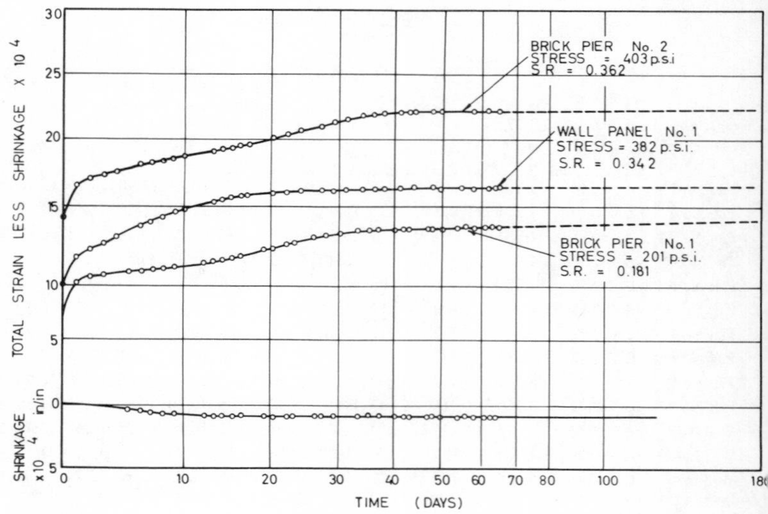

Figure 9-1a. Creep strain time curves for model brickwork.

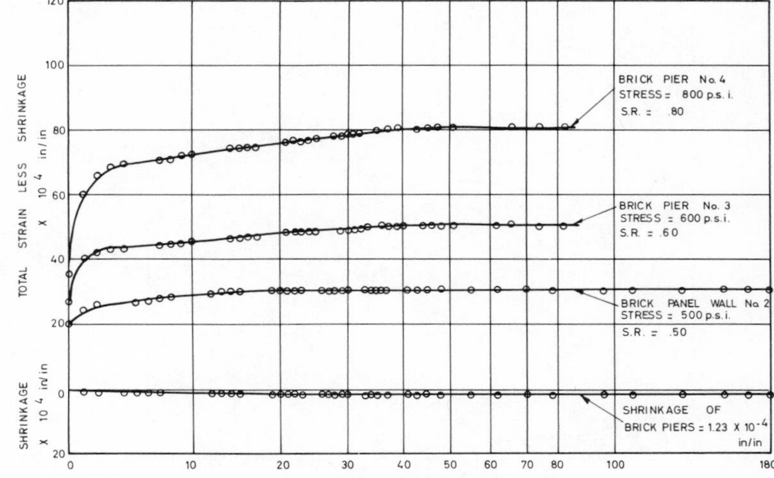

Figure 9-1b. Creep strain time curves for model brickwork.

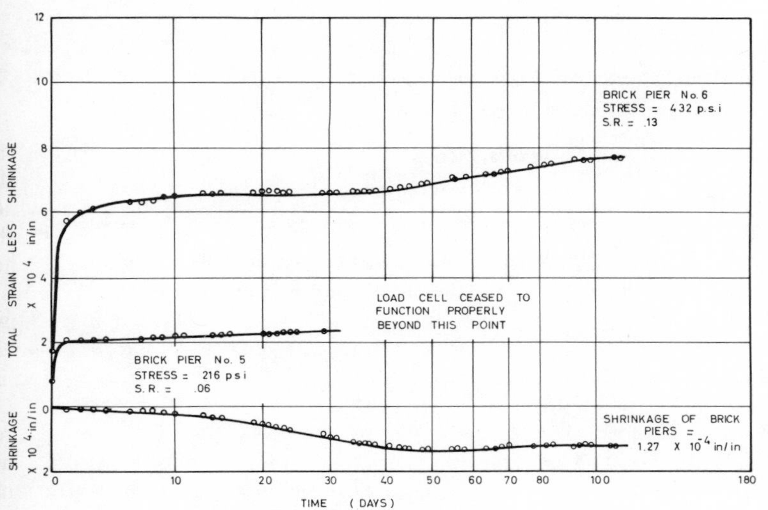

Figure 9-1c. Creep strain time curves for model brickwork.

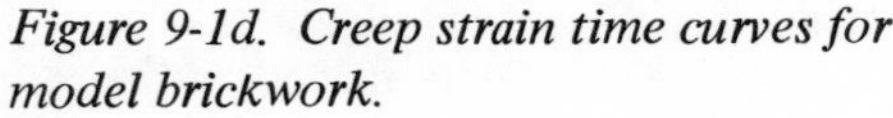
Figure 9-1d. Creep strain time curves for model brickwork.

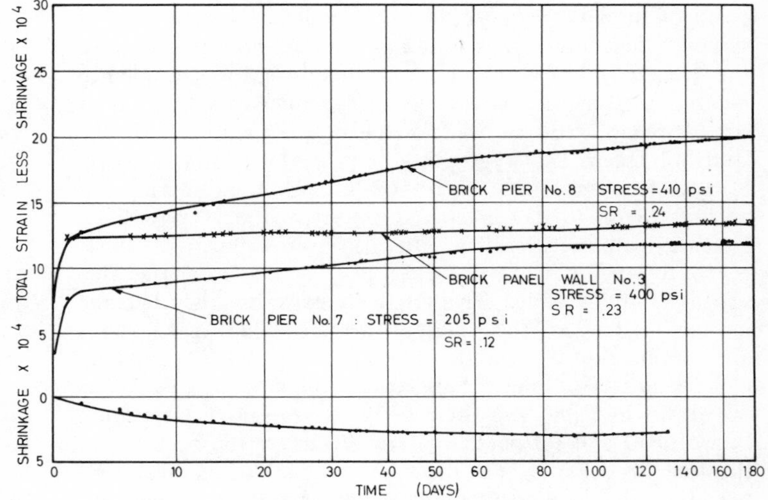

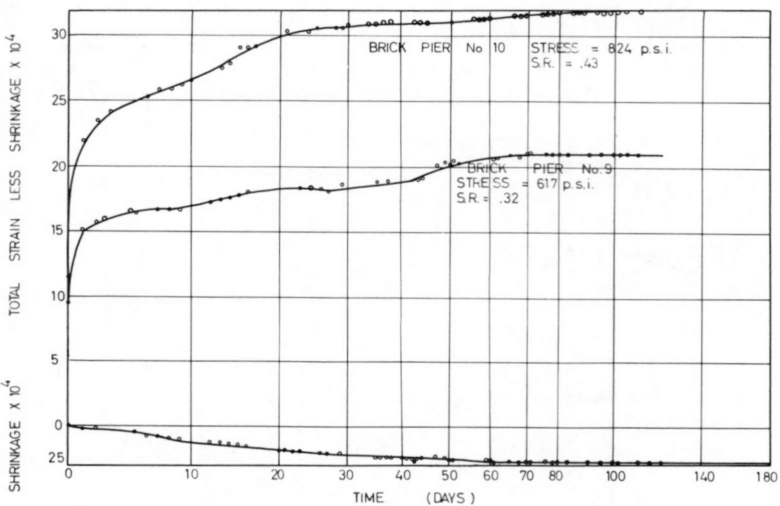

Figure 9-1e. Creep strain time curves for model brickwork.

Table 9-3

Values of Relative Creep in Model Brickwork Piers with Brick A (extruded Along Its Length) and Different Stress Levels

Load applied at 28 days $\quad$ **SR = $\frac{\text{Applied stress}}{\text{brickwork strength}}$**

	Average brick strength psi	Average Brickwork Strength @ 28 days psi	Applied Stress psi	SR	Creep x 10^6 after 70 days under load	Relative creep as a percentage of 70-day creep after a period under load of				
						1 day	3	7	14	28
1	4,214	1,117	201	.18	730	43	48	55	67	91
2	4,214	1,117	402	.36	830	30	41	50	63	87
3	4,004	997	600	.60	2,425	59	70	75	84	96
4	4,004	997	800	.80	4,677	56	72	77	84	93

tested. In an attempt to investigate the effect of stress on the creep of model brickwork, it was intended to keep the other variables constant. It was found impossible, however, to keep the strength of brickwork constant; therefore it was decided to use the ratio applied stress over brickwork strength (SR) or stress/strength ratio in brief as one of the parameters in the study of creep. Table 9-3 gives the values of relative creep in brickwork piers 1 – 4 built with bricks A expressed as a percentage of 70 day creep. As expected, the 70 day creep increases with the stress/strength ratio from 730 x 10^{-6} at SR = .18 to 4677 x 10^{-6} at SR = .80. There is an appreciable scatter in the 1 and 3 days relative creeps, but they become more consistent at longer periods. It is significant that 28 days after application of load, 87 to 96 percent of the 70 day creep had already taken place. This trend is repeated for piers 7 – 10 shown in Table 9-4 where bricks C were used. Here again between 80 and 90 percent of the 70 day creep occurred in the first 28 days. In both cases, the amount of relative creep one day after loading was mainly between 40 to 55 percent.

Results from tests over longer periods of time (up to six months in one case) show that there is very little creep in brickwork at working stresses after 12 weeks. Table 9-5 gives values of relative creep in model brickwork walls at different stress/strength values using both bricks A and C. The 70 day creep strains for the brickwork piers and walls are plotted against the stress/strength ratio in Figure 9-2.

Reference has already been made to the difficulty in determining the instantaneous strains and the resultant errors in creep values derived by subtracting the first from the total strains. In view of this difficulty, more emphasis was put on the total strains which can be read off directly. Table 9-6 gives total and relative strains at 70 days for brickwork piers, and Table 9-7 gives this information for brickwork walls. Note in Table 9-6 that, although again a considerable scatter in the instantaneous strains is expressed as percentages of the corresponding 70 day strains (excluding moisture strains), the relative strains become much more constant for longer periods. A similar trend existed for the brickwork walls, although here

Table 9-4
Values of Relative Creep in Model Brickwork Piers with Brick C (Extruded Normal to Its Length) and Different Stress Levels
Load applied at 28 days

	Average brick strength psi	Average Brickwork Strength @ 28 days psi	Applied Stress psi	SR	Creep × 10^6 after 70 days under load	Relative creep as a percentage of 70-day creep after a period under load of				
						1 day	3	7	14	28
7	5,355	1,700	205	.12	822	52	59	64	71	28
8	5,355	1,700	410	.24	1,143	42	49	56	65	79
9	6,250	1,915	617	.32	1,160	48	55	62	71	78
10	6,250	1,915	824	.43	2,105	50	60	68	77	90

Table 9-5
Values of Relative Creep in Model Brickwork Walls
Load applied at 28 days

Type of Brick	Average Brick Strength psi	Average Brickwork Strength @ 28 days psi	Applied Stress	SR	Total creep after 70 days x 10^6	Relative creep as a percentage of 70-day creep					
						1 day	3	7	14	28	56
A	4,214	1,117	382	.34	747	29	41	65	88	96	100
A	4,004	997	505	.50	1,115	48	58	75	91	98	99
C	5,355	1,700	385	.23	583	86	89	90	92	93	97

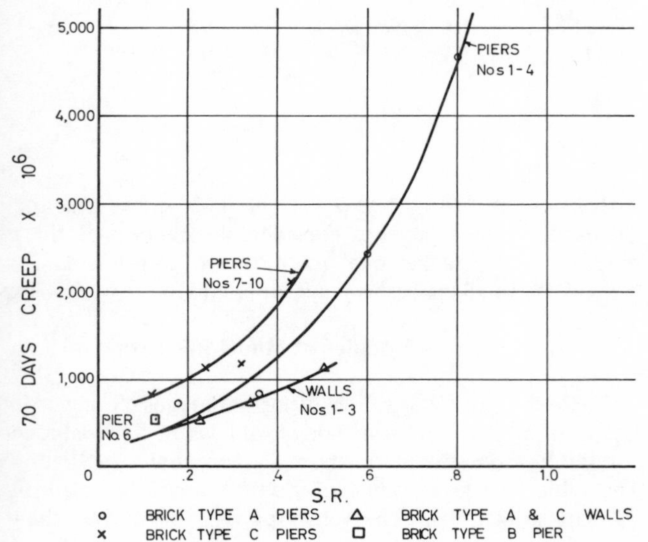

Figure 9-2. 70 days creep in model brickwork piers and walls vs ratio of applied stress/brickwork strength.

the variation in the relative strains is more pronounced up to 7 days when they again become more or less equal. One can conclude from these results that the relative strain rate in model brickwork is virtually independent of the stress/strength ratio or the type of brick used. In brickwork piers between 65 and 80 percent of the 70 day strain occurred after one day, and in brickwork wall the corresponding value ranged approximately between 70 and 90 percent.

The results from Tables 9-6 and 9-7 have been plotted in Figures 9-3 and 9-4. Figure 9-3 plots the instantaneous strains for brickwork piers 1 – 4 and 7 – 10, the 1 day and 70 day total strains for all brickwork piers and the 70 day strains for brickwork walls. The results suggest that the total strains (except the instantaneous strains) do not depend on the type of brick used but are solely a function of the stress/strength ratio. Brickwork walls show 20 percent smaller 70 day strains than the brickwork piers and are only slightly higher than the 1 day brickwork pier strains. The 70 day strains in brickwork piers follow the law:

$$\log_{10} \epsilon_{70} = 1.25\,(SR) - 3.05 \qquad (9\text{-}1)$$

and the 1 day strain in brickwork piers follows the law:

$$\log_{10} \epsilon_1 = 1.31\,(SR) - 3.23 \qquad (9\text{-}2)$$

Table 9-6
Values of Relative Total Strains (Excluding Shrinkage) in Model Brickwork Piers with Brick A and C and Different Stress Levels
Load applied at 28 days

Type of Brick	Average Brickwork Strength @ 28 days psi	Applied Stress	SR	Total strain after 70 days x 10^6	Relative total strain as percentage of 70-day total strain						
					Instant	1d	3	7	14	28	56
A	1,117	201	.18	1,359	46	71	72	76	82	95	99
A	1,117	402	.36	2,236	63	74	78	82	87	96	99
A	997	600	.60	5,055	52	80	86	88	92	98	100
A	997	800	.80	8,177	43	75	84	87	91	96	100
C	1,700	205	.12	1,172	30	66	71	75	79	86	97
C	1,700	410	.24	1,803	40	65	69	73	79	87	96
C	1,915	617	.32	2,110	45	72	76	79	84	88	97
C	1,915	824	.43	3,245	35	68	75	78	86	95	99

Table 9-7
Values of Relative Total Strain (Excluding Shrinkage) in Model Brickwork Walls
Load applied at 28 days

Type of Brick	Average Brick Strength psi	Average Brickwork Strength @ 28 days psi	Applied Stress	SR	Total Strain @ 70 days x 10^6	Relative total strain as a percentage of 70-day total strain						
						Inst	1d	3	7	14	28	56
A	4,214	1,117	382	.34	1,655	55	68	74	84	95	98	100
A	4,004	997	505	.50	3,135	64	81	86	91	97	98	100
C	5,355	1,770	385	.23	1,313	56	93	95	96	97	97	98

where:

ϵ_{70} = 70 day strain
ϵ_1 = 1 day strain
SR = ratio of applied stress to brickwork strength at 28 days.

The 70 day and 1 day strains for brickwork piers are plotted in Figure 9-4 on a semi-logarithmic scale where they yield practically straight lines.

Table 9-8 gives the values of 70 day linear shrinkage strains of control brickwork piers as well as relative shrinkage expressed as a percentage of the 70 days values. The shrinkage was measured from 28 days after casting. The most probable reason for shrinkage of the brickwork rather than expansion[6] which occurs more frequently in full-size brickwork is that the model bricks were stored for a considerable time and were wetted to a saturated, surface dry condition prior to laying. The shrinkage of model brickwork with bricks C (250 – 257 x 10^{-6}) was approximately 2.5 times that of model brickwork with bricks A (88 – 122 x 10^{-6}). This shows that for lo values of applied stress a considerable fraction of the com bined strain can be due to moisture movements in th brickwork. In all cases shrinkage stopped after 7 weeks.

Young's Modulus of Model Brickwork

Table 9-9 gives the values of instantaneous Young's Modu E_{inst} of model brickwork piers and walls. The values wer computed from the stress-strain curves shown in Figure 9-: The table also gives values of Young's modulus based on th 70 day strains E_{70}. The values of E_{inst} are lower than th normally accepted values for full-size brickwork. To chec whether this was solely a feature of the model brick geometrically similar brickwork piers were built with full-siz bricks, and these gave values of E_{inst} ranging from 0.29 – 0.6 x 10^6 p.s.i. with an average value of 0.35 x 10^6 p.s.i. whic was of the same order as the values obtained previously. allowance was made for the strength of brickwork constructe

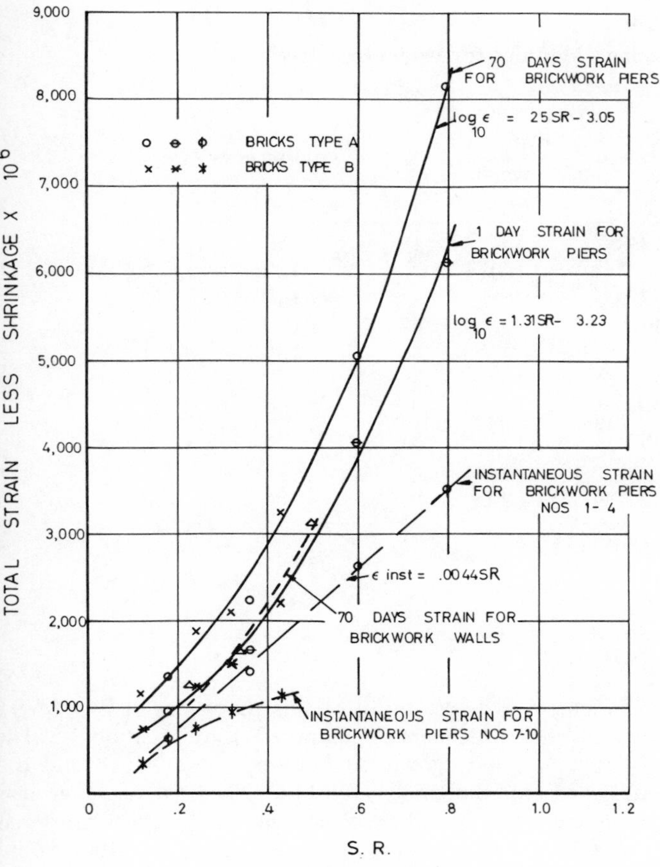

Figure 9-3. Instantaneous 1 day and 70 days strains in model brickwork piers and walls against ratio applied stress/brickwork strength.

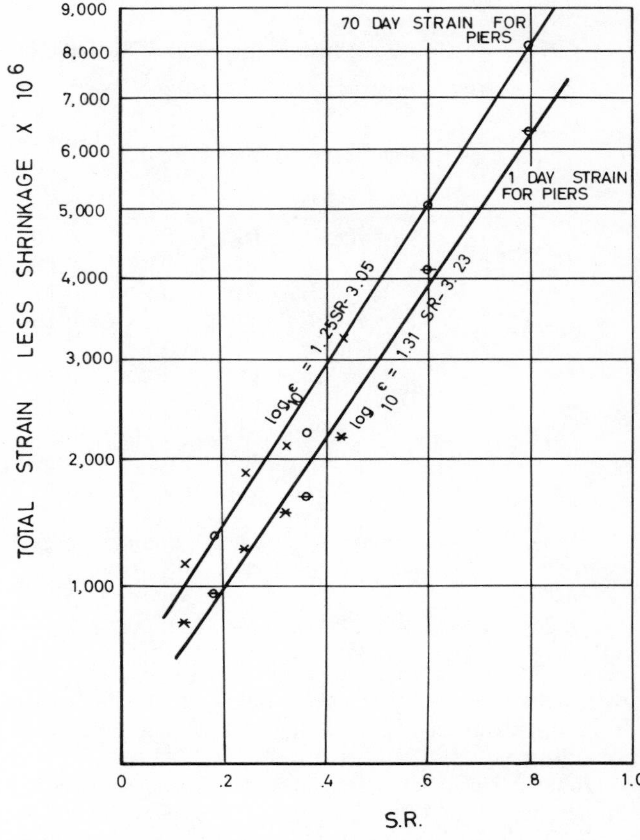

Figure 9-4. Semi-log plots of 1 day and 70 days strains in model brickwork piers against ratio applied stress/brickwork strength.

Table 9-8
Values of Relative Shrinkage of Model Brickwork Specimens Measured From 28 days After Casting

(Time of Application of Load)
Temperature 70° F, RH = 50%, Bricks saturated surface dry at time of casting.

Type of Brick	Average Brick Strength psi	Average Brickwork Strength @ 28 days psi	Shrinkage @ 70 days x 10^6	Relative shrinkage as percentage of 70-day shrinkage					
				1 day	3	7	14	21	28
A	4,214	1,117	88	17	28	68	96	100	100
A	4,004	997	122	9	27	62	92	99	101
C	5,355	1,700	257	8	22	46	68	81	88
C	6,250	1,915	250	4	12	28	52	72	84
B	14,206	3,400	120	2	6	13	28	49	61

Table 9-9
Instantaneous and 70-Days Values of Young's Modulus for Model Brickwork

Specimen	SR	E_{inst} × 10^{-6} psi	E_{70} × 10^{-6} psi	$\frac{E_{70}}{E_{inst}}$	$\frac{E_{70}}{\text{B/W strength}}$	SR	$1100(SR)e^{-2.88(SR)}$
Pier No. 1	.18	0.32	0.15	0.47	134	.1	83
” 2	.36	0.29	0.18	0.62	161	.2	123
” 3	.60	0.23	0.12	0.52	119	.3	140
” 4	.80	0.23	0.10	0.44	98	.4	139
” 5	.06	2.28	—	—	—	.5	131
” 6	.13	2.30	0.55	0.24	162	.6	117
” 7	.12	0.59	0.17	0.29	102	.7	103
” 8	.24	0.55	0.21	0.38	127	.8	88
” 9	.32	0.65	0.29	0.45	152	—	—
” 10	.43	0.72	0.25	0.35	133	—	—
Wall No. 1	.34	0.43	0.23	0.53			
” 2	.50	0.25	0.16	0.64			
” 3	.23	0.59	0.29	0.49			

with the two types of bricks then the ratios of E_{inst}/brickwork strength was higher for model brickwork than for full-size brickwork.

Table 9-9 also gives the ratios E_{70}/E_{inst}. For piers 1 – 4 these range from .44 to .56. For pier 6 built with high strength model brick B the ratio is .24 and for piers 7 – 10 built with model brick C the ratio varies from .29 to .45. For brickwork walls the ratio varies from .49 to .64. The average value of E_{70}/E_{inst} for piers is .42 and for walls it is .56. These values show that to allow for long term movements the values of Young's modulus based on short duration laboratory tests must be reduced by a factor of approximately 2 to 2.5.

Referring again to Equation 9-1 this can be rewritten in the form:

$$\epsilon_{70} = 912\, e^{2.88\,(SR)} \times 10^{6} \qquad (9\text{-}3)$$

or

$$\frac{1}{\epsilon_{70}} = 1100\, e^{-2.88\,(SR)} \qquad (9\text{-}4)$$

Now from previous definition $SR = \frac{\sigma}{B.W.S.}$

where:

σ = applied stress
B.W.S. = brickwork strength at 28 days

$$\therefore \frac{SR}{\epsilon_{70}} = \frac{\sigma/BWS}{\epsilon_{70}} = \frac{E_{70}}{BWS} = 1{,}100(SR)\, e^{-2.88(SR)} \qquad (9\text{-}5)$$

where:

$$E_{70} = \frac{\sigma}{\epsilon_{70}}$$

Figure 9-5 shows in dotted line the values of E_{70}/BWS fo model brickwork piers as computed from Equation 9-5. The is a fairly good agreement between these values, and tho obtained experimentally (full line). These curves, contrary t usual expectations, where the Young's modulus either remai constant or decreases with increasing stress, the modul actually goes up with the applied stress (for a consta brickwork strength) reaching a maximum value at SR = 0.3 and then decreases again. This unusual behaviour is a dire consequence of the stress-strain relationship for the mod brickwork given by Equation 9-1.

Conclusions

A series of creep tests on half scale model brickwork pie and walls showed the following:

1. The 70 day strain in brickwork piers (excluding moistu movements) followed the law:

$$\log_{10} \epsilon_{70} = 1.25(SR) - 3.05$$

and the 1 day strain followed the law:

$$\log_{10} \epsilon_{1} = 1.31(SR) - 3.23$$

The strain is a function of time and ratio of applied stre over brickwork strength. It is independent of type of mod brick or its direction of extrusion.

2. The 70 day strains in single leaf model panel walls a some 20 percent smaller than the corresponding strains i piers.

3. The 70 day relative strain rate for model brickwork i virtually the same after 3 days for different ratios of applie stress to brickwork strength. The instantaneous strains whe

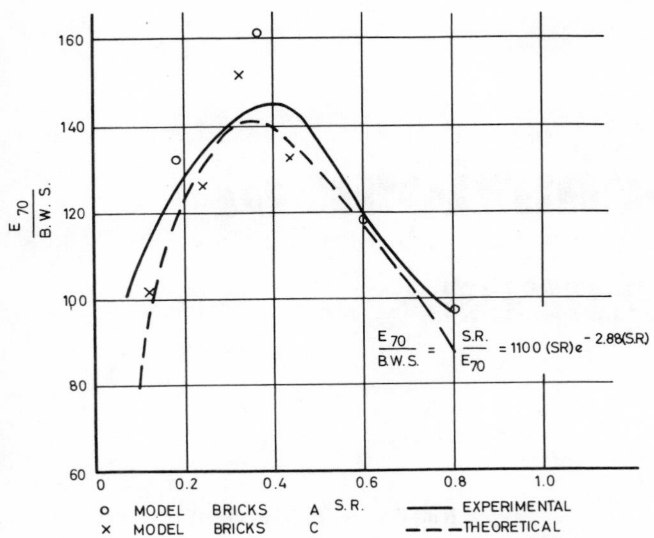

Figure 9-5. Variation of E_{70}/brickwork strength with ratio applied stress/brickwork strength for model brickwork piers.

expressed as percentages of 70 day strain show a wider scatter due to the errors introduced in extrapolating the initial strain-time curve to zero time.

4. In model brickwork piers between 65 and 80 percent of 70 day strain occurred in the first 24 hours. For model panel walls the value was between 70 and 90 percent. In both types of brickwork, very little creep occurs after 12 weeks, even at stress levels exceeding half the ultimate strength of brickwork.

5. The value of Young's modulus for model brickwork based on 70 day strains are approximately one half of the instantaneous Young's modulus. The instantaneous Young's modulus for model brickwork piers was constant for different stress levels when using brick A extruded in the direction of its length, but it decreased with increasing stress when using brick C extruded normal to its length. There was a fairly good agreement between the ratios of instantaneous Young's modulus to brickwork strength for model and full-size brickwork piers.

Acknowledgements

The author wishes to express his gratitude to the Brick Development Association who sponsored the greater part of the work described in this paper, to the British Ceramic Research Association of Great Britain for supplying the model bricks, and to Professor R. C. Coates who provided the laboratory facilities for carrying out this work.

References

1. Lenczner, D. "Design of Creep Machines for Brickwork", Proc. Brit. Ceram. Soc. No. 4, July, 1965. pp. 1-8.
2. Skeen, J. W. "The Strength of Brickwork built with Plasticized (Aerated) Cement-Sand Mortars", Trans. Brit. Ceram. Soc. Vol. 62, 1963, pp. 631-643.
3. Davey, N., and Thomas, F. G., "The Structural Uses of Brickwork", Inst. Civ. Engrs., Struct. and Bldg. Div., Struct. and Bldg. Paper No. 24, I.C.E., London, 1950.
4. Stedham, M. E. C. "Quality Control for Load-Bearing Brickwork II. 9 in.-Cube Tests: Further Results", Proc. Brit. Ceram. Soc., No. 4, July, 1965, pp. 9-23.
5. Lenczner, D., "Strength and Elastic Properties of the 9-in. Brickwork Cube", Trans. Brit. Ceram. Soc., Vol. 65, No. 6, June, 1966. pp. 363-382.
6. West, H. W. H., "Moisture Movement of Bricks and Brickwork" Trans. Brit. Ceram. Soc. Vol. 66, April 1967, pp. 137-160.

10. Rheological behaviour of masonry structures.

Dr. P. T. Mikluchin, P. E., P. T. Mikluchin and Assoc., Toronto, Ontario, Canada

Introduction

Latest progress in design and construction of modern masonry structures and buildings requires, from a designer, an adequate knowledge of long-term effects of applied loads on the general performance of buildings. The evaluation of these long-term effects must be based on the data derived from general principles of engineering rheology.

Rheology, as applied to structures, is a study of problems connected with changes in stress distributions and deformations taking place in structures and buildings subjected to the action of long-term loading.

The knowledge of rheological behaviour of structures in general[1,2] and masonry structures in particular[3,4] is very important for the design and construction of buildings where masonry is combined with other materials possessing different characteristics of creep, as in reinforced concrete or structural steel frame-works, working together with the masonry, or where masonry elements are built of units with different physical characteristics.

The phenomenon of differential creep must also be considered in structures subjected to variations in the intensities of external loads acting on various elements of the buildings.

Tests have shown that long-term deformation of masonry under the action of loads is accompanied by the change in magnitude of modulus of elasticity[1,3]. Changes in deformation characteristics due to such loading affect the rigidity of structures and must be taken into account in the design of structures subjected to dynamic forces and in all problems requiring the determination of the frequency of vibrations and other dynamic characteristics of the structure. These considerations are important in seismic design of masonry buildings.

Rheological Behaviour of Masonry

Since masonry is a composite building material, eac component influences, in its own way, the overall rheologic behaviour of masonry structures.

Masonry Units

As far as masonry units are concerned, they possess variou degrees of creep. Creep characteristics of these units depen on the materials used for their fabrication and the type o process utilized for their manufacture.

For instance, creep of hard burnt clay units, for all practica purposes, is negligible. Soft brick units are subjected to higher degree of creep.

Mortars

Mortars possess a very considerable degree of creep Stabilization of creep deformations usually takes place 4 to hours after application of load. After the stabilization period creep deformations are proportional to applied stress provide the stresses do not exceed $0.5 - 0.6\ R_m$.

Main source of creep in masonry is the mortar. Magnitud of creep is, essentially, a function of the volumetric content o cement paste in mortar joints[5].

Creep increases with the increase in water-cement ratio i mortar.

Nonreinforced Masonry

Masonry, being a composite material, has definite rheo logical properties. The most pronounced increase of creep deformations in masonry takes place in 3 to 4 months afte the initial moment of loading. Stabilization of creep defor mations begins after 8 to 10 months. After one year, tota deformations of masonry is approximately 1.8 to 2.0 time greater than instantaneous deformations at the moment o first load application.

Tests on masonry specimens to study the creep phenomena[3] have shown that creep deformations take place during the whole process of loading.

These tests have proven that there exists, for all practical purposes, proportionality between creep and the applied stress. Such proportionality holds true for stress levels not exceeding 0.5 to 0.6 of ultimate strength of masonry (R_m). In this case, we have a phenomenon of linear creep.

For stress levels between 0.6 to 0.85 R_m proportionality ceases to exist, and the phenomenon of non-linear creep takes place.

For stress levels exceeding 0.85 R_m creep does not become smaller with the time but increases, leading to failure of masonry.

Among other factors influencing creep are relative ambient humidity of the surrounding medium and temperature. Creep increases with a decrease in the relative humidity, and with an increase in temperature.

Creep of masonry also depends on thickness of mortar joints and shape and size of the masonry units.

There is certain amount of decrease in creep with an increase in thickness of masonry elements.

Age of masonry at the time of loading also affects creep. With the increase of age, creep diminishes.

Recent rests conducted on vibrated masonry[3] show pronounced reduction of creep. Creep deformations of non-vibrated masonry are approximately twice as large as the creep deformations of vibrated masonry.

If a masonry element consists of several masonry materials with different creep characteristics then, in the course of time, stresses from the material with greater creep characteristics will be partially transferred to the material with lower creep characteristics.

It means that stresses in materials possessing higher degree of creep will be reduced, whereas stresses in materials with lower degree of creep will be increased.

Such stress transfer can result in overstressing of one of the masonry materials. It is often the case with the walls covered with the exterior cladding. In such cases special measures shall be undertaken to make sure that the cladding would not take part in resisting forces applied to such masonry walls.

Reinforced Masonry

All above mentioned considerations are valid for plain masonry. In reinforced masonry, the study of rheological behaviour indicates that the magnitude of creep is considerably smaller as compared with plain masonry.

In reinforced masonry columns subjected to the action of axial loading, redistribution of normal stresses in longitudinal reinforcement and surrounding masonry takes place due to the phenomenon of creep.

For instance, tests have shown that, after a period of 1 year, stress in steel reinforcement can be 1.6 to 1.7 times higher than at the moment of load application, whereas stress in masonry can be reduced to 0.6 – 0.65 of the original stress magnitude[3]. This fact must be considered during the design of reinforced masonry structures.

Relationship Between Stresses and Deformations Under Sustained Loads

Case of Linear Creep

In order to establish the relation between stresses and deformations for long-term loading, the following assumptions will be made:

1. masonry can be considered as uniform building material,
2. the relationship between creep deformation and stress is linear,
3. the law of superposition is valid for creep deformations.

To differentiate between two kinds of deformations taking place in masonry under the action of applied stresses, deformations at the moment of load application will be called instantaneous elastic deformations, and deformations developing with the time will be called creep deformations.

The magnitude of the instantaneous deformations depends on the age of masonry. Magnitude of creep deformations depends on both the age of masonry and the duration of loading.

If the age of masonry is τ and the instant for which the deformation is to be found is t, then the total unit deformation for masonry element subjected to the action of an axial force at any time can be determined from the equation:

$$\Delta(t,\tau) = \Delta_{EL}(t,\tau) + \Delta_{CR}(t,\tau) \tag{10-1}$$

where:

$$\Delta_{EL}(t,\tau) = \frac{1}{E(\tau)}$$

$$0 < \tau \leqslant t$$

is the instantaneous elastic unit deformation and,

$$\Delta_{CR} = F(t,\tau)$$

is the creep unit deformation.

If at the instant $t = \tau$, normal stress, $\sigma = \sigma(\tau_1)$ which changes with time then the total relative deformation $\epsilon(t)$ will be;

$$\epsilon(t) = \sigma(\tau_1) \cdot \Delta(t,\tau_1) + \int_{\tau_1}^{t} \frac{a\sigma(\tau)}{a\tau} \cdot \Delta(t,\tau) \cdot d\tau \tag{10-2}$$

or after the integration by parts:

$$\epsilon(t) = \frac{\sigma(t)}{E(t)} - \int_{\tau_1}^{t} \sigma(\tau) \frac{\delta}{\delta\tau} \Delta(t,\tau)\, d\tau \tag{10-3}$$

From this equation follows that total relative deformation consists of instantaneous elastic relative deformation:

$$\epsilon_{EL} = \frac{\sigma(t)}{E(t)} \tag{10-4}$$

and creep relative deformation:

$$\epsilon_{CR} = -\int_{\tau_1}^{t} \sigma(\tau) \frac{\delta}{\delta \tau} \Delta(t, \tau) \cdot d\tau \tag{10-5}$$

Relative creep deformation , Equation 10-5, is always positive, if $\sigma(\tau)$ is greater than zero.

thus:

$$\epsilon(t) = \epsilon_{EL}(t) + \epsilon_{CR}(t) \tag{10-6}$$

If the normal stress $\sigma(\tau)$ due to the action of long-term loading is constant, $\sigma(\tau)$ = const. as it is the case for the majority of buildings, then the Equation 10-2 becomes:

$$\epsilon(t) = \sigma(\tau_1) \Delta(t, \tau_1) = \sigma(\tau_1) \left[\frac{1}{E(\tau_1)} + F(t, \tau_1) \right] \tag{10-7}$$

Equation 10-7 can be presented in the following form:

$$\epsilon(t, \tau) = \frac{\sigma(\tau_1)}{E_D(\tau_1)} \tag{10-8}$$

where:

$$E_D(\tau_1) = \frac{E(\tau_1)}{1 + \beta(t, \tau_1)} \tag{10-9}$$

with:

$$\beta(t, \tau_1) = F(t, \tau_1) \cdot E(\tau_1)$$

Preceeding analysis holds true for axial stress conditions. Identical relationships between elastic and creep deformations can be established for shear stresses and shear deformations.

The knowledge of normal and shear stresses with corresponding deformations is important for analysis of various stress conditions. In the general case of three-dimensional stress distribution, a definite functional relationship between components of deformations and stresses can be established. This relationship would fully describe stress-strain condition in the structure subjected to the action of external forces, taking into account the influence of creep and change of modulus of instantaneous deformations.

Case of Non Linear Creep

The above mentioned considerations of the theory of cree are valid for cases when stresses do not exceed 0.5 R_m an consequently when linear relationship between creep defo mations and corresponding stresses holds true.

If σ is greater than 0.5 R_m, but does not exceed 0.85 R_m then non-linear creep takes place. In this case, the relationshi between stresses and deformations can be described by th equation:

$$\epsilon(t, \tau) = \frac{\sigma(\tau_1)}{E(\tau_1)} + F(t, \tau) \cdot F_o(t, \tau) \qquad (10\text{-}10$$

Here, as before, $\epsilon(t,\tau)$ is total relative deformation of masonr at the instant t, subjected to stress $\sigma(\tau)$ applied to the age o τ_1, $E(\tau_1)$ is modulus of elasticity, and $F_o(t,\tau)$ is a functio determined from experiments. This function expresses nor linear relationship between stress and creep deformations.

It can be shown that the total deformation $\epsilon(t)$ can b expressed in the following form:

$$\epsilon(t) = \epsilon_{EL}(t) + \epsilon_{L.CR}(t) \left[1 + a(t) \right] \qquad (10\text{-}11$$

where ϵ_{EL} (t) is instantaneous elastic deformation, $\epsilon_{L.CR}$ (t is linear creep deformation and $a(t)$ is a function expressin the influence of non-linearity of relationship between stresse and deformations. When $a(t)$ = O, then Equation 10-11 describes the functional relationship between stresses an deformations for the case of linear creep. The relationship Equation 10-11, is the general equation of the theory o non-linear creep.

Design of Masonry Elements

Engineering design of masonry structures must be based o the simultaneous consideration of strength, stability, an deformability criteria.

Design methods based on classical working stress analysi only, do not take into account the redistribution of internal stresses due to rheological phenomena taking place in struc tures, caused by creep and shrinkage of masonry.

Sizes of many structural elements may be dictated by consideration of their deformability and not by the magnitude of stresses obtained from the classical stress analysis. Analysis of the effect of long-term loads on stress distribution in structural elements is of paramount importance for prope design of masonry structures.

Creep affects the strength and stability of all structural elements of a building and a building itself as a whole. This means that the design of modern masonry structures must take creep into account in every element of the structure and consider the overall rheological behaviour of the building in its totality.

It has been established that massive masonry elements, under the influence of long-term loading, within the limits of linear creep, show certain amount of increase in ultimate strength.

But if the stresses produced by long-term loads exceed the stress level corresponding to linear creep, then the ultimate compressive strength of masonry will be reduced.

Design for Strength and Stability

Tests have proven that, for all stress levels, slender masonry elements (columns, walls) with slenderness ratios greater than 8, subjected to long-term loading, show a reduction of the ultimate strength[3]. Therefore, allowable loads on such elements must be reduced.

Nonreinforced Masonry

Case of Concentric Compressive Load. Allowable load can be determined on the basis of the following formula:

$$P \leqslant \phi \cdot A \cdot R_m \qquad (10\text{-}12)$$

where:

$$P = \frac{P_{d\,.\,1}}{C_c} + P_{1\,.\,1} \qquad (10\text{-}13)$$

or

$$\frac{P_{d.1}}{C_c} + P_{1.1} \leqslant \phi \cdot A \cdot R_m \qquad (10\text{-}14)$$

here:

- P – total design load,
- $P_{d.1}$ – design compressive force due to dead load,
- C_c – coefficient taking into consideration the effect of creep on strength of an element,
- $P_{1.1}$ – design compressive force due to live load,
- ϕ – stress factor, taking into consideration the slenderness ratio of the element[6,7,8]
- A – cross sectional area of an element,
- R_m – basic allowable compressive stress.

Coefficient C_c depends on the slenderness 1/h ratio of an element[3]. It can be determined from the following formula:

$$C_c = 0.021\,(55.7 - 1/h)$$

where:

$$8 \leqslant C_c \leqslant 20$$

The above mentioned considerations are valid for the uniform distribution of compressive stresses across the cross section of masonry elements.

A series of tests conducted on the eccentrically loaded masonry elements have shown that if the compressive stresses do not exceed 0.5 R_m the hypotheses of plane sections can be considered as valid, for both instantaneous and long-term load applications.

Neutral axis changes its position with time but not considerably; as a result, one can assume for all practical design calculations that the position of neutral axis remains unchanged. Such assumption greatly simplifies design calculations.

Case of an Eccentric Axial Load. For small eccentricities allowable load can be determined from the formula:

$$P \leqslant \psi \cdot \phi \cdot A \cdot R_m \qquad (10\text{-}15)$$

where:

- ψ – coefficient of stress reduction, taking into consideration the magnitude of the excentricity of applied compressive load.[6,7,8]

Other factors have the same meaning as in the previous case.

For larger excentricities some modification of the above mentioned formula shall be made.

Case of an Eccentric Axial and Transversal Loads. In the case of a bending forces acting together with the axial loads, design bending moment can be determined from the following formula:

$$M = \frac{M_{d.1}}{C_c} + M_{1.1} \qquad (10\text{-}16)$$

here:

- $M_{d.1}$ = bending moment due to dead load,
- $M_{1.1}$ = moment due to live load,
- C_c = coefficient taking into consideration the influence of creep.

Reinforced Masonry

Design of reinforced masonry is based on the following assumptions:

1. hypothesis of plane sections is applicable,
2. all tensile forces are resisted by the reinforcement,
3. modulus of elasticity of reinforcement and masonry remain constant.

Theory of design of reinforced masonry elements should take into consideration the influence of elastic and inelastic phenomena which are taking place in these elements.

For instance, for elements subjected to axial loads, allowable load P can be determined from the following formula:

$$P \leqslant \phi \cdot A(a \cdot b\ R_m + p \cdot R_s) \qquad (10\text{-}17)$$

where:

ϕ – coefficient taking into account the influence of slenderness ratio,
A – cross-sectional area of the element,
R_m – ultimate strength of masonry,
R_s – allowable stress in reinforcement,
p – percentage of reinforcement,
a – factor of safety,
b – coefficient taking into account the influence of creep.

Eccentrically loaded reinforced masonry elements, depending on the magnitude of eccentricity, can be designed according to formulas analogous to formulas for reinforced concrete elements. The same holds true for the design of reinforced masonry subjected to bending forces.

Shearing stresses and diagonal tension shall be checked as well.

Design of Masonry Structures on the Basis of Deformability Criteria

In addition to the design for the required degree of strength and stability, masonry structures must be designed for the required degree of rigidity.

For all elements of masonry structures and the structures themselves, deformations, due to applied loads, should not exceed certain limits. For instance, high masonry walls, working together with the structural frame of the building, should not be subjected to deformations which would result in cracking of these walls.

If the deformations exceed the allowable, either the rigidity of the building frame must be increased or the strength of masonry made greater. The latter can be achieved by using stronger masonry, by increasing its thickness, or by introducing proper reinforcement.

Deformations must be reduced to a minimum in reinforced masonry walls, beams, lintels and similar structural elements. Limited deformations are very important for such structures as reinforced masonry water tanks, reservoirs, water filtration plants and the like.

Masonry walls, carrying exterior cladding must also be checked for deformations.

In general, the evaluation of the linear and non-linear creep can be obtained from Equations 10-8 and 10-11.

Without going into any details, it can be shown that unit deformations ϵ_A, due to axial forces should satisfy the following simple requirement:

$$\epsilon_A = \frac{P}{E_m \cdot A} \leqslant \epsilon_{ALL.} \qquad (10\text{-}18)$$

Unit deformation due to the action of bending moments should not exceed the allowable:

$$\epsilon_B = \frac{M}{E_m \cdot I}\left(\frac{h}{2} - y\right) \leqslant \epsilon_{ALL.} \qquad (10\text{-}19)$$

here:

P – is an axial load,
E_m – modulus of elasticity for masonry,
A – cross-sectional area of a masonry element,
M – bending moment,
I – moment of inertia,
h – thickness of masonry,
y – distance from the center of gravity to the poi under consideration,
$\epsilon_{ALL.}$ – allowable unit deformation.

In case of eccentrically applied load, unit deformation w be:

$$\epsilon = \frac{\Sigma M}{E_m \cdot A}\left[e\left(\frac{h}{2} - y\right)\frac{A}{I} - 1\right] \leqslant \epsilon_{ALL.} \qquad (10\text{-}2$$

where:

ΣM – sum of moments due to axial and transversal force
e – eccentricity of an axial load,

other factors are similar to the previous cases.

If the deformations due to these forces exceed t allowable, an opening of the horizontal joints in the tensio zone of a wall will take place.

It means that such a wall must be made thicker reinforced in the zone where opening of the joints could tak place.

The design of reinforced masonry against excessive defo mations must be based on the considerations analogous t relevant design methods used in reinforced concrete structure

In prestressed masonry elements, all deformations must als be checked.

The study of deformability of masonry structures, seen the light of rheological behaviour of masonry, must b intensified to solve new problems arising from the moder developments in masonry construction.

Conclusion

It is impossible, within the confines of this paper, t present all material research and theoretical investigatio devoted to the rheological behaviour of masonry buildings an structures.

An attempt was made to show the importance of co sidering creep phenomena for the adequate design an construction of modern masonry buildings and to indica certain quantitative and qualitative approaches to the solutio of problems arising from analysis of rheological behaviour c such structures.

Present state of progress in the area of engineering design c masonry warrants the inclusion of a series of recommend tions, concerning the rheological aspects of masonry co struction, into Building Codes.

In conclusion, we would like to reiterate once more th necessity of continuing research in the area of rheologic behaviour of plain and reinforced masonry building material

Such research will provide creative architects and engineers with all necessary data for the design of new modern buildings and structures.

References

1. "Symposium on Creep of Concrete", ACI, Publication SP-9, 1964.
2. Arutyunyan, N., "Some Problems in the Theory of Creep", Pergamon Press, New York, 1966.
3. Polyakov, S. V., and Falevich, B. N., "Masonry Structures", Moscow, 1960.
4. "Methodes de Calcul des Murs", Etude Bibliographique, Cahiers du Centre Scientifique et Technique du Batiment, #68, Paris, 1964.
5. Neville, A. M., "Role of Cement in the Creep of Mortar", ACI Journal, March, 1959.
6. Haller, P. "The Technological Properties of Brick Masonry in High Buildings", Translation from Schweiz. Bauz. #76, 1958, National Research Council of Canada, Ottawa, 1959.
7. "Recommended Building Code Requirements for Engineered Brick Masonry", SCPI, Washington, May, 1966.
8. National Building Code, National Research Council, Ottawa, Canada, 1965.

11. Experimental investigation on structural performance of brick masonry prisms.

Dr. R.N.S. Rao, P. E., Civil Engineering Dept., Prairie View A and M College, Prairie View, Texas

In the past the bricks were extensively used to build monumental structures requiring high structural strength. With the development of steel and concrete, use of bricks as structural materials has receded. Though bricks are being continuously used in modern structures, their structural strength has often been ignored. Visualizing this, the Clay Products Association of the Southwest has been promoting many research activities to remedy this economic waste and to focus attention on the structural strength of brick masonry.

The results presented in this paper are based on one such study conducted at the Prairie View A and M College of Texas sponsored by the Clay Products Association of the Southwest. The study involved correlating the compressive strength of brick masonry piers with the strength of bricks and mortars used and with the curing time.

Materials

Bricks

Bricks No. 20 BDD and No. 91 were used. The bricks were supplied by Elgin Butler Brick Company in one batch. The first type, made of 100 percent plastic fine clay, was burned at 2200°F. The second type, made from a mixture of fine clay and top clay which is not so dense was burned at 2200°F. The strength properties are indicated under the test section of this report. The dimensions of bricks used are shown in Figure 11-1.

Mortar Materials

The portland cement used was Lone Star Portland Cement of Houston, Texas type 1. The cement needed was purchased fresh in one bulk supply. The type of lime used was the Magnolia type S building lime of Birmingham, Alabama. The lime needed was obtained fresh in one bulk and used immediately.

The clear fine sand, locally available, was used. Seive analysis results of the sand are shown in Figure 11-2 and Table 11-1. The fineness modulus of the sand was 2.60. The test and the computations were conducted according to the standard procedure which is specified in ASTM C-125-66 and ASTM C-136-63.

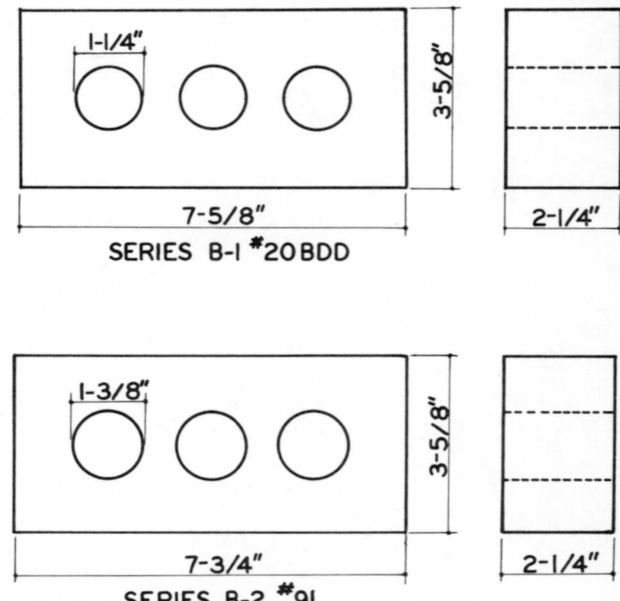

Figure 11-1. Brick dimensions.

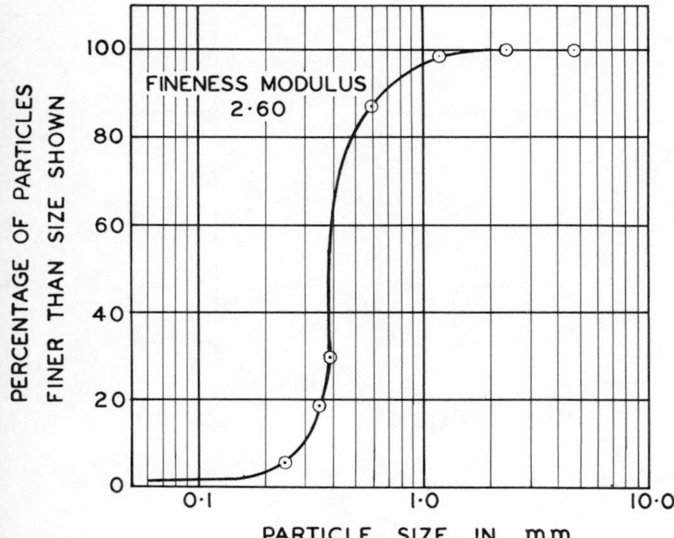

Figure 11-2. Particle size cumulative curve of sand.

Table 11-1
Sieve Analysis of Sand

Sieve No.	Dia. of Openings	% Retained on Each Sieve	Cumulative Finer	Cumulative Retained
4	4.760 mm	0	100.00	0
8	2.380 mm	0	100.00	0
16	1.190 mm	0.65	99.35	0.65
30	0.595 mm	12.05	87.30	12.70
50	0.297 mm	57.75	29.55	70.45
60	0.250 mm	10.93	18.62	81.38
100	0.149 mm	12.96	5.66	94.34
Pan	–	5.48	0	100.00

Table 11-2
Mixing Batches for Mortar in Tests

Mix	Proportions of ingredients by volume			Quantities		
	Cement	Lime	Sand	Cement in lbs.	Lime in lbs.	Sand in CFT.
M	4	1	15	47.00	6.25	1.83
S	2	1	9	47.00	12.50	2.25
N	1	1	6	23.50	12.50	1.50
O	1	2	9	23.50	12.50	2.25

Table 11-3
Compressive Strength of Bricks
Series B-1-#20BDD

Test No.	Compressive Stress in KSI		$(X - \overline{X})^2$	Coefficient of Variation
	X	$\overline{X}$		$\frac{100}{\overline{X}}\sqrt{\frac{\epsilon(X-\overline{X})^2}{n-1}}$
1	7.14	6.32	0.6724	
2	4.67	6.32	2.7225	
3	7.14	6.32	0.6724	
4	6.79	6.32	0.2209	
5	7.29	6.32	0.9409	
6	6.19	6.32	0.0169	
7	4.19	6.32	4.5369	
8	6.49	6.32	0.0225	
9	5.85	6.32	0.2209	
10	7.58	6.32	1.5876	
11	5.73	6.32	0.3481	
12	6.56	6.32	0.5760	
13	6.57	6.32	0.6250	
Total	32.17	$\frac{82.17}{13}$	13.1630	16.61%

Mortars

The strength variation of the masonry with respect to mortar used was tested using four types of mortars with each type of brick. The types of mortars used were: M-type, N-type, S-type and O-type. The entire quantity of each type of mortar needed for testing was mixed separately at one time and used immediately for making the masonry piers. Each batch was mixed by machine with just enough water to give good workability. The mixing was done in a paddle-type mixer. The mortar was used in less than two hours after mixing. The batches used for mixing are given in Table 11-2.

Tests

To correlate the strength properties of the bricks, the mortars, and the masonry, as well as to identify the properties of the materials, the following tests were conducted.

Compression Tests on Bricks

Selected bricks were cut into approximate cubes (some having one hole, some exactly into half, and some having two holes), and were shellacked. After 24 hours, they were coated with plaster-of-paris capping. After hardening for two days, they were tested for compression in the universal testing machine with bricks laid flat-wise. Load was applied uniformly at about 20 to 30 kips per minute. The ultimate load when the brick failed was noted. The results of the tests are shown in Table 11-3.

Moisture Absorption by Bricks

The test was conducted according to the ASTM standard C 67-62, and the results of the absorption of moisture in 24 hours are given in Table 11-4.

Compression Strength of Mortar

Immediately after mixing, mortar cubes of 2" x 2" x 2" were cast. After 24 hours, they were taken out of the mold and kept in a moist cabinet. The cubes were placed high above water level in a pan with water and covered with a cardboard box which was kept wet. After 7 days, the cubes were taken out and were completely immersed in water for the remainder of 28 days.

At the end of the 28 day period, the cubes were taken out, wiped, and cross-section measured, before subjecting them to compression test in the universal testing machine: The load was applied uniformly and slowly so as to see that the specimen failed in not less than 20 sec. and in not more than 80 sec. The load at failure was noted.

Compression Test on Brick Masonry Prisms

The masonry blocks were built in seven layers with 3/8" thick joints as shown in Figure 11-3. The workmanship was of good quality and all specimens were made on the same day. The specimens were air-cured. The temperature and the humidity in the laboratory where the specimens were cured varied from 38°F to 98°F and from 9 percent to 88 percent respectively during this period. In all, sixty-four specimens were built using two types of bricks and four types of mortar. One of each type was tested at the end of 2 days, 4 days, 7 days, 14 days, 28 days, 3 months, and 6 months.

The length, width, and height of each block was measured to the nearest 1/8" before testing. Measurements used in computation were the average of measurements at the top and the bottom of the specimens. Before testing, the side of the specimen was checked for plumb. The top and the bottom were levelled by filling with plaster-of-paris powder as needed. The specimen was placed between the two steel plates 1/4" thick, one at the bottom and one at the top. The whole setup was centered underneath the spherical bearing block of the universal testing machine. Two dial gages were fixed symmetrically on either side of the specimen to measure the compressive deformation of the masonry block. The average of two dial gage readings was taken as the compressive deformation of the specimen.

The load was applied slowly at a constant rate. The deformation was observed at every 5000 lbs load increment. The rate of deformation was kept below 0.001" per inch length of the specimen. The dial gages were removed when the load reached approximately about 75% of the rupture load.

The loading was continued at the same rate further till the block failed. The Figures 11-4 and 11-5 show the specimen under the experimental set up before and after the test.

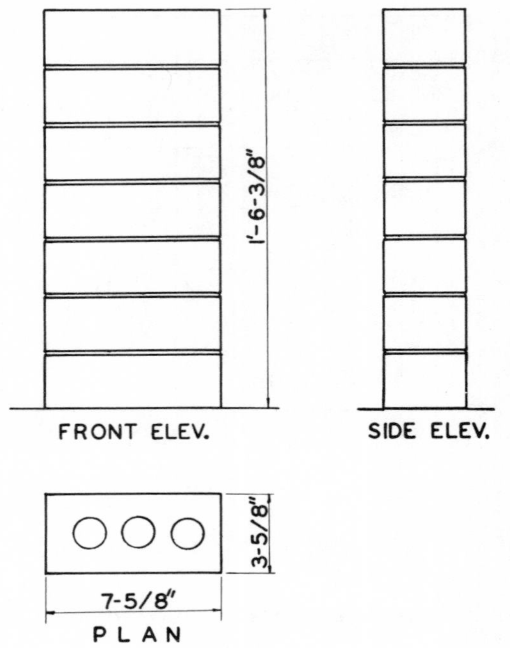

Figure 11-3. Dimensions of brick masonry tiers.

Test Results and Discussion

The test results show that the strength of the masonry block is greatly affected by the type of mortar. Even with the best mortar, the strength of the masonry was found to be only 93% of the strength of the brick in weaker types of brick and 75% of the strength of the brick in stronger types of brick. The contributing factors for reduction of the strength are: percentage of mortar content, thickness of joint, workmanship, and column effect. However, the breaking of the specimen occurred each time by the split failure of bricks, though the pattern of split was modified by the joint and the layers.

There was less strength reduction in masonry piers with mortar containing a higher proportion of cement and lime, and there was more strength reduction in masonry piers with mortar containing a smaller proportion of cement and lime. The setting of mortar depends on the type of curing and on the proportions of cement and lime in the mortar. The author believes that the strength would be larger with rich cement mix cured with moisture and also with rich lime mortar cured in air. Table 11-6 and Figure 11-6 show the effect of using different types of mortars on the compressive strength of the brick masonry units.

The duration of curing definitely affects the strength of the masonry. The tests reveal that the six months strength is nearly 30% more than the two days strength. In practice, air-cured, lime-rich mortar masonry units increase more in strength. This means that if the structure is safe under

Figure 11-4.

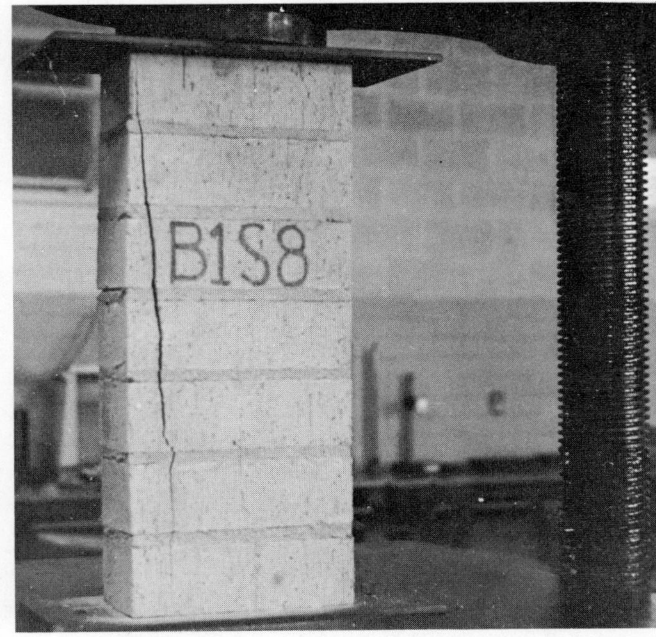

Figure 11-5.

Table 11-4
Moisture Absorption by Brick After 24 Hours Submersion in Water

Brick Type B-1, #20 BDD				Brick Type B-2, #91			
Specimen No.	Wt. of Bricks in grams		Absorption %	Specimen No.	Wt. of Bricks in grams		Absorption %
	Before	After			Before	After	
B1- 1	826.6	869.9	5.26	B2- 1	846.8	913.6	7.88
B1- 2	840.4	883.5	5.11	B2- 2	906.2	978.6	7.98
B1- 3	922.0	970.0	5.20	B2- 3	921.3	994.6	7.95
B1- 4	869.1	914.5	5.25	B2- 4	874.9	944.5	7.97
B1- 5	862.8	908.0	5.25	B2- 5	831.2	896.4	7.85
B1- 6	866.9	913.0	5.32	B2- 6	894.5	966.6	8.07
B1- 7	854.7	901.3	5.46	B2- 7	857.8	926.8	8.05
B1- 8	899.8	947.3	5.28	B2- 8	909.4	980.5	7.83
B1- 9	870.8	917.0	5.40	B2- 9	846.8	913.8	7.92
B1-10	900.8	950.1	5.43	B2-10	895.6	966.3	7.90
B1-11	661.6	698.0	5.50	B2-11	584.2	630.6	7.95
B1-12	667.2	702.2	5.25	B2-12	632.4	682.4	7.92
B1-13	664.2	697.6	5.03	B2-13	676.7	732.0	8.18
B1-14	1067.2	1122.2	5.16	B2-14	1143.3	1232.7	7.80
B1-15	1076.4	1132.6	5.22	B2-15	1054.1	1139.4	8.10
B1-16	1087.1	1146.9	5.52	B2-16	1103.9	1189.1	8.23
		Average	5.30			Average	7.97

Table 11-5
Compressive Strength of Mortar

Type of Mortar	Mix of Mortar			28 Days Strength of Mortar
	Cement	Lime	Sand	PSI
M	4	1	15	3465
S	2	1	9	2506
N	1	1	6	1488
O	1	2	9	603

Table 11-6
Effect of Mortar on the Compressive Strength of Brick Masonry Units

Test No.	Day Test	Type of Mortar Stress in PSI			
		M	S	N	O
1	2	3,360	2,630	2,550	2,130
2	4	3,530	3,250	2,650	1,720
3	7	3,420	3,200	3,850	2,440
4	14	4,340	2,990	3,280	2,740
5	28	4,080	3,780	3,510	2,850
6	3 (MTH)	3,310	4,340	3,240	2,680
7	6 (MTH)	4,360	3,700	3,480	2,420

designed heavy loads during the construction, it will be safer afterwards.

The stress-strain curve pattern of the masonry units slightly deviates from the regular pattern of such curve for elastic materials. The tangent modulus of elasticity seems to increase with increasing stress before reaching an almost constant value. As the yield point approaches, the modulus decreases with further increase in strength.

The author feels that the initial increasing trend of the elasticity modulus cannot be explained by slackness of experimental set-up alone. At the outset of the test, the test specimen and especially the mortar joints are not dense enough. As compression load increases, the material becomes denser, and there is a certain amount of increase in the elasticity modulus due to this increase in density of the material. The decreasing trend of the tangent modulus near the yield point can be explained by the general yielding of the material. The densification effect is more pronounced in masonry units where mortar joints are thick and also where the mortar used is less dense. As mortar ages, the mortar sets and gives more resistance to densification. Therefore, the densification rate decreases, and, consequently, the increasing tendency of the tangent modulus persists for longer time. This effect is illustrated in Figure 11-7.

Limitations of the Study and Its Future

The conclusions are based on limited experimental study. The author believes that a greater number of similar experiments will substantiate the foregoing conclusions.

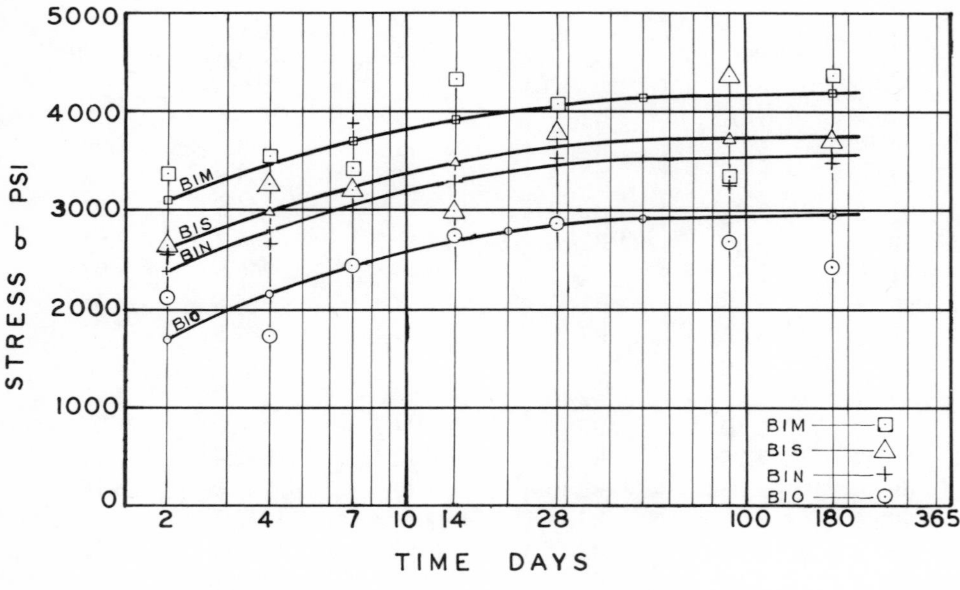

Figure 11-6. Effect of mortar on compressive strength of brick masonry units.

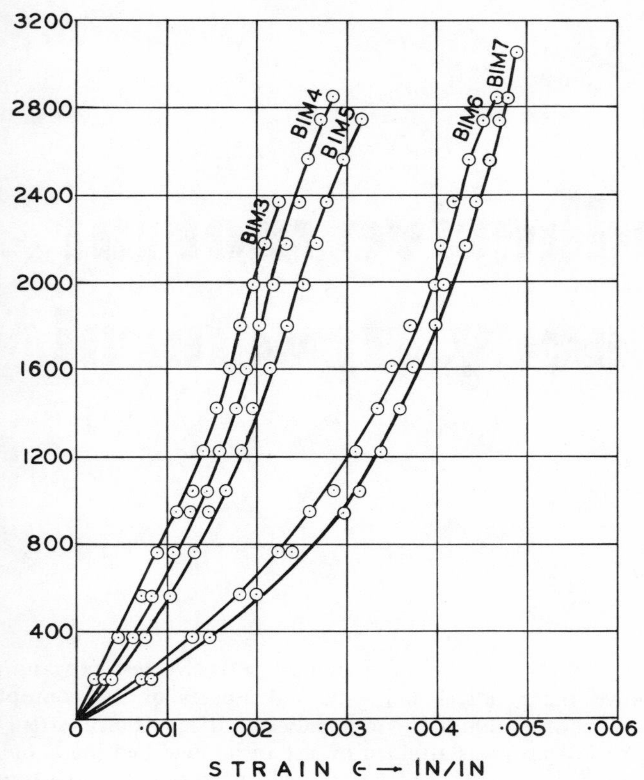

Figure 11-7. Stress strain curve for specimen BIM.

The experimental study could include different thickness of joints; different types of curing; different sizes of masonry units; and different kinds of bricks and mortars.

Acknowledgements

The author wishes to express his deep gratitude and thanks to Mr. C. T. Grimm of Clay Products Association of the Southwest for his interest and sponsorship of this study. Many thanks to Prairie View A and M College for helping me with this study. Thanks are due to Mr. C. T. Edwards of Prairie View A and M College and numerous students of Prairie View A and M College for their assistance.

References

1. *Standards in Building Codes,* American Society of Testing Materials, Philadelphia, 1966.
2. *Compressive Transverse and Racking Strength of Four Inch Brick Walls,* Structural Clay Products Research Foundation, Research Report No. 9, Geneva, Illinois, August, 1965.
3. *Compressive and Transverse Strength Tests of Eight Inch Brick Walls,* Structural Clay Products Research Foundation, Research Report No. 10, Geneva, Illinois, October, 1966.

For additional discussion on this chapter see Remarks *by Bob D. Campbell in chapter 6.*

12. High strength adhesive mortar in concrete masonry structural systems.

M. Schupack and A. McDonald, Schupack and Associates, Stamford, Connecticut

High strength adhesive mortar, when used with concrete block, is generally applied along the face shells. It is applied as a bead and then thinly spread by the weight of the block in the next superimposed course. The thinness of the mortar joint requires the block to be dimensionally accurate so that a straight plumb wall can be obtained. Compensations for out-of-square block are not as readily made with thin joints as with normal 3/8-inch thick cement-lime mortar joints.

The most stringent dimensional requirement is for parallel bedding surfaces with all blocks of the same height. One method of obtaining this is to put the blocks through a grinding operation. Essentially, the blocks are milled-to-bear. As can be seen in Figure 12-1 even, level beds can be obtained. The grinding operation is a process which few block manufacturers are equipped to do. Consequently, in the early stage of adhesive mortar use, this system was limited by the grinding facilities available. The first applications were also limited to basement walls and industrial buildings. Here it was found that the advantages of adhesive mortar could support the additional costs which the grinding operation imposed.

Nevertheless, to widen the field of application, another method for obtaining dimensional accuracy was developed. It entailed up-ending blocks with their cores parallel to the floor. Thus, the mating surfaces are the molded faces of the blocks. With an accurate mold used in the production process, few problems are encountered. This system is identified under the trademark applied for name of MONOWALL with patents pending. It is illustrated in Figure 12-2 which shows the tight bearing surfaces which are obtained. The vertical head joints are open because it was realized in the early developmental stages that adhesive mortar in the head joints was probably not required structurally and slowed production. This, and other innovations described, initiated an extensive test program to prove the practical and structural aspects of the concepts. Among other things, the tests indicated that sufficient strength for most uses was attained by use of bonded bed joints only. The space in the head joints could be covered with various coatings.

The prime motivation in pursuing this concept is economy. This is achieved by substantially increasing field production rates and by better utilizing the block material which will be described in this chapter.

Figure 12-1. Concrete block with ground surfaces.

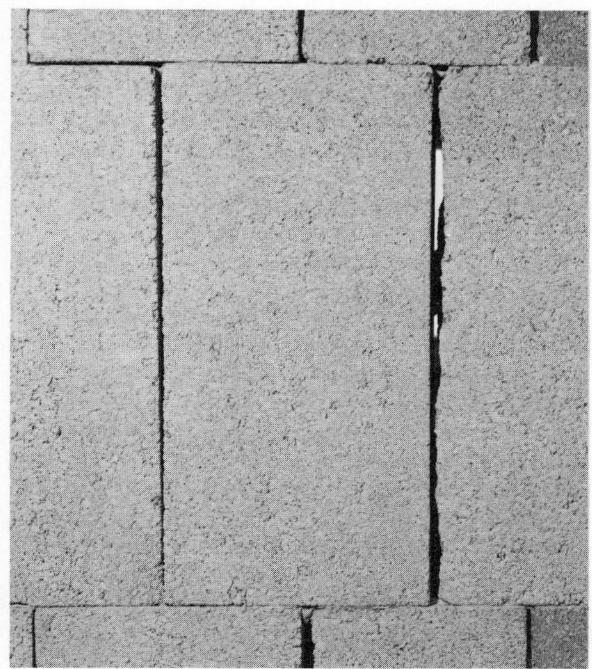

Figure 12-2. Orientation of concrete block in Monowall construction.

Figure 12-3. Foundation wall with stacked bond, ground block.

History

The concept of thin-bed adhesive mortar, using an epoxy resin with latex and cement additives combined in an oil in water emulsion, was conceived by Al Barrows and developed by Raybestos-Manhattan, Inc. The concept was developed in 1960, and the marketing and further development of this concept were taken over by the Dow Chemical Company in 1963. The Plasticrete Corporation of Hamden, Connecticut, a large block producer, under their own initiative undertook development of the use of the adhesive mortar in general masonry construction. Since that time, Intercon Research Incorporated has become the distributor of THREADLINE® brand adhesive mortar.

Since the introduction of the concept, close to 2 million blocks have been assembled by this process. This is a very small portion of the block industry, but it is a beginning of a breakthrough in the concrete masonry field and shows much promise.

General Considerations in Using Thin-Bed Adhesive Mortar

When using thin-bed adhesive mortar, the following points require special attention:

1. Adhesive of this nature is expensive and should be used sparingly.
2. Application is best done by a caulking gun procedure which puts down a 3/16″ bead. The adhesive then spreads under the weight of a superimposed block and permits small adjustments for the tolerances.
3. The pot life of the adhesive material must be reasonable for both hot and cold weather. In excessively hot weather, the material may have to be stored in a cool place several hours prior to mixing.
4. Clean-up of tools and equipment by dispersion in water must be simple and complete.
5. The setting time should be reasonable under all weather conditions so that laying successive lifts of blocks will not be delayed.
6. Layout courses, generally set in conventional mortar, must be level and straight to give a starting point which produces a good interface contact and a plumb wall.
7. Blocks should be clean and free of dust. They should be reasonably dry and have low shrinkage characteristics.
8. Dimensional tolerances of the block should be checked by dry lay-up of small panels on a true and level bed.

Examples of Application

Adhesive mortar with ground blocks can be used in most applications where conventional mortar is applicable. However, proper control joints are even more important with adhesive mortar because the joints are always stronger than the block material. If shrinkage or settlement cracks occur, they will crack the block instead of opening at a joint.

A typical application of ground block is shown in Figure 12-3. Figure 12-3 illustrates stacked bond construction in basement wall construction with a lintle joining the block piers which have unmortared head joints.

Designs are now being prepared using ground block in high-rise bearing wall apartments. The system lends itself to nonreinforced, partially reinforced, or reinforced masonry systems depending on design requirements. Continuing research indicates that load-bearing capacity can be developed and upon completion of more research, such applications are envisioned.

Another interesting use of thin-bed adhesive mortar lies in various patterned screen walls obtainable with either ground block or MONOWALL concepts. Examples of such applications are shown in Figures 12-4 and 12-5.

Strength Tests

Strength test results from several sources are summarized in Table 12-1. The tension stresses reported are flexural tension, while the compression stresses are from axially loaded prisms or eccentrically loaded wall panels.

One of the summarized series of tests is shown in more detail in Figure 12-6. This figure shows the compression tests conducted on 8 foot high wall panels of MONOWALL construction. The tests were conducted with an eccentricity of one-sixth the panel thickness as prescribed in ASTM E72. Superimposed on this plot are test results on conventional walls taken from data collated by the National Concrete Masonry Association. Indications are that bearing wall capacity of MONOWALL construction can be based on the same procedures as standard block construction.

The tension stresses shown in Table 12-1 are based on a linear distribution of the elastic stresses on a representative mortared area which was about 1 inch-wide and centered over the face shells. The stresses are all based on midspan bending moments, although failure on the 8-foot-long specimens sometimes occurred slightly off center. Bending test procedures such as the air bag test followed ASTM E72 procedures. A more convenient bending test was later developed as is shown in Figure 12-7.

All bending tests to date have resulted in fracture of the block material. A typical example of this is shown in Figure 12-8 which shows the ruptured face shells where the adhesive mortar had been placed.

The indicated 67 psi strength across the open head joints of MONOWALL construction is again based on air bag tests. The stresses are arbitrarily computed on the basis of the net cross sectional area of the face shells. Since this cross sectional area is interrupted at the open head joint, the procedure is not a true representation of the stress situation. It is given only for comparison with other types of construction. A more rigorous approach is to be developed.

Two series of tests have not been included in Table 12-1. The first was a group of two beams 8-feet-long made with ground block and loaded to produce a maximum tensile strength of 200 psi at midspan and allowed to remain loaded to see if long term effects would weaken the beams. For more than a year, they have withstood this test without failure.

Figure 12-4. Screen wall with adhesive mortar in head and bed joints.

Figure 12-5. Screen wall with block spaced intermittently.

Table 12-1
Summary of Strength Tests
Concrete Block with High Strength Adhesive Mortar

	Type		Performed by	No. Tests	Average Net Stress	Remarks
Ground Block	Bed Jt. Tension		Dow Chemical Corp.	6	255 psi	Air bag-7′ – 6″ span
			Copeland & Saxer	3	250	28″ beam span
			Schupack & Assoc.	7	270	7′ – 4″ beam span
	Compression		Plasticrete Corp.	15	1730	prism tests
Monowall	Tension	Bed Jt.	Schupack & Assoc	40	275	8 – 7′ beam spans 32 – 1½ to 2½″ spans
		Head Jt.	Dow Chemical Corp.	2	67	1 @ 4′ & 1 @ 8′ span
	Compression		Schupack & Assoc.	15	1150	8′ wall tests
	Shear		Schupack & Assoc.	5	490	

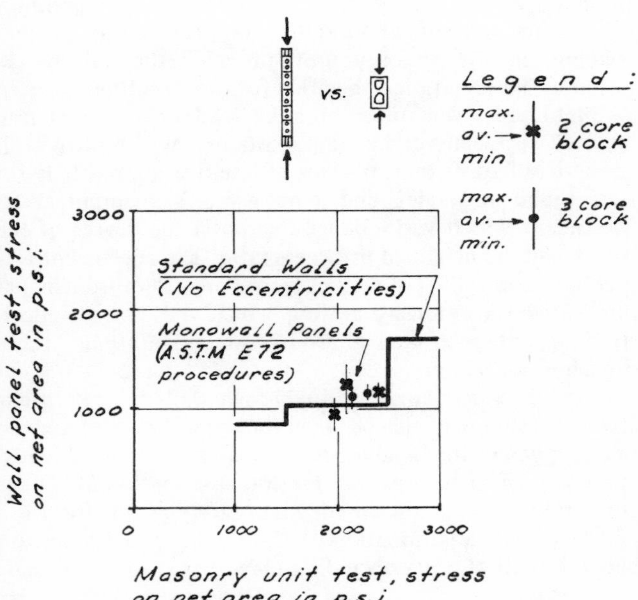

Figure 12-6. Compression tests of wall panels in the Monowall system. Notes: (1) Ratio h/t varied from 8 to 16 but appears not to be of significant effect. (2) Block thickness varied from 6″ to 12″. (3) Plot for standard walls is an average of data collated by N.C.M.A.

Figure 12-7. Bending test of beam with ground blocks.

Figure 12-8. Mode of failure at adhesion interface.

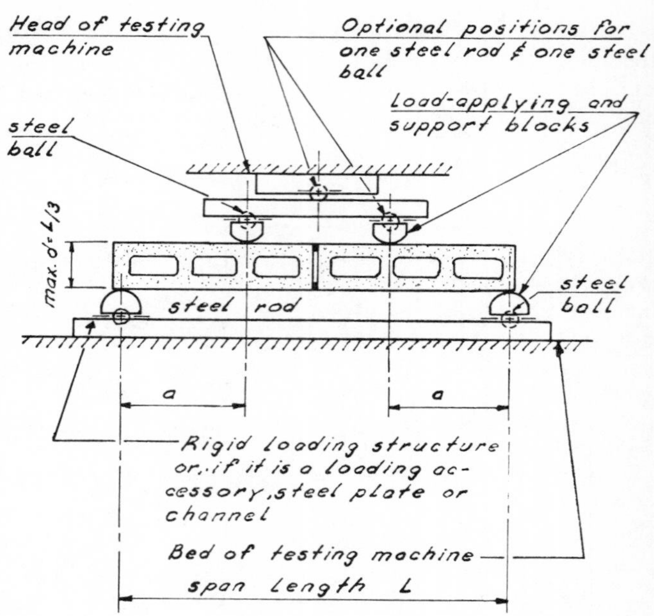

Figure 12-9. Suggested apparatus for flexural test of block with high strength adhesive mortar. Note: apparatus may be used inverted.

The second series of tests not included in Table 12-1 were impact tests on MONOWALL panels conducted according to ASTM E72 procedures. Two panels 4-inches-thick and one panel 3-inches-thick were tested. Failure occurred on the 4-inch panels when a 60-lb. bag fell against it from a 3-foot-height. The 3-inch panel failed when 60-lb. bag fell from a 2-foot fall. This can be compared to the New York State Building Construction Code which requires the panels to sustain a 60-lb. bag falling from a 1-1/2-foot height.

Other Physical Tests

In addition to the strength tests, extensive testing has been conducted to determine other characteristics of adhesive mortar and assembled walls. These included about 500 crossed brick tests conducted under various conditions to determine what conditions caused adhesive mortar to fail. The tests are summarized in Table 12-2. In all cases, the mortar used was the THREADLINE adhesive mortar manufactured by the Dow Chemical Corporation. It should not be assumed that all formulations of adhesive will perform identically. Care must be exercised to prove an adhesive's performance, strength, and applicability in field conditions.

Design

Design of bearing walls using high strength adhesive mortar can follow the rational approach currently being fostered for masonry construction. Compression stresses resulting from axial loads and bending can be combined in the commonly used interaction equation, $f_a / F_a + f_b / F_b = 1$. In this equation, the allowable stresses can be basedon the masonry's strength, which can be determined from either preliminary prism tests or assumed from the compressive strength of the concrete in the masonry unit, provided the unit has been tested in the orientation specified for the structure.

Simplified calculations of axial load only should not be resorted to whenever bending exists in a wall built with high strength adhesive mortar. This alternative approach is sometimes used in codes and employs a semiempirical stress coefficient which varies depending upon the degree of eccentricity and the height to thickness ratio. The coefficient is then used for controlling the axial load alone. Because it is partly predicated on extensive testing which did not include high strength adhesives nor MONOWALL orientations, this approach is nor recommended.

Tension stresses may occur in high walls subject to lateral loads. Tension may also occur in the upper floors of a high-rise building where the axial loads are small and the wind loads are increased. In such cases, the tension stresses should always be computed to maintain an adequate safety factor for a brittle material. The determination of the tensile strength across the bed joints of the masonry should be based on tests made in advance of operations, using beam specimens built of similar materials under the same conditions as for the structure. Beam specimens such as the one shown in Figure 12-9 can be tested in accordance with the ASTM C78-64 procedures. Results should be based on net areas. Safety factors from 3.0 to 6.0 should be used, depending on the nature of the loading, the type of connections employed, and the familiarity with the reliability of the particular product involved.

No simple tests have been devised for determining shear strength or tensile strength across the head joints, but limited data available indicate that values currently used for unreinforced block masonry can be conservatively used.

Construction

The construction procedures involved with adhesive mortar are highly adaptable to existing methods and crafts. The proper layout of the starter course requires the most attention, but, thereafter, no special precautions are required. Indeed, the main economy of the system lies in the speed of operations. While local conditions vary and affect specific production rates, generally the construction rates are more than double those obtained with conventional mortar. With the MONOWALL system on straight runs, the highest rates are obtained.

Contractors and craftsmen have sometimes been hesitant with the new approach, but, once accepted, it has been endorsed. The Bricklayers, Masons, and Plasterers International Union of America has specifically endorsed the procedure. This endorsement has been accepted by many locals to which the system has been presented.

Detail consideration for ground block are almost identical with good practice in conventional mortar. Detail requirements for MONOWALL construction are sometimes different. These details are now being developed.

The surface finish of the walls will vary with different architectural requirements. Unmortared head joints are a predominant influence in selection of the finish. Where fire

Table 12-2

Summary of Physical Tests

Type	Procedure	No. of Tests	Performed by	Failure: Block	Failure: Mortar	Results
Sound Transmission	ASTM E90-61T	2	Cedar Knolls			44 & 49 STC ratings of 6" Monowall with thin coat plaster and dry wall coatings, respectively.
Fire Resistance	ASTM E119-58	2	Ohio State U.	✓		3 & 4 hr. ratings for 8" ground block with head joint mortar and no coating.
		1	Factory Mutual	✓		4 hr. rating for 8" Monowall with thin coat plaster, each face
Flamability	ASTM D635-56T	2	Thompson & Lichtner			THREADLINE classified as non-burning and non-flamable
Compression	ASTM C270-57T	27	Thompson & Lichtner			50,000 psi did not fail the mortar specimens
Bond	ASTM C321-57	500	Raybestos-Manhattan	✓		maximum stress on cross bricks of granite = 750 psi
Freeze-Thaw	ASTM C310-57T	4	Thompson & Lichtner	✓		no deterioration of THREADLINE after 100 cycles
Weather Resistance	ultra-violet & water	4	Thompson & Lichtner			no adverse effects after 50 cycles of exposures
Fungus Growth	innoculated mortar	1	Hudson Laboratories			no deterioration nor support of fungus growth after 3 months.
Chemical Resistance	7 day immersion	29	Raybestos-Manhattan		✓	THREADLINE stable under medium solution of acids and bases which commonly degrade cement-lime mortar

Additional tests investigated the variation in mortar strength obtained with various curing times and temperatures and with variations in temperature at time of test. Results are reflected in manufacturer's recommendations.

resistance is a requirement, plaster coatings will be required unless the head joints are closed with mortar as can be done with ground block. Some of the recent developments in thin coat plasters successfully employ one coat applications. Veneers and insulation can be used for weather resistance and temperature control. Ground water resistance has been provided by simple pargeting. Other finishes such as dry wall, panelling, and simple painting have been used.

In this connection, it can be seen from the illustrations that MONOWALL construction produces a roughhewn appearance, while ground blocks with a tongue and groove interlock give a finished appearance.

Future Research and Further Developments

To fully utilize the advantages of block construction with adhesive mortar, the following developments are being pursued:

1. Development of 24" long block which can be used for ground block or MONOWALL constructions.
2. More sophisticated grinding equipment to decrease the grinding cost.
3. Development of a block manufacturing technique which would do away with the need for grinding.
4. Tests and quality control procedures which would permit greater utilization of block material in rational design procedures.
5. Automated mixing and placing procedures for the adhesive mortar.

Limitations

Earthquake loadings can be analyzed and resisted using high strength adhesive mortar. However, these loadings are only approximations of greatly fluctuating and random motions imposed under seismic conditions, and the motions are best resisted by ductile materials which can mobilize reserve energy in the inelastic range. This material is not recommended by itself in earthquake regions. It can be used in conjunction with grouted and reinforced cores and would then conform to the recommendations of the Structural Engineers Association of California which requires masonry elements to be reinforced. In this approach, the economy of the system must be carefully evaluated.

References

1. THREADLINE® is a registered trademark of the Dow Chemical Company.

13. Miniature tensile and panel flexure properties of brickwork.

V. A. Youl and Dr. P. K. Foster, Amalgamated Brick and Pipe Co., Ltd., Auckland, New Zealand

Introduction

Since the coming of man, his need for shelter has been a prime requirement of his environment. Research in building and construction is often neglected because of this traditional need, whilst developments such as air-craft, power, space travel, and synthetics have been born of research and are further nurtured by large research expenditures. Within the building industry, this analysis applies to the use of materials and structural systems. Stone and brick were two of the earliest construction materials known to man, these materials provided many of man's early forms of shelter. Their survival today as building systems is due to the inherent advantages of the system and not to research and development.

New Zealand is in a belt of high seismic activity. This, more than any other factor, increases building costs and restricts the use of masonry structural systems.

Through research in England, Europe and the U.S.A. have developed the design of multi-story brick buildings. These buildings take into account lateral loads occasioned by wind. Such forces seldom equate the dynamic conditions imposed by earthquake in relation to the period of the building. Further, multiple lateral partitions restrict the building design and limit the structural systems.

Until earthquakes of 1929 and 1931 brick was a major structural and facing material in New Zealand building. The failure of many brick buildings in these disasters caused engineers and architects to distrust masonry. Such distrust will not be allayed until sound design criteria are established through research on, and dynamic testing of, materials and practices used in building construction.

Recognizing that the most fundamental factor governing the strength of unreinforced brickwork was the bond between brick and mortar, the N.Z. Pottery & Ceramics Research Assn., in 1959 embarked upon an extensive research programme to evaluate the effect of the properties of materials on bond mechanism and bond strength. Results of early work, published by Youl[1], Tytherleigh & Youl[2] illustrate the mortar properties necessary to achieve maximum bond strength. Many other parameters remain to be investigated. A mathematical analysis by Kenna[3] of types of brickwork showed that in a brick veneer construction some 90 percent of lateral loads are carried by the veneer and only 10 percent by the frame, which had been previously assumed to carry all the loads. This analysis has been confirmed by face loads tests on small panels reported by Kenna [13]

This chapter presents results on the tensile strength of the brick-mortar interface as determined by minature tests and by the flexure of brick masonry panels. The work is part of a long-term project designed to examine factors affecting the tensile strength of masonry; it includes criteria of importance to successful design and use of masonry in addition to establishing the validity of miniature or model testing as a basis for future work.

The need for establishing the tensile behaviour of masonry is dictated largely by ignorance both of its optimum properties and of the sensitivity of these optimum properties to variations in materials. The low figure of 6.7 p.s.i. for the maximum tensile load permitted by the New Zealand Model Building By-law[4] in the design of uninspected masonry reflects the uncertainty surrounding the properties and variability of masonry.

Confirmation of brick masonry's properties using New Zealand materials would be necessary even if published oversea's work gave a sufficient understanding of masonry to permit full advantage of materials to be taken in design. The latter, however, is far from being the case. Inevitably much of the work suffers from inadequate specification of materials used in experiments. It is not until relationships between properties are established that the necessity for their specification in description of experiments becomes apparent. The resulting lack of detail in much of the published work makes it impossible to relate the results of different experiments. Comparisons can be made only in very broad terms, and difference between results must remain largely unexplained.

Cement-lime-sand mortars have received most attention and high values of initial flow, high values of water retentivity and low values of the initial rate of absorption of brick emerge clearly as being criteria beneficial to the strength of brick-mortar bond. The importance and interaction of such factors as sand/cement ratio, sand grading, sand particle shape, physical and chemical properties of the cement and lime (or other plasticizer) in affecting the tensile bond strength of brick masonry, have been far from adequately studied.

Thus there is an urgent need for a thorough investigation of the tensile bond strength of masonry, and the present work is one of the first steps. Because of many factors to be investigated, a miniature test method was essential to obtain information at reasonable cost and in reasonable time. This paper reports on the development of a miniature test method, and compares the data it gives with data from panels tested in flexure and with data from the literature. Work has been restricted to cement-lime-sand mortars at this stage because this gave most scope for comparison of results with published data. Future work will use the miniature test method in statistically planned experiments on the effects of variables using other plasticisers in common use in New Zealand. The intention is to confirm the more important results with full-size tests from time to time. This will go far towards achieving the objections of determining the optimum bond strength; the properties of the mortar and brick to give that strength, and its sensitivity to deviations from the optimum properties.

Definitions and Standard Test Methods

All testing and reporting on properties of mortar and bricks is based on standard test methods wherever these apply.

Mortar Tests and Properties

The two properties measured, initial flow and flow after suction, are standard ASTM methods. In comparisons between results in this paper and other work, the only reliable comparison is when flow after suction is expressed as a percentage of initial flow.

Initial Flow. This property is examined in accordance with ASTM C109-58[5] and is a measure of the workability or flow of mortar.

Flow after Suction. This property is examined in accordance with ASTM C91-60[6]. As it is a measure of mortar's resistance to loss of water due to brick suction, it is called *water retentivity* in this paper. It is also a measure of mortar's workability after placing.

Brick Tests and Properties

From early work it was well established that the rate at which brick absorbs water in the first minute of contact with the mortar bed is of prime importance in establishing a good bond performance. After checking scale effect, all samples, both for the miniature tests and full-size bricks, were measured by the same method.

Initial Rate of Absorption (IRA). This measurement is taken in accordance with ASTM C67-62[7] all results of miniature and full-size brick are corrected and expressed in grams of water per 30 sq. inches of brick bedding surface.

Experimental

Miniature Tests

Mortars. Cement-lime-sand mortars, with a constant ratio of cement to sand of 1:5 by weight, were used throughout. The cement and lime came from New Zealand in sealed drums of the same bulk, thus preventing variation between deliveries. Natural river sand, screened to pass 3/16", was separated into size fractions and reconstituted to give the grading analysis shown in Table 13-1.

Table 13-1

Sieve Size (NZSS 196)	Percent Retained Each Sieve
7	0
14	14.7
25	29.1
52	38.8
100	12.0
Pan	5.4

All mortar preparation was carried out in a constant temperature room (25°C) because previous work showed this increased reproducibility in mortar properties for a given composition. The dry hydrated lime was soaked in distilled water overnight, and mortars were then prepared following a procedure based on ASTM C305-59T[8]. Mortars were characterised by their initial flow and retentivity properties determined according to ASTM C109-58[5] and C91-60T[6] respectively. The required levels were obtained by adjusting the amounts of lime and water only.

Bricks. Special mini-bricks made commercially from a Canterbury loess in a shape approximating to a 2 in. cube, had two opposite wedge shaped faces to facilitate gripping for tensile testing. The bricks were subsequently re-fired in a laboratory kiln to give 'Initial Rate of Absorption' (IRA) values less than 25, and selected into three ranges as follows: 3-6, 8-12, and 15-20. The bonding face was ground smooth because preliminary work showed this improved the reproducibility of bond strength tests.

Bonding, Curing, and Testing. Five replicate couplets were prepared from each mortar. A non-absorbent plastic mold produced a mortar bed 1/2 in. thick, covering the bonding face. The brick was then placed mortar-bed upwards in the bonding machine and the upper brick, positioned in the grips of the machine, was lowered pneumatically. A pressure of 1½ p.s.i. was exerted on the mortar bed. Two procedures were followed; the second of which included relative motion between the bricks to simulate the sliding imparted by the bricklayer.

Method A: Pressure was maintained for 10 sec. and the grip-head was then retracted.

Method B: The upper brick was oscillated through one cycle of ± 15° about its axis perpendicular to the mortar bed while under pressure. The grip-head was then retracted.

The miniature method (b) has advantages over the method described in ASTM E149-59T[9]. Comparison of coefficients of variation obtained in the present work and elsewhere e.g., Monk [11], show that accuracy is no less, while the reduction in size of the test pieces and therefore in time and cost of materials and test equipment is significant.

The couplets were cured for 7 days at 25°C and 65 per cent relative humidity. Each couplet was then subjected to a tensile load perpendicular to the mortar bed in a Hounsfield tensometer. A tension spring was connected in series with the couplet to give a sufficiently slow and reproducible rate of load with the motorized drive.

Panel Tests

Mortars

The materials were the same as used for the miniature tests. Because larger quantities of mortar were needed, a different mixer and longer mixing times were required. The latter reduced the initial flow and increased the retentivity for a given composition. The water and lime contents were adjusted accordingly to attain the same retentivity levels. The constant temperature room was not used. Three mixes were prepared for each panel.

Bricks

Commercial wire-cut perforated brick, 2½ x 3¾ x 8 in., were used. The Initial Rate of Absorption (IRA) range was 110 to 133 as received. Experiments showed that two minutes submersion in water, followed by three hours draining, reduced the IRA to between 7 and 23, with a mean of 12. Increasing the draining time by two hours increased the mean to 14. Two minutes submersion followed by three hours draining at the start of laying each panel was adopted for the work.

Laying and Testing

The procedure was generally that used by Kenna[13]. Seven panels were laid in stretcher bond by a bricklayer, each 16 courses high and three bricks wide and measuring approximately 48 inches by 24 inches. The panels were aged at room temperature and humidity for 28 days. Laying time for each panel was approximately 1½ hours.

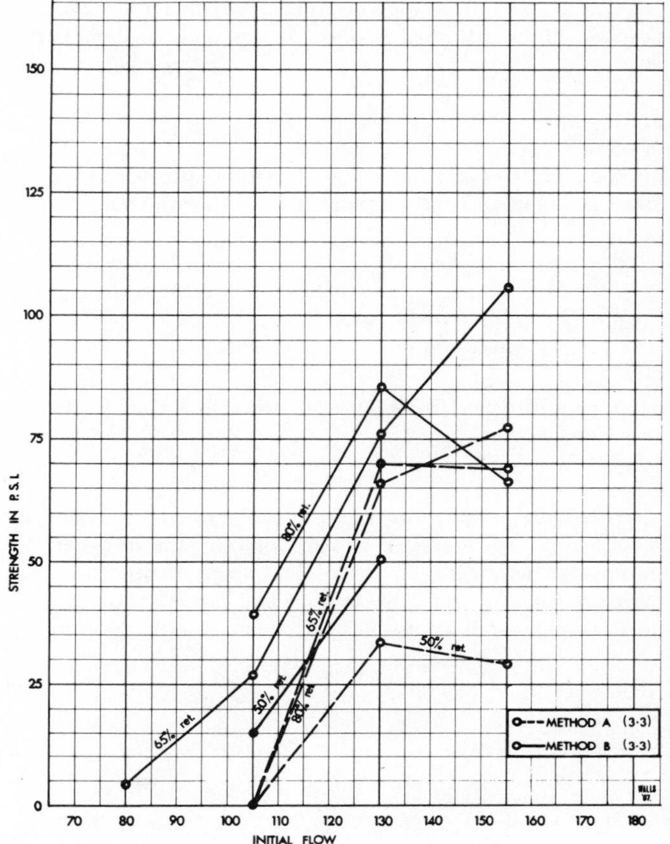

Figure 13-1. Effect of initial flow and retentivity on bond strength using bonding methods A and B.

Quarter-point live loads were applied in 100 lb. increments in a Baldwin Universal Testing Machine.

Results

Miniature Test

IRA was found to have no significant effect on bond strength, for the three ranges studied (3-6, 8-12 and 15-20).

Figure 13-1 gives the results for the bond strengths obtained with the two test methods, for mortars with different flow and retentivity properties, and bricks with IRA in the range 8-12. Each point is the mean of five couplet results.

As discussed later, the method described in Bonding, Curing, and Testing (B) was preferred, and accordingly its results were examined more closely. The lines for three values of retentivity and the values of initial flow of 105 and 130 per cent were tested statistically for significance, using the coefficients of variation for the six points which averaged 22 percent. It was shown that the three lines could be taken as parallel; it was confirmed statistically that their slope was highly significant. More important were that the difference between the 50 and 65 percent retentivity lines was highly significant, and that the difference between the 65 and 80 percent retentivity lines were significant only at the 5 percent level.

Panel Tests

The results of the flexural tests were expressed as the fibre stress at failure, (f) and were calculated from the relation

where

$$f = M/Z \quad (13\text{-}1)$$

M = bending moment, and

Z = section modulus.

They are shown in Figure 13-2 for the seven panels tested.

Discussion

In this discussion, the limitations imposed by insufficient specification of materials (mentioned in the Introduction) must be remembered. At the present stage of this work these limitations apply to a large extent, and care must be exercised in making generalisations on the detailed results reported here.

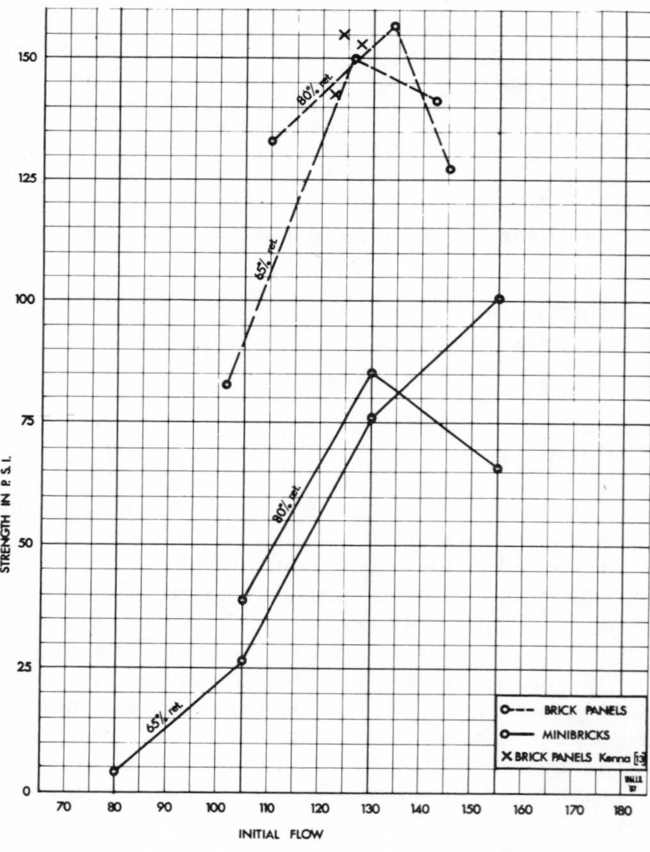

Figure 13-2. Correlation between brick panels and minibrick couplets.

The results will first be compared with other published work. ASTM method E149-59[9] has been used for miniature investigations. Ritchie and Davison[10] investigated brick IRA presenting a curve with a maximum bond strength at IRA of 15 to 20. Their data is such, however, that the bond strength could well be constant over the IRA range 5 to 20, within experimental error, and therefore not inconsistent with the present work. Ritchie and Davison[10] also published a curve of tensile bond strength using bricks of IRA 19-22 as a function of initial flow of 1:1:6 mortars, but they do not state water retentivity. The results are approximately equal to the present results for 50 percent retentivity, using the method described in Bonding, Curing, and Testing (B). In comparing the properties of conventional cement-lime-sand mortars with latex-bearing cementitious mortars, Monk[11] compiled bond data using 16 cement-lime-sand mortars in crossed-brick couplet tests. His results are similar, but lower than those in this experiment. Fishburn[12] reported the results of many crossed-brick couplet tests and obtained bond strengths of up to 70 p.s.i. at high flows (140 to 145 percent) and high retentivities (83 to 88 percent) with brick of IRA of 4 to 9. The Figure 13-2 compares the panel results with those obtained by Kenna in the same laboratory, but using a different source of bricks. Monk[11] reported an average stress of 77 p.s.i. for 4 by 8 feet panels tested vertically in flexure using 1:1:6 mortar, (curing period unstated) and stresses of 42 to 61 p.s.i. obtained in diagonal tension tests on 16 in. by 16 in. wallettes using 1:1:6 and 1:1:4½ mortars cured for 7 days. The flow and retentivity properties of the mortars were not specified so that little comparison with the present work is possible.

The preceding general comparisons with recently published work show that there are no major inconsistencies, but that significantly high stresses have been achieved, both with the miniature tests in the present work, and particularly with panels constructed in this laboratory (Figure 13-2). Present work, Kenna[13] and Ryder[14], achieved stresses up to 260 p.s.i. but Ryder's[14] method required fracture through brick as well as through mortar, and is therefore not a test of the bond strength alone. The differences in degree between the various sets of data confirm the need for investigating the many possible variables outlined in the Introduction.

A major object of the present study was to test the validity of miniature test methods for investigations of the factors influencing the ultimate tensile strength of the brick-mortar junction in masonry. A broad comparison of the results in Figure 13-2 shows that this has been achieved in that, with increase in initial flow up to 130 percent, all methods give an increase in strength, and with initial flow values greater than 130 percent there is no comparable increase in performance. In making these comparisons, remember that the miniature test results in Figures 13-1 and 13-2 are each the mean of five tests, while the panel results are from one panel at each level. The three results in Figure 13-2 obtained by Kenna[13] give some indication of the reproducibility to be expected under the conditions of test.

Figure 13-2 shows that the tensile strength of miniature samples is approximately half that of the panels tested. This is probably largely due to a combination of the smooth, machined surface of the miniature bricks, the 7-day curing for the miniature couplets as opposed to 28 days for the panels, and imperfect simulation of the tradesman's action in the miniature tests.

The importance of curing time is shown by failures in the mortar, which occurred at high values of initial flow with the miniature test but were not reproduced by the panels. This points to the desirability of 28 day curing for the miniature test in future work.

A number of points of general importance concerning the engineering properties of brick masonry arise from the results:

1. Attention must be drawn to the inter relation between the variables initial flow, retentivity of mortar, and brick IRA. The first determines the amount of water in the mortar during initial setting if given values for the two others. The retentivity can be a measure of the ability of the mortar to retain water against the suction exerted by the brick, while the value of IRA of the brick can be a measure of its ability to reduce the water content of the mortar.

The results in Figure 13-1 apply only to brick with IRA in the ranges given in the experimental section of this paper, and it is emphasized that strengths of the order given in Figure 13-1 for the same mortars would not necessarily be obtained with these mortars in contact with brick of higher IRA.

2. Retentivity is confirmed as an important property, which should be maintained at a sufficiently high value. The statistical examination of the results obtained with method B, *Bonding, Curing and Testing,* suggests that, with brick of IRA less than 20, little is gained by increasing the mortar retentivity beyond 65 percent. The improvement was significant only at the 5 percent level. The results obtained with the panels confirm this, to the extent that of five panels at 120 to 135 percent initial flow giving approximately constant strength, one was constructed from mortar with 65 percent retentivity. Results obtained by Ritchie and Davison[10] also indicate that the small effect of varying retentivity between 70 and 78 percent. No significance is attached to the lower strength obtained for Panel No. 7 (80 percent retentivity) compared with Panel No. 5 (65 percent retentivity); the results are probably within experimental variations and the slightly shorter curing period (24 days) of Panel No. 7 is not significant. The gain accruing from retentivities greater than 65 percent require further quantitative investigation.

3. Of all the system parameters so far studied, initial flow of mortars exerts the greatest effect on bond strength. The results in Figure 13-1 clearly indicate the magnitude of the effect. It also shows that for mortars with a cement-sand ratio of 1:5 by weight in contact with brick of IRA 5 to 20, optimum strength is obtained at an initial flow near 130 percent. Strengths consistently attainable with controlled materials are approximately twenty times the loads currently permitted in design.

Previous work has indicated that maximum bond strengths will be achieved at about 130 initial flow or above. The *Handbook on Reinforced Grouted Brick Masonry Construction*[15] states "Mortar when used should have an original flow of from 135 to 145%". Plummer and Blume[16] state, "The substantial increase in tensile bond strength with increased mortar flow indicates the importance of controlling this variable in assembling tensile bond specimens, and also of maintaining a high flow in mortar used in masonry construction". The "high flow" in this case refers to a range of 125-135%.

It is believed that strengths obtained with initial flows greater than 130 are irrelevant to brick masonry, when used in conjunction with brick of mean IRA in the range 8-12. Under laboratory conditions, they were not considered workable by the bricklayer, and certainly resulted in excessively dirty and therefore unacceptable brickwork. To this extent, the lower strengths obtained for the panels at high initial flows are unlikely to be met in practice, and differences between the results of the two miniature test methods need not be resolved. Figure 13-1 shows that loss of strength is large with values of initial flow lower than 100 percent. Accordingly, it is concluded that for brick of IRA range less than 20, the range of initial flow of interest is 100 to 130 percent.

Summary

A good correlation exists between strengths obtained from panel tests and from a miniature test method. The latter is suitable for further investigation of the effects of variables on brick mortar bond strengths.

At present, considerable care must be exercised in generalising from particular experimental results.

For the cement-lime-sand mortars used, properties have been found in broad agreement with published work as follows:

1. Bond strength was found to increase with initial flow up to a value of about 130, and remained approximately constant up to 155, for brick IRA of 8-12.

2. Bond strength was found to increase strongly with retentivity up to a value of 65% and only slightly from 65% up to 80%.

3. Bond strength was insensitive to IRA of brick for the range 3 to 20. For IRA less than 20, the range of initial flow of practical interest is given an upper limit of 130 by workability, and a lower limit of 100 by loss of bond strength.

Consistent flexural strengths of brick panels 20 times greater than the figure permitted by the N. Z. Standard Model Building By-law[4] can be obtained.

References

1. Youl, V. A., "Design of Buildings," Paper 2 C.B.I., Part I, Australian Building Research Congress. 1961.
2. Tytherleigh E. St. J. and Youl, V. A., "Design of Buildings," Paper 2 C.B.I., Part II, Australian Building Research Congress.
3. Kenna, L. F., "Some structural features of brick veneer construction," Technical Report No. 12, New Zealand Pottery & Ceramics Research Assn., 1963.
4. "Design and Construction: Masonry," Chapter 9.2 *New Zealand Standard Model Building By-Law,* NZSS 1900, New Zealand Standards Inst., 1965.

5. "Standard method of test for compressive strength of hydraulic cement," ASTM C105-58, American Society for Testing and Materials, 1958.
6. "Standard specification for Masonry cement," ASTM C91-60T, American Society for Testing and Materials, 1960.
7. "Standard method of sampling and testing brick," ASTM C67-62, American Society for Testing and Materials, 1962.
8. "Tentative method for mechanical mixing of hydraulic cement pastes and mortars of plastic consistency," ASTM C305-59T, Amer. Soc. for Testing and Materials, 1959.
9. "Tentative method of test for bond strength of mortar to masonry units," ASTM E149-59T, American Society for Testing and Materials, 1959.
10. Ritchie, T. and Davison, J. I., "Factors affecting bond strength and resistance to moisture penetration of brick masonry," ASTM Special Tech. Publ. 320:16-30, 1963.
11. Monk, C. B., "Testing high-bond clay masonry asse blages," ASTM Special Technical Publication 320:31-6 1963.
12. Fishburn, C. C., "Effect of mortar properties on strength masonry," Monograph 36, US National Bureau Standard 1961, p. 45.
13. Kenna, L. F., "Brickwork and earthquakes in Ne Zealand," Proc. 3rd World Conference Earthquake E gineering, 3, Session IV:292-311, 1965.
14. Ryder, J. F., "The use of small brickwork panels for testi mortars," 62(8):615-29 Trans. Brit. Ceramic Society, 196.
15. *Handbook on Reinforced Grouted Brick Masonry Co struction,* 2nd ed, Brick Institute of California, L Angeles, 1962.
16. Plummer, H. C. and Blume, J. A., "Reinforced bric masonry and lateral force design," Structural Clay Produc Inst., Washington, D. C., 1953.

Part 3: Structural performance

14. Design of brick masonry columns.

Donald E. Anderson and Edward S. Hoffman, Engineers Collaborative, Chicago, Illinois

Introduction

The use of reinforced and nonreinforced brick masonry as a structural material has recently been given new freedom which permits the design of such building elements to be based on rational and scientific procedures. This was accomplished by the introduction in May 1966 of "Recommended Building Code Requirements for Engineered Brick Masonry" by the Structural Clay Products Institute (SCPI). These recommendations have subsequently been adopted by the National, BOCA, and Southern Building Codes.

The ultimate strength design method is not being used by present-day masonry codes. Future codes will give even further freedom to the design of reinforced brick masonry.

Standard working stress masonry codes in effect prior to SCPI 1966 and previously and presently being used in most cities for reinforced and nonreinforced brick masonry are:

1. ASA – A41.2 – 1960 – National Bureau of Standards Handbook 74 – "Building Code Requirements for Reinforced Masonry."
2. ASA – A41.1 – 1953 – National Bureau of Standards Publication 211 – "American Standard Building Code Requirements for Masonry."

Working stresses allowed by the ASA-A41.1 – 1953 code have not been changed for some time and are essentially the same as those of the 1944 edition and similar to those specified in the "1931 Modifications in Recommended Minimum Requirements for Masonry Construction of the Building Code Committee of the U. S. Department of Commerce". An exception in the 1931 code was an attempt to consider the importance of workmanship as a factor in establishing working stresses by permitting a 50% increase for properly constructed and inspected masonry. This was omitted in 1944.

Purpose

To the writer's knowledge, there have been no test conducted on eccentrically-loaded, reinforced brick column Present-day masonry code requirements for reinforced bric columns with moment are not based on test data. This stud purposes to determine by exploratory tests on eccentrically loaded-reinforced-brick (RBM) columns if these test dat indicate that the Ultimate Strength Design (USD) method o the American Concrete Institute (ACI), ACI 318-63, fo reinforced concrete columns (RCC) is applicable as a desig method for reinforced brick masonry columns.

This study also purposes to compare the test results wit results calculated by the present-day working stress cod requirements of SCPI-66, ASA 41.1 and 41.2, for reinforce and non-reinforced brick masonry and the Working Stres Design Method (WSD) of ACI 318-63 for reinforced concret columns. It also examines the resulting factors of safety o ratio of test load to calculated load.

The ultimate-strength design theory of reinforced concret is a consistent method for designing columns in accordanc with actual behavior. This is an advantage, because it remove most of the ambiguity now attending the design of eccentri cally loaded columns. This concept simplifies the design o members subject to combined bending and axial load an clarifies the effect of the load-thrust relationship.

Design Method

The fundamental difference between the working stress o straight-line and the ultimate-strength theories is in th stress-strain relationship assumed for stresses near the ultimat load. The straight-line theory assumes that stress and strain ar proportional up to the ultimate capacity. The ultimate strength theory is based on the hypothesis that, as the ultimat capacity is approached, the plastic range of the material i reached in which stress and strain are no longer proportional At ultimate load, the stress distribution in the compressio zone is not triangular but curvilinear, which can be approxi mated by various shapes.

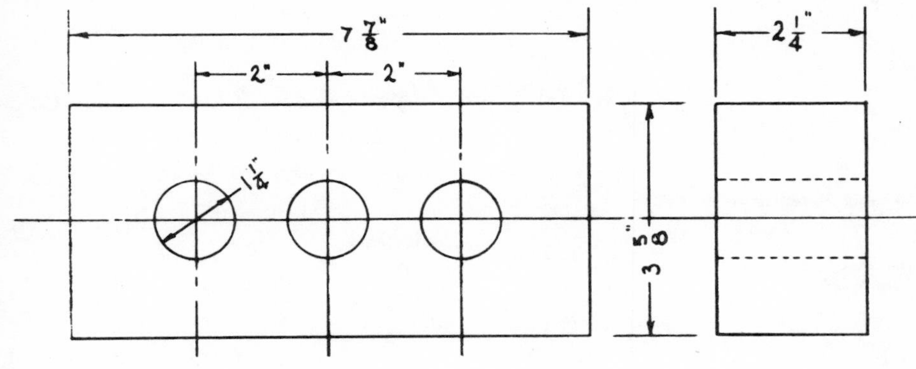

GEOMETRIC PROPERTIES

Height 2.25 in.

Width 3.63 in.

Length 7.88 in.

Areas :

Gross 28.5 in.²

Net 24.8 in.²

Percent Voids 13.0 %

Sketch of void pattern

PHYSICAL PROPERTIES

Compressive Strength*	$\bar{X}$ = 13,500 psi,	V = 18.9 %	Color	Buff
Modulus of Rupture*	$\bar{X}$ = 1,248 psi,	V = 17.6 %	Texture	Velour
Initial Rate of Absorption	$\bar{X}$ = 4.46 gm./min.,	V = 14.1 %	Weight	4.32 lbs.

* based on gross areas

Figure 14-1. Unit information sheet.

For this study, a rectangular stress-distribution block has been chosen as a basis for calculating ultimate loads.

When working stresses are based on the straight-line theory, the actual factor of safety against failure cannot be calculated. With ultimate-strength design, the actual load and moment are multiplied by a specific load factor which approximates the safety factor to obtain the ultimate load used for design.

Tests

Compression tests were made on 12" x 16" x 10'2" long RBM columns hinged at the top and fixed at the bottom with eccentricities of 0 to 34% of their depth. Tests were conducted at the Structural Clay Products Research Laboratories in Geneva, Illinois. Test columns were constructed with inspected workmanship from the following components:

1. Brick: 13,500 psi minimum compressive strength
2. Mortar: ASTM 270, Type S
3. Grout: 3197 psi minimum and 3616 psi average compressive strength
4. Masonry: 5250 psi average compressive strength as determined by prism tests
5. Reinforcing Steel: ASTM A15-4- # 5 intermediate grade deformed bars with minimum yield strength of 40,000 psi

Unit information sheet (Figure 14-1) gives the physical properties and geometry of the brick units used in the test.

Figure 14-2 shows a sketch of the RBM test columns with the instrumentation dials. C1, 2, 3 and 4 represent the dials measuring shortening of the four corners. The dials C6 and C8 measure the lateral movement about the major axis. After the first test, the C5 and C7 deflection readings were discontinued because of little or no deflection about the minor axis. The deflection dials were placed 1/3 the column height from the top as this is the point of maximum deflection for a column hinged at the top and fixed at the bottom.

Table 14-1 contains a summary of the test results taken from data submitted by SCPI.

Table 14-2 contains load and average strain measurements for test WUGIA which was conducted with a concentric load. Strain measurements were taken at each corner of the column and averaged. The measurements were stopped at 70% of the ultimate load.

Test WUGIA, conducted as a concentric load, did not fail in the million pound machine when the machine's capacity was reached. Consequently, the first three specimens were tested with an eccentricity of 1/20 (specimens WUGI1, WUGI2 and WUGI3). Preloading the first specimen, WUGIA, did not appear to affect its strength when tested as WUGI1 with an

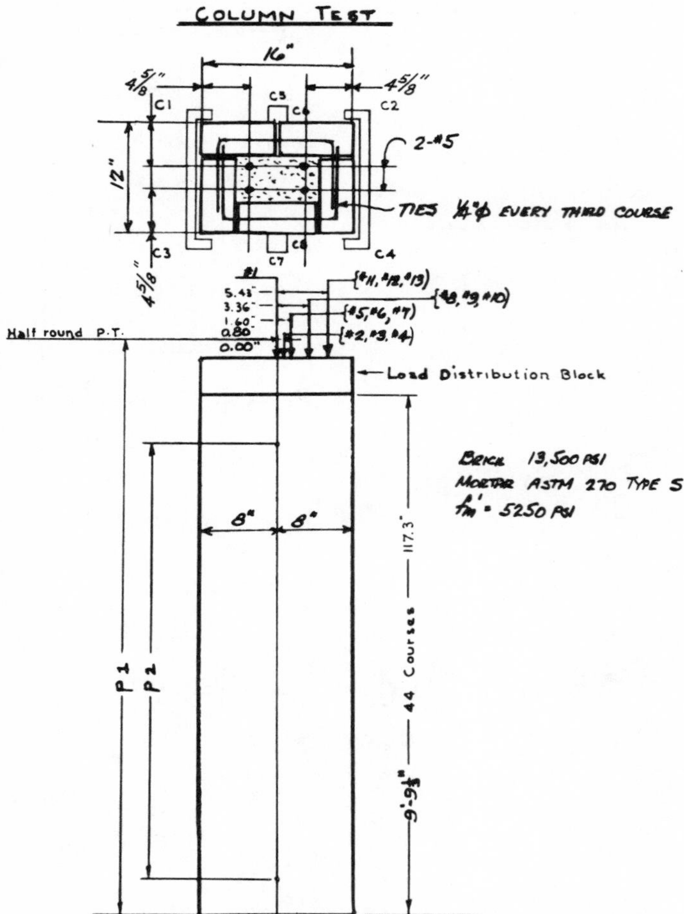

Figure 14-2. RMB test arrangement.

Table 14-1
Summary of Test Results
on
12" x 16" x 10'2" Reinforced Brick Masonry Columns
f'_m (average from prism tests) = 5250 psi

Test No.	Load Eccentricity e inches	Ultimate Load in kips	Mortar S Strength psi	Average Grout Cylinder Strength psi
WUGI A	0	(974.2)*	1805	3522
WUGI 1	.80	928.0	1805	3522
WUGI 2	.80	928.0	2353	3522
WUGI 3	.80	921.0	1512	3522
(Average)	(.80)	(925.7)	(1890)	(3522)
WUGI 4	1.60	839.0	2415	3522
WUGI 5	1.60	791.5	2032	3898
WUGI 6	1.60	792.5	2143	3898
(Average)	(1.60)	(807.7)	(2197)	(3773)
WUGI 7	3.36	603.0	2103	3898
WUGI 8	3.36	608.0	2404	3898
WUGI 9	3.36	549.2	2227	3429
(Average)	(3.36)	(586.7)	(2245)	(3772)
WUGI X	5.43	406.0	1782	3429
WUGI Y	5.43	418.5	1733	3429
WUGI Z	5.43	426.0	2153	3429
(Average)	(5.43)	(416.8)	(1889)	(3429)

* No failure at 974.2 kips

eccentric load. The last three tests conducted, with an eccentricity of 5.43 inches, are coded WUGI X, Y and Z as there are not normally twelve specimens in a given test series.

Table 14-2
Load-Strain Results for Test WUGI A

Load kips	Average Stress Based on Gross Masonry Area psi	Average Strain inches/inch
52.0	271	.00006
104.0	542	.00012
156.0	813	.00020
210.2	1095	.00027
262.8	1370	.00033
312.2	1630	.00041
359.7	1872	.00048
406.0	2120	.00056
451.0	2330	.00063
499.0	2600	.00072
547.0	2850	.00080
591.5	3080	.00088
974.2	5070	—

Discussion

The results of ultimate test loads at various eccentricities are compared with calculated ultimate and working stress capacities as determined by ACI 318-63 and ASA-41.1 and ASA41.2 in Table 14-3 and Figure 14-3.

ACI 318-63 USD

Ultimate loads for RBM columns were calculated according to the USD (ultimate strength design) method for short reinforced concrete columns and compared with the test results. Figure 14-4. These calculations were based on assumed maximum strain at the extreme compression fiber at ultimate strength equal to .003, a stress intensity at ultimate strength equal to 100% f'_m $\phi = 1$, k, = .80, f_y = 40,000 psi and E_s = 29,000,000 psi.

Table 14-3
Tabulation and Comparison of Ultimate Test Loads and Calculated Loads for Eccentrically Loaded Brick Masonry Columns

		TEST	CALCULATED BY												
			Reinforced Concrete Method				Reinforced Brick Masonry				Non-Reinforced Brick Masonry				
			ACI 318-63 USD		ACI 318-63WSD		SCPI-66		ASA-41.2-60		SCPI-66		ASA-41.1-53		
e inches	e/t	P_T Average kips	Pu kips	P_T/Pu	Pc kips	P_T/Pc	P_c kips	P_T/P_c	P_c kips	P_T/P_c	P_c kips	P_T/P_c	P_c kips	P_T/P_c
0	0	—	1051	—	363*	—	214	—	215	—	192	—	67	—
.80	.050	926	943	.98	296*	313	186	4.98	181	5.12	192	4.82	52	17.8
1.60	.100	808	837	.97	250*	3.23	165	4.90	156	5.18	166	4.87	42	19.2
2.38	.149	710**	733	.97	217	3.27	148	4.80	138	5.14	140	5.06	36	19.7
2.67	.167	670**	694	.97	—	—	143	4.68	132	5.08	130	5.15	34	19.7
3.36	.210	587	605	.97	—	—	131	4.48	120	4.89	111	5.29	—	—
5.33	.333	425**	386	1.10	—	—	107	3.97	96	4.43	60	7.08	—	—
5.43	.340	417	377	1.11	—	—	—	—	—	—	—	—	—	—

* These values were obtained using the basic formula, but exceed the arbitrary code limitation of (Formula 14-1) which would make the maximum allowable load = 231 kips.

** Extrapolated from test results.

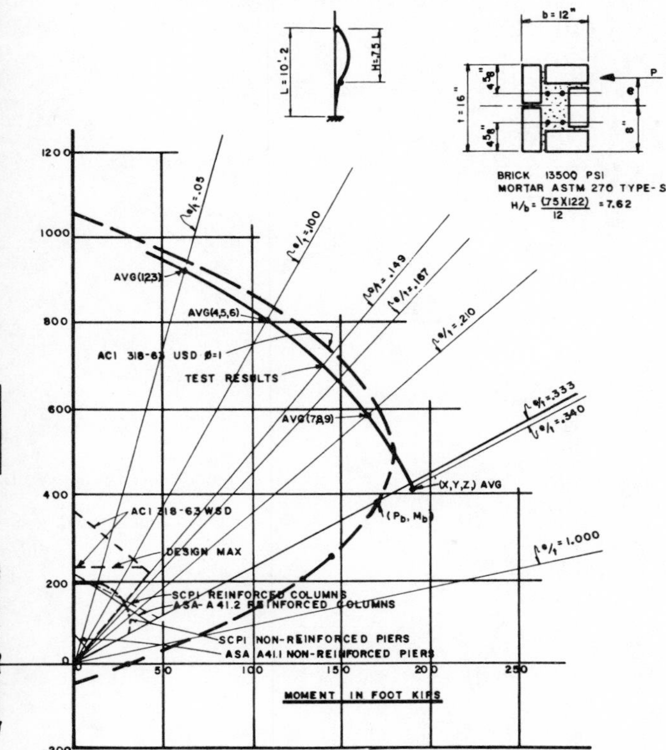

Figure 14-3. Comparison of brick masonry column load-moment interaction diagrams.

The assumed stress intensity of f'_m = 5250 psi at ultimate strength as shown in Figure 14-5 based on tests made by SCPI, indicates that there is no dip in the compression stress strain curve of brick masonry after ultimate stress is reached as there is for concrete. An examination of Table 14-3 and Figure 14-3 shows that the ultimate loads calculated by the USD method compare very favorably with the ultimate test loads, the ratio of P_T/P_u varying from .97 to 1.11.

ACI 318-63 WSD

Working loads for short RBM columns were calculated according to the WSD (working stress design) method (Figure 14-6) for reinforced concrete and compared with the test results. These calculations were based on an uncracked section in the compression failure zone and a modular ratio of 2n for all vertical reinforcing. The factor of safety or ratio of P_T/P_c ranged from 3.13 to 3.27 and neglected the ACI 318-63 WSD code limitation for maximum design load at minimum eccentricity e = .10t.

Reinforced Masonry Columns

Working loads for RBM columns were calculated by the ASA 41.2 and SCPI-66 codes and compared with the test results. These similar codes are based on P = AG [$.20f'_m$+ .65 P_g f_s], $e/_t$ = 1/3, an uncracked section in the compression failure zone, a modular ratio equal to 2n, and appropriate length reduction factors for long columns. No reduction for length is required by the ASA 41.2 code (Figure 14-7) for

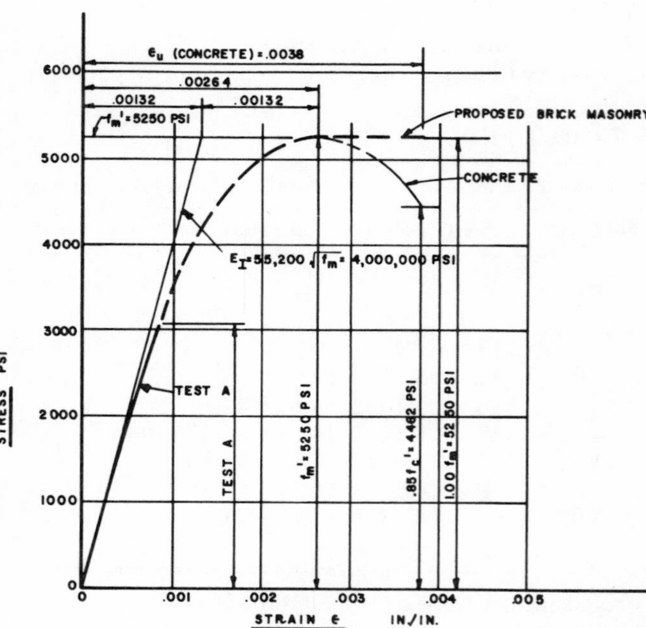

Figure 14-4. Proposed stress-strain diagram for brick masonry.

$f_m' = 5250$ psi
$f_y = 40,000$ psi
$k_1 = .80$
$u = .003$
$b = 12''$
$t = 16''$

Eccentricity Inches	P_u kips	M_u Ft.-kips
0	1051	0
.80	943	63
1.60	837	112
2.38	733	145
2.67	694	154
3.36	605	169
5.33	386	171
5.43	377	170
6.49	268	145
7.44	197	122
8.46	146	103
—	0	31
0	−49	0

Figure 14-5. Calculations for reinforced brick columns by USD method from IBM 1130 computer.

columns with an $H/_b \leqq 10$. The SCPI-66 code (Figure 14-8 reduction factor was equal to .993. The essential difference i these two methods, in addition to the length reduction facto is in the value of E_m and E_s. SCPI specifies that $E_m = 1000$ f but 3,000,000 psi max. and $E_s = 29,000,000$ psi. ASA 41.2 - 1960 specifies that $E_m = 1000\ f_m'$ and $E_s = 30,000,000$ psi.

The factor of safety or ratio of P_T/P_c for SCPI-66 varie from 3.97 to 4.98 and for ASA-41.2 from 4.43 to 5.12.

Nonreinforced Brick Masonry Piers

Because there is a great difference in the SCPI-66 an ASA-41.1 codes for nonreinforced brick masonry piers an because the test columns were reinforced with a nea minimum steel percentage $P_g = .645\%$, it was thought that comparison of calculated working loads by code with tes loads might be of interest.

The SCPI-66 code recognizes brick strengths in excess c 14,000 psi and permits eccentricities up to 1/3 the depth c the section. The ratio of ultimate test loads for RBM columr to working loads for non-reinforced piers calculated b SCPI-66 varied from 4.80 to 7.08.

The ASA-41.1 code permits no tension in brick masonry. I addition, the maximum masonry strength permitted for Typ S mortar is 350 psi and no increase in masonry strength allowed for brick compressive strengths in excess of 8,000 ps The ratio of ultimate test loads for RBM columns to workin loads for non-reinforced brick piers calculated by ASA A41.1-53 (Figure 14-9) varied from 17.8 to 19.7.

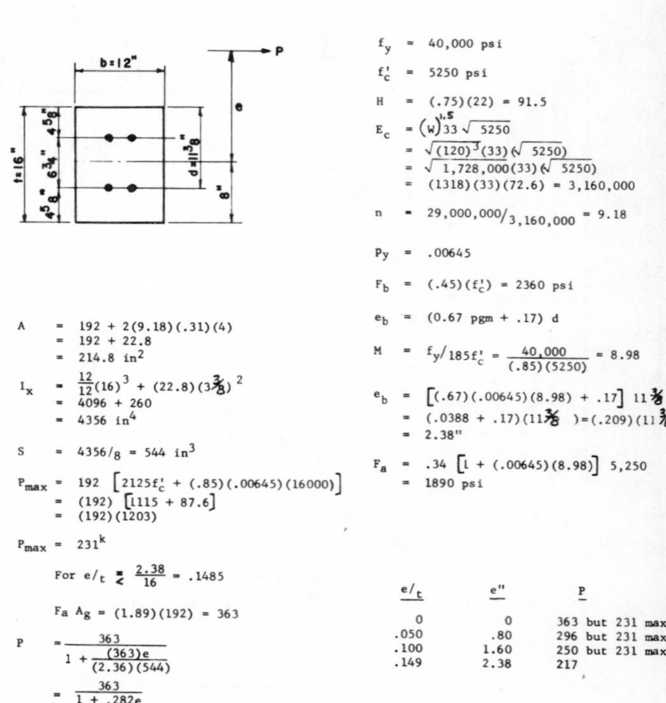

f_y = 40,000 psi
f_c' = 5250 psi
H = (.75)(22) = 91.5
$E_c = (W)^{1.5}\ 33 \sqrt{5250}$
$= \sqrt{(120)^3}(33)(\sqrt{5250})$
$= \sqrt{1,728,000}(33)(\sqrt{5250})$
$= (1318)(33)(72.6) = 3,160,000$
$n = 29,000,000/_{3,160,000} = 9.18$
$P_y = .00645$
$F_b = (.45)(f_c') = 2360$ psi
$e_b = (0.67\ pgm + .17)\ d$
$M = f_y/185f_c' = \frac{40,000}{(.85)(5250)} = 8.98$
$e_b = [(.67)(.00645)(8.98) + .17]\ 11\frac{3}{8}$
$= (.0388 + .17)(11\frac{3}{8}) = (.209)(11\frac{3}{8})$
$= 2.38''$
$F_a = .34\ [1 + (.00645)(8.98)]\ 5,250$
$= 1890$ psi

$A = 192 + 2(9.18)(.31)(4)$
$= 192 + 22.8$
$= 214.8\ in^2$
$I_x = \frac{12}{12}(16)^3 + (22.8)(3\frac{3}{8})^2$
$= 4096 + 260$
$= 4356\ in^4$
$S = 4356/_8 = 544\ in^3$
$P_{max} = 192\ [2125f_c' + (.85)(.00645)(16000)]$
$= (192)\ [1115 + 87.6]$
$= (192)(1203)$
$P_{max} = 231^k$
For $e/_t \leqq \frac{2.38}{16} = .1485$
$F_a A_g = (1.89)(192) = 363$
$P = \frac{363}{1 + \frac{(363)e}{(2.36)(544)}}$
$= \frac{363}{1 + .282e}$

$e/_t$	e"	P
0	0	363 but 231 max
.050	.80	296 but 231 max
.100	1.60	250 but 231 max
.149	2.38	217

Figure 14-6. Calculations for reinforced brick masonry, AC 318-63 WSD.

Conclusions

Based on the exploratory tests on RBM columns, and this study, it appears that the ACI 318-63 USD method for reinforced concrete columns could be applicable for RBM columns. Before it can be adopted in masonry codes, however, further research is needed. It is necessary to establish by test the true shape of the compression stress-strain curve for brick masonry and determine the ultimate strain at ultimate strength, the intensity of maximum stress at ultimate strain (whether or not there is a dip in the stress-strain curve after ultimate stress is reached), the action of RBM columns in the tension failure zone and the effect of different percentages of reinforcing. Any code recommendation for design of reinforced brick masonry columns by the USD method should include appropriate load factors for dead and live load to provide an adequate factor of safety and an appropriate capacity reduction factor ϕ that recognizes the variations in quality of materials and tolerances in bar and column dimensions as well as approximations inherent in the analysis.

The USD method should enable us to design more economical structures if we can predict failure loads and establish appropriate factors of safety. This work needs to be done now in order that RBM can follow the recent advances of reinforced concrete.

Technical Notation

a Depth of equivalent rectangular stress block $a = k_1c$

A_g Gross column area

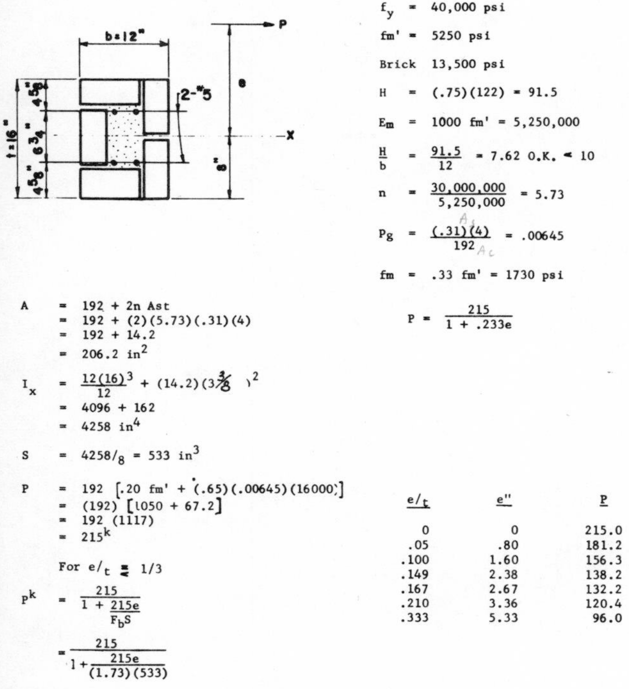

Figure 14-7. Calculations for reinforced brick masonry, ASA-A41.2.

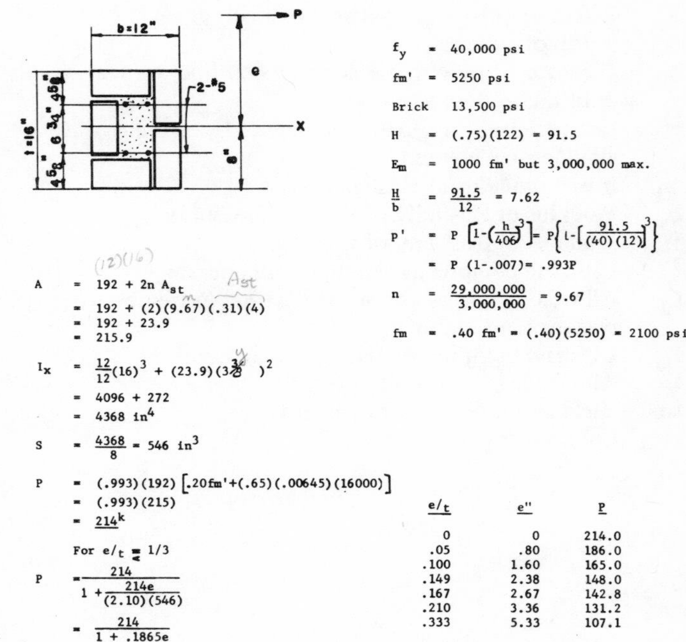

Figure 14-8. Calculations for reinforced brick masonry, SCPI-66.

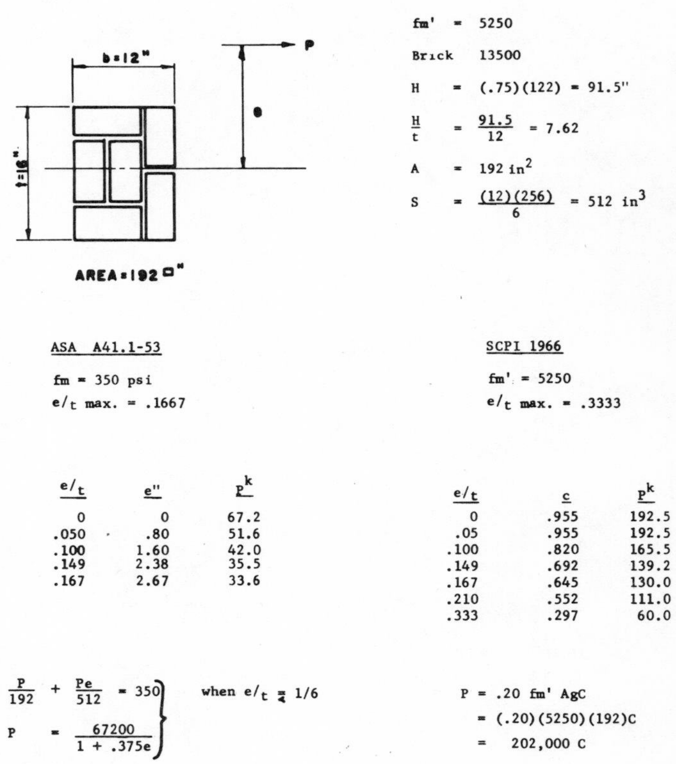

Figure 14-9. Calculations for non-reinforced masonry piers.

A_s	Effective cross sectional area of steel
b	Width of column
c	Distance from extreme compression fiber to neutral axis at ultimate strength
e	Eccentricity of load measured from centerline of symmetrical column
E_1	Initial modulus of elasticity
E_m	Modulus of elasticity of the brick masonry
E_s	Modulus of elasticity of the steel
f'_c	Ultimate compressive strength of concrete
f_m	Allowable compressive stress in extreme fiber of masonry in flexure
f'_m	Ultimate compressive strength of masonry
f_s	Allowable steel stress = .40 f_y
f_y	Yield strength of reinforcement
H	Column length
k_1	Fraction of distance from extreme compression fiber to neutral axis that equals depth of equivalent rectangular stress block at ultimate strength
M_b	Ultimate moment at balanced failure
M_u	Ultimate moment
n	$Es/_{Em}$
Pg	$As/_{Ag}$
P	Column load
P_b	Ultimate column load at balanced failure
P_c	Calculated column load
P_T	Ultimate column test load
P_u	Ultimate column load as calculated by USD method
t	Overall depth of column
ϕ	Capacity reduction factor
ϵ_u	Strain in masonry at ultimate load
ϵ_s	Strain in steel

15. Preliminary crushing tests on storey-height cavity walls.

R. E. Bradshaw, Leeds School of Architecture, Leeds, England and Prof. A. W. Hendry, University of Edinburgh, Edinburgh, Scotland

Introduction

The object was to investigate the structural behaviour of storey height cavity walls 10-1/2 in. thick subjected to vertical load, with particular reference to the distribution of load and bending moment to the two leaves of the wall at the floor slab/wall junction.

This chapter details the first seven walls (six 10-1/2 in. cavity walls and one 9 in. solid wall) built of average workmanship and tested to assess the performance of the newly installed test frame and to provide data on cavity wall tests.

Experimental Method

Loading Frame

A loading frame of 600 tons capacity was designed and erected to accommodate wall panels up to 8 ft. 2 in. high and 4 ft. 6 in. wide. Figure 15-1. This panel size is within the limits of 8 ft. to 9 ft. by 4 ft. to 6 ft. recommended in the British Standard Code of Practice C.P.111 1964 for test wall panels. A full description of the test frame has been given elsewhere [1,2].

Materials

A summary of the brick properties is given in Table 15-1. Two building sands were obtained locally to Table 1 of BS.1200, and stored in the open and used damp.

A rapid hardening Portland Cement (Ferrocrete) was used for all mortars to give early strength. Walls 1 and 2 were constructed during a period of cement shortage and lower mortar strengths than normal were obtained.

The mortar was batched by volume and mixed by hand. For each mix the bricklayer was allowed to add sufficient water to give optimum workability. After 24 hours the cubes were removed from the moulds and stored in water until tested. The mortar cube strengths are included in Table 15-2.

Wall Tests

General. Each wall was constructed by a professional bricklayer, within the loading frame shown in Figure 15-1. Both the upper and lower 6 in. thick reinforced concrete slabs were cast in position prior to construction of the test walls and, to facilitate this, the upper slab was raised 1/2 in. at the test wall

Figure 15-1. 600 ton test frame with 10½ in. cavity wall ready for test.

end. The wall was then constructed in the normal manner, the centre line of each wall being marked on the sides of each slab. A bed of mortar 5/8 in. thick was placed on top of the wall and the upper slab then lowered 1/2 in. onto the fresh bed of mortar which reduced in thickness from 5/8 in. to 3/8 in.

The bricklayer constructed the walls plumb, true to line, level, and with all joints completely filled with mortar. A storey height course rod was supplied to the bricklayer and a nominal 3/8 in. mortar joint adopted for all the test walls.

Walls were built overhand, workmanship was typical of that found on the average site. Wall 4 was built 3/4 in. off plumb for half the wall width. For wall 5, the load was applied 3/4 in. eccentric towards the inner leaf. Brickwork cubes 9 in. x 9 in. by 3 and 4 courses high were constructed as each wall was built and later tested with the walls. Each wall was 8 ft. 2 in. high between slabs and comprised 31 and 33 brick courses respectively when the 2-7/8 in. and 2-5/8 in. thick bricks were used.

The walls were tested after curing by applying the load through the loading beam which was seated on a 9 in. thick single course of brickwork laid on edge, on the upper slab.

Instrumentation. For cavity walls 1 and 2 and the 9 in. solid wall test, four vertical extensometers were fixed to the wall, two on each outside face, as shown in Figure 15-4b.

For cavity walls 3, 4, 5 and 6, four additional vertical extensometers were fixed to the end of each leaf on the centre of the 4-1/8 in. leaf thickness.

The load on the wall was recorded at intervals by measuring the electrical output from each of the 200 ton load cells using a digital voltmeter 1, 2; the load cells having been previously calibrated.

Tests. Failure was generally by shearing within the 4-1/8 in. brick thickness (Figure 15-2) in the top 4 or 5 courses. This was seen as spalling on the wall face (Figure 15-3).

Figure 15-2. Typical failure by shearing within 4-1/8 in. bri[ck] thickness in top courses (wall 2).

During the tests on walls 5 and 6 the upper slab crack[ed] over the outer leaf at a load of approximately 100 tons. T[his] transferred all the load to the inner leaf and accounts for t[he] considerably lower strengths for walls 5 and 6 when compar[ed] with wall 4.

Results

A summary of the results of the 7 wall tests and comparison with the permissible design stresses based on t[he] Code of Practice C.P.111 1964 is given in Table 15-2.

Table 15-1
Brick Properties

Type of Brick	Crushing Strength B.S. 1257 and 3921 (lb/in²)	Strength Range (lb/in²)	Water Absorption 24 Hour (% wt.)	Wall No.
Single frog 2-5/8 in. deep	3710	1350	17.7	1 and 2 and 9 in. solid wall
Pressed double frog (batch 2) 2-7/8 in. deep	7110 6625 mean 6855	3640 2110	6.1	3
Pressed double frog (batch 3) 2-7/8 in. deep	4345	1950	10.0	4, 5 and 6

Figure 15-3. Typical spalling of face in top courses (wall 4).

A typical stress/strain curve is given in Figure 15-5 and the distribution of load on each leaf for walls 3 – 6 incl. is given in Figure 15-6.

The strains due to bending for walls 3 – 5 incl. are given in Figure 15-7.

Calculations

The permissible design stresses given in Table 15-2 have been calculated according to the Code of Practice CP111 1964. as follows:

$$\text{10-1/2 in. cavity wall} - \text{slenderness ratio} = \frac{\text{effective height}}{\text{effective thickness}}$$

$$= \frac{\tfrac{3}{4} \times 8.17 \times 12}{2/3\,(4\tfrac{1}{2} + 4\tfrac{1}{2})} = 12.25$$

Reduction factor for axial loading (from Table 4 of C.P.111) = 0.75. The basic permissible compressive stress for a brick strength of 3,710 lb/in^2 and 1:3 cement/sand mortar mix is 285 lb/in^2 (by interpolation Table 3 C.P.111 1964).

The maximum permissible compressive design stress = 285 x 0.75 = 213 lb/in^2. Similarly for brick strengths of 6,855 and 4,345 lb/in^2 the basic permissible stresses are 471 and 321 lb/in^2 respectively and the maximum permissible compressive stresses are 353 and 241 lb/in^2 respectively.

Discussion of Results

Test Frame

The operation and performance of the test frame for the 7 preliminary tests was generally satisfactory.

Table 15-2
10½ in. Cavity Wall Tests in 600 Ton Frame
Summary of Results

a	b	c	d	e	f	g	h	i	j	k
Wall No.	Brick Strength (lb/in^2)	Mortar Strength (lb/in^2)	Ultimate Load (tons)	Average compressive stress (lb/in^2)	Permissible design stress (C.P. 111, 1964) (lb/in^2)	Load factor	Duration of loading (minutes)	Strength ratio/bwk/brick	Loading	Age at test (days)
9" solid	3710	495 (1.1.6)	150	725	202	3.6	30 to 93^t 30 to 150^t	0.19	axial	75
1	3710	335	153	770	213	3.6	45	0.21	axial	7
2	3710	670	169.5	855	213	4.0	45	0.23	axial	12
3	6855	2360	345	1735	353	4.9	45 to 75^t 150 to 100^t 15 to 345^t	0.25	axial	114
4	4345	1215	244.5	1230	241	5.1	75	0.28	3/4" ecc. at one end	7
5	4345	1100	150	755*	241	3.1	60	–	3/4" ecc.	99
6	4345	1100	128	645*	241	2.7	40	–	axial	9

* R.C. Slab over wall cracked transferring all load to inner leaf.

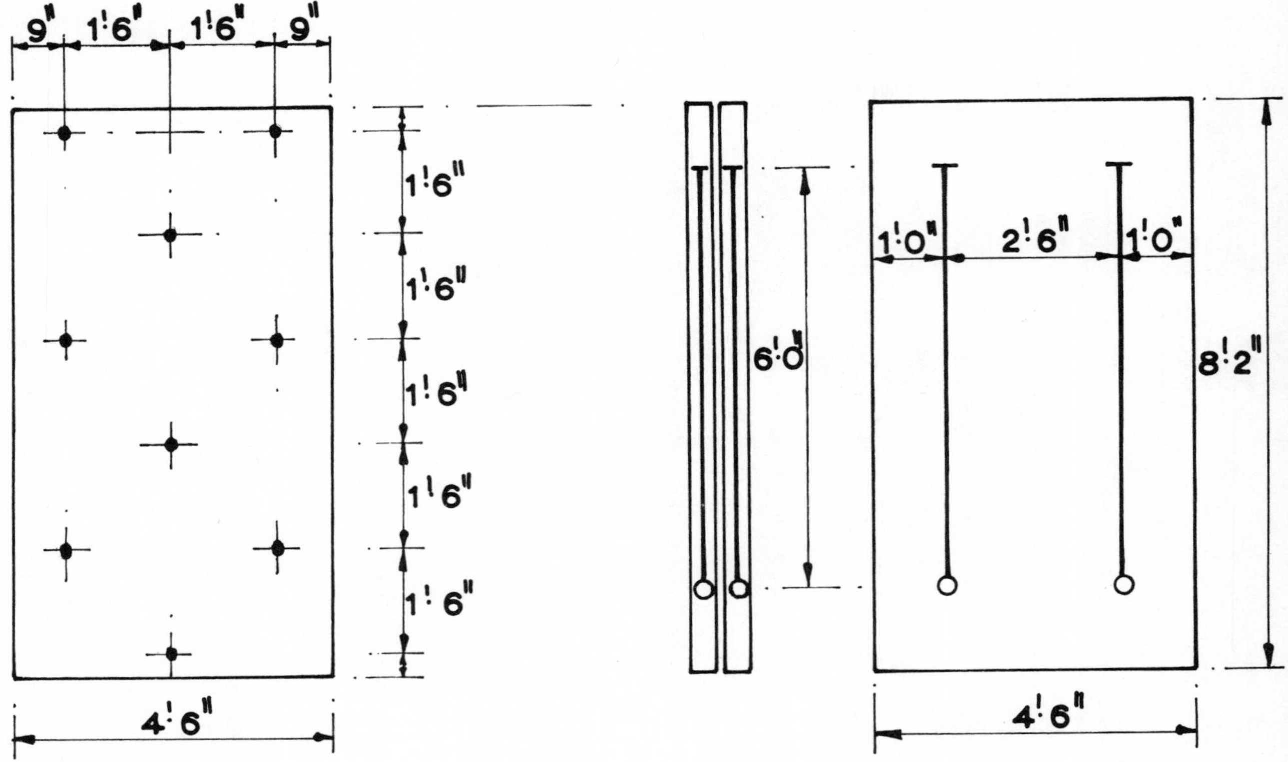

Figure 15-4a. Position of wall ties.

Figure 15-4b. Position of extensometers.

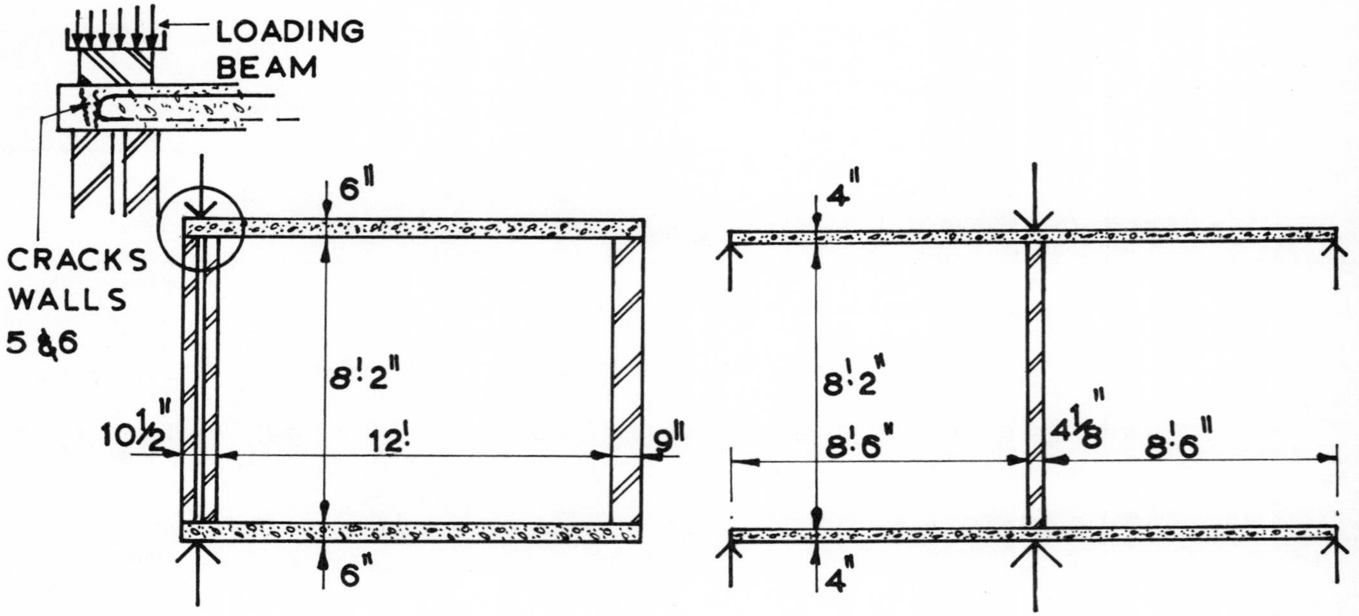

Figure 15-4c. Cavity wall test arrangement.

Figure 15-4d. Single leaf wall test arrangement.

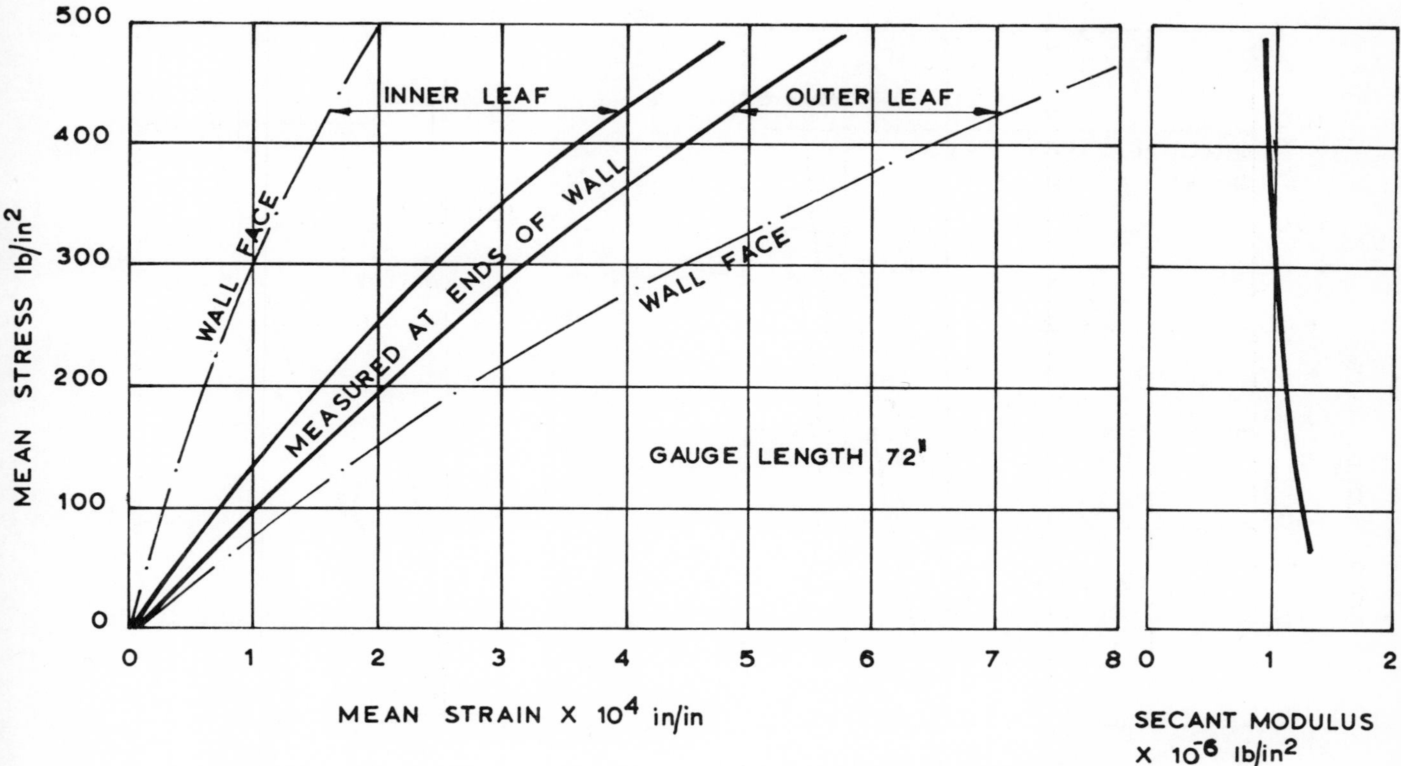

Figure 15-5. Typical stress/strain curve and values for secant modulus (wall 4).

Mortar Strength

Wall 1, having a mortar strength half that of the otherwise similar wall 2, failed at a load of 10% less. This agrees with empirical formulae used in Europe which assume that for axial loading the brickwork strength is proportional to the cube or fourth root of the mortar strength.[1]

Brickwork Strength

The average compressive strength for the cavity walls 1 and 2 was 770 and 855 lb/in^2 respectively (Table 15-2). These compare quite well with a manufacturers results[3] for two 9 in. solid walls of 925 and 890 lb/in^2, constructed of a slightly stronger brick and mortar (Walls A and B, Table 15-3).

The walls were 28% weaker than three single-leaf walls constructed of similar materials (Walls C,P and E Table 15-3) having crushing strengths of 1265, 1085 and 1040 lb/in^2 respectively[1], and a mean strength of 1130 lb/in^2.

Cavity wall 3 having a strength of 1735 lb/in^2 was 28% weaker than the single-leaf walls F,G,H and I in Table 15-3 having crushing strengths of 2110, 2450, 2330 and 2670 lb/in^2 respectively and a mean strength of 2390 lb/in^2. Cavity wall 3, however, was constructed of slightly stronger materials. The strength of the cavity walls tested was approximately 30% less than that of two leaves of similar materials constructed and tested separately, and this is partly due to the noticeably lower standard of workmanship for the cavity walls when compared with the single-leaf walls.

Two other factors that were unequal for both the single-leaf and the cavity wall tests may also have influenced the differences in ultimate wall strength. The test walls were all 8 ft. 2 in. high, but the cavity walls were 4 ft. 6 in. in length and the single leaf walls only 3 ft. in length.

The difference in the height to length ratio and the restraining influence of the upper and lower r.c. slabs acting on different lengths of wall may have contributed to the differences in wall strengths.

A further factor concerns the restraint afforded to the wall/slab junction by the reinforced concrete floor slabs. For the single-leaf wall tests, the floor slabs extended 8 ft. 6 in. on either side of the test walls, representing an internal load-bearing wall. For the cavity wall tests, the floor slab extended 12 ft. on one side of the wall only. In this case, the cavity wall would absorb a greater part of any bending moment due to eccentric loading than would the single-leaf wall, having the floor slab extending on either side.

Distribution of Load and Bending Moment for Walls 3-6 Inclusive

It can be seen in Figure 15-6 that the load is not distributed equally between the two leaves, when it is assumed that the

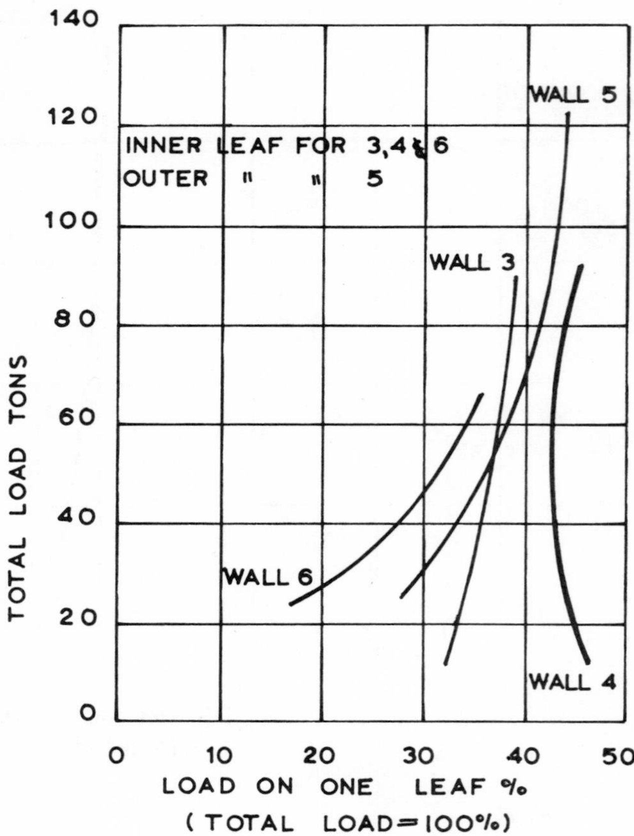

Figure 15-6. Distribution of load on each leaf for walls 3-6.

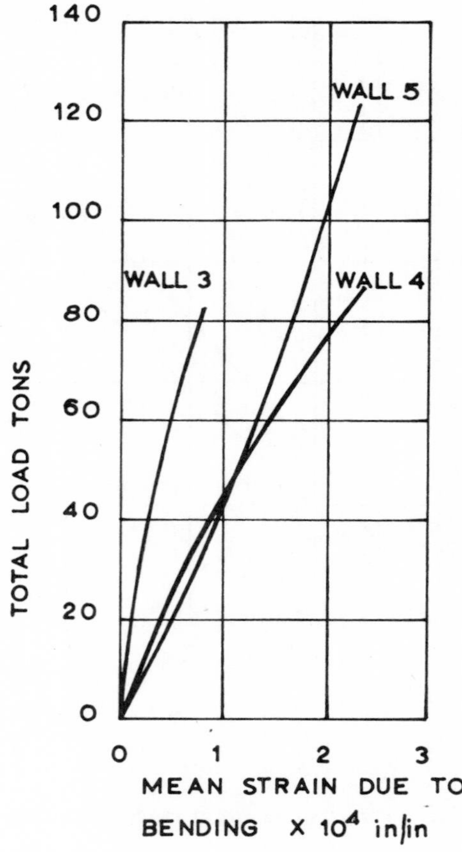

Figure 15-7. Strain due to bending for walls 3-5.

load is directly proportional to the shortening measured at the ends of the wall on the centre of the 4-1/8 in. thicknesses.

When workmanship and materials are dissimilar the load will be distributed to the two leaves in proportion to their stiffnesses. For walls 3, 5 and 6 the difference in load supported on each leaf is a maximum at low loads and decreases as the load increases. At a load of 100 tons, the load distribution between the two leaves is in the ratio of approximately 2 to 3.

The tensile and compressive strains due to bending were generally within ± 5% of the mean curves in Figure 15-7 indicating that the moment is shared equally between the two leaves.

For the nominally axially loaded wall 3, the bending moments were about half those for the eccentrically loaded walls 4 and 5.

Load Factors

The maximum load factor for the cavity wall tests was 5.1 for wall 4 (Table 15-2) and values were generally half those obtained for the single leaf walls constructed of similar materials. This would seem to be partly due to the lower standard of workmanship found in cavity walls, resulting in an unequal load distribution between the two leaves and introducing some bending into the wall. Also, the method of supporting the cavity wall by floor slabs spanning from one side only (external wall) might provide less restraint than that given to an internal wall having floor slabs spanning on both sides (internal wall).

Brickwork Cubes

The strength ratio of the cavity wall/brickwork cube ranged between 0.52 and 0.73. The strength ratio of the brickwork cubes 3 courses high/4 courses high ranged between 1.04 and 1.24.

Cracking of Upper Slab

The upper reinforced concrete slab cracked over the line of the outer leaf (Figure 15-4c) during tests on walls 5 and 6. The load was then supported by the inner leaf only, and the failure loads of 150 tons for wall 5 and 128 tons for wall 6 were appreciably less than the load of 244.5 tons for wall 4 constructed of similar materials and loaded on both leaves.

Inspection of the cracked slab after failure of wall 5 revealed that the fabric reinforcement in the top of the slab had been displaced during the placing and vibrating of the concrete. The cracked slab was repaired for the test on wall 6 to avoid replacing the entire upper slab. This did not prove satisfactory, however, and the slab failed whilst wall 6 was under test.

The failure of the r.c. slab during the test on walls 5 and 6 indicated that the r.c. slab may be subjected to considerable shearing and bending stresses which could result in failure of the r.c. slab before failure of the cavity wall.

Consideration should therefore be given to assessing the magnitude of these stresses, to providing the necessary steel reinforcement in the r.c. slab, and to checking the position of the reinforcing on site.

Conclusions

The results of the preliminary cavity wall tests indicate that:

1. The 600 ton testing frame operated satisfactorily.
2. The cavity walls tested were approximately 30% weaker than two leaves of similar materials constructed and tested separately. The support conditions were typical of those in normal buildings. The cavity walls were loaded between 6 in. thick r.c. slabs, top and bottom, spanning 12 ft. from one side only, representing an external wall. The single-leaf walls were loaded between 4 in. thick r.c. slabs spanning 8 ft. 6 in. on either side representing an internal wall.
3. Workmanship for the cavity wall was noticeably poorer than for the single-leaf walls because of the difficulty in flushing up the joints completely.
4. The load distribution between the two leaves was approximately 60% and 40% at half failure load. The difference lessened as the load increased.
5. At high loads, the local bending and shearing stresses in floor slabs where they have to transmit loads from above to the wall below are likely to be severe. Failure of the upper slab occurred during two cavity wall tests, drawing attention to the importance of correct detailing and placing of reinforcement at such locations.

Acknowledgements

Thanks are due to the Brick Development Association who sponsored the cavity wall tests and to the British Ceramic Research Association who sponsored the single-leaf wall tests. Also to the Castle Fire Brick Company and the London Brick Company for supplying bricks.

References

1. Bradshaw, R. E., "Loadbearing Brickwork Walls". M.Sc. Department Civil Engineering, Edinburgh University, March, 1964.
2. Hendry, A. W. and Bradshaw, R. E., "The Design of a 600 Ton Multi-Purpose Testing Frame". Civil Eng. and Public Works Review, Nov. 1966, pp. 1383-1385.
3. Private Communication, T. G. W. Boxall, London Brick Company, 1965.

Table 15-3
Comparison Single Leaf Wall Tests in 200 Ton Frame
Summary of Results

Wall No.	Brick Strength (lb/in^2)	Mortar Strength (lb/in^2)	Ultimate Load (tons)	Average compressive stress (lb/in^2)	Permissible design stress (C.P. 111 1964) (lb/in^2)	Load factor	Duration of Loading (minutes)	Strength ratio/bwk/brick	Loading	Age (days)
A * (9 in. solid)	4260	1140	–	925	240	3.86	–	.217	axial	28
B * (9 in. solid)	4780	1095 (1.1.6)	–	890	260 (basic S.R. = 4.5)	3.42	–	.186	axial	28
C. 4 1/8″	3710	805	81.5	1265	77	16.4	30	.34	3/4″ off plumb	19
D. 4 1/8″	3710	770	70	1085	140	7.7	25	.29	axial	7
E. 4 1/8″	3710	940	67	1040	140	7.4	30	.28	axial	13
F. 4 1/8″	6235	1540	135	2110	217	9.7	90 to 135^t 15 to 135^t	.34	axial (t/40)	18
G. 4 1/8″	6235	2450	157	2450	217	11.3	30	.39	axial (t/62)	78
H. 4 1/8″	6235	865	150	2330	217	10.7	30 to 90^t 8 to 150^t	.37	axial (t/67)	2
I. 4 1/8″	6235	2335	172	2670	217	12.3	20 to 22.5^t 60 to 172^t	.43	axial (t/24)	18

*Walls A and B tested by London Brick Company.

Table 15-A

e/d	P_{one}/P_E	P_{two}/P_E	P_{one}/P_{two}
0.0	1.00000	2.00000	0.50
0.0002	0.99868	1.76517	0.57
0.0004	0.99737	1.57968	0.63
0.0007	0.99605	1.42948	0.70
0.0009	0.99473	1.30535	0.76
0.0011	0.99341	1.20107	0.83
0.0013	0.99210	1.11221	0.89
0.0016	0.99078	1.03559	0.96
0.0018	0.98946	0.96885	1.02
0.0020	0.98815	0.91019	1.09
0.0022	0.98683	0.85823	1.15
0.0024	0.98551	0.81188	1.21
0.0027	0.98420	0.77028	1.28
0.0029	0.98288	0.73274	1.34
0.0031	0.98156	0.69868	1.40
0.0033	0.98025	0.66765	1.47
0.0035	0.97893	0.63926	1.53
0.0038	0.97761	0.61319	1.59
0.0040	0.97630	0.58916	1.66
0.0042	0.97498	0.56694	1.72
0.0044	0.97366	0.54634	1.78
0.0047	0.97235	0.52718	1.84
0.0049	0.97103	0.50932	1.91
0.0051	0.96971	0.49263	1.97
0.0053	0.96840	0.47700	2.03
0.0055	0.96708	0.46233	2.09
0.0058	0.96576	0.44853	2.15
0.0060	0.96445	0.43554	2.21
0.0062	0.96313	0.42328	2.28
0.0064	0.96182	0.41168	2.34
0.0067	0.96050	0.40071	2.40
0.0069	0.95918	0.39031	2.46
0.0071	0.95787	0.38043	2.52
0.0073	0.95655	0.37104	2.58
0.0075	0.95524	0.36210	2.64
0.0078	0.95392	0.35359	2.70
0.0080	0.95260	0.34546	2.76
0.0082	0.95129	0.33770	2.82
0.0084	0.94997	0.33028	2.88
0.0086	0.94866	0.32318	2.94
0.0089	0.94734	0.31638	2.99
0.0091	0.94602	0.30986	3.05
0.0093	0.94471	0.30360	3.00
0.0095	0.94339	0.29759	3.17
0.0098	0.94208	0.29182	3.23
0.0100	0.94076	0.28626	3.29
0.0102	0.93945	0.28091	3.34
0.0104	0.93813	0.27576	3.40
0.0106	0.93682	0.27079	3.46

Tensile Strength Buckling Strength 0.01.
P_{two} = Cracking Load for the loadfree wythe of a cavity wall.
P_{one} = Cracking load for a single wythe wall.
E = Distance from center of the loaded wythe to the force.

Table 15-B

e/d	P_{one}/P_E	P_{two}/P_E	P_{one}/P_{two}
0.0	1.00000	2.00000	0.50
0.1000	0.41415	0.03279	12.63
0.2000	0.04000	0.01653	2.42
0.3000	0.01216	0.01105	1.10
0.4000	0.00706	0.00830	0.85
0.5000	0.00496	0.00664	0.75
0.6000	0.00383	0.00554	0.69
0.7000	0.00211	0.00475	0.66
0.8000	0.00262	0.00416	0.63
0.9000	0.00227	0.00370	0.61
1.0000	0.00199	0.00333	0.60
1.1000	0.00178	0.00303	0.59
1.2000	0.00161	0.00277	0.58
1.3000	0.00147	0.00256	0.57
1.4000	0.00135	0.00238	0.57
1.5000	0.00125	0.00222	0.56
1.6000	0.00116	0.00208	0.56
1.7000	0.00108	0.00196	0.55
1.8000	0.00102	0.00185	0.55
1.9000	0.00096	0.00175	0.55
2.0000	0.00091	0.00167	0.54
2.1000	0.00086	0.00159	0.54
2.2000	0.00082	0.00151	0.54
2.3000	0.00078	0.00145	0.54
2.4000	0.00074	0.00139	0.54
2.5000	0.00071	0.00133	0.53
2.6000	0.00068	0.00128	0.53
2.7000	0.00066	0.00123	0.53
2.8000	0.00063	0.00119	0.53
2.9000	0.00061	0.00115	0.53
3.0000	0.00059	0.00111	0.53
3.1000	0.00057	0.00107	0.53
3.2000	0.00055	0.00104	0.53
3.3000	0.00053	0.00101	0.53
3.4000	0.00051	0.00098	0.53
3.5000	0.00050	0.00095	0.52
3.6000	0.00048	0.00093	0.52
3.7000	0.00047	0.00090	0.52
3.8000	0.00046	0.00088	0.52
3.9000	0.00045	0.00085	0.52
4.0000	0.00043	0.00083	0.52
4.1000	0.00042	0.00081	0.52
4.2000	0.00041	0.00079	0.52
4.3000	0.00040	0.00077	0.52
4.4000	0.00039	0.00076	0.52
4.5000	0.00038	0.00074	0.52
4.6000	0.00038	0.00072	0.52
4.7000	0.00037	0.00071	0.52
4.8000	0.00036	0.00069	0.52

Tensile strength/ buckling strength 0.01.
P_{two} = Cracking load for the loadfree wythe of a cavity wall.
P_{one} = Cracking load for a single wythe wall.
E = Distance from center of the loaded wythe to the force.

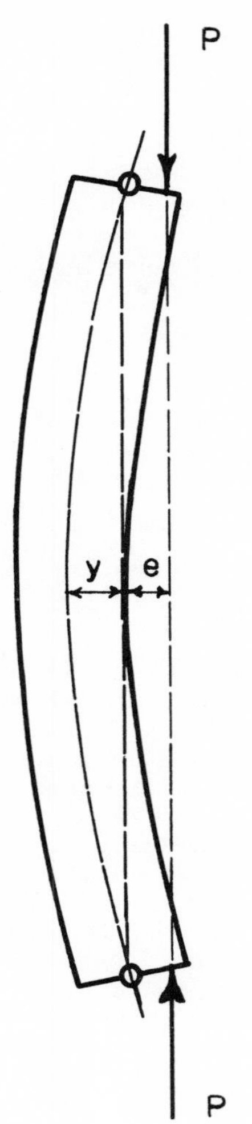

Figure 15-A.

Remarks

By Sven Sahlin
Department of Civil Engineering, University of Illinois

Consider a pin-ended single wythe wall, Figure 15-A. The moment at midheight due to an eccentric load P is approximately:

$$M = \frac{Pe}{1 - P/P_E} \quad (15\text{-A})$$

The tensile stress, which governs cracking is:

$$\sigma = \frac{P}{A} + \frac{M}{W} = \frac{-P}{A} + \frac{M6}{Ad} \quad (15\text{-B})$$

for a rectangular section with thickness d. With the ratios $P/P_E = P_{one}$, e/d = e ov d, and $\sigma \cdot A/P_E = T$ Equation 15-B can be solved for P_{one} by inserting the value of M from Equation 15-A.

$$P_{one} = \frac{(1 - T - 6\ eovd)}{2} + \sqrt{\frac{(1 - T - 6\ eovd)^2}{2} + T} \quad (15\text{-C})$$

If a second identical wall is tied to the first one in such a manner that both walls have the same curvature but the second wall does not carry any axial load, the buckling load will be doubled due to the doubled stiffness. Thus:

$$M = \frac{Pe}{1 - \frac{P}{2P_E}} \quad (15\text{-D})$$

with the same notations as before and the first wall still loaded as in Figure A.

This moment is now shared equally by the two walls (they have the same curvature).

The wythe without axial load cracks at the stress σ:

$$\sigma = \frac{0.5M}{W} = \frac{M6}{2 \cdot A \cdot d} \quad (15\text{-E})$$

Solving Equations 15-E and 15-D for $P_{two} = P/P_E$ gives:

$$P_{two} = \frac{2T}{T + 6\ eovd} \quad (15\text{-F})$$

The cracking loads for single (P_{one}) and two wythe (P_{two}) walls have been calculated for varying eccentricities and they are shown in Tables A and B together with the ratios of the two loads. The fact that the cavity wall has a lower cracking load for certain eccentricities does not necessarily mean that it has a lower ultimate load since the uncracked wythe more or less acts as a single wall, with the cracked one acting as a pure load or, eventually, as a partial stiffener. If both wythes are axially loaded simultaneously and identically, then the total load carrying capacity would be doubled for all eccentricities.

For loading cases in between, i.e., when both wythes carry load but in unequal amounts, the cracking load can be higher or lower than that for a single wall, depending upon the actual fractions of load on each wythe and the load eccentricities.

16. Reinforced masonry revisited, ten years later.

Walter L. Dickey, Masonry Research, Los Angeles, California

The author presented a paper in 1956 before the Building Research Institute of the National Academy of Sciences in Washington, D. C. entitled "Reinforced Brick Masonry"[1]. It discussed reinforced brick masonry then in use in California. That article will be summarized briefly and then reviewed herein, particularly to confirm some earlier points and to discuss advances that have been made in this decade.

It will be reviewed especially in the light of improvement of use and of increased earthquake resistance design data.

This latter is important because the discussion of the Long Beach Earthquake in that 1956 article is still valid, namely that unreinforced and unengineered structures may be hazards during earthquakes. One comment made then is that "some of the brick structures that were demolished by the Long Beach Quake were identical to many of the brick structures now being built in the East (since that last big earthquake occurred in that area). The first earthquake for many of those buildings will probably be their last . . ." We do not predict a quake soon, but records as shown on seismic charts indicate that quakes have occurred in those areas in the past, and therefore may probably occur again. (See Figure 16-1)

In confirming that we cannot predict occurrence of earthquakes one authority stated, "The only thing we may state for certain is that the farther we are from the last quake the closer we are to the next one." (See Figure 16-1.)

The conclusion of that earlier article of a decade ago is as follows:

> We have described the details, advantages, and disadvantages of RBM. Although RBM was developed initially in the West to meet a need for an economical earthquake resistant construction, it has certain inherent qualities making it effective in any area. As a consequence it may make the use of masonry feasible and more desirable than some other material in many instances. Furthermore, no area is entirely free from earthquakes, some of the strongest known have occurred in the East. It might, therefore, be well to take advantage of RBM's inherent safety factor.
>
> To sum up:
>
> RBM is the technique of laying exterior and interior wythes of masonry with a grout collar joint in which reinforcement is placed.
>
> It provides masonry surfaces of elements of different heights, types, and coursing, all incorporated into a homogeneous structure.
>
> It has an adaptability and freedom of expression which could be more fully realized.
>
> Design theory is identical to reinforced concrete design theory.
>
> Validity of the principles and theory have been established by test.
>
> It has a tremendous factor of safety over permitted design values.
>
> It is subject to some typical masonry disadvantages, namely, modular restrictions of size or placement, and sensitivity to human workmanship. It is new and masons must be trained in slightly different techniques.
>
> It has several advantages; for instance:
>
> An ageless and warm beauty, with interesting texture and pattern.
>
> A relatively low cost of placement.
>
> An elimination of certain human equation factors.
>
> A low maintenance cost.
>
> Excellent resistance to cracking and differential settlement.
>
> A finish wall that serves as a structural element.
>
> High earthquake resistance.
>
> Good atomic blast resistance.
>
> Good weather resistance.
>
> This discussion will, I hope, help enrich the vocabulary of the architect and engineer who seeks full, free, uninhibited expression of his creative imagination as well as function. It may also provide food for thought for those who seek economy—better buildings at lower cost.

Purpose

This Chapter proposes to extend that earlier paper, to examine the validity, to bring it more up to date, and to discuss changes made.

The RBM advantages listed therein are still valid, such as savings in steel reinforcement compared to concrete, savings in structural steel support, economy of reinforcing and laying, improvement of confidence in workmanship, savings due to

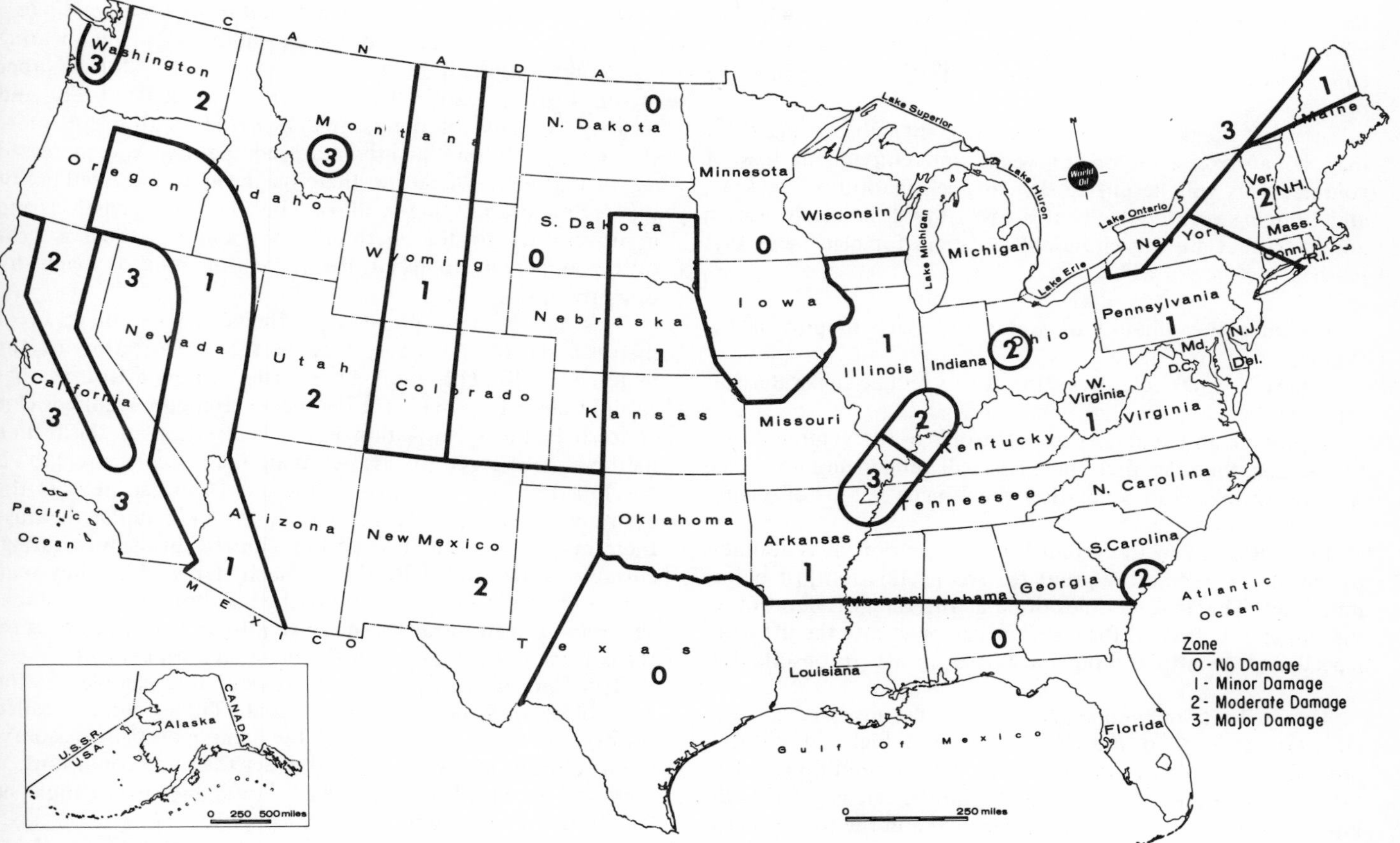

Figure 16-1. Chart indicating where quakes have occurred and are therefore likely to occur again.

the use of reinforced walls, along with the other many aesthetic and intrinsic advantages of brick.

Code Design Revisions

The structural design method for RBM was stated then to be identical with the design procedure for reinforced concrete. This is noted to be correct in the ranges of stress permitted by the codes, i.e. with that tremendous factor of safety. However, reinforced concrete design is becoming more sophisticated and changing in details not applicable to masonry; therefore, in the newer codes such as the 1967 *Uniform Building Code,*[2] the design provisions were put into the masonry chapter rather than included merely by reference to the concrete chapter. Also, since that time it has been found that a proper consideration of Es/Em, or "n", and the percentage of steel, that is the "np" value, is influential. This is because the percentage of reinforcement is considerably less than used in concrete, and more economical design can be achieved, i.e. use of less steel for the same factor of safety. There is economy of design in using proper values of k and j instead of the approximate values.

There have been improvements in methods and techniques, some of which are as follows:

Joint Reinforcing

There has been a wider use and development of joint reinforcing. This is a very convenient economical method of placing reinforcing in masonry walls[3] There are now examples such as Dur-O-Wall, AA mesh, K mesh, Wallmesh and so forth in the California area.

High Lift Grouting

High lift grouting is an improvement of the method of placing grout in grouted reinforced masonry. It was developed and promoted first in the San Francisco Bay area, then spread to Southern California and to other parts of the country[4]. This consists essentially of building the brick wythes full height with wire ties between them to serve as form ties, cleaning out the interior, inspecting the steel placement, and then grouting in lifts to the full height of a wall[5]. Conventionally such grouting is done in 4′ lifts, between vertical barriers which control the flow, and then vibrating for intimate placement. Subsequently, after it has partially solidified, another 4′ height is added, and then another and another until the wall is complete. The grout is generally pumped into place, which makes for economical placing and also assures that the grout will be wet when it is placed. Being wet and fluid, it develops an intimate bond with the brick. The vibration at time of placing assures a thorough intimate contact and placement around the reinforcing and against the masonry.

In some areas where the brick is highly absorbent, there may be an excessive loss of water and consequent loss of volume. This will permit settlement, segregation or cracking, and bridging or arching. In this case, it is desirable to use an admix to alleviate this situation[6]. One aid for placement that has been developed will

1. reduce the amount of water necessary to provide the fluidity,
2. have a water retentive capacity to reduce the water loss that might occur,
3. provide an expansion or slight increase in volume during the setting time, so that the mass will remain homogeneous with no shrinkage or separation phenomena at time of setting.

In some areas, with certain brick absorption, it is desirable to vibrate or puddle the grout for reconsolidation just before initial set. This is sometimes done at the time of vibration of the upper lift, that is, the vibrator can penetrate the lift being placed and go into the previously placed lift, reconsolidating it.

This high lift technique adds to the other many advantages. Of most import to the designer is that high lift grouting provides a greater assurance of satisfactory conditions within the wall. Inspection at the time of grouting can assure that the interior is clean, that the steel is clean and in the proper place, and that it is there! Other items that might be missed by observation, such as improper bed joints or head joints or improper mortar will be disclosed when the grout is placed, because the 4′ or 5′ head of grout as a fluid will "proofload" the wall subjecting it to greater stresses than any design stresses to which it may be subjected later under actual loads. Also this technique is self disciplining. Once a wall fails, due to omission of ties, improper workmanship, or whatever, it is a costly mess to clean up. One can visualize the tangle of brick, reinforcing, grout, mortar, braces, scaffolding and so forth that might result. It is not likely to happen a second time!

Prism Testing

Prism testing was mentioned in the authors 1956 article, and although this method was in existence at that time it is now more widely accepted. It seems obvious that the best way to determine the actual capacity of a heterogeneous collection of materials under load is actually to test them, rather than to try to predict from a brick or mortar strength grout strength, and steel strength what might be developed. For example, in a specific job one would not know the actual effect of the absorption of the brick wythes on the water cement ratio of the grout collar joint unless he tested a sample of the actual construction.

This principle was used so little initially that it was almost taken out of the *Los Angeles City Code* because for the 10 or 15 years that it had been in, there had been no use for it. Even now, it is in only by reference to *Uniform Building Code*[2] However, with the advent of higher buildings and load-bearing wall construction, it became more important, if for no other reason than to assure the engineer of adequate safety and security. The use of the assured higher strength means more efficiency and consequently more competitive and increased use of masonry. Therefore, there has been an increased use of this technique, and there will soon be additional variations and improvements to the method. For example, there is now testing underway to refine the corrections due to height-to thickness ratio.

This requirement of testing affects the specification of materials in several ways. One is the specification of the material itself. This must be a little different from earlier specifications to provide for the higher strengths required. One concern in the specification is the description of the testing method necessary to assure that the design strength is developed in the actual construction. Another item is the definitive stipulation of the purchasing of material because there may be a production period required for manufacturing, curing, testing, and delivering of such items, since they may not be in the usual production schedule nor always in stock. There have been instances in which jobs were delayed because the contractors did not order the material soon enough.

The *Uniform Building Code* provides that samples of the assemblage may be made and tested. These samples called prisms, are to be fabricated of the same materials, masonry grout, mortar, and so forth, and under the same conditions, as they will be installed in the wall. Preferably, they should be laid by the same mason.

According to the present code, they are to be a sample of wall 16″ high and 16″ wide and of the thickness and type of the wall to be tested. In the code, the basis for the standard is a two to one height-to-thickness ratio. If the samples are made higher or lower than this ratio, they should be corrected to obtain the corrected answer, related to the standard.

These prisms are cured for a 28-day period and tested in compression to determine an f'_m, which is called the ultimate compressive strength. This is the f'_m that is used in the code tables to determine the permitted design stresses. Seven-day results may be used if the relationship to the 28-day strengths have been established. Similar samples are made during the conduct of the job to assure that the materials being incorporated into the project will meet the desired strength. This, obviously, is very similar to the method used in inspection of concrete work where test cylinders are made during the conduct of the job to insure that the strengths are being met.

For specification purposes, one may use the paragraphs as spelled out in the *Uniform Building Code,*[2] which has proved to be a reasonable wording in usage over several years. Portions of the Code are reprinted below.*

1. (c) Determination of Masonry Design Strength. 1 General. The value of "f'_m" shall be determined by tests of

*Reprinted with permission of International Conference of Building Officials, Pasadena, California.

masonry assemblies in accordance with the provisions of paragraph 2 of this Subsection or shall be assumed in accordance with the provisions of paragraph 3 of this Subsection.

2. Tests.

A. General. When the strength "f'_m" is to be established by tests, they shall be made using prisms built of the same materials, under the same conditions and, insofar as possible, with the same bonding arrangements as for the structure. The moisture content of the units at time of laying, consistency of mortar, and workmanship shall be the same as will be used in the structure. The value of "f'_m" shall be the average of all specimens tested but shall be not more than 125 per cent of the minimum value determined by test, whichever is less.

Testing shall include tests in advance of beginning operations and at least one field test during construction per each five thousand square feet (5000 sq. ft.) of wall but not less than three such tests for any building.

The compressive strength "f'_m" shall be computed by dividing the ultimate load by the net area of the masonry used in the construction of the prisms. The gross area may be used in the determination of "f'_m" for solid masonry units as defined in U.B.C. Standard No. 24-1-67.

B. Prisms. For walls, prisms shall be sixteen inches (16") high and sixteen inches (16") long. The thickness and type of construction of the specimen shall be similar to the wall under consideration.

For columns, prisms shall be sixteen inches (16") high and not less than eight inches by eight inches (8" x 8") in plan. Cores in hollow masonry shall not be filled, except for solid filled construction.

The symbol "f'_m" shall be taken as the compressive strength of the specimens multiplied by the following correction factor:

Ratio of "h/d"	1.5	2.0	2.5	3.0
Correction factor	.86	1.00	1.11	1.20

where:

h = height of specimen in inches.
d = minimum dimension of specimen in inches.

C. Storage of Test Prisms. Test prisms shall be stored for seven days in air, at a temperature of 70 degrees, plus or minus 5°F., in a relative humidity exceeding 90 per cent, and then in air at a temperature of 70 degrees, plus or minus five degrees, at a relative humidity of 30 per cent to 50 per cent until tested. Prisms shall be capped and tested in compression similar to tests for molded concrete cylinders as specified in U.B.C. Standard No. 26-10-67.

D. Sampling. Not less than five specimens shall be made for each initial preliminary test to establish "f'_m." Not less than three shall be made for each field test to confirm that the materials are as assumed in the design. The standard age of test specimens shall be 28 days, but seven-day tests may be used, provided the relation between the seven-day and 28-day strengths of the masonry is established by adequate test data for the materials used.

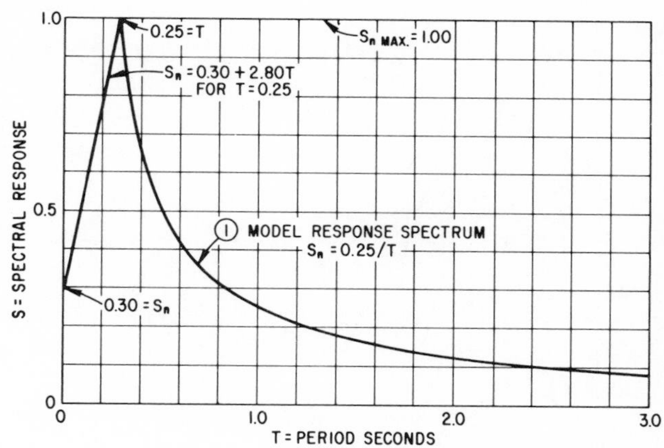

Figure 16-2. Response spectrum showing response of single mass elements of various periods of vibration T.

Testing

Tests show that masonry has extremely high values in compression and that reasonable tension values can be developed. Also, tests show that masonry does not buckle within the range of wall sizes that may be built. This confirms the indications of the buckling theory of thin plates such as presented by Timoshenko. This indicates, for example, that a wall 3" thick would not be subject to shear buckling until it is about 16'. Obviously, there is a much greater safety factor in bearing walls than in almost any other type of construction. Tests have confirmed this and steps are being taken to correct codes accordingly. The extensive testing is not listed here in detail.

Damping

Damping is an important factor in the response of a building to shaking, such as due to earthquake, and tests have shown that masonry under vibration will develop tremendous damping characteristics[12]. How great these characteristics are is not yet well documented, but tests are being made to determine this. The great damping characteristic is probably one of the factors contributing to the excellent performance of masonry in earthquakes[9]. (Note Figures 16-2 and 16-3.)

Earthquake Performance of Masonry

To recognize a negative note, masonry has a poor image in many locales because of the poor performance of some unengineered, unreinforced, or unanchored masonry. Some unreinforced structures have shown satisfactory performance e.g., some of the massive or conservatively built structures.

However, reinforced masonry has performed quite well in even the most severe quakes. For example, 85 percent of the masonry buildings that were reinforced and properly tied showed no damage in the major earthquake in Anchorage, Alaska. The difficulty in Anchorage was, not enough anchor-

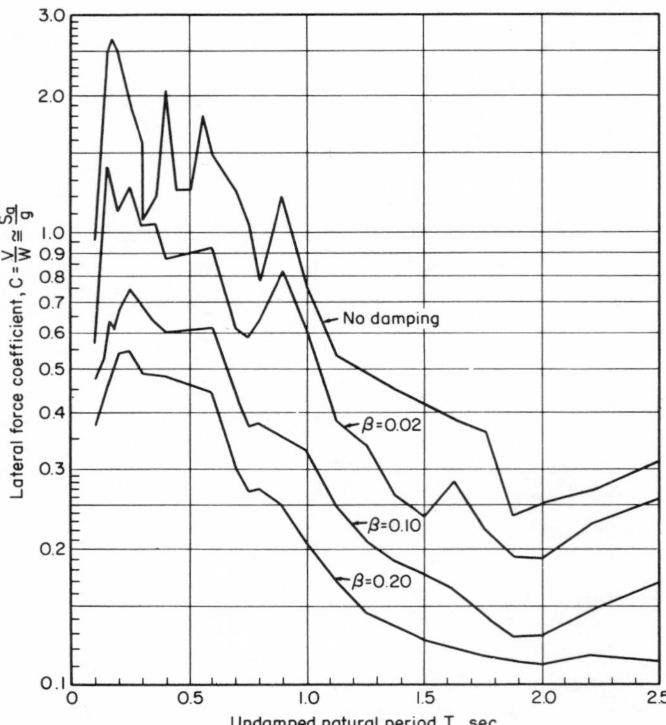

Figure 16-3. A plot of response to quake against period T for various conditions of damping.

age. This includes major industrial, commercial, and institutional buildings as well as residential.

The author's design experience confirms the satisfactory performance. A series of concrete masonry warehouses was designed by him for Elmendorf Air Force Base near Anchorage. These were 30′ high with wide spacing of reinforcing, 4′ and more. These showed no distress whatever, even though subjected to that major quake. It is to be noted that some tilt-up warehouses were built on the site prior to the author's masonry wall designs and were similar in size, i.e., 200′ x 1000′. Two segments of the tilt-up buildings collapsed and three were seriously damaged, confirming that the quake was major, or catastrophic, at least to those buildings[9]. Figure 16-4 shows the damaged buildings on the site, confirming the quake intensity at the site, and the Figure 16-5 shows the complete lack of damage to the masonry buildings.

The author was pleased to note that two other structures of his design in Alaska were not damaged, the Power Plants at Elmendorf Air Force Base, and at Fort Richardson.

The above factual observations confirm that properly designed reinforced masonry structures perform quite well in resisting quakes, better than might be popularly anticipated.

Research is now being done in order to understand the reasons. There are several probable contributory facts, e.g.:

1. Properly designed buildings perform in a dramatically satisfactory manner compared to unanchored, undesigned buildings of Zero factors of safety to lateral loads.

2. The damping characteristics of masonry reduce the response to quakes.

3. The natural frequency of these stiff structures may place them in the short period range where they have less response to quakes, though there is no lessening of the code design requirements. See Figure 16-2.

4. Failures in reinforced masonry are of the ductile type which is a very effective type of resistance to catastrophic quakes. The avoiding of brittle or sudden complete failures is regarded as very important.

Multi-story Bearing Wall Construction

There has been a greater recognition of the tremendous bearing capacity of masonry since there has been greater assurance of earthquake resistance and capacity of such structures when properly engineered. In actual practice, this scheme has turned out to be a surprisingly effective one. It might be called a natural use of masonry. There have been very many side benefits derived. The construction is fast, economical, can be operated on a production line type of operation, and, properly designed, provides extremely high security and factor of safety. (SCPI and NCMA as well as others have developed many publications describing examples and further explaining of the method.) There have been many high rise, or multi-story programs in other countries and some in the U.S.A. Apparently, the highest one in the U.S.A. is the Park Mayfair complex in Denver. This is not in a Zone 3 but with slight revisions could have been made to comply.

Earthquake Design Factors and Codes

The Structural Engineers Association of California has been intensely concerned with earthquake design for many years especially because of the relatively great frequency of earthquakes in the California area. The quakes may not be more severe in California than in other areas, but their frequency is much greater. Therefore building officials and structural engineers are constantly aware of the subject, perhaps even hypersensitive.

The action of earthquake on a building is not a simple static consideration, although a simplification is to consider static lateral loads assumed applied on the building in the hope that the assumption can be adjusted in magnitude so that the forces assumed would be comparable to those that would actually occur in event of a quake.

We might say that the earthquake considerations are divided into two basic types: (1) general considerations of layout, rotation, distribution of masses, actual effect of vibration on the buildings and (2) manipulation of numbers to arrive at a reasonable order of magnitude of the assumed forces to be resisted.

The first factor, "general considerations," is more the application of judgement, common sense, and experience. Many times slight revisions to the layout of the building can change it from one that might fail due to torsion or disastrous distribution of loads and deflections in a quake to one that would be highly resistant to earthquake.

Perhaps the most important factor to consider in earthquake resistance is recognition that it is not a static load function but a vibrating load or shaking load that can occur in any direction, east, west, north, south, up, or down. In general, the up and down factors are not considered in earthquake load assumptions because there is already so much factor of safety for vertical load that additional is not required for the short-time additional load and the slight probability of full design load at time of quake. For certain conditions this must be considered, though, such as for possibility of cantilever projections coming in tune with the random vibration with consequent great response. However, as a result of experience with earthquakes, and study, the "Lateral Force Recommendations" of the Structural Engineers Association [10] has been developed as the best earthquake considerations for major earthquake areas, such as Zone 3 (some of the arbitrary requirements might be deleted for Zones 0, 1 or 2 with their lesser requirements, although the "General Considerations" would be applicable.)

Figure 16-4. Tilt-up warehouses at Elmendorf Air Force Base after Alaskan earthquake.

Figure 16-5. Warehouses at Elmendorf Air Force Base, showing no damage, after the Alaskan earthquake, 200 ft. wide by 1000 ft. long.

Design

Nomenclature[2] (Taken from the *Uniform Building Code* of the State of California.)

Box System is a structural system without a complete vertical load-carrying space frame. In this system the required lateral forces are resisted by shear walls as hereinafter defined.

Shear Wall is a wall designed to resist lateral forces parallel to the wall. Braced frames subjected primarily to axial stresses shall be considered as shear walls for the purpose of this definition.

(c) Symbols and Notations. The following symbols and notations apply only to the provisions of this Section.

- C = Numerical coefficient for base shear as specified in Section 2314 (d) 1.
- C_p = Numerical coefficient as specified in Section 2314 (d) 2 and as set forth in Table No. 23-1. (Table 16-1, this Chapter).
- D = The dimension of the building in feet in a direction parallel to the applied forces.
- D_s = The plan dimension of the vertical lateral force resisting system in feet.
- F_i, F_n, F_x = Lateral forces applied to a level "i," "n," or "x," respectively.
- F_p = Lateral forces on the part of the structure and in the direction under consideration.
- F_t = That portion of "V" considered concentrated at the top of the structure, at the level "n." The remaining portion of the total base shear "V" shall be distributed over the height of the structure including level "n" according to Formula (14-5).
- H = The height of the main portion of the building in feet above the base.
- h_i, h_n, h_x = Height in feet above the base to level "i," "n," or "x," respectively.
- J = Numerical coefficient for base moment as specified in Section 2314 (h).
- J_x = Numerical coefficient for overturning moment at level "x."
- K = Numerical coefficient as set Forth in Table No. 23-H.
- Level i = Level of the structure referred to by the subscript "i."
- Level n = That level which is uppermost in the main portion of the structure.
- Level x = That level which is under design consideration.
- M = Overturning moment at the base of the building or structure.
- M_x = The overturning moment at level "x."
- N = Total number of stories above exterior grade.
- T = Fundamental period of vibration of the building or structure in seconds in the direction under consideration.
- V = Total lateral load or shear at the base.
- W = Total dead load including partitions using the actual weight of the partitions or the partition loading specified in Section 2302 (b).

$$W = \sum_{i=1}^{n} w_i$$

Exception: "W" shall be equal to the total dead load plus 25 per cent of the floor live load in storage and warehouse occupancies.

w_i, w_x = That portion of "W" which is located at or is assigned to level "i" or "x" respectively.
W_p = The weight of a part or portion of a structure.
Z = Numerical coefficient dependent upon the zone as determined by the map shown in Figure 16-1. For locations in Zone No. 1 "Z" shall be equal to one-fourth. For locations in Zone No. 2 "Z" shall be equal to one-half. For locations in Zone 3 "Z" shall be equal to one.

Table 16-1 is for selection of the factor C_p in the equation for calculation of forces on various portions of the building, not for determination of load on the building.

$$F_p = ZC_pW_p \qquad (16\text{-}1)$$

The values of "C_p" are set forth in Table 16-1. The distribution of these forces shall be according to the gravity loads pertaining thereto.

(h) Combined axial and flexural stresses. Members subject to combined axial and flexural stresses shall be so proportioned that the quantity

$$\frac{f_a}{F_a} + \frac{f_b}{F_b} \text{ shall not exceed 1}$$

where:

f_a = Computed axial unit stress, determined from total axial load and effective area.
F_a = Axial unit stress permitted by this Code at the point under consideration, if member were carrying axial load only, including any increase in stress allowed by this Section.
f_b = Computed flexural unit stress.
F_b = Flexural unit stress permitted by this Code, if member were carrying bending load only, including any increase in stress allowed by this Section.

This is not always true nor accurate, but it is used as an acceptable expression that the percent a member is developed in bending plus the percent it is developed in direct stress must not add to more than 100% developed.

Design Synopsis

Occupancy

Type of occupancy and use, with the area required will govern the type of construction, fire rating, etc.

Area
Type of Construction
Req. Fire Rating, Walls
Reg. Fire Rating, Floors
Floor Load – L. L.
D. L.

These will be based on the above, as defined elsewhere.

Partition Load

Partitions are generally fixed so the specific load as applied may be used in lieu of an "average" floor load.

Equipment Load
Roof Load – L. L.
D. L.
Vert. Wall Load
Wind Load

As determined by the site, and height, etc.

Shape Factor

This will generally be appropriate only in special structures.

Seismic

Zone = 3 i.e. Z = 1.0

This Zone 3 factor of course is 1.0 in California.

K (Table 23-H)

Shearwall.	K = 1.33
25% Frame.	K = .80
100% Frame.	K = .67

Once this factor K is determined according to this scheme of framing, that scheme must be followed through—like considering a chain, link after link. The Box system is considered in this text as the most appropriate use of Masonry.

Scheme of Structure

For example: Floor and roof slabs with integral finish are 1 way slabs, simply supported for vertical load, and bear on walls. Lateral loads are carried by shear through the slabs to the walls which act as vertical cantilevers from mat footings.

$$T = \frac{0.05h_n}{\sqrt{D}}$$

$$C = \frac{0.05}{\sqrt[3]{T}}$$

A Table may be provided to simplify this period determination which uses a simple calculation based on dimension. Other type calculation to determine could be used in lieu of this simplification and may be more correct.

A Table is provided to simplify calculation of this constant, the factor of C dependent on period.

T – 4	3	2.5	2.0	1.5	1.0	.8	.6	.4	.2
C – .0316	.0348	.037	.040	.0435	.050	.054	.060	.068	.086

Table 16-1

Horizontal Force Factor "C_p" for Parts or Portions of Buildings or Other Structures

(Table 23-I, Uniform Building Code – reference 2)

Part of Portion of Buildings	Direction of Force	Value of C_p
Exterior bearing and nonbearing walls, interior bearing walls and partitions, interior nonbearing walls and partitions over ten feet (10′) in height, masonry or concrete fences over six feet (6′) in height[1]	Normal to flat surface	0.20
Cantilever parapet and other cantilever walls, except retaining walls	Normal to flat surface	1.00
Exterior and interior ornamentations and appendages	Any direction	1.00
When connected to or a part of a building: towers, tanks, towers and tanks plus contents, chimneys, smokestacks, and penthouses	Any direction	0.20[2]
When resting on the ground, tank plus effective mass of its contents	Any direction	0.10
Floors and roofs acting as diaphragms[3]	Any direction	0.10
Connections for exterior panels or for elements complying with Section 2314 (k) 5	Any direction	2.00
Connections for prefabricated structural elements other than walls, with force applied at center of gravity of assembly[4]	Any horizontal direction	0.30

[1] See also Section 2312 (b) for minimum load on deflection criteria for interior partitions.
[2] When "h_n/D" of any building is equal to or greater than five to one increase value by 50 per cent.
[3] Floors and roofs acting as diaphragms shall be designed for a minimum value of "C_p" of 10 per cent applied to loads tributary from that story unless a greater value of "C_p" is required by the basic seismic formula V = ZKCW.
[4] The "W_p" shall be equal to the total load plus 25 per cent of the floor live load in storage and warehouse occupancies.

The above factors can now be substituted in the basic equation V = ZKCW. This represents the total base shear, to be distributed up the building according to the forces determined in equation below.

$$\left(\frac{h_n}{D_s}\right)$$

This represents the ratio of height and plan dimension, in the direction being considered.

$$F_t = .004V\left(\frac{h_n}{D_s}\right)^2$$

This represents the assumed portion of the shear to be concentrated at the top, the so-called "whiplash" effect.

$$F_x = \frac{(V - F_t)\, w_x h_x}{\sum_{i=1}^{n} w_i h_i}$$

This represents the assumed force to be applied to the level x and may be simply calculated by tabular form.

Overturning Moment

$$J = \frac{0.5}{\sqrt[3]{T^2}}$$

The value of "J" need not be more than 1.00.

This represents the overturning moment coefficient depending upon the period of the building. The calculation is simplified by tabular listing:

T –	40	30	2.5	2.0	1.5	1.0	.8	.6	.4	.2	.1
J –	.199	.241	.272	.315	.382	.500	.58	.70	.92	1.46	2.32

$$M = J\left(F_t h_n + \sum_{i=1}^{n} F_i h_i\right)$$

and

$$M_x = J_x\left[F_t (h_n - h_x + \sum_{i=x}^{n} F_i (h_i - h_x)\right]$$

where:

$$J_x = J + (1 - J)\left(\frac{h_x}{h_n}\right)^3$$

This represents the overturning moment determined for the base.

The overturning moment M_x at any level "x" shall be determined thus. This, and M, can be solved rather simply by a table.

References

1. Dickey, W. L., "Reinforced Brick Masonry," Modern Masonry Publication 446 of the Building Research Institute, National Academy of Sciences, 1956.
2. *Uniform Building Code,* Vol. 1, International Conference of Building Officials, 1967 Edition.
3. Dickey, W. L., "Joint Reinforcement," *Masonry Industry Magazine,* April 1965.
4. Person, Oscar F., Sahlberg, Manley W., Harrington, Robert W., "High Lift Grouting System," Testing Project 922, September 1959.
5. Dickey, W. L., "High Lift Grouting," *Masonry Industry Magazine,* March 1965.
6. "Report of Investigation of Suconem G. A. (Grout Aid)," Lowry Testing Laboratory, August 1966.
7. "Sportsmans Lodge Hotel," Portland Cement Association.
8. "Hanalei Hotel Addition," Portland Cement Association.
9. Kunze, Walter E., Sbarournis, John A., Amrhein, James E., "The March 27, 1964 Alaskan Earthquake," Portland Cement Association, 1965.
10. "Recommended Lateral Force Requirements," Structural Engineers Association of California, Revised 1966.
11. Joint Committee ASCE, SEAONC, "Lateral Forces of Earthquake and Wind," *ASCE Proceedings,* Separate No. 66, April 1951.
12. Mackintosh, A., Dickey, W. L., "Effective Width in Flexure," Test Report, CMA, Masonry Research.
13. Renfro, Walter C., "Reinforcing Bar Positioners," *Masonry Industry Magazine,* October 1965.
14. "Contemporary Bearing Wall," Architectural Studies, SCPI.
15. "Contemporary Bearing Wall," Structural Design, SCPI.
16. "Contemporary Bearing Wall," Construction Techniques, SCPI.
17. "Contemporary Bearing Wall," Wall Types and Details, SCPI.
18. "General Publications on Testing and Bearing Wall Construction," SCPI.

17. Effect of edge load on flexural strength of clay masonry systems utilizing improved mortars.*

Dallas G. Grenley, Dow Chemical Co., Midland, Michigan, Louis E. Cattaneo, and Edward O. Pfrang, U.S. Dept. of Commerce, Washington, D.C.

Introduction

Masonry design in the United States, until very recently, was largely empirical in approach; historical example is the most common justification for the masonry systems we use. Designers have assumed neither tensile strength nor interaction in engineered structural situations, an approach necessitated by very low tensile, flexural, and bond strengths of masonry systems which use conventional mortar. Recently, mortars of much higher strengths have become available. Tensile and compressive strengths of mortars approaching those of brick and bond strengths as great as the tensile strength of the brick call for new concepts in masonry design. Our work proposes to supply data which will assist in rational masonry design utilizing such improved mortars.

Scope

This work involved studying the interaction between flexural stress and compressive stress on brick wall specimens of single-wythe-running-bond construction, utilizing three varieties of brick and two types of mortar. All walls were four feet wide by eight feet high, except those loaded only in compression; these were two feet by eight feet. The brick were typical of American production, but by no means embrace the extremes. The mortars are a conventional masonry type and a high bond mortar utilizing a synthetic polymer dispersion[3] designed specifically for masonry construction. The work reported here considers only uniform flexural loads and uniform-axial compressive loads. Future work will expand the data beyond these limits.

Theory

If a modulus of rupture specimen is constructed so that no bond developes between the masonry unit and the mortar, and if, then, this specimen could be tested in the usual fashion as shown in Figure 17-1a, a zero value for modulus of rupture is established. A second specimen is constructed in a similar manner. If this specimen is first subjected to a small compressive thrust and then tested with that thrust maintained (Figure 17-1b), a pseudo modulus of rupture results. If the axial compressive thrust is increased in subsequent tests, a general trend of increasing pseudo modulus of rupture with increasing axial thrust is established for moderate levels of compression. However, if this process continues, a level of compression is eventually reached above which further increases in thrust result in a reduction rather than an increase in pseudo modulus of rupture.

This phenomena can readily be predicted by considering elementary mechanics. Figure 17-1c shows a free body portion of the specimen of Figure 17-lb. If now it is assumed that[1] tensile bond is again zero,[2] that the masonry construction obeys a linearly elastic stress-strain relationship up to some crushing stress, f'_m, and[3] that the usual assumptions regarding plane sections in bending are invoked, then the compressive stress distribution at failure is as shown in Figure 17-1d. Expressions for axial thrust, P, and moment, M, can now be written:

$$P = 1/2\, f'_m k_1 tb$$

$$M = 1/2\, f'_m k_1 tb\left(\frac{t}{2} - \frac{k_1 t}{3}\right)$$

*Contribution of the National Bureau of Standards, not subject to copyright.

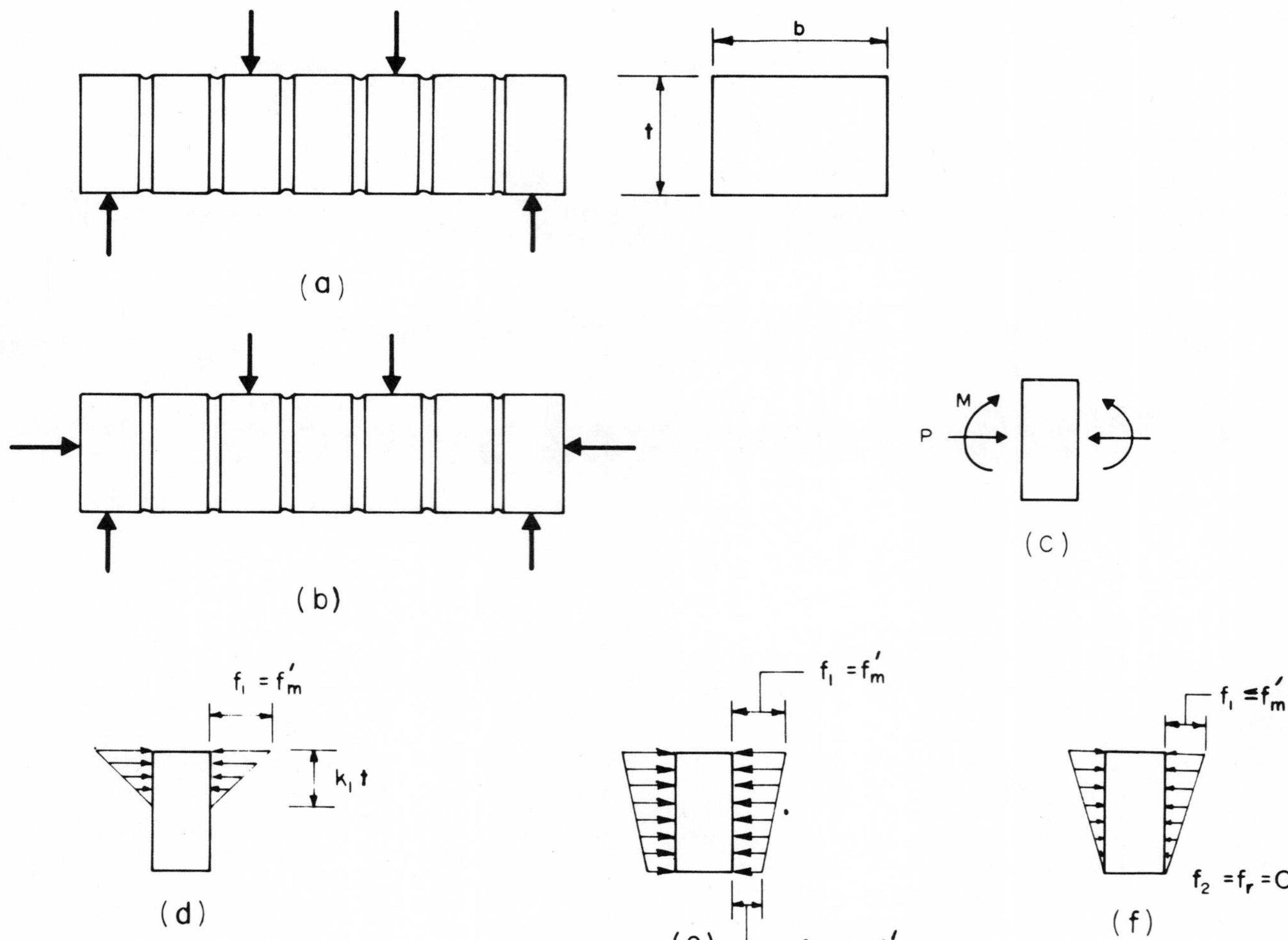

Figure 17-1. Loading conditions and stress distributions.

where:

f'_m = masonry crushing strength
t = thickness of test specimen
b = width of test specimen
$k_1 t$ = depth to neutral axis

These expressions can be rewritten in dimensionless form as:

$$\frac{P}{f'_m bt} = \frac{k_1}{2}$$
$$\frac{M}{f'_m bt^2} = \frac{k_1}{2}\left(\frac{1}{2} - \frac{k_1}{3}\right) \quad (17\text{-}1)$$

These expressions are valid over the range of values of k_1:

$$0 \leqslant k_1 \leqslant 1$$

or

$$0 \leqslant \frac{P}{f'_m bt} \leqslant 1/2$$

For values of axial thrust greater than $\frac{P}{f'_m bt} = 1/2$ the stress distribution shown in Figure 17-1(e) results. This distribution of stresses leads to the following:

$$\frac{P}{f'_m bt} = \frac{1}{2}(1 + k_2)$$
$$\frac{M}{f'_m bt^2} = \frac{1}{12}(1 - k_2) \quad (17\text{-}2)$$

where:

$$0 \leqslant k_2 \leqslant 1$$

or:

$$1/2 \leqslant \frac{P}{f'_m bt} \leqslant 1$$

Plotting Equations 17-1 and 17-2 leads to Figure 17-2. The resultant curve is the crushing-failure interaction diagram for the masonry section in question. The significance of this interaction diagram is that it represents the locus of all combinations of axial thrust and moment which result in cross-section failure by crushing. It could, of course, be plotted in terms of unit stresses in compression and flexure. The crushing-failure interaction diagram corresponds to the onset of crushing and does not necessarily represent maximum combinations of thrust and moment which can be resisted by the cross-section. However, for most engineering materials the failure interaction diagram is not significantly exceeded by the maximum interaction diagram. For the particular materials properties assumed above, the crushing-failure interaction diagram is also the maximum interaction diagram.

In addition to the crushing-failure interaction diagram, the interaction diagram for first cracking is also of interest. Using the same assumptions as before and the stress distribution shown in Figure 17-1f which represents a family of distributions having a maximum compressive stress f_1 and a minimum compressive stress, f_2, equal to zero, the assumed cracking stress leads to the following:

$$\frac{P}{f'_m bt} = \frac{1}{2}\frac{f_1}{f'_m}$$

$$\frac{M}{f'_m bt^2} = \frac{1}{12}\frac{f_1}{f'_m} \qquad (17\text{-}3)$$

Here, the modulus of rupture $f_r = f_2 = 0$.

These expressions are plotted as the dashed line of Figure 17-2. The significance of the cracking interaction diagram is that it represents the locus of all combinations of thrust and moment which result in first cracking. Thus, those combinations of thrust and moment below the dashed line, but within the crushing-failure interaction diagram, all involve various extents of tensile cracking.

Point B in Figure 17-2, the intersection of the crushing and cracking interaction diagrams, is generally designated as the balance point. It represents the combination of thrust and moment which cause simultaneous cracking and crushing. For values of thrust less than balance, crushing is always preceeded by cracking; for values of thrust above balance, crushing is not preceeded by cracking; for upon reaching crushing, the specimen fails abruptly.

Using the analysis indicated interaction diagrams can be developed for cross sections possessing almost any properties. Figure 17-3 shows an interaction diagram for a cross section identical to the preceeding, except that it possesses a degree of tensile or bond strength. Note that the general form of the two interaction curves is quite similar. There is, however, a feature of Figure 17-3 which is not present in Figure 17-2, in that for very small values of thrust, cracking moment exceeds crushing moment. The cause of this phenomenon can readily be appreciated by reference to Figure 17-4, which shows the development of moment with increasing curvature under a constant small value of thrust. Figure 17-4, besides showing the development of moment with increasing curvature, also shows the stress distribution on the cross section at several critical stages. Note that the section behaves elastically up to cracking (point G). With increasing curvature, beyond the initiation of cracking, the section develops an increased moment, but at a decreasing rate. The moment on the section eventually reaches a maximum and then experiences a decrease down to crushing (point H). Thus, for the level of thrust used

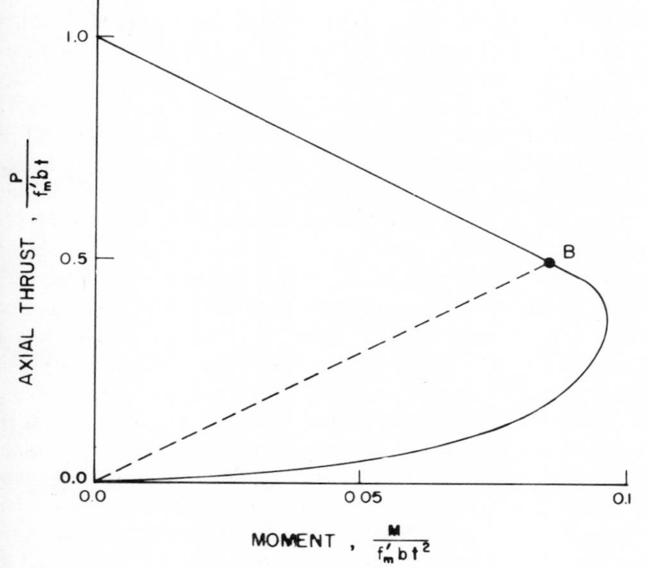

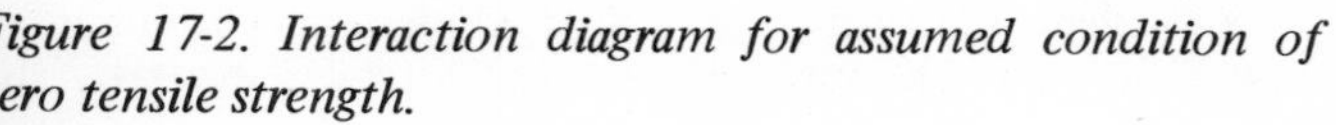

Figure 17-2. Interaction diagram for assumed condition of zero tensile strength.

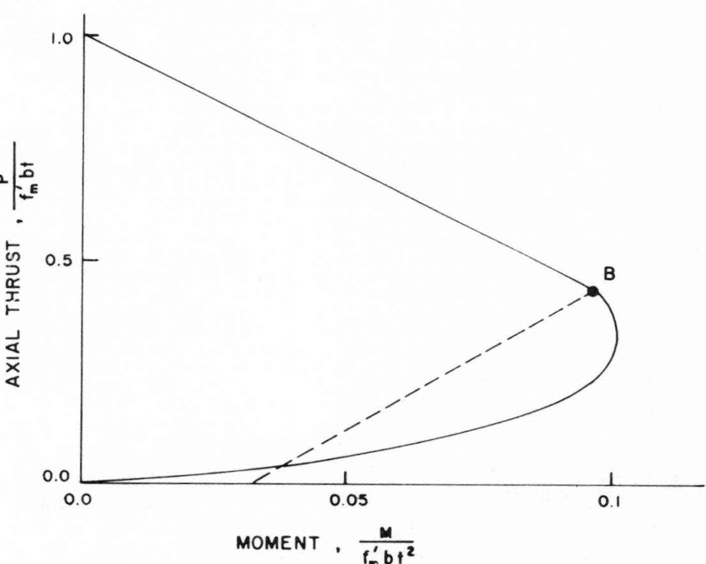

Figure 17-3. Interaction diagram for a cross section possessing tensile strength.

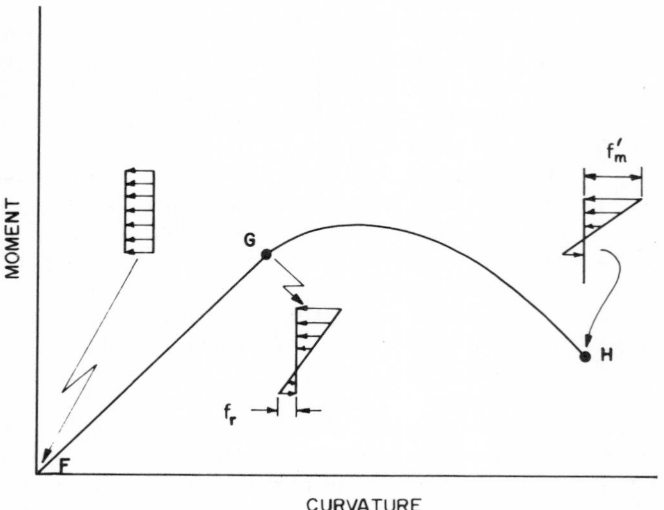

Figure 17-4. Development of moment with increasing curvature.

in this case the cracking moment exceeds the crushing moment, and the maximum moment exceeds both of these. Generally, the maximum-moment interaction diagram does not greatly exceed that which is developed by taking the larger of the cracking and crushing values of Figure 17-4. Thus, for ease and simplicity, the larger of these is taken for the remainder of this paper.

In the preceeding discussion, no consideration has been given to the secondary effects of slenderness or to boundary conditions. Thus, the interaction diagrams presented have, of necessity, been for the cross section without considering such effects. In addition to cross-section interaction diagrams it is also possible, by accounting for these additional affects, to construct interaction diagrams for wall systems. In developing the wall interaction diagrams presented here, the applied moments resulting from transverse force have been magnified for axial thrust effect by use of the expression:

$$M' = M \frac{1}{1 - \frac{P}{P_e}}$$

where

M' = magnified moment taking into account deflection
M = applied moment
P = axial thrust
P_e = Euler buckling load

This expression has been shown by Timoshenko[1] to be correct for ideal columns and has been shown by Spang[2] to yield reasonable values for reinforced-concrete columns. Since the walls reported in this paper were effectively pin-loaded at their upper end but were flat-ended at their lower end, an effective length coefficient K = 0.85 has been used in determining the Euler load.

Table 17-1
Brick Properties

Brick Designation	Compressive Strength psi	Modulus of Rupture psi	Initial Rate of Absorption, grams in 1-min	24 Hour Immersion %	5 Hour Boil %
A	14,480	848	6.2	3.3	5.1
B	20,660	761	2.6	2.7	3.3
S	17,560	741	19.8	7.6	10.5

The brick dimensions in inches are:

	Length	Width	Height
A	7.97	3.63	2.25
B	8.08	3.75	2.25
S	8.00	3.62	2.26

Materials

Three types of bricks were selected for this work, based on a small scale study reported elsewhere[3] and on the advice of the Structural Clay Products Institute. They were chosen to cover a reasonable range of compressive strengths and absorption rates that might be found in better quality brick in common use today. Their physical properties, determined in accordance with ASTM test method C-67, are tabulated in Table 17-1. The brick are described in greater detail elsewhere.[3]

Two mortars were selected for this study. The first was a typical masonry mortar; the second a mortar to which was added a commercially available polyvinylidene chloride* intended to produce high-bond strength. The first mortar was selected to indicate the performance of conventional masonry under interaction stresses; the second was selected to illustrate what can be accomplished in engineered masonry as better mortars become available, permitting a masonry structure to more fully utilize the inherent high strength of the individual brick. The conventional mortar contained 1 sack (94 lb) of Type I portland cement, 50 lb of lime, and 360 lb. of washed masonry sand. The cement and sand conformed to ASTM specifications C-150 and C-144 respectively. The high-bond mortar was mixed according to the additive manufacturer's specifications. Within these specifications, the mason selected a quantity of sand and of water to produce a mix with a workability which suited him. It contained one sack (94 lb) of Type I portland cement, 50 lb. of fine limestone, passing a No 200 sieve, 360 lb. of washed masonry sand, and four gallons of the liquid additive. Both mortars were mixed in a conventional barrel-type mixer with rotating blades. Retempering was permitted, but no mortar was used which was more than three hours old. The sand and cement for all batches of mortar came from the same source, respectively, and each was purchased as a single lot to minimize variability.

Walls were built and aged under ambient conditions in an air-conditioned structures laboratory. All were built by the

Figure 17-5. Test apparatus prior to installation of wall.

Figure 17-6. A 4 x 8 ft. wall panel in place for flexural testing under edge load.

same experienced mason using full bed joints and head joints. No furrowing of the bed joint was permitted. The mason was paid on an hourly basis and asked to emphasize quality rather than productivity. He averaged 750 to 800 brick per eight-hour day, including preparation and cleanup time. Both sides of the walls were finished with a struck joint. The walls were erected between 2 x 4 wooden frames braced in two planes, perpendicular to the floor. The courses of brick were laid to a horizontal line as in customary masonry practice. The bottom course of brick was imbedded in mortar laid in a suitable length of 6-in. steel channel to facilitate handling and placement in the testing machine.

Walls were transported and tested at 35 ± 1 days age as illustrated in Figures 17-5, 17-6, 17-7. Care was taken to avoid tensile or flexural stresses during handling. The walls were positioned with a forklift truck in a hydraulic testing machine of 600,000 pounds capacity. The steel channel in which the walls had been built rested on half-inch fiber board which in turn was supported by polished steel blocks on the machine platen. The bottom horizontal axis of the wall was positioned parallel to the overhead loading beam of the machine and centered directly under the centerline of this beam. Markings scribed in the steel platen facilitated this positioning. The vertical axis of the wall was then adjusted until perpendicular to the floor, assuring that the top horizontal centerline was parallel to and centered under the loading beam. A one-inch square steel bar, a two-inch steel plate, and a one-half-inch fiber board transmitted the load to the top of the wall.

For flexural loading, an air bag was held against one wall surface by a sheet of plywood suitably reinforced by a reaction frame. The air bag was wide enough to exert uniform pressure over the entire width of the wall (nominally four feet). The air bag was 84″ high and symmetrically positioned to the 82-1/2″ test span of the wall. The face of the wall opposite the air bag was restrained by upper and lower horizontal bars, 82-1/2″ apart. The bars were faced with quarter-inch resilient material and were supported by a mobile frame. As the bars were brought into contact with the wall, this frame was bolted at each corner to the frame supporting the air bag. The air bag was provided with an inlet tube connected to a hand-controlled compressed air supply; an outlet tube from the air bag was connected to a pressure transducer.

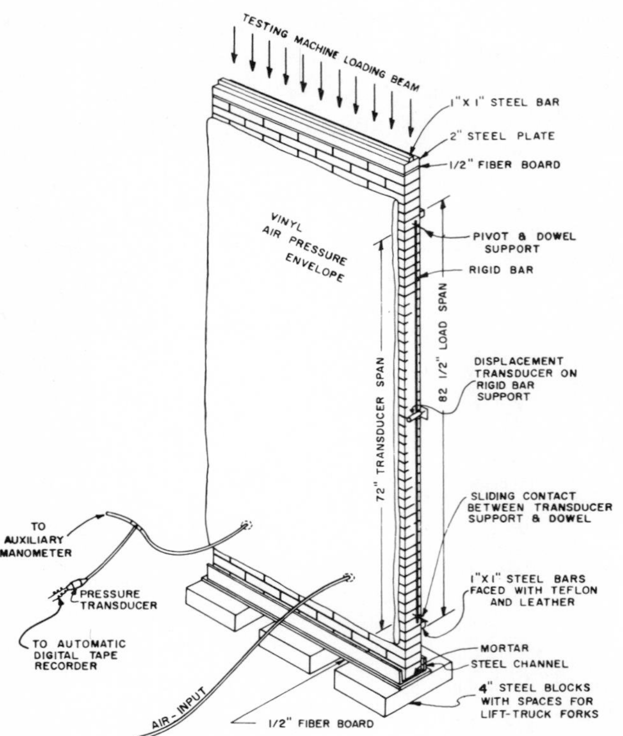

Figure 17-7. Schematic diagram of flexural test under edge load.

All walls tested in flexure or in combined compression and flexure were handled in this manner. Those tested in compression only were positioned in the machine similarly except that the fiber board at the top and bottom of the wall was replaced with plaster, grouted in place, and allowed to harden before testing. All compressive loads were applied at the rate of 60,000 pounds-per-minute; all flexural loading was applied at the rate of 0.30 to 0.35 psi of air-pressure-per-minute. The mortar used each day was sampled, air cured with the walls, and tested in compression at 35 ± 1 days according to ASTM test method C 91. The average compressive strength of the high-bond mortar was 7870 psi with a standard deviation of 515 psi for 39 specimens. The average compressive strength of the conventional mortar was 958 psi with a standard deviation of 49 psi for 12 specimens.

Instrumentation

Flexural deflection of the walls was measured with two variable inductance displacement transducers, calibrated to read increments of ± .0001", and recorded on an automatic multi-channel, data logging system. The transducers were attached in the following manner: A six-foot rigid rod was suspended along the edge of the wall from a dowel pivot just below the horizontal reaction bar at the top of the wall. The bottom of the rod was attached to another dowel so that it could slide vertically without lateral movement. The dowels were equidistant from the mid-span of the wall. Another rod was attached similarly on the opposite edge of the wall. The transducers were then clamped normal to the rods at the mid-span of the wall. A small aluminum plate with a tapped hole for the transducer's core was fastened to the wall face. The core was inserted into the transducer coil and then loosely threaded into the plate so that, when the wall began to deflect, the core did not bind when moving in or out of the transducer coil while measuring deflection. Figures 17-6 and 17-7 show a typical wall complete with instrumentation and ready for test.

The air-bag pressure was measured with a semi-conductor pressure transducer. This transducer's output provided a signal which was recorded along with the displacement transducer readings on automatic, data-recording equipment. A complete cycle of readings was recorded every five seconds. The printed tape output was converted to load/deflection plots for the full span by standard computer techniques. Due to space limitations, these data will not be presented in this paper.

Results

Data from the destructive testing of 39 walls appear in Table 17-2 and are plotted in terms of the flexural and compressive stresses in Figures 17-8 through 17-11. Each interaction diagrams indicates those combinations of flexural and compressive stresses which caused wall failure.

Using data computed from Table 17-2 and other known parameter values[3] listed in Table 17-3, theoretical curves of the type illustrated in Figure 17-3 were developed for each of the four systems studied in this work. These curves appear on the appropriate interaction diagrams.

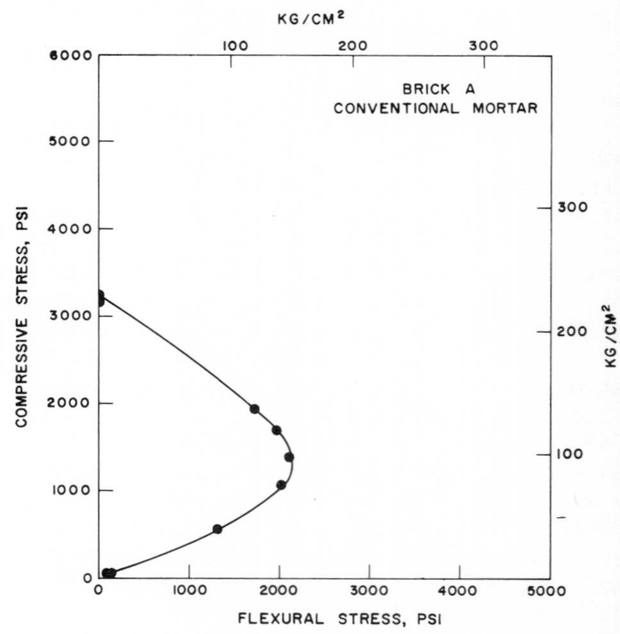

Figure 17-8. Interaction diagram for wall panels of brick A with conventional mortar.

Table 17-2
Test Results of Wall Specimens

Brick A $\frac{1}{m}$ conventional mortar

Edge-Load (psi)	Modulus of Rupture (psi)
0	80.6
0	77.5
559	1314
1119	2013
1398	2122
1678	1989
1957	1724
3161	Compressive failure
3217	Compressive failure

Brick A $\frac{1}{m}$ high-bond mortar

Edge-Load (psi)	Modulus of Rupture (psi)
0	359
0	360
560	1562
1118	2747
1398	2821
1678	2781
1957	2711
2237	3340
4755	Compressive failure
4911	Compressive failure

Brick B $\frac{1}{m}$ high-bond mortar

Edge-Load (psi)	Modulus of Rupture (psi)
0	376
0	474
854	2505
1707	4082
1707	3510
2187	3888
2667	3762
3200	4067
5108	Compressive failure
5226	Compressive failure

Brick S $\frac{1}{m}$ high-bond mortar

Edge-Load (psi)	Modulus of Rupture (psi)
0	225
0	212
781	1523
1228	2069
1618	2763
1953	2789
2232	2702
3348	2094
6122	Compressive failure
5959	Compressive failure

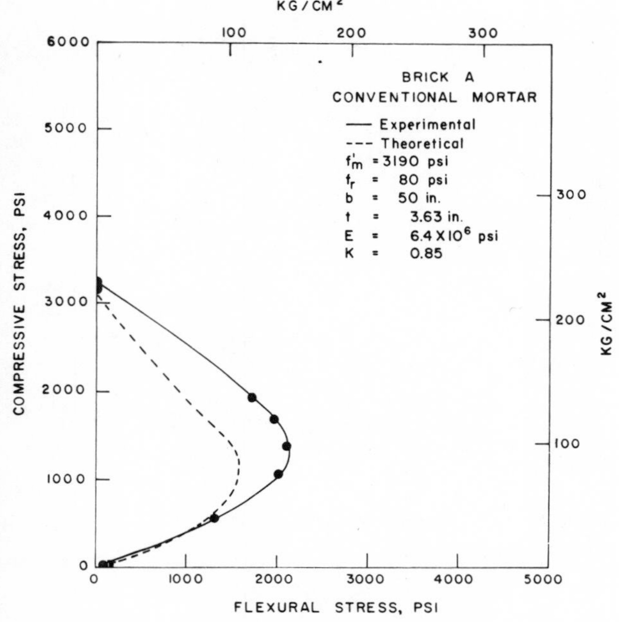

Figure 17-9. Interaction diagrams for wall panels of brick A with conventional mortar.

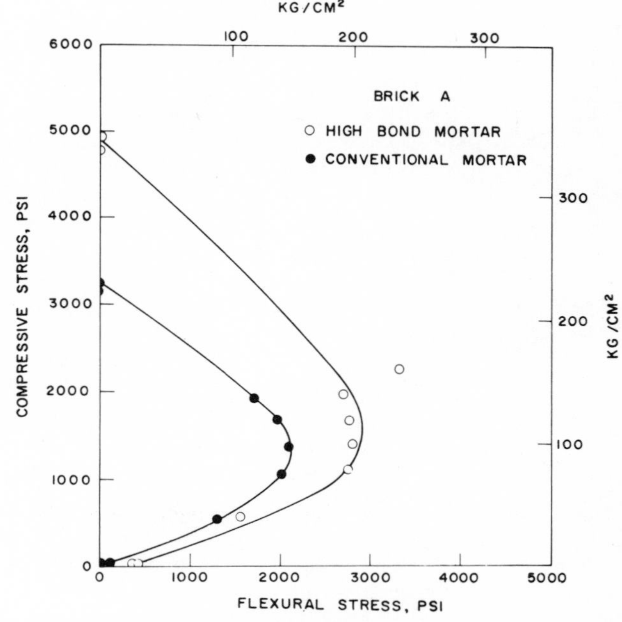

Figure 17-10. Interaction diagrams for wall panels of brick A with two mortars.

Discussion

Figure 17-8 indicates that a significant increase in the flexural strength of a masonry system due to applied edge-load may be anticipated, even when assuming working stresses as high as 40% of the ultimate compressive strength. Figure 17-9 shows that the theoretical curve fits the experimental data favorably, although somewhat on the conservative side. Nonetheless, the theoretical interaction diagram suggested here gives a much better approximation of actual masonry system performance than those diagrams which assume either no interaction or only negative effects due to interaction.

Figure 17-10 illustrates the effect of an improved mortar on the interaction diagram of wall panels built from brick A. The high-bond mortar yields more than a 50% increase in compressive strength and over a fourfold gain in flexural strength. Clearly, a much better structural performance can be obtained from these masonry systems by simply improving the mortar.

Edge-load, in part, affects flexural behavior in a manner similar to adhesion. It may be noted, particularly from Figure 17-10, that the relative improvement due to high-bond mortar is most striking at low edge loads or where no edge-load is

Table 17-3
Parameter Values

	Brick A Conventional Mortar	Brick A High-Bond Mortar	Brick B High-Bond Mortar	Brick S High-Bond Mortar
Masonry crushing strength, psi	3190	4830	5170	6100
Masonry modulus of rupture, psi	80	360	425	220
Test specimen width, in.	50	50	50	50
Test specimen thickness, in.	3.63	3.63	3.75	3.62
Effective length coefficient	0.85	0.85	0.85	0.85
Modulus of elasticity of wall, 10^6 psi	6.4	6.4	5.0	3.8

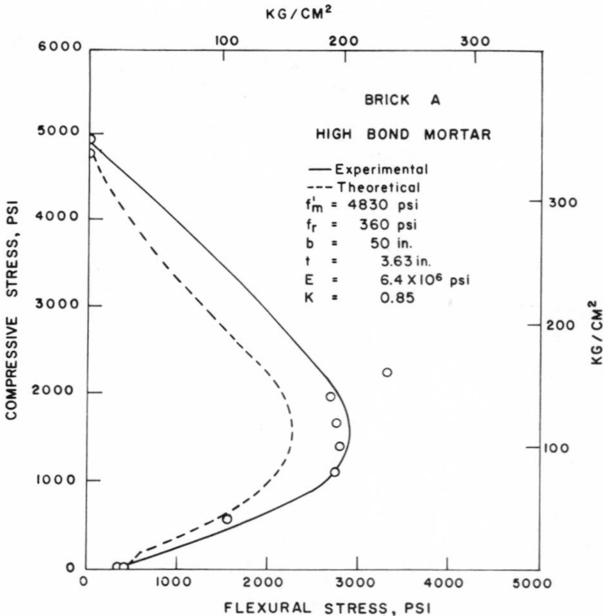

Figure 17-11. Interaction diagrams for wall panels of brick A with high bond mortar.

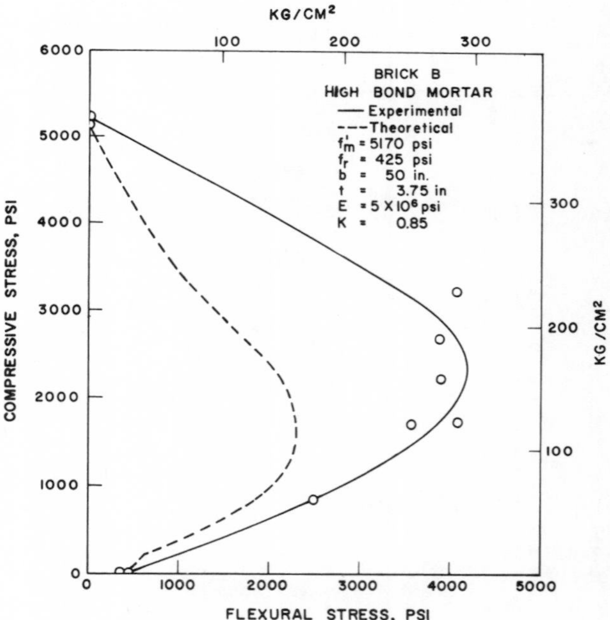

Figure 17-12. Interaction diagrams for wall panels of brick B with high bond mortar.

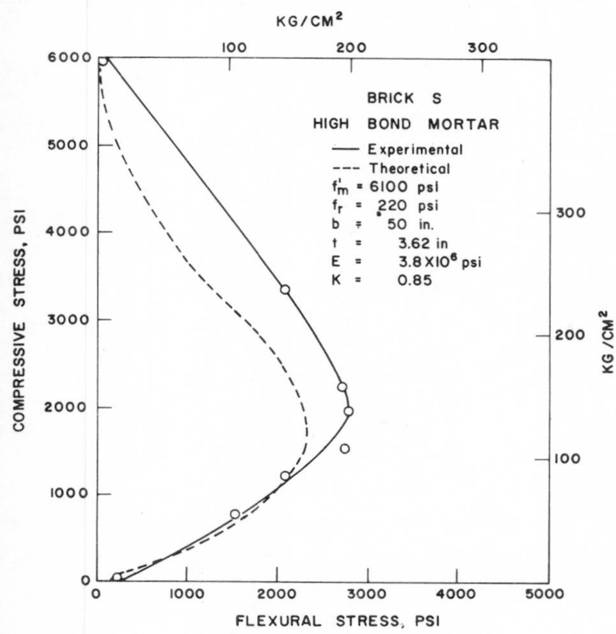

Figure 17-13. Interaction diagrams for wall panels of brick S with high bond mortar.

Figure 17-15. Typical failure at moderate edge load.

Figure 17-14. Typical failure at low edge load.

Figure 17-16. Typical failure at high edge load.

applied. However, even at high edge-loads, a substantial increase in flexural strength is experienced. Figures 17-11 through 17-13 illustrate the effect of edge-load on the flexural strength of wall panels which use the three bricks selected for this work bonded with high-bond mortar. These systems also exhibit a good correlation between the experimental data and their theoretical curves based on Equations 17-1, 17-2 and 17-3.

Figures 17-14 through 17-16 illustrate typical failures experienced in this work. At low edge, loads failure occurs by cracking on the tensile side of the wall (Figure 17-14). As edge load is increased, a point is reached where flexural failure is initiated by crushing the compressive side of the panel (Figure 17-15). At very high edge-loads the failure occurs by crushing, but forces are released explosively (Figure 17-16).

Summary

The results presented in Figures 17-9, 17-11, 17-12, and 17-13 show that the theoretical interaction curve can safely predict the combined effect of edge load and flexural load on the ultimate strength of clay masonry wall panels. Further, Table 17-2 illustrates that a notable increase in bond and compressive strength of these mortars can be used advantageously in the rational design of such wall panels.

Acknowledgement

The authors are indebted to Mr. James Raines for advice and assistance on data measurement and collection; to Mr. Harvey Shirley and Mr. Timothy Miles for assistance in physical testing, all of whom are members of the Structures Section, Building Research Division, IAT at the Bureau; and to Mr. Frank Rankin, a masonry contractor whose craftsmanship and cooperative spirit were a significant contribution to this work.

References

1. Timoshenko, S. P., and Gere, J. M., *Theory of Elastic Stability,* 2nd edition, 1961, McGraw Hill, Inc., New York City, pp. 15.
2. Spang, J. M., *Design Method for Long Reinforced Concrete Columns,* M. S. Thesis, University of Delaware, June 1966.
3. Grenley, D. G., *A Study of the Effect of Certain Modified Mortars on the Compressive and Flexural Strength of Clay Masonry,* Proceedings of International Conference on Masonry Structural Systems, University of Texas, Austin, Texas, November 1967.
4. Known as Sarabond®, manufactured and supplied for these tests by the Dow Chemical Company.

Remarks

By Sven Sahlin
Department of Civil Engineering, University of Illinois

The author's excellent paper can be supplemented by some theoretical solutions of interacting axial and lateral loads on walls with large height-to-thickness ratios.

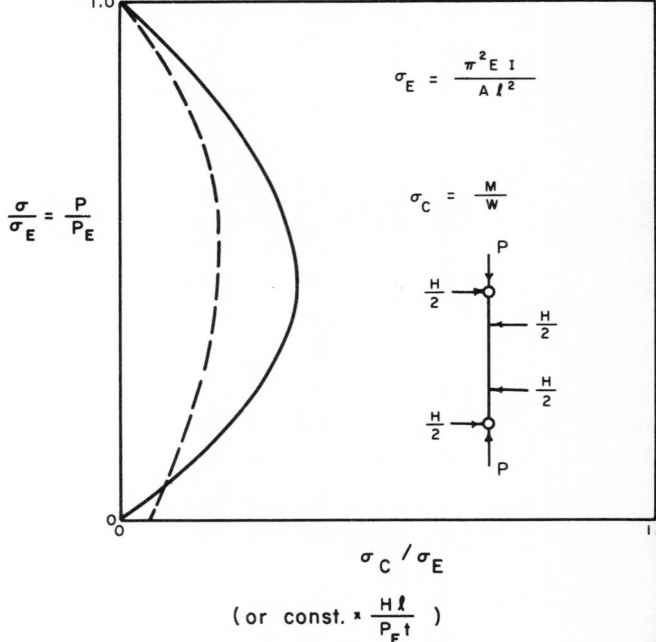

Figure 17-A.

For slender walls, when crushing is not imminent, th lateral instability load for varying normal force has bee computed, from the differential equation, for a wall having n tensile strength, loaded as shown in Figure 17-1b and with th stress distribution as in Figure 17-1d. The cracking load for wall with known tensile strength, and with the same bucklin load as the wall described above, has also been computed an compared with the instability load for a wall without tensil strength. See "Transversely Loaded Compression Membe Made of Material Having No Tensile Strength." by Sahlir IABSE Vol. 21, p. 243, Zurich 1961.

The results are presented as the lateral load times th slenderness of the wall divided by the Euler buckling loa ($Hl/P_E t$) as a function of the ratio of axial load to the Eul buckling load (P/P_E). The results obtained for 3rd poi loading directly converts tc an interaction diagram of the typ shown in Figure 17-A.

It is interesting to note that Point B (Figure 17-3) moves t the end point $P/P_E = 1$ when the wall is slender. It can also b noted that for low axial forces the moment capacity of th wall is governed by the tensile stress, while for higher axi forces the moment capacity is governed by a stability criteri For high tensile strengths the calculation of the momer capacity of the wall becomes a stress problem for all axi loads except for $P = P_E$.

Recently the case with uniform lateral load and arbitraril chosen eccentricities of the axial load has been solve theoretically by Hellers: "Eccentrically Compressed Colum Without Tensile Strength Subjected to Uniformly Distribute Lateral Loads", Report No. 35/67 från Byggforskninge Stockholm, 1967 (also as a Lic. Thesis at Roy. Inst. of Techn Stockholm 1966).

18. Load capacity of brick masonry.

Prof. P. Haller, EMPA, Swiss Federal Laboratories for Testing Materials and Research, Bern, Switzerland

Introduction

The present report is the outcome of a long series of investigations at the Swiss Federal Institute for Testing Materials and Research in Dübendorf, conducted over 20 years mainly for the brick industry. Results of tests on masonry structures have yielded a better understanding of the interaction between masonry brick and mortar and have been utilized by the brick industry. They have succeeded in manufacturing bricks that are truer to size, less absorptive, and having higher compressive strength. This development then made possible the construction of buildings up to 18 storeys high and of 16-storey buildings with bearing walls measuring 5-7/8" in thickness Figure 18-1 [5,6]. Knowledge acquired in the laboratory, on the one hand, and considerable experience in high-rise construction, on the other, led to the formulation of "SIA-Standards 113 for the Calculation and Construction of Masonry Made from Artificial and Natural Stone", which has been in effect since 1964.

The following report relates the development of brick masonry in Switzerland. It also contains results of shear tests on brick masonry still in progress.

The Two-Material System of Masonry

Masonry erected with mortars composed of inorganic bonding agents (Portland cement, hydraulic lime) possesses a property which must be taken into account when evaluating its bearing capacity. It cannot sustain tensile stresses perpendicular to the course joints. The tensile strength is small to begin with and is further reduced by the uneven shrinkage of the mortar layer from the outside towards the inside, resulting in a separation of the contact layer between brick and mortar or in crack formation in the mortar. The test results agree well with theoretical derivations if the tensile strength is neglected.

Masonry should therefore be loaded centrically and perpendicularly to the course joints whenever possible, for only then can optimal utilization be achieved.

Eccentric loadings can hardly be avoided, however. Thus, bending of floors that are imposed on walls causes displace-

Figure 18-1. High-rise apartment house in Biel, constructed in 1959/61 in brick masonry.

Internal Masonry (bearing):	*5-7/8" (15 cm)*
Outside masonry:	
Inner wythe (bearing):	*5-7/8" (15 cm)*
Insulation layer: mineral wool slabs	*1-1/2" (3 cm)*
Outer wythe: (self-supporting) with stucco	*4-3/4" (12 cm)*
Floors: reinforced concrete	*6-3/4" (17 cm)*

ment in wall loading. The effect of eccentric loadings on the bearing capacity of walls, varying from thick walls to the thin walls used nowadays, has been intensively investigated. This has led to a better understanding of properties responsible for failure of brick and of mutual interactions between brick and mortar when joined to form masonry.

Loading a stout masonry structure results in compaction of both the masonry brick and the mortar, accompanied by a transverse elongation of both elements. If the elongation of the mortar is inherently greater than that of the brick, then the latter will become subject to a transverse tensile stress, since no displacement between the two is possible across the area of contact. Thus, both will suffer the same transverse deformation:

$$q\epsilon_m = q\epsilon_s$$

where:

$q\epsilon_m$ = transverse deformation of the mortar
$q\epsilon_s$ = transverse deformation of the brick

If no external forces are acting normal to the line of pressure one must have the relation:

$$q\sigma_m \cdot F_m - q\sigma_s \cdot F_s = 0$$

where:

$q\sigma_m$ = transverse stress in the mortar
$q\sigma_s$ = transverse stress in the brick
F_s, F_m = cross-sections of brick and mortar respectively parallel to the line of pressure

If $q\epsilon_m > q\epsilon_s$, tensile stresses will appear in the brick and compressive stresses will occur in the mortar. Tensile stresses in the brick increase with increasing thickness of mortar layer, with increasing void fraction in the brick, i.e. with decreasing cross-section offering resistance, and with increasing difference between transverse elongation of brick and mortar.

On the basis of this one can draw the following conclusions:

1. course joints should not be thick,
2. small transverse elongation of the mortar, i.e. high strength,
3. no excessively large perforations in the brick,
4. no cracks in the brick,
5. high tensile strength of the brick,
6. the ratio h_s/h_m to be as high as possible, i.e. tall bricks.

These remarks are valid because the strength of masonry is generally very much smaller than the compressive strength of bricks, and because bricks tend to split open parallel to the direction of pressure.

These transverse tensile stresses are most pronounced above the vertical joints in the cross section, as indicated by the fact that even natural stones will develop cracks above the vertical joints.

The number of headers and the bonding-in length play a decisive role in determining the bearing capacity of bonded, multiple-wythe masonry, where headers have to assure the

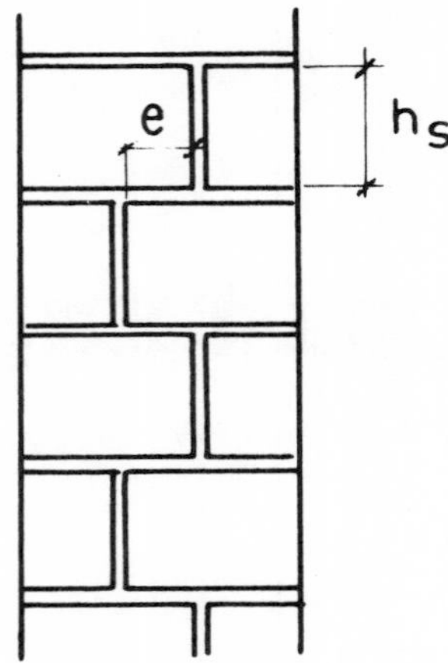

Figure 18-2. Bonded masonry structure bonding-in coefficien e/h_s where e = bonding-in length, h_s = height of brick.

firm joining of masonry components in the cross sectio perpendicular to the wall, Figure 18-2. The bonding-i coefficient e/h_s must not fall below 0.44.

Thick, single wythe masonry, containing only headers, ha greater strength than bonded, multiple-wythe masonry.

Bonding-in along the wall is indispensible if bending an tensile stresses are to be transmitted toward the course joint (wind), if the masonry is subjected to locally concentrate loads, or if angle-shaped walls must act as a single unit.

Theoretical Treatment and Its Agreement with Test Results

Tests to determine the bearing capacity of experimenta brick walls are conducted to understand the factors affectin the properties of brick and mortar to define the permissibl loading, and to yield basic calculational methods for appl cation to brick walls of arbitrary height, subjected to the usua range of eccentric equilateral or crossed loadings. This goal i reached if the relevant factors are related in such manner tha calculated and experimental load capacities are in agreement

As a first step, it is necessary to demonstrate the validity o Bernoulli's hypothesis: cross sections normal to the axis of th wall stay plane after load deformation. Results of tests on a eccentrically loaded brick wall measuring 38 cm in thicknes conclusively prove this assumption, Figure 18-3[2].

Information concerning the relation between stress an resulting deformation is obtained from the stress-strain dia gram.

This relation between stress and strain can be derived fror the measured deformation of a thick masonry structure o typical construction under centric loading in a power press.

Whether the relation between stress and deformatio derived thusly may be used to calculate bearing capacities o walls having different dimensions, including the bucklin region, will be discussed here.

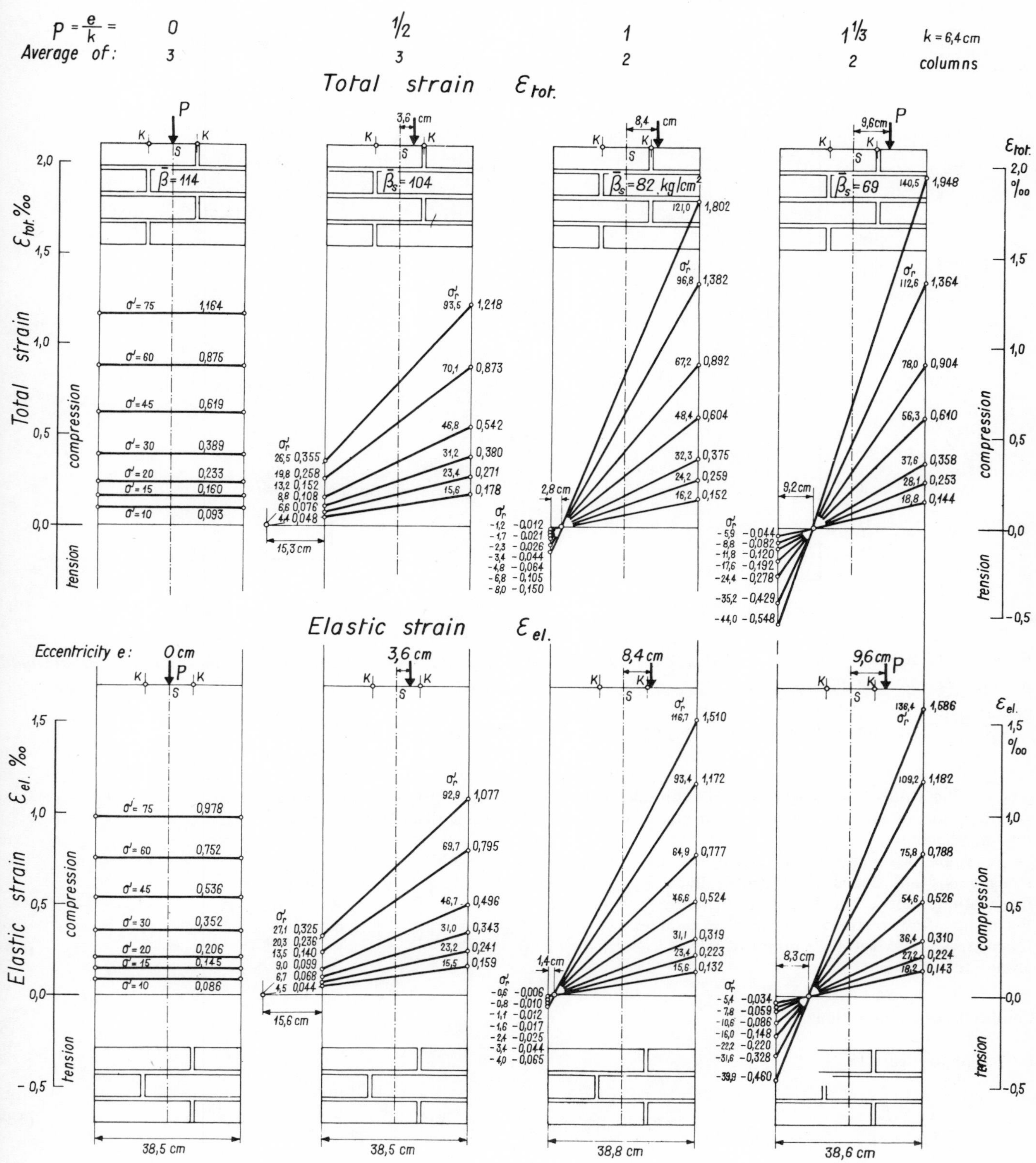

Figure 18-3. Brick pier 15″ x 20″, buckling length 11′2″, knife edge supports. Loading: near-centric, eccentric with e = 1-1/2″, 3-1/3″, and 3-3/4″, measured total and elastic deformations.

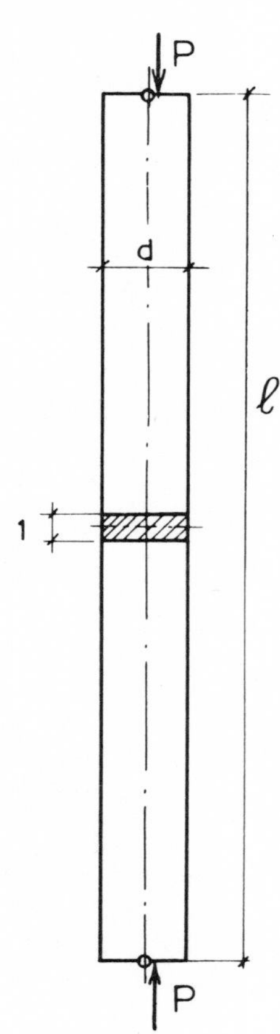

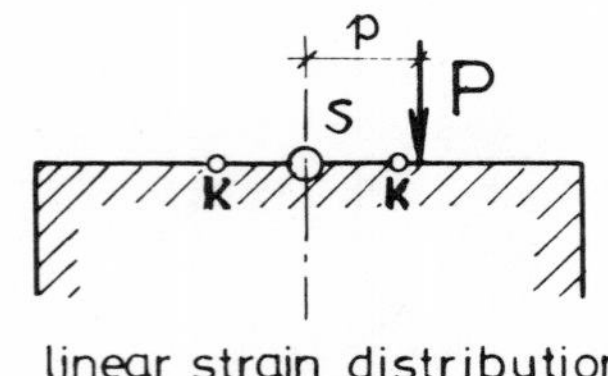

linear strain distribution
(Navier — Bernoulli)

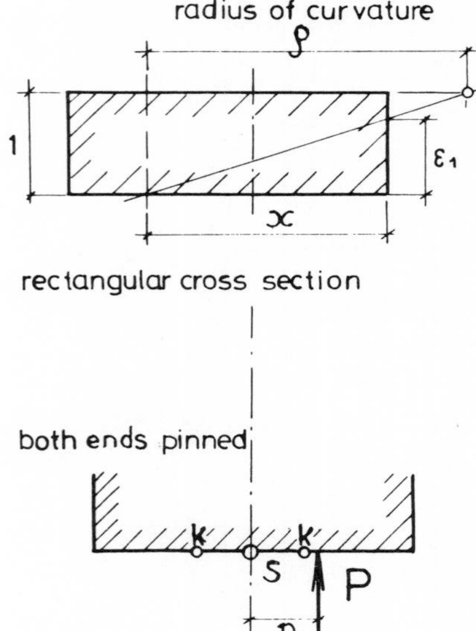

Figure 18-4a. Masonry structure loaded eccentrically. Section at middle height.

Figure 18-4b. Deformation of the element cut at midd. height.

Figure 18-4. (Above and next page). Second order stress problem and stability state.

Only the stress-strain diagram will be considered to be at our disposal up to the failure point of a representative masonry structure.

A completely homogeneous structure, having a perfectly straight axis and loaded 100% centrically, exists only in the imagination; centric buckling must therefore be relegated to the realm of abstractions. Centric buckling does not occur in practice; hence, a certain amount of initial eccentricity must always be considered.

Conditions of Deformation

According to Figure 18-4b:

$$\frac{1}{\varsigma} = \frac{\epsilon_1}{x} \qquad \text{(Bernoulli) (18-1)}$$

$$\frac{1}{\varsigma} = \frac{y''}{(1 + y')} \approx y'' \qquad (18\text{-}2)$$

Assumption of sufficient accuracy: the deformed axis assume a sine shape. Figure 18-5.

$$y = f \cdot \sin\frac{\pi}{1} u$$

$$y' = \frac{\pi}{1} \cdot f \cdot \cos\frac{\pi}{1} u \qquad (18\text{-}$$

$$y'' = -\frac{\pi^2}{1^2} \cdot f \cdot \sin\frac{\pi}{1} \cdot u = -\frac{\pi^2}{1^2} \cdot y$$

$$u = \frac{1}{2} : \; y = f \qquad (18\text{-}$$

$$y'' = \frac{\pi^2}{1^2} \cdot f \qquad (18\text{-}$$

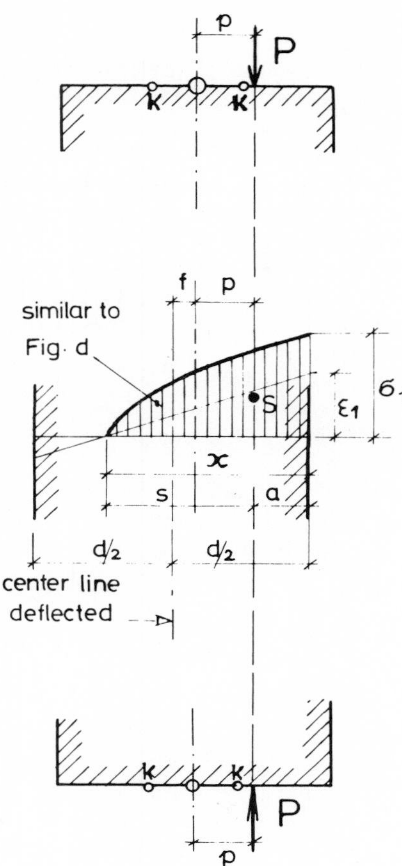

Figure 18-4c. Plane of deformation and stress distribution when the neutral axis lies inside the cross section (load outside of kern).

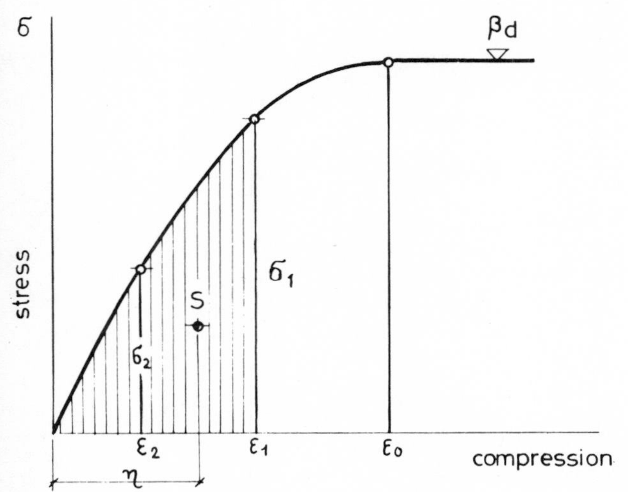

Figure 18-4d. Stress-strain diagram up to the compressive strength for a small masonry structure made up of at least 5 layers of brick loaded as near-centrically as possible. $\epsilon > \epsilon_o : \sigma = \beta d$.

From Equations 18-1, 18-2, and 18-5 it follows that:

$$y^{11} = \frac{\epsilon_1}{x} = \frac{\pi^2}{l^2} f$$

$$f = \frac{\epsilon_1}{x} \frac{l^2}{\pi^2} \qquad (18\text{-}6)$$

Equilibrium Conditions

At equilibrium the force P must pass through the center of gravity of the area of stress (derivation for $x < d$). According to Figure 18-4c:

$$a = x - s = \frac{d}{2} - p - f \qquad (18\text{-}7)$$

$$a = x \cdot (1 - g) \qquad (18\text{-}8)$$

where:

$$s = g \cdot x$$
$$g = 1/3 \text{ to } 1/2$$

The following expression for the bearing capacity may be derived from the two conditions:

Using Equation (18-6):

$$x(1 - g) = \frac{d}{2} - p - \frac{l^2}{\pi^2} \cdot \frac{\epsilon_1}{x} \qquad (18\text{-}9)$$

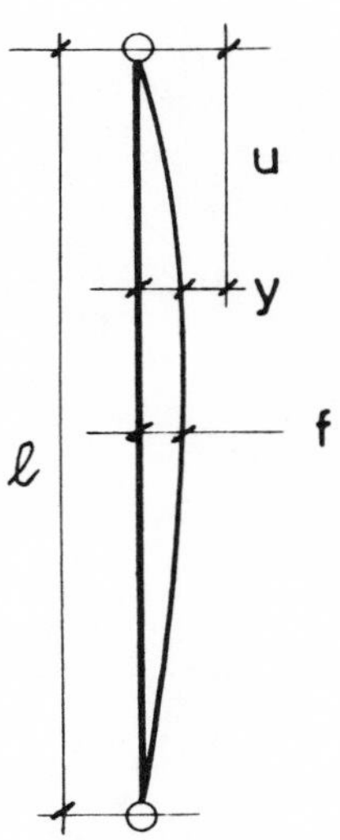

Figure 18-5. Line of flexure of a masonry structure, hinged supports both ends. Largest deflection f.

$$x^2 (1 - g) - x\left(\frac{d}{2} - p\right) + \frac{l^2 \cdot \epsilon_1}{\pi^2} = O \qquad (18\text{-}9a)$$

$$x = \frac{1}{2} \cdot \frac{\frac{d}{2} - p}{1 - g} + \sqrt{\frac{1}{4}\left(\frac{\frac{d}{2} - p}{1 - g}\right)^2 - \frac{\epsilon_1 \cdot l^2}{(1 - g) \cdot \pi^2}} \qquad (18\text{-}10)$$

$$\frac{x}{d} = \frac{1}{4 \cdot (1 - g)} \cdot \left[A + \sqrt{A^2 - B \cdot \epsilon_1 \cdot (1 - g)}\right] \qquad (18\text{-}10a)$$

where:

$$A = 1 - \frac{m}{3} \quad m = \frac{p}{k} = \frac{6p}{d} \qquad \text{[rectangle]}$$

$$B = \frac{16}{\pi^2} \cdot \left(\frac{l}{d}\right)^2$$

If the load acts on a point inside the kern, i.e., if the neutral axis lies outside the cross-section ($x > d$), Equation 18-14, Figure 18-6 must be satisfied in addition to Equation 18-10 by choosing an ϵ_2 appropriate to the value of ϵ_1.

The value of x decreases with increasing ϵ_1, i.e. f increases rapidly according to Equation 18-6.

Known quantities are: d, p, l

The variables are: ϵ_1 and g

g for every value of ϵ_1 can be taken from the stress-strain diagram shown in Figure 18-4d:

$$\frac{s}{x} = \frac{\eta}{\epsilon_1} = \frac{g \cdot x}{x}$$

$$g = \frac{\eta}{\epsilon_1}$$

$$1 - g = 1 - \frac{\eta}{\epsilon_1} = \frac{\epsilon_1 - \eta}{\epsilon_1} \qquad (18\text{-}11)$$

$$P = \bar{\sigma} \cdot d \cdot 1 = \frac{F'}{\epsilon_1} \cdot x \cdot 1 \qquad (18\text{-}12)$$

$$\boxed{\bar{\sigma} = \frac{P}{F} = \frac{F'}{\epsilon_1} \cdot \frac{x}{d}} \qquad (18\text{-}13)$$

where:

$\bar{\sigma}$ = mean stress

η resp. g is taken from the stress-strain diagram for different values of ϵ_1. The distance x of the neutral axis and $\bar{\sigma}$ can be calculated. Figure 18-7 shows $\bar{\sigma}$ in function of the ϵ_1-values.

The largest mean stress, $\bar{\sigma}_{max.}$, and the greatest bearing capacity $P_{max.}$, is reached at the highest point of the curve. For still larger values of ϵ_1, or for larger deformations, equilibrium can be maintained only under reduced loads. No equilibrium is possible if the strain ϵ_1 exceeds ϵ_1''.

If the neutral axis lies outside of the cross section, the chosen values of ϵ_1 and ϵ_2 must satisfy Equations 18-10 and 18-14. The computed mean stresses $\bar{\sigma}$ are shown in Figure 18-8 as a function of ϵ_1 and ϵ_2.

If ϵ'_1 is larger than ϵ_o ($\sigma = \beta_d$) one has a strength problem (1st or 2nd order stress problem). If, however, ϵ'_1 is smaller than ϵ_o one is dealing with a stability problem, namely the buckling problem.

The structure now becomes unstable before reaching its compressive strength at the extreme fiber.

When $\epsilon'_1 \geqq \epsilon_o$ one is dealing with a strength problem where the extreme fiber reaches compressive strength (Figure 18-9).

We are dealing with a stability problem if ϵ'_1 is smaller than ϵ_o.

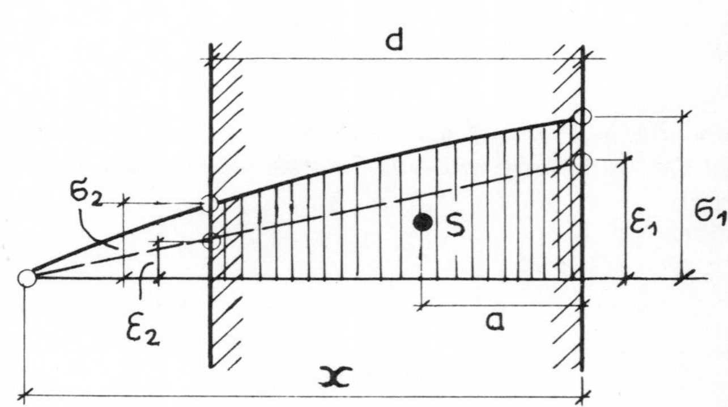

$$\frac{\varepsilon_1}{\varepsilon_2} = \frac{x}{x - d} \qquad \varepsilon_2 = \varepsilon_1 \frac{x - d}{x}$$

$$\boxed{x = \varepsilon_1 \frac{d}{\varepsilon_1 - \varepsilon_2}} \quad (14)$$

Figure 18-6. Flexure plane and stress distribution of the median section when the neutral axis lies outside the cross section. At equilibrium, the external load must pass through the center of gravity of the stress area.

Figure 18-10 shows curves for various slenderness ratios and coefficients of eccentricity calculated for a given quality of brick masonry by the method outlined. Also entered in the same drawing are experimental points for the masonry whose stress-strain diagram was used in computing the curves.

A comparison of this curve with the test results allows the following conclusions to be drawn:

1. The calculational method developed in the preceding section, based on an experimentally determined stress-strain diagram, yields results in practically perfect agreement with experimental values both in the strength region and in the stability range.

Load was applied via knife edge supports top and bottom. This arrangement allowed the scatter of experimental points to be kept small, especially in eccentrically loaded test walls. At near concentric loading, small inaccuracies in centering and deviations of the axis from the line connecting the contact lines of the two knife edges become noticeable, sometimes more strongly and sometimes less so.

2. Masonry with inorganic bonding agents cannot sustain any significant tensile stress perpendicular to the course joints. This is demonstrated by the good agreement between curves and test values, especially for greater eccentricities of the point of load application.

3. The assumption on which the derivation was based, namely that the axis of deformation has a sine shape, has been proven.

4. Only the curve with an eccentricity of p ′= l/1000 agrees with the experiment. This proves that one must always consider the lack of straightness of the wall axis.

5. The bearing strength of masonry without tensile stresses decreases rapidly with increasing eccentricity.

6. The transition from the strength region to the stability region is continuous, as expected. For increasing eccentricities, the test structure will enter the buckling region at smaller slenderness ratios.

7. Euler's buckling equation, assuming proportionality of stress and strain, yields values lying far beyond the practical range, Figure 18-10.

Is it possible to replace the stress-strain diagram by a curve of similar shape, for instance by a parabola having the same value of ϵ_o?

Figure 18-11 shows a comparison between the real curve and a parabolic σ-ϵ-curve. Computed $\bar{\sigma}$-values based on the latter are up to 90% higher for higher slenderness ratios and greater eccentricities.

Hence, the question must be answered negatively. This calculational procedure, utilizing the stress-strain diagram

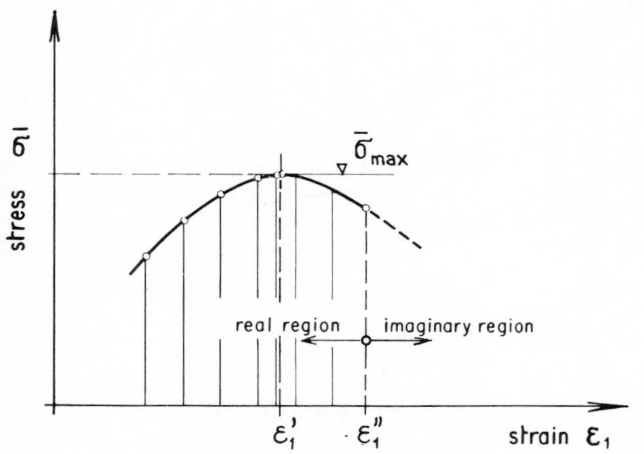

Figure 18-7. Representation of average stresses for various assumed values of ϵ_1 ($x < d$). The highest point on the curve corresponds to the buckling stress $\bar{\sigma}_{max}$.

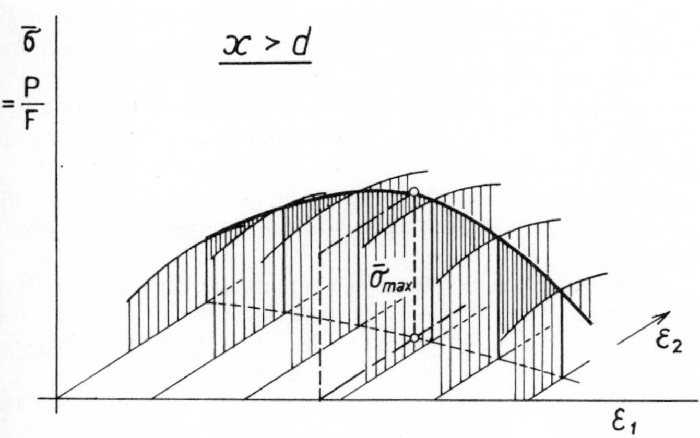

Figure 18-8. Representation of mean stresses for ϵ_1 and ϵ_2 satisfying Equations 18-10 and 18-14. Plane through the highest point and parallel to the $\epsilon_1 - \epsilon_2$ plane gives value $\bar{\sigma}_{max}$ in the strength or buckling region.

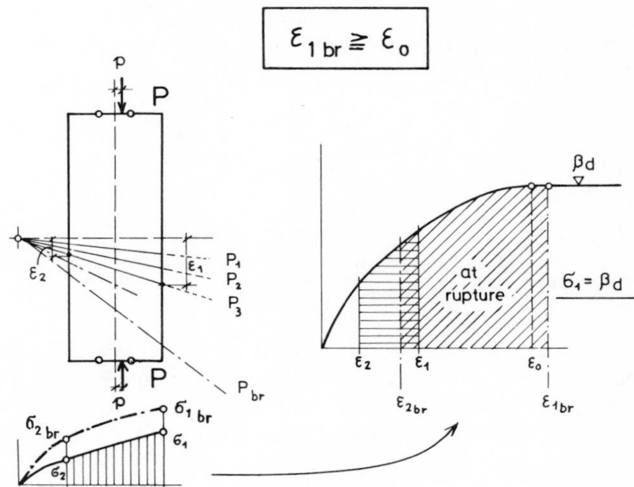

Figure 18-9. Stout masonry structure showing planes of deformation. 1st order stress problem (without bulging). Stress distribution taken from stress-strain diagram.

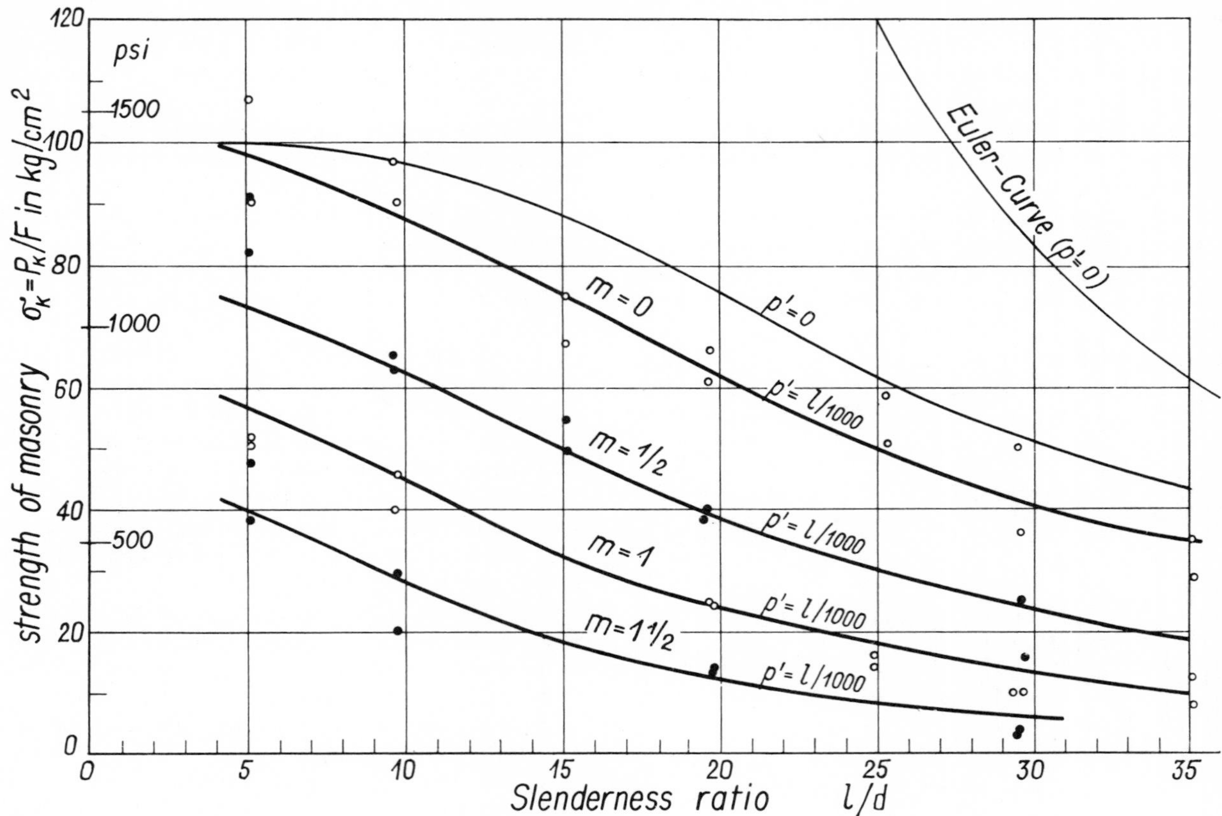

Figure 18-10. Bearing capacity of 12 cm brick masonry. Slightly absorptive bricks 5.3" high with round perforations. Mean compressive strength of unit 4'110 psi. Cement lime mortar: Compressive strength after 29 days: = 410 psi. Width 31", knife edge supports. Curves calculated theoretically from the stress-strain diagram. p' = estimated initial eccentricity.

obtained from experiments with a small masonry structure, goes over into Euler's buckling formula if the actual σ-ϵ-diagram is replaced by Hooke's law of proportionality between stress and strain:

$$\overline{\sigma} = \frac{E \cdot \pi^2}{12(lk/_d)^2} = \frac{E \cdot \pi^2}{(l/_i)^2}$$

where:
i = radius of gyration
E = modulus of elasticity

In this case, eccentrically loaded structures will not buckle but will be crushed due to attaining their compressive strength (bending). Hence, buckling may be expected to occur only when the stress-strain diagram is non-linear.

The Effect of Properties and Peculiarities of Masonry Brick and Mortar on the Bearing Capacity of Masonry

1. In the strength region, it is the resistance to transverse tensile stress which plays the decisive role in determining the bearing capacity of masonry. Large-size perforations, such as hand holes, can reduce the cross section for transverse tension to an extent which seriously diminishes the bearing strength of masonry. The bearing capacity of stout structures can even be reduced to that of slender masonry structures, where transverse tensile strength is not the determining feature.

This property gradually loses importance as the slenderness ratio increases, while the deformability of the brick gains correspondingly greater influence on the bearing capacity.

2. The larger the compressive strength of the brick, the larger also is its deformation resistance. The same is true of mortar.

It is found that bulging is the greater and bearing capacity is the smaller when the total deformation of brick and mortar is larger, i.e., the more gradual is the rise in stress with growing deformation in the stress-strain diagram.

3. Good trueness to size, i.e., small deviations from the mean of the dimensions of individual bricks, and small deviations of the mean from the rated value not only has a decisive influence on the performance of the mason, but also has a beneficial effect on the bearing capacity of brick. Bricks showing deviations from rectangularity are inconvenient to use (deviation of the body axis from a straight line).[8]

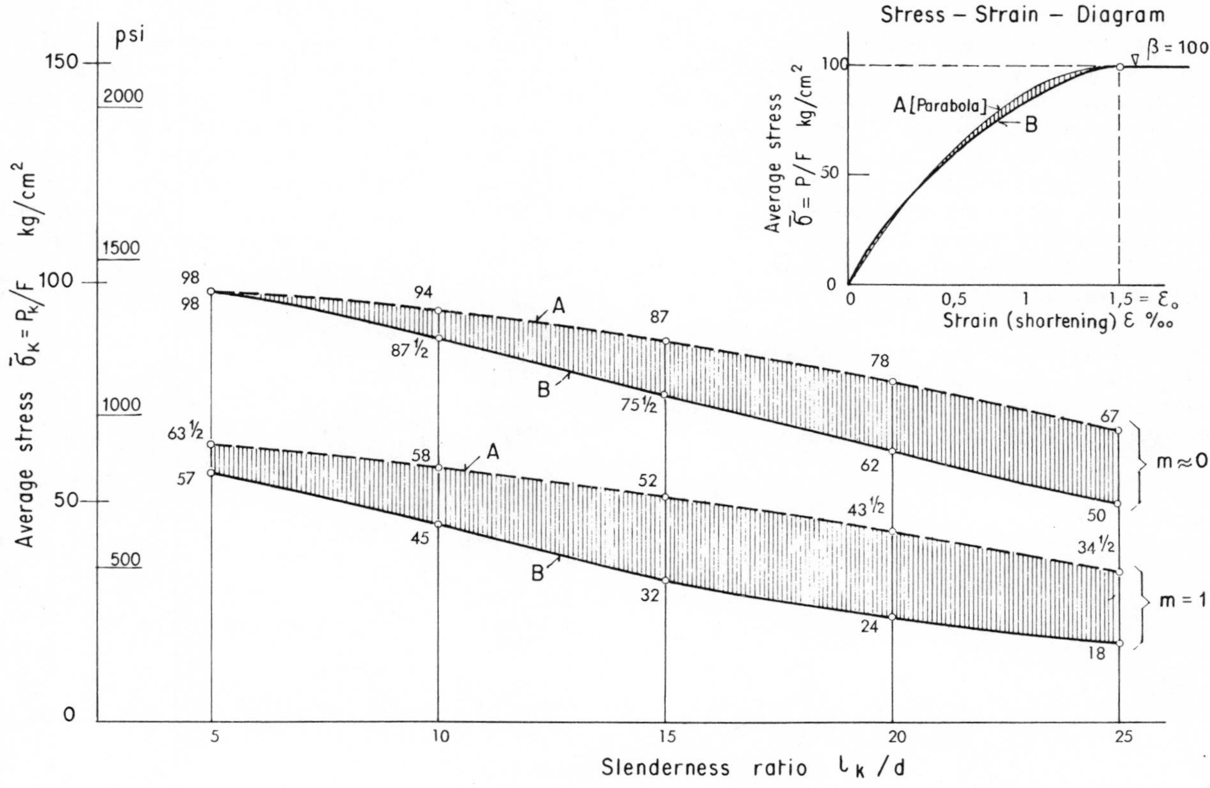

Figure 18-11. Comparison of calculated bearing capacity of brick walls using the stress-strain diagram obtained from deformation tests with that determined from the parabolic stress-strain diagram. Wall thickness: 4-3/4", lime cement mortar, eccentricity of load (equilateral) p' = l/1000 = 0.13". Slightly absorptive brick.

4. Thick-bond multiple-wythe masonry exhibits lower bearing capacity than single-wythe masonry, because it is weakened as a consequence of containing fewer headers. Following SIA-standards 113, half the bricks must be laid as headers.

The cross section for transverse tension diminishes in importance with growing slenderness ratio, while the capacity for deformation (bulging) gains correspondingly increasing influence on the bearing strength of the masonry. The purpose of headers in slender structures is to generate sufficient shear resistance to prevent displacement of masonry components relative to each other.

5. High suction masonry bricks withdraw from the mortar an excessive amount of water needed for the full development of its bonding strength. For this reason, slender walls of thickness d less than 10" tend to bulge more strongly.

In addition, the newly applied mortar loses elasticity. Dewatering renders the mortar plastic so that it is deformed when the upper section of the masonry moves back and forth during laying (wobble effect). The layer of mortar is squeezed out and gaps develop between brick and mortar. (Figure 18-12)

These gaps promote bulging of walls and piers to such an extent, especially under eccentric loading, that the bearing

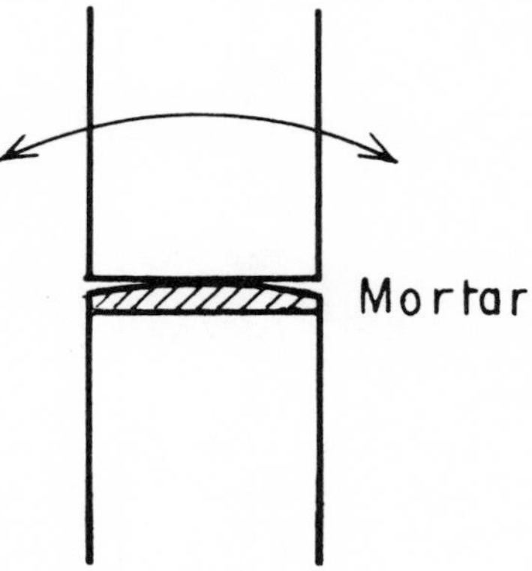

Figure 18-12. Highly absorptive bricks dewater the mortar in the joints to such a degree that it will lose its elasticity. The mortar remains plastically deformable only, and is rounded off during building by the back-and-forth movement of the unit above, giving rise to gaps.

strength of the masonry is reduced nearly to zero (Figure 18-13.[7] Because of this, it is imperative to take the initial rate of absorptivity of masonry brick into account when judging the quality of bricks. Deformation measurements on small samples of masonry are insensitive to the wobble effect. Hence tests performed with piers of storey height, built from strongly absorbent bricks, are indispensable. Conclusions reached in the preceding paragraphs can therefore be extended to strongly absorbent bricks in slender walls.

Cement mortars are more sensitive to dewatering than cement lime mortars, so that use of cement mortar together with high suction bricks, where s $>$ 100 g/min 30 sq. in., will not lead to any appreciable increase in bearing capacity.

6. Shrinkage of the mortar from the outside towards the inside likewise produces gaps which increase the bulging effect of slender walls. This leads to a corresponding reduction in bearing strength, at least temporarily, i.e., until the mortar has dried out completely to the level of moisture equilibrium.

The quality of brick and mortar are not the only factors influencing the bearing capacity of masonry. It also depends to an important extent on the manner in which the masonry is put together, i.e., on the mason's professional qualifications.

7. Transverse tension and tensile stress in bricks forming part of stout masonry increase with increasing thickness of joints. The thicker and softer layer of mortar leads to greater bulging in slender structures, resulting in a falling-off of bearing capacity of the masonry. SIA-standards 113 [1] limits the joint thickness as follows:

MS (Special Quality)	:	3/8" – 5/8",
MH (High Quality)	:	3/10" – 5/8",
MN (Normal Quality)	:	3/10" – 3/4".

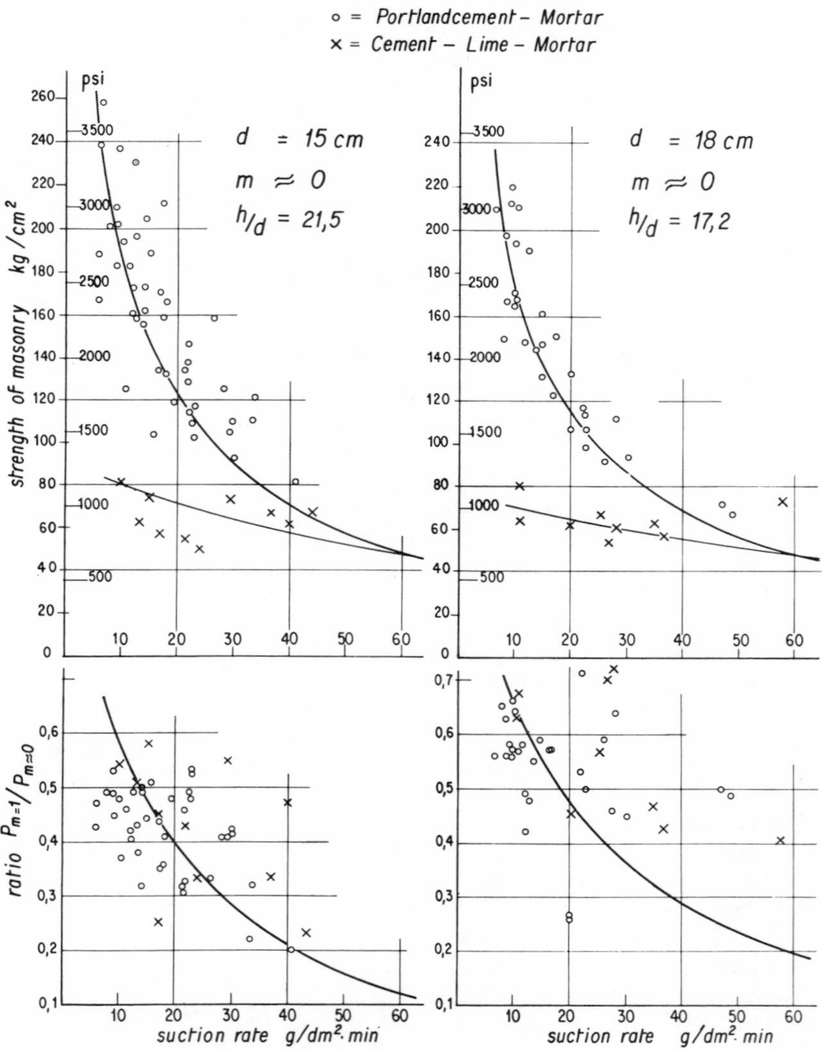

Figure 18-13. Masonry made of bricks from various brickworks. Wall thickness: 5-7/8" and 7-1/10". Cement mortar and lime cement mortar. Bearing strength as a function of absorptive capacity of bricks in g/min dm^2 (g/min. 30 sq. in. = 1,94 g/min dm^2). Loading: Centric and at kern edge. (The large scatter is due to differences in brick strength, perforations, etc.)

8. Clearly, masonry should be erected with an axis that is as straight and as vertical as possible, to keep the initial eccentricity which tends to diminish the bearing strength to a minimum. Only highly qualified masons should erect heavily loaded masonry.

According to SIA-standards 113[1] the following deviations of masonry structures are tolerated (measurement distance: 8 ft.):

Deviation of the axis from a straight line and deviation of the latter from the vertical:

MS (Special Quality) : 0.12″
MH (High Quality) : 0.16″
MN (Normal Quality) : 0.24″

Allowable Compressive Stresses

The admissible stresses are average stresses, obtained from tests on piers having a slenderness ratio of $l_k/d=8$ and a buckling length of approximately 10 ft., loaded nearly concentrically as well as eccentrically at the kern edge (m=1).

The brick manufacturer must guarantee the masonry strength as specified in SIA standards 113. Figure 18-14[1]. This is a supplementary guarantee given by the brick producer. It is necessary, however, because it is impossible to include in the standards all formats and perforations as well as all masonry bonding agents for bricks newly appearing on the market, including those made of other materials.

The allowable average stress can be determined by dividing the masonry strength by the safety factor. The choice of safety factor for a given building material must take into account; i.e., uncertainties in static calculations (Hooke's assumption), unavoidable scatter both in dimensions and material properties, inaccuracies in the laying of units (departure of the wall axis from rectilinearity and from the vertical), and deformation under permanent loads (shrinkage and creep).

A safety factor of 5 has been established if no results of masonry tests are available from the brickworks, but if the brick quality corresponds to SIA-standards 113. A safety factor of 4 may be used if the masonry strength is determined experimentally and if, furthermore, the brick is tested 3 times annually and proves to be of the same quality as the masonry used in the tests.

Allowable stresses in special quality masonry, high quality masonry, and normal quality masonry are shown in Figure 18-15 for near centric loading and for eccentric loading acting on the same side at the kern edge.

Figure 18-14 contains information concerning the strength of masonry to be guaranteed by the manufacturer. Brick properties that are required to meet specifications are summarized in Table 18-1. The decrease in admissible stress as a function of slenderness ratio l_k/d and coefficient of eccentricity m=p/k for special quality masonry is seen in Figure 18-16.

Shear Strength of Masonry and Allowable Shear Stresses

Wind and earthquakes acting on a building generate bending effects and produce shear stresses. In a two-material system

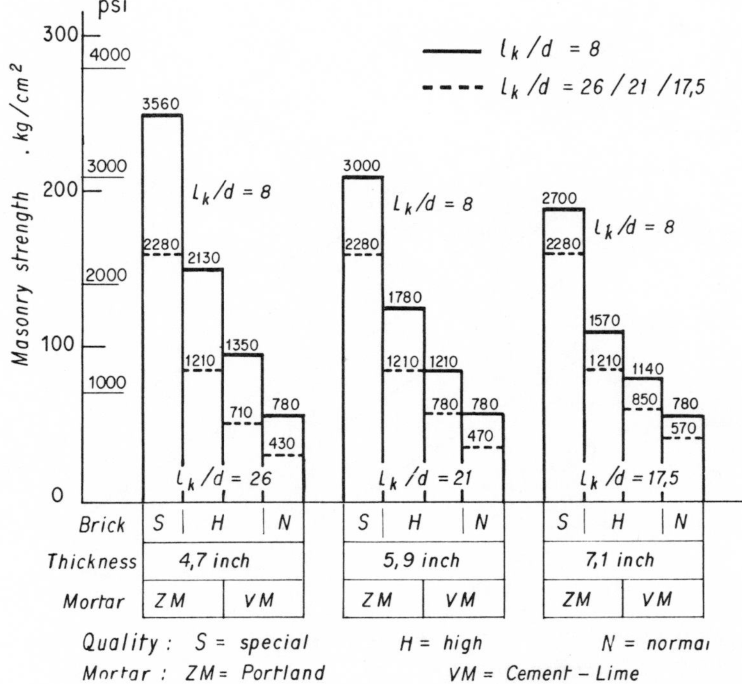

Figure 18-14. Single wythe and bonded masonry strengths specified by SIA-standards 113 for the three masonry qualities and for near-centric as well as eccentric loading (at kern edge). Knife edge support. Buckling length: 10′4″. Cement mortar and lime cement mortar.

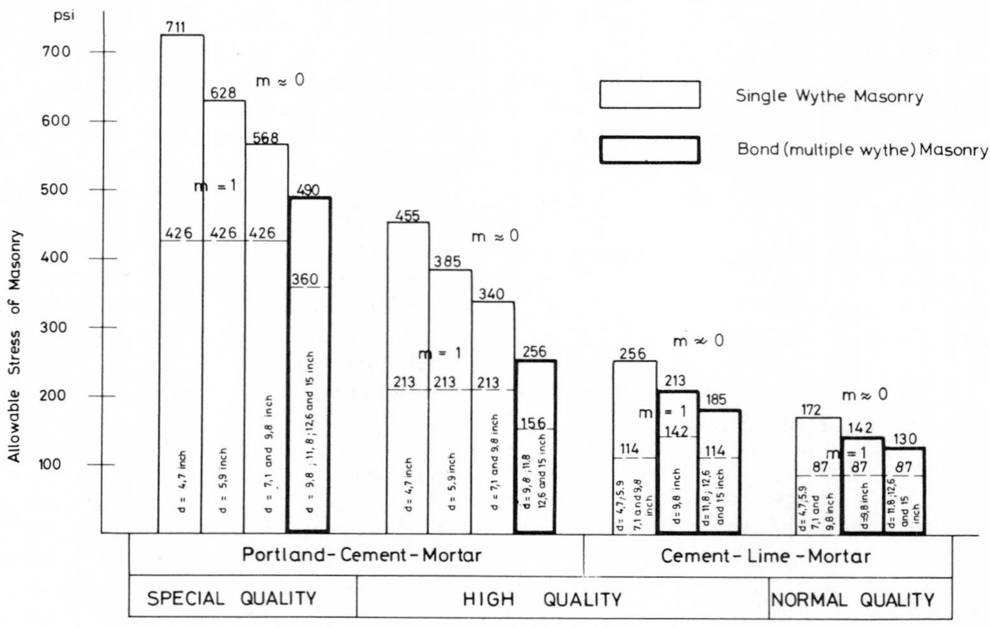

Figure 18-15. Allowable stresses specified by SIA standards 113 for the three masonry qualities and the two mortars. Single wythe and bonded masonry. Loading near-centric and at the kern edge (m = 1).

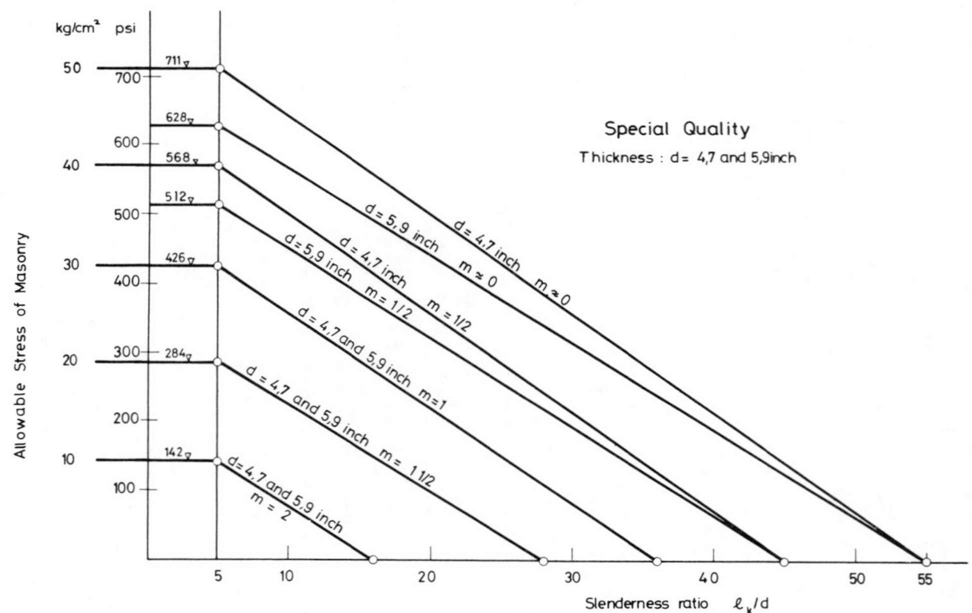

Figure 18-16. Allowable stresses for masonry made from special quality bricks for near-centric and eccentric loading: m = 1/2, 1, 1-1/2, and 2. Thickness 4.7" and 5.9". Slenderness ratio $l_k/d = 55$.

Table 18-1

Properties of Brick	Type of Brick				
	Normal Quality	High Quality			Special Quality
Specific Absorptive Capacity in g/min 30 sq in Deviation (max) in g/min 30 sq in	Optional Optional	≦ 62 ± 30	≦ 78 ± 40	≦ 98 ± 50	≦ 33 ± 10
Compressive strength in psi Deviation (max) in %	≧ 2150 ± 30	≧ 3600 ± 20	≧ 4300 ± 20	≧ 5000 ± 20	≧ 5700 ± 15
Maximum Perforations in %	Optional	15 – 40			± 15
Dimensional Tolerances: Max. Deviation of individual value from mean value in % Length Width Height	 ± 2.5 ± 2.5 ± 3	 ± 1.5 ± 1.5 ± 2			 ± 1 ± 1 ± 1.5
Max. Deviation of mean value from rated value in inch Length Width Height	 ± 1/4 ± 1/7 ± 1/8	 ± 1/5 ± 1/8 ± 1/10			 ± 1/6 ± 1/10 ± 1/12
Cracking Average per Brick	1 Crack full Height 3 Cracks of max. 1-1/4" Length	4 Cracks of max. 3%5" Length			No Cracks

like masonry, whose tensile strength normal to the course joints is negligibly small, it becomes particularly important to know quantitatively the shear strength existing between masonry brick and mortar. Consequent investigations in numerous countries, including Switzerland, have led to fractures similar in appearance to the cracks produced by earthquakes. A quantitative interpretation of the strongly positioned, dependent stresses occurring in these realistic tests meets with considerable difficulty. Only when certain assumptions are made can the shear strength be calculated approximately. Moreover, these tests are expensive. (Figure 18-17)

Thus, it was attempted to derive quantitative results for the shear strength by using smaller test structures and subjecting them to various stresses in a stress field held as uniform as possible. (Figures 18-18 and 18-19).

The height of test walls was limited by the distance between the columns of the 2000 t (4400 kip) power press. (Figure 18-20)

The maximum applicable stress was limited by the compressive strength of the masonry bricks normal to the perforations, since this is less than the strength parallel to the perforations.

Tests were conducted on two of the three kinds of brick manufactured in Switzerland: normal quality and special quality.

Tests on normal quality material used bricks 2-7/8" and 5-1/3" tall, all other tests employed only 5-1/3" bricks.

Normal quality bricks were laid with lime cement mortar, while those of special quality were laid with ordinary cement mortar, Table 18-2.

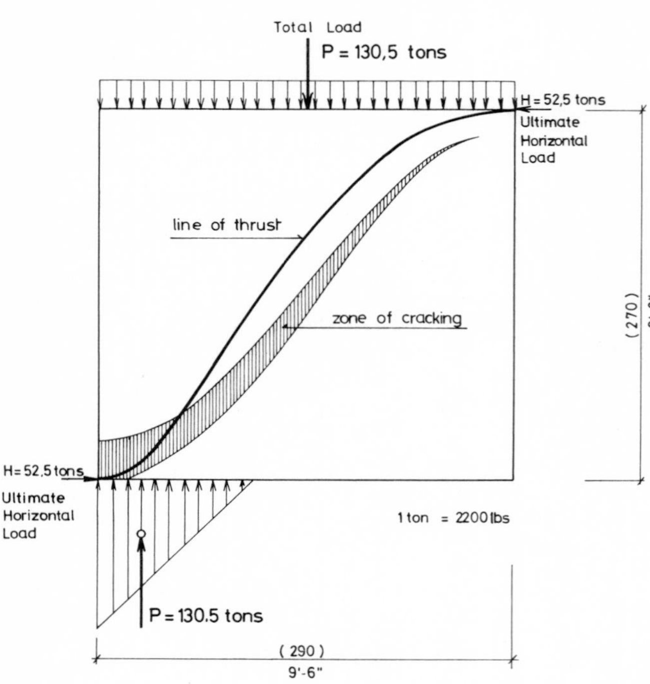

Figure 18-17. Representation of test walls 9'6"/8'8" (d = 6"), loaded uniformly at the top with 427 psi (30 kg/cm²). Reaction at bottom assumed to be triangular. Horizontal fracture load H = 115 kip (52.5 t). Region of crack formation adjacent to line of thrust.

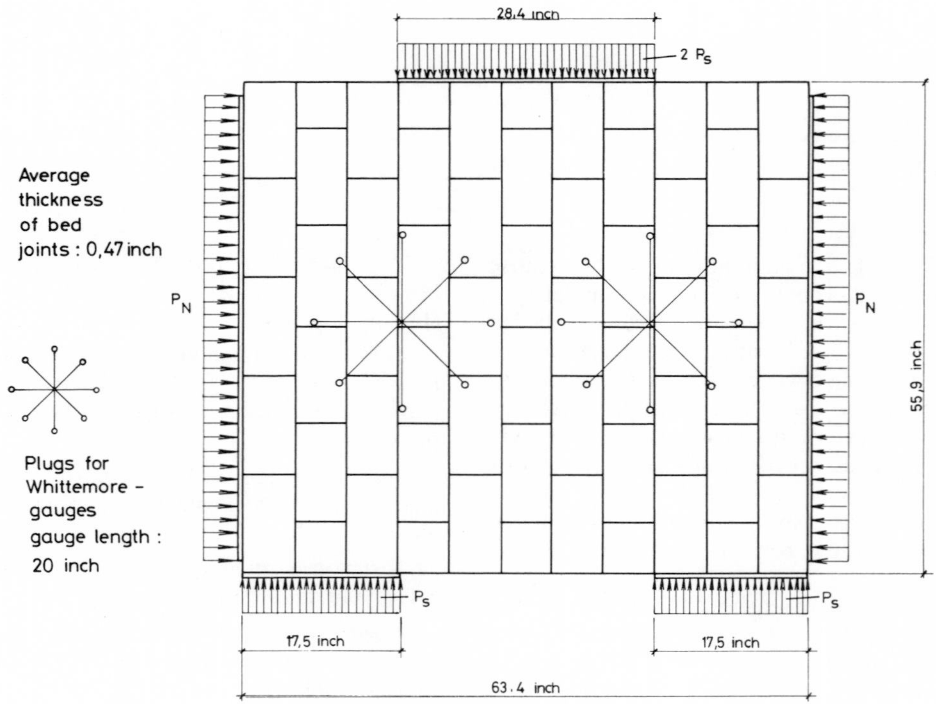

Figure 18-18. Picture of test structure for shear tests turned through 90°, showing its position in the press. 11 layers of brick with lime cement mortar and cement mortar. Position of the altogether 16 gauges of 20" length each.

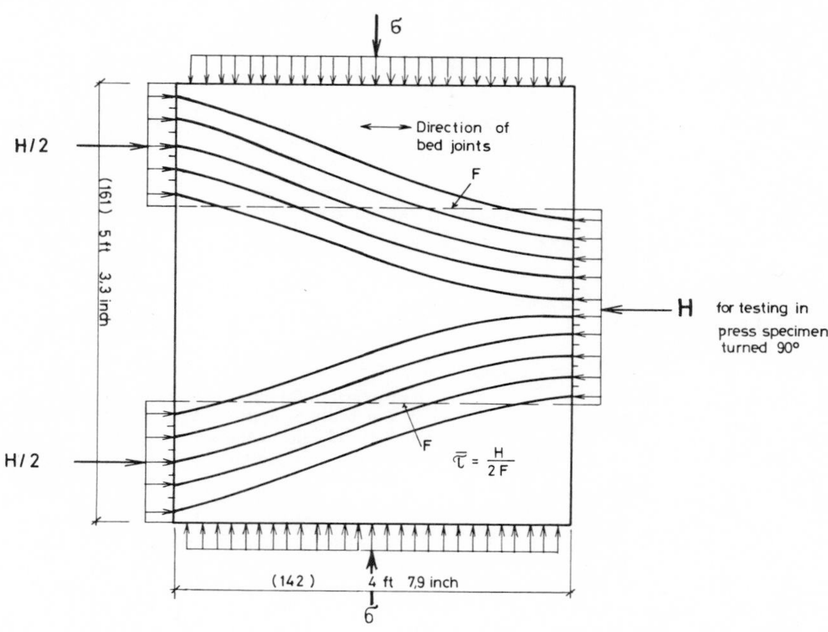

Figure 18-19. Test specimen for shear tests, 4'8"/5'3", under several compressive stresses varying from 14 psi to 357 psi. Approximate pattern of lines of force, almost uniform distribution of shear stresses.

Figure 18-20. Test structure for shear tests, turned through 90° in the press. Normal stresses horizontal, shearing forces vertical. Position of Whittmore gauges of 20" each: Location on both sides and in both halves of the test structure.

Table 18-2

	Composition by Weight–%				Age: 28 Days [1]				Number [4]	Age: Average [2] 94Days [3]			
	Portland Cement	Hydrated Lime	Sand + Ground Limestone (5%)	Water	Flexural Tensile Strength		Cube Strength			Flexural Tensile Strength		Cube Strength	
					Average	max. Deviation	Average	max. Deviation		Average	max. Deviation	Average	max. Deviation
Portland Cement Mortar	18.2	–	69.4	12.4	655	6.6	2890	1.5	7	888	7.2	3620	2.5
Portland Cement-Lime Mortar	4.6	11.6	70.0	13.8	411	3.8	1225	1.9	6	469	6.2	1440	3.6

Sand Grading:

0 – 0.12	mm:	10.2%
0.12 – 0.2	mm:	15.0%
0.2 – 0.5	mm:	17.0%
0.5 – 1	mm:	20.0%
1 – 2	mm:	18.5%
2 – 4	mm:	18.4%
>4	mm:	0.9%

1) Number of Samples: Average of 3 Prisms each
2) Number of Samples: Average of 4 Prisms each
3) Portland Cement Mortar: 83–104 Days, Average 95 Day
Cement Lime Mortar: 90– 99 Days, Average 94 Day
4) Series

All data concerning dimensions, perforations, etc., of the masonry bricks are contained in Table 18-3.

Masonry structures were stored in an air-conditioned room at 68°F and 60% relative humidity for a period varying between 83 and 104 days, with a mean storage period of 94 days.

Results of shear tests are given in Table 18-4. Mean values for the two wall qualities are shown graphically in Figure 18-21.

With a single exception, walls of all three thicknesses made from bricks of normal quality have yielded practically the same shear strength. Bricks 5-1/3" wide were crushed at the higher stress of 171 psi; hence the shear strength is greater.

The special quality masonry made from bricks of high compressive strength and smaller absorptivity, using cement mortar, possesses about twice the shear strength of normal quality bricks at a stress of 171 psi. The scatter of results for the three wall thicknesses is also greater.

As the stress $\overline{\sigma}$ increases, so does the shear strength $\overline{\tau}$. The following analytical expressions represent curves which follow the total mean values with sufficient accuracy (Figure 18-22). They also allow a determination of the allowable shear stress $\overline{\tau}_a$ as a function of the compressive stress. A safety factor of ν = 3 for unusual building loads is deemed suitable.

Normal quality : $$\overline{\tau}_a = 0.9 \cdot {}_0\overline{\sigma}_5 \cdot \left[\sqrt{\frac{\overline{\sigma}}{{}_0\overline{\sigma}_5} + 1.64} - 1.20\right]$$

Special quality : $$\overline{\tau}_a = 0.45 \cdot {}_0\overline{\sigma}_5 \cdot \left[\sqrt{\frac{\overline{\sigma}}{{}_0\overline{\sigma}_5} + 0.185} - 0.24\right]$$

where:
$\overline{\sigma}$ = actual compressive stress
${}_0\overline{\sigma}_5$ = allowable compressive stress for 1/d=5, m ≈ O
all stresses in psi

The shear strength is composed of the adhesion of the mortar to the masonry brick, the shear resistance of mortar plugs, i.e., of mortar having penetrated into the perforations and forming a single unit with the course joints, and the friction forces which increase with rising compressive stress.

In the absence of compressive stress only the first two effects, i.e., adhesion and shear resistance, are active. A comparison between shear strengths of masonry of both qualities in unstressed condition (σ = 0) shows that the absorptivity of bricks and the strength of mortar, including plugs, has a considerable effect on the shear strength: adhesion and plug resistance of special-quality masonry erected with cement mortar is about 4-1/2 times greater than that of normal quality brick masonry built with lime cement mortar. Preloading the masonry by compressing it causes the shear strength to increase. The steeper rise of the shear strength of the special quality masonry brick compared with that of normal brick apparently is due to the higher tensile strength of the cement mortar.

It is planned to publish the detailed evaluation of the test series in a separate report.

Methods for Calculating Wall Thicknesses

The Effect of Restraints

If the wall is restrained top and bottom, or just at one end, allowable stresses may be chosen according to the reduced buckling length or slenderness ratio. In general, because only partial restraints occur in buildings, one usually neglects the effect in very tall buildings.

Calculation of Bearing Capacity or Allowable Stress for Crossed and Unequal Eccentricities of the Point of Load Application at Top and Bottom

The allowable stresses are specified for equilateral load application. The empirical relations shown in Figure 18-23

Table 18-3

		Normal Quality				Special Quality		
	Dimensions of brick	24½ x 11½ x 6	24½ x 12 x 13½	25 x 15 x 13½	25 x 18 x 13½	25 x 12 x 13½	25 x 15 x 13½	25 x 18 x 13½
1	Dimensions							
	Mean Value in cm — Length	24.5	24.4	24.9	24.8	24.8	24.9	24.9
	Width	11.7	11.8	15.0	17.9	11.9	14.8	18.0
	Height	6.0	13.4	13.5	13.5	13.5	13.5	13.5
	Maximum Deviation in % — Length	± 0.4	+ 1.2	± 0.4	± 0.4	- 0.4	+ 0.4	- 0.4
	Width	- 0.8	± 0.8	± 0.7	- 1.1	± 0.8	+ 0.7	0
	Height	± 1.7	± 0.7	- 1.5	+ 1.5	- 0.7	+ 0.7	± 0.7
2	Perforations in %	22.7	29.5	30.3	30.9	24.7	30.9	27.0
3	Absorptive Capacity g/min 30 sq inch	69.7	63.2	83.2	73.0	25.1	24.2	21.7
4	Maximum Deviation in %	- 10.7	- 16.0	+ 28.8	+ 14.4	+ 10.5	- 15.2	- 18.0
5	Compressive Strength in psi	6520	4140	3760	3280	9510	8050	9800
6	Maximum Deviation in %	- 8.6	+ 11.3	- 17.8	+ 23.0	- 3.0	+ 10.1	+ 4.2

Number of Samples: 1., 5. and 6. : 10 Samples
3 and 4. : 6 Samples

Table 18-4
Shear Tests Shearing Strength in psi

	Masonry Width	Height of Bricks	Compressive Stress in psi							
			14.2	42.7	71.1	170.6	213.3	234.6	289.6	355.5
BS	4-3/4	5-1/3	188		335		422			609
			194		258		465			593
			191		297		444			601
BS	5-7/8	5-1/3	246		261		385			472
			181		261		426			515
			214		261		406			494
BS	7-1/10	5-1/3	114		268		414			
			167		278		418			
			140		273		416			
BN	4-1/2	2-3/8		93*		217*				
				98		201				
				95		209				
BN	4-3/4	5-1/3		90		200*				
				100		215				
				95		208				
BN	5-7/8	5-1/3		93		198				
				93		208				
				93		203				
BN	7-1/10	5-1/3		93		168*				
				93		178*				
				93		173				

Note: *Rupture of bricks due to lateral compression, shearing strength must be slightly higher.

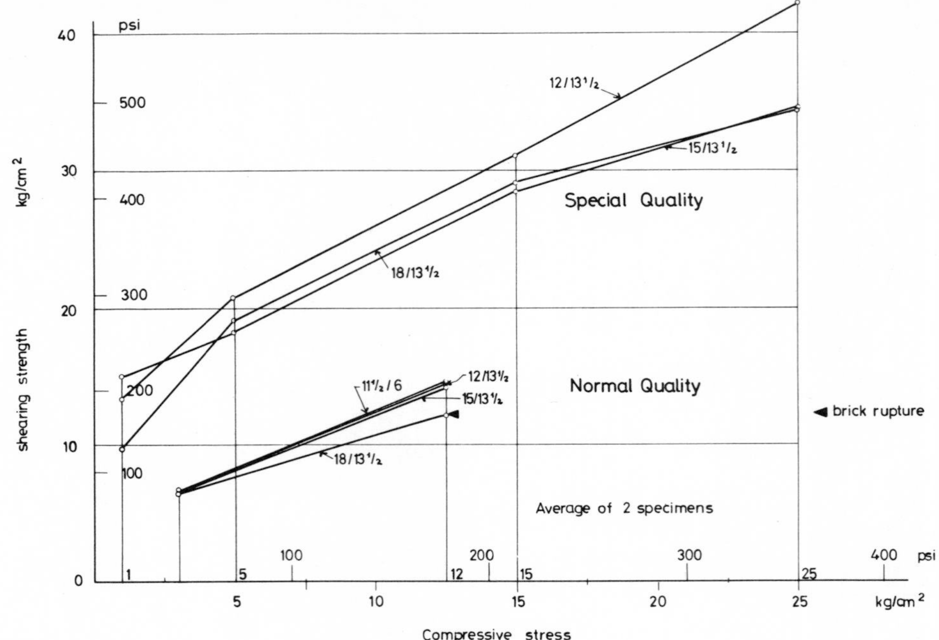

Figure 18-21. Graphical representation of test parameters used in shear tests: Mean shear stress $\bar{\tau}$ as a function of normal stress $\bar{\sigma}$. Normal quality and special quality. Wall thickness: 4-3/4" (12 cm), 5-7/8" (15 cm), and 7-1/10" (18 cm). Brick sizes: 2-3/8" (6 cm) and 5-1/3" (13,5 cm). Specified formats indicate width and height of bricks.

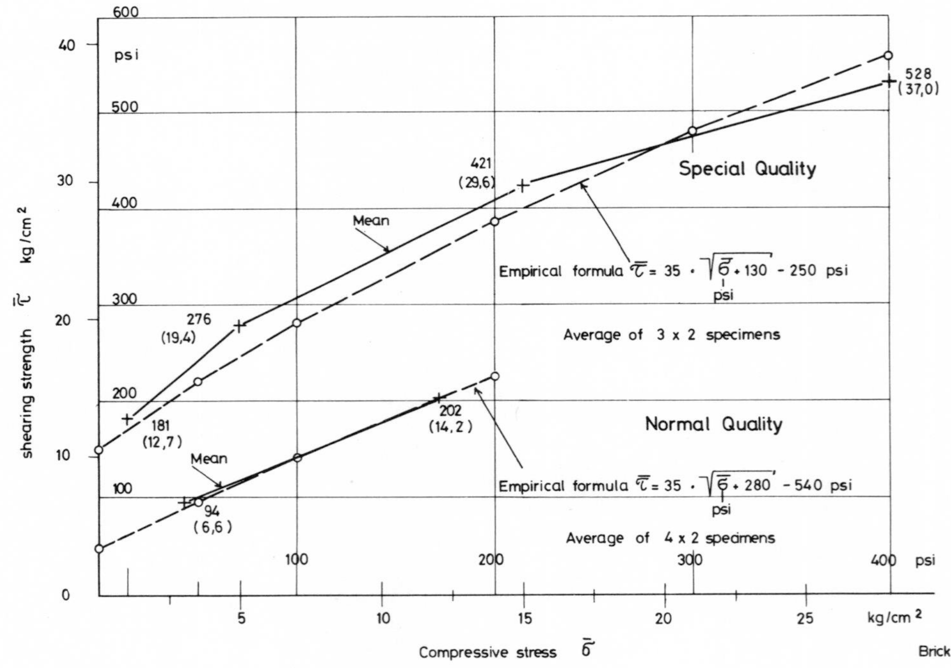

Figure 18-22. Graph showing mean values of results of shear tests for normal and special quality bricks under various normal stresses. Empirical curves.

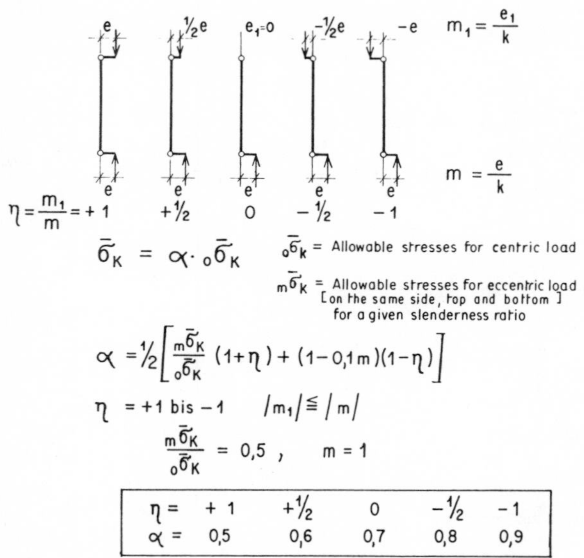

Figure 18-23. Empirical formula for calculation of allowable stresses for various equilateral or crossed coefficients of eccentricity.

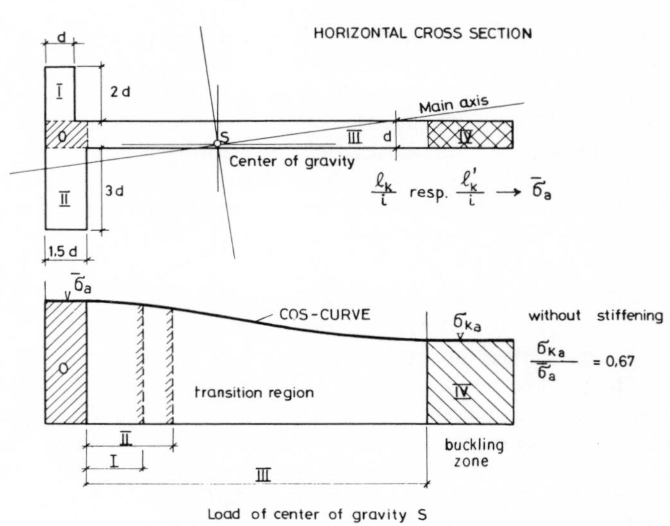

Figure 18-24a. Calculation of allowable stress $\overline{\sigma}_a$ for l_k/i and $\overline{\sigma}_{ka}$ for l_k/d, increased by wall stiffening, from the tables of allowable stresses. Transition zone 12 d.

were tested by a number of experiments. They are valid when the eccentricities of the points of load application differ at top and bottom and, in particular, if they are crossed.

$$\overline{\sigma}_k = a \cdot {}_o\overline{\sigma}_k \qquad \eta = \frac{m_1}{m} \qquad |m_1| \leqq |m|$$

$$a = \frac{1}{2} \cdot \left[\frac{{}_m\overline{\sigma}_k}{{}_o\overline{\sigma}_k} \cdot (1 + \eta) + (1 - 0.1\ m)(1 - \eta) \right]$$

The Stiffening Effect of Wall Sections Placed at an Angle

Included in SIA-standards 113[1] is an attempt to utilize the stiffening effect of wall sections placed at an angle, thus allowing heavier loading of masonry. Since comprehensive tests of masonry to determine this effect do not exist, an attempt was made to work out a calculational method based on present-day knowledge (plane cross sections, stress-strain diagram). First, one calculates the smaller radius of gyration for the entire horizontal cross-section after having determined the principal axes (Figure 18-24).

The allowable stress corresponding to the slenderness ratio l_k/i is determined. Assuming the wall to be half restraint, the slenderness ratio may be reduced by 25%. With the assumption that the stiffening effect extends over a length of 12 d (d = wall thickness), one can calculate the allowable stresses for individual wall sections, provided a cosine dependence is

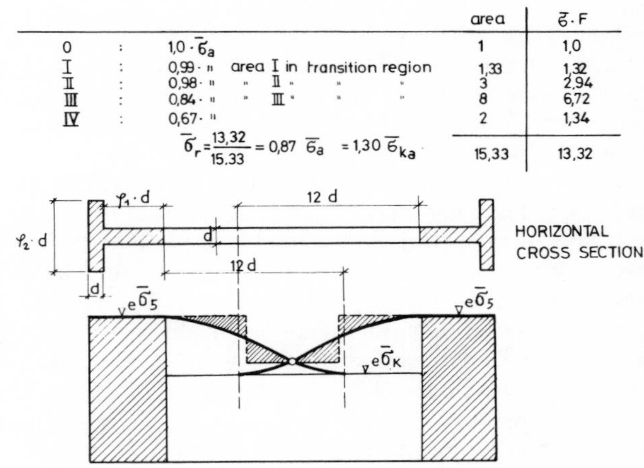

Figure 18-24b. Evaluation for intersecting cosine curves of a wall stiffened on both sides.

assumed for the transition curve in the transition region between $\overline{\sigma}_a$ and $\overline{\sigma}_{ka}$

The example shown in Figure 18-24 illustrates the procedure. If the point of application does not coincide with the center of gravity S, then load components corresponding to the deflection must be assigned to the wall sections, keeping the cross section flat. The laborious procedure is normally used only if the bearing capacity of walls is to be fully exploited.

Calculation of the Coefficient of Eccentricity[6]

Calculating the eccentricity of the point of a wall's load application from the deflection of floors and walls is simplified by visualizing a cut-out, double cross with flexibly supported end points (Figure 18-25). The coefficient of eccentricity m = p/k to be used in stress calculations of masonry is obtained by dividing the moments at top and bottom by the vertical load. Possible eccentricities of building sections lying above are, of course, also taken into consideration.

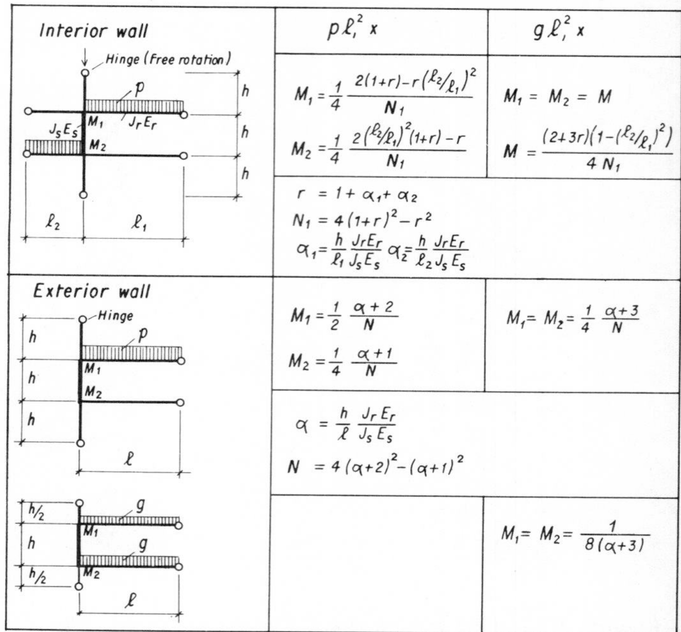

Figure 18-25. Simplified calculations of the coefficients of eccentricity using the double cross method for an interior wall and an exterior wall. Moments top and bottom for checkerboard loading and for the ceiling weight. Equal storey heights.

Supplementary Remarks

To guarantee the availability of high grade material for building construction, several further conditions, outlined below, must be met by the calculations and during the phases of construction planning and execution. Additionally, no measures should be taken which would tend to reduce the bearing capacity and no unallowable alterations should be made[8].

1. The greatest possible uniformity in the deformation of individual walls within a given storey should be striven for in high buildings to avoid restraining stresses and cracks in ceilings and walls resulting therefrom.

2. Calculation of reinforced masonry requires a knowledge of the allowable edge stresses. The allowable average stress $\overline{\sigma}_5$, i.e., the stress at a slenderness ratio of $l_k/d=5$, may be increased by 40% and used as edge stress.

3. Masonry bricks used in Switzerland generally are 3-1/2″ high; this limits the minimum thickness of bearing walls to 4-3/4″. Using thinner walls is dangerous because it may lead to a considerable departure of the wall axis from a straight line during erection.

4. Floors must be imposed on the entire wall if the wall thickness is less than 6-1/2″.

5. Special quality masonry bricks, because of their brittleness, may not be split. Instead, smaller units must be ordered from the supplier.

6. No slots or openings shall be made in special quality masonry. The construction of recesses shall be shown on the course-plans which are obligatory for this type of masonry. In high-grade masonry, vertical slots may be cut, subsequent to erection, only into walls, but not into piers.

7. For cavity masonry, non-corrosive ties are required only at storey height. Wind pressure should be transferred to the floor by insulating material having high compressive strength (cork). Bulging of the outside wythe as a result of heating by the sun can then take place without affecting the bearing wythe and without inducing undue stresses. Horizontal corner reinforcements prevent opening of the outside wythe. Water vapor, which may diffuse through the wall from the inside towards the outside, is condensed at the inner surface of the outside wythe. Thus, the latter should either be built out of absorptive masonry units (Bricks), or else a 1″ gap should be left open between the outside wythe and the insulating material to enable the water condensation to run off.

8. Roof slabs of reinforced concrete will shrink, drawing walls bearing small loads into the interior. This may cause cracks to appear in the masonry of the top floor. The insertion of slabs made of foamed polyester resin, about 2/5″ thick, can prevent a tight connection to the masonry, thus avoiding harmful frictional forces. Taking this measure does, however, require cutting the plaster all along the walls of the top floor ("Swedish cut"). (Arching of floors at the corners and the effects of lifting-off from the heavier outside walls should be hidden from view and shielded from rain by placing a brick in front, entirely separated from the face of the concrete floor).

9. The impermeability of exposed masonry is assured only if the mortar is removed to a depth of 3/4″-1″ and if the joints are subsequently grouted with a highly workable joint mortar or, alternatively, if a suitable mortar is used that can be smoothed out immediately.

10. If, under exceptional circumstances, masonry is executed at freezing temperature of 32 to 23°F, the following measures must definitely be taken if the mortar is to develop its full strength: mortar temperature of 50°F, brick temperature not below 32°F, work to stop at 4 p.m. at the latest. The masonry is to be covered immediately on both sides and over its entire height[9].

Notations

d	Wall thickness
l_k	Buckling length measured between hinges
l_k/d	Slenderness ratio
p	Load eccentricity

$m = \frac{p}{k}$ Coefficient of eccentricity k = width of kern (middle third)

p' Initial eccentricity = deviation of wall axis from straight line through hinges.

i Radius of gyration $i = \sqrt{\frac{J}{F}}$

J = Moment of inertia

F = Area of cross-section

f Deflection of wall axis at middle height

x Distance of neutral axis

g Distance between neutral axis and centre of gravity of stress area

η Distance between centre of gravity and o-point in σ-ϵ-diagram, or ratio of smaller to larger eccentricity at both ends m_1/m

$_q\epsilon_m$ Transverse deformation of the mortar

$_q\epsilon_s$ Transverse deformation of the brick

ϵ_1 Largest compressive strain in %

ϵ_2 Smallest compressive strain in %

ϵ_o Compressive strain at compressive strength of masonry (β_d)

β_d Compressive strength of masonry, lk/d $\approx$ 4

E Modulus of elasticity in psi (kg/cm^2)

$\overline{\sigma}$ Average stress in psi (kg/cm^2)

$_m\overline{\sigma}_k$ Average buckling stress for any slenderness ratio lk/d and a coefficient of eccentricity of m

$_o\overline{\sigma}_k$ Average buckling stress for any slenderness ratio lk/d for near-centric loading

$_o\overline{\sigma}_5$ Average stress for a slenderness ratio of lk/d = 5 and near-centric loading

$\overline{\sigma}_a$ Allowable average stress in psi (kg/cm^2)

$\overline{\tau}$ Average shear stress in psi (kg/cm^2) for a compressive stress $\overline{\sigma}$ perpendicular to the bed joints

M_1, M_2 Moments top and bottom of wall

S Absorptive capacity of the dry brick during one minute per dm^2 (1 dm^2 = 15.5 sq. in.)

a Reducing coefficient for the load capacity for equilaterally or crossed eccentric loading

25/15/13½ Format: length, width, height in cm

h_s height of brick

h_m thickness of mortar layer

References

1. SIA-Norm 113 – Norm für die Berechnung und die Ausführung von Mauerwerk aus künstlichen Steinen 1964. Schweiz. Ingenieur- und Architekten-Verein Zürich.
2. Haller P., "Physik des Backsteins" I. Teil "Die Festigkeitseigenschaften" – Verband schweiz. Ziegel- und Steinfabrikanten, 1949.
3. Haller, P., Knickfestigkeit von Mauerwerk aus künstlichen Steinen Schweiz. Bauzeitung Nr. 38, 67. Jahrgang, 1949.
4. Haller, P., "Der Ziegelbau in der Schweiz" "Die Ziegelindustrie" Heft Nr. 15, 1953.
5. Haller, P., Teglmurverk i Höchuskonstruktionen "Tegl" Nr. 1, Stockholm, 1955.
6. Haller, P., "Die technischen Eigenschaften von Backsteinmauerwerk für Hochhäuser" Schrift des Verbandes schweiz. Ziegel- und Steinfabrikanten 1959. Translation "The technological properties of Brick Masonry in high Building" National Research Council of Canada NRC TT 792, 1959.
7. Haller, P., L'évolution de la maçonnerie en Suisse Recherches et essais sur les structures en terre cuite Symposium Rilem-Milan 1962, Roma, 1965.
8. Haller, P., "Mauerwerk im Ingenieurbau" Betrachtungen zu der neuen SIA-Norm 113 Schweiz. Bauzeitung 83. Jahrgang, Heft 7, 18. Februar 1965. Translation "Masonry in Engineered Construction" National Research Council of Canada NRC TT 1270, 1967.
9. Haller, P., "Bericht über den Einfluss der Frosttemperaturen auf das Mauerwerk aus künstlichen Bausteinen" Mitteilungsblatt des Delegierten für Arbeitsbeschaffung 9. Jahrgang, Heft 1, 1953.

19. Correlation of tests of masonry assemblages with strength characteristics of reinforced masonry beams.

Dr. Frank B. Johnson and Prof. J. Neils Thompson, The University of Texas at Austin, Austin, Texas

Introduction

Masonry assemblages have some of the same basic characteristics as do comparable units of plain concrete; they both have excellent compressive strength and limited tensile strength. In some cases, the configuration of masonry units does not permit a convenient, economical placement of reinforcement. Longitudinal bars can be placed in the bed joints of masonry assemblages, but it is extremely difficult to utilize vertical steel bars effectively in a single wythe of masonry.

Of the components of a masonry assemblage, brick and mortar, mortar is the weaker of the two. The compressive strength of brick is sufficient, generally, to resist ordinary stress. The same is also true for most mortar used in the assemblage. In addition, over 94 percent[1] of the clay units manufactured have a modulus of rupture exceeding 500 psi, and the average clay unit has sufficient-in-tension for most conditions. The deficiency in tensile strength and bond strength of mortar has limited the use of masonry to applications requiring only compressive strength. Some building codes limit the allowable tensile working stress to approximately 10 psi[2]. This value is a severe limitation, and any significant improvement could change materially the potential utilization and economic attraction of masonry as a competitive structural building material. Comparative tests were made to determine the strength characteristics of standard portland cement masonry mortar and of a special high-bond mortar manufactured by the Dow Chemical Company in 1963.

Testing Program

General

The testing program developed for this investigation as herein presented was performed in several phases as follows:

Phase 1. This phase was primarily exploratory. Six reinforced masonry beams with a span of 10 feet were constructed, using high-bond mortar. These beams are shown in Figure 19-1. Using the same batch of mortar, masonry panels, 16 x 16-in.-square, were built, and three companion mortar cubes were cast for each beam. These simply supported beams were loaded with two symmetrically placed concentrated loads. The distance from the support to the point of load (the shear span) was varied from beam to beam to determine the critical shear span to depth of beam ratio. This critical shear span was used to determine the points of loading for the beams in Phase 2.

Phase 2. This phase attempted to establish the relationships of the shearing stresses found in actual reinforced masonry beams with the strength characteristics of masonry disc assemblages. Beams were constructed to investigate the diagonal tensile strength as affected by variations in depth of beam, shape of beam, and type and strength of mortar used.

Sixteen beams were constructed. These were divided into two main groups, eight with high-bond mortar and eight with regular mortar. Each of the two main groups was composed of four subgroups of two each. Three of these subgroups were

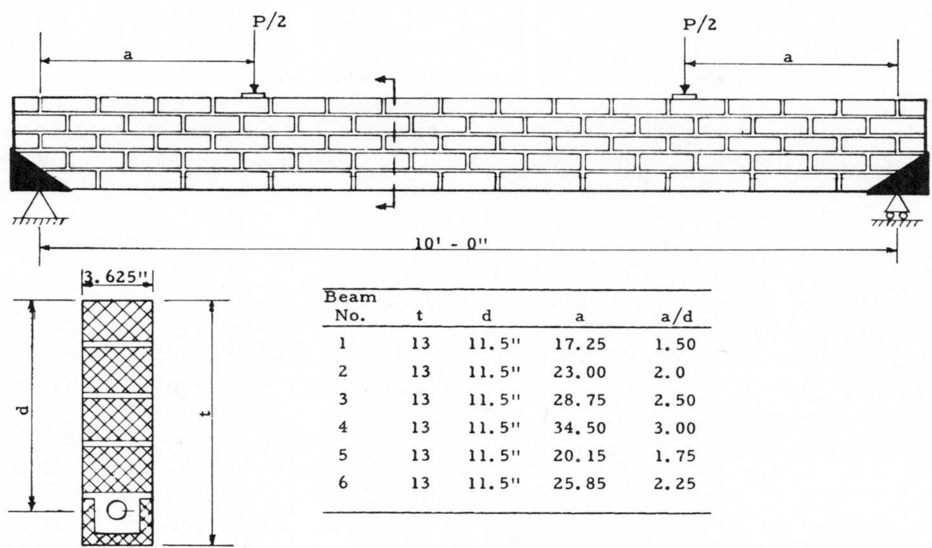

Beam No.	t	d	a	a/d
1	13	11.5"	17.25	1.50
2	13	11.5"	23.00	2.0
3	13	11.5"	28.75	2.50
4	13	11.5"	34.50	3.00
5	13	11.5"	20.15	1.75
6	13	11.5"	25.85	2.25

Figure 19-1. Dimensions of Phase 1 – reinforced masonry beams.

rectangular beams with effective depths of 12, 14-1/2, and 17 inches (two of each depth). The fourth subgroup consisted of two beams with an effective depth of 12 inches, but with a flange at the top.

For each beam the following control specimens were constructed for testing: two 15-inch-diameter masonry discs, three 3-inch-diameter mortar discs, and three 2-inch mortar cubes. Each beam, and the corresponding specimens for the diametral and compression tests, were prepared from the same mortar batch. The water-cement ratio was carefully controlled.

Masonry Assemblages

The 15-inch-diameter masonry discs were cut from 16-inch-square masonry panels of one brick wythe that were laid up by skilled masons. All panels were identically constructed as shown in Figure 19-2, using 3/8-inch bed joints and 1/2-inch head joints. Joints were full and the surface of the joints were tooled slightly. Upon completion of a panel, four bricks were placed on top of the panel to provide some weight on the bed joints of the upper courses. The panels were not disturbed for 14 days to permit the mortar to gain sufficient strength for handling. A 15-inch-diameter circle was then inscribed on the panel and the corners were removed with a diamond saw. These cuts, done quickly, approximated a circle. The final shaping was done on a large grinder using an abrasive disc.

Beams

Construction of the beams begun by laying out channel tiles to the proper length. Wax paper separated the tile from the floor, preventing any mortar from bonding to the floor. Mortar was placed in the channel tiles until the grout filled the space. Number 9 steel reinforcing bar was then forced into the grout (Figure 19-3). From this point, the construction of the beams proceeded normally. The mortar as with construction of the masonry panels, was provided in such quantity that a beam, the corresponding masonry panels, and other required samples would come from a single batch. Retempering of the mortar was not permitted. Workmanship was uniform. To prevent a bond or slip failure between the grout and the reinforcing steel, it was necessary to provide a positive-end

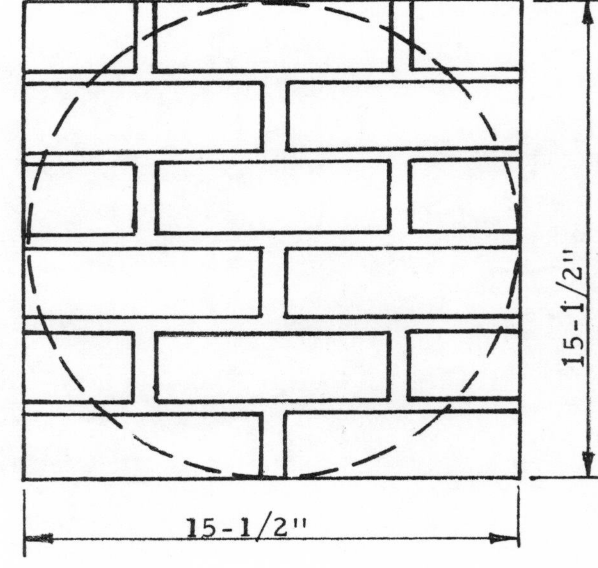

Figure 19-2. 16 in. square panel – source of masonry disc.

anchorage of the ends of the reinforcing bars. This anchorage was furnished by attaching a steel shoe to each end of the beam.

This shoe provided not only end anchorage for the reinforcing steel, but also acted as a bearing plate for the end reaction. The beams were whitewashed prior to testing to aid in the visual examination for cracks that occur during loading.

All beams were treated similarly for loading and instrumentation. They were precisely centered under the head of a Young testing machine, and the supports were leveled to provide uniform bearing. The supports consisted of one rocker which provided free beam rotation for one end, and one roller which provided free beam rotation and horizontal movement at the other end (Figure 19-4).

The load was applied in 2000-lb increments. At each load increment, the machine head movement would be stopped and the load recorded along with the deflection indicated by five dial-gauge readings. At this time, a visual examination of the sides of the beam was made to mark the extent of cracking. As the load approached the ultimate, the load would fall off after movement of the machine head had been stopped for the reading of dial gauges. Warning of the approach of failure was generally indicated by a rather severe drop in load.

Figure 19-3. Placement of reinforcing steel in masonry beam.

Results

Results of Phase 1 Tests

The program for this phase consisted of testing the following specimens prepared with high-bond mortar:

1. Six reinforced-masonry beams as shown in Figure 19-1.
2. Two 16 × 16-in. masonry panels with each masonry beam, making a total of 12 panels.
3. Three 2-in. mortar cubes with each masonry beam making a total of 18 cubes.

All of the specimens were tested after a curing for 28 days. The high-bond mortar cubes were cured in air as they contained a latex polymer and could not be cured according to the ASTM specifications. All beam failures were definitely shear failures, with a crack developing at mid-depth at the interface of the mortar and brick. Figure 19-5 shows photographs of beam No. 2 and clearly illustrates the type of failure. The small, vertical arrow painted on the beam indicates the point of load application, and the lower, stair-stepped crack extending to the point of load application was the first diagonal shear crack to form.

Table 19-1 numerically tabulates the results of the beam tests and the compression tests of the corresponding mortar cubes. The beam results were the average of two load values

Figure 19-4a. Reinforced masonry beam in position for testing.

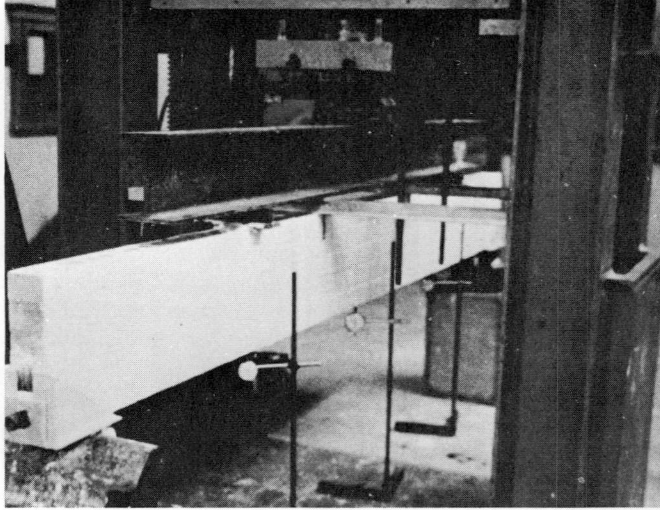

Figure 19-4b. Steel anchorage on bearing in sleeve resting on pin end support.

the applied load at which the first shear crack appeared or when the actual shear failure began and the final ultimate load that the beam would carry. The compression strength (f'_m) of the mortar cubes is the average of the results of three mortar cubes tested in compression.

The only variation in the physical make up of the beams was the mortar strength. The only other controllable variable was the point of application of the load. The load was placed at a different distance (distance "a") from the support. This variation was varied to find the critical distance from the support that would yield a shearing failure that would not be complicated by the effect of nearby load. This effect had been observed and studied in reinforced concrete structures for many years. One of the first reports on this subject appeared in a paper by Mr. Arthur P. Clark[3].

Upon analyzing the numerical results, it became apparent that the compressive mortar strengths were related to the load capacity of the beams. A linear relation was assumed, and the loads were modified by a factor C, which was simply a ratio of the actual mortar cube compression strength divided by an arbitrary compression strength of 2400 psi. (This value was, in actuality, the average mortar cube compression strength of beam No. 1.) The coefficient thus obtained was used to modify the corresponding load obtained in the testing. The curve obtained from modifying the loads strongly indicated that in reinforced masonry beams of this general dimension, the critical ratio of a/d was near 2.5. A graphic representation of the results of this phase is shown in Figure 19-6 where adjusted ultimate and initial cracking loads (P_u and P_i) are plotted against the ratio of a/d for each beam. Determining a critical shear-span-to-depth ratio of 2.5 was significant inasmuch as it was used as the criterion for locating the load position in the beams tested in the subsequent phase of this investigation.

Results of Phase 2 Tests

Beam Results. The final phase consisted of 16 beams with two main variations, as to mortar type, of eight beams each. Each mortar group of beams was composed of three subgroups of two rectangular like beams with effective depths of approximately 12-in., 14-1/2 in., and 17-in., and a fourth subgroup of two beams with an effective depth of 12-in., but with a brick flange at the top. The exact dimensions and loading diagram for all of these beams may be seen in Figures 19-7, 19-8, 19-9, and 19-10. In addition to the beams, a group of subsidiary test elements were prepared using mortar corresponding to each particular beam. Each of these groups consisted of two 15-in. masonry discs and three 3-in. mortar discs for diametral testing and three 2-in. mortar cubes for the standard compression testing.

The behavior of the beams under load and the mode of failure were important in understanding and interpreting the results. In general, all of the beams failed similarly, with only

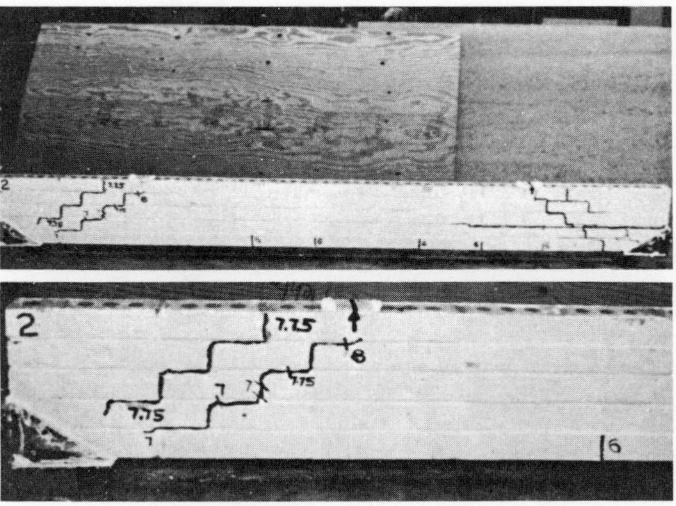

Figure 19-5. Typical failure pattern of Phase 1 reinforced masonry beams.

Table 19-1
Results of Phase 1 Beam Test

Beam No.	Load P_i	Load P_u	Average f'_m	C	P_i/C	P_u/C	a/d
1	11,000	14,220	2400	1.00	11,000	14,220	1.50
5	9,600	11,670	2420	1.01	9,500	11,500	1.75
2	7,000	8,770	2300	0.96	7,300	9,170	2.00
6	9,300	11,370	3280	1.36	6,840	8,390	2.25
3	8,000	9,420	2740	1.14	7,000	8,270	2.50
4	6,950	8,020	2650	1.10	6,320	7,450	3.00

P_u = Ultimate applied load that beam would carry – lb

P_i = Load on beam when first diagonal shear crack appeared – lb

C = Coefficient for adjusting loads P_u and P_i $\left(\frac{f'_m}{2400}\right)$

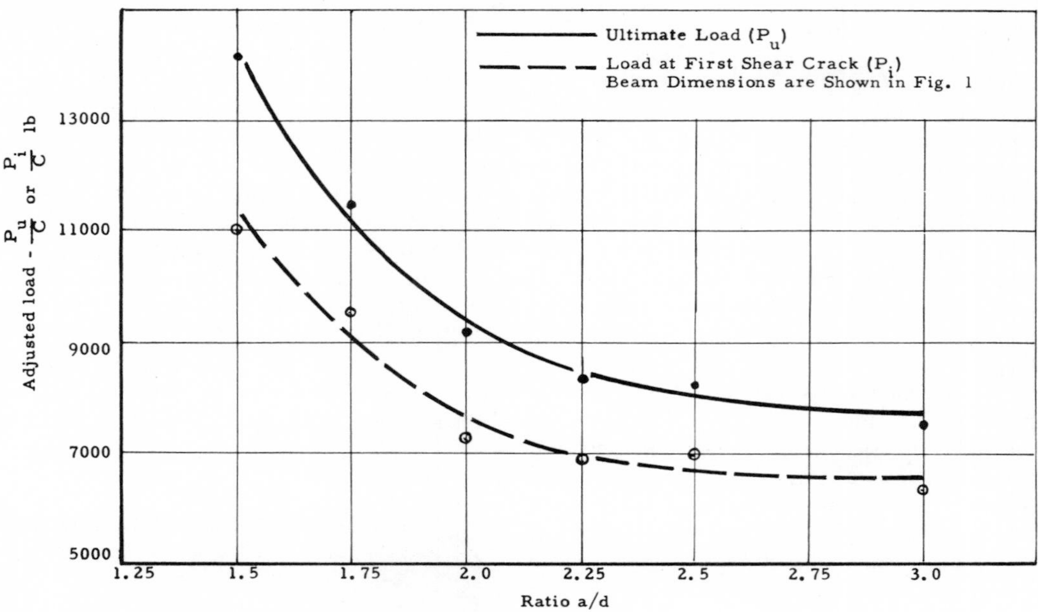

Figure 19-6. Effect of position of load on capacity of reinforced masonry beam failing in shear.

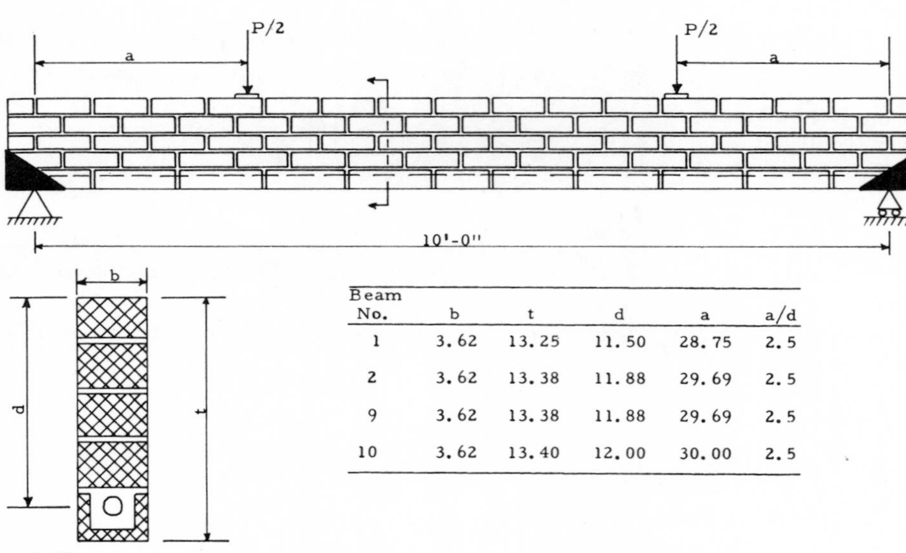

Beam No.	b	t	d	a	a/d
1	3.62	13.25	11.50	28.75	2.5
2	3.62	13.38	11.88	29.69	2.5
9	3.62	13.38	11.88	29.69	2.5
10	3.62	13.40	12.00	30.00	2.5

Figure 19-7. Dimensions and position o loads for Phase 2 beams 1, 2, and 10.

minor variation in the details. At low applied loads (below 6000 lbs), the load held steady throughout the data-recording period, but as the applied load increased, a drop of around 200 to 300 lbs. occurred while the recordings were being made. This drop in load was typical of all beams tested throughout the middle and upper range of the applied load. A drop of 500 lbs. or more, while recording data, was an indication of imminent failure. With beams made with the Type M cement-lime mortar, the shear failure occurred during the application of the next 2000 lbs. load increment. Beams made with high-bond mortar with low water-cement ratio would, i some instances, sustain loads through a further 2000 lbs increment before failure occurred.

When the beam actually failed, the load-carrying capacit of the beam was suddenly reduced. The actual, initial shea crack could usually be found before the ultimate load wa reached. The initial shear cracking normally began nea mid-beam depth and a similar distance (d/2) outside of th point of load application. In beams using high-bond morta with low water-cement ratio, the initial cracking occurred i

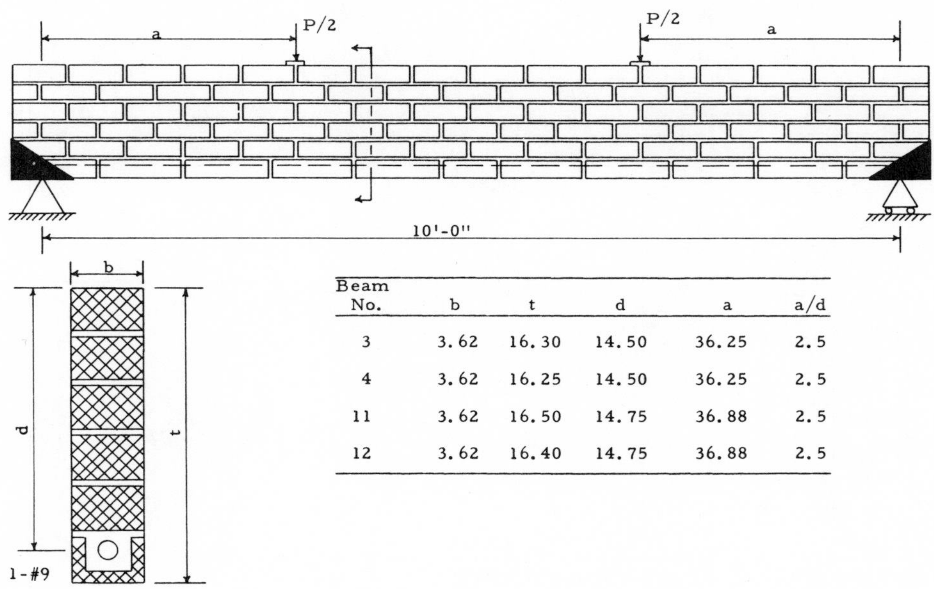

Beam No.	b	t	d	a	a/d
3	3.62	16.30	14.50	36.25	2.5
4	3.62	16.25	14.50	36.25	2.5
11	3.62	16.50	14.75	36.88	2.5
12	3.62	16.40	14.75	36.88	2.5

Figure 19-8. Dimensions and position of loads for Phase 2 beams 3, 4, 11, and 12.

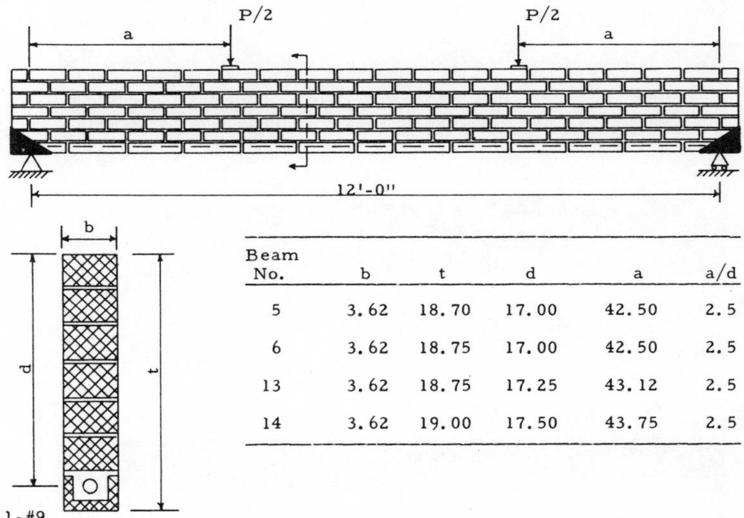

Beam No.	b	t	d	a	a/d
5	3.62	18.70	17.00	42.50	2.5
6	3.62	18.75	17.00	42.50	2.5
13	3.62	18.75	17.25	43.12	2.5
14	3.62	19.00	17.50	43.75	2.5

Figure 19-9. Dimensions and position of loads for Phase 2 beams 5, 6, 13, and 14.

the masonry and proceeded on a 45° diagonal toward the point of load in one direction and toward the bearing plate in the other. In beams where Type M cement-lime mortar was used, the cracking usually began along the mortar joint at the brick-mortar interface and followed the mortar joint interface in stair-step fashion toward the reinforcing steel and point of load application. Figures 19-11 and 19-12 are photographs of the typical failures obtained in the testing and illustrate these failure patterns. In every beam tested, the primary failure produced the typical shear failure pattern. A secondary failure involved splitting of the beam at the level of the reinforcing steel. This splitting progressed from the intercept of the shear crack along the steel and toward the reaction. The value recorded was the ultimate applied load corresponding to the beam shear failure and was completely recognizable from the behavior of the beam.

The results of the beam tests are shown in Table 19-2. The ultimate applied load, the calculated total shear, and the calculated unit shear strength are shown for each beam. Also included are the corresponding water-cement ratios of the

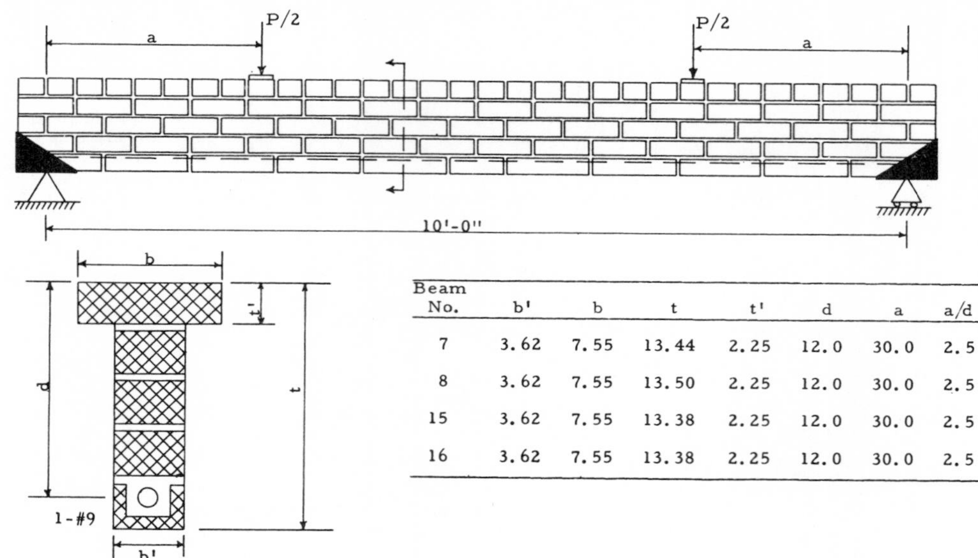

Beam No.	b'	b	t	t'	d	a	a/d
7	3.62	7.55	13.44	2.25	12.0	30.0	2.5
8	3.62	7.55	13.50	2.25	12.0	30.0	2.5
15	3.62	7.55	13.38	2.25	12.0	30.0	2.5
16	3.62	7.55	13.38	2.25	12.0	30.0	2.5

Figure 19-10. Dimensions and position of load for Phase 2 beams 7, 8, 15, and 16.

Figure 19-11. Typical failure pattern of reinforced masonry beams made with high-bond mortar.

Figure 19-12. Typical failure pattern of reinforced masonry beams made with type M Mortar.

beams, the type of mortar used, and a brief description of the beam. Figures 19-7 through 19-9 show the position of the loads and the physical dimensions for each beam. The shear values presented in Table 19-2 were based on the following:

$$V_u = \frac{w_b\, L}{2} + \frac{W_{wf}}{2} + \frac{P}{2} - w_b\left(\frac{a}{12} - \frac{d}{24}\right)$$

where:

V_u = total ultimate shear in lb
w_b = weight of beam in lb/ft
L = span of beam in ft
W_{wf} = weight of steel loading beam WF section in lb
a = shear span in inches
d = effective depth of beam in inches
P = applied load in lb

The above calculations for the total shear V_u are self-explanatory except for the last term $[\, w_b \,(\frac{a}{12} - \frac{d}{24})\,]$. This term represents the weight of a portion of the beam bounded by the reaction point and the point where the initial shear crack originated. Then, the total shear was found for the point where the failure originated.

The unit shear calculation v was based on the following:

$$v = \frac{1.5\, V_u}{bd}$$

where:

V_u = total shear in lb
b = width of beam stem (3.625 in.) in inches
d = effective depth of beam in inches

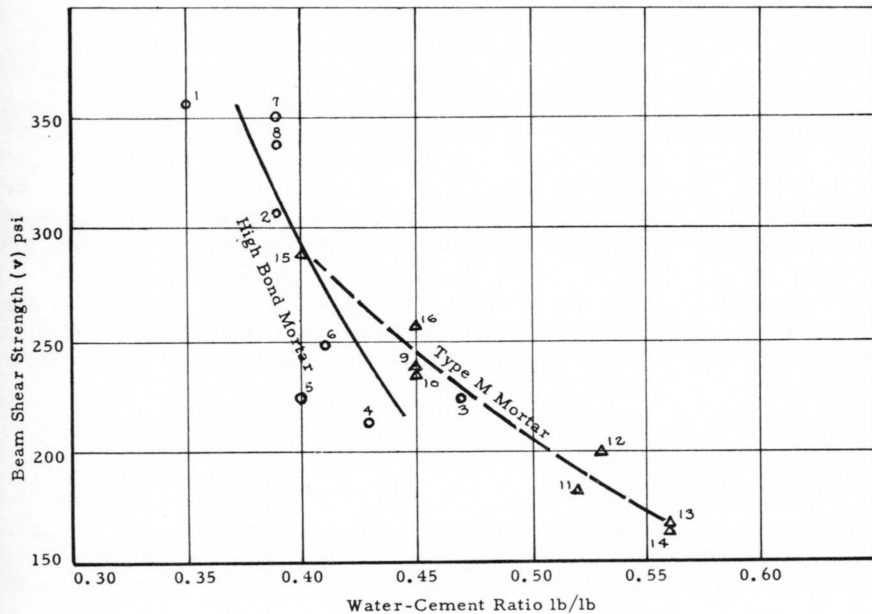

Figure 19-13. Effect of water-cement ratio on beam shear strength.

Table 19-2
Result of Phase 2 Beam Test

Beam No.	Mortar Type	W/C Ratio	Depth d	Beam Type	Applied Ultimate Load	V_u Total Shear	v Unit Shear
1	high bond	.35	11.5	Rectangular	22,000	11,261	406
2	"	.39	11.875	"	20,000	10,255	357
3	"	.47	14.5	"	18,700	9,611	274
4	"	.43	14.5	"	18,000	9,211	263
5	"	.40	17.0	"	22,000	11,269	274
6	"	.41	17.0	"	24,000	12,269	298
7	"	.39	12.0	Tee	22,000	11,282	401
8	"	.39	12.0	"	21,250	10,907	388
9	Type M	.45	11.875	Rectangular	16,000	8,255	288
10	"	.45	12.00	"	16,000	8,250	285
11	"	.52	14.75	"	16,000	8,260	232
12	"	.53	14.75	"	17,400	8,859	249
13	"	.56	17.25	"	17,500	9,022	216
14	"	.56	17.5	"	17,400	9,067	214
15	"	.40	12.0	Tee	18,500	9,529	338
16	"	.45	12.0	"	16,700	8,629	307

Note: a/d for all beams = 2.5.

This calculation for unit shearing stress was based on the width of the beam for rectangular sections and the width of the stem for T-beams, which was an approximation of the maximum unit shearing stress in the beam and was used as an arbitrary measure of the shear strength of the beams. Only minor flexural cracking near the shear failure was observed for all but four of the beams tested. Several other methods of evaluating shearing stress were tried and discarded. These included calculations based on the transformed uncracked sections and the transformed cracked sections. These methods did not produce values that significantly improved the relationship between calculated unit shearing stress and the other variables.

Beam-Unit-Shear Strength vs Mortar Water Cement Ratio. Figure 19-13 presents the data given in Table 19-2. As in the diametral tests of the masonry discs where it was established that the tensile strength of the masonry assemblage was a function of the water-cement ratio, the beam test results showed a corresponding relationship existed for the shear strength of the masonry beams. However, beams with low water-cement ratios constructed with high-bond mortar developed higher shear strength than did beams constructed with Type M mortar. This superiority of the high-bond mortar was observed in other tests in this investigation.

Beam Shear Strength vs Corresponding Mortar and Masonry Disc Strengths. Figure 19-14 plots the beam shear strength and the average values of the three corresponding mortar cube compressive strengths. Figure 19-15 plots the beam shear strength and the average value of the three corresponding mortar cylinder tensile strengths. In a similar manner, the average of the masonry disc tensile strengths is compared with the beam shear strengths in Figure 19-16. An individual examination of the curves indicates that an increase in beam shear strength corresponds to an increase of mortar tensile strength, an increase of mortar compressive strength, and an increase of masonry-disc tensile strength. A comparison of Figures 19-14, 19-15, and 19-16 show the change in the relation of the position of the Type M mortar curve to the high-bond mortar curve. The curves representing the mortar strengths (Figures 19-15 and 19-16) show Type M mortar falling to the left of high-bond mortar, while in curves based on the masonry disc tensile strengths, the Type M and high-bond curves are closer together, indicating the validity of the disc tensile strength. In actuality, the behavior of masonry assemblages in discs and in beams was subject to the variations of not only mortar materials, mortar proportions, and brick properties, but also workmanship. The testing of homogeneous mortar specimens did reflect the brick properties or the workmanship of a masonry assemblage. While both the mortar tensile strength and mortar compressive strength could be used as an indication of the beam shear strength, only the masonry-disc tensile strength reflected all the variables of the masonry assemblage. Thus, it is for these reasons that the authors believe that the masonry disc tensile strength (Figure 19-16) is more nearly a true measure of the beam shear strength.

Conclusion

The results of the investigation provided information that established definite relationships between the shear strength of the beams and the properties of the mortar and those of the masonry discs. The more important findings from these results were as follows:

1. The shear strength of reinforced-masonry beams depended upon the water-cement ratio of the mortar. This relationship, illustrated in Figure 19-13, showed that an

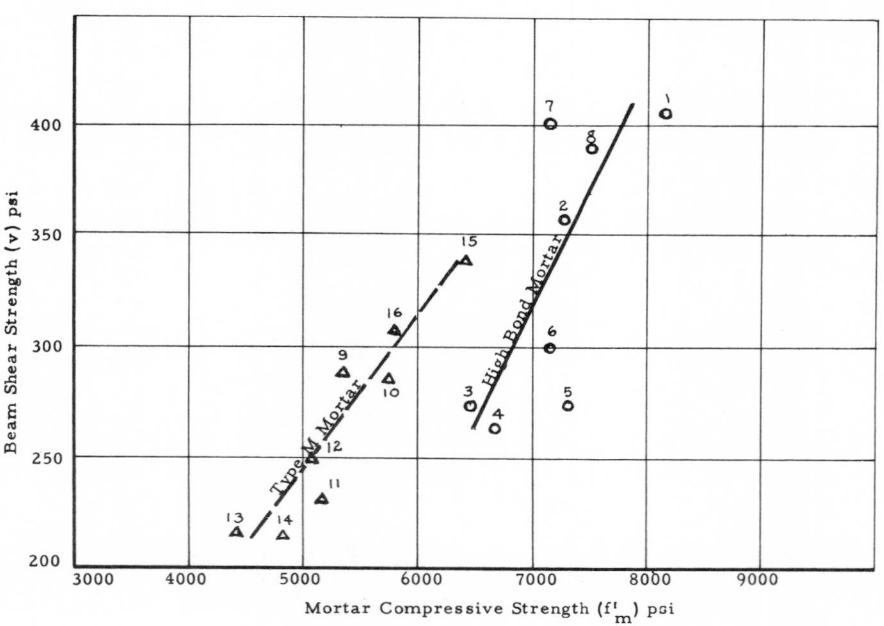

Figure 19-14. Comparison of mortar compressive strength with beam shear strength.

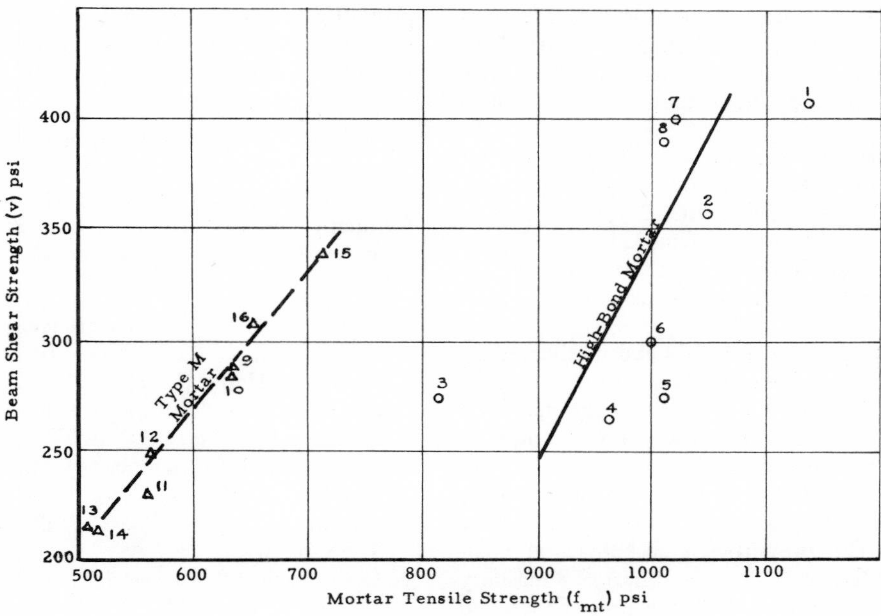

Figure 19-15. Comparison of mortar tensile strength with beam shear strength.

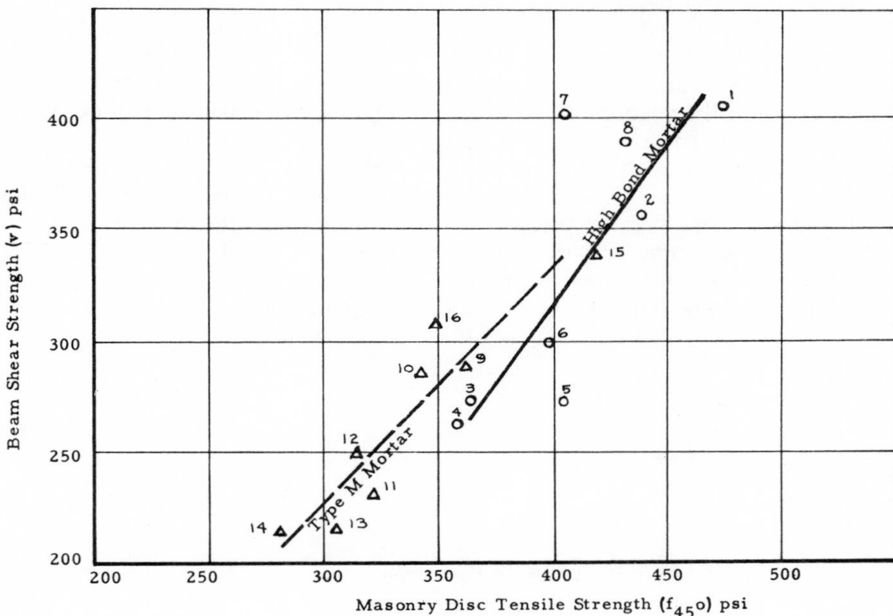

Figure 19-16. Comparison of masonry disc tensile strength with beam shear strength.

increase in the water-cement ratio of the mortar was accompanied by a decrease in beam shear strength. Figures 19-13 also indicates the different behavior of beams constructed with high-bond mortar as compared with beams constructed with Type M mortar.

2. Reinforced-masonry beams made with high-bond mortar developed shear strengths that ranged from 263 to 406 psi. Reinforced masonry beams made with Type M mortar developed shear strengths that ranged from 214 to 338 psi. These values were all sufficiently high to indicate the feasibility of using reinforced masonry assemblages as a flexural structural unit.

3. The diametral testing of mortar discs and masonry discs proved to be a simple and feasible procedure for measuring the respective tensile properties. It is believed that the diametral testing of mortar discs was far superior to the briquette method of determining tensile strength.

4. The diametral testing of mortar discs can only provide information concerning the properties of the mortar as a monolithic specimen. The properties and behavioral characterisitics of mortar acting as a component part of a masonry assemblage depended not only on the batch proportions and properties of the mortar, but also on the properties of the individual masonry units and the individual workmanship exercised by the mason.

5. Diametral testing of masonry discs provided an inexpensive method of determining the behavioral properties of masonry assemblages and provided results that included all of the variables mentioned. Rectangular test panels can be easily constructed and converted into the masonry discs, and the actual testing was no more complicated than the procedure for testing the standard concrete cylinder in compression. The within-test coefficient of variation for the masonry disc testing was unusually low for this type of material and indicates the reliability of results that may be obtained with the composite unit.

6. Quality control in masonry construction, at present, is nearly absent. Mortar performance is normally specified in terms of mortar type, but the specification is rarely enforced effectively. The masonry disc not only has the composite properties of the mortar and the masonry units, but it also ha the individual mason's skill integrated into the assemblages i the form of workmanship.

Acknowledgement

The authors express their gratitude to the Dow Chemic Company and the Structural Clay Products Research Foun ation for their support of this project.

References

1. Plummer, Harry C., *Brick and Tile Engineering Handboo of Design*, First Edition, Washington, D. C., Structural Cla Products Institute, 1950, p. 87.
2. International Conference of Building Officials, *Unifor Building Code,* Vol. 1, 1958 Edition, Los Angele California, Pacific Coast Building Officials Conferenc 1958, p. 109.
3. Clark, Arthur P., "Diagonal Tension in Reinforced Concre Beams," Title No. 48-11, *Journal of the American Concre Institute,* Vol. 23, October 1951, pp. 145-156.
4. Monk, C. B., Jr., "Testing of High-Bond Clay Mason Assemblages," paper presented at the Symposium o Masonry Testing held in conjunction with the Annu Meeting of the American Society for Testing and Material New York, New York, June 28, 1962.
5. Portland Cement Association, *Design and Control c Concrete Mixtures,* Tenth Edition, Chicago, Illinois, Por land Cement Association, 1952, pp. 5-7.
6. Carneiro, F. L. L. B., and A. Barcellos, "Concrete Tensil Strength," Union of Testing and Research Laboratories fo Materials and Structures, No. 13, March 1953.
7. Mitchell, Neal B., Jr., "The Indirect Tension Test fo Concrete," Materials Research and Standards, Vol. 1, No 10, October 1961, pp. 780-788.
8. Rudnick, A., A. R. Hunter, and F. C. Holden, "An Analys of the Diametral-Compression Test," *Materials Researc and Standards,* Vol. 3, No. 4, April 1963, pp. 283-289.

20. Column action of clay masonry walls.

Clarence B. Monk, Jr., School of Civil Engineering, Purdue University, Lafayette, Indiana

Historical Survey

Masonry has been used as a building material in compression from antiquity. It reached its highest aesthetic expression in Gothic architecture. This spanning of space in compression was largely based on empirical experience in construction, as an art not as an engineering science. The first application of stress analysis was the masonry dome of St. Peter's in Rome in 1742. The first compression tests on stone and mortar were reported in 1771 on materials from the Pantheon in Paris. Although Galileo (1564-1642) had established strength of materials as a scientific subject, it was not until Navier (1785-1836) that structural engineering, as it is practiced today, was organized as a professional body of knowledge.

Rational building design was first applied to masonry structures. Modern steel and reinforced concrete did not exist much before the latter half of the nineteenth century. Yet both of these materials enjoyed, from the start, a rational basis for design. Steel, because of its relative high price, required detailed analysis. Concern over the nonhomogeneity of reinforced concrete resulted in special regulations on the calculations of this material by many European governing bodies at the beginning of the twentieth century. Thus, paradoxically the use of masonry materials, was until now largely based on "rule of thumb" design aids dating from such medieval works as Alberti (1404-1472) and Fontana (1634-1714), though this area was the first to benefit from modern engineering.

Testing of clay masonry in the United States dates from 1880, when work was started on pier testing at the Watertown Arsenal. This work was actively continued by the National Bureau of Standards from its beginning until about 1930. During this period, significant work on clay masonry in compression was done at Cornell, Purdue, Illinois, and Columbia Universities. When the Hoover Committee on building codes, appointed in 1921, considered masonry materials, it had available a large body of knowledge from the sources indicated on clay masonry. The recommendations of this committee, amended by further study in the early 1930's, resulted in the masonry code regulations in many governing bodies in the USA. These regulations do not encourage or provide means for rational design of masonry structures. While the available compressive-strength data was considered, it was conservatively interpreted because of the lack of data on flexural action, either due to lateral loads or due to column action. The fear of tension in masonry and the lack of information concerning it perpetuated the "rule of thumb" design procedures in many modern building codes which sharply contrasts to the sophisticated design knowledge available for steel, concrete, and wood.

Work at the National Bureau of Standards in their Building Material and Science series and at the Structural Clay Products Research Foundation, resulted in data on column action, racking strength, and bond tension data. This work, plus the work in Europe, particularly in Switzerland and in England justified the publication in May 1966 of the *Recommended Building Code Requirements for Engineered Brick Masonry.* Chapter 4 "Structural Design of Brick Masonry" provides for a rational basis of clay masonry design. This paper examines one feature of this code in detail: column action. A full discussion of prism strength is to be found in "A Historical Survey and Analysis of the Compressive Strength of Clay Masonry", Structural Clay Products Research Foundation's Report No. 12 and of column action in "The Behavior of Clay Masonry Wall Columns", Structural Clay Products Research Foundation's unpublished report. These papers exhaustively examine prism strength and provide substantial detail, including recommended design column factors on column action.

Recent Methods of Column Action Analysis

Through the effort of the C.I.B. (International Building Council) a comprehensive survey was made of this subject recently in the publication, "Methods of Design of Masonry

Walls", Transactions of the International Building Council No. 68. Roughly from 1935 to 1960, many European investigations contributed to both analytical and experimental investigations of the subject. These efforts centered on the following specific topics:

1. The strength of masonry piers, including modes of failure.

2. The mathematical description of the stress-strain diagram.

3. The influence of boundary conditions, particularly the location of eccentric loading.

4. The limitation of cracked section action.

While the current writer is indebted to all prior investigators, he acknowledges his special indebtedness to Onichtchyk's work on modes of failure of piers, Haller's comprehensive experimental work on pin-ended columns, and Shalin's extended analytical investigations. Prior to these authors, the literature reveals the work of D. H. Young, "Rational Design of Steel Columns", a PhD. Thesis 1934, University of Michigan. This classic effort, though applied to steel columns, contains the basis of the analytical work established here. The current author has extended this to cracked section theory by analytical work similar to that of Shalin but benefited by the extensive experimental work discussed in this paper.

Modes of Failure

A compressive system of mortar and clay units has a characteristic mode of failure: splitting perpendicular to the bed joint. This characteristic mode of failure is observed only when the h/t of the specimen is four or greater. For shorter specimens, particularly $h/t < 2$, the mode of failure becomes diagonal shear, yielding, of course, higher apparent masonry strength. It is strongly urged to use prism proportions whose mode of failure is tensile splitting ($h/t \geqq 4$) for the shear mode of failure believed due to the restraining action of the head of the testing machine yields artifically high strength.

This mode of failure is readily understood when it is realized that the strength of the mortar is much less than that of the clay unit. Also, the compressive elastic modulus of the mortar is probably about one-fifth that of the clay body. Under compression, the lateral extension of the mortar creates a tensile strain in the clay unit. Even if the cube compressive strength of the mortar is exceeded, due to friction, the mortar between the mortar-unit interface remains confined within the joint. Paradoxically, experiments on joints merely filled with sand may produce stronger masonry systems than those filled with mortar. Typically a 10,000 psi brick built with a 1,500 psi mortar will test over 4,000 psi as a masonry assemblage. Since brick are tested flat between the steel heads of a testing machine, their strength is also due to a shear failure and consequently is higher than a tensile mode of failure would yield. See Figure 20-1.

Figure 20-1. Typical difference between shear mode of failur of brick halves tested with steel plate (right) and tensil splitting failure of those tested with a plexiglass plate (left).

Column Analysis

General Theory

The chief concern in column behavior is bending due t eccentricities. Three sources of eccentricity are recognize here:

1. <u>Design eccentricity</u> due to the geometric position of beam or slab reaction (or the equivalent virtual eccentricit induced by continuity plus the known effects of differenti movement).
2. <u>Chance eccentricity</u> due to fabrication inaccuracies an to non-homogeneity of the materials themselves.
3. <u>Bending eccentricity</u> due to the deflection induced b the design and chance eccentricities themselves.

Axially loaded columns thus become a combined direct an bending stress problem in which the maximum stress f_m expressed as follows:

$$f_m = \frac{P}{A} \pm \frac{M_x}{S} \qquad (20\text{-}1$$

In this equation M_x is the bending moment due to the source of eccentricity and is expressed as follows:

$$M_x = P\,(e_x + y) \qquad (20\text{-}2$$

where:

e_x = the design eccentricity which, in turn, is the loa eccentricity at a distance "x" from the top

y = the bending eccentricity

In general, the deflection "y" may be expressed as:

$$y = \frac{ZP(e_x + y)h^2}{E\,I} \qquad (20\text{-}3$$

The moment of inertia I must be adjusted when a cracke section exists. Equation 20-3 is not an explicit equation fo "y", since the deflection is a function of the deflection itsel To avoid this analytical difficulty, "y" may be expressed as:

$$y = \left[\frac{Z\,Pe_x\,h^2}{E\,I}\right]\left[\frac{1}{1-\frac{P}{P_E}}\right] \qquad (20\text{-}4)$$

The term $1/(1 - \frac{P}{P_E})$ may be considered a magnification actor. While three kinds of eccentricities have been discussed, nly the design and bending cases have been mathematically ntroduced into the analysis by the expression $(e_x + y)$. However, the influence of chance eccentricities are introduced n work to follow by adjusting the theory to coincide with xperimental data and by requiring a minimum $\frac{e}{t}$ value of $\frac{1}{20}$.

Treating the problem at all times as a combined axial and ending problem enables the analytical work to treat the whole range of slenderness values as a single analytical entity without recourse to regions of "short compression blocks", "intermediate columns", and "long Euler columns". No dependence is placed upon an empirical column formula of the traight line or parabolic variety for relatively short columns, with special adjustment for long columns. Not only is the lenderness ratio readily dealt with in this approach, but also he degree of eccentricity is easily introduced.

Analysis Neglecting Slenderness

A non-linear stress-strain relation is assumed as shown in Figure 20-2. For purposes of mathematical simplicity, three asic parameters describe the stress-strain curve:

1. An initial modulus of elasticity, E_i
2. An ultimate critical strain ϵ'_m
3. An ultimate compressive stress f'_m

It is useful to create the parameter:

$$\omega = \frac{E_i\,\epsilon'_m}{f'_m} \qquad (20\text{-}5)$$

which becomes the degree of the parabola assumed to fit the data. Further, the slope is assumed horizontal at the point of critical strain. With this assumption in mind, some properties of the geometry surrounding the stress-strain curve can be derived as shown in Figure 20-2.

The so-called kern condition is the situation when the cracked section is about to occur at the cross section of maximum stress. For solid rectangular cross sections, the eccentricity corresponding to the kern condition is shown to be a function of:

$$k_k = \frac{1}{2\omega + 4} \qquad (20\text{-}6)$$

For the elastic condition $\omega = 1$, the familiar value of $\frac{1}{6}$ is obtained. This value becomes $\frac{1}{8}$ and $\frac{1}{10}$ for values of ω equal to 2 and 3 respectively.

Based on the non-linear stress-strain assumption, the column analysis neglecting slenderness, as shown in Figure 20-2, can proceed. For both the uncracked and cracked sections, the "c" value has been derived.

Uncracked case:

$$c = \frac{1}{1 + \frac{2k\,(\omega + 2)}{\omega}} \qquad (20\text{-}7)$$

Cracked case:

$$c = \frac{\omega\,(\omega + 2)}{(\omega + 1)^2}\,(1 - 2k) \qquad (20\text{-}8)$$

In this instance "c" is defined as the ratio of the average stress in a cross section to the maximum stress which is presumed to be either the ultimate strength of the material or the maximum allowable working stress. The equations for the two

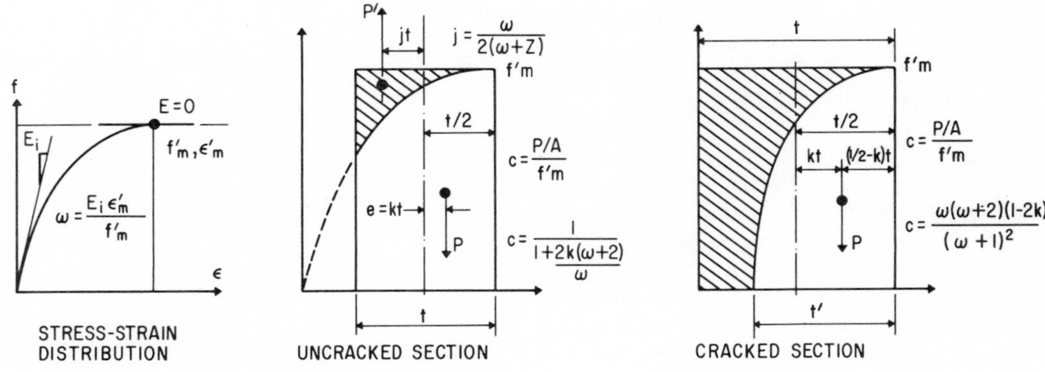

Figure 20-2. Column analysis neglecting slenderness.

conditions have a common value at the kern condition which is:

$$c_k = \frac{\omega}{\omega + 1}$$

Analysis Including Slenderness

Derivation of the Uncracked Section Equation.* Reference is made to Figure 20-3 for column geometry, deflection curve, and moment diagram. The position of maximum stress may be either at the column top or at the distance x = uh from the top. It remains at the column top until the deflection is such that:

$$e_x + y \geqq e_t$$

In the limiting case of $\beta = +1$ or y = O, the maximum stress always occurs at the mid-height. The point of maximum stress, in general, doesn't coincide with the point of maximum deflection; it generally is above it.

For $\omega = 2$ Equation 20-7 becomes:

$$c = \frac{1}{1 + 4k} \qquad (20\text{-}9)$$

This choice of ω is based on extensive prism stress-strain data. Now k is equal to either k_t or $(k_x + k_y)$ depending on the location of the maximum moment. Proceeding on the assumption that the maximum occurs below the top,

$$k_y = \frac{1}{4}\left[\frac{1}{c} - 1\right] - k_t\ (1 - u\gamma) \qquad (20\text{-}10)$$

since $k_x = k_t\ (1 - u\gamma)$. Rather than compute the deflection "y" by the formula previously stated, it is more general to derive it by moment area methods yielding the following expression:

$$k_y = \frac{A\ u\ k_t}{\Psi} \qquad (20\text{-}11)$$

By the usual process for maximizing a function u must satisfy the following relation if M_x is to be a maximum:

$$\Psi = \frac{1/2 - u - \gamma/6 + \gamma u^2/2}{\gamma} \qquad (20\text{-}12)$$

From Equations 20-10, 20-11, and 20-12 it is possible to derive the uncracked section formula as follows:

$$\sqrt{\Phi} = \sqrt{\frac{n\,\pi^2}{c}}\ \sqrt{\frac{1}{n\,\pi^2\,\Psi + 1}} \qquad (20\text{-}13)$$

*For meaning of algebraic symbols see "List of Mathematical Definitions," p. 170.

where u must satisfy the following criteria:

$$Wu^3 + Xu^2 + Yu + Z = O \qquad (20\text{-}14$$

Derivation of the Cracked Section Equation. This part of th derivation can proceed identically as the uncracked case onl taking into account the cracked section analysis as expresse by Equation 20-8 which for $\omega = 2$ becomes:

$$c = \frac{8}{9}\ (1 - 2k) \qquad (20\text{-}15$$

Noting again that k below the top equals $(k_x + k_y)$ and k_x = $k_t\ (1 - y)$ yields the expression:

$$k_y = (1/2)\ (1 - 9/8c) - k_t\ (1 - uy) \qquad (20\text{-}16$$

The deflection is again determined by moment area method taking into account that at the point of maximum stress th contact depth is:

$$\frac{t'}{t} = \frac{3c}{2}$$

The depth of the contact area on either side of the critica section towards the ends is assumed to vary as a ρ degre parabola, the cross section becoming its full value at the ends regardless of the point of application of the loads. This i assumed in the face of the realization that the end section wil be cracked theoretically when the kern eccentricity is ex ceeded. This assumption is crucial, and its justification will b discussed upon examination of the experimental evidence Suffice it to say at this point that confinement at the colum ends, due to a test plate of steel in an experiment or due to th actual disposition of boundary conditions in a real structure exists to suppress cracking to a remarkable degree. Further cracking occurs only at the joint interface as the tensil strength of the clay units is generally sufficient to suppres cracking. With the added complication of the presence of cracked region, it is possible to proceed as above for k_y:

$$k_y = (A + BC)\ u\,k_t/\Psi \qquad (20\text{-}17$$

Again the criterion for u to locate the position of maximu stress is:

$$\Psi = \left((1/2 - u - y/6 + y\,u^2/2) + C(1 - 2u - 2y\,u + 3y\,u^2)\right)/y \qquad (20\text{-}18$$

From these equations of the cracked section, it is possible t show:

$$\sqrt{\Phi} = \sqrt{(n\,\pi^2/c)}\ \sqrt{\left(1/(n\,\pi^2\Psi + 1)\right)} \qquad (20\text{-}19$$

where u

$$Wu^3 + Xu^2 + Yu + Z = 0 \qquad (20\text{-}20$$

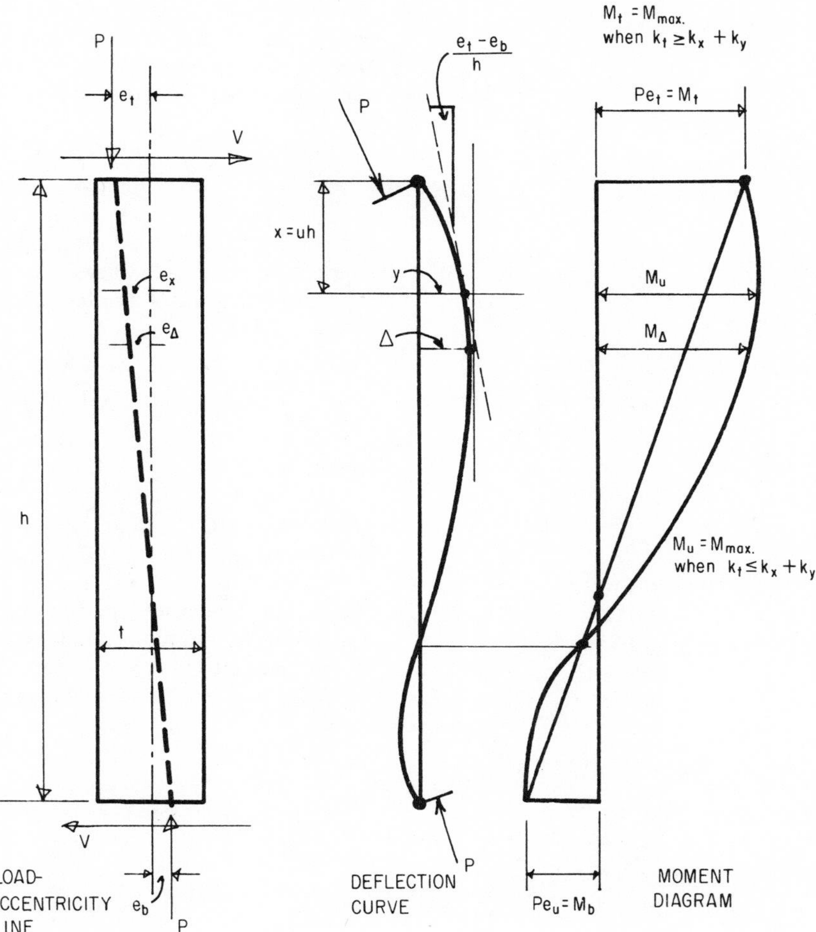

Figure 20-3. Column action of a wall column.

This reduces the expression to that identical for the uncracked case except the value of ψ W, X, Y, and Z are different as summarized in Computer Formulation of Column Formulae.

Stability Limit. As the slenderness increases under cracked section action, a limiting condition called the stability limit is reached wherein the internal resistive moment becomes a maximum. This limiting condition occurs when the deflection is:

$$k_y = (1/6)\ (1 - 2k_x) \qquad (20\text{-}21)$$

This is true regardless of the value of ω. Combining Equations 20-16 and 20-21 yields:

$$c^* = (16/27)\ \big(1 - 2k_t\ (1 - uy)\big) \qquad (20\text{-}22)$$

The value of c at which the stability region starts is that value of c which satisfies both 20-20 and 20-21 simultaneously. This is referred to as a c* value. Values of $c < c^*$ are governed by the stability limit Equation 20-21.

Computer Formulation of Column Formulae. The column formulae are far too complicated for simple engineering use. The solution of the cubic equation alone is prohibitive. However, a simple formulation for computer input is outlined below:

$$\sqrt{\Phi} = \sqrt{(n\,\pi^2/c)} \cdot \sqrt{\big(1/(n\,\pi^2\,\Psi + 1)\big)}$$

$$\Psi = N/D \qquad N = (A + BC)u \qquad D = K + u\,y$$

$$A = 1/2 - u/2 - y/6 + y\,u^2/6$$

$$B = 1 - u - y\,u + y\,u^2$$

Uncracked Case

$C = 0$

$K = (1/(4k_t))\ ((m/c) - 1) - 1 \qquad 1 \leqq c \leqq (2m/3)$

Cracked Case

$C = ((2m/3c)^3 - 1)\ \phi \qquad (2m/3) \leqq c \leqq c^*\ k_t \geqq 1/8$

$K = (1/2k_t)\ (1 - (9c/8m)) - 1$

$(8m/9)\ (1 - 2k_t) \leqq c \leqq c^*\ k_t \leqq 1/8$

Stability Case

$C^* = ((2m/3c^*)^3 - 1)\ \phi$

$K^* = (1/2k_t)\ (1 - (9c^*/8m)) - 1$

$c^* = (16m/27)\ (1\ 0\ 2k_t\ (1 - u\ y)) \qquad c^* \leqq c \leqq 0$

$u = 1/2$ when $y = 0$

u: $Wu^3 + Xu^2 + Yu + 2 = 0$ when $y > 0$

$W = 1$

$FX = (3/2y)\ (K - 1) + (3C/y)\ (3K - y - 1)$

$FY = (-3K/y^2) + (-6C/y^2)\ (1 + y)\ (K)$

$FZ = (K)\ ((3/2y^2) - (1/2y) + (3CK/y^2)$

$F = 1 + 6C$

Two experimental constants are introduced, one reflecting th magnitude of the chance eccentricity k_t^* and the other th degree of cracking through the use of a suitable nth degree (parabola. These experimental constants are defined as follow

$$m = 4\ k_t^* + 1$$

$$\phi = 1/(\rho + 2)$$

Several trials in fitting tested data has suggested that $k_t^* = 1/2$ and $\rho = 8$ are "good" values.

The final form of the basic equation may be expressed a

$$\frac{h}{r} = \sqrt{M} \cdot \sqrt{E} \cdot \sqrt{\frac{1}{n\,\pi^2 G + 1}} \qquad (20\text{-}2$$

where:

$M = E_i/f'_m$

$E = n\,\pi^2/c$

$G = \psi\,(n, k_t, y)$

where the slenderness is a function of the material ratio M, th Euler limit E, and the geometric function G which is a functic of the eccentricity parameters, k_t and y, and the degre of fixity n. Since slenderness is expressed as h/r instead of h/

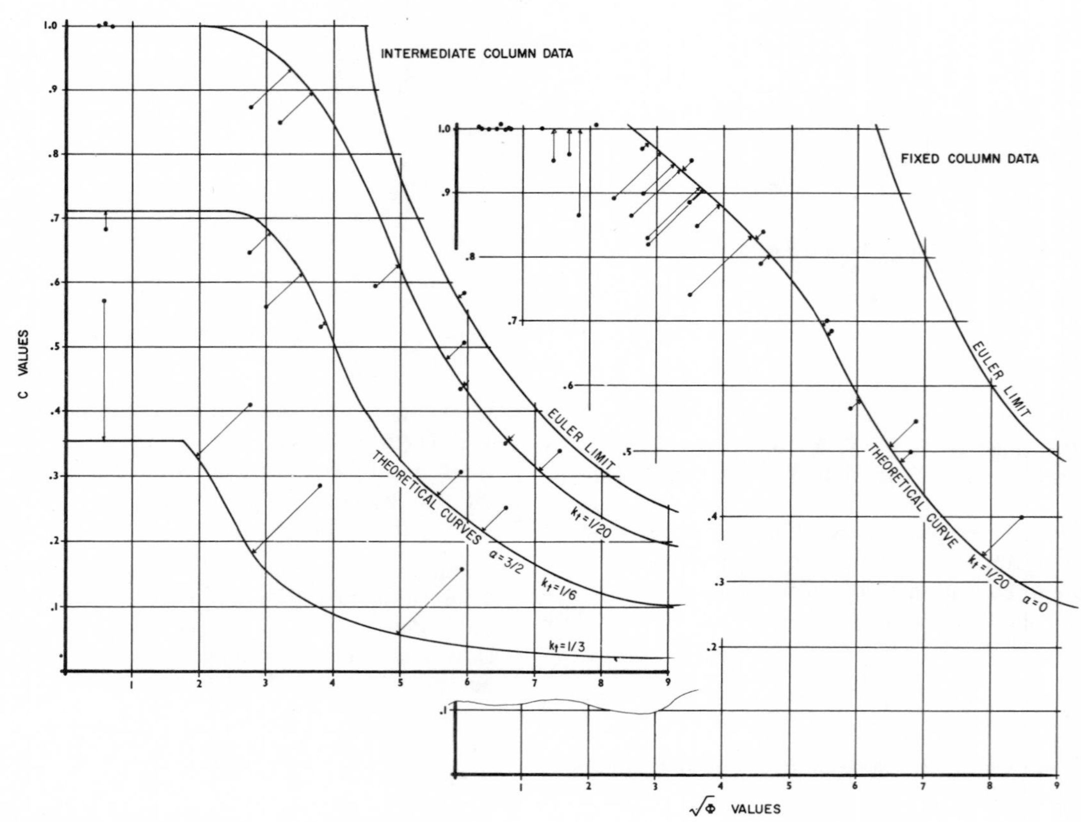

Figure 20-4. Plot of experimental wall column data.

hollow as well as solid cross-sections may be considered in the uncracked equations without revision. The cracked section equations may be used as an approximation for the hollow case.

Experimental Data and Discussion

Wall Column Data

Since 1961, the Structural Clay Products Research Foundation has conducted some 420 wall column tests. The results of the wall column test are reviewed in some detail in Figures 20-4 and 20-5.

The scope of the wall column tests was as follows:

Program Description	Specimen Types	Planned Replications	Specimens Tested
Eccentricity Study Part I	19	3	56
Eccentricity Study Part II	33	3	120
Four-Inch Solid Walls	11	5	54
Eight-Inch Solid Walls	9	5	45
4, 5, 6 and 8-Inch Units	17	3	54
Four-Inch Glazed Facing Tile	16	3	48
High-Bond Mortar Study	14	3	43

In general, the strengths of the brick used are believed to be typical of the average strengths available (10,000 to 12,000 psi) for solid brick units (i.e. less than 25 percent cored). A few high strength (16,900 psi) and a few low strength (6,310 psi) units were also used.

The strength of all hollow units is based on gross area. Type S mortar (1:1/2:4-1/2 proportion by volume) was used throughout these programs except for the high-bond mortar study which consisted of a special mortar mix as follows:

	Proportions by Volume	Percent of Sarabond Additive*
Part I	1:0:2-1/4	15
Part II	1:0:3	20

*Relative to weight of cement
Dow Chemical Company proprietary material

Three basic boundary conditions were tested:

H – Hinged (n = 1)
I – Intermediate (n = 2)
F – Fixed (n = 4)

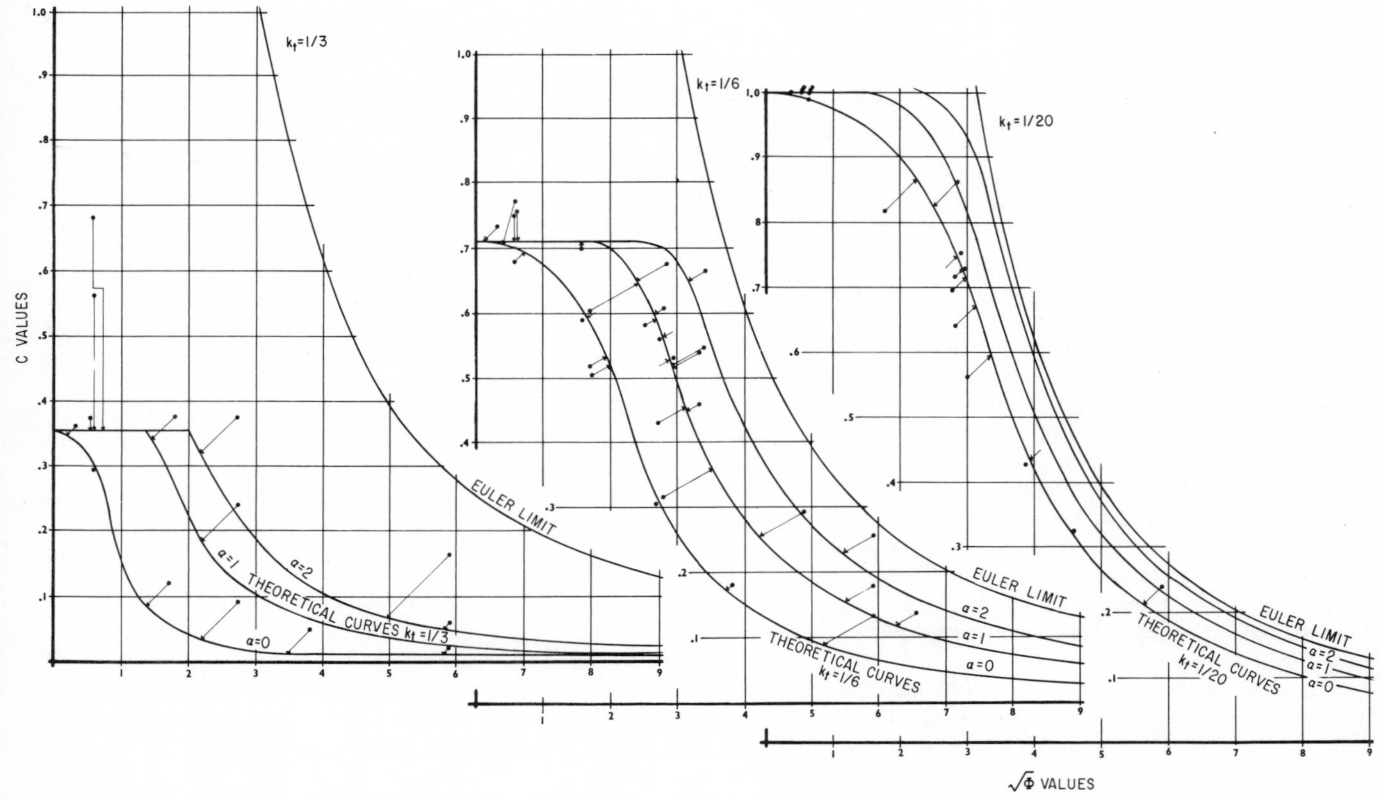

Figure 20-5. Plot of experimental hinged wall column data.

The top eccentricity, k_t, was confined to three values: 0, 1/6, and 1/3. The relative positions of the bottom eccentricity, y, were 0, 1 and 2 for the hinged conditions, and 0 for the fixed case. The intermediate case inherently has a y value of 3/2 at the base. Height, h, of all specimens takes into account the precise position of the hinge and includes the thickness of any intervening bearing plates. Values for h/t are based on actual (not nominal) dimensions. The stress-strain data are based generally on the values of f'_m and E_i obtained from short compression prisms (h/t = 4). Stress reduction factors, c, were obtained by dividing each ultimate P/A value by the compression block value f'_m. The $\sqrt{\phi}$ values are computed from the h/t values by the following formula:

$$\sqrt{\Phi} = \frac{h}{t}\sqrt{\frac{12\,f'_m}{E_i}}$$

The theoretical work previously derived is plotted on Figures 20-4 and 20-5. The theoretical curves are based on the equations derived in Section 2:

$$\sqrt{\Phi} = \sqrt{\frac{n\,\pi^2}{c}} \cdot \sqrt{\frac{1}{n\,\pi^2\,\Psi + 1}} \qquad (20\text{-}24)$$

The data from the tables are also plotted for comparison. The best fit occurs with the hinged case (k_t = 1/20, y = 0, Figure 20-5). For each condition of fixity, a k_t value of 1/20 for the centroidally loaded case has been assumed instead of 0, resulting in a better fit of the data. Such a k_t value represents the degree of inherent eccentricity due to chance misalignment of the load-line relative to the centroid of the cross section. For the intermediate case and the fixed case (Figure 20-4), the data are generally above the theoretical curve for high h/t values and generally below for the low h/t values. The low values probably reflect the difficulty in achieving true fixed end conditions in any experimental apparatus. The high values for the more slender walls, perhaps, reflect a degree of "arching" action prior to failure, which the theory does not take into account. The fact that all theoretical curves underestimate the experimental results for high slenderness ratios is a favorable one from the viewpoint of safety factors. It is not uncommon to use a higher safety factor for more slender columns. The theoretical curves significantly underestimate experimental results for the hinged case: k_t = 1/3, at all values of y. This degree of eccentricity represents the upper limit as allowed by code. The case of y = 0 is most difficult to execute in the laboratory, since an arbitrary pre-load must be used merely to hold the specimen in the test machine, and prevent it from falling out during load cycles. It is not unreasonable to have a conservative position in this extreme case of eccentricity.

The plots of the data in Figures 20-4 and 20-5 are based on an average value of E_i/f'_m assumed at 666 for Type S mortar and 444 for high-bond mortar. These arbitrary numbers are based on a reasonable fit to the data. The current state of knowledge doesn't permit much refinement of this parameter. In the absence of better data, the values of 666 for conventional mortar and 444 for high-bond mortar ar assumed as adequate fits of the available column data.

Column Design Factors

Based on the foregoing data and theoretical study, the bes adjusted theoretical curves (m = 6/5 and ϕ = 1/10) are show in Figure 20-6. The three basic conditions of fixity are shown The chance eccentricity of 1/20 and the design top eccen tricities of 1/6 and 1/3 (which include the effect of chanc eccentricity) are shown. For the hinged case, the variety o base eccentricities ranging over y = 0, 1/2, 1, 3/2, 2 ar plotted. Based on the non-linear stress strain assumption, ω = 2, the start of the cracked region is at c = 0.8. The beginnin of the stability limit is so labeled on the graph. Assuming a E_i/f'_m value of 666, corresponding h/t values have bee plotted up to 52, the range of the experimental data. Fo high-bond walls, these h/t values should be increase $\sqrt{(666/444)}$ or 1.225. Values of the stress reduction factor, c from the graph have been tabulated in Table 20-1 fo conventional mortars and for h/t values ranging from 4 to 52

Summary

The wall column study made here by both analytical an experimental methods may be summarized as follows:

1. The following formula relating wall column slendernes h/r to the c-value is a reasonable fit to the wall column data

$$\frac{h}{r} = \sqrt{M}\,\sqrt{E}\,\sqrt{\frac{1}{n\,\pi^2\,G + 1}}$$

where:

$M = \dfrac{E_i}{f'_m}$ (material parameters)

$E = \dfrac{n\,\pi^2}{c}$ (Euler limit)

$G = \Psi(n, k_t, y, c)$ (loading and boundary conditions)

The function G is set forth in detail in Column Analysis. A plot of the equation for engineering use is found in Figur 20-6 and presented numerically in Table 20-1.

2. The magnitude of the minimum "chance" eccentricity i established at k_t = 1/20.

3. A non-linear stress-strain relation has been justified. Thi has been related to the parameter $\omega = \dfrac{E_i\,\epsilon'_m}{f'_m}$ which for the clay masonry materials tested here has a value equal to 2 corresponding to an E_i/f'_m = 666 and a critical strain, ϵ'_m, o 0.003 in/in. for systems with ordinary cement-lime mortars (For the high bond mortar examined here (Sarabond) E_i/f'_m = 444.)

4. Recognition that the magnitude of the "chance" eccen tricity exists in interpretating all experimental work, togethe

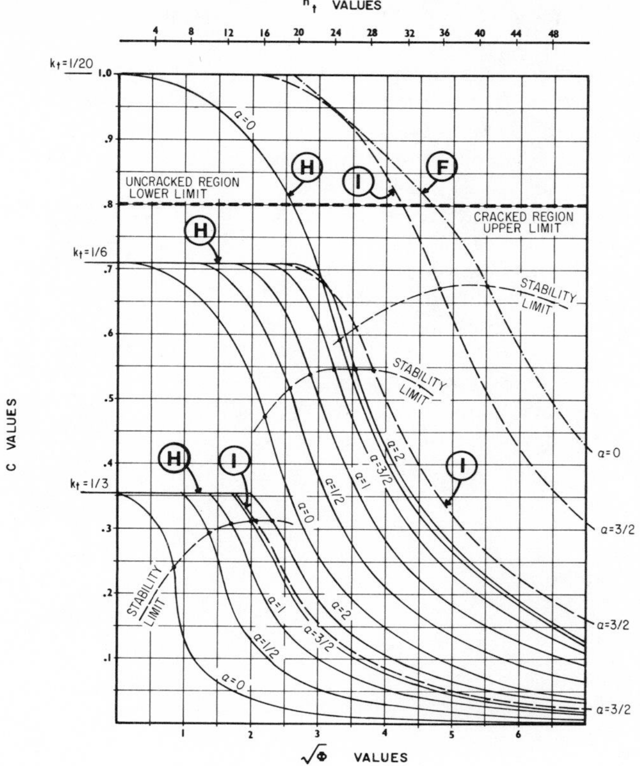

Figure 20-6. Graph of column formula.

Table 20-1

C – VALUES*

h/t	Hinged 1/20	Hinged 1/6 α=0	Hinged 1/6 α=½	Hinged 1/6 α=1	Hinged 1/6	Hinged 1/6 α=2	Hinged 1/3 α=0	Hinged 1/3 α=½	Hinged 1/3 α=1	Hinged 1/3	Hinged 1/3 α=2	Intermediate 1/20	Intermediate 1/6	Intermediate 1/3	Fixed 1/20	h/t
4	0.99	0.70	0.71	0.71	0.71	0.71	0.31	0.35	0.35	0.35	0.35	1.00	0.71	0.35	1.00	4
8	0.97	0.67	0.71	0.71	0.71	0.71	0.12	0.34	0.35	0.35	0.35	1.00	0.71	0.35	1.00	8
12	0.93	0.61	0.69	0.71	0.71	0.71	0.06	0.21	0.32	0.35	0.35	1.00	0.71	0.35	1.00	12
16	0.87	0.48	0.61	0.68	0.71	0.71	0.03	0.11	0.20	0.28	0.33	1.00	0.71	0.31	1.00	16
20	0.78	0.33	0.48	0.60	0.68	0.71	0.02	0.07	0.13	0.18	0.25	0.98	0.70	0.20	0.99	20
24	0.62	0.22	0.33	0.44	0.55	0.66	0.02	0.05	0.09	0.13	0.17	0.94	0.66	0.14	0.95	24
28	0.47	0.17	0.24	0.32	0.41	0.48	0.01	0.03	0.06	0.09	0.12	0.88	0.55	0.10	0.90	28
32	0.35	0.13	0.18	0.24	0.31	0.37	0.01	0.03	0.05	0.07	0.09	0.78	0.43	0.07	0.84	32
36	0.28	0.10	0.15	0.20	0.25	0.30	0.01	0.02	0.04	0.06	0.08	0.67	0.35	0.06	0.78	36
40	0.23	0.07	0.12	0.16	0.20	0.24	0.01	0.02	0.03	0.04	0.06	0.54	0.28	0.05	0.70	40
44	0.19	0.06	0.09	0.13	0.16	0.20	0.01	0.02	0.03	0.04	0.05	0.43	0.23	0.04	0.59	44
48	0.15	0.05	0.08	0.11	0.13	0.16	0.01	0.01	0.02	0.03	0.04	0.36	0.19	0.03	0.50	48
52	0.12	0.04	0.07	0.09	0.11	0.13	0.01	0.01	0.02	0.02	0.03	0.31	0.16	0.03	0.43	52

* values tabulated are for conventional cement: lime: sand mortars; for 'high bond' mortars increase C values by 1.225.

with the non-linear stress-strain relationship, yields theoretical results more in accord with test results. This is particularly obvious when considering eccentricities in the vicinity of the kern. Classical maximum c-values here are predicted at 0.50 whereas test data suggests values closer to 0.75.

5. The degree of cracking, as evidenced by its effect primarily on the order of magnitude of the deflections, is substantially less than classical linear theoretical considerations would have anticipated. One mechanism probably responsible for this is confinement against cracking at the points of end bearing.

6. Column deflections are ultimately limited by the stability limit which has been defined in terms of that degree of deflection which corresponds to the development of the maximum internal moment of resistance. Mathematically this is expressed as $k_y = 1/6\,(1 - 2k_x)$.

List of Algebraic Symbols

A – column area
E – modulus of elasticity
E_i – initial modulus of elasticity
I – moment of inertia
M_b – column moment at the bottom = Pe_b
M_t – column moment at the top = Pe_t
M_x – column moment at distance "x" from the top = $P(e_x+y)$
M_Δ – column moment at the point of maximum deflection
M_u – column moment at the point of maximum moment i.e. at $x = uh$
N – safety factor
P – column load
P_E – initial Euler load $= \dfrac{n\pi^2 EI}{h^2}$
S – column section modulus
V – horizontal column shear $= \dfrac{P(e_x - e_b)}{h}$
Z – general parameter relating column boundary conditions in computing deflection
c – ratio of average column stress to maximum column stress
e – load eccentricity
e_b – bottom eccentricity
e_k – kern eccentricity
e_t – top eccentricity
e_x – load eccentricity at distance "x" from the top
e_Δ – load eccentricity at point of maximum deflection
f_m – compressive strength
f'_m – ultimate compressive strength
h – column height
k_t^* – top "chance" eccentricity
k $= \dfrac{e}{t'}, k_x = \dfrac{e_x}{x}, k_x = \dfrac{e_x}{x}, ky = \dfrac{y}{x}, k_b = \dfrac{e_b}{x}$
n – column fixity, parameter: hinged = 1, intermediate = 2, fixed = 4
r – radius of gyration
t – column thickness
t' – contact depth in a cracked section
u – ratio distance x to h
x – distance from top of column
y – column deflection
γ $= 1 - \beta$
β $= \dfrac{e_b}{e_t}$
ϵ – unit strain
ϵ'_m – ultimate or critical strain
Δ – maximum deflection
ρ – degree of parabolic curve
ω $= \dfrac{E_i\,\epsilon'_m}{f'_m}$

List of Mathematical Definitions

$$A = 1/2 - \frac{u}{2} - \frac{y}{6} + \frac{yu^2}{6}$$
$$B = 1 - u - yu + yu^2$$
C = see Section 2.34
$$D = K + uy$$
$$F = 1 + 6C$$
K = see Section 2.34
$$N = (A + BC)\,u$$
$$W = 1$$
$$X = \left[\left(\frac{3}{2y}\right)(K-1) + \left(\frac{3C}{\gamma}\right)(3K - \gamma - 1)\right] + F$$
$$Y = \left[\left(-3\frac{K}{\gamma^2}\right) + \left(-\frac{6C}{\gamma^2}\right)(1+\gamma)(K)\right] + F$$
$$Z = \left[K\left(\frac{3}{2\gamma^2}\right) - (1/2\,\gamma) + \left(\frac{3CK}{\gamma^2}\right)\right] + F$$
$$\Phi = \left(\frac{f'_m}{E}\right)\left(\frac{h}{r}\right)^2$$
$$\Psi = \frac{N}{D}$$
$$\left.\begin{aligned} \phi &= \frac{1}{(\rho+2)} \\ m &= 4k_t^* + 1 \end{aligned}\right\}\text{experimental constants}$$

21. Research on load-bearing masonry in Belgium since 1963.

Ing. Henri Motteu, Centre Scientifique E Technique de la Construction, Bruxelles, Belgium

Introduction

The investigations in this report have been carried out in collaboration with the "Centre scientifique et technique de la Construction" (contractor association), the "Centre de Recherche de l'industrie cimentière" (cement producers association) and the Belgian Ministry of Public Works, with the financial aid of the National Institute for Scientific Research in the Industry (IRSIA) and the associations of producers of clay bricks and cement blocks. The tests were made by the cement industry and the universities of Louvain and Liège.

In Belgium, excellent standards have been set up concerning the properties of masonry materials such as solid, perforated, and hollow bricks; concrete blocks; cement mortar; and sand.

There does not exist any standard for calculating brickwork and blockwork, giving the allowable stress in these structures in relation to several factors such as:

1. The properties of the materials: bricks and concrete blocks, mortar.
2. The dimensions, especially the slenderness of the wall.
3. The size and bond of the units.
4. The thickness and regularity of the joints.
5. The method of applying the loads (distributed, local, axial and eccentric loads).
6. Workmanship (wetting of the bricks or blocks prior to laying, filling of the joints, flatness and regularity of the courses, hardening of the masonry, etc.).

The whole research program comprises the following stages, only the first of which is terminated:

1. Determination of the masonry basic strength R′ on walls in relation to the quality of the materials (bricks, concrete blocks) and of the mortar.
2. Comparison of the basic strength measured on storey-height walls, the elements having a small slenderness (near 7).
3. Determination of the effect of eccentricity of loads on the strength of storey-height walls.
4. Determination of the influence of workmanship on masonry strength.

Research Program

In this first biennal research stage, the tests mainly attempted to determine, for as many types of clay bricks and concrete blocks as possible, the relations between the physical and mechanical properties of the materials and the behaviour-under-load of walls built with these materials for several mortar compositions.

Materials Used for the Masonry Tests

The bricks and concrete blocks tested and the masonry mortar used are included in Table 21-1.

Table 21-2, taken from the Belgian Standard NBN 476–Perforated or Hollow Clay Bricks for Common Brickwork, gives the differences between solid, perforated and hollow bricks.

For concrete blocks NBN 538 draws the following distinction, based on the maximal volume weight (expressed in t/m3):

Extra light blocks	type 0.55
Very light blocks	type 0.75
Light blocks	type 1.2
Medium-heavy blocks	type 1.9
Heavy blocks	heavy type

Mortar Components

Binders. The following binders were used in preparing the mortar: ordinary portland cement, fat-lime powder complying with the prescriptions of issue II of the building specifications of the Ministry of Public Works, ordinary hydraulic lime of current quality.

Table 21-1
Masonry Materials Subjected to Tests

	Symbol	Materials (bricks and blocks)	Nominal size (mm) (L x T x H)	Mortar Symbol	Composition binder*	sand**	water***
Clay	A1	High-strength solid bricks	192 x 90 x 65	M1	C250 G50	B	21.5
				M2	C300	B	21.0
				M2′	C300	D	18.0
				M2″	C300	C	25.0
				M3	H350	B	21.0
				M4	C200 G100	B	22.0
				MI	C370	1/2C-1/2Rh	19.3
				MII	C400	Rh	17.8
				MIII	C500	D	16.65
	A2	Medium-strength solid bricks	192 x 90 x 65	M1	C250 G50	B	21.5
	A3	Low-strength solid bricks	192 x 90 x 65	M1	C250 G50	B	21.5
	A3′	Lower-strength solid bricks	192 x 90 x 65	M1	C250 G50	B	21.5
	A4	Hollow bricks type 0.8	290 x 190 x 190	M4	C200 G100	B	22.0
	A5	Bricks with holes (10.4% voids) considered as solid	192 x 90 x 65	M4	C200 G100	B	22.0
	A6	Perforated bricks (29.5% voids) type 1.1	290 x 190 x 90	M4	C200 G100	B	22.0
Concrete	B1	Extra light-weight solid cellular concrete blocks (type 0.55)	390 x 190 x 250	M5	C100 G100	B	23.0
	B1′	Very light-weight solid cellular concrete blocks (type 0.75)	390 x 190 x 250	M6	C125 G125	B	22.2
	B2	Very light-weight hollow cinder concrete blocks (type 0.75)	390 x 190 x 190	M6	C125 G125	B	22.2
	B3	Light-weight hollow pumice concrete blocks (type 1.2)	390 x 190 x 190	M5	C100 G100	B	23.0
	B4	Light-weight solid expanded clay concrete blocks (type 1.2)	390 x 190 x 190	M6	C125 G125	B	22.2
	B5	Medium-heavy hollow gravel concrete blocks (type 1.9)	390 x 190 x 190	M4	C200 G100	B	22.0
	B6	Heavy solid gravel concrete blocks (heavy type)	390 x 190 x 190	M1	C250 G50	B	21.5

* The mortar composition is indicated according to NBN 578: Masonry and plaster mortars. The capitals indicate the type of binder according to the following code:

C : cement.
G : fat lime powder.
H : ordinary hydraulic lime.

The numbers indicate the binder content in kg per m3 dry sand. Example: C250 G50 mortar is composed of 250 kg cement and 50 kg fat lime powder for 1 m3 dry sand.

The mortars have the compositions prescribed by NBN 578, except in type A5 bricks, type B1 and B3 blocks, and series A1 mortars.

** For the investigation three different types of sand were used, marked B, C, and D. These are set out in sand. For the MI and MII mortars Rhine sand (Rh) (fineness modulus m = 1.30) was used.

*** The water quantity is expressed as a percentage of the dry sand and binder weight.

Table 21-2

	Voids %	Volume weight (kg/m3)	Type
Solid bricks	less than 15		
Perforated bricks	from 15 up to 25	not exceeding 1.600	1.6
	from 25 up to 40	not exceeding 1.400	1.4
	from 25 up to 40	not exceeding 1.100	1.1
Hollow bricks	from 40 up to 60	not exceeding 1.100	1.1
	60 and more	not exceeding 800	0.8

Each binder was supplied at one time for the whole research.

Sand. The choice of the sand was based on results of a sieve analysis test on several types of pit sand commonly used for masonry mortar. A medium-sharp sand, indicated by B, was used for the whole investigation.

For the M2′ mortar, a coarse-grained sand, indicated by B, was chosen, because it is completely within the grain band proposed by the I.B.N. (Institut Belge de Normalisation). For the M2″ mortar, a medium-soft, medium-sharp C sand (equal volume parts) was used that is also used as masonry sand, although the grain-size distribution curve falls completely outside the prescribed band. Although C sand is not suitable for mortar preparation, it has been used for a series of walls to determine its influence on the mechanical properties of masonry.

Figure 21-1 gives the grain distribution curve of the B, C, and D sand and also their main characteristics.

Water Content. The quantity of water to be used for each mortar was first determined in the laboratory; then the advice of the mason was asked who found the proper mortar workability. The corresponding quantity of water is expressed as a percentage of the dry sand and binder weight.

Test Walls

Number and Size. There was a specified mortar composition for each material. Five identical walls were built up with the following nominal dimensions:

Width	60 cm
Thickness	19 cm
Height	105 cm.

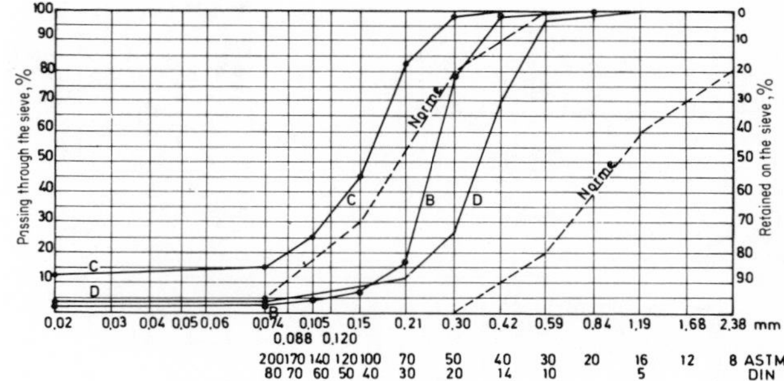

Figure 21-1. Grain size distribution curve and main characteristics of B, C, and D sands used.

Preparation of the Bricks and the Blocks. Prior to constructing the walls, the bricks and the blocks were put in a moisture saturated room for 48 hours. These materials were not dipped in the water prior to use, except for the A3 bricks (very porous).

Construction of the Walls. The walls were built in a hall wherein the temperature (20°C) and the relative moisture (65%) of the air fluctuated little. The masonry bond had staggering cross joints. The solid brick masonry consists of alternate courses of headers and stretchers. For the other materials, the thickness (19 cm) was equal to that of the wall.

The cross and bed joints were properly filled with mortar, except in the voids of the hollow of perforated blocks. Jointing was done as the work progressed. The thickness of the joints was uniform (1 cm). The regularity of the laying and the horizontal lie of the courses were checked carefully.

The base and the upper slab are identical (Figure 21-2). Both consist of a metal URN 30-S profile with light reinforced concrete fill. Both slabs are tied with four threaded bars, enabling a little vertical pretensioning force to be exerted by turning the tightening-nuts fixed on the threaded end of the bars. Thus, no joint can be opened and no fixing be severed during transport.

Storage of the Walls. After construction, the wall is enveloped in a plastic foil for 28 days. To avoid moisture exchange with the laboratory air, the borders of the foil are sealed below and above the slabs. This storage method equals a stay in a moisture-saturated atmosphere of about 20°C.

Table 21-3

Name of the sand	⩽74 μ %	⩽ 20 μ %	Fineness modulus ASTM	Organic matter congent	Sand equivalent %
B 1/2	3.7	2.8	1.155	traces	32
C 1/2 soft – 1/2 sharp	14.0	12.45	0.570	traces	26.5
D coarse-grained	3.7	3.62	1.690	traces	27

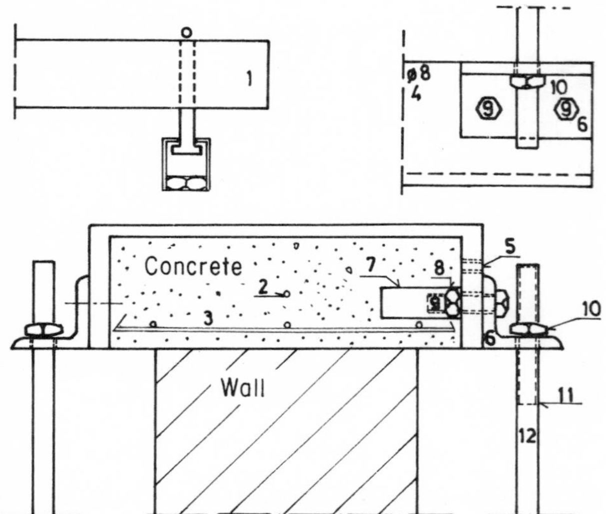

Figure 21-2. Scheme of wall slabs. Notes: 1. Lever bar. 2. ∅ 8 polished drawn steel. 3. Reinforcement 2 x 3 ∅ 8. 4. UPN 30-S. 5. hole ∅ 8 with screw thread. 6. Angle iron 60 x 60 x 10. 7. Protection pipe. 8. Hexagonal nut 5/8″. 9. Hexagonal bolt 5/8″. Hexagonal screw bolt 3/4″. 11. Part with screw thread. 12. Bar ∅ 3/4″.

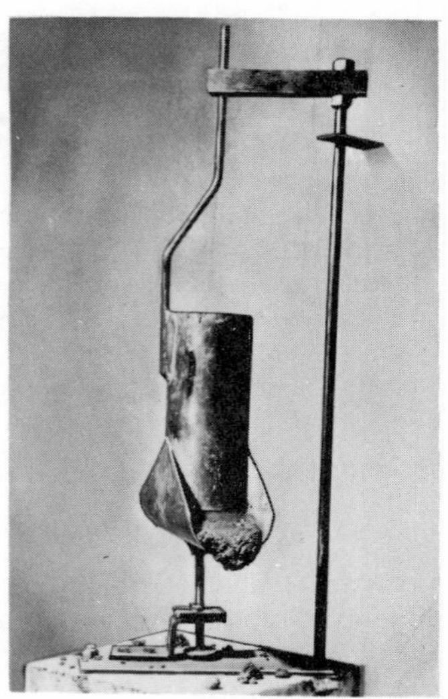

Figure 21-3. Mömeter for the measurement of the mortar fluidity.

Tests Made

Brick and Concrete Block Tests. Table 21-4 includes the tests carried out on bricks and concrete blocks to determine as completely as possible the mechanical and physical properties. In general, the methods described in NBN 118, 476 and 538 were applied.

Mortar Tests. To determine the mechanical and physical properties, the mortar was first thoroughly investigated.

During construction, a mortar sample was taken for each wall to determine the mechanical bending tensile strength and compressive tensile strength. The specimens were 4 x 4 x 16 cm3 test units which were stored in a plastic foil after demoulding. Their fluidity was measured with the DIN-TABLE or Mömeter (Figure 21-3).

Wall Tests. The walls were crushed 28 days after storage at 20°C in waterproof plastic foil.

During the test, the load was applied in increments of one tenth of the calculated crushing load, the load being kept constant during 1 minute at each loading stage. For each loading stage, the time-of loading application was 30 seconds. The longitudinal (vertical) deformations of the wall on the four faces and the transverse expansions between the opposite vertical faces were measured.

With some walls, the elastic behaviour could be determined by first loading to two tenths of the crushing load, then unloading to 0, and reloading to the ultimate load as in the above-described process.

Test Results

The main test results are included in Tables 21-5 and 21-6. The first applies to brick and block wall tests; the second applies to concrete block and concrete-block wall tests. For each measured characteristic, the average value is indicated in brackets as is the coefficient of variation (which is a measure of the dispersion) equal to the standard deviation divided by the average value:

$$\delta = 100 \frac{\sigma}{M} \text{(in \%)*}$$

If not indicated, the sand used for the mortar preparation is B sand. The other types of sand are indicated by SC, SD or Srh as it concerns C, D or Rhine sand described under Sand.

Analysis of and Main Comments on the Test Results

Comparison of the Several Brick Compression Tests

Figure 21-4 indicates that the different compression tests carried out on solid bricks give a similar classification of this bricks in relation to their mechanical strength.

The compression test on two, superposed half-bricks did not give results which could be reproduced in the laboratory.

$$* \quad \delta = \frac{\sigma}{M} = \frac{1}{M}\sqrt{\frac{\Sigma \epsilon^2}{n-1}}$$

where ϵ is the difference between each measuring result and the average value M
n is the number of measures done.

The compression test on bricks laid flat with the faces smoothed with standard mortar seems to present the most advantages for the following reasons:

1. The results of the tests on the same brick supply exhibit an average with little dispersion.
2. The smoothing of the faces with mortar reduces some irregularities on the brick surfaces which corresponds to use of the bricks in masonry. This situation does not exist with the test on bricks with surfaces struck off smooth.
3. The difference between the brick properties is apparent, but not excessive.
4. The test is made on entire bricks, and the smoothing of the surfaces can take place on a brick with flat or grooved test surfaces (case of hollow bricks).

Thus, this test applies to all types of bricks and if a great advantage for the comparison of the mechanical properties of the different types of bricks used. This advantage, however, is limited to the bricks where the height-to-cross section ratio are nearly the same. This is due to the warping of the bearing plates during the test. This strongly influences the measured results, especially for test units with little slenderness.

Tensile Strength of Bricks and Blocks

The test results exhibit a large dispersion. Although the tensile strength of a material increases in the same sense as the compressive strength, there is no general relation between both properties.

Capillary Absorption Capacity of Bricks and Blocks (Haller Method)

The Haller method consists of measuring the weight increase of the material put in water during 1 minute 1 cm deep. This weight increase is compared with the total immersed surface of the material (unities: g/dm2.min.).

Table 21-4
Tests Made on Clay Bricks and Concrete Blocks

Tests	Belgian standards	Materials tested
Check of dimensions	NBN 118, 476 and 538	All types of bricks and blocks
Compression test on two superposed half bricks	NBN 118	Only solid bricks
Compression test on two half bricks with a joint of the same mortar as that used in the test walls (test after 28 days)		
Compression test on solid brick or block with test faces smoothed with standard mortar *	NBN 476 and 538	All types of bricks and blocks
Compression test on whole brick of block with test faces struck off smooth		All types,except hollow bricks
Tensile test **		All types
Capillary absorption capacity (Haller method)		All types
Water absorption capacity by immersion	NBN 118, 476 and 538	All types
Volume weight (specific and effective)	NBN 476 and 538	All types
Adhesion of the mortar to the brick or blocks **		All types

* Standard mortar contains one part PDR cement, 2 parts dune sand passing through 0.4 mm mesh width sieve and retained on the 0.09 mm mesh width sieve; the mixing water represents 20% of the total dry sand and cement weight. In practice this percentage could not be applied and had to be reduced.

** This test consists in sticking small steel plates on the opposite small faces of the bricks or blocks. Each plate is provided with a bar hinged at one end and anchored in the jaws of the tensile strength testing machine.

Table 21-5
Results of the Main Brick and Brick Wall Tests

Tests	Number of tests per material	Unity	Solid bricks A 1 C250 G 50	C300	C300 SD	C300 SC	H350	C200 G100	C370 SC;Rh	C400 SRh	C500 SD	A 2 — C250 G 50	A 3 — C250 G 50	A 3' — C250 G 50	Hollow bricks type 0.8 A 4 62.4 C200 G100	Solid bricks with holes A 5 10.4 C200 G100	Perfo-rated bricks type 1,1 A 6 29.5 C200 G100
Brick tests																	
1. Nominal dimensions L x W x H		mm					192 x 90 x 65					192 x 90 x 65	192 x 90 x 65	192 x 90 x 65	290 x 190 x 190	192 x 90 x 65	290 x 190 x 90
2. Compression test on two half bricks (according to NBN 118.41)	15	kg/cm^2 (%)	445 (11)									307 (23)	214 (15.2)	146 (34)			
3. Item 2 but with joint of the same mortar as for the walls	15	kg/cm^2 (%)	192 (10)	196 (11.9)	220 (17.4)	212.4 (9.7)	69.25 (29.5)	137.7 (11.7)	294.3 (10.4)	321.9 (13.9)	367.4 (8.3)	188.5 (10)	140 (7.9)	102 (13.6)			
4. Compression test on entire brick with faces smoothed with standard mortar	15	kg/cm^2 (%)	493 (8.4)									360 (18)	277 (15.7)	149.3 (33)	46.6 (24)	242 (15)	181.7 (8.2)
5. Compression test on entire brick with faces struck off smooth	15	kg/cm^2 (%)	762 (22.6)									597 (16.9)	263 (13.1)	151.3 (25.3)		245.5 (13.1)	184.7 (7.6)
6. Tensile test	15	kg/cm^2 (%)	21.5 (37.2)									23.4 (30)	7.8 (31)	3.37 (22.2)		9.28 (27.7)	1.45 (27)
7. Capillary absorption capacity (Haller method)																	
–on brick in supply condition	15	$g/dm^2 \times 1'$ (%)	6.6 (35.4)									14.2 (19)	26.9 (12.3)	27.3 (14.6)	4.5 (16.1)	32 (14.6)	32.2 (14.8)
–on dried brick	15	$g/dm^2 \times 1'$ (%)	8.5 (27.4)									14.2 (21)	27.8 (12.8)	29.3 (12.9)	5.61 (8.7)	36.2 (11.7)	32.0 (5.8)
8. Water absorption capacity (in weight)	15	% (%)	6.8 (11.4)									10.6 (8)	19.9 (8)	19.3 (8.3)	10.03 (14)	20.6 (9)	20.1 (3.6)
9. Volume weight of body	15	kg/dm^3 (%)	2.01 (1.3)									1.85 (0.6)	1.52 (3)	1.554 (8.4)	1.85 (7)	1.64 (2.31)	1.627 (0.5)
Volume weight of the brick = dry weight x (1 – v)	15	kg/dm^3													0.695	1.47	1.15
10. Adhesion on bricks in cross-shape	15	kg/cm^2 (%)	3.6 (12.5)	3.9 (12.3)	3.8 (11.8)	3 (13.7)	1.1 (27)	2.19 (31)	3.72 (16.9)	5.58 (14.3)	3.88 (21)	2.4 (30)	1.9 (42)	1.57 (32)	1.53 (10.4)	2.04 (22)	0.97 (23)
Mortar tests																	
11. Mechanical tests																	
compression	6 per wall	kg/cm^2 (%)	68.9 (6.85)	104.7 (6.25)	142.6 (4.4)	110.9 (7.45)	4.03 (11.2)	38.5 (4.8)	213.5 (6)	224.4 (9.87)	339 (2.8)	76.7 (6.5)	71.3 (3.8)	76.8 (4.2)	41.4 (3.6)	42.0 (5.7)	47.0 (16.7)
bending	3 per wall	kg/cm^2 (%)	20.3 (4.95)	28.3 (6)	34 (7.7)	29.4 (5.65)	0.66 –	12.47 (7.1)	42.7 (3.2)	42.4 (7.65)	49.7 (6.26)	22.1 (5.5)	20.1 (4.5)	20.9 (5.3)	12.77 (2.7)	11.2 (4.4)	14.3 (14.8)
12. Fluidity measured with Mömeter	1 per wall	Number of blows (%)	40 (5.15)	44 (4.7)	48 (4.5)	36 (4.5)	46 –	44 (2)	66 (2.2)	61 (5.9)	52 (5)	39 (10)	41 (7.3)	49 (4)	41.6 (4.3)	47 –	46 –
Wall tests	5	kg/cm^2 (%)	160.8 (2.85)	179.6 (3.69)	205.8 (4.68)	191.7 (6.12)	59.6 –	120 (8.51)	236.6 (6.76)	229.1 (10)	262.9 (6.10)	144.4 (6.21)	97.1 (3.61)	48.75 (5.8)	17.53 (11.8)	66.6 (13.4)	54 (6)

Table 21-6
Results of the Main Concrete Block and Concrete Block Wall Tests

Tests	Number of tests per material	Unity	Cellular concrete blocks B1 – extra-light C 100 G 100	Cellular concrete blocks B1' – very-light C 125 G 125	Cinder blocks B2 40 very-light C 125 G 125	Pumice blocks B3 34 light C 100 G 100	Expanded clay blocks B4 – light C 125 G 125	Gravel concrete blocks B5 40 med.-heavy C 200 G 100	Gravel concrete blocks B6 – heavy C 250 G 50
Block tests									
1. Nominal dimensions L x W x H		mm	390 x 190 x 250				390 x 190 x 190		
2. Compression test on block with faces smoothed with standard mortar (on total section)	15	kg/cm^2 (%)	30.87 (7.3)	55.67 (9.25)	58.1 (19)	45.26 (12.2)	49.2 (16.7)	130.6 (12.3)	181.8 (33)
3. Compression test on block with faces struck off smooth (on total section)	15	kg/cm^2 (%)	23.95 (9.3)	50.66 (5.5)	58.3 (30.2)	43.32 (9.4)	40.5 (15.3)	120.4 (15.7)	165 (35.3)
4. Tensile test	15	kg/cm^2 (%)	1.48 (27)	2.25 (49)	6.54 (17.6)	6.55 (18.3)	4.93 (19.7)	12.2 (13.9)	10.55 (22.3)
5. Partial shrinkage + 2/3 of expansion	5	mm/m (%)	0.405 (7.7)	0.255 (8.1)	0.499 (11.5)	0.276 (32.7)	0.499 (12.3)	0.175 (8.3)	0.142 (44.8)
6. Capillary absorption capacity (Haller method)									
– on block in supply condition	15	g/dm^2 x1' (%)	21.71 (5.5)	17.04 (14.1)	21.9 (44.9)	18.0 (33.7)	10.03 (33.2)	6.23 (36.2)	5.71 (96)
– on dried block	15	g/dm^2 x 1' (%)	22.89 (14.4)	23 (22)	35.0 (45.4)	19.6 (31.2)	16.95 (19.2)	5.40 (41)	9.47 (74)
7. Water absorption capacity (in weight)	15	% (%)	58.86 (3.45)	64.28 (1.8)	19.73 (7.6)	19.58 (13)	24.9 (4.5)	6.11 (10.8)	6.87 (17)
8. Volume weight of concrete	15	kg/dm^3	0.560	0.70	1.283	1.27	0.82	2.25	2.039
Volume weight of block	15	kg/dm^3 (%)	0.560 –	0.70 –	0.775 –	0.841 (20.2)	0.82 (4.6)	1.374 (4.8)	2.039 (3.2)
9. Adhesion									
–on blocks in cross-shape	5	kg/cm^2 (%)	0.31 (62.7)	0 –	0.385 –	0.58 (20.6)	0.51 (15.7)	0.834 (28.2)	2.554 (38)
–on blocks by opening of the joint (ASTM)	10	kg/cm^2 (%)	1.337 (25.3)	0.664 (30.8)	1.553 –	1.724 (18.3)	2.06 (24.5)	3.64 (34.2)	3.72 (21.5)
Mortar tests									
10. Mechanical tests on 4 x 4 x 16 cm3 tests units									
–compression	6	kg/cm^2	7.65	14.2	13.5	9.9	16.88	44.5	89.69
–bending	3	kg/cm^2	4	5.25	5.3	4.2	5.50	13.58	19.9
11. Fluidity measured with DIN table	1 per wall	–	1.38	1.35	1.19	1.41	1.28	1.35	1.38
Wall tests	5	kg/cm^2	22.07 (6.42)	37.89 (2.06)	24.47 (8.0)	30.84 (4.16)	33.86 (12)	59.87 (7.10)	94.12 (7.42)

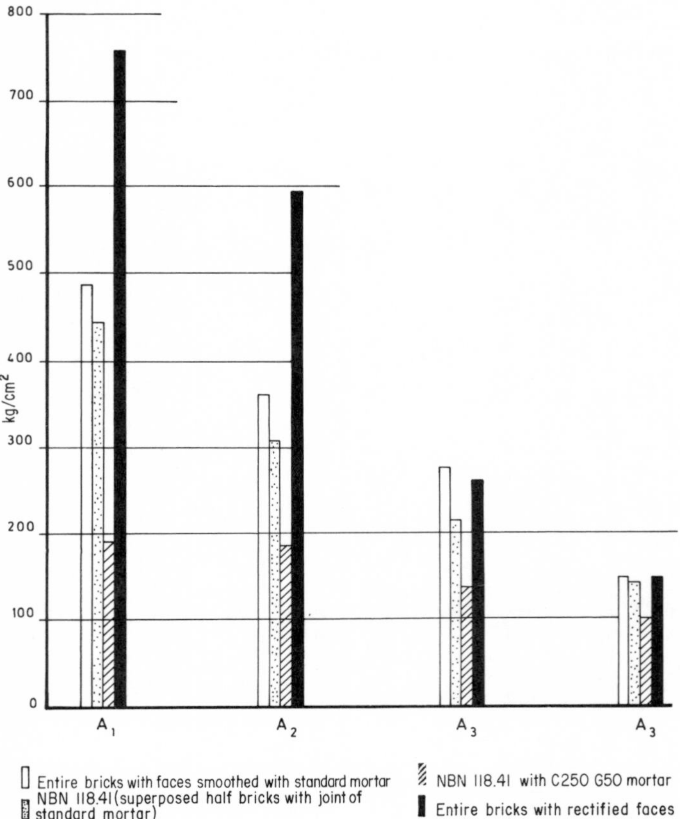

Figure 21-4. Compressive strength of solid bricks.

The absorption test was made on dry bricks and blocks in supply condition without having undergone a preliminary treatment. It should be noted that, in the second case, the stored materials were sheltered from rain and exterior moisture.

In general, the ascertained differences are small, except in some very porous concrete blocks. For medium-heavy and heavy, ordinary concrete blocks, the capillary absorption capacity is very small and the determination of the weight increase is uncertain because of the influence exerted by the dripping water which makes weighing very inaccurate (Figure 21-5).

For perforated blocks or bricks, the Haller value is obtained by deviding the weight increase by the gross section of the brick or the block plus the perimeter of the immersed surface multiplied by 1 cm. Thus, the Haller value measures the quantity of water absorbed out of the mortar by the brick or block used.

The decrease of the water in the joint mortar counteracts the normal bond and hardening of this mortar, especially near the exterior faces of the wall, where the drying of the bricks and the mortar occurs faster than inside the masonry. Because of this, according to Haller, the decrease of wall strength greater as load eccentricities and wall slenderness increase.

The importance of the Haller value is especially perceptibl with materials having a strong capillary absorption capacit when used without preliminary wetting. The results of the A series (very porous bricks), A5 (bricks with holes), A (perforated bricks) and B2 (cinder blocks) show that th strength of the walls are abnormally low when taking int account the properties of the materials and mortar used. Th can be explained by the fact that during the construction thes materials drained an excessive quantity of water out of th mortar (in relation to the Haller value), diminishing th strength of the joints and, thus also of the masonry. For A bricks, B2 blocks and heavy B6 blocks, the compressiv strengths determined on bricks or blocks yield very disperse results and lead to premature failure.

Water Absorption Capacity of Bricks and Blocks by Immersio

Generally water absorption capacity by capillarity (Halle and by immersion are physical properties varying in the sam sense. Nevertheless, except for B1 and B1′ cellular blocks, th percentages of water absorption (according to Belgian stan ards) vary little from material to material, whereas the Hall value indicates these materials differ from each other (Figu 21-6).

Because of the mechanical properties of masonry, th Haller value is a more important characteristic than th percentage of water absorption by immersion.

With cellular concrete blocks, the water absorption b immersion goes very slowly. When complying with th instructions of NBN 538, § 7.07, some weeks must sometim elapse before a constant weight of the water saturated materi

Figure 21-5. View of the Haller test apparatus.

can be obtained. It is also very difficult to get the material in dry condition. For cellular concrete, instructions should be drawn up which are more suitable for this material. For example: the absorption percentage can be determined by immersion in boiling water or in water under pressure.

Adhesion of Blocks or Bricks to Mortar

The numerous tests yield very dispersed results. It appears that by measuring the release between bricks or blocks built in cross shape, the adhesion conditions existing with materials and mortar used in masonry are not reproduced. In this contest, the ASTM test to open the joint by eccentric stress conforms more with reality.

The adhesion capacity is strongly influenced by the preliminary wetting of the bricks and blocks. With a dry material, this adherence to the mortar is very small. A short immersion (some seconds) suffices to increase considerably the adhesion capacity.

Quality of Used Mortars

Mechanical Tests. Tests on 4 x 4 x 16 cm3 prisms yields tensile and compressive strengths which also can be reproduced with mortar of the similar composition. The dispersion of the results is small.

Fluidity Tests. The measurement of fluidity by the Mömeter yields results with very little dispersion and can be reproduced. This measuring-method, worked out in Sweden, will be embodied in the Belgian standard concerning the mortar test methods now being drawn up.

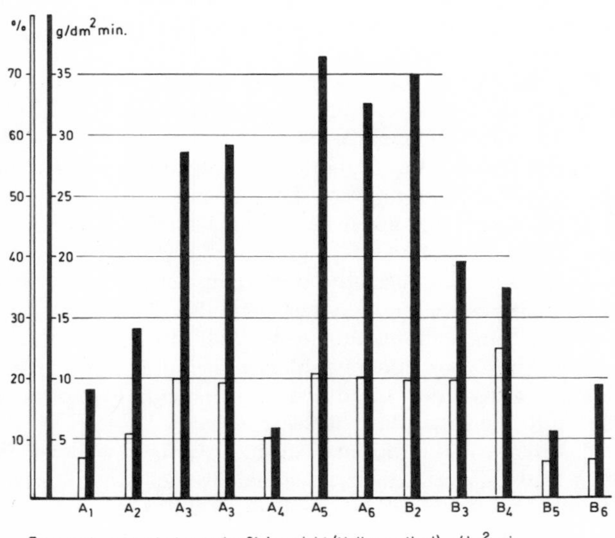

Figure 21-6. Percentages of water absorption by immersion and by capillarity.

Wall Tests

Figures 21-7 to 21-12 show some walls after being compressed.

Figure 21-7. Failure of a wall, side view (A1M3). H 350 mortar.

Figure 21-8. The mortar comes out the joints (A1M3). H 350 mortar.

Figure 21-9. Failure of a wall, front view (A1MII). C 400 mortar (very strong).

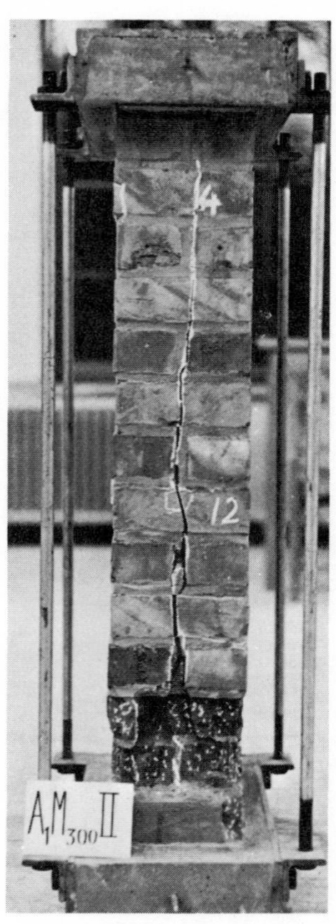

Figure 21-10. Failure of a wall, side view (A1MII). C 400 mortar (very strong).

The dispersion of the results is small (2.8 to 13.4%) indicating that the construction of the walls and the tests ran a normal course. This dispersion is also small, whether the elements (bricks or blocks) are small or large.

The results of the 9 series of tests on walls built with the same A1 bricks and mortars of different quality are included in Figure 21-13.

On the abscissa is plotted the average wall strength and on the ordinate the mortar compressive strength determined after 28 days from 4 x 4 x 16 cm3 test units. The experimental points lay on a curve and in this context the following remarks can be made:

1. The ordinate at the origin of the experimental curve indicates that even with strengthless mortar, the masonry has a considerable compressive strength. This corresponds with a joint carried out with a material having no cohesion (sand for example), which would distribute the loads.

2. The law of the increase of strength in relation to that of the mortar gets near a asymptote. It is useless to increase the mortar strength over a certain value. In the special case of the curve of Figure 21-14, this asymptote is situated near 280 kg/cm2 of the boundary strength of the wall. For example, it may be assumed that over point P of the experimental curve, the increase of the mortar quality is becoming prohibitive considering the small improvement in masonry quality.

For example, to increase the wall strength from 243 to 270 kg/cm^2, the mortar quality should increase from 245 to approximately 400 kg/cm2.

On the basis of the findings and reservations, the following simple and empiric rule can be recommended for the construction of high masonry where the mechanical strength is the main sought characteristic.

For load-bearing masonry, it is recommended to use mortar with a compressive strength measured after 28 days on 4 x 4 x 16 cm2 test units about equal to the half of the strength of the material (brick or concrete block) measured on the entire element with faces smoothed with standard mortar and reduced to the net section of the material.

In this way the optimal mortar strength is determined which leads to better mechanical achievements and takes into account the brick or block quality and the economy of construction.

This simply means that mortar quality corresponds to each material; a mortar with strength lower than this quality (misuse of the brick qualities) or higher (too strong mortar for the material) gives a bad yield and is thus too expensive.

Figure 21-11. Failure of a wall, front view (A6M4). Perforated bricks, type 1,1. C 200 G 100 mortar.

Figure 21-12. Failure of a wall, side view (A6M4). Perforated bricks, type 1,1. C 200 G 100 mortar.

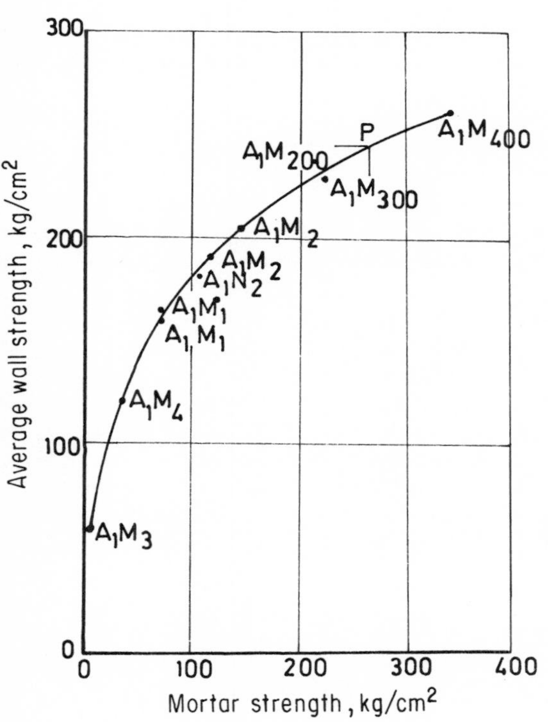

Figure 21-13. Influence of the mortar quality on the basic strength of masonry for bricks of a given quality (A1). The quality of the mortar (M) can be determined to obtain the best possible results of the masonry (P).

Except for the AlMI, A1MII, A1MIII and A4 series, the mortar strength was much less than that of the bricks or blocks used. In this case, creep of the joint mortar might be expected through which the bricks were subjected to tensile stress.

Failure of the walls often occurs rather suddenly, and the cracks visible on the surface often occur only near nine tenths of the crushing load. The cracks appear on the section as well as on the major surfaces of the walls.

An examination of the strain-deformation diagrams (Figure 21-14) shows that during a test the behaviour of the wall can be classified in the following stages:

1. Elastical stage.
2. Internal breakdowns, observable sometimes by audible cracking; the extension values increase more or less suddenly.
3. Crushing stage.

It seems that the destruction of the wall starts with internal cracks. At this moment the measured expansion increases (rather sudden flexure of the $\sigma' - \epsilon_h$ curves); the bricks and blocks show tensile failures and vertical loosenings.

It is often stated that the strain-deformation curves do not run through the origin which means that, with a little load, significant deformations of the wall occur. This is because the components (mortar and brick) settle at the beginning of the test.

A certain number of walls were tested by loading to 0.2 R′, unloading to 0, then reloading. This showed that, except for the A1M3 series (see Table 21-7), the behaviour under compression of the masonry up to the 0.2 R′ load boundary may be considered as elastic and that the deformations disappear when the load decreases to 0.

Table 21-7 gives the average modulus of elasticity at the moment of one half (5/10) of the crushing load (angle coefficient of the tangent on the experimental curve on the point of the ordinate 0.2 R′) for each series of 5 walls. The values of the modulus of elasticity for the brick A1 wall series show the influence of the mortar quality.

For the hollow brick A4 series (voids consisting of horizontal canals) the modulus of elasticity at 0.R′ is small (28.000 kg/cm2): the longitudinal deformation at the moment of failure is less than 1 mm/m, whereas it is near 2 mm/m for the other brick walls. This indicates that hollow brick masonry is crushed a good deal before the proper strength of the bricks is reached. (Figure 21-15.)

These premature failures occur by shearing the bricks on the spot of the connections of the vertical exterior walls with the horizontal parts.

Tentative Conclusions

The general conclusions drawn from the tests made during the first stage of this program are tentative conclusions. In this context, they should be confirmed by continued testing, applying mainly to the influence of the loads and the slenderness of the wall on the mechanical strength of the masonry. Efforts will also be made to determine the influence exerted on this strength by workmanship factors such as the exact filling of cross and bed joints, the regularity of the courses, the joint thickness, the wetting of the materials prior to use, etc. Finally, other investigations will aim at deter-

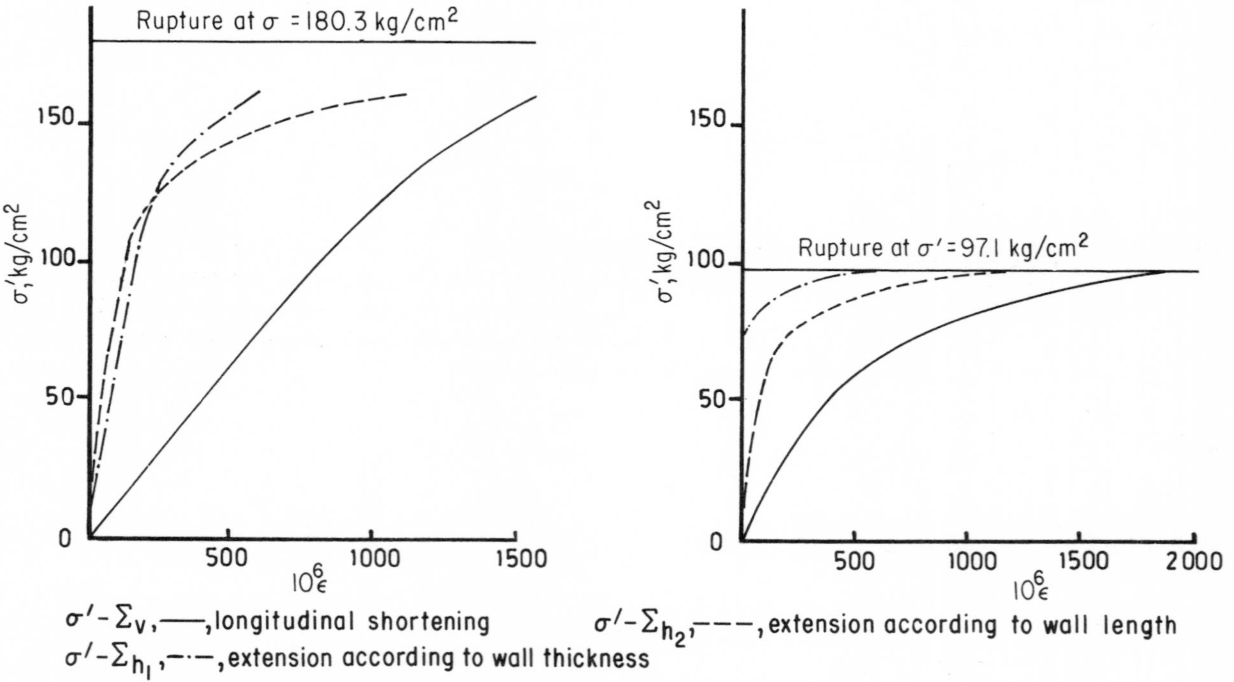

Figure 21-14. Strain deformation curves. On the left a wall of the A1M2 series, on the right a wall of the B6 series.

Table 21-7

Series	(E) 0,2 R′ in kg/cm2
A1M1	132.200
A1M2	138.800
A1M2′	143.200
A1M2″	137.000
A1M3	9.500
A1M4	102.750
A1MI	152.400
A1MII	155.000
A1MIII	138.200
A2M1	75.500
A3M1	58.000
A3′M1	41.300
A4M4	28.000
A5M4	50.600
A6M4	47.800
B1	16.560
B1′	21.000
B2	31.980
B3	30.240
B4	37.700
B5	91.250
B6	129.200

mining the methods for calculating walls, taking into account the assembling of elements and the deformation mechanisms. Some tentative conclusions or recommendations are given in the following paragraphs.

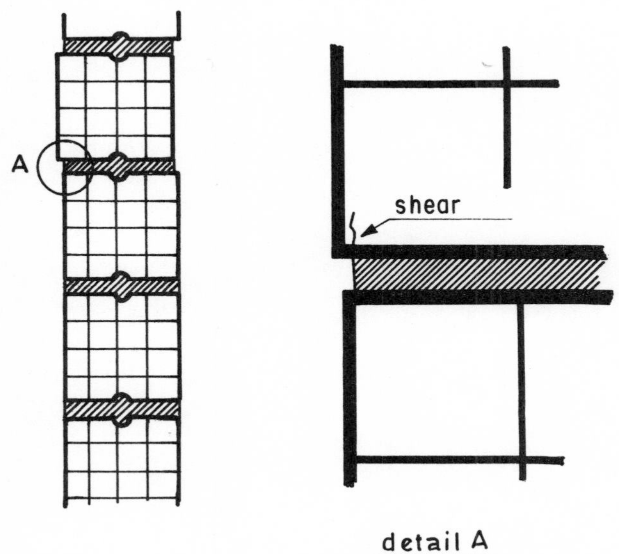

Figure 21-15. Failure of a hollow brick wall by shearing of jutting wall.

Regarding the Masonry Materials. The results of the compressive test on two superposed half-bricks are hard to compare from laboratory to laboratory. This also applies to results obtained in the same laboratory when tests are carried out with intervals of some days. This is because the testing procedure inherently has errors. The quality of the joint mortar also exerts a great influence on the final result.

We propose to perform the compression test on entire brick or block with faces smoothed with standard mortar. This test presents the advantage of being applicable to all types of materials, giving an exact classification of the mechanical properties of the materials in relation to those of the masonry, yielding few dispersed results and giving a valuable indication for calculating the masonry's basic strength.

Mechanically mixing mortar improves its homogeneity. It is recommended to prepare the mortar with a mixer, for load-bearing masonry subjected to high work strains.

Masonry's basic strength is influenced by the capillary absorption capacity. For bricks or blocks having a high Haller value (higher than 20 g/dm2.min for example), it is important to wet them prior to use (immersion of several minutes suffices). These materials may not be used in frosty weather. It is recommended to use the bricks or the blocks in dry condition. For some materials, special glue mortars meet the difficulty of wetting.

It is necessary for the construction of load-bearing masonry subjected to high work strain to adapt the mortar quality to the quality of the brick or the block. It is recommended to use mortar having a compressive strength after 28 days measured on 4 x 4 x 16 cm3 test units of about equal to half the strength of the material (brick or block) measured on the whole element with faces smoothed with standard mortar (1 part PDR cement and 2 parts dune sand) and referred to as the net section of the material.

Regarding the Masonry

The strength of hollow brick masonry (with horizontal voids) is determined by jutting some bricks out from the wall faces. The wall strength is considerably less than that of the brick or the mortar considered separately.

For all these types of materials (bricks or blocks), work strains must be adopted for the calculation of this strong loaded masonry built up with this materials, based on the ultimate strains measured on walls or test walls. The properties of the brick and the mortar only do not suffice as criteria for determining this work strain. This remark applies especially to hollow bricks and to bricks or blocks with a high capillary absorption capacity. We recommend building up the wall, to store them, to carry out the compression test, and to measure the deformations according to what is said in Test Walls and Wall Tests.

Provisory and under reserve of confirmation by subsequent tests, the allowable work strain of masonry under axial load and for a slenderness h/d (°) less than 8, may be calculated on the ground of the ultimate strain measured on walls by dividing the average ultimate strength obtained on 3 test walls by a factor 5 (factor of safety). The work strain determined in this way should be reduced to take account of the slenderness of the wall and the eccentricity of the load.[1] The determination of these reduction factors will be investigated later by the C.S.T.C.-C.R.I.C. working committee within the framework of the masonry research.

The test walls and the masonry proper should be constructed in similar conditions, namely regarding the bond of the elements, the regularity and the filling of the joints, the moisture condition (preliminary wetting or not) of the bricks or blocks, the nature and the mixing of the components, and the preparation (mechanical or not) of the mortar.

[1]In order to calculate the slenderness, taking into account assemblage elements of the wall, it is recommended to take the British Standard "Structural Recommendations for Loadbearing Walls" *British Standard Code of Practice CP 111, 1964)* as a basis.

22. Static racking tests on concrete masonry walls.

r. J. C. Scrivener, Dept. of Civil Engineering, Massachusetts
stitute of Technology, Cambridge, Massachusetts

Introduction

The paper reports a series of tests on reinforced-concrete, ollow, masonry walls subject to static racking loads. In an arlier series of tests[1], flexural failure of 8′-8″-high by 8′-long alls in 4″ and 6″ concrete blocks was experienced. The 6″ alls of this series were made to fail in shear, by applying a ertical load which was just sufficient to balance, at each crement of racking load, the moment of the racking load bout the wall toe. A pattern of cracks parallel and close to e diagonal joining the loaded corner and wall toe was btained in each case.

The objectives of the tests, the results of which are to be sed as aids in the design of load-bearing reinforced masonry alls subjected to earthquake loads, were to determine:

1. The pattern of behaviour as the percentage of reinforcing as increased.

2. The relative effectiveness of vertical and horizontal einforcing.

3. The difference between the behaviour of walls where the ertical steel was peripheral and where the steel was distributed over the length of the wall.

Wall deflections, crack patterns, and cracking and failure ads are reported. The influence of varying the amount and istribution of the vertical and horizontal reinforcing is etermined. The test equipment used, readings taken, and tests n component materials are given. The test set-up is illustrated d graphs and tables of results are recorded.

The techniques and results of masonry wall racking tests ported by Schneider[2] and Converse[3] are compared with ose of the author.

Test Walls and Test Procedures

Description of Walls

12 walls, 8′-8″ high and 8′ long, in 6″ hollow concrete blocks, were tested in two groups. Series C, of 6 walls, was tested over one week, and three months later Series D, of 6 walls, was tested over a similar period. The numerical designation of each wall refers to the amount and distribution of reinforcing, which was altered for each wall, and is the same designation as that adopted in Series A walls of the earlier series[1]. A typical wall is detailed in Figure 22-1 where the numbers on the blocks refer to the type of concrete blocks (Vibrapac) used.

The walls were constructed on reinforced concrete bases and anchored by welding the mild-steel, vertical, deformed bars to 3/4″ diameter screwed rods projecting from the bases.

The reinforced cavities were filled by gravity feeding of site mixed grout, and rodded three or four courses at a time.

The mortar and grout specifications were:

Laying mortar: 1800 lb/in.^{2} nominal, as NZSS 1900, 9.2:1964, mix. No. 1. 1:4 by weight of ordinary Portland cement and sand with 10% lime and 6% Onoda (a plasticiser) by weight of cement.

Grout: 1:3 by weight of cement and sand (3/16″ maximum size aggregate), water cement ratio 0.5, Onoda 6%.

Concrete block, mortar, and grout cylinder compressive strengths and tensile test results of the deformed mild steel reinforcing are given in the Appendix.

Loading Frame

Figure 22-2 shows the side view of the loading frame. The M.S. frame consists essentially of two identical halves, separated by 10″, which straddle the wall. Each half is constructed of a vertical member (8″ x 3″ x 16# R.S.C.), a diagonal member, and a horizontal member (each 7″ x 3″ x 14# R.S.C.) welded at their junctions. Bearing brackets at the junction of the vertical and diagonal members carry the horizontal racking and vertical loads applied to the wall at its top. The loads are transferred to the concrete foundation via the frame and 2/3″-diameter pins at each end of the horizontal member.

Method of Testing, Instrumentation

Sixty ton hydraulic jacks provided the horizontal racking load and vertical load. So that the vertical jack should not restrain the horizontal wall movement, the 6″-diameter jack acted through a roller bearing of twelve 3/8″-diameter, 8″-long, silver-steel bars between, two 1″-thick mild-steel plates, each with a 1/8″-thick surface of hardened steel. The bottom plate was seated to the top of the wall by using a high-strength dental plaster. The horizontal jack applied its load through an 1½″-diameter hemispherical ball on to an indented plate seated with dental plaster against the vertical end of the wall. For load measurement, precalibrated pressure gauges were used.

Racking load was increased from zero in 4000 lb. increments until failure, which was taken to be the maximum load that could be applied to and held by the wall. At each increment and prior to applying the racking load, a vertical load, just sufficient to balance the overturning moment of the racking load about the toe of the wall, was applied. The geometry of the set-up was such that the ratio of horizontal to vertical load was 0.9.

Longitudinal horizontal deflections were recorded at the 2nd, 6th, and 10th courses of the loaded end of the wall using Mercer dial gauges mounted on an independent light steel frame.

Using two Mercer dial gauges, one towards each end of the walls, transverse deflections of up to 0.12″ were observed, probably due to slight off-centre application of the loads. No attempt was made to restrain the walls from bending sideways or twisting. When cracking occurred on the wall sides, unsymmetrical behaviour was not apparent.

The walls were whitewashed to ease finding cracks which were marked in coloured chalk with their load incidence. Crack widths were measured using a lens with magnification of 20 and etched with a graduated scale. As cracks were mostly at the mortar-block interfaces, accurate measurement was extremely difficult. The results quoted must be considered as very approximate. It was found that cracks which had just become visible to the naked eye were of the order of 0.001″ width.

After failure, some of the reinforced cavities were checked for grout filling and bond of grout to steel. In all cases, completely satisfactory filling and bonding was found.

Figure 22-2 shows the test set-up with 6 walls built on their bases, and the loading frame, jacks and dial gauges positioned on one wall. The pumps and pressure gauges for the jacks are in the foreground.

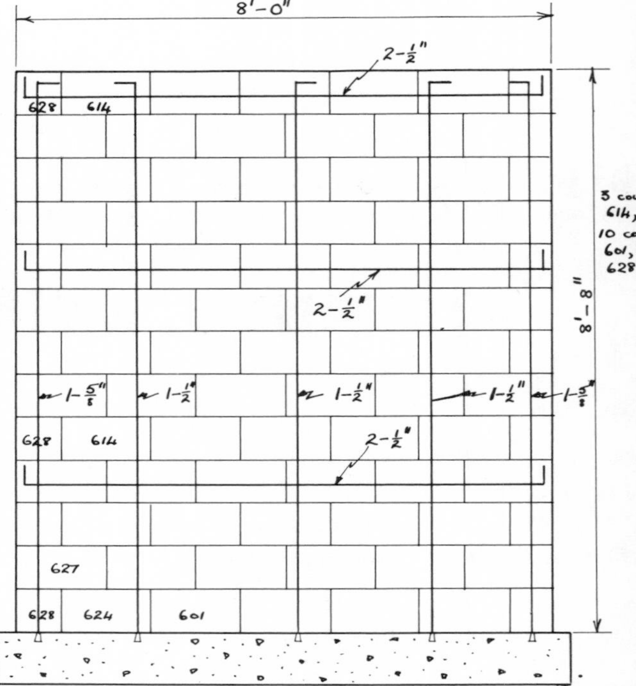

Figure 22-1. Wall D4.

Test Results and Interpretations

General Behaviour of Walls Under Load

Under load the walls all behaved similarly. At low loads, tl loaded-end deflections were very small and gradually increase with increasing load until, with a deflection at the 10th cour of between .01″ and .02″, the first crack was usually notice A crack of .001″ width could be seen with the naked ey particularily when the likely position of these cracks becan known, namely along or adjacent to the diagonal joining tl loaded corner and the wall toe. Further increments of loa produced extensions of these first cracks and addition cracking along or parallel to this diagonal line. Although crac were most often in the mortar, there were many instances cracks across the concrete blocks, even at moderately lo loads. Severe cracking, defined as the stage where some crac reached .01″ width, was accompanied by much larger incr mental deflections. Finally further load could not be mai tained, and failure was considered to be reached. Failure w never achieved suddenly.

Even after failure, with further load application produci dramatic increases in the deflection and crack widths, it w found that, particularly with the more heavily reinforce walls, a very high proportion (80 - 95%) of the failure loa could still be carried by the walls.

Cracking and Deflection

Figure 22-3 shows the crack pattern of wall D12 with tl typical diagonal cracking from loaded corner to toe. Earli

Figure 22-2. Test set-up.

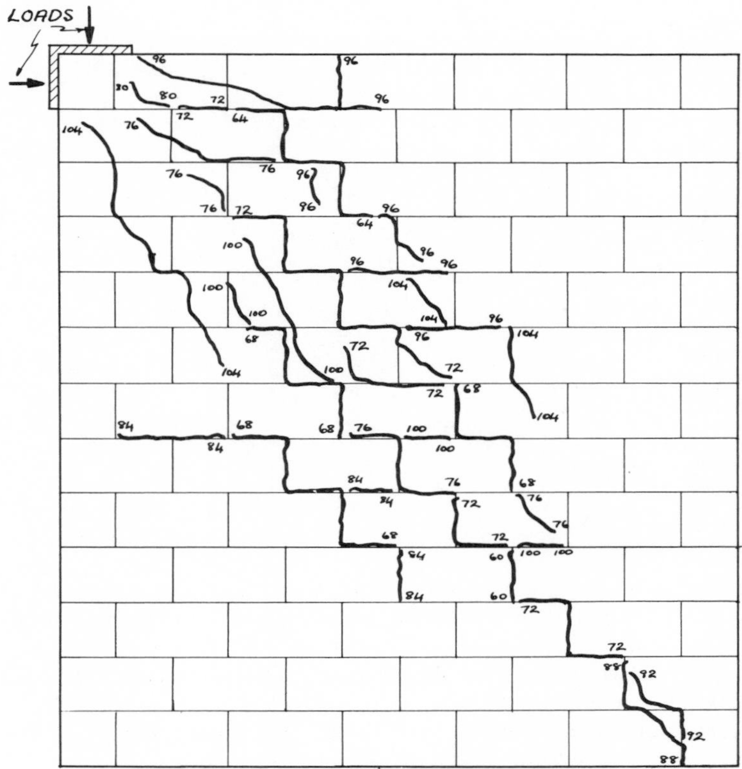

Figure 22-3. Crack pattern, wall D12. Note: Numbers represent crack incidence in Kips.

researchers, Schneider[2] and Converse[3], obtained the same diagonal cracking in their tests.

The behaviour of the walls, as given by (a) the loads causing first crack, severe cracking, and failure and (b) the stiffness at first crack and severe cracking, are given in Table 22-1. The stiffness is calculated on the requisite load divided by the deflection at the 10th-course loaded end. Accordingly, the stiffness is not that usually defined, since the walls exhibited little linear-elastic behaviour. This is clearly indicated in Figure 22 4, giving the load deflection curves of walls C1, C8, D4 and D13 which are fairly representative of all walls.

Up to severe cracking, the deflections at the 2nd and 6th courses (lower part of wall) were generally related to the 10th-course deflection in ratio of the heights of the courses above the wall bases, indicating that the loaded wall ends remained approximately straight. From severe cracking to failure, however, the deflection at the 10th course was much larger, in relation to the 2nd and 6th-course deflections, than would be obtained if the walls remained straight.

Because of considerable variations in the shapes of the load deflection curves and the lack of initial linear behaviour, the *stiffnesses* either at first crack or severe cracking showed no trend in values as quantity of reinforcing increases. At first crack, the stiffness varies indiscriminately from 1.9×10^3 to 5.5×10^3 kip/inch and at severe cracking the stiffness varies indiscriminately from 1.1×10^3 to 4.4×10^3 kip/inch.

The cracking behaviour brought out one important point. Walls C9 and D11 had the same amounts of vertical reinforcing but D11, with all of its bars in the periphery of the wall, had a much earlier onset of severe cracking than C9 with its evenly-distributed reinforcing. The failure loads of these two walls were similar.

On numerous occasions, a comparison was made between the deflection immediately after load application and the deflection some few minutes later. Very small differences, even near failure where maximum differences of the order of .003" were observed, indicated that creep under load was small for these walls.

Table 22-1
Behaviour of Walls Under Test

Wall	Reinforcing				First Crack (d)		Severe Cracking (e)		Failure
	Vertical Bars Peripheral	Vertical Bars Within	Horizontal Bars (a)	Percentage (b) (%)	Load Causing (kip)	"Stiffness" $\times 10^{-3}$(c) (kip/in.)	Load Causing (kip)	"Stiffness" $\times 10^{-3}$(c) (kip/in.)	Load (f) (kip)
C1	—	—	—	0	16	5.3	28	1.1	28
D2	2–5/8"	—	—	.104	32	4.9	48	4.4	68
C10	—	—	2–5/8" & 2–1/2"	.173	24	3.0	28	2.3	48
C7	2–5/8"	—	2–1/2"	.173	40	2.7	48	2.7	60
C8	2–5/8"	1–1/2"	1–1/2"	.173	44	2.1	48	1.9	56
C9	2–5/8"	2–1/2"	—	.173	52	2.0	56	1.6	60
D11	2–5/8" & 2–1/2"	—	—	.173	36	1.9	40	1.6	65
C3	2–5/8"	3–1/2"	—	.205	48	3.0	56	2.5	70
D12	2–5/8"	3–1/2"	2–1/2"	.272	60	2.8	72	1.8	104
D4	2–5/8"	3–1/2"	4–1/2"	.340	64	4.9	92	3.2	In excess of 112
D13	2–5/8"	3–5/8"	3–5/8"	.420	44	5.5	76	2.0	96
D14	2–5/8"	3–5/8"	4–5/8"	.470	48	2.4	80	2.0	112

Notes:

a. The horizontal reinforcing in the top bond beam, which for each wall consisted of 2–1/2" bars (except for walls D13 and D14 where 2–5/8" bars were used), is not included in the table or in the percentage of reinforcing.

b. The percentage of reinforcing is calculated on the percentage area of steel divided by the gross cross sectional area of the wall i.e., in this case 8' – 8" x 5-5/8".

c. The "stiffness" is calculated on the requisite load divided by the deflection at the loaded end, 10th course.

d. First crack is the first crack visible to the naked eye – some .001" wide.

e. Severe cracking is the stage where some part of the crack pattern has cracks of width .01".

f. Failure load is that maximum load which could just be sustained by the wall.

Ultimate Load

Table 22-1 records the failure loads of all walls. Several points emerge from a study of these results and those of the cracking and deflection behaviour.

Firstly, with low percentages of reinforcing, failure occurs soon after the load, causing severe cracking. With higher percentages of reinforcing, a great deal more load must be applied, after the load causing cracks of .01" width, before failure is attained.

Secondly, vertical and horizontal reinforcing appear to be equally effective as witnessed in walls C7, 8, 9, and D11. These walls, with the same percentage of reinforcing, have very similar failure loads, but they have different ratios of vertical to horizontal reinforcing. Of the same group, however, wall C10 exhibited a significantly lower failure load, but this is because with only horizontal reinforcing provided, this wall had no vertical equivalent to the top horizontal beam of all walls. C10 failed in lifting the top two courses off the lower ones; this failure was greatly different from those of the other walls of the group with their diagonal-cracking pattern right up to failure.

In series A [1], with flexural failure, it was found most advantageous to concentrate the steel vertically in the wall periphery. For walls in shear, however, although this distribution would not effect the failure load, it would produce an earlier onset of cracking than in walls with more evenly distributed reinforcing (see Cracking and Deflection).

Thirdly, it can be seen that the failure load increases as the quantity of reinforcement increases from zero up to approximately 0.3% of the gross cross-sectional area of the wall where the failure load is approximately 100 kip. Further increase of reinforcing percentage, even up to 0.47%, gave little if any increase in the failure load. Confirmation of this trend is shown in the results of Schneider[2], who found a maximum effective quantity of reinforcement of 0.2%. In his tests a racking load only was applied, but sufficient, peripheral, vertical reinforcement was placed in the walls to preclude this

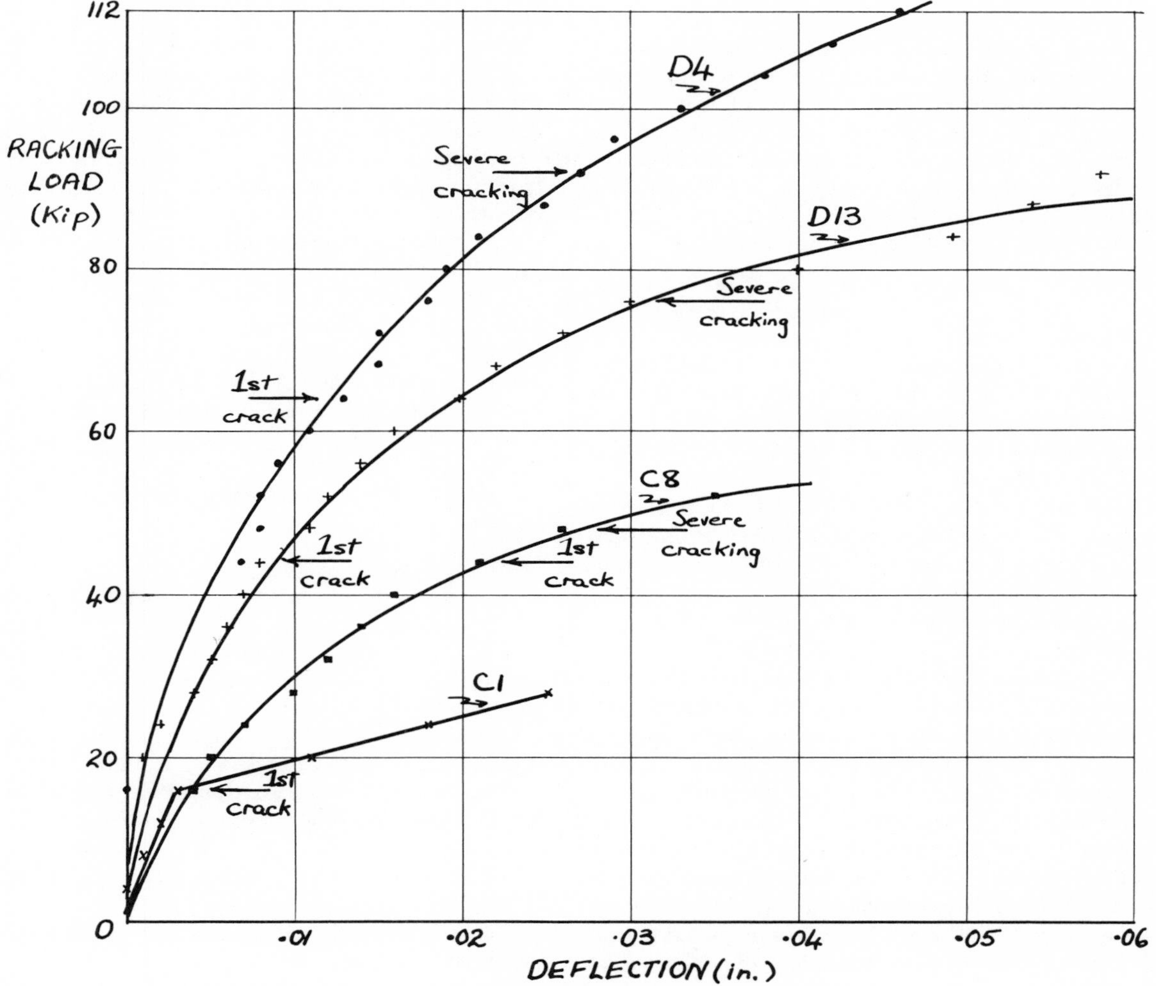

Figure 22-4. Load deflection curves, 10th courses, walls C1, 8, D4, and 13.

steel being stressed beyond its yield point when subjected to the tensile forces induced by the maximum-overturning moment. Consequently, Schneider's walls failed in shear with the typical diagonal cracking. The difference between his test walls and those reported here are in the boundary conditions on the vertical sides.

If one calculates the ultimate horizontal shear stress (ultimate load divided by the gross cross sectional area of the wall) for the walls with maximum failure loads (those walls with 0.3% reinforcing or greater) the stress obtained is 170 $lb./in.^2$ The equivalent figure from Schneider's tests is 143 $lb./in.^2$ These may be compared with the NZSS 1900, Chapter 9.2:1964 allowable stress in shear for reinforced, filled, wall units of 50 $lb./in.^2$

The compressive strengths of concrete blocks, mortar, and grout cylinders and the tensile strengths of the reinforcing bars show that Series D walls were a little stronger in all specimen tests than Series C walls. The walls reflect this in the slightly higher failure loads achieved in Series D walls over Series C walls where comparable walls were tested.

Repeated Loading

Walls D4 and D14 were loaded beyond the severe cracking zone, the loads removed, the residual deflections recorded, and then the walls were reloaded. This sequence of loading was repeated twice. Even though some relatively large deflections were not recoverable on unloading after severe cracking, the walls still behaved on the reloading cycle much as they did on the first loading. The extent of this phenomenon very likely depends on the amount of reinforcing in the wall.

Wall D4

Even after repeated loading of wall D4, as explained above, it proved to be too strong for the 60-ton jacks to fail the wall in shear. As the use of larger capacity jacks would have entailed major alterations in the test frame, D4 was failed in a predominantly flexural mode.

Racking load together with vertical load was applied, as in the shear tests, up to a 32-kip vertical load. From then onwards, only racking load was applied until flexural failure occurred, as in the earlier test series[2]. This failure was typified by horizontal cracks in the mortar of the lower courses near the loaded wall end, at a racking load of 72 kip.

It is interesting to predict the failure load on the basis determined in the earlier series. The theoretical failure load, neglecting the effect of the vertical load, would be approximately 25 kip. This failure load is calculated on the assumption that failure occurs when all of the vertical steel away from the wall toe has yielded and the moment of these yield loads about the wall toe equals the moment of the failure load about the wall toe. To balance the restoring moment, about the toe, of the 32-kip-vertical load would require an additional racking load of 29 kip. This gives a predicted failure load of 54 kip. As this figure is much less than the actual failure load of 72 kip, it seems that, in the above calculation, the effect of the vertical load is grossly underestimated. The situation is of considerable practical importance as masonr walls are very often carrying vertical loads much in excess o their dead weight. It is hoped to consider this problem i future tests and theoretical studies.

Conclusions

The conclusions which may be drawn from this series o tests on approximately square reinforced masonry wall subjected to a racking load, and to vertical load (to balanc flexural effects) and typified by cracking along or parallel t the diagonal from loaded corner to wall toe are:

1. Vertical and horizontal reinforcing are equally effectiv in providing satisfactory crack behaviour and failure loads.
2. Walls with evenly distributed reinforcing have a late onset of severe cracking than walls where the reinforcement i concentrated in the wall periphery.
3. With a low percentage of reinforcing, failure occurs soo after the onset of severe cracking (some crack width exceeding 0.01"). With higher percentages of reinforcing, th failure load is much greater than the load causing sever cracking.
4. As the load-deflection curves showed no linear portio and the curved shapes showed no pattern from wall to wall the stiffness (or load-deflection ratio at a point on the curve did not seem to bear any direct relationship with th percentage of reinforcement. However, for steel percentage from zero to 0.4%, at first crack (width approximately .001" the stiffness varied from 1.9×10^3 to 5.5×10^3 kip/in. A severe cracking (some widths exceeding .01"), the stiffnes varied from 1.1×10^3 to 4.4×10^3 kip/in.
5. Higher failure loads were obtained with walls with highe percentages of reinforcing up to 0.3% of the gross cross sectional area of the wall, which corresponds approximately t 100-kip failure load. Above this percentage, additional reinforcing had little effect on the failure load. From the walls with the optimum (0.3%) or higher percentage of reinforcing the ultimate horizontal shear stress (ultimate load divided by the gross cross-sectional area of the wall) was found to be 170 lb/in^2.

Acknowledgements

For their assistance in this research the author is grateful to the other members of the Test Walls Committee: T. D. Hempstalk, I. L. Holmes, J. Ince, A. H. Johnston, G. M. Jones, P. J. Moss, and T. H. Moynihan and to the following organizations: Christchurch City Council, Concrete Masonry Association, I. L. Holmes Consulting Engineers, Ministry of Works, University of Canterbury, and Vibrapac Blocks.

Appendix

Table 22-2 details the compressive strength of the concrete blocks, mortar and grout cylinders.

The tests on the deformed reinforcing bars gave average yield loads on 2 or 3 specimens:

Table 22-2
Compressive Strength of Concrete Blocks, Mortar, and Grout Cylinders

Specimen	Walls	Average Compressive Strength (lb./in.^{2})	Number of Specimens	Highest Strength (lb./in.^{2})	Lowest Strength (lb./in.^{2})	Coefficient of Variation (%)
Mortar Cylinders	C	2880	13 sets of 3	3790	2020	19
"	D	3180	13 sets of 3	3980	1780	21
Grout Cylinders	C	4570	3 sets of 3	5330	3820	–
"	D	5230	6 sets of 3	5700	4440	8
Concrete Blocks	C	2050	4	2090	2030	–
"	D	2700	6	2920	2320	–

Notes:

a. Mortar and grout cylinders were 4" diameter and 8" high, cured in accordance with NZSS 192 and tested at 28 days age.

b. Concrete blocks were cured in air and tested at ages approximately 2 months. Their compressive strength was calculated on the gross area of block including projections.

Yield load, nominal 5/8" diam. bars - Walls C = 12,700 lb.
Walls D = 12,900 lb.

Yield load, nominal 1/2" diam. bars - Walls C = 8,600 lb.
Walls D = 8,600 lb.

References

1. Scrivener, J. C., "Concrete Masonry Wall Panel Tests – Static Racking Tests with Predominant Flexural Effect", New Zealand Concrete Construction, Vol. 10, 1966, pp. 119-124.

2. Schneider, R. R., "Lateral Load Tests on Reinforced Grouted Masonry Shear Walls", University of Southern California Engineering Center, Report No. 70-101, 1959, pp. 1-47.

3. Converse, F. J., "Tests on Reinforced Concrete Masonry", *Building Standards Monthly*, Feb., 1946.

23. Racking tests on storey-height shear-wall structures with openings, subjected to pre-compression.

B. P. Sinha and Prof. A. W. Hendry, Dept. of Civil Engineering, University of Edinburgh, Edinburgh, Scotland

Introduction

In recent years, there has been increasing interest in load-bearing brickwork walls for frameless cross-wall construction. In a multi-storey building of this type, to safeguard against 'pack of cards' collapse, shear walls are provided at right angles to the cross-walls. These walls will generally be in discontinuous lengths and may have various openings in them. Due to the tendency in the past to avoid the structural use of walls containing openings, little attention has been paid to the investigation of the structural behaviour of such walls. The primary object of this work was, therefore, to investigate the rigidity and shear strength of a single-storey, shear-wall structure consisting of three shear panels, with floor slab above, stiffened by cross-walls and having door openings between two of the panels.

Some exploratory tests were carried out on model brickwork couplets[1], and a relationship was established between vertical compressive stress and horizontal shear stress. These couplet tests, however, did not fully represent the conditions existing in a shear wall, since in the couplet tests no shear stress was developed in the brick. This condition occurred because the shear load was applied in the plane of the mortar joint. In an actual structure, the presence of shear stress both in the brick and mortar will give rise to diagonal tension and compression in the masonry as a whole. Hence, in the tests described here, 1/6-scale-model structures were subjected to vertical precompression to simulate the actual loading condition in a building before being subjected to racking loa Formulae for calculating the ultimate shear strength brickwork were derived, and experimental values compare with the theoretical failure criteria.

Materials and Construction Details

Bricks

One-sixth-scale model bricks with an average crushi strength of 4332 lb/in.^{2} and 4221 lb/in.^{2} were used constructing single-leaf walls, representing a thickness 4½-in.-at-full-scale. The average water absorption (by weigh according to the 24-hour test was 12.65% for all the bric used in the test structures.

Cement and Sand

The sand and cement were in accordance with t requirements of B.S. 12: 1958 and B.S. 1200: 1950 respe tively.

Mortar

A ratio 1:4 cement and sand mortar by weight (1:3 volume) was used for the construction of the walls. T average crushing strength of 1-in. mortar cubes[2] for shear wa in different structures varied from 1500 to 2234 lb/in. Details are given in Table 23-1.

A mortar mix of 1:1 (cement: sand) was used f assembling walls and joining them to the slab. The avera

Table 23-1
Shear Strength of One-Sixth Scale Storey-Height Shear-Wall Structures with Openings, Subjected to Precompression

Test No.	Average compressive strength of mortar (lb/in^2)	Normal compressive stress (lb/in^2)	Ultimate racking load (lb)	Ultimate shear stress (lb/in^2)	Ultimate shear stress according to couplet formulae (lb/in^2)	Max. perm. stress in shear according C.P. 111: 1964 (lb/in^2)	Safety factor over C.P.111: 1964
1	2172	55	1640	77.66	78.0	20.0	3.88
2	1926	78	2064	97.77	96.0	26.0	3.76
3	2234	109	2404	115.07	117.0	30.0	3.84
4	1881	151	2170	103.84	146.0	30.0	3.45
5	1500	147.5	2492	119.30	143.0	30.0	3.97

Brick strength = 4332 and 4221 lb/in.^{2}
Co-efficient of friction between bricks and mortar = 0.74.

crushing strength of the cubes of this mortar at the time of testing the structures was 1120 lb/in^2.

Assembly

The wall panels were built vertically in jigs and then assembled according to the layout shown in Figure 23-1. While assembling, care was taken to see that the walls remained plumb and level. The joints between panels, as well as those between the slab and the panels, were completely filled with cement mortar. The walls were bedded in mortar in steel-base channels attached to the loading frame. The structures were tested on the third day after assembly.

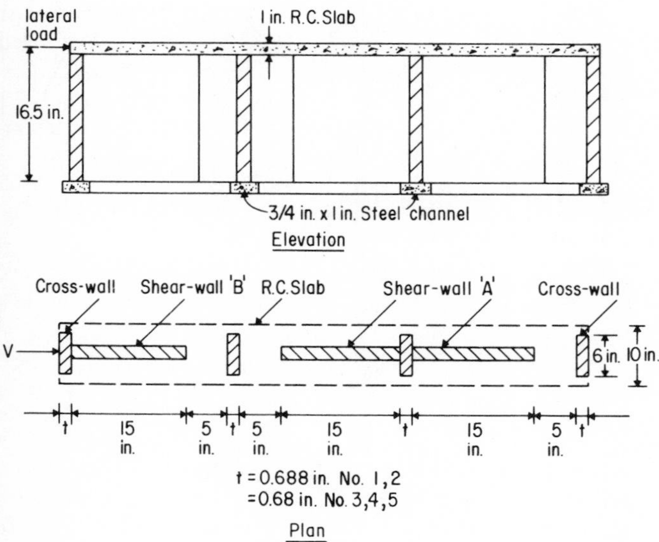

Figure 23-1. Shear wall test structure; plan and elevation.

Testing Equipment

Vertical load was applied to the structure by lead billets and concrete slabs as shown in Figure 23-2. The racking load was applied by a 6-ton hydraulic jack seated on a semi-circular hinge at the centre of a 1″ x 1¼″ x 10″-long, high-tensile, steel beam, supported on ½-inch-diameter rollers spaced 9 in. apart. The rollers transmitted the load to the slab, through a channel embedded along the edge of the slab, as shown in Figure 23-3.

The racking load was determined by measuring the central deflection of the 1″ x 1¼″ x 10″ high tensile steel beam by means of a dial gauge carried by a steel bridge piece between the support points of the loading beam. This device had a capacity of 6,000 lbs. and was calibrated in an Avery universal testing machine.

Experimental Results

Five model structures with door openings, subjected to precompression of 55, 78, 109, 151 and 147.5 lb/in.^{2}, respectively, were tested to failure under a racking load. The horizontal deflection at the slab level was measured at regular intervals during loading up to failure. The five structures all failed similarly with cracks passing through the horizontal and vertical mortar joints. Figure 23-2 indicates the typical form of damage at failure. In almost all cases first failure was noticed on the left of the panel ‘A’, (see Figure 23-1) and was then followed by cracks in panel ‘B’, which resulted in the ultimate failure of the structure.

Figure 23-4 shows for each test the relationship between the racking load and the horizontal deflection measured at slab level, whilst Figure 23-5 shows the variation of the shearing modulus of the brickwork with applied shear stress, as calculated from the deflection measurements.

The ultimate shearing stress in the brickwork is plotted against precompression in Figure 23-6. Also shown in this diagram are points relating to tests on model brick couplets and to test carried out on full-scale specimens by other investigators.

Figure 23-2. Shear wall test structure; general view.

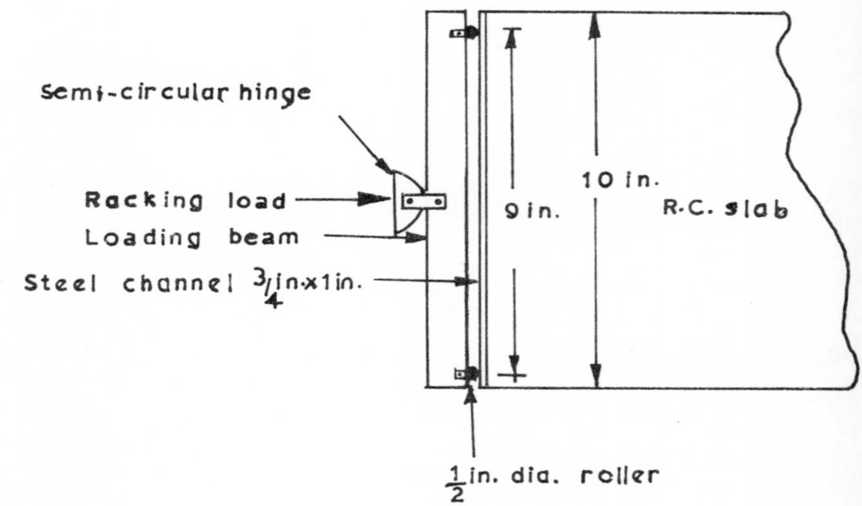

Figure 23-3. Shear wall test structure; application of horizontal load.

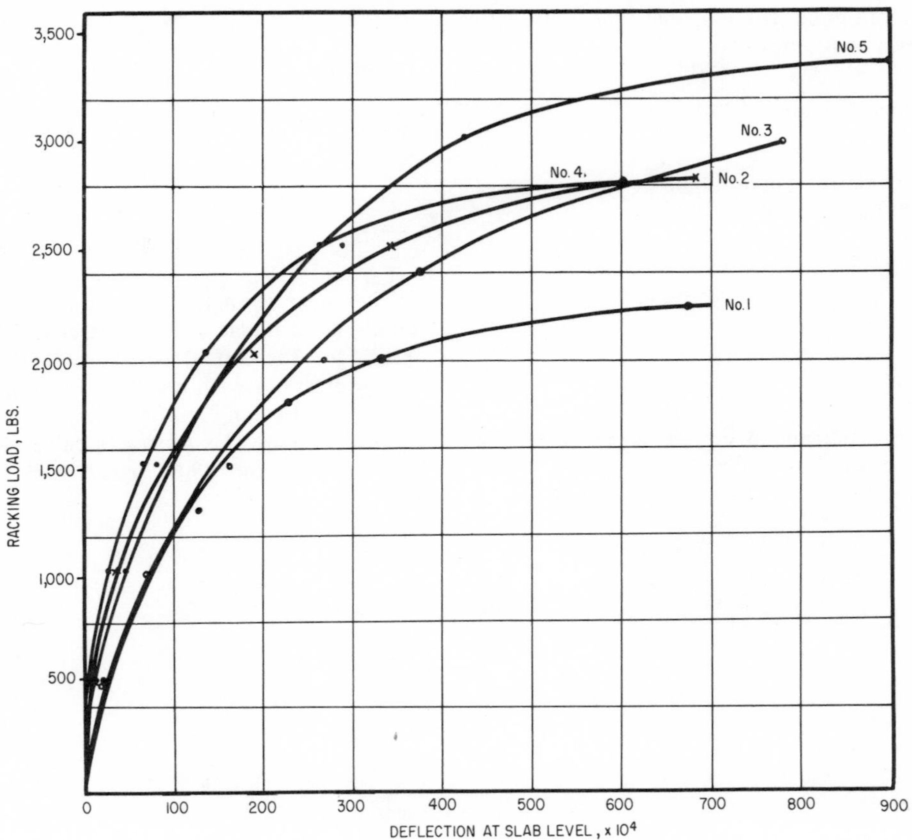

Figure 23-4. Load-deflection curves for shear wall structures.

Formulae for Predicting Shear Strength of Brickwork

Brickwork subjected to combined compression and shear exhibits two distinct types of failures:

1. By shear failure at the brick/mortar interface. The shear strength consists of initial bond shear and the resistance, proportional to the normal stress, due to friction between brick and mortar.
2. By diagonal tensile cracking through bricks and mortar, governed by constant, maximum, tensile strain or stress.

The diagonal tensile strength of the brickwork was estimated based on experimental work carried out in America[3] as described below. It is well-known that a circular specimen of brittle material, when loaded along the vertical diameter, fails by splitting along this diameter; the maximum stress occurs at the centre of this disc and is given by:

$$f_t = \frac{2P}{\pi Dt} \quad (23\text{-}1)$$

If the circular specimen is brickwork, oriented as shown in Figure 23-7, the stress f_t gives a measure of the diagonal tensile strength of the brickwork. The results have been reported of numerous such tests on 15-in.-dia. circular discs of brickwork, and the diagonal tensile strength has been correlated with the compressive strength of 16-in.-high brickwork prisms of the same thickness. These results showed that:

$$f_t = K\sqrt{f_m} \quad (23\text{-}2)$$

where K (referred ɔ as the "splitting ratio" $\geqslant 2$

Similar tests on six-course-high prisms of the model brickwork used in the shear panel tests were carried out to find the average compressive strength f_m. Assuming that splitting ratio of 2 to hold good, the diagonal tensile strength of the model brickwork was found to be:

$$f_t = 2.\sqrt{1814} = 85 \text{ lb/in}^2.$$

If it is assumed that failure is determined at a certain stage by the criterion of maximum tensile stress, then:

$$f_t = \sqrt{\frac{\sigma_y 2}{4} + \tau^2} - \frac{\sigma y}{2} = \text{constant} \qquad (23\text{-}3)$$

For failure: $\tau \geqslant f \cdot \sigma y$ (23-4)

We assume that the condition of equation (23-4) will be fulfilled by two values σy_1 and σy_2 of σy.

We can re-write equation (23-3) for the two conditions of equation (23-4):

$$f_t = \sqrt{\frac{\sigma_y{}^2 V}{4} + (V_{bo} + f \cdot \sigma y_1)^2} - \frac{\sigma y_1}{2} \qquad (23\text{-}5)$$

as:

$$\tau = V_{bo} + f \cdot \sigma y_1$$

or:

$$f_t = \sqrt{\frac{\sigma y_2^2}{4} + (f \cdot \sigma y_2)^2} - \frac{\sigma y_2}{2} \qquad (23\text{-}6)$$

where:

$$\tau = f \cdot \sigma y_2$$

If f_t, V_{bo} and f are known we can calculate σy_1 and σy_2. Between the precompressive stresses σy_1 and σy_2 failure of the structure will occur by attaining maximum tensile strength.

Below and above this range, failure will be governed by shear at the brick/mortar interface. Precompression above σy_2 will suppress the inherent failure due to diagonal tension and modify its value. Eventually at very high precompression values, failure of the brickwork will take place in compression, typically by vertical splitting. The limiting shear stress at values of precompression approaching the compressive strength of the brickwork are, however, not considered in the present work.

Hence, ultimate shear may be calculated from the following formulae:

$$V_b = V_{bo} + f \cdot \sigma y \qquad (23\text{-}7) \quad y\sigma y \leqslant \sigma y_1$$

$$f_t = \sqrt{\frac{\sigma y^2}{4} + V_b{}^2} - \frac{\sigma y}{2} \qquad (23\text{-}8) \quad \sigma y_1 \leqslant \sigma y \leqslant \sigma y$$

$$V_b = f \cdot \sigma y \qquad (23\text{-}9) \quad \sigma y_2 \leqslant \sigma y \leqslant \text{cor}$$

pressive strength o
brickwork

Discussion of the Results

The shear strength of the brickwork was calculated fr the above formulae and compared in Figure 23-6 with the t results for the model structures and, over a wide range precompression, with results from couplet tests, taking f_t = lb/in.^{2}, f = 0.74 and V_{bo} = 40 lb./in.^{2}.

The ultimate shear stresses calculated from the suggest formulae (Figure 23-6) agree well with the experimen

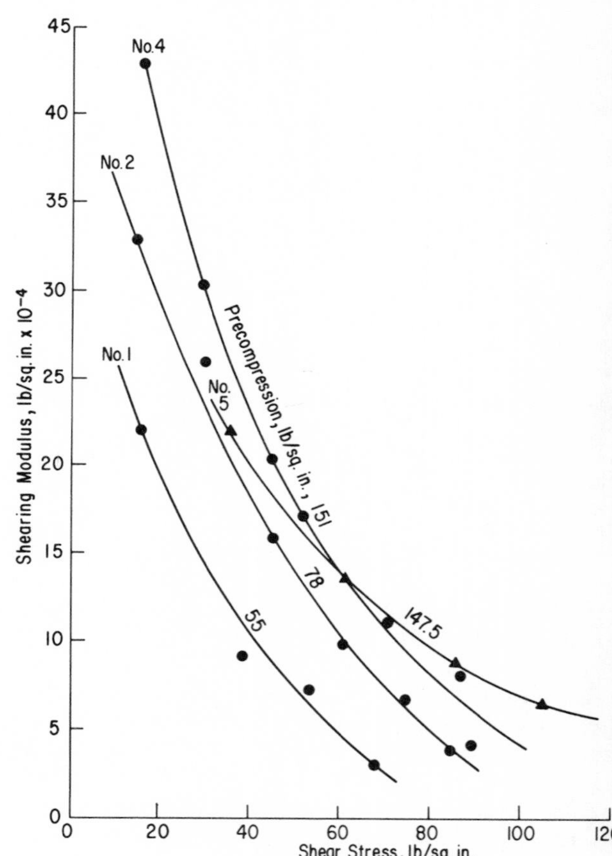

Figure 23-5. Variation of shearing modulus of brickwork.

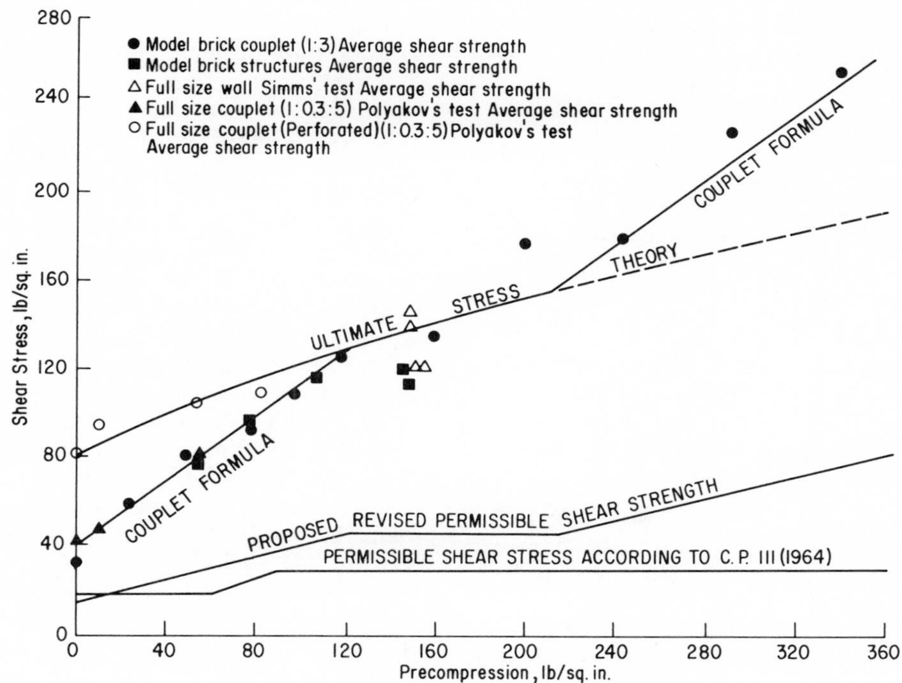

Figure 23-6. Relationship between ultimate shearing stress and precompression.

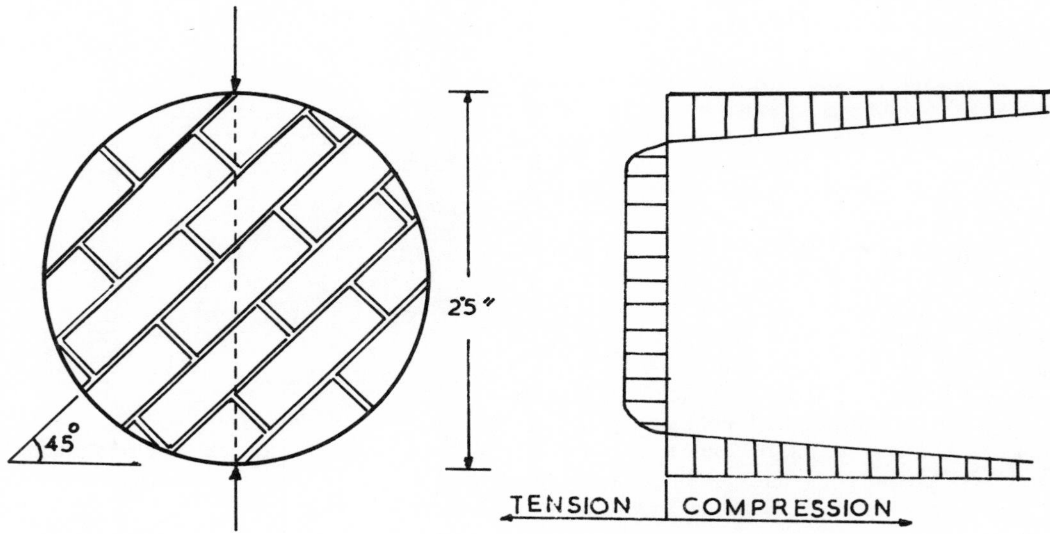

Figure 23-7. Test for diagonal tensile strength of brickwork and stress distribution.

results for the couplets and the model structures and also with the test results for full-size brickwork specimens, obtained from other sources [4,5].

Practically no increase in the shear strength of the structure was noticed when the precompression was increased from 120 to 150 lb/in.^{2}. A similar phenomenon was noticed, while carrying out the couplet tests, and is also apparent from the test results of Murthy[2]. The shear strength of couplets subjected to 160 lb/in^2 precompression ranged from 105-165 lb/in^2, which overlaps the actual shear stress obtained from the racking test of structures 4 and 5.

In Simm's tests, the shear stress in full-size walls having mortar strengths of 1000 lb/in^2, when subjected to 150 lb/in^2 precompression, ranged from 100 to 150 lb/in^2 with an average of 122 lb/in^2. This agrees well with the model test results of 119 lb/in^2 and 104 lb/in^2.

The small increase in shear strength with increase in precompression from 120 lb/in^2 to 150 lb/in^2 is because, over this range, failure is governed by the ultimate strength of the brickwork in diagonal tension (Figure 23-6). Also it is clear from Figure 23-6 that, within the limits of precompression σy_1 to σy_2, there is only a small increase in the shear strength, which, for practical purposes, may be assumed constant over this range.

In Figure 23-6 the curve of shear strength based on maximum tensile strength of brickwork has been extended to cover values of precompression down to zero. With perforated bricks, Polyakov assumed a straight line formula, based on an equation similar to Equation 23-7 in this paper and from it he calculated the coefficient of friction as 0.15, which is a very low value for brick and mortar interface. Examination of his results suggests that the failure was governed by the maximum tensile stress theory. At the values of precompression used in his tests, the frictional effect was not pronounced, and the slope of the curve would give a fictitious value of the coefficient of friction.

From Figure 23-6 it will be seen that below precompression σy_1, if the shear strength of a wall built of wire-cut bricks is calculated by the maximum stress theory, the shear strength will be over-estimated. Above the precompressive stress of σy_2 the shear strength will be underestimated. In the case of perforated or frogged bricks, the mechanical key established between brick and mortar ensures that failure in diagonal tension takes place in the range of precompression values between zero and σy_1. This suggests that such bricks are to be preferred for brickwork subject to shear at low precompression.

In model structures 3,4, and 5 the crack passed through some of the bricks. The failure of these structures first started at the interface of the vertical mortar joints of the compression diagonal in the panel and subsequently passed through the bed joints. At the point of failure, therefore, cracks may develop above and below a particular brick, as suggested in Figure 23-8, and final failure may take place through this brick, although the calculated principal tension may be much below the tensile strength of the brick in diagonal tension.

The relationship between the racking load, horizont deflection at slab level, and the shearing modulus of the te structures are non-linear. The rigidity and shearing modulu both decrease with an increase of load. Precompressio generally increases the rigidity, shearing modulus and the she strength of the structure, which confirms the test results Murthy and Hendry[2].

In test 3, when the structure was unloaded, cracks we noticed in the slab. It appears that, due to repeated loading the same slab, it was damaged during the test and th measured deflection at the slab level was somewhat more tha others.

The shear stress without external precompression found b Benjamin and Williams[6] was 16 lb/in^2 and by Polyakov[5] 4 lb/in^2 in full-size brickwork. Murthy and Hendry[2] have foun a value of 28 lb/in^2 in model brickwork set in 1:3 morta Polyakov[5] found 0.7 as the coefficient of friction betwee full-size bricks and mortar (which is almost the same as th found for model brickwork by the authors). Assuming th value of the coefficient of friction to hold good in Simm tests[4], the initial bond shear works out to be 17 lb/in^2.

All these results indicate that the lower limit of shear stre of 20 lb/in^2 recommended by the British Standard Code Practice CP.111[7] (cf. Figure 23-6) without external precon pression is somewhat high, with possibility no safety factor unperforated wire-cut or single-frog bricks. The shear strengt of brick masonry without precompression depends mainly the strength of the bond between the brick and mortar, an this is affected by a great many factors such as consistency mortar, surface characteristics of the bricks, treatment bricks before laying, moisture absorption of the bricks, an

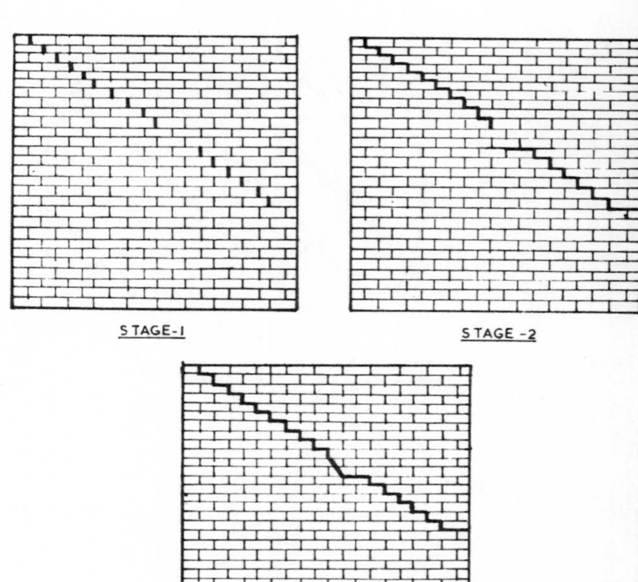

Figure 23-8. The progressive failure of brickwork panel shear.

workmanship. It is impracticable to closely control all these factors on site.

With this limitation in mind and with a safety factor of 3, based on the tests described in this paper, a permissable shear stress of only 15 lb/in^2 without external precompression appears to be more reasonable for wire-cut or single-frog bricks. It is also suggested that (for walls built with solid bricks in 1:3 mortar), the permissable shear stress without precompression should be increased by adding one-quarter of the vertical stress up to a maximum of 45 lb/in.^{2} . Above a precompression of 200 lb/in.^{2} the shear strength may be increased by adding one-quarter of the precompression in excess of this value up to the maximum allowable compressive stress for the brickwork in question.

Conclusions

1. The formulae proposed in the paper give a reasonable estimate of the ultimate shear strength of model brickwork structures with and without openings. From such tests as are available, it would appear that these formulae are also applicable to full scale brickwork.

2. Failure of a storey-height shear walls with openings under a racking load is generally due to breakdown of the bond at the interface, leading to diagonal cracks stepping down through the vertical and horizontal mortar joints or sometimes passing through bed joints only.

3. Over a certain range of vertical compression, the failure of a shear wall occurs in diagonal tension. In this type of failure, the crack passes through mortar joints and through some of the bricks.

4. Precompression increases the shear strength of the brickwork up to a certain limit, which will depend on the compressive strength of the brickwork.

5. The effective rigidity and shearing modulus of brickwork decrease nonlinearly with increase of racking load. The rigidity, shearing modulus and shear strength increase with precompression.

Notation

f_t = Failing stress of brickwork in diagonal tension lb/in^2.
P = Diametral load on disc specimen for splitting test, lbs.
D = Diameter of splitting test specimen, in.
t = Thickness of disc specimen, in.
K = Splitting ratio
f_m = Compressive strength of brickwork prisms, lb/in^2.
σ_y = Precompression applied to brickwork panels or couplets lb/in^2.
τ = Shear stress, lb/in^2
f = Coefficient of friction at brick/mortar interface.
V_{bo} = Initial bond shear strength between bricks and mortar, lb/in^2.

References

1. Sinha, B. P. "Model Studies Related to Load Bearing Brickwork" Ph.D. Thesis, University of Edinburgh, 1967.
2. Murthy, C. K., Hendry A. W. "Model Experiments in Load Bearing Brickwork" Building Science, Vol. 1 pp. 289-298.
3. "Small Scale Specimen Testing" National Testing Programme, Progress Report No. 1, Structural Clay Products Research Foundation, Geneva, Ill., 1964.
4. Simms, L. G. "The Shear Strength of Some Storey-height Brickwork and Blockwork Walls" Clay Products Technical Bureau (London), Technical Note No. 1, 1964.
5. Polyakov, S. V. "Masonry in Framed Buildings" Gosudatst Vennoe Izdatel' stvo Literature po Straitel' stvu' i Arkhitekture, Moscow, 1956. (Translated by Building Research Station and published by National Lending Library for Science and Technology, Boston Spa, England)
6. Benjamin, J. R., Williams, H. A. "The Behaviour of One Storey Brick Shear Walls" Proc. Am. Soc. C. E., J. of Struct. Div. Vol. 84, No. ST, 4, 1958.
7. "Structural Recommendations for Load Bearing Walls" C.P. 111, British Standards Institution, 1964.

24. A prestressed clay masonry floor.

R. J. Wass, B. E., and D. J. Turner, B. E., Amalgated Brick and Pipe Co., Ltd., Auckland, New Zealand

Introduction

Stahlton Flooring is a prefabricated flooring system consisting of prestressed planks and hollow infill blocks of fired clay, bonded together by a cast in situ concrete topping and characterised by speed and simplicity in erection, versatility, and economy.

Originally developed in Switzerland in the late 1940's, the system has spread to 22 countries and is presently manufactured by 41 different factories. The system was adopted in 1963 by the Amalgamated Brick & Pipe Company Limited, New Zealand, who operate under license to B.B.R.B. Zurich, the original developers of the system.

How the Stahlton Floor System Works

The planks are prefabricated off the site and are centrally prestressed, thus inducing a symmetrical compression over the plank cross section. The concrete topping bonds to this plank, forming a composite structural section. When this is subjected to an applied bending moment, the plank resists the tensile stresses induced while the concrete resists the compression stresses. The filler blocks are regarded as formers only and assumed to carry no structural loads.

Static and dynamic tests have demonstrated that the bond between plank and topping concrete and the elastic characteristics of the composite section are preserved very close to the point of ultimate failure.

Assembly

Temporary props and bearers are erected to provide support for the Stahlton Planks at approximately 5 ft. to 6 ft. centres, and the prestressed planks are set out with a clear distance between them, equal to the nominal width of the infill block plus ¼ inch.

The infill blocks are placed between the planks, and t plank stirrups are bent upward. A light-gauge reinforcing me is laid over the whole area, lapping it as necessary, a additional nominal deformed steel is placed over areas likely be subjected to cracking forces.

The edges of the floor are boxed up and screed bars plac in position. Immediately prior to pouring the concr topping, the planks and blocks must be thoroughly saturat with water. The topping concrete is placed into positic vibrated, and screeded off.

It is essential, after placing, that great care be given curing the concrete. After five days every second line of pro can be removed, and after ten days all props can be remov

Construction of Stahlton Planks

Stahlton planks are made to the required length fo particular span by setting the plank tiles on the bed a cutting the necessary closure tiles. The sides of the tiles cramped up to ensure that the planks are straight, and t prestressing wires are run in the plank grooves and stress Grout is vibrated into the plank grooves and around t prestressing wires, and then the stirrups are placed a vibrated into position. The plank tiles have a bevelled e which allows grout to penetrate between adjacent ti forming a joint. Immediately after placing the grout, t planks are covered with polythene sheets and left to cu Note Figure 24-1.

Test cylinders are broken to ensure that the grout reached its required strength before destressing. (1.67 immediate prestress or 4000 p.s.i.) The wires are then releas and cut at the ends of each plank. The planks are fina cleaned, strapped up in bundles, and stacked ready despatch.

"In Situ" Topping Concrete. Minimum crushing strength 28 days f_c' = 3000 p.s.i. (Cylinder strength). Maxim aggregate size 1/2″. Slump 4″ – 5″.

Placing plank tiles

Placing the grout

Placing the stirrups

igure 24-1. Construction of Stahlton planks.

olerances. ASTM tolerances of ± 3 percent give an allowable ariation of 12″ ± 3/8″. Consumer requirements have meant hat tolerances of ± 1 percent only are acceptable. These finer olerances are obtained by grading the planks and blocks into hree nominal widths as shown in Table 24-1.

Material Specifications

lank Tiles

Component plank tiles have a cross section 6″ x 2-3/8″ and re 12″ long. (Gross Area = 14.25 in.^{2} Net Area = 10.12 in.^{2}). hey are made of high quality clay by an extrusion method nd have a crushing strength not less than 6,000 lb. per sq. in. Nett area).

Prestressing Steel Tendons

Tendons are of high-tensile steel, cold-drawn, and stress relieved with indentations to improve bond. Combinations of .160″-diameter and .200″-diameter wires are used to provide the varying amount of prestress required by design conditions.

Filler Blocks

Standard Hollow Blocks are 12″ long, and three-quarter lengths are available to permit easy adjustment to required spans. The blocks are made of high-quality, medium-density clay with compressive strength not less than 3000 lb. per sq. in. All blocks (with the exception of V blocks) may be inverted to give a deeper, stronger, and cheaper floor provided

Table 24-1

	Oversize	Common Size	Undersize
V & W Blocks	18″ ± 1/8″	17-3/4″ ± 1/8″	17-1/2″ ± 1/8″
A, B, C, D, E, F, P & X Blocks	12″ ± 1/8″	11-3/4″ ± 1/8″	11-1/2″ ± 1/8″
Planks	6-1/8″ ± 1/8″	6″ ± 1/16″	5-7/8″ ± 1/16″

a ribbed soffit to the floor is acceptable. P trays are used to make up space at edges of floors and to make stronger sections at the supports for continuous designs. The various filler blocks are illustrated in Figure 24-2.

The nominal wall thickness of the filler blocks is 1/2 inch.

Fundamental Engineering Principles

Design Specification

Although originally designed to comply with the New Zealand Model Building Code, the design tables have recently been recalculated according to the ACI Code.

Stresses in Stahlton Planks

Loss of Prestress. Loss of prestress may be due to:

elastic shortening of plank $= \frac{100n \quad A^W}{A^p + nA^W}\%$

relaxation of stress relieved wire = 4%
creep and shrinkage of plank = 3%

The structural clay tile is stable, and there is no loss due to creep and shrinkage. The grout forms only approximately 25 percent of the total cross-section.

Final Prestress

$$f_e^p = \frac{.93 \quad f_i^W \quad A^W}{A^p + nA^W}$$

Allowable Compressive Stress for Negative Bending

Ultimate compressive strength of prestressed planks = Compressive strength of unstressed plank – Strength utilized by effective prestress + Strength contribution of prestressing wire.

$$P_{ec}^{p'} = A^p f_c^{p'} - A^p f_{ec}^p + nA^W (f_c^{p'} - f_{ec}^p)$$

$$= (f_c^{p'} - f_{ec}^p)(A^p + nA^W)$$

Effective ultimate compressive stress of prestressed planks =

$$\frac{P_{ec}^{p'}}{A^p}$$

∴ Using a safety factor of 3

Allowable compressive stress:

$$f_c^p = \frac{f_c^{p'} - f_{ec}^p}{3} \times \frac{A^p + nA^W}{A^p}$$

Calculation of Properties of Composite Section

The calculations to determine the Moment of Resistanc are based upon the following assumptions:

1. The planks and concrete will resist no tensile stresses.
2. Young's Modulus of Prestressing Wire:

$$E^W = 29{,}000{,}000 \text{ lb/sq.in.}$$

Young's Modulus of Plank:

$$E^p = 3{,}500{,}000 \text{ lb/sq.in.}$$

Young's Modulus of Concrete:

$$E^c = 3{,}150{,}000 \text{ lb/sq.in.}$$

These give modular ratios:

$$E^W/E^p = 8.30$$

$$E^c/E^p = .90$$

Procedure. The procedure is as follows:

1. Establish neutral axis of composite section. A numeric procedure for finding the neutral axis is used which converg rapidly.
2. Calculate Moment of Inertia of composite section abo its neutral axis in terms of E^p and reduce this to the Mome of Inertia/ft. width = I in 4/ft.
3. Calculate Section Modulus for tension:

$$Z_t = \frac{I}{y} \text{in.}^3\text{/ft.}$$

4. Calculate Section Modulus for compression:

$$Z_c = \frac{I}{x}\,\frac{E^p}{E^c} \text{ in.}^3\text{/ft.}$$

5. Calculate Moment of Resistance in tension:

$$M_t = f_e^p Z_t \text{ lb. in./ft.}$$

6. Calculate Moment of Resistance in compression:

$$M_c = f_c^c Z_c \text{ lb.in./ft.}$$

The section properties obtained are very dependent on t area of plank tile. Changes in dimensions give a variation of ± percent to the area, and the effective area (including effect creep and shrinkage) by about ± 7 percent.

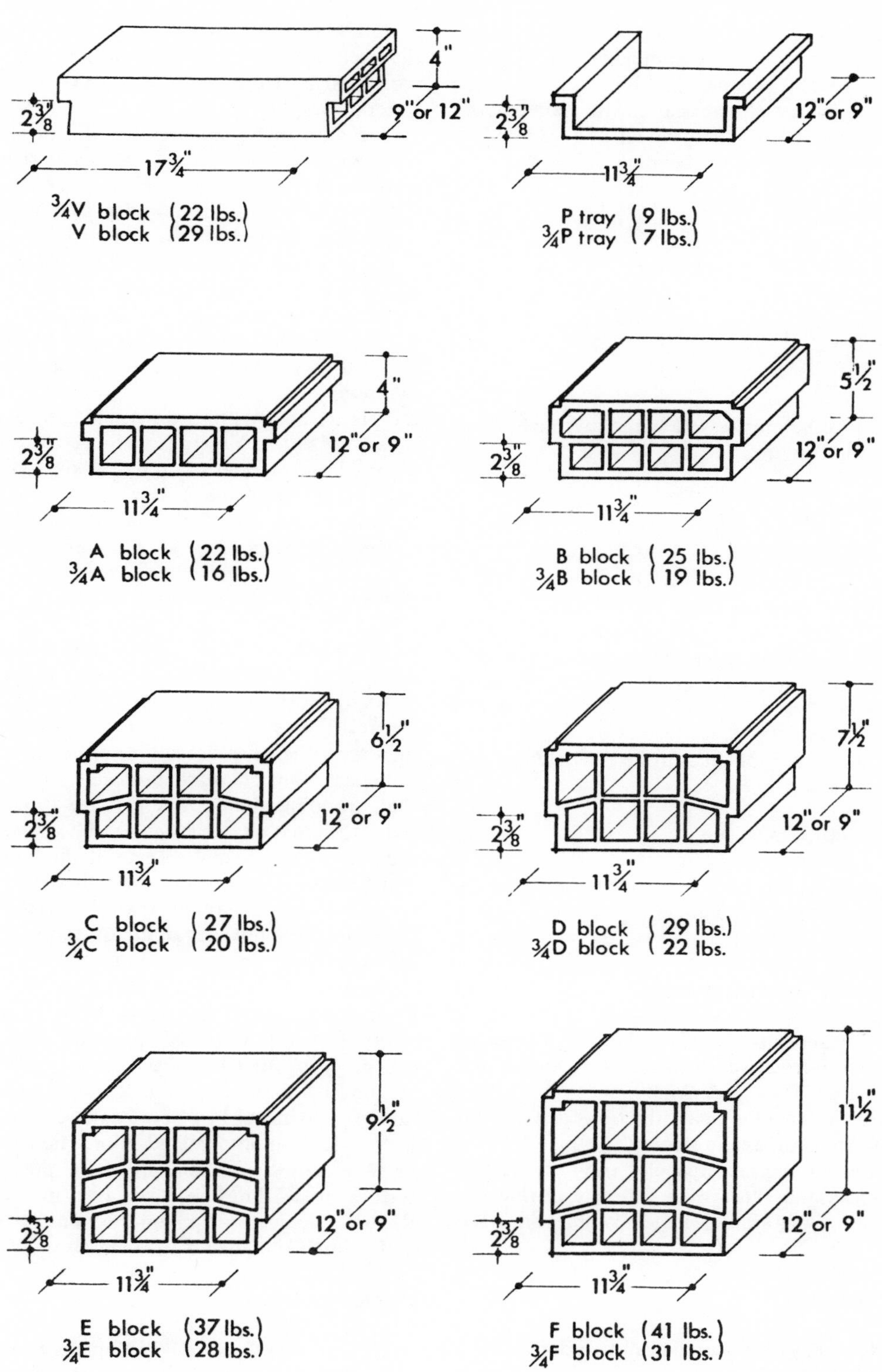

Figure 24-2. Stahlton filler blocks.

In calculating the stress for a 13 percent decrease in area, there is a 13 percent increase in compressive stress, and approximately an 11 percent decrease in the tensile section modulus. The variation in the theoretical elastic moment of resistance is only 1 percent (being the product of 1.13 x .89 = 1.01). There is no variation in ultimate bending moment.

Ultimate Strength in Bending

The ultimate strength in bending is given by:

$$M' = A^{w} f^{wu} d \left(1 - \frac{.59pf^{wu}}{f^{c'}}\right)$$

where f^{wu} is the stress in the prestressing wire at ultimate load f^{wu} is obtained from the equation:

$$\epsilon u^{wu} = \frac{fe^{w}}{29{,}000{,}000} + .003 \frac{(.72 f^{c'} - 1)}{pf^{wu}}$$

and from the stress/strain curve of the prestressing wire used.

Although this must be solved by a trial-and-error method, the results can be graphed for a given steel, concrete strength and initial tension in the steel, against the variable p (percentage of steel).

The equation for ultimate moment can be rewritten in the form:

$$M' = A^{w} K.d.$$

where K is a constant depending only upon p. The stress/strain curves and the K/p curves for the wires used in New Zealand are shown in Figures 24-3 and 24-4.

Continuity and Design for Negative Moments

The preceding notes apply to the floor design for positive moments. The design for negative moments is as for normal reinforced concrete design. Two cases exist:

1. When the negative moment is small, the rib of the section alone is able to resist the compression stresses.
2. When the negative moment is large, clay trays are used to replace the filler blocks and filled with concrete during the placing of the topping, giving a much larger compression face to resist bending.

Shear Bond and End Bearing

Numerous shear tests have been carried out to determine a general expression for the shear strength of the Stahlton Floor. Although no general expression has been obtained, the following qualitative conclusions have been reached.

1. The presence of the plank only increases the strength of the web for normal strength concrete, i.e., the shear and compressive strength of the plank is far greater than the concrete's.
2. Failure by bond between the prestressing wire and the plank occurred only when the shear strength of the section was much higher than normal, i.e., a new failure mode appeared to be introduced when a very high strength concrete was used in the web.
3. No evidence of bond failure between the plank and in situ concrete was ever recorded.
4. Even for the lowest result obtained, a Safety Factor of 4.5 existed when compared with the shear strength allowed by the ACI Code. A minimum safety factor of 11 existed against failure-by-bond between the poured in situ concrete web and the plank. Because of the variable nature of the shear strength it is prudent to design according to the ACI Code requirements. Bond stresses of up to 160 lb./sq.in. are used, when .1? percent of mechanical ties are provided, and up to 10? lb./sq.in. are allowed without any mechanical ties except at the ends of the planks where ties are always provided.

Stresses Due to Propping and Camber

For planks propped at five-foot centres and placed with a camber of 1/4″ per 10 ft. span, propping stresses can be ignored. However, it will often be convenient to prop planks at centres greater than five feet. This can be achieved by increasing the prestress and/or the camber according to results obtained from standard prepared tables. It should be noted that propping stresses and camber do not effect the ultimate strength and that resultant tensile stresses on the top side of the plank do not matter even if the plank does crack during construction. Tests have shown that the ultimate moments of the planks are far greater than the cracking moments and that cracking does not occur unless tensions in excess of 140? lb./sq.in. occur during erection.

Because of this, and because if the elastic state is maintained throughout erection (by calculation) a very high safety factor is obtained, propping stresses are not checked except when the Checking Authority insists on it. No sign of yielding or distress has ever been recorded in the history of Stahlton operations in New Zealand, nor has a crack appeared in the plank in any erected floor. The ultimate moment of the plank is almost independent of the prestressing wire content since a plastic hinge is formed in an over-reinforced section Right up to just before failure, almost complete recovery of deflection is obtained if the plank is unloaded.

Diaphragm Action

New Zealand is an earthquake-prone country and the writers of Building Regulations are very conscious of seismic damage. Structural Mechanics has not produced a general solution for diaphragm action, and the various restrictions

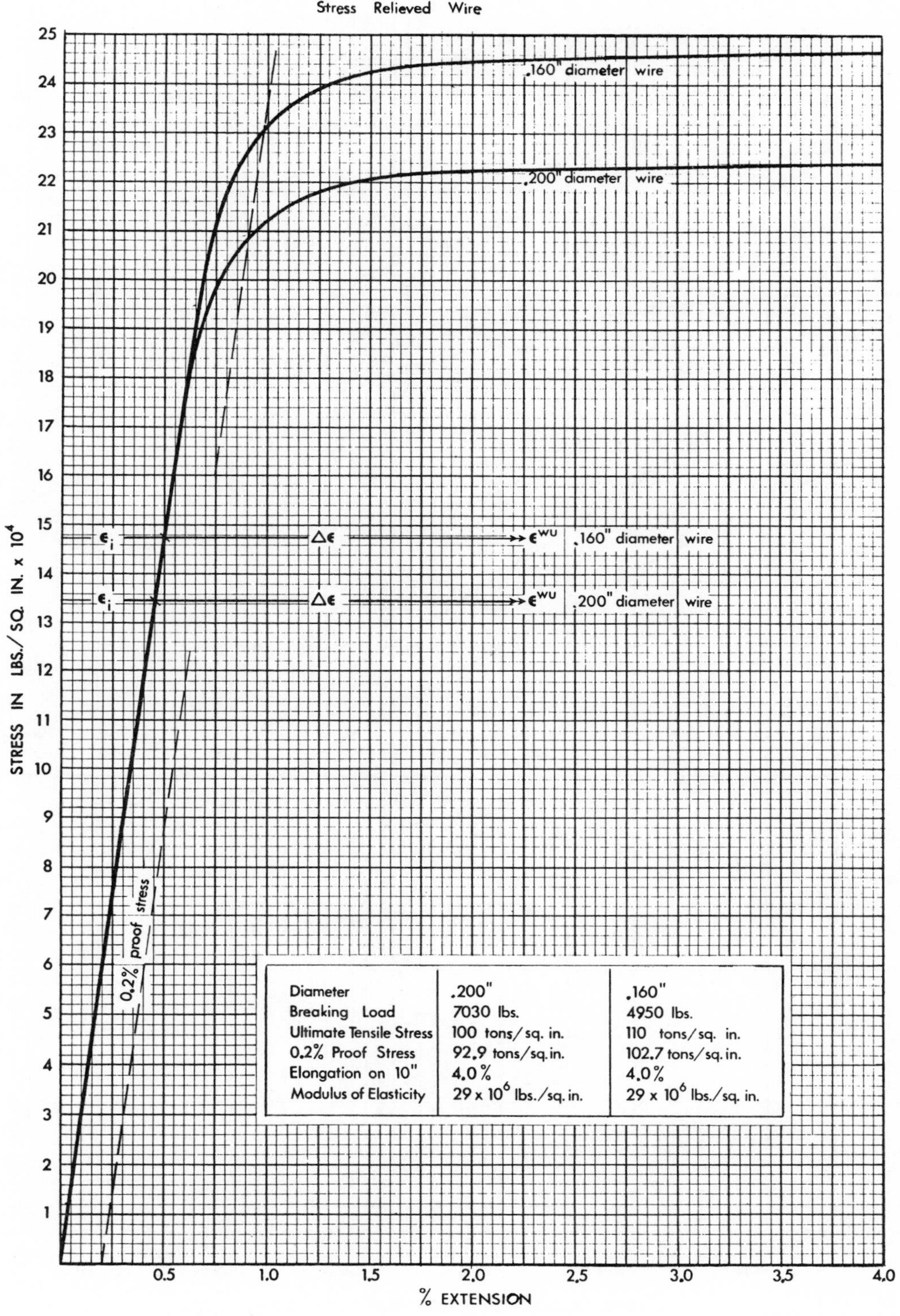

Diameter	.200"	.160"
Breaking Load	7030 lbs.	4950 lbs.
Ultimate Tensile Stress	100 tons/sq. in.	110 tons/sq. in.
0.2% Proof Stress	92.9 tons/sq. in.	102.7 tons/sq. in.
Elongation on 10"	4.0 %	4.0 %
Modulus of Elasticity	29×10^6 lbs./sq. in.	29×10^6 lbs./sq. in.

Figure 24-3. Design load extension curves.

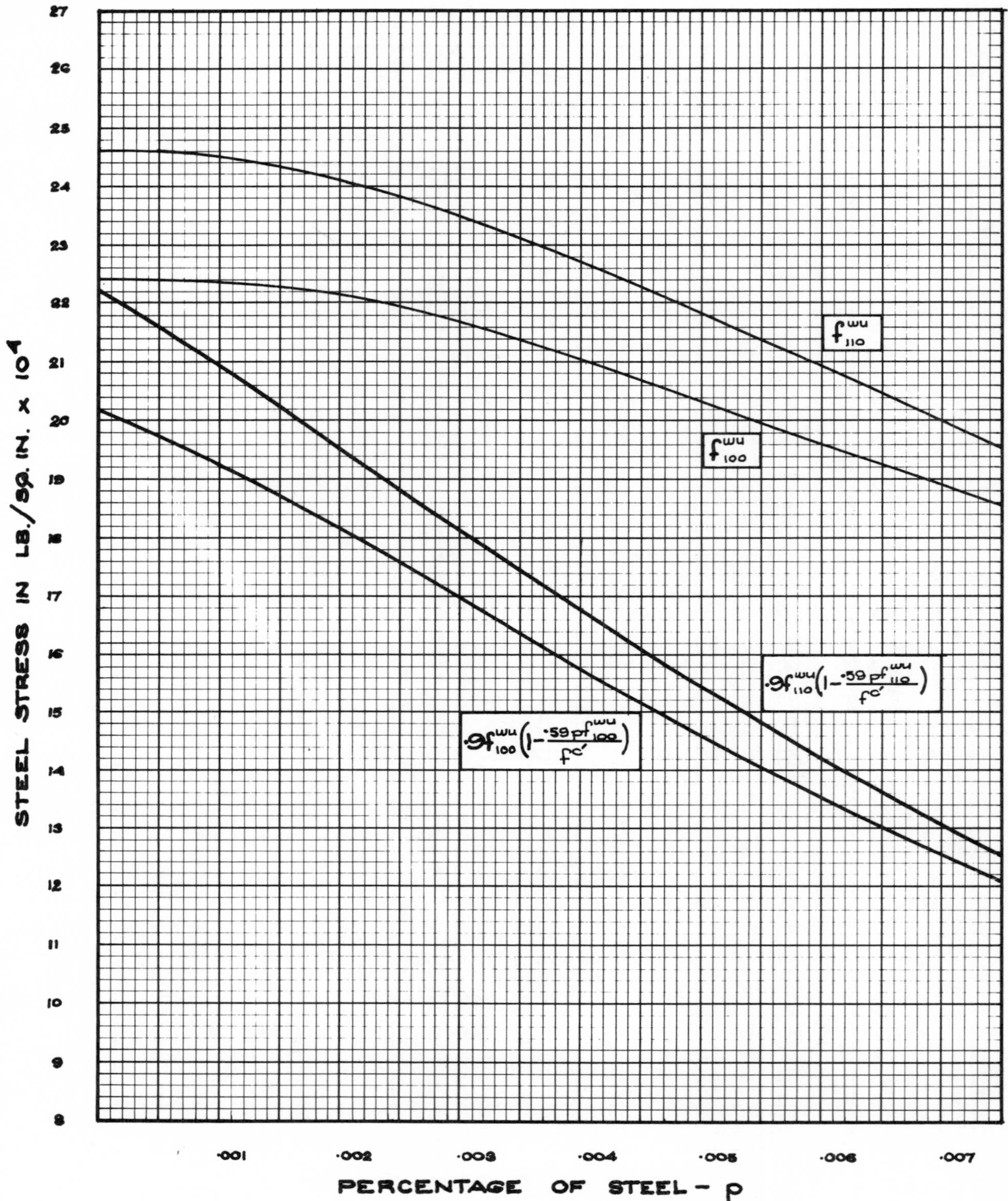

Figure 24-4. Graph for determining ultimate bending moment. Note: 3000 lb. concrete: .9 capacity reduction factor.

imposed have been of a very empirical nature, with most of these based on the assumption that failure will be by structural instability. The authors of this paper are presently working on this problem at a theoretical level, and their results, although not yet in a simplified form, indicate that structural instability is unlikely for floor slabs of normal dimensions (where the span to depth ratio is generally controlled by deflection requirements).

Regardless of this, stresses at instability tend to be related to the ratio $\frac{\text{radius of gyration}}{\text{length}}$ and to Young's Modulus. Stahlton Flooring, with its ribbed section running in one direction, is a more complex problem, but both of these above two factors are higher than for a reinforced concrete floor of the same depth. Stahlton's practice to date is to use the same stresses allowed in a concrete floor of the same depth, but to allow this stress to be developed only in the topping, plus top surface of the infill blocks.

The instability against buckling at right angles to the ribbed section without considering the influence of the supporting walls or beams is very low, but the floor cannot buckle in this direction without the ribs buckling in the other direction. Therefore the problem is almost the same as before.

When the floor is governed by shear stresses, the diagonal compression presumably could lead to buckling, and this will occur at a 45° angle to the web, but the ribs must still buckle and the same position is reached.

Deflection of Stahlton Floors

The stiffness and deflections of Stahlton Floors are generally controlled by limiting the span-to-depth ratio to 32 for simply supported spans and to 36 for continuous spans. It should be noted that the total depth of the floor acts structurally c.f. reinforced concrete.

Sag is controlled by propping the planks to the required camber before placing the topping concrete. This camber is a minimum of 1/4" per 10 ft. of span.

The accurate prediction of the deflection of Stahlton Floors depends upon the correct choice of Young's Modulus, Creep and Shrinkage coefficients, moments of inertia, and the degree of end fixity.

No creep or shrinkage will occur in the planks and filler blocks. For calculating moments of inertia, the area of the filler blocks in contact with the concrete, based on a thickness of 1/2", should be included.

The present method of designing Stahlton Floors is to design a fully continuous floor or a simply supported floor supplying sufficient nominal steel over the supports to ensure that the steel does not yield under full design load. Because of the high steel stresses, deformed steel is used, and the mesh is carried over the supports.

Accurate deflection calculation is so involved that it could only be obtained quickly by preparing tables giving the moments of inertia of the standard sections, including the effect of infill blocks before and after creep. Three moments of inertia must be calculated: the uncracked section, the cracked section due to positive moments, and the cracked section due to negative moments (the cracked section due to negative moment will have a moment of inertia dependent upon the percentage of steel).

The graphs would then have to be prepared to give the position of the point of inflexion for various ratios of moment of inertia at centre and supports depending on the end connections.

From this the "true" Bending Moment Diagram can be calculated. The elastic and long-term deflection can be calculated as a multiple of the simply supported deflection, using the moment of inertia of the cracked composite section.

An additional deflection must then be added to allow for shrinkage, which depends on: (a) shrinkage coefficient, (b) moment of inertia, (c) depth of section, and (d) points of inflexion.

Then, this must be multiplied by a factor allowing for some rotation at supports, depending on the restraint.

The theory of all this has been completed, and a series of deflection tests have been planned in which hopefully the deflection due to shrinkage can be separated.

From two experiments in which elastic creep and shrinkage deflections were all lumped together, it has been found that, for a floor nominally reinforced at one end and simply supported at the other, under working loads, the deflection is reduced by 30-40 percent, when compared to the deflection of a simply supported floor of the same span. The initial deflection is far less than that predicted by using the moment of inertia of the cracked section, neglecting the effect of the infill block (i.e., the moment of inertia of the structural section), but the final total deflection is about 30 percent greater.

Some Commercial Aspects

It is convenient and logical for Stahlton prestressed planks to be manufactured by the company which manufactures the component plank tiles and infill blocks.

The Stahlton Department is responsible for designing, pricing, and manufacturing the planks, despatching of components, and supervising erection.

The capital expenditure required to establish a Stahlton plant is relatively low. To operate efficiently, a minimum of two prestressing beds is required to provide work continuity for the labour force. Four days are allowed for curing. The prestressing beds used in New Zealand are 220 ft. long. Planks are set eight across on each bed and built three layers high, each bed holding approximately one mile of plank.

An efficient plant can produce 20 ft. of plank per man hour. This figure includes the production foreman and all despatching work.

Thus, a two-bed plant can produce approximately 30,000 ft. of plank per month with a gang of 9 men working 8 hrs. per day. This gives an annual turnover of \$(NZ)360,000 for prestressed planks and the accompanying infill blocks.

Estimated capital outlay to establish a two bed plant is \$(NZ)70,000. This figure includes the two prestressing beds, anchor blocks and wedges, stressing equipment, concrete mixer, vibrators, etc., but does not include the purchase of land and a building to cover the beds.

Minimum staff required for administration and design is a manager, an engineer, two draughtsmen, a field supervisor, and a typist/clerk. Experience has shown that a design and draughting service is of great assistance in establishing a market for Stahlton. This service also minimizes errors during production of planks and erection on the site.

Cost Considerations

In selecting the optimum sizes for the range of Stahlton components (i.e. plank and block dimensions and topping concrete thickness), it is necessary to find the most economical range of units which will satisfy the structural requirements and also be readily handled on the site.

The prestressed planks are more costly per unit area of laid floor than the filler blocks. Therefore the aim is to provide the minimum cross-sectional area of plank which is satisfactory for shear, bending, and deflection in the composite section. Planks must be light enough to be manhandled on the site but of sufficient strength to support the filler blocks and topping concrete during construction with a minimum of temporary support.

To obtain a range of floors, it is possible to vary the dimensions of planks or blocks or both. It is believed best to use one plank size and to vary the block sizes. The amount of prestress in the planks is varied by combining two sizes of wire. For heavy loads, double planks are used rather than a deeper floor.

The range of floors which are supplied vary in depth from 6″ to 16″ and are suitable for spans up to 40 ft. It is found however, that the most competitive range of spans is from 12 ft. to 28 ft.

The plank cross section adopted is 6 in. wide x 2-3/8 in. deep, and this is combined in with a range of hollow blocks which vary from 4 in. to 11-1/2 in. deep.

Until recently, the design of Stahlton in New Zealand has been based on the British Codes of Practice (CP114 and CP115) but has now been changed to the ACI Design Code which is also to be adopted as the basis for the N.Z. Design Standards. The ACI Code allows higher prestress in the planks and also higher shear stresses, both factors resulting in more economical sections.

Table 24-2

ITEM	DESCRIPTION	QUANTITY	UNIT	RATE	AMOUNT
				$(NZ)	$(NZ)
1.	Quotation for design manufacture and delivery at site of prestressed planks and hollow infill blocks.	5000	sq. ft.	0.59	2950.00
2.	Propping of planks including bearers, props, wedges and removal on completion.	5000	sq. ft.	0.04	200.00
3.	Take delivery, place prestressed planks, place infill blocks.	5000	sq. ft.	0.05	250.00
4a.	Box edges, etc.	300	lin. ft.	0.20	60.00
b.	Box construction joints	200	lin. ft.	0.08	16.00
5.	Set up screeds	600	lin. ft.	0.05	30.00
6.	Supply and lay reinforcing steel mesh.	5000	sq. ft.	0.06	300.00
7.	Supply and lay additional reinforcement required at supports.	5.6	cwt.	12.00	67.20
8.	Supply concrete topping.	34.0	cu. yds.	16.00	544.00
9.	Lay, compact & screed concrete.	34.0	cu. yds.	9.50	323.00
10.	Finish off surface. Power float and steel trowel.	5000	sq. ft.	0.03	150.00
	Price per sq. ft. – $0.98				4890.20

Table 24-3

DESCRIPTION	QUANTITY	UNIT	RATE	AMOUNT
			$(NZ)	$(NZ)
Supply, erect and remove soffit shuttering.	5000	sq. ft.	0.45	2250.00
Box edges, construction joints and set up screeds.				100.00
Supply and place reinforcing steel.	105	cwt.	12.00	1260.00
Supply and place concrete.	77.2	cu. yds.	25.00	1930.00
Power float and steel trowel.	5000	sq. ft.	.03	150.00
	Price per sq. ft. = $1.14			5690.00

For many floors the planks need now only be placed at 24 in. centres and a range of 18-in.-wide blocks has been introduced. This floor is lighter and uses less concrete to fill the webs.

Table 24-2 is typical pricing for the erection in New Zealand of a 6″-deep Stahlton floor (DL = 50 lb./sq.ft.) spanning 16 ft. This example is for an area of 5,000 sw.ft. of floor.

As a comparison, costs are shown in Table 24-3 for a 5″ reinforced-concrete slab (D.L. = 62 lb./sq.ft.) also spanning 16 ft. and covering an area of 5000 sq.ft.

Advantages of Stahlton Flooring

When selecting a type of floor construction it is necessary, in addition to direct cost comparisons, to consider the materials in relation to the total project.

Of particular importance is the effect of light weight in reducing footing, column and beam sizes. A Stahlton floor is approximately 2/3 the weight of a solid reinforced concrete slab designed for the same span and load.

In New Zealand there is a marked lack of skilled carpenters. Stahlton, by eliminating soffit shuttering, has helped relieve this scarcity. At the same time, timber is conserved.

Stahlton has good sound insulation (airborne sound reduction varies from 45 to 50 decibels for floors of 6″ to 12″ deep) and good thermal insulation properties.

The floor qualifies for a two-hour fire rating which can be further increased by plastering or spraying the soffit. The underside is a uniform clay surface ideal for plastering.

Service pipes and wiring can be accommodated within the floor depth.

A floor system must be versatile to be generally acceptable. Stahlton can be used with either steel-frame, reinforced concrete, or reinforced masonry construction. Although this is a precast floor, it can, in some respects, be regarded as an in situ construction with the planks acting as reinforcement. The planks and topping concrete can be readily tied into the supporting structure.

The need for temporary propping during construction may be regarded as a disadvantage, but it is this propping which gives the system its versatility and allows the use of lightweight components.

Notation Used

The notation used in this chapter consists of three characters. The symbol; a subscript, and a superscript.

Symbol

- A — Area
- d — Effective depth from extreme compression fibre to centroid of tendons
- E — Young's Modulus
- f — Stress
- I — Moment of inertia
- M — Moment
- NA — Neutral Axis
- n — Modular Ratio
- P — Longitudinal load
- p — Ratio of area of steel reinforcement to effective area of beam
- x — Distance from N.A. to top of concrete
- y — Distance from N.A. to bottom of plank
- Z — Section modulus
- ϵ — Strain
- ϕ — Capacity reduction factor

Subscript

- c — Compression
- e — Effective
- i — Initial
- t — Tension

Superscript

- c — Concrete
- p — Plank
- u — Ultimate load
- w — Prestressing wire
- ′ — Ultimate

Example:

f_i^w Initial stress of prestressing wire

f_e^p Effective stress of plank

25. Prestressed masonry-reinforced concrete space structure.

John S. Gero, Dept. of Architectural Science, University of Sydney, Sydney, Australia

Introduction

With the present trend of increasing urbanization in Western civilization, the number and use of motor vehicles have markedly increased. In areas of high density development, street parking has always been totally inadequate. Building regulations have nearly always specified the size of the building be provided within site boundaries.

In most cases, this has meant that at least one parking floor, and in many instances more than one, had to be provided at the base of the building. Fixed column-grid sizes accompanied this provision to satisfy vehicle turning circles and vehicle space requirements. Particularly in multi-storey apartments or home-unit buildings, this has led to the introduction of these column grids into the living areas, even though the grid dimensions were determined for vehicles. This gave rise to drastic changes in the floor planning of the living areas to accommodate these supports.

The resurgence of masonry as a structural material and its subsequent use in multi-storey construction has basically been due to new design concepts which eliminated the need for the masonry to take significant tension and shear[1]. This can be achieved by either judicial planning of the building so that tension, due to lateral loads such as wind, are always cancelled by gravity loads or by reinforcing the masonry so that these forces are taken not by the masonry but by the reinforcement. However, in both of these cases the original problem still remains, viz. the position of load-bearing masonry walls in multi-storey, home-unit buildings is determined by the vehicular parking requirements and not by the living area requirements.

A further problem with using load-bearing masonry walls in multi-storey buildings has been the need to provide reasonably large, open, public areas. In hotels and similar buildings, this is a major requirement which cannot readily be satisfied when designing in masonry even though load-bearing masonry is ideal for construction of cellular-type areas required on the upper floors. Generally, in hotels these spaces are not on the ground floor. The solution has been to use a framed structure up to the ballroom floor and then to provide heavy beams to support the remaining residential floors of load-bearing masonry.

The structure described below, which has been designated as a "prestressed masonry-reinforced concrete space structure", has been invented to solve these problems. It has effectively eliminated contact of parking area supports with those required for the living areas. Furthermore, this structure can have one or a number of intermediate floors virtually free of central supports, thus providing large, uninterrupted areas such as those required in hotel ballrooms and reception rooms.

Structural Interaction

In its simplest form, the prestressed masonry-reinforced concrete space structure consists of two thin, reinforced concrete floors, one supported on the other by load-bearing masonry walls. The masonry walls are then post-tensioned vertically using the floors as anchors. This structure can then be supported on only four columns near the corners so that it spans at least 70 feet. In effect, two floors and the prestressed masonry act as a three-dimensional Vierendeel girder. This leaves the plan area of at least 70 feet by 70 feet (this figure could easily be 100 feet by 70 feet) column-free. This concept can be very simply extended to a multi-storey building where it becomes even more efficient.

Thus, it is possible to provide a complete break between the parking areas and living areas in a home-unit building or to provide a large column-free space on floors apart from the ground floor, as shown in Figure 25-1 representing the sectional elevation of a hotel designed on this basis.

Vertical prestress in the walls provides sufficient structural interaction between floors and wall so that the combination will resist web shearing forces produced in the wall and tension in the wall due to lateral wind loading.

To place this concept within the existing framework of research on structural interaction in composite masonry-

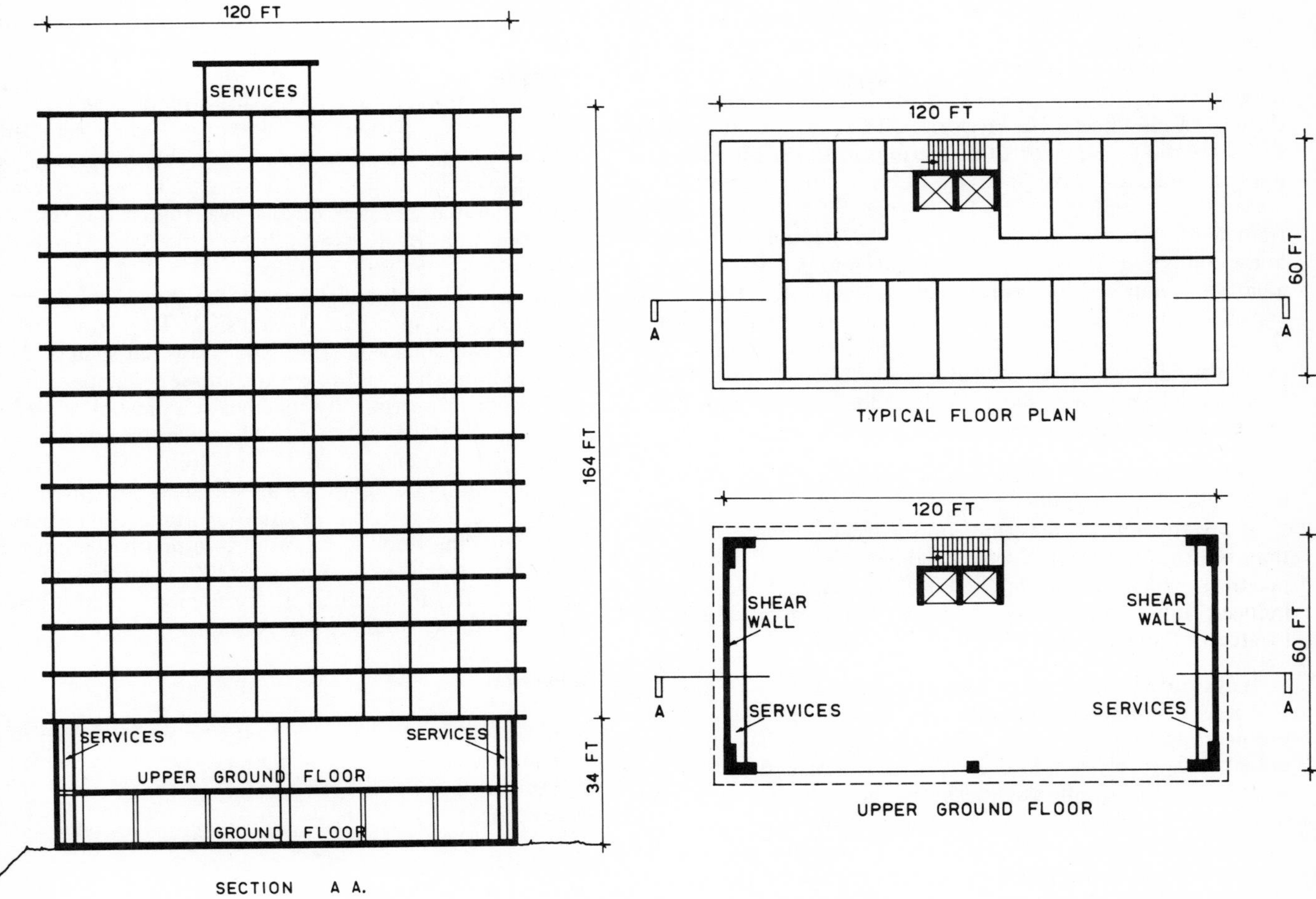

Figure 25-1. Plan and section of hotel project utilizing the prestressed masonry-reinforced concrete space structure principle to provide open areas.

concrete construction, a short review of pertinent research will be presented.

Structural interaction in composite construction has been investigated by numerous research workers. In 1932 Dischinger made a "Contribution to the Theory of Wall-Like Girders"[2] in which he examined the stress distribution for deep walls resting on multiple supports in the form of continuous beams. Wood[3] in 1952 investigated the composite action of brick panel walls supported on reinforced concrete beams and found that "due to arching effects in the brickwork, the bricks in fact formed a composite beam of a much greater depth than the supporting beam".

Rosenhaupt[4,5] in studying the composite action of masonry walls supported on reinforced concrete beams, found the following:

1. the shearing stresses at the beam-wall boundary induce the composite action of the structure. The tensile stresses concentrate in the foundation beam and the compressive stresses are distributed over the whole height of the masonry.

2. the vertical compression forces are transferred by the wall to the supports, where high stresses concentrate.

3. the vertical shear stresses are taken by the masonry part of the wall.

4. the horizontal shear stresses between foundation beam and masonry concentrate near the supports.

In all the above investigations, the walls were composed of unreinforced masonry. Reinforced brick masonry has been used for many years, and considerable work has been performed in determining its action[6,7]. However, of particular interest in this context is the work done at Structural Clay Products Limited (England) by Foster, Sutherland, Couzens and Plowman[8]. They performed experiments on the combination of reinforced brickwork with thin reinforced concrete slabs to form storey height beams. Among the conclusions they drew from their experiments was that "post stressing markedly reduced the deflections and cracking".

In 1966 Hinkley published two papers[9,10] dealing with both analytical and experimental results of stress determinations in composite prestressed masonry walls with in-plane lateral loading. The theoretical analysis is based on Hrennikoff's lattic analog [11,12] since the problem becomes a plane stress problem. In this method of analysis, an analogy is drawn between the deflections of an elastic plate element and those of a pin-jointed frame work of the same external shape and dimensions. Equality of deflections is possible for cases of uniform axial or shear load by defining the cross-sectional areas of the members of the framework. With the areas of the framework members so defined, the deflections of an elastic body composed of rectangular elements and the deflections of a lattice composed of corresponding pin-jointed frames are considered to be analogous. Hinkley, using this method, found reasonable agreement with the experimental results. The experimental results [10] of full scale tests of prestressed, masonry, composite shear walls, loaded as previously mentioned, indicated that:

1. the strength and reliability of brickwork shear walls can be increased by vertically prestressing the walls.
2. prestressing of the ends of the walls is more efficient than uniform prestress. There is a limit to the amount of end prestress which can be applied to the masonry because of induced horizontal tensile stresses. Anchorages should be located in the beam above the wall.

Beresford [13] using the lattice analogy method, has developed a computer program which enables plane stress problems of the type generated in two-dimensional composite prestressed masonry-reinforced concrete structures to be solved. The program assembles the appropriate equations, solves them to obtain displacements, and evaluates stresses in detail. The results are tabulated, and a contour map of the principal stress trajectories is also produced by the graph-plotting facility of the computer system. In that paper, he presents an example of a 33-ft.-long, 8-ft.-high masonry wall vertically post-tensioned between top and bottom tie beams of reinforced concrete. A door aperture was included. A bending condition was imposed in the wall by vertical loads at the ends, while the bottom tie beam was fixed at the third points. The masonry was considered to possess uniform elastic properties, and the variable elastic modulus facility of the program allowed for material differences of the tie beam. A very good agreement existed between the computed value of vertical stress and those derived from strain measurements during testing of a full-scale model.

Thus, there has been a logical progression in the research into composite masonry structures. However, virtually all the work done to date has been to determine the feasibility of structural elements rather than full or complete structures. This somewhat narrow approach has, therefore, restricted the application of some of the concepts developed. The prestressed masonry-reinforced concrete space structure described earlier has expanded these concepts into three dimensions to produce a meaningful structural entity.

Small-Scale Model

To test the feasibility of this structure, it was decided to investigate a small-scale plastic model simulating what might be the worst vertical loading condition in an actual structure. This condition was considered to occur in a two-storey structure, the top floor of which was this prestressed masonry-reinforced concrete space structure and the ground floor open for parking. In buildings higher than this, the vertical stiffness increases at a considerably faster rate than the vertical load. Plastic (methyl methacrylate) was chosen as the model material because of the availability of commercially produced, uniform thickness sheets which could be readily cut to form the model walls and floor.

The use of commercially produced plastic sheets restricted the choice of possible thicknesses. The structure to be modelled was square in plan with an overall span of 75 ft. On the first floor this was broken into three equal spans of 25 feet. each in both directions by load-bearing prestressed walls. The interior walls are completely solid, whilst the exterior walls are broken by openings equal to one third of its area. At the openings no bending or shear stiffeners are provided. The storey height was taken as 10 ft. Particularly to accentuate deflections, the floor slabs were made relatively thin for their span. An overall scale factor of 30 was chosen and was maintained for all dimensions. A summary of both prototype and model dimensions is given below.

Dimensions

Span	l_p = 75 ft.	l_m = 30 in.
Slab depth	S_p = 5.8 in.	S_m = 0.19 in.
Wall thickness	t_p = 7.5 in.	t_m = 0.25 in.
Storey height	h_p = 10 ft.	h_m = 4 in.

Material properties

Elastic modulus	$E_p = 3 \times 10^6$ psi (throughout)	$E_m = 0.46 \times 10^6$ psi (throughout)

The effect of differing Poisson's ratios was neglected.

Thus, the model ratios become:

$$\lambda_l = 30:1, \quad \text{and}$$
$$\lambda_E = 6.5:1$$

where λ_l stands for the ratio of prototype to model for property l.

Loads

The model load required can be determined from the relationship:

$$\lambda_W = \lambda_E \, (\lambda_l)^2 \tag{25-1}$$

which is derived using dimensional analysis [14].

So that rewriting Equation 25-1:

$$W_m = W_p / \{\lambda_E \, (\lambda_l)^2\} \tag{25-2}$$

The prototype vertical loading consisted of the floor slab, the finishes on the floor slab, the brick partitions, the live load on floor, the ceiling and horizontal services, the roof slab, the built-up roofing, and the roof live load. This load was therefore taken as 250 psf. The total load to be supported by the structure comes to W_p = 1400 kips. Substituting this value of W_p, with the known values of λ_E and λ_l into Equation 25-2, the required model load is W_m = 230 lbs. or 0.26 psi vertical load. The load was applied by means of an air bag pushing against a reaction frame, Figure 25-2. It was simpler to provide load readings in terms of millimeter increments on the manometer gauging the applied pressure so that the load on the model for the test discussed below was equivalent to 0.37 psi or 333 lbs. This means that a load factor, Q, must be applied to the resultant readings to bring them back to those that would be produced when W_m = 230 lbs.

$$\text{Load factor Q} = \frac{\text{Actual load}}{\text{Required load}} = \frac{333}{230}$$

$$\therefore Q = 1.45.$$

Prestressing

An initial prestress, equivalent to 100 psi in the prototype was applied to the model.

Now $\lambda_\sigma = \lambda_E$ from dimensional analysis

where λ_σ is the ratio of prototype to model stresses, i.e.

$$\sigma_m = \frac{1}{\lambda_E} \cdot \sigma_p = \frac{100}{6.5}$$

$$= 15 \text{ psi.}$$

Spacing ten bolts (to simulate prestressing rods) along each 30 in. length of wall; a load of 10 lb. per bolt is needed to produce the required prestress in the model. The positioning of the bolts is shown in Figure 25-3.

Deflection Results

The model as described above was tested for vertical deflections which were measured by dial gauges. The model was cycled through several loadings before readings were taken. Figure 25-4 shows the deflected shape of the soffit of one exterior wall and one interior wall. Of particular interest is the distinct difference in shape of the deflection curves. The

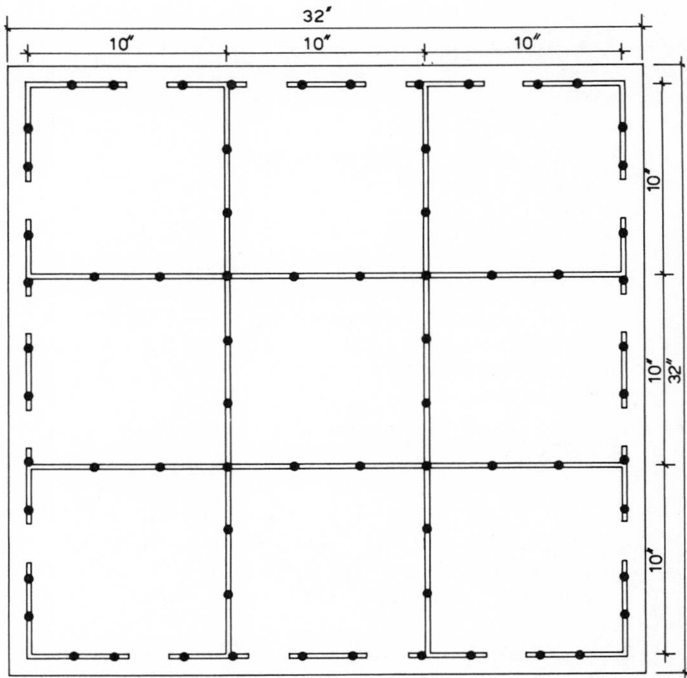

Figure 25-3. Plan of the model showing the positioning of the prestressing bolts.

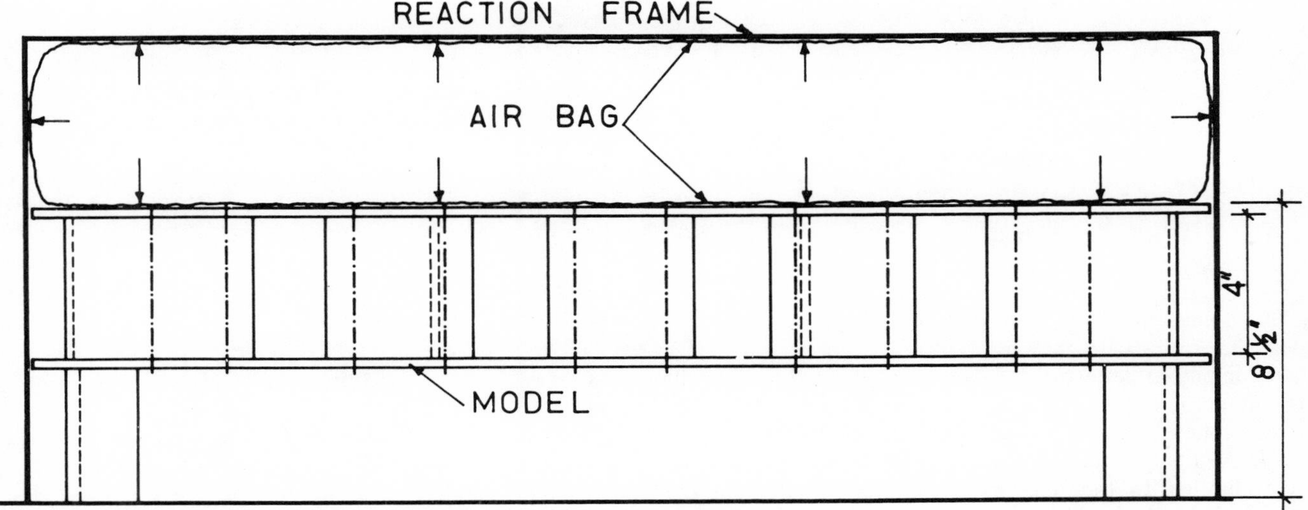

Figure 25-2. Air pressure bag method of loading the model with a uniformly distributed vertical load.

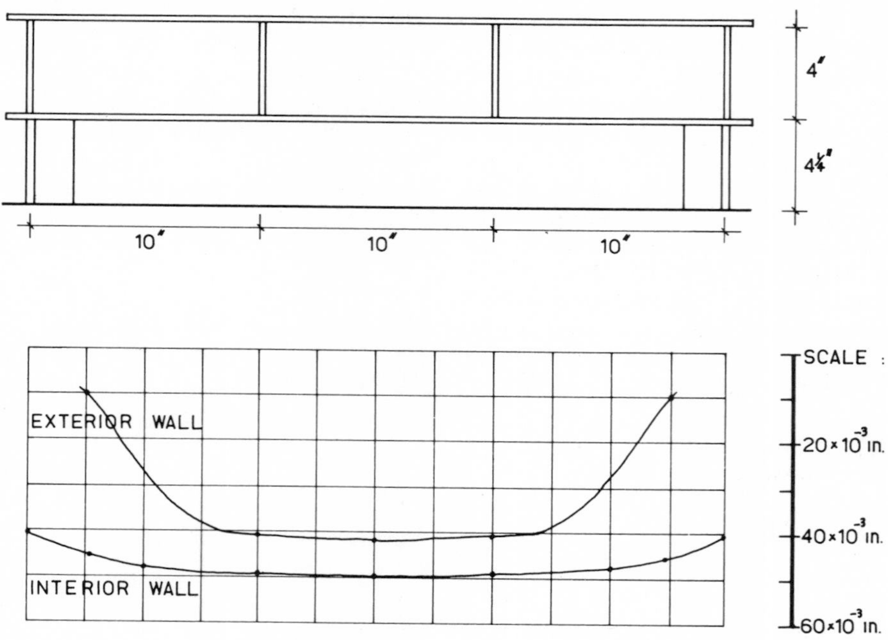

Figure 25-4. The deflected shapes of the soffit of one exterior wall and one interior wall.

exterior wall has 30 percent of its area as unstiffened openings running from slab to slab. The absolute value of the deflections in the exterior walls could be sharply reduced by providing compensatory shear and bending stiffness at these openings.

The maximum deflection of the unstiffened exterior wall is 0.042 in. when the model is under a total load of 333 lb. Applying the load factor to this deflection, the maximum deflection of model, δ_m, under a total load of 230 lb. becomes:

$$\delta_m = \frac{0.042}{Q} = 0.029 \text{ in.}$$

From the length scale ratio:

$$\begin{aligned} \delta_p &= 30 \times {}_m \\ &= 30 \times 0.029 \\ \therefore \delta_p &= 0.87 \text{ in.} \end{aligned}$$

i.e. the equivalent deflection of the exterior wall of the prototype.

The maximum deflection of the centre of the interior walls of the model relative to their ends is approximately 0.010 in. Therefore, the equivalent prototype deflection is 0.21 in.

Under normal circumstances the deflection in most structures is limited to the span/360. This gives a value for the allowable deflection in this structure of 2.5 in. Even allowing for a factor of span/1000, the allowable deflection comes to 0.9 in. which is of the order of the maximum deflection in the model. For the interior walls this is considerably bettered.

Thus, the deflections of the prestressed masonry-reinforced concrete space structure satisfies the most stringent of deflection criteria and indicates the validity of the structure.

Stress Results

Strains were measured on both top and bottom plates as well as on the walls by electric resistance strain gauges. Complete results are not yet available, but preliminary results indicate that:

1. There is compression as well as bending in the roof slab.
2. There is tension as well as bending in the floor slab.
3. The distribution of axial forces in the slabs is not uniform.
4. The walls sustain vertical compression bending moments (although this may be due to the end fixing conditions) and shear.

A more detailed study is being undertaken to determine complete stresses in the walls.

Future Research

Previous research into the effect of vertical prestressing in composite masonry-reinforced concrete wall elements indicated the validity of using the two materials in this way. However, numerous problems still have to be investigated before one can adequately design a complete structure:

1. The actual load distribution along the length of the wall is needed. Once this is known, it is relatively simple to determine the stress distribution in the wall using the method outlined by Beresford[13].
2. Magnitude of shear stresses in walls and slabs immediately over supporting columns needs to be investigated in more detail.
3. The effect of varying the vertical prestress should be investigated to determine if an optimum level of prestress exists.
4. The spacing of walls and the percentage of openings possible in walls as well as whether compensatory stiffness over openings produces significantly different results needs to be examined.

The model described earlier has, so far, been tested to determine the feasibility of the concept and the problems outlined above, which are regarded as being details, are being investigated in the second stage of testing.

Conclusion

A composite structure designated as a prestressed masonry-reinforced concrete space structure has been shown to be a feasible structure with a particularly high degree of stiffness. It is expected that this structure will be utilised in load bearing masonry construction where large open areas are required within the building.

Acknowledgments

The author would like to thank Mr. A. Jacob, Research Student, who assisted with the testing; the technical staff of the Department of Architectural Science, University of Sydney, who manufactured the model; Mr. J. G. Pohl, who drew the figures; and to Mr. A. Wargon, for his helpful suggestions.

Notation

E Elastic modulus
h Storey height
l Span
m,p Subscripts denoting model and prototype respectively
Q Load factor $= \frac{\text{actual load}}{\text{required load}}$
s Slab thickness
t Wall thickness
W Load
δ Deflection
σ Stress
λ_E Scale ratio for elastic modulus
λ_l Scale ratio for length
λ_W Scale ratio for load
λ_σ Scale ratio for stress

References

1. Anon., "Calculated Loadbearing Brickwork", No. 11, Brick Development Research Institute (Australia), 1967, p. 4.
2. Dischinger, F., "Beitrag zur Theorie der Halbscheibe und des wandartigen Balkens", Vol 1, *International Association for Bridge and Structural Engineering,* 1932, pp. 69-93.
3. Wood, R. H., "Studies in Composite Construction, Part 1", Research Paper No. 13, National Building Studies, Her Majesty's Stationary Office, London, 1952, p. 25.
4. Rosenhaupt, S., "Experimental Study of Masonry Walls on Beams", *Proceedings,* Vol. 88, ST3, A.S.C.E., 1962, pp. 137-166.
5. Rosenhaupt, S., "Stresses in Point Supported Composite Walls", *Proceedings,* Vol. 61, No. 7, A.C.I., 1964, pp. 795-810.
6. Hammam, C. W. and Burridge, L. W., "Reinforced Brickwork", *The Structural Engineer,* Vol. 17, 1939, pp. 198-250 and 350-363.
7. Thomas, F. G. and Simms, L. G., "The Strength of Some Reinforced Brick Masonry Beams in Bending and in Shear", *The Structural Engineer,* Vol. 17, 1939, pp. 330-349.
8. Foster, D., Sutherland, R. J. M., Couzens, M. L., and Plowman, J. M., "Reinforced Brickwork Box Beams", SCP-3, Structural Clay Products Limited, 1966, p. 33.
9. Hinkley, A. T., "Analysis of a Shear Wall Supported by a Beam", *Proceedings,* Vol. 92, ST1, A.S.C.E., 1966, pp. 121-130.
10. Hinkley, A. T., "Tests on One-story Prestressed Brickwork Shear Walls", *New Zealand Engineering,* Vol. 21, No. 6, 1966, pp. 245-252.
11. Hrennikoff, A., "Solution of Problems of Elasticity by the Framework Method", *Journal of Applied Mechanics,* Vol. 8, 1941, p. 169.
12. Hrennikoff, A., "Framework Method and its Technique for Solving Plane Stress Problems", Vol. 9, International Association for Bridge and Structural Engineering, 1949, pp. 217-248.
13. Beresford, F. D., "Computer Solution of Plane Stress Problems", Preprint, Third Australian Building Research Congress, Melbourne, 1967, p. 4.
14. Cowan, H. J., "Some Applications of the Use of Direct Model Analysis in the Design of Architectural Structures", *Jnl. Institution of Engineers,* Australia, Vol. 33, 1961, pp. 259-267.

26. Tests on storey-height brickwork panels and development of site control test for brickwork.

N. F. Astbury and H. W. H. West, British Ceramic Research Association, Stoke-on-Trent, England

Introduction

There has been a resurgent interest in calculated load-bearing brickwork in the U.K., and this has been encouraged by the revision in 1964 of the British Standard Code of Practice III, "Structural Recommendations for Load-bearing Walls". As a result of this, some impressive examples of multi-storey load-bearing masonry can now be seen and as structural engineers become more aware of the possibilities of this medium, they are demanding more design data. In particular, there has been interest in developing site control tests of workmanship and more laboratory testing of brickwork strength.

In November 1965 the British Ceramic Research Association installed a wall testing frame capable of applying a compressive load of up to 900 tons to a storey-height (8 ft. 4 in.) wall up to 6 ft. long. This machine[1] has been used to study the effect of essentially ceramic characteristics on the brickwork properties, while the structural implications of different end-conditions and interactions of more than one wall are being studied by Professor A. W. Hendry at Edinburgh University under B.C.R.A. sponsorship. The present chapter describes part of the programme undertaken at the Mellor-Green Laboratories of B.C.R.A. and, in particular, experiments to establish the validity of a site control test using a 9-in. brickwork cube as a guide to the strength of brick walls.

Stedham carried out a series of preliminary tests[2,3] while West, Everill and Beech examined various forms of cube and established a standard testing procedure for a 9-in. brickwork cube consisting of 6 bricks laid with 2 mortar joints in 3 courses of 2 bricks[4]. In a more recent paper[5] at the Essex Symposium, Stedham compared the strength of laboratory-made brickwork cubes with that of storey-height (8 ft. 4 in.) 9-in. walls built from the same materials and concluded that there was a consistent relationship.

At the same Symposium, West, Everill and Beech[6] reported on experiments verifying the usefulness of the brickwork cube test as a site-control test in which they showed that even when brick batches were deliberately chosen so that the strength of the individual bricks was highly variable, and the composition of the mortar was not closely controlled, there is a good correlation between the compressive strength of the wall and the 9-in. cube. An analysis of the site-control tests carried out during the building of the first residential tower at Essex University was also given.

The 9-in. cube test has been included as an Appendix to the B.C.R.A. "Model Specification for Load-bearing Clay Brickwork"[7] and is now being specified by some engineers. The present chapter describes some further results on the effect of the joint condition and gives the results of wall tests used to obtain a correlation between cube strength and wall strength for different mortars and different wall thicknesses.

Effect of the Joint Condition

Earlier work[8] has shown that the character of the joint surface between the brick and the mortar is of considerable

Table 26-1
Ground Brick Cubes, 2 x 3/8 in. Mortar Joints

Mean Compressive strength of cubes, lb./in.^{2}	10200
Number in sample	5
Standard deviation, lb/in.^{2}	897
Coefficient of variation, %	8.8
Mean mortar strength, lb/in.^{2}	380

Table 26-2
Properties of Soft Mud Bricks and Brickwork Cubes

	Light Bricks			Dark Bricks		
	Brick	Cube		Brick	Cube	
		7 days	28 days		7 days	28 days
Mean compressive strength lb/in.^{2}	4000	1420	1610	2590	1050	1170
Number in sample	20	5	5	20	5	5
Standard deviation lb/in.^{2}	281	198	75	260	70	56
Coefficient of variation, %	7.0	13.9	4.7	10.1	6.7	4.8
Mean mortar strength, lb/in.^{2}		274	595		249	595
Number in sample		2	2		2	2

significance in determining the strength of brickwork. Not only does the number of "effective" joints control the strength of brickwork cubes, but minor irregularities in the bed faces of the brick also markedly affect it. Thus, a cube of 6 bricks ground to have their bed faces plane and parallel and assembled without mortar has a crushing strength of 14500 lb./in.^{2} This is not significantly different from the mean crushing strength of the individual ground bricks which is 15800. The mean crushing strength of unground bricks assembled as cubes without mortar was 8274 lb./in.^{2} and with two 3/8 in. mortar joints 9111, despite the fact that these were well-shaped wirecut bricks with very few blemishes.

Further supplies of these same bricks have been ground and have now been made into cubes with two 3/8-in. mortar joints (1:1:6 mortar tested at 7 days). The results are given in Table 26-1.

This compares with one isolated value obtained earlier of 10900 lb./in.^{2}

For most load-bearing brickwork, stiff-extruded or pressed bricks are used. These are, on the whole, reasonably well-shaped with sharp arrises and approximately parallel bed faces. It is not, however, necessary to have high strength bricks for all load-bearing work, and there is a place for hand-made and soft-mud* bricks so that it is also pertinent to examine the effect of shape.

Table 26-2 gives the results of strength tests on individual bricks and cubes from two batches of clamp-fired† single-frog, soft-mud bricks.

The B.S. method of determining crushing strength requires the frogs to be filled flush with 1:3 mortar; this was done for both individual bricks and the cubes. In fact, the top surface of the mortar was struck off flush both on the individual bricks and on the cubes. It will be noted that the coefficients of variation are within the range usually accepted as satisfactory reproducibility for the strength of industrial ceramic materials.

At the Essex Symposium[6] single-frogged, stiff-plastic pressed bricks of very variable strength had been tested. In this case, the brick is similar in aspect to the soft mud brick, but here the shape is regular and the strength very variable with coefficients of variation of the 10 batches of brick which ranged from 14.8 percent to 29.2 percent.

Table 26-3 compares the ratios of brickwork cube strength to brick strength for all the bricks discussed above and for completeness includes some results for bricks with 3/8-in. epoxy mortar joints.

Considering first bricks 2, 3 and 4, it seems that irregular shape or high variation in strength gives brickwork cubes the mean strength which is between 35 percent and 45 percent of the mean strength of the bricks. Construction with stronger mortars or testing at later ages increases the ratio somewhat. When the brick is well-shaped,the ratio rises to 0.6. When the bed faces are ground to provide a plane boundary between brick and mortar, a more even stress distribution may be expected, and here the ratio rises to 0.65. When the strength of the mortar material approaches that of the ceramic,then the cube begins to behave almost as a monolith and reaches over 80 percent of the brick strength.

In the classical work of Davey and Thomas[9], the ratio of pier strength to brick strength became smaller with high strength bricks due to the low mortar strength, although stronger mortars again increased the ratio. In the present case, however, the stronger brick with the weak 1:1:6 mortar still gives a higher ratio both in the ground and unground condition. In this case, the junction with the mortar is an important determinant.

Curiously enough, with very strong mortars the strength of the mortar is more important than the junction between brick and mortar. In the example quoted, with a 3/8-in. epoxy joint, ground bricks give a lower ratio than unground bricks. It seems that some lateral strain is occurring even in this high-strength mortar, so that there is a proportion of tensile stress transmitted to the brick. When no mortar of any kind intervenes between the faces of the brick, then—as noted

* "Soft-mud" is used in the English context of a machine moulded brick and not a soft extruded brick.

† "A kiln constructed, except for the permanent foundations, of the bricks that are to be fired, together with combustible refuse and breeze." E.A. Dodd Dictionary of Ceramics.

Table 26-3
Variation of Cube: Brick Ratio with Regularity of Bricks

Brick No.	Type of Brick		Mean Brick Strength lb./in.^{2}	Age tested days	Mortar Type	Mean Mortar Strength lb./in.^{2}	Mean Cube: Brick Strength Ratio
1	Extruded bed faces:	ground		7	3/8" Epoxy	10840	0.732
1		unground	15100	7	3/8" Epoxy	11280	0.817
1		ground		7	1:1:6	380	0.646
1		unground		7	1:1:6	381	0.603
2	Soft mud single frog:	light	4000	7	1:1:6	274	0.355
3		dark	2590	7	1:1:6	249	0.405
2		light	4000	28	1:1:6	595	0.403
3		dark	2590	28	1:1:6	595	0.450
4	Stiff-plastic pressed, single frog, common		4810	28	1:¼:3	1909	0.428

*Single result

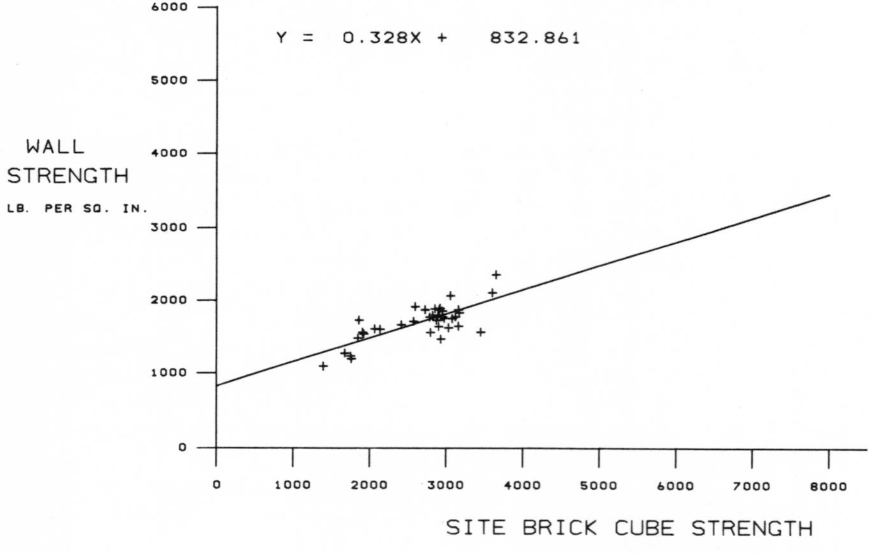

Figure 26-1. 9 in. walls, axially loaded, 1:¼:3 mortar, tested at 28 days.

above–the strength of a cube is not significantly different from the mean strength of the brick.

Correlation of Wall and Cube Tests

The British Ceramic Research Association often closely cooperates with industry and with government laboratories, and in the programme of wall testing full advantage has been taken of this. Thus when the wall frame was first installed, a correlation exercise[1] compared the performance of the machines at B.C.R.A., Edinburgh University and Structural Clay Products, Ltd., with the 1000 ton Amsler machine at the Building Research Station. In a more recent programme, several brick companies cooperated to provide materials and facilities to enable a large programme of wall testing to be completed more quickly than would otherwise be possible. Some of these results have been used in drawing up the following tables. The contributing laboratories are appropriately identified.

All walls are storey-height (approx. 8 ft. 4 in.) and 4 ft. 6 in. long. In the early work the walls were 9 in. thick, laid in

Table 26-4
9-in. Walls, Axially Loaded, 1:¼:3 Mortar, Tested at 28 days.

Wall No.	Brick Type	Mean Brick Strength lb./in.^{2}	Mean Mortar Strength lb./in.^{2}	Mean Wall Strength lb./in.^{2}	Mean Site Cube Strength lb./in.^{2}
BCRA 1	Wirecut perforated	8880	1850	1840	3170
2			1920	1925	2590
3			1970	1653	3160
4			1790	1880	3160
5			1830	1635	3030
6			1680	1570	2790
7			1750	1650	2900
8			1860	1735	2870
9			1690	1900	2920
10			2420	1675	2410
BCRA 11	Wirecut perforated	8920	3050	1760	2977
12			2320	1880	2720
13			2850	2350	3650
14			2730	2110	3600
15			1425	2070	3053
16			1410	1880	2910
17			1480	1760	3080
SCP 18	Wirecut perforated	8880	1680	1775	2780
19			1600	1800	2890
20			1560	1475	2930
21			1510	1890	2850
22			1660	1860	2950
BRS 23	Wirecut perforated	8880	1810	1780	2950
24			1860	1720	2570
25			1750	1800	2820
26			1590	1570	3450
27			1510	1780	3120
BCRA 28	Stiff-plastic, single frog	3400	2173	1280	1673
29		5960	1953	1613	2066
30		5960	2260	1490	1846
31		4710	1800	1200	1760
32		4870	2020	1735	1860
33		4860	2370	1610	2136
34		4840	2447	1550	1920
35*		4560	2280	1570	1903
36**		4420	926	1240	1750
37		4520	1030	1100	1393

* Curing time for wall 35 was 46 days and for its cubes 35 days
** Curing time for wall 36 was 41 days and for its cubes 34 days

English bond with 1:¼:3 mortar, and tested by axial loading at 28 days. The brick strengths are the mean of 10 tested, soaked in water according to B.S.3921. The mortar strengths are the means of 3 or 4 cubes taken as the wall was being built. The "site" cubes are the mean of 3 and, in the case of walls 1-10 means of 6, built by the bricklayer as he built the wall. The results are given in Table 26-4 and the computer plot with regression line is shown at Figure 26-1.

Two walls cured for more than 28 days are included. It will be noted that these give the same sort of relationship and have been included in the analysis. The correlation coefficient is 0.759 and is significant at the 0.1 percent level.

The regression equation is:

$$y = 0.328 X + 832.861$$

The regression equation for the results reported by Stedham[5] is:

$$y = 0.377 X + 433.825$$

(Note Figure 26-2)

The two gradients do not show a statistically significant difference, but the lines differ significantly in position. No comment is offered on this at present. Stedham's correlation coefficient was 0.932, significant at the 0.1 percent level.

Subsequently a number of nominal 4-1/2-in. walls have been tested. The actual thickness of the wall is 4 to 4-1/8 in. In this case a variety of bricks covering a wide range of strengths has been used, and the walls have been tested both axially and with an eccentricity of 1/2 in. (equivalent to $^t/_8$ on a 4-in. wall).

Some results are given in Table 26-5 and plotted at Figures 26-3 and 26-4. All the strength tests were carried out at 14 days. The bricks are all wirecuts. All the axial tests were on the wall frame at S.C.P. Ltd. and the eccentric loading tests at B.C.R.A. In the axially loaded walls, the mortar and cube strength are each the mean of two. For eccentric loading, mortar strength is the mean of 3 or 4, and brick cubes the mean of 3.

No differentiation has been made between 1:¼:3 and 1:1:6 mortar. The correlation coefficients and their significance are:

Axial 0.520, significant at 1 percent level
Eccentric 0.732, significant at 0.1 percent level

The effect of eccentricity is clearly shown, but the estimate of wall strength from the cubes is not very precise.

A larger number of results from an extension of this programme are plotted at Figures 26-5, 26-6, 26-7, and 26-8

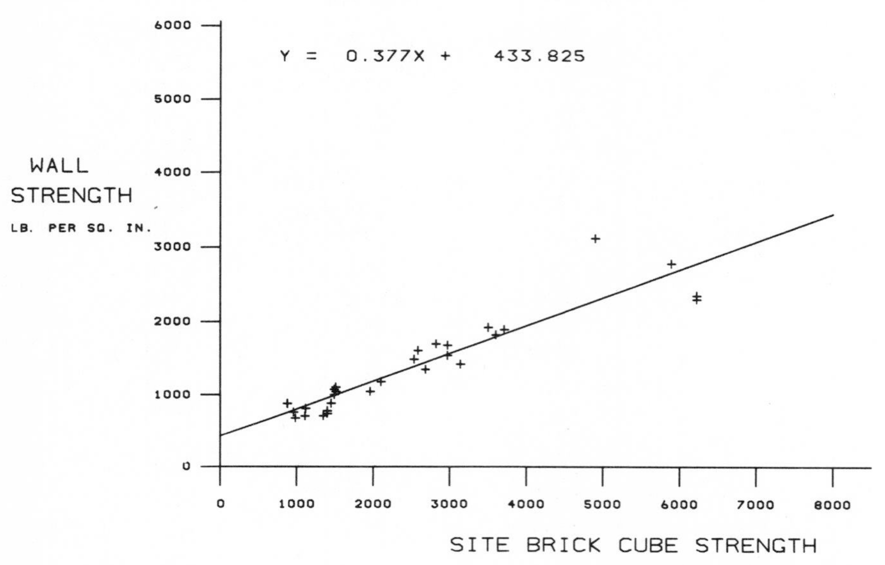

Figure 26-2. Stedham's results for 9 in. walls.

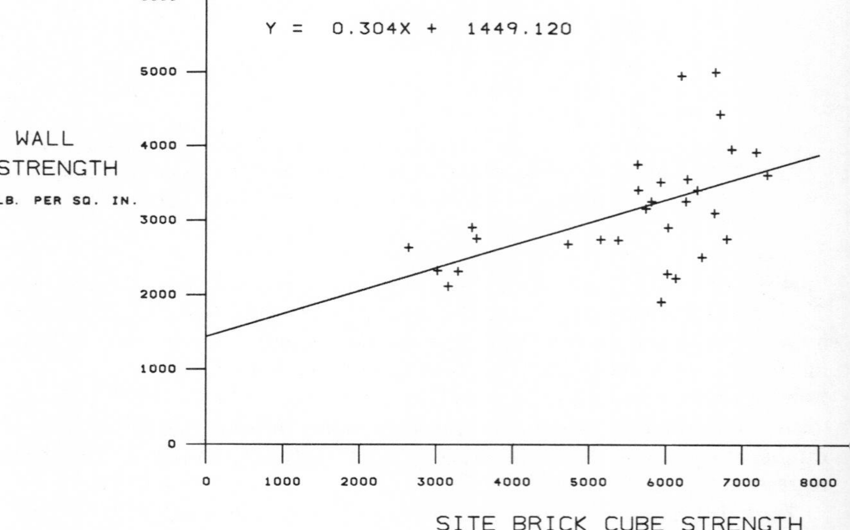

Figure 26-3. 4½ in. walls from Table 26-5, axially loaded.

Table 26-5
4½ in. Walls Tested at 14 days

		AXIAL LOADING			ECCENTRIC LOADING		
Mortar Type	Mean Brick Strength lb./in.^{2}	Mean Mortar Strength lb./in.^{2}	Wall Strength lb./in.^{2}	Mean Site Cube Strength lb./in.^{2}	Mean Mortar Strength lb./in.^{2}	Wall Strength lb.//in.^{2}	Mean Site Cube Strength lb./in.^{2}
1:¼:3	12450	1565	4950	6200	2478	2780	5803
		1870	5000	6650	1901	2245	4769
		2340	3960	6860	2334	2476	6298
	13060	2090	3520	5930	2226	2505	5990
		1910	3410	6410	2309	2495	5192
		2380	3260	5810	2189	2055	5447
	6060	2060	2760	3530	2440	1415	3157
		1540	2910	3470	2615	1081	3270
		1480	2640	2640	2423	935	2747
	15120	1610	3610	7325	2193	2370	5720
		1630	3920	7180	2215	2060	5413
		2600	4430	6710	1963	2880	5317
	11980	2005	3100	6640	1771	1410	4340
		2120	3160	5740	2248	2130	5460
		1940	3410	5640	1815	1730	4760
1:1:6	12450	1062	3760	5630	464	1347	4515
		889	3560	6280	501	1674	4879
		582	3260	6260	502	1946	5379
	13060	747	2230	6130	650	1910	4880
		636	1920	5940	651	1664	4837
		601	2290	6020	684	1720	4730
	6060	815	2330	3020	522	938	2183
		696	2320	3290	353	741	2263
		655	2120	3160	506	763	2283
	15120	748	2760	6800	517	1745	6423
		591	2510	6470	494	1272	6616
		760	2910	6030	409	1525	6235
	11980	685	2750	5150	530	1210	3510
		974	2740	5380	534	1400	3673
		760	2690	4720	471	1093	3923

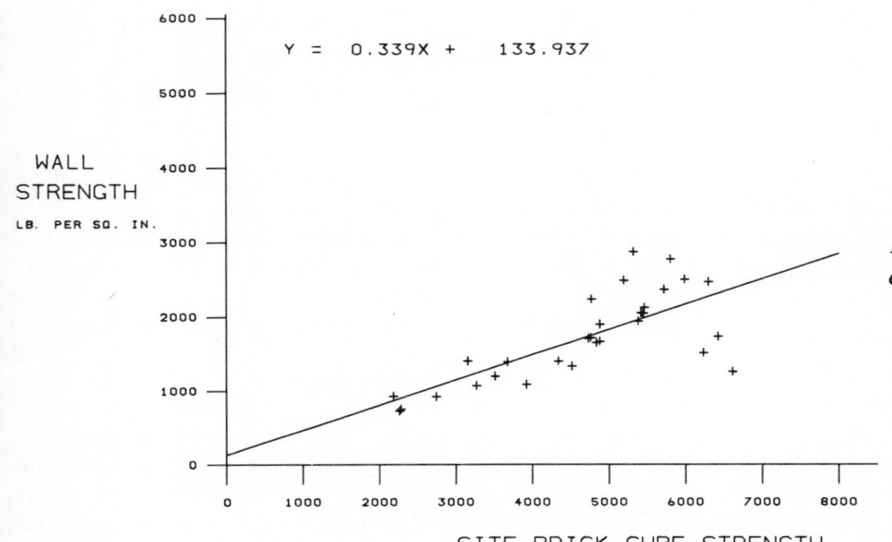

Figure 26-4. 4½ in. walls from Table 26-5, eccentrically loaded.

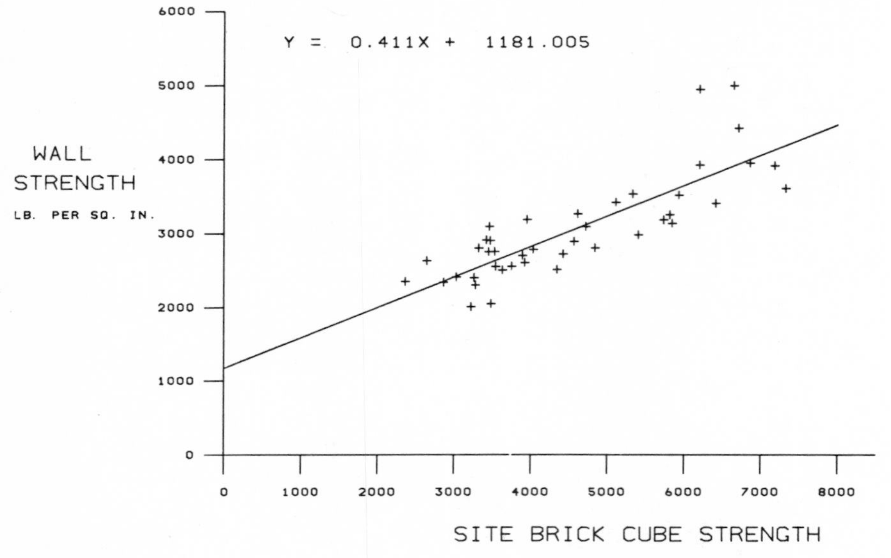

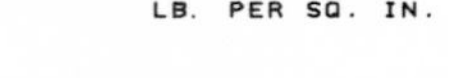

Figure 26-5. 4½ in. walls, 1:¼:3 mortar, tested at 14 days, axially loaded.

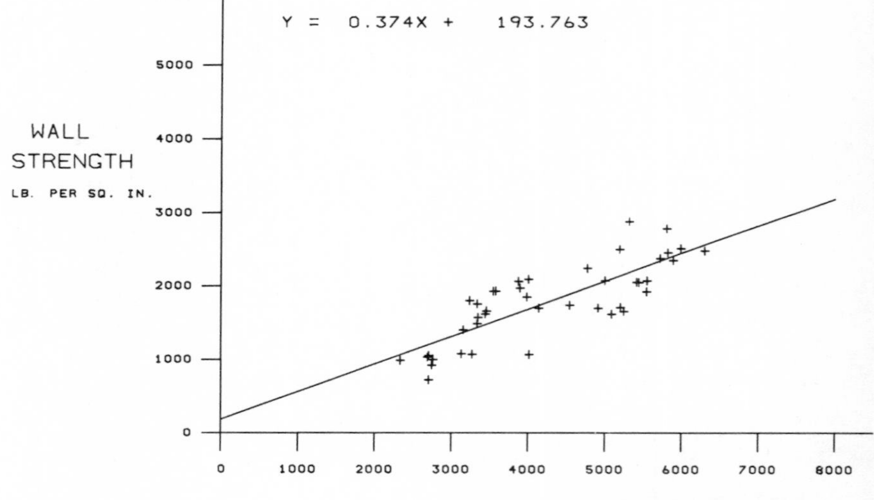

Figure 26-6. 4½ in. walls, 1:¼:3 mortar, tested at 14 days, eccentrically loaded.

and here the separation of 1:¼:3 and 1:1:6 mortar is possible but the spread of the results is still large. The correlation coefficients are as follows:

1:¼:3	Axial	0.824
1:¼:3	Eccentric	0.810
1:1:6	Axial	0.693
1:1:6	Eccentric	0.688

All are significant at the 1 percent level.

In comparing these various results, it is apparent that, for a given brick and mortar as represented by the cube test, the compressive strength of a 4 1/2-in. wall is greater than that of a 9-in. wall by about 30 percent. Similarly the effect of an eccentricity of 1/2-in. with these walls is to reduce the strength by about 1000 lb./in.^{2} from that obtained under axial loading conditions with 1:¼:3 mortar, while with 1:1:6 mortar the reduction range is from about 1200 lb./in.^{2} to about 600 lb./in.^{2} over the range of cube strength considered.

Conclusions

The development of a 9-in. brickwork cube test has involved considering two aspects. There is first the desirability of developing a site-control test for load-bearing brickwork, and second the wish to find an experimental method which will lead to some more rational explanation of the curious physics of a brick and mortar composite.

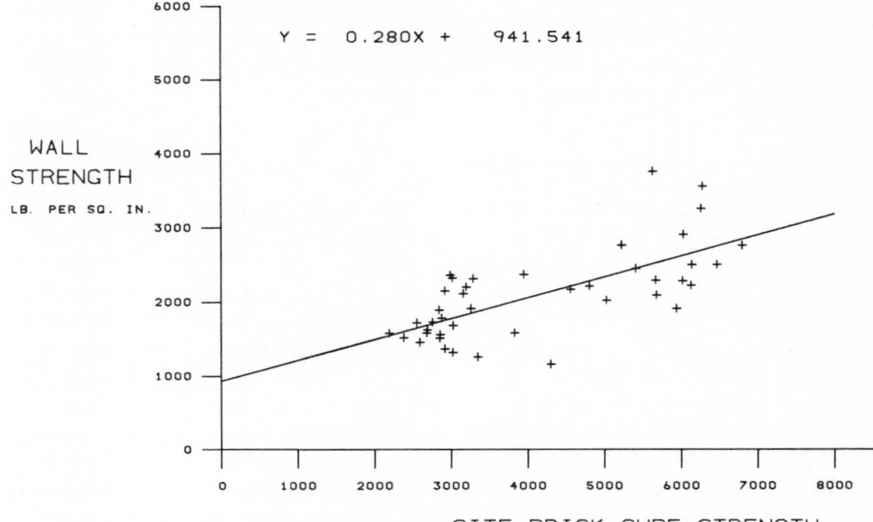

Figure 26-7. 4½ in. walls, 1:1:6 mortar, tested at 14 days, axially loaded.

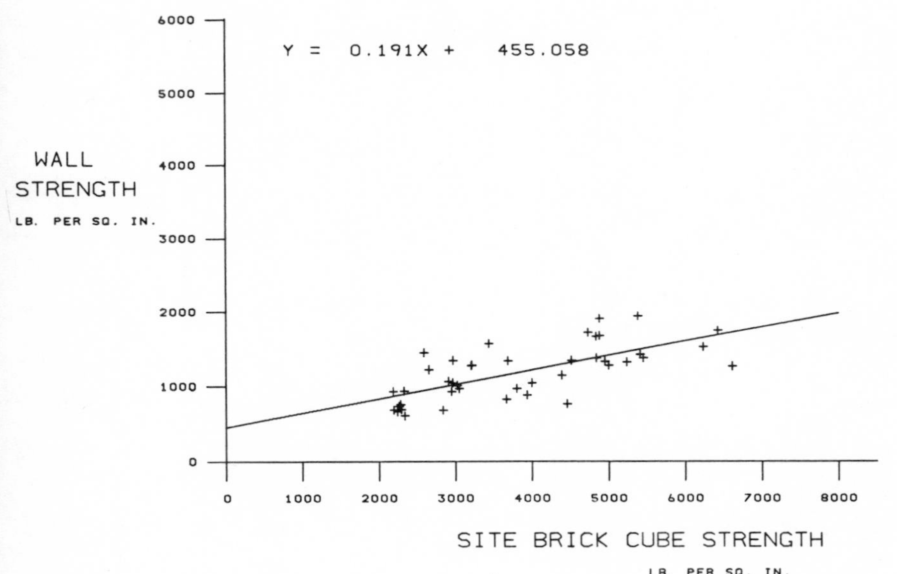

Figure 26-8. 4½ in. walls, 1:1:6 mortar, tested at 14 days, eccentrically loaded.

For the first task, while undoubtedly using site control methods – any site control method – tends to aid supervision and to give more uniform workmanship, we are not yet satisfied that the test is sufficiently precise to be mandatory. This caution was expressed by placing it in the appendix to the Model Specification and, in that document, engineers were recommended to use the test to accumulate evidence.

In the second respect, however, the test has already yielded useful results as a laboratory tool. It has, for example, enabled the effect of the joint condition to be examined with less effort and perhaps more precision than when storey-height walls are tested. While it is true that the present code calculations based on the brick strength and the mortar strength may be adequate, our own experience suggests that the compressive strength of the mortar is of marginal importance except at very high mortar strengths, and thus the 9-in. brickwork cube provides an additional check on the behaviour of this complex material called brickwork.

Acknowledgments

The wall tests are part of a large cooperative programme for which materials have been manufactured by G. H. Downing and Co., Ltd., J. and A. Jackson, Ltd., and Redland Bricks, Ltd. The 4 1/2-in. axially-loaded walls have been tested by S.C.P., Ltd. under the direction of Mr. S. T. E. Davenport. The authors gratefully acknowledge the assistance of their colleagues, Mr. H. R. Hodgkinson, who has responsibility for wall testing, and Mr. G. N. Vaughan and Miss M. Ravenscroft, who have carried out the computer programmes. Thanks are due to the Council of the British Ceramic Research Association for permission to present this information.

References

1. Hodgkinson, H. R., Powell, B., and West, H. W. H., "The Design of a Wall Testing Machine and Comparative Tests", *Proc. Brit. Ceram. Soc.*, No. 11 (under publication).
2. Stedham, M. E. C., "Quality Control for Loadbearing Brickwork; Part 1. 9-in. Cube Tests–Preliminary Results",*Transactions of British Ceramics Society, 64,* 1965, 1.
3. Stedham, M. E. C., "Quality Control for Loadbearing Brickwork: Part 2. 9-in. Cube Tests–Further Results," *Proc. Brit. Ceram. Soc., 64,* 1965, 9.
4. West, H. W. H., Everill, J. B., and Beech, D. G., "Development of a Standard 9-in. Cube Test for brickwork", *Transactions of British Ceramics Society, 65,* 1966, 111.
5. Stedham, M. E. C., "Quality Control for Loadbearing Brickwork; Part 3. Wall Tests", *Proc. Brit. Ceram. Soc.*, No. 11 (under publication).
6. West, H. W. H., Everill, J. B., and Beech, D. G., "Some Experiments in the Use of the 9-in. Brickwork Cube for Site Control Testing", *Proc. Brit. Ceram. Soc.*, No. 11 (under publication).
7 "Model Specification for Load-Bearing Clay Brickwork" drafted by the Structural Ceramics Advisory Group of the Building Science Committee, B.C.R.A. Spec. Pub. No. 56, 1967.
8. West, H. W. H., Everill, J. B., and Beech, D. G., "The Testing of Bricks and Blocks for Load-Bearing Brickwork", *Trans XIth Int. Cer. Congress,* Stockholm, 1966.
9. Davey, N. and Thomas, F.G., "The Structural Uses of Brickwork", Paper No. 24 I.C.E., Inst. Civ. Engnrs. Struct. and Bldg. Div., Struct. and Bldg. London, 1950.

Part 4: Structural interaction

27. Structural behavior of masonry infilled frames subjected to racking loads.

C. Carter and B. Stafford Smith, Dept. of Civil Engineering, University of Southhampton, Southampton, England

Introduction

When a masonry panel is subjected to an in-plane racking load, failure occurs by one of the following modes:

1. local crushing of the masonry or mortar close to the applied load or at its reaction.
2. tension cracking along the mortar joints or through the masonry
3. shear cracking along the mortar joints.

These modes are illustrated in Figure 27-1a and Figure 27-1b.

The particular mode depends on such factors as the extent of the region over which the racking load is applied, the presence of other external loads, the length-height proportions of the panel, and the relative values of the compressive, tensile, and bond shearing strength of the masonry-mortar composite. Although the panel thickness will influence its strength, generally it will not influence the failure mode since it affects the strength of each mode by the same proportion. Usually, occurrence of one of the modes is sufficient to precipitate collapse.

When a masonry panel is bounded by a frame and the composite structure is subjected to a racking load, similar modes of panel failure will occur. In this case, some factors influencing both the strength and the failure mode will result from the frame's restraining influence. Indeed, the containment of the frame is such that even after failure of one of the modes, it may be possible to increase the racking load by a substantial proportion before complete collapse occurs.

Failure modes 1. and 2. are particularly relevant to panels of a relatively homogeneous material such as concrete; this problem has been considered previously.[1,2] The introduction of a mortar-jointed masonry panel immediately raises the significance of mode c) because of the lowered shear strength along the mortar joints. Therefore, this investigation has been concerned primarily with accounting for mode c), although not ignoring the possibility of the other modes. As the investigation has also allowed an assessment of the stiffness of infilled frames, this aspect is also briefly considered.

The Interaction of the Frame and Infill

The resistance of masonry to shearing stresses is provided by combining bond shear strength and friction between the masonry and mortar. To estimate the ultimate racking load, it is necessary to know the following:

1. the shear and compressive stresses induced in the panel by the racking load,
2. the bond shear strength between the masonry and mortar,
3. the coefficient of friction between the masonry and mortar.

Therefore, it is necessary first to consider more closely the nature of the frame-infill interaction and to examine the resulting stresses in the infill. The following paragraphs describe briefly the behaviour and analysis of infilled frames; for greater detail the reader is referred to a previous paper.[2]

When an infilled frame is subjected to a racking load, the frame separates from the infill except in regions around the end of the compression diagonal, as illustrated in Figure 27-2a. The load is transmitted from the frame to the infill through these regions or "lengths of contact" and, in effect, the infill behaves as a diagonal strut to brace the frame, as shown in Figure 27-2b.

The importance of the lengths of contact is that they influence the stress distribution in the panel and, therefore, its

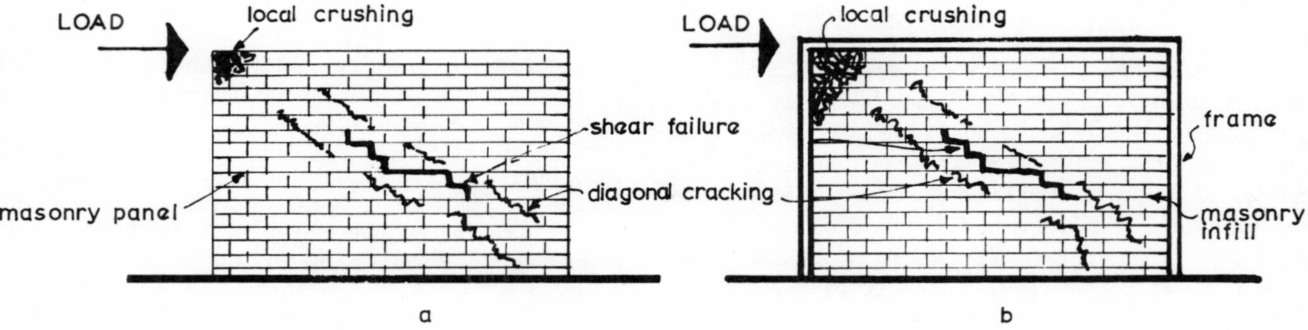

Figure 27-1. Modes of failure.

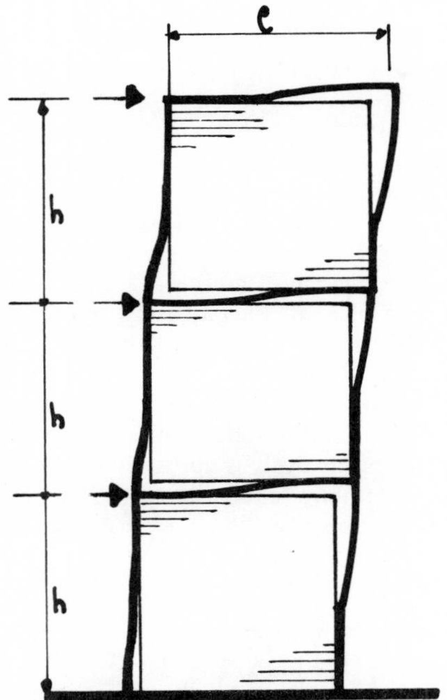

Figure 27-2a. Laterally loaded infilled frame.

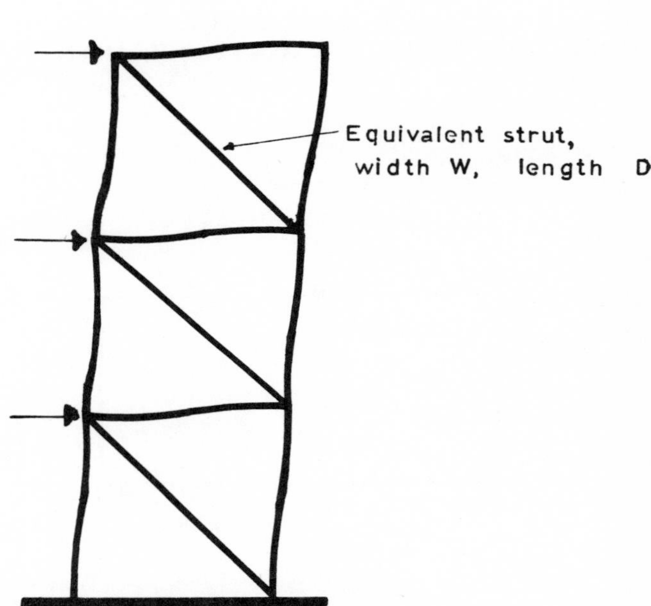

Figure 27-2b. Equivalent frame.

stiffness and strength. In multi-storey infilled frames, the length of contact against the beam is equal to about half the span. However, against the columns it varies significantly according to the flexural stiffness of the column relative to the in-plane stiffness of the infill. Hence, the stiffness and strength of the infill partly depends on the relative stiffness of the column to the infill. This relative stiffness may be aptly expressed by a dimensionless parameter λh, where

$$\lambda = \sqrt[4]{\frac{E_c t \sin 2\Theta}{4EIh}} \tag{27-1}$$

in which h is the vertical spacing between beams; E_c and t are Young's modulus and thickness, respectively, of the infill; Θ is the slope of the infill diagonal to the horizontal, and EI is the flexural rigidity of the column.

Using this parameter, an approximate value of the length of contact against the column is given by

$$\frac{a}{h} = \frac{\pi}{2\lambda h} \tag{27-2}$$

The parameter λh has proved an appropriate function against which to plot other structural properties of the infilled frame, such as stiffness and strength.

On the basis of the length of column contact, which is known in terms of λh, and the half-span length of contact against the beam, then, by assuming an arbitrary diagonal load to be triangularly distributed over each length, as shown in Figure 27-3, the stresses in the infill were analyzed by a finite difference solution of the biharmonic equation. This analysis was repeated for panels of different length-height proportions, each with a range of values for the length of column contact, i.e. accounting for variations in λh. Thus, values of the direct and shear stresses were obtained throughout the panels.

Pursuing the diagonal strut concept for the infill, the stresses were used to calculate the diagonal strains and thus obtain effective widths w for different panel proportions and values of λh, as shown in Figure 27-4. However, model experiments showed these theoretical values to be excessive, and so the more realistic experimental values are also included on Figure 27-4.

As the horizontal deflections of an infilled frame are very small compared with those of the open frame, the influence of the bending stiffness of the frame members on the overall

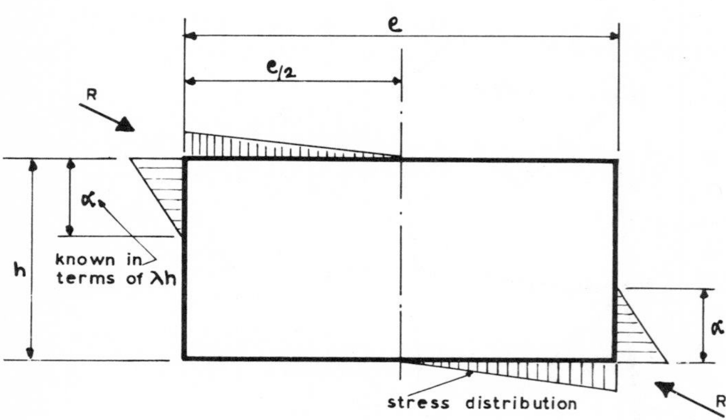

Figure 27-3. Assumed panel loading.

horizontal stiffness is negligible; therefore, it is a reasonable approximation to assume the frame to be pin-jointed and, by replacing the infills with equivalent struts, estimate the horizontal stiffness of the infilled frame by a conventional pin-jointed frame calculation.

It remains, therefore, in predicting the horizontal stiffness of a masonry infilled frame to decide a value for the effective Young's Modulus of the masonry composite. This will depend on the quality of the bricks, the mortar, and the workmanship. In the absence of any particular values, the reader should estimate a value between 1.0×10^6 lb./in^2 and 3.0×10^6 lb./in^2.

With the indeterminables described above, and others such as the fit of the panel against the columns and the upper beam, any prediction for stiffness is likely to be grossly in error, especially in the initial stages of loading, and should be used only to indicate the order of horizontal stiffness.

The Strength of Masonry Panels

As described previously, the authors carried out elastic stress analyses for a series of panels of varying proportions, considering each panel with varying lengths of contact against the surrounding frame. Thus, the stresses were established throughout the panel, and from these the principal shear stresses and associated normal stresses were also determined. Two typical panels are shown in Figures 27-5 and 27-6 indicating the directions and values of the principal shear stresses.

The lines of the principal shear planes correspond to the diagonal cracks which usually occur in masonry panels subjected to a racking load. Also, in tests on masonry infilled frames, the first cracks occur at the centre of the panel, which is the region where the mortar joints are approximately mutually inclined with the planes of the maximum shear stress. The fact that the first cracks appear at the centre and not in the compressed corners of the panel probably results from the high bi-axial compression occurring at the loaded corners and assisting the strength of the masonry, in contrast to the condition at the panel's centre where low normal compressive stresses and maximum shear stresses produce a more critical failure condition. This condition applies throughout the early stages of failure with the result that, when the loading is further increased, additional cracks appear parallel to the initial cracks in the adjacent mortar joints, thus producing a band of cracks stepping down through the mortar joints along the loaded diagonal.

As the behaviour of brickwork is approximately linear up to both tension and shear failure, is is justifiable to assume that an elastic stress analysis is appropriate for predicting the panel stresses at failure and, therefore, the ultimate load. Although the masonry infilling is non-homogeneous, the

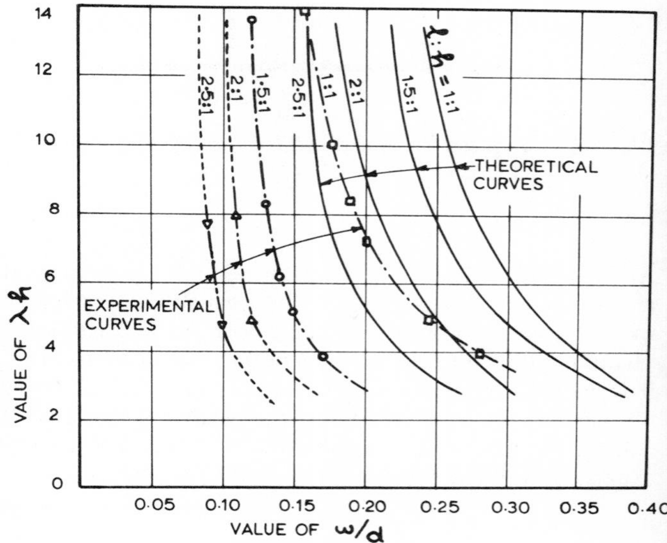

Figure 27-4. Effective width of infill as a function of λ h.

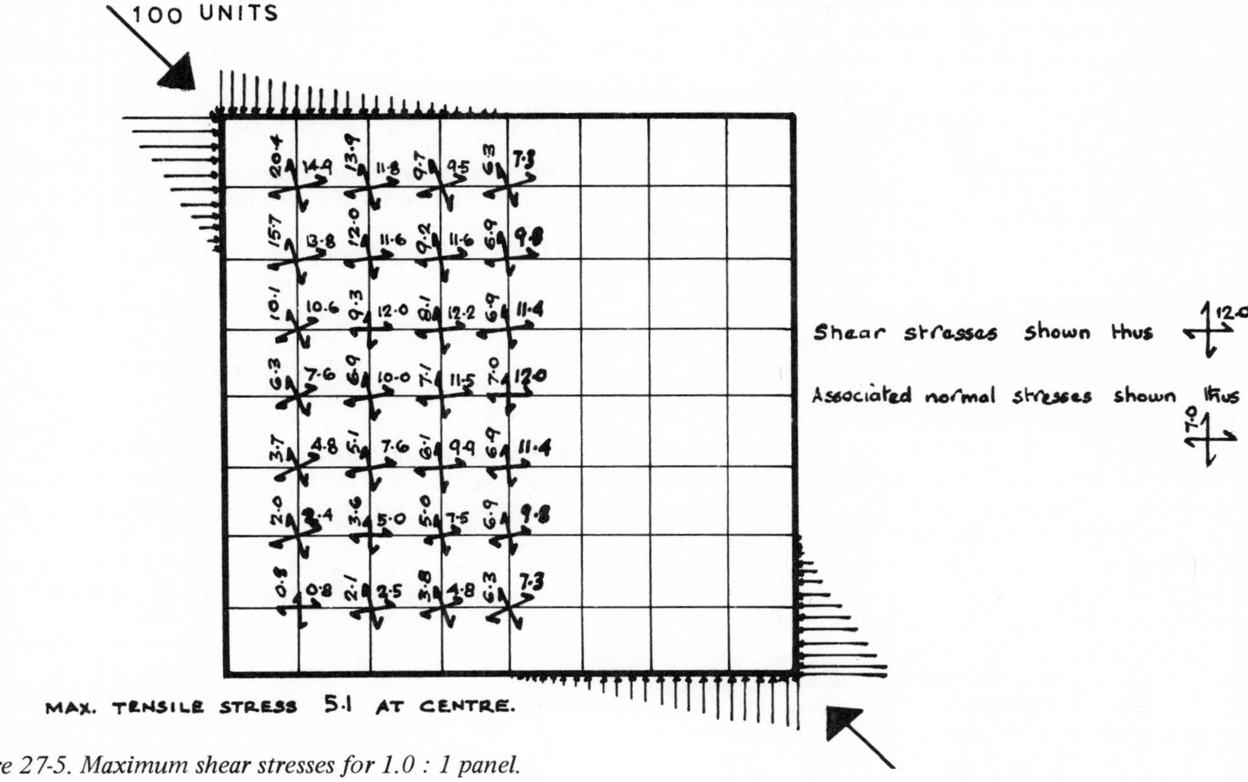

Figure 27-5. Maximum shear stresses for 1.0 : 1 panel.

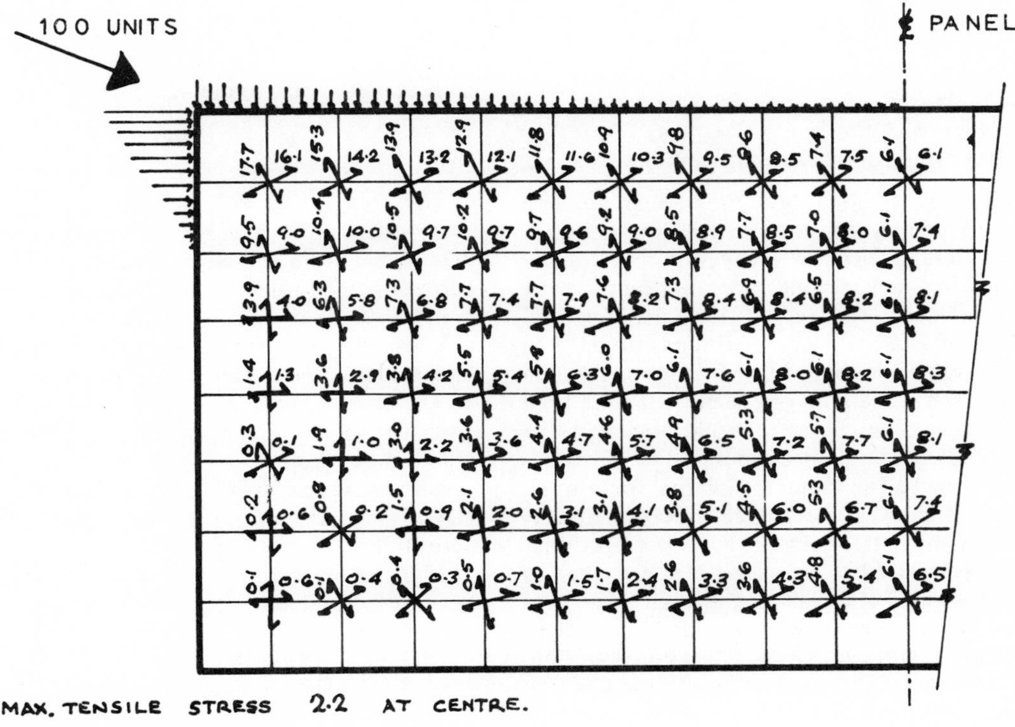

Figure 27-6. Maximum shear stresses for 2.5 : 1 panel.

authors assumed that the relatively small size of the components compared to the overall panel size allows the results of the homogeneous stress analysis to be applied to the masonry infilling.

One mode of failure of a masonry infill could be by local crushing at the application point of the load; this may be realized if a relatively low strength brick were used with a high strength mortar. However, this combination is unlikely to occur in an infilled frame deliberately designed as a shear wall. Therefore, rather than considering this mode in detail here, the reader is referred to one of the authors' earlier papers on the subject.[2]

Bond Shear Strength (f_{bs}) and Bond Tension Strength (f_{bt})

The bond shear strength of masonry has recently been given considerable attention, and, as a result, it is possible to predict the value of the bond shear strength for a given mortar strength and type of masonry block. This chapter does not propose to discuss the many factors which govern the bond shear strength since these have been thoroughly investigated by Polyakov.[3] However, one aspect of bond shear strength will be considered as it is necessary for the development of this chapter.

When a vertical compressive stress is applied to masonry, the shear resistance is increased by the increase of friction between the masonry and the mortar. The following relationship for the shear strength of the brickwork has been suggested.[3]

$$f_s = f_{bs} + \mu f_n \tag{27-4}$$

where

- f_s the shear strength of the brickwork
- f_{bs} the bond shear strength of the brickwork
- f_n normal compressive stress
- μ coefficient of internal friction of the brickwork.

When the infilling is of solid brick the shear strength depends, to an approximately equal degree, on the bond shear strength and the internal friction; whereas, for perforated brick assemblies their strength depends primarily on the value of the bond shear strength. Test results show that for solid brick the coefficient of internal friction (μ) varies from 0.6 to 1.7, with a typical value of about 0.7, and for perforated brickwork a much lower value averaging about 0.15 has been found. It is useful to note also that for solid brickwork the coefficient of internal friction has been found to be independent of the mortar strength. The values for internal friction can vary considerably depending on the surface state of the bricks and, in the absence of any better data, the authors suggest that for solid brick and perforated brick, values of μ are taken as 0.6 and 0.1, respectively. These values are given only as a rough, conservative guide for average brickwork; higher values may be used if known for the brickwork under consideration.

The permissible shear stress for brickwork given in the current British Standard, when a 1:¼:3 or stronger mortar is used, is 20 lb./in^2, or one third of the compressive stress produced by the dead load, whichever is the greater, with a maximum value of 30 lb./in^2. This value is low compared with results obtained under laboratory conditions but, from a study of actual structures, it is probably a realistic figure for average workmanship on the site.

The bond tension strength is usually taken as approximately half the bond shear strength; however, there is no general agreement that this value is correct for all types of brickwork. The probable relation between bond shear and bond tension is characterized by a decrease of f_{bs}/f_{bt} with and increase of f_{bt}. For practical purposes, the value of $f_{bs}/f_{bt} = 1.7$ is quoted as a useful guide,[4] although Murthy and Hendry[5] find that for solid bricks in a 1:3 cement mortar $f_{bs} = 2.3\ f_{bt}$.

Design Curves

From a knowledge of the properties of the masonry infill and the surrounding frame, one can predict the value of the racking force to cause the initial cracking of the masonry.

The equation for the shear mode of failure is derived as follows:

If R_S is the diagonal load to cause the shear failure of a panel of particular length/height proportions, it may be shown that:

$$R_S = \frac{100}{8}\,\frac{f_{bs}}{f_{st}}\,.\,ht + \mu R_S\,\frac{f_{nt}}{f_{st}} \tag{27-5}$$

where f_{st} and f_{nt} are the theoretical maximum shear and corresponding vertical stresses given by a 100-unit load acting diagonally on an 8-unit-high, 1-unit-thick panel.

$$\therefore\ R_S = \left(\frac{100}{8}\cdot\frac{f_{bs}}{f_{st}}\cdot ht\right)\Big/\left(1-\frac{\mu f_{nt}}{f_{st}}\right) \tag{27-6}$$

and converting this to non-dimensional parameters,

$$\frac{R_S}{f_{bs}\,ht} = \frac{100}{8f_{st}}\Big/\left(1-\frac{\mu f_{nt}}{f_{st}}\right) \tag{27-7}$$

A panel of particular length/height proportions, can now be determined from the stress analyses values of f_{st} and f_{nt} for corresponding values of λh. These may be substituted in the right-hand side of Equation 27-7, together with a value for μ, to allow the curve for the shear failure load, expressed by the dimensionless parameter $R_S/f_{bs}ht$, to be plotted as a function of λh, as in Figures 27-7, 27-8, 27-9, and 27-10. Curves are given for values of μ equal to 0 and 0.6 to cover a range of practical possibilities.

Curves representing diagonal tension failure of the infill may also be plotted on the same graphs from the following derivation:

If R_T is the diagonal failure load to cause diagonal tension failure, in an infill of particular length/height proportions, then:

$$R_T = \frac{100f_{dt}\,.\,ht}{8f_{tt}} \tag{27-8}$$

where f_{dt} is the brickwork diagonal tensile strength and f_{tt} the maximum theoretical tensile stress caused by a 100-unit load acting on a 8-units-high, 1-unit-thick panel.

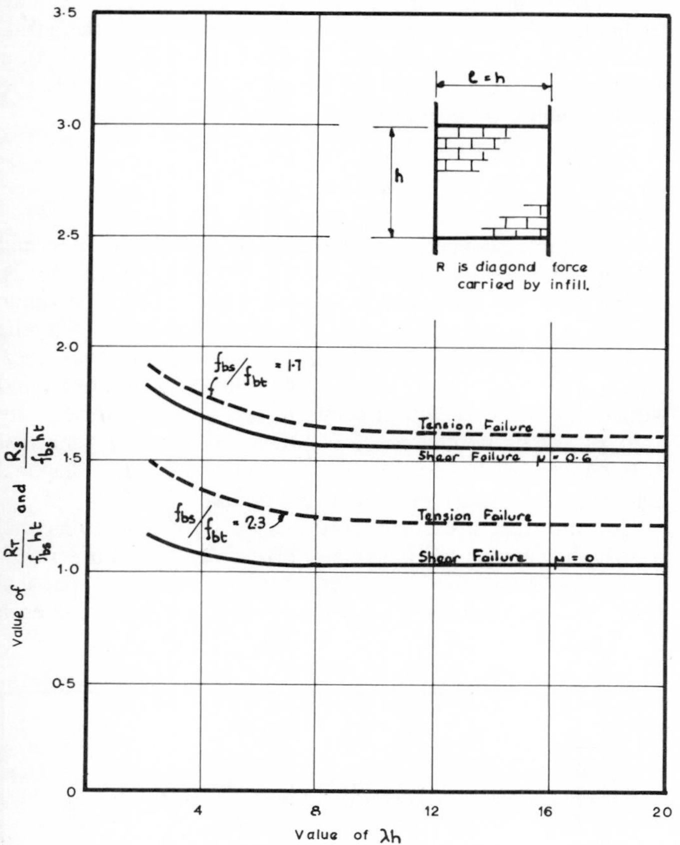

Figure 27-7. Panel strengths for masonry infilled frames as a function of λ h.

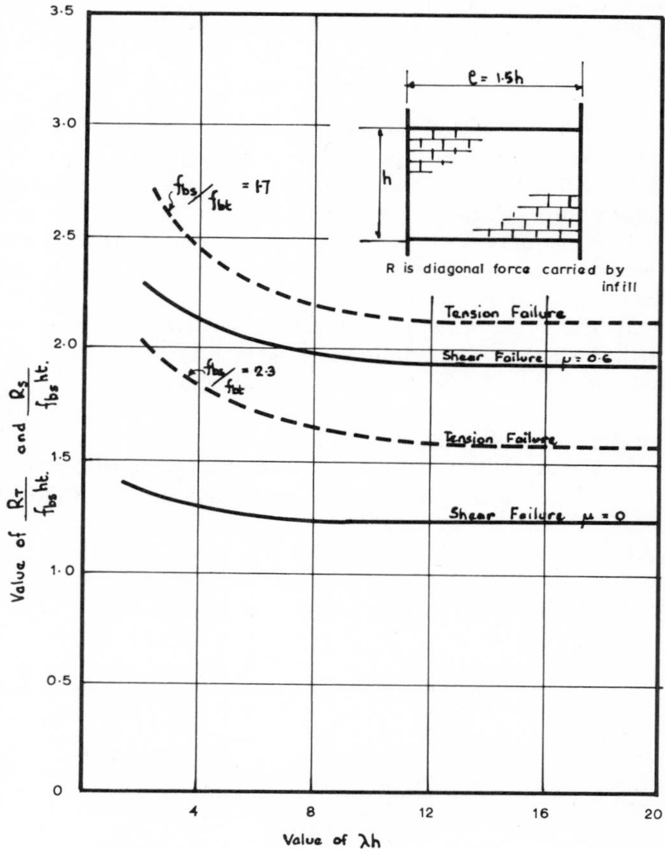

Figure 27-8. Panel strengths for masonry infilled frames as a function of λ h.

The diagonal tensile strength of the masonry may be related to the bond shear strength by the following approximate relationships:

$$f_{dt} = 1{\cdot}25\, f_{bt} \qquad (27\text{-}9)$$

where f_{bt} is the bond tensile strength of the brickwork. Equation 27-9 is a linear approximation to an experimentally derived curve[6].

$$\frac{f_{bs}}{f_{bt}} = 1{\cdot}7 \rightarrow 2{\cdot}3 \qquad (27\text{-}10)$$

$$\therefore f_{dt} = 0{\cdot}74\, f_{bs} \rightarrow 0{\cdot}54\, f_{bs} \qquad (27\text{-}11)$$

substituting for f_{dt} into Equation 27-8, and converting to non-dimensional parameters:

$$\frac{R_T}{f_{bs}\,ht} = \frac{9{\cdot}3}{f_{tt}} \rightarrow \frac{6{\cdot}8}{f_{tt}} \qquad (27\text{-}12)$$

Values of f_{tt}, the maximum theoretical tensile stress, have been determined for corresponding values of λh for infills of various proportions. Substituting these into Equation 27-12 allows $R_T/f_{bs}ht$ to be plotted as a function of λh for the two ratios of bond shear to bond tension given in Equation 27-10. These curves are shown in Figures 27-7, 27-8, 27-9, and 27-10. Once again the probable range of practical values has been covered.

It is clear from the relatively higher position and, therefore, from the strength of the tensile failure curves, that shear failures are generally more likely to occur.

The appearance of the initial shear failure cracks does not necessarily imply that collapse is imminent; indeed, the structure may withstand a considerable additional load before the infill disintegrates enough to allow complete collapse. From a practical point of view, however, the appearance of the initial cracks would not be acceptable in most circumstances, and the occurence of the cracks would define failure.

In Table 27-1, a number of published test results are given and the corresponding theoretical values of strength calculated to compare with them. Because a value of μ had to be estimated, it is difficult to comment on the accuracy of the proposed method. However, the order of accuracy of the theory is such that, by judiciously selecting an appropriate, but practical, value in each case, it would have been possible to show good correlation between experiment and theory. The results may therefore be considered encouraging.

Concluding Remarks

1. When an infilled frame is subjected to a racking load the horizontal stiffness may be estimated by considering the infill to be replaced by an equivalent diagonal strut and analysing the structure as a pin-jointed triangulated frame.

2. A masonry panel normally fails either by shear along the mortar joints, or by tension through the mortar, or through the mortar and brickwork.

3. The mode of failure is governed partly by the geometry of the structure, which influences the relative size of the shear and normal and diagonal tensile stresses in the panel.

The greater the length/height ratio of the panel, the less is the possibility of a tension failure.

5. The mode of failure is governed also by the relative size of the bond shear strength, internal friction, and diagonal tensile strength of the masonry.

The lower the value of internal friction or the greater the ratio of the bond tension strength to the bond shear strength, the less likely the panel is to fail by the tensile mode.

6. The design curves may be used to give an approximate prediction of the strength and mode of failure of the infill. However, the factor of safety adopted for such a prediction should allow for the statistical nature of the materials and the variable quality of workmanship.

Summary

The chapter concerns an investigation into the stiffness and strength of masonry infilled frames subjected to racking loads.

When an infilled frame is subjected to racking, the frame remains in contact with the infill only in regions close to the ends of the compression diagonal. The lengths of contact, which are a function of the frame-infill relative stiffness and which may be predicted in terms of this relative stiffness, are used as the basis of a series of stress analyses for panels of different length-height proportions with arbitrary diagonal loads acting over different lengths of contact.

The resulting stresses allow the calculation of the diagonal strains and, hence, the diagonal stiffness of each infill which is expressed as an effective width for an equivalent diagonal strut. By assuming the frame pin-jointed, and replacing each

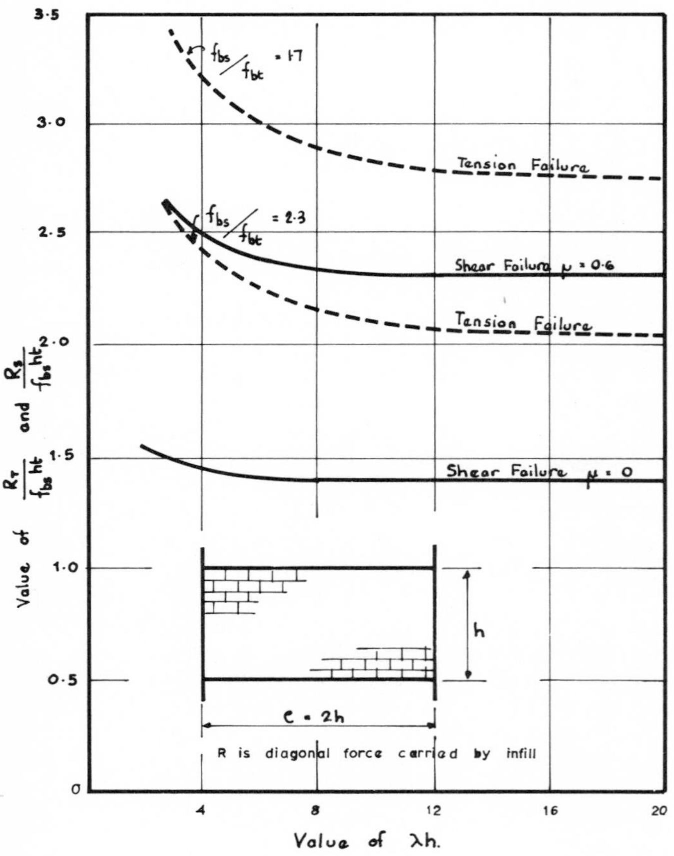

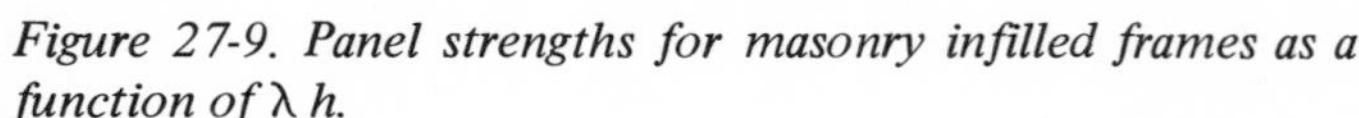

Figure 27-9. Panel strengths for masonry infilled frames as a function of λh.

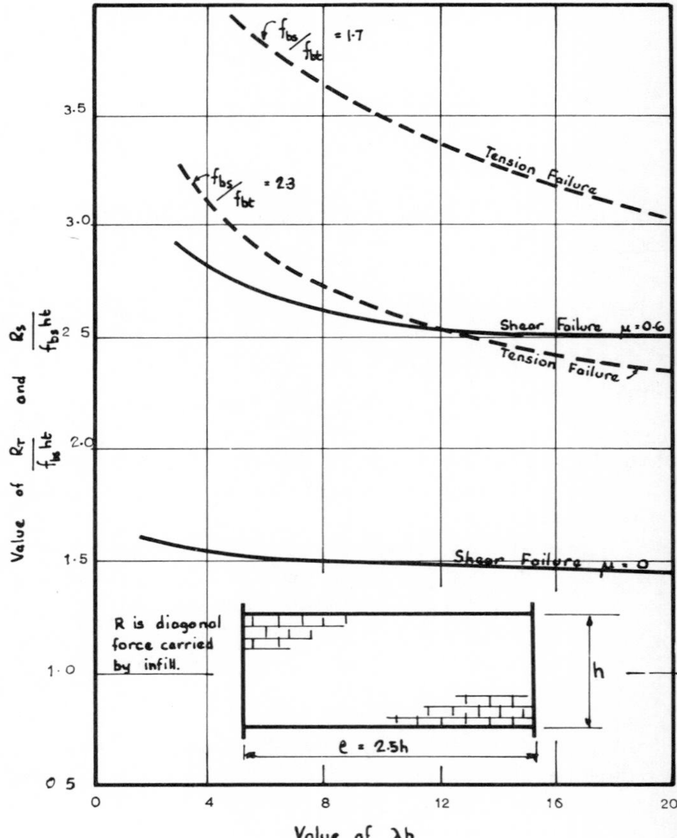

Figure 27-10. Panel strengths for masonry infilled frames as a function of λh.

Table 27-1
Shear Strength of Masonry Panels

No	Specimen Size h x 1	Thickness	Infill	Frame	λh	Bond Shear	Theoretical Load	Actual Load
1	4-1/2″ x 9″	1″	Bricks	Steel	12	28 lb/in^2	220 lb	130 lb.
2	8 ft x 8 ft	4-3/16″	Solid Brick	None	Equiv. to 20	90 lb/in^2	18.0 ton	13.0 ton
3	8 ft x 8 ft	8-3/4″	″	″	″	″	36.0 ton	28.0 ton
4	8 ft x 15 ft	4-3/16″	″	″	″	″	31.2 ton	15.0 ton
5	8 ft x 8 ft	6″	Hollow Block	″	″	″	12.8 ton	14.1 ton
6	8 ft x 8 ft	6″	″	″	″	″	12.8 ton	13.0 ton
7	8 ft x 8 ft	6″	Perforated Brick	″	″	″	12.8 ton	14.0 ton 17.1 ton
8	8 ft x 8 ft	4-1/8″	″	″	″	″	13.2 ton	23.0 ton
9	1.2m x 1.2m	0.25m	″	Steel	7.0	4.4 kg/cm^2	10.2 tonne	7t, 11t, 8t.
10	1.2m x 1.2m	″	″	″	8.0	6.4 kg/cm^2	14.8 tonne	13t, 12t, 15t, 15t.
11	1.2m x 1.2m	″	″	″	7.2	5.5 kg/cm^2	12.7 tonne	23t
12	1.2m x 1.2m	″	″	″	9.0	5.1 kg/cm^2	11.8 tonne	12t, 12t.
13	1.2m x 1.2m	″	Solid Brick	″	6.0	3.1 kg/cm^2	10.3 tonne	19.0t, 19.0t.
14	9 ft x 11 ft	4-1/2″	″	Steel Encased	4.0	90 lb/in^2	30.0 ton	35t, 30t.
15	9 ft x 11 ft	3″	″	″	3.0	″	20.4 ton	21t
16	9 ft x 11 ft	3″	Clinker Block	″	3.0	″	20.4 ton	22t, 24t.
17	9 ft x 11 ft	3″	Hollow Block	″	3.0	″	20.4 ton	22t
18	9 ft x 11 ft	13-1/2″	Solid Brick	″	8.0	″	84.0 ton	110t.

Note:
Test 1. Model Experiments at Southampton
Tests 2-8 Experiments carried out by L.G. Simms,[7] Building Research Station.
Tests 9-13 Experiments carried out by S.V. Polyakov,[3] Moscow.
Tests 14-18 Experiments carried out by R.H. Wood,[8] Building Research Station.

infill with an equivalent strut, the horizontal stiffness of the infilled frame may be calculated.

The results of the stress analyses are used next to determine the principal shear stresses and planes in the panel which, in conjunction with the internal friction caused by the compressive stresses, provide the criterion for predicting the shear failure of the infill. The principal tensile stresses are determined also and used to predict the possibility of diagonal tension failure.

Finally, the results of the proposed methods for predicting failure are compared with a number of published test results on masonry infilled frames. The correlation between the theoretical and test results is encouraging.

References

1. Smith, Stafford, "Behaviour of Square Infilled Frames". *Jnl. Struct. Div.,* Proc. A.S.C.E., Feb. 1966.
2. Smith, Stafford, "Methods for Predicting the Lateral Stiffness and Strength of Multi Storey Infilled Frames;" *Building Science* Vol. II.
3. Polyakov, "Masonry in Framed Buildings", published by Gosudarstvennoe izdatel'stvo Literatury po stroitel'stvu i arckhitecture, Moscow 1956.
4. Sementsov, "Masonry Structures", published by Gosudarstvennoe izdatel'stvo Literatury po stroitel'stvu i arckhitecture, Moscow 1953.
5. Murthy & Hendry, The British Ceramic Research Association, *Technical Note* No. 65. 1965.
6. Structural Clay Products Research Foundation, Geneva, Illinois, *Progress Report No. 1.* Oct. 1964.
7. Simms, "The Shear Strength of Some Storey-Height Brickwork and Blockwork Walls", *Technical Note,* C.P.T.B. 1964.
8. Wood, "The Stability of Tall Buildings", *Proc.,* Vol II, I.C.E., 1958.

28. Case study of brick used as floor and roof structure.

Nat W. Krahl and Harry S. Ransom, School of Architecture, Rice University, Houston, Texas

Introduction

In Guadalajara, second largest city in Mexico and capital of the state of Jalisco, a local handmade brick serves as a structural element for building not only walls but also floors and roofs. To serve as the structure of floors and roofs, the brick is laid in shallow, almost flat, barrel vaults which are supported on a framework of structural steel (Figure 28-1) or reinforced concrete. This type of structure is employed in a wide variety of building types, including office buildings, churches, schools, and residences. Typical vaults are laid without any formwork. This system is widely used today in Guadalajara and is an outgrowth of centuries of experience in this geographic region with this and similar systems.

Conventional System

Description

This structural system apparently stems originally from the Terrado building system in which the Mexican Indians used wood beams to support tree branches which were covered with earth. The Spanish modified this method to the Catalan system in which wood beams supported short-span multiple brick vaults that, in turn, supported an earth or concrete fill and wearing surface.

With the introduction of structural steel, some builders used rolled steel beams in lieu of wood beams to support the brick vaults. Then, someone observed that the shape of the steel beam would allow it to be placed between two adjacent vaults, thereby containing the depth of the arch rib and being virtually concealed itself, and the final step in the evolution of the method had been taken (Figure 28-2).

Any description of this system must first recognize that it combines two separate structures: first, the brick vaults, which support the floor and the loads imposed on the floor and carry these loads to the supporting structure; and, second, the supporting framework of steel or concrete beams, girders, and columns which directly support the vaults.

A typical cross section through this type of construction is shown in Figure 28-2. Typically the supporting beams are placed 80-130 cm. (32-51 in.) center-to-center, and this distance becomes the span of the barrel vault. As mentioned before, the bricks comprising the barrel vaults are laid without formwork, each successive row of bricks in itself becoming an arch rib spanning between steel beams. The vaults themselves are almost flat, the rise usually being only 3-8 cm. (1.5-3 in.). The bricks are handmade mud bricks of local manufacture, are very light in weight, and are laid with the large side flat against the adjacent arch rib. The bricks are laid without prewetting, and the mortar's suction against the side of each brick helps keep it in place until its arch rib has been completed. It should be noted that the humidity in Guadalajara is usually very low. Also, the vertical axis of each brick is tilted slightly so that each brick is partly supported by the newly-completed

Figure 28-1. Vaulted brick floor and roof systems under construction on steel framework.

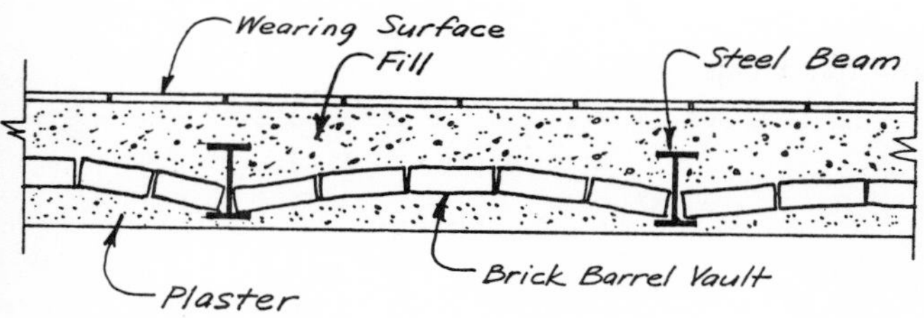

Figure 28-2. Cross section through vaulted brick floor system on steel framework.

adjacent arch rib until its own rib is completed. The mortar in which the brick is laid is made from lime and sand.

A level surface above the vaults and beams is achieved by filling with a lightweight concrete made from hydrated lime and "Jal", which is a local pumice sand and gravel. The State of Jalisco takes its name from this volcanic material. The thickness of the fill varies, particularly on roofs, which are usually sloped for drainage. For example, a variation of fill thickness from 5 to 20 cm. (2 to 8 in.) over a roof would not be unusual.

A wearing surface of burnt clay brick or tile is usually placed on top of the concrete fill. On roofs a waterproofing layer of asphalt or cement is placed between the concrete fill and wearing surface.

Finally, the undersides of the vaults are almost always covered with a plaster made from lime and sand to give a perfectly flat ceiling which conceals the vaults and beams. In some cases, a wire mesh is attached to the beam flange to support the plaster below the flange. In a few cases, the brick vaults and steel beams have been left exposed to view from below and achieve a dramatic architectural effect because of the varying colors of the brick and the apparent daring of the flatness of the vaults.

The brick vaults described above are widely used in Guadalajara to support the typical floor loads and roof loads encountered in houses and office buildings. The floor live load used locally for design of dwellings is 150 kg./m.^{2} (30.8 lb./ft.^{2}), and the maximum office floor live load for which this type of construction would be considered suitable by local engineers is about 350 kg./m.^{2} (71.8 lb./ft.^{2}). The brick vaults themselves are not considered suitable for resisting heavy, concentrated loads. If such loads are anticipated in this type of construction, it is customary to support these loads on small beams of steel or reinforced concrete, which replace the arch ribs in that immediate location and carry their loads directly to the supporting framework of beams, girders, and columns. These allowable loads and practices seem to be based primarily on accumulated experience.

The beams which directly support the vaults are usually steel beams placed 80-130 cm. (32-51 in.) apart. Typical beam sizes range from 4 inch to 8 inch 1-beams, depending on their span and their supported load. Usual spans are in the range of 4-6 meters (13-20 ft.). Most often the steel beams are supported by steel girders that, in turn, are supported by steel columns. Occasionally, small precast concrete beams of

Figure 28-3. Handmade brick stacked for firing at Tateposco.

1-section are used in lieu of steel beams to support directly the brick vaults, and the remainder of the supporting structure may then become reinforced concrete.

At an interior beam under uniformly distributed load, the lateral thrust from the vault on one side balances that from the other side; but, at edge beams under any loading and at interior beams under unsymmetric loadings, there are unbalanced thrusts to be resisted. For this purpose, tie rods are used between adjacent beams at intervals along the length and the lines of rods are extended across the building. The rods are eventually concealed within the floor construction.

Individual members of the supporting structure are, of course, designed according to the live and dead loads, the conditions of support, and the span or length of members.

Properties of Materials

The brick used for vault construction is handmade in the country-side nearby and is trucked into the city. The primary ingredient is a mud made from water and Jal, which is readily available throughout the area. In addition, certain amounts of manure and maguey fiber are used in the mixture. The bricks are formed in wood molds, dried in the open air, then stacked in large piles, and fired with mesquite logs, which are placed in slots left in the piles. Figure 28-3. The resulting brick is light in weight, very porous, and has beautiful variations in color, which depend largely upon the degree of firing. Predominant colors range through various shades of yellow, ocher, orange, red, and brown. Table 28-1 contains the quantitative measurements of certain mechanical properties of samples of brick

Table 28-1
Results of Tests of Jalisco Handmade Brick

		From the brickyards of "Las Pintas."						From the brickyards of "Tateposco."					
		Sample						Sample					
Test	Units	1	2	3	4	5	Average	1	2	3	4	5	Average
Volumetric Weight, Dry	kg/m^3	1180	1070	1180	1180	1180	1158	1260	1255	1200	1210	1370	1259
	lb/ft^3	73.7	66.8	73.6	73.6	73.6	72.3	78.6	78.4	75.0	75.5	85.5	78.6
Modulus of Rupture	kg/cm^2	11.4	11.9	13.55	16.50	11.35	12.94	15.4	9.41	16.7	15.6	25	16.42
	lb/in^2	162	169	193	235	161	184	219	134	237	222	356	234
Compressive Strength	kg/cm^2	33.15	43.2	72.2	61.2	14.6	44.87	50.35	55.5	37.0	66.0	118.5	65.47
	lb/in^2	472	615	1,026	870	208	638	716	789	526	939	1,685	931
First Crack	kg/cm^2	12.3	14.7	15.7	30.3	9.9	16.58	16.9	30	17.2	20	19.8	20.78
	lb/in^2	175	209	223	431	141	236	241	427	245	285	281	296
Absorption (24 hours)	%	37.8	31.4	36.35	30.8	38.8	35.03	27.6	32	32.8	31.6	27.5	30.3
Absorption (5 hrs. boiling)	%	37.4	44.2	45.5	41	46	42.82	36.5	38.7	33	38.2	32	35.68
Coefficient of Saturation	—	1	0.71	0.79	0.75	0.84	0.818	0.75	0.83	1.0	0.83	0.86	0.854

coming from the brickyards of Tateposco and Las Pintas. These tests were performed at the Universidad Autonoma de Guadalajara.

Mortar such as is typically used, made from lime and yellow sand, showed a compressive strength of 8.8 kg/sq.cm. (125 lb./sq. in.).

Typical Jal concrete for leveling above the vaults is mixed in the following proportions by volume: Jal, 2 parts; yellow sand, 1 part; lime, 0.75 part; water, 0.50 part. At six days samples had a density of 1048 kg./cu.m. (65.5 lb./cu.ft.). At ten days the same samples had a density of 939 kg./cu.m. (58.5 lb./cu.ft.). Tests indicated a compressive strength of 4.35 kg./sq. cm. (61.9 lb./sq. in.).

Samples of the burnt clay brick used as a wearing surface over the fill showed a density of 1464 kg./cu.m. (91.4 lb./cu. ft.).

Test of Floor Panel

A load test of full-scale brick vaults was performed on the campus of the Universidad Autonoma de Guadalajara to study the structural behavior and strength of the brick vaults under uniformly distributed load.

A drawing of the structure which was tested is shown in Figure 28-4. Photographs of the test are shown in Figure 28-5. To obtain a measure of the strength of the vaults, without a premature failure on the part of the supporting structure, the steel beams supporting the test vaults were made arbitrarily oversize, 10-inch I-beams on a 3-meter (9 ft. 10 in.) span,

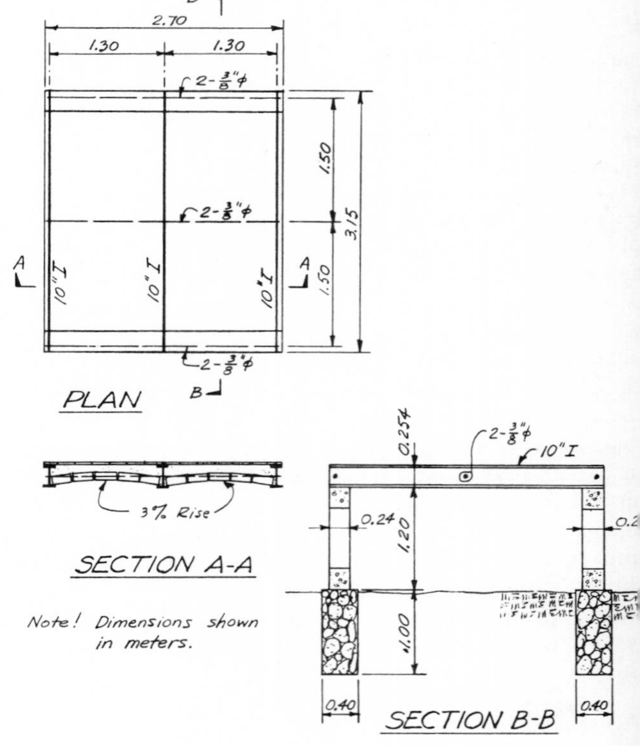

Figure 28-4. Test vaults.

Figure 28-5. Test vaults supporting 388 lbs. per square foot.

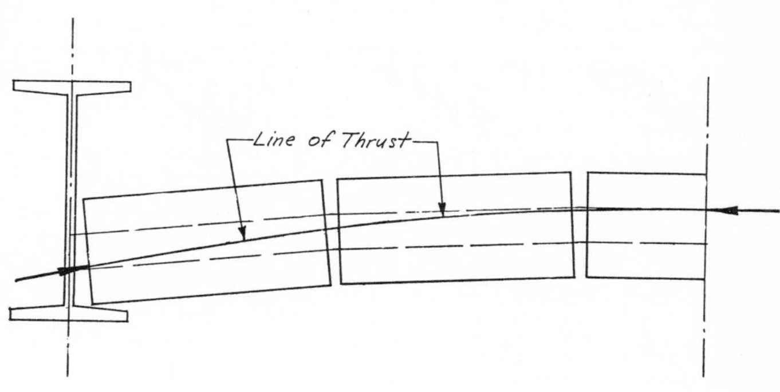

Figure 28-6. Line of thrust of brick vaults.

while the vaults were constructed of conventional proportions and materials.

Sacks of river sand were used to simulate a uniformly distributed load on the structure. The test was stopped prematurely because of a heavy rain, but the experiment was successful in demonstrating that the structure could sustain a superimposed uniformly distributed load of 1893 kg./m^2 (388 lb./ft.^{2}) without appreciable damage and without excessive deflection. Based on the maximum live load in current use for this type of construction, which is 350 kg./m^2 (71.8 lb./ft.^{2}), there is a factor of safety which must be greater than 5.4.

This great strength of the brick vaults can be confirmed by analytical methods. Figure 28-6 shows a scale drawing of a cross section of the barrel vault used in the load test. If we consider a unit thickness of vault perpendicular to the plane of the paper, we can analyze the vault as an arch rib. Since these vaults in practice are constructed without framework, it must be realized that the actual curve of the underside, or intrados, of the rib will vary somewhat from one cross section to another. But, since the rise of the arch is so small, only about 3 percent of the span, all smooth curves of this rise and span will lie very close to one another. Hence, the small variations in construction are likely to be unimportant. For simplicity, the placement of bricks in Figure 28-6 is shown approximating the curve of a second-degree parabola. Because this arch is of relatively short span and, in practice, supports a relatively light, uniformly distributed load, the so-called "line of thrust" analysis is considered to be the most suitable basis for analysis[1]. According to this analysis, the line of thrust under uniformly distributed load becomes parabolic, the crown thrust is horizontal, and its resultant lies at the upper extremity of the middle third of the arch rib, while the resultant thrust at the skewback lies at the lower extremity of the middle third of the arch rib.

The line of thrust following these restrictions is shown in Figure 28-6.

An investigation of possible modes of failure and of stresses under working loads, using this line of thrust, indicates that the behavior of the vaults under working loads should be quite satisfactory, thus confirming results of the load test.

Adaptation of System to Campus Design

Criteria for use

Universidad Autonoma de Guadalajara (U.A.G.) is, at the present time, embarking upon a vast expansion of its physical facilities.

In the architectural programming for all of the proposed new buildings for the U.A.G., it became evident that a system of architectural flexibility must be an integral part of the structural skeleton. It is imperative that, with relative ease, walls may be relocated, modules added, spaces rearranged. Versatility is essential. The barrel brick vault system satisfied these requirements to a workable degree. But, it was recognized as basically a one-way growth system with the opportunity to expand or move in only one direction. For example, partitions can be reasonably relocated only at the supporting beams, framing in the same direction. (Figure 28-7.)

A two-way directional system was therefore desired so that expansibility could occur in either of two directions. Such a system can be seen today in one building in Guadalajara, "La Casa de las Artesanias". In this handsome structure two-way doubly curved brick vaults are employed, spanning approximately 16 feet and supported upon square steel-framed bays. But elaborate formwork was necessary to achieve this striking result.

Experiments

Consequently, a subsequent series of tests was undertaken by the architectural design group in Guadalajara to discover that dimension of supporting structural network that would permit the doubly curved brick vaults to be constructed without the use of forms; and to retain a low rise of the vault capable of inclusion within a normal ceiling-floor thickness

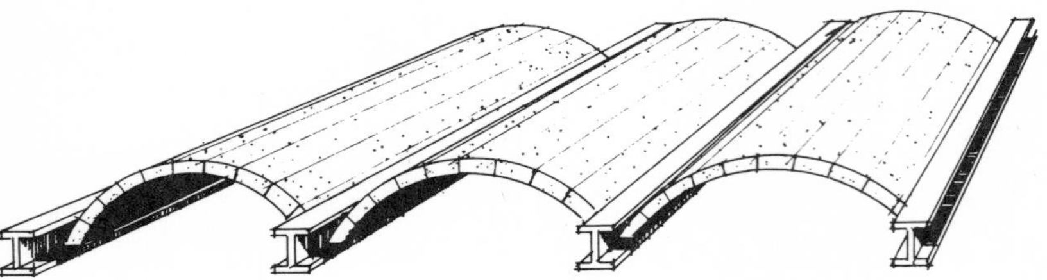

Figure 28-7. One-way growth system.

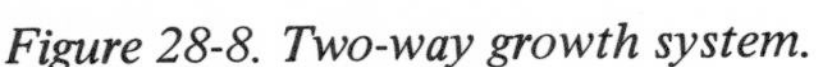

Figure 28-8. Two-way growth system.

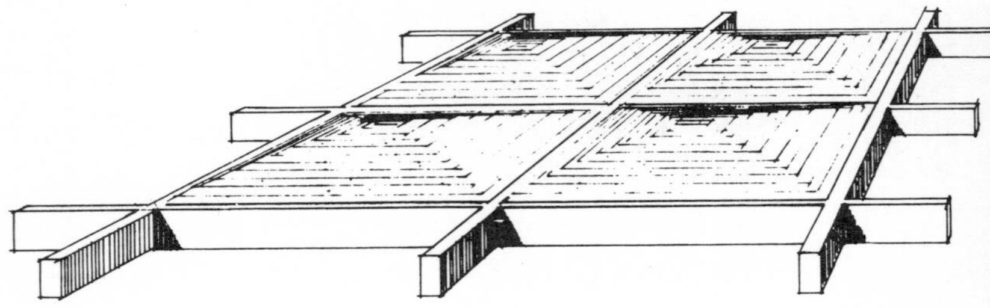

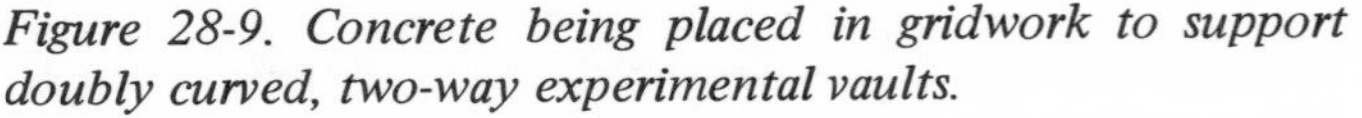

Figure 28-9. Concrete being placed in gridwork to support doubly curved, two-way experimental vaults.

Figure 28-10. Diagonal and circular doubly curved vault constructed for study purposes.

(Figure 28-8). Several trial-and-error, full-size tests were conducted; calculations reviewed and refined; and visual details studied. (Figures 28-9 to 28-12.)

Design

The original tests acted as a springboard for developing a more sophisticated method of building vaults of brick; in this instance, doubly curved brick vaults—built without the use of forms—spanning 1.60 m. (5 ft. 2 3/8 in.), rising 10 cm. (3.9 inches). These vaults are in turn supported upon an aggregate network of reinforced concrete beams and columns. The underside of the brick vaults will be exposed to take advantage of their rich color and textural surface. (Figure 28-12).

Construction documents for seventeen buildings have been completed. The first phase of the University building program, containing the basic academic nucleus of Library, Institutes and Schools, broke ground in November, 1967.

This evolved system then becomes the structural desig determinant for all of the architecture of the new campus c the Universidad Autonoma de Guadalajara—a system rich i both the past and the present.

Acknowledgements

In 1963 a group of universities in the United States forme a consortium to assist the U.A.G. in its academic and physica development. One of these universities is Rice University c Houston, Texas, whose Chancellor, Dr. Carey Croneis, ha participated in the work of the consortium from the firs meeting. Professor William W. Caudill, Director of the Ric School of Architecture, also participated in the early stages c

Figure 28-11. The diagonal two-way vault system. Electrical outlet box fully recessed in brick depth.

Figure 28-12. Rectangular two-way brick vault. Labor time: 1 hour, 10 minutes. This is the vaulting system that will be used in the new university buildings.

organization. Professor Harry S. Ransom spent two years at the U.A.G. in the detailed planning of the overall campus planning program. Professor Nat W. Krahl participated in this work as a structural consultant.

The authors wish to express particular thanks to the following individuals whose efforts have contributed to the work reported in this paper: Dr. Luis Garibay G., Rector of U.A.G., for his dedication to and guidance of the campus expansion; Dr. Angel Morales Castro, Vice-Rector, for his personal involvement in the project; Arq. Francisco Camarena, Director of the School of Architecture at the U.A.G., and Arq. Ernesto Ramirez Sotomayor, who, together with Professor Ransom, directed preparation of architectural plans and specifications for the new campus buildings; Ing. Carlos Trujillo del Rio and Ing. Francisco Nuñez Farias, who performed the tests referred to herein; Ing. Adelberto Brito and Ing. Jose Luis Amezcua S., who furnished a wealth of information on conventional brick vaults and furnished structural consultation on preparation of architectural plans and specifications; and the faculty and students of the Schools of Architecture and Engineering at U.A.G., who assisted in preparation of plans.

The expansion of the facilities of U.A.G. has received support from the Ford Foundation and from the A.I.D. Program of the United States Department of State.

Reference

1. Plummer, Harry C., *Brick and Tile Engineering*, Structural Clay Products Institute, Washington, D.C., 2nd ed., 1962, pp. 199-214.

29. Structural performance of clay tile wall panels.

Dr. Dimitrij Pume, Praha, Czechoslovakia

Introduction

Clay products meet the demands made on a safe and durable building, since they possess excellent, constant physical and mechanical properties, such as sufficiently high strength, satisfactory standards of thermal insulation, a favourable thermal conductivity-strength ratio, and a low stable moisture content. For these reasons, they are particularly suitable for load-bearing structures that act simultaneously as thermal protection. Such structures are load-bearing exterior walls in residential, industrial, and other buildings.

Characteristics of Precast Clay Tile Wall Panels

The term precast clay tile wall panels denotes such wall panels, the most significant component of which are structural load-bearing wall tiles. These wall tiles are bonded together with mortar of acceptable quality. In mortar joints, reinforced bars may be embedded. The outer and the inner face of the panels may be provided with plaster, facing, etc.

The advantages of precast clay tile wall panels may be summarized as follows:

1. The panels are made of structural clay, load-bearing wall tiles, the volume of which is three to five times the volume of solid brick. The wall tiles are provided with rows of cores and sometimes have reduced density. This is why the exterior walls may be thickened.

2. Precast-clay tile wall panels give the brick industry a chance to utilize its products in buildings erected by industrial methods.

3. Precast-clay tile wall panels are manufactured with the aid of vibration, which results in a higher compressive strength of wall panel masonry compared with nonvibrated masonry made of the same materials.

On the other hand, the following difficulties arising from use of precast-clay tile wall panels are to be mentioned:

1. Up to the present time, the appropriate mechanization of manufacture of these panels remains an unsolved problem. This is why mechanized mass production has not yet been provided.

2. Freedom in designing these panels is restricted because of the rather small number of structural tile sizes available for manufacturing panels.

This chapter gives the results of investigating the structural performance of single-wythe, load-bearing clay tile wall panels designed for both exterior and interior walls.

Description of the Investigated Single-Wythe Clay Tile Wall Panels

The single-wythe clay tile wall panels consist of one wythe (leaf) of structural load-bearing wall tiles bonded together with lime-cement or cement mortar; internal and external mortar ground coats are also made. These panels are manufactured in horizontal position with compacting mortar by vibration.

In determining the properties of clay wall tiles and mortar, it is reasonable to follow instructions[8] which also include principles concerning the structural features of the panels.

In load-bearing exterior wall panels, the properties of structural clay wall tiles depend first on climatic conditions of the surrounding atmosphere. Let us point out the properties of clay wall tiles and mortar for the average Czechoslovakian winter outdoor temperature of -15°C.

The structural clay wall tiles are provided with vertical, relatively small rectangular cores arranged in 10 to 13 successive rows (when observed in the transverse direction). The volume of the clay wall tiles is three to five times the volume of traditional solid brick.

When considering panels having a thickness of 30 to 33 cm (11-13/16″ to 13″) including finishing plasters, the volume weight of the clay tiles ranges from 1150 to 1300 kg. per cu. m. (0.0415 to 0.0470 lb. per cu. in.) and their ultimate compressive strength from 100 to 200 kp. per sq. cm. (1422 to 2845 psi/). The mortar in the joints is made from normal sand.

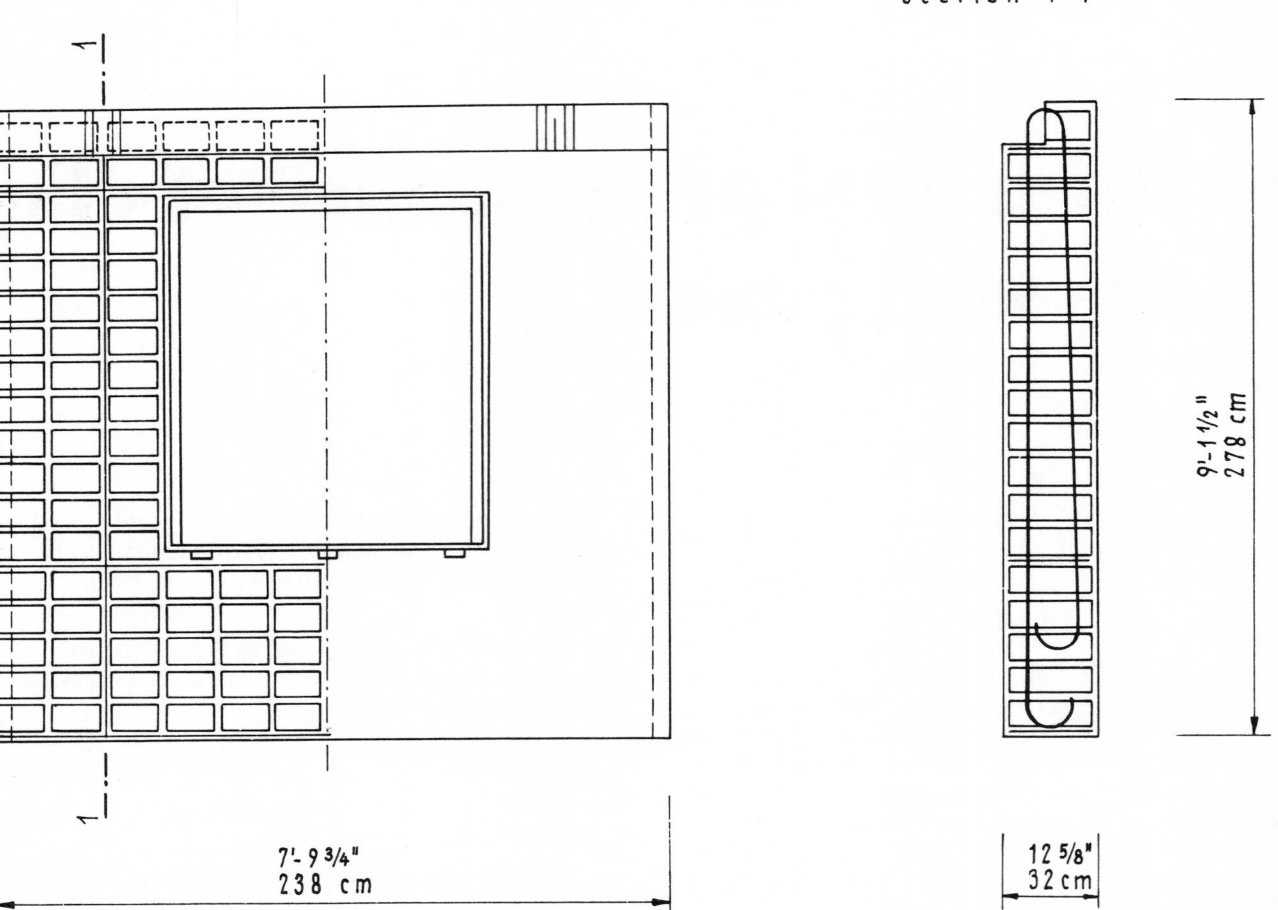

Figure 29-1. The single-wythe clay tile load-bearing wall panel.

The volume weight of mortar is 1900 – 2000 kg. per cu. m. (0.0686 – 0.0723 lb. per cu. in.).

If the wall panels have a reduced thickness of 25 to 27 cm. (9-7/8" to 10-5/8"), the volume weight of the clay tiles should range from 900 to 1050 kg. per cu. m. (0.0325 to 0.0379 lb. per cu. in.), their ultimate compressive strength being, as a rule, approximately 100 – 150 kp. per sq. cm. (1422 to 2133 psi). The volume weight of mortar ranges from 1100 to 1500 kg. per cu. m. (0.0397 to 0.0542 lb. per cu. in.).

Figure 29-1 demonstrates a 32-cm-(12-5/8")-thick load-bearing clay tile panel for exterior load-bearing walls as designed by the enterprice Pražské stavební závody (Prague Construction Works) according to Reference 8 of this chapter.

Ultimate Compressive Strength of Single-Wythe Clay Tile Wall Panels

Experimental Investigations

The ultimate compressive strength values for single-wythe structural clay tile wall panels have been determined from the results of experimental investigations on the load-bearing capacity of test specimens made as cut-outs of actual panels[6,7]. These test specimens were 19, 21 and 31 cm (7-1/2", 8-1/4" and 12-3/16") thick, 56 and 70 cm. wide (22-1/16" and 27-9/16") wide and 125 – 134 or 250 cm (49-1/4" – 52-3/4" or 59-1/16") high. The specimens were made by using three different types of vertically cored structural clay wall tiles (see Table 29-1) and two different types of cement mortar, i.e. M 50 having a cube strength of 50 to 80 kp. per sq. cm./711 to 1138 psi) and M 100 having a cube strength of 100 to 130 kp. per sq. cm. (1422 to 1849 psi). In addition, 15 handmade masonry piers from the same clay wall tiles and mortar have also been examined (see Table 29-2).

Average ultimate compressive strength values derived from these results are given for vibrated test wall units in Table 29-3 and those for test masonry piers in Table 29-4 respectively. The average ultimate compressive strength values for both masonry piers and wall units have been found to be higher than those given in the Czechoslovakian standard for design of

Table 29-1
Properties of Vertically Cored Clay Wall Tiles

Type	Dimensions	Volume Weight (kg per cu. m)	Volume Weight (lb. per cu. in.)	Compressive Strength (kp. per sq. cm.)	Compressive Strength (psi)
PDt	36.5 x 17.8 x 17.5 cm 14-3/8" x 7" x 6-7/8"	1274	0.0460	110	1564
CDK 19	29.0 x 19.0 x 15.0 cm 11-7/16" x 7-1/2" x x 5-1/2"	1168	0.0422	147 213	2091 3029
CDK 24	29.0 x 24.0 x 11.3 cm 11-7/16" x 9-7/16" x x 4-7/16"	1303	0.0471	155	2204

Table 29-2
Survey of Test Specimens

Vertically cored clay wall tiles			Masonry piers			Wall elements		
Type	Compressive Strength kp per sq cm	Compressive Strength (psi)	Number	Mortar Compressive Strength kp per sq cm	Mortar Compressive Strength (psi)	Number	Mortar Compressive Strength kp per sq cm	Mortar Compressive Strength (psi)
PDt	100	1564	6	50	711	10	50	711
			3	100	1422	9	100	1422
CDK 19	147	2091	—	—	—	11	100	1422
	213	3029	—	—	—	7	100	1422
CDK	155	2204	6	50	711	9	50	711
						30	100	1422

masonry structures[2] relating to masonry of 29 x 14 x 6.5 cm (11-7/16" x 5-1/2" x 2-9/16") solid brick and 24 x 11.5 x 11.3 cm. (9-7/16" x 4-1/2" x 4-7/16") vertically cored brick, as shown in Figure 29-2 for wall elements bonded with mortar M 100.

The increase of compressive strength values for masonry piers and wall elements, compared with standard values, may be explained thusly: both the larger size of structural clay wall tiles and the type of masonry bond exert their influence.

As for the precast wall elements, the higher ultimate compressive strength was, apart from both above factors, also enhanced by their vibration.

Derivation of Standard Values of Ultimate Compressive Strength

As will be seen from Tables 29-3 and 29-4, the values of ultimate compressive strength of precast wall elements were an average of 43 percent higher than those of the corresponding comparison masonry piers and an average of 79 percent higher than the standard compressive strength values (see Figure 29-2). It is to be emphasized, however, that for structural design of precast wall elements it is not possible to introduce values as increased as it follows from the increase of average strength values. Account must also be taken of the spread of the sets of values already found.

The standard values of compressive strength of masonry listed in[2] are computed by applying L. I. Onishcziks formula[5]:

$$f'_m = \frac{100 + f'_u}{100 + 3\,f'_u} \cdot f'_u \cdot \left(1 - \frac{0.2}{0.3 + \frac{f_{mr}}{2f_u}}\right) \qquad (29\text{-}1)$$

The validity of this formula has been verified by structural testing of approx. 300 masonry piers during the years 1954 – 1958[5]. Some of these test results are demonstrated in Figure 29-3, each point presenting the average value obtained from results of testing six masonry piers.

In the standard[2] it is presumed that the coefficient of homogenity characterizing the spread of values of compressive

Table 29-3

Comparison of Average Ultimate Compressive Strength Values of Masonry According to Test Results and Standard Requirements[2]

Test Specimens	Compressive strength of clay wall tiles			Compressive strength of mortar		Compressive strength of masonry: Test results			Compressive strength of masonry: Standard requirements		
	kp per sq. cm		psi	kp per sq cm	psi	kp per sq cm	psi	%	kp per sq cm	psi	%
Masonry piers	PDt 110		1564	50	711	48.2	686	161	30	427	100
	PDt 110		1564	100	1422	52.8	751	151	35	498	100
	CDK 155		2204	50	711	50.6	720	145	35	498	100
	Average			—	—	—	—	152	—	—	100
Well elements	PDt 110		1564	50	711	68.8	978	229	30	427	100
	PDt 110		1564	100	1422	86.1	1225	246	35	498	100
	CDK 19	147	3029	100	1422	67.1	954	149	45	640	100
	CDK 19	213	3029	100	1422	69.2	984	138	50	711	100
	CDK 155		2204	50	711	62.7	892	179	35	498	100
	CDK 155		2204	100	1422	61.0	868	135	45	640	100
	Average			—	—	—	—	179	—	—	100

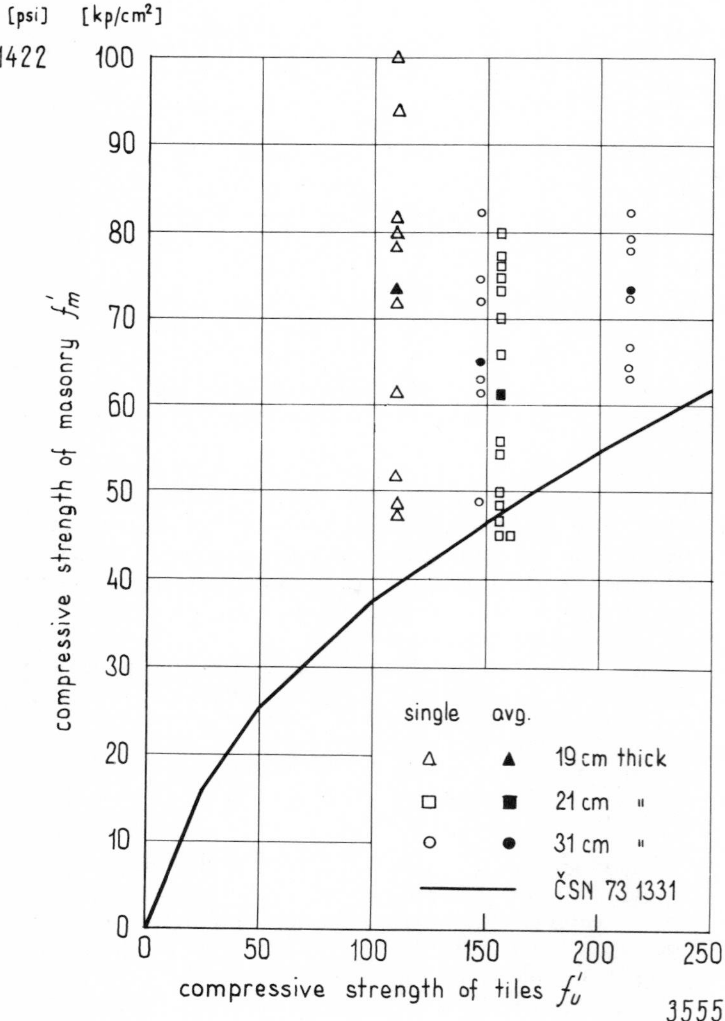

Figure 29-2. The relation between the ultimate compressive strength of masonry in the clay tile wall panels and the compressive strength of tiles with the use of the mortar M 100.

Table 29-4
Comparison of Average Ultimate Compressive Strength Values of Masonry Piers and Precast Wall Elements

Compressive strength of clay wall tiles		Compressive strength of mortar		Compressive strength of masonry					
				Masonry piers			Wall elements		
kp per sq. cm	psi	kp per sq. cm	psi	kp per sq. cm	psi	%	kp per sq. cm	psi	%
PDt 100	1564	50	711	48.2	686	100	68.8	978	143
PDt 110	1564	100	1422	52.8	751	100	86.1	1225	163
CDK 155	2204	50	711	50.6	720	100	62.7	954	124
Avg.		—	—	—	—	100	—	—	143

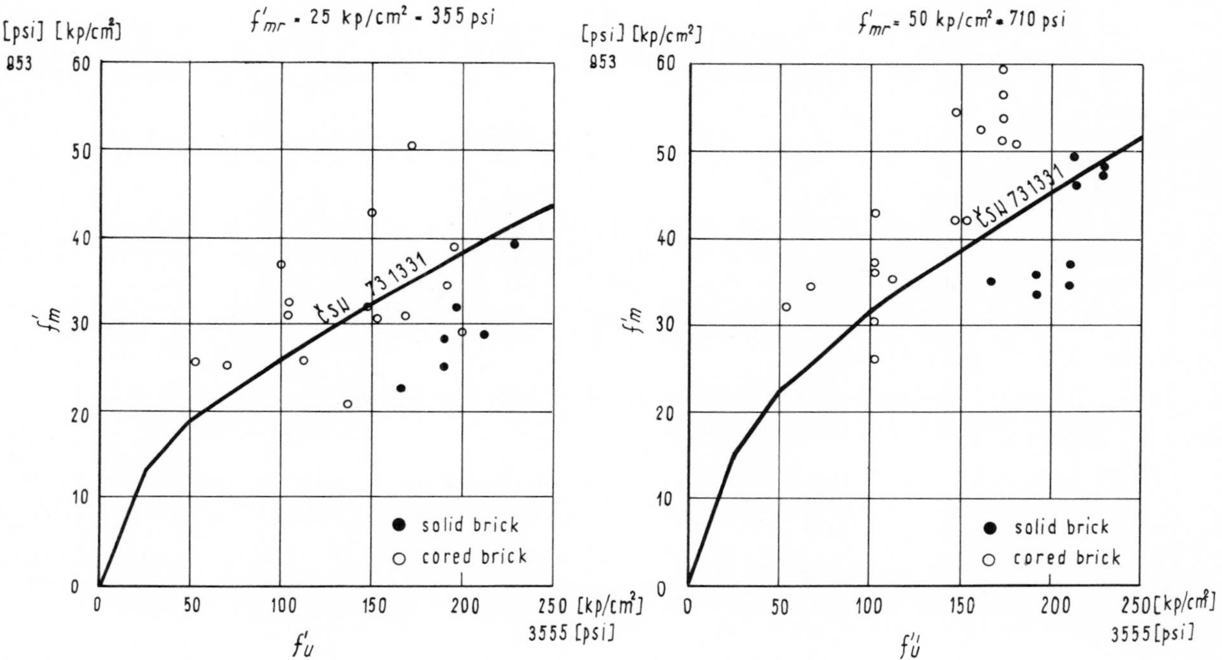

Figure 29-3. The relation between the ultimate compressive strength of masonry and the compressive strength of bricks.

strength is equal to k = 0.5. This coefficient k indicates the ratio of the lowest value of ultimate compressive strength min f'_m to the average value of ultimate compressive strength $\bar{f}'_m$

$$k = \frac{\min f'_m}{\bar{f}'_m} \qquad (29\text{-}2)$$

The lowest value may be computed with a probability of 1.10^{-3} by application of the following formula:

$$\min f'_m = \bar{f}'_m \,(1 - 3.09\,S) \qquad (29\text{-}3)$$

The sets of results obtained by testing masonry piers[5] showed an average value of k = 0.54. The sets of results obtained by testing precast wall elements revealed that the k-value had always been lower than 0.5, e.g. elements 19 cm (7-1/2") thick showed k = 0.39 and members 31 cm (12-3/16") thick showed k = 0.36.

For these reasons, standard values of compressive strength of precast clay tile wall panels might be increased to the lowest minimum values of f'_m, as determined by testing and are higher than the minimum values of f'_m provided by the standard[2].

Having taken account of still another circumstances affecting the load-bearing capacity of masonry walls, it was recommended in standard specifications to provide for increased ultimate compressive strength values of vibrated structural clay tile wall elements, as listed in Table 29-5. The values of ultimate compressive strength for wall elements having a thickness of 25 cm. (9-7/8") and less are higher by 33 percent and those for wall elements having a thickness of 30 cm (11-13/16") and more are higher by 14 percent compared with the standard values for normal masonry composed of brick and mortar of equal strength. For masonry thicknesses of more than 25 cm. (9-7/8") and less than 30 cm. (11-13/16"), linear interpolation is used. The increased values apply provided that the vertical spacing between bed joints is at least 10 cm. (4") and that the thickness of both head and bed joints is 1.2 – 2.0 cm. (1/2" – 3/4").

Relation between Stress and Strain of Single-Wythe Clay Tile Wall Panels

The relation between stress and strain was determined by measuring the compressive strain of test specimens 120 – 125 cm (47-1/4" – 49-1/4") high. As in normal masonry, the stress-strain relation may be expressed by the following formula

$$\epsilon_{st} = -\frac{1.1}{a} \ln \left(1 - \frac{\sigma}{1.1\, f'_m}\right) \tag{29-4}$$

where a = strain factor, the magnitude of which varies with the type of brick, clay wall tile and mortar used. For precast clay tile wall elements, if mortar type M 25 is used, a = 1200, whereas when using mortar types M 50 and M 100, a = 1500.

Influence of Eccentric Load and Buckling on the Bearing Capacity of Single-Wythe Clay Tile Wall Panels

The influence of eccentric load and buckling has been investigated by structural testing of several test specimens since this influence had already been examined in detail earlier on masonry piers[5].

In design, precast clay tile wall elements are considered in the same manner as handmade masonry piers and walls.

The influence of buckling is considered. In computation formulas a buckling factor is introduced, the values of which depend on the slenderness of the wall and on the magnitude of the strain factor a, i.e, on the strain properties of the masonry.

Experimental Investigation on Structural Performance of Clay Tile Wall Panels in the Walls of Multistorey Residential Buildings

Description of the Building

The subject of the investigation was an eight-storey precast residential house shown diagrammatically in Figure 29-4. The principal vertical load-bearing system was represented by load-bearing cross walls and short longitudinal walls. All walls

Table 29-5
Compressive Strength Values of Vibrated Clay Tile Wall Elements

Wall Thickness (cm)	Compressive strength of clay wall tiles (kp per sq cm)	Compressive strength of masonry (kp per sq cm) provided compressive strength of mortar (kp per sq cm)		
		≧ 100	99 + 50	49 + 25
≦ 25	75	—	32	26
	100	45	39	32
	150	58	45	39
	200	71	58	45
≧ 30	75	—	28	22
	100	40	34	28
	150	51	40	34
	200	62	51	40
(inch)	(psi)	≧ 1422 psi	1408 + 712 psi	697 + 356 psi
≦ 9-7/8"	1067	—	455	370
	1422	640	555	455
	2133	825	640	555
	2845	1010	825	640
≦ 11-13/16"	1067	—	398	313
	1422	569	484	398
	2133	725	569	484
	2845	882	725	569

were assembled of storey-high and room-wide panels. On cross walls, prestressed concrete floor panels 19 cm (7-1/2″) thick were positioned. The floor panels were interconnected by longitudinal wall tiles located in the seating face of floor panels resting on wall panels. The longitudinal facades were executed of structural clay tile bracing wall elements 600 x 120 x 27 cm (19′ – 8-1/4″ x 3′ – 11-1/4″ x 10-5/8″) and strips of windows. The lateral facades (gables) consisted of solid wall panels.

In the test building, an extensive set of measurements has been effected to determine the structural, moisture, and thermal properties of the precase elements used. In this chapter, we shall deal merely with the measurements concerning the precast clay tile wall panels and walls erected. The target of the measurements was the gable wall, and the internal load-bearing cross wall nearest to the former.

The gable wall panels were 33 cm (13″) thick and were like the panel in Figure 29-1. They had, however, no window openings. They were manufactured of vertically cored clay wall tiles 29 x 24 x 15 cm (11-7/16″ x 9-7/16″ x 6-1/3″) in size, having a volume weight of 1250 kg. per cu. m. (0.0452 lb. per cu. in.) and an ultimate compressive strength of 150 kp. per sq. cm.(2133 psi). The cube crushing strength of the mortar was 100 kp. per sq. cm. (1422 psi).

Panels for the interior load-bearing cross walls were of similar design; they were, however, only 19 cm (7-1/2″) thick. Clay tiles used in their manufacture measured 16 x 24 x 15 cm (6-5/16″ x 9-7/16″ x 6-1/8″) and had a volume weight of 1550 kg. per cu. m (0.0560 lb. per cu in.) and an ultimate compressive strength of 200 kp. per sq. cm. (2845 psi). The cube crushing strength of mortar was 200 kp. per sq. cm.(2845 psi). Panels with door openings were made of concrete provided with reinforcement as required in the door lintel.

Test Procedure

Vertical strains in individual panels and horizontal strains (closing and gaping) in vertical joints between panels were measured in the groundfloor and in the first floor of both exterior gable wall and the interior cross wall. The strains were measured by a Huggenberger type Berry strain gauge and by means of permanently attached mechanical strain gauges, the accuracy of reading being 1 x 10^{-5}.

In addition, strains of the entire height of both the gable wall and the interior cross wall measured by the geodetic method of depth zone. With a gauge length of 23 m (75′ – 5″), an accuracy of ± 0.2 mm (± 0.08″) has been attained.

The measurements were taken over a two-year period and will probably be extended for at least another year.

As integral part of every individual strain measurement, the temperature of the surrounding atmosphere and that of the investigated wall panels was measured. Temperature measurements are of major significance because, as the preliminary evaluation clearly pointed out, the strains in panels due to

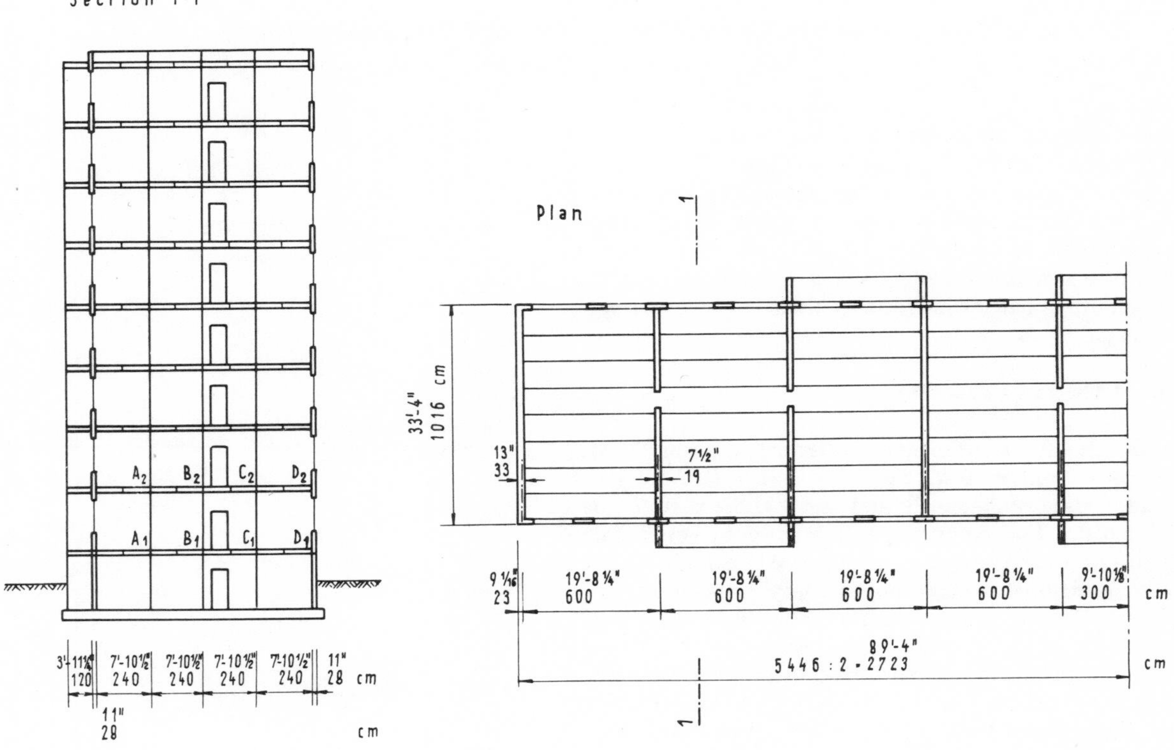

Figure 29-4. The investigated eight-storey residential building.

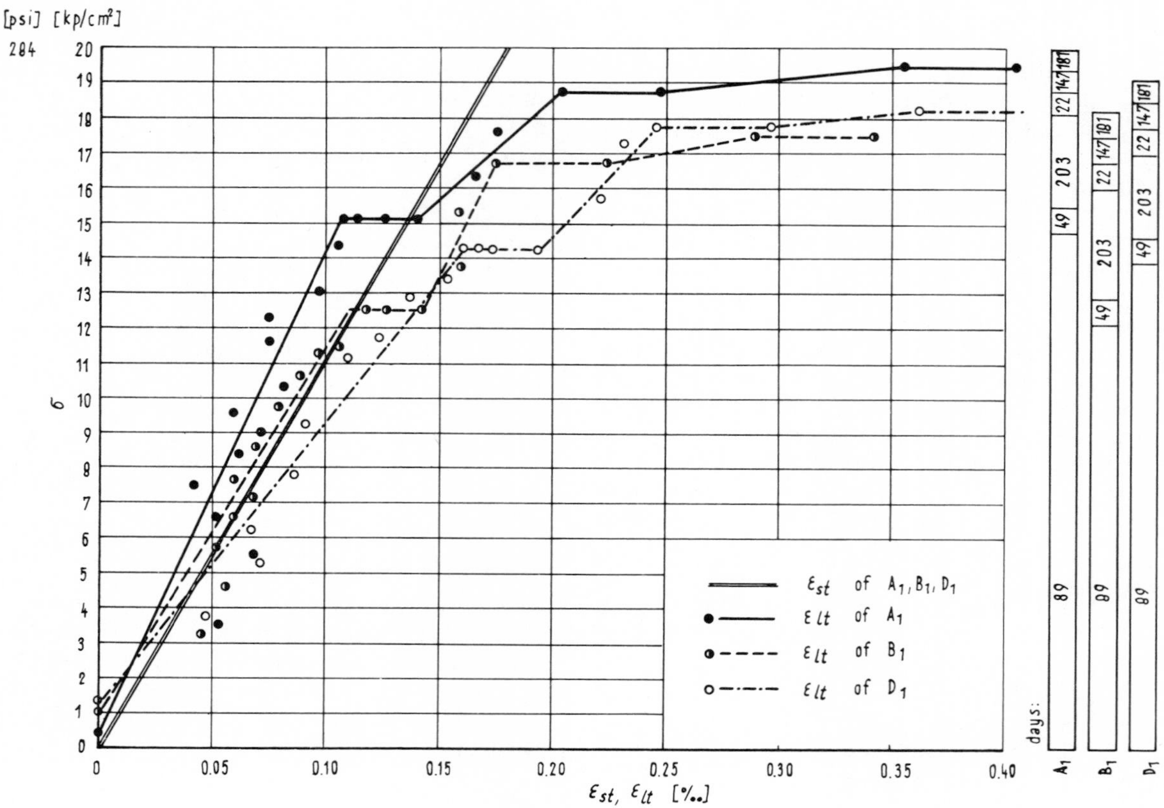

Figure 29-5. The long-term strains of the clay tile wall panels in the ground floor of the building.

temperature variations were frequently more extensive than those due to stress, shrinkage, and creep variations.

Along with the measurements on site, laboratory tests were made. In these tests, relation between stress and relative compression variations under short-term loads were ascertained and linear strains and deflections of clay tile wall panels due to temperature changes induced by their one-side heating were investigated.

Coefficient of Thermal Expansion

The value of the coefficient of thermal expansion, as determined by laboratory test, was $a_{th} = 0.71 \times 10^{-5}$ for the interior load-bearing wall panels and $a_{th} = 0.83 \times 10^{-5}$ for gable wall panels. For comparison, let us point out that according to requirements of the appropriate Czechoslovakian standard specification for designing masonry structures[2] the coefficient of thermal expansion for solid brick masonry bonded with lime or lime-cement mortar is $a_{th} = 0.5 \times 10^{-5}$. As for concrete, in the appropriate Czechoslovakian standard specification for designing concrete structures[1], the coefficient of thermal expansion of $a_{th} = 1.2 \times 10^{-5}$ is required. The test programme was not of large enough scale to demonstrate different values of a_{th} in horizontal and vertical direction as given for example in[4].

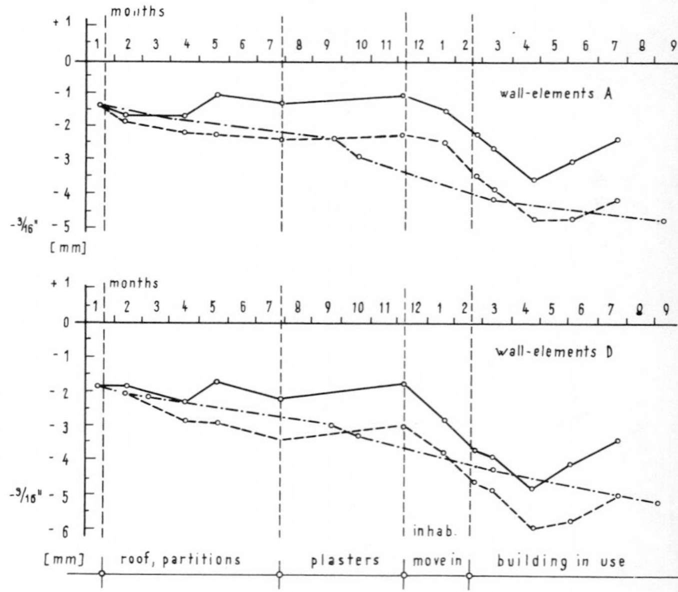

Figure 29-6. The long-term strains of the building-high wall assembled from the clay tile panels.

trains of Clay Tile Wall Panels under Long-Term Loads

According to generally known presumptions, the total rains ϵ_t, as measured on the site, were the sum of short-term rains ϵ_{st} appearing almost simultaneously with the applica- on of load, long-term strains ϵ_{lt} appearing delated in the ourse of several years, and, thermal strains ϵ_{th} brought about y changes in temperature.

$$\epsilon_t = \epsilon_{st} + \epsilon_{lt} + \epsilon_{th} \tag{29-5}$$

Since both short-time strains ϵ_{st} and thermal strains ϵ_{th} ere known from laboratory tests, it has been possible to ompute the virtual long-term strains ϵ_{lt} from the total strains t.

The values of short-term relative strains ϵ_{st} were estab- shed by laboratory loading tests on test specimens which had een made along with the investigated wall panels. It has been ound that the relation between short-time stress and strain ay be, for the range of stresses occurring in the investigated anels, taken for linear with sufficient accuracy.

The thermal strains ϵ_{th} were determined by the well-known quation applying to thermal expansion, use having been made f the values of the coefficient of thermal expansion a_{th} given coefficient of Thermal Expansion.

As in concrete structures, the long-term relative strains ϵ_{lt} cluded two types of strain. On one hand, it was creep that epends on stress; on the other hand, it is shrinkage that is dependent from stress and thermal expansion. Since there xisted no possibility of measuring shrinkage on special unloaded test specimens, no computations of virtual creep from long-term strains determined by measuring shrinkage on special unloaded test specimens, no computations of virtual creep from long-term strains determined by measuring were made.

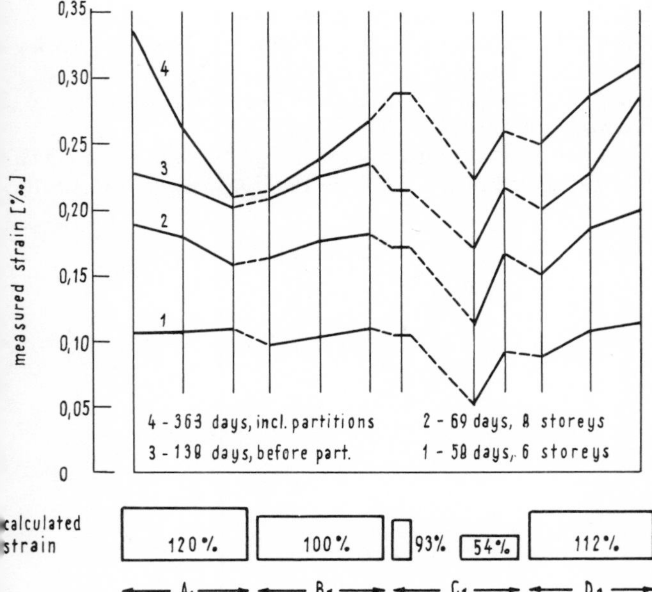

igure 29-7. The long-term strains along the length of the nterior load-bearing wall.

In Figure 29-5 the derived values of relative strains in the ground-floor interior cross-wall panels are demonstrated. The values of ϵ_{lt} show great dispersions caused by non-uniform properties of panels and the selected method of calculation. It is well-known that long-term strains of concrete depend on many factors. Concerning the clay tile wall panels, a parallel phenomenon may be observed, due to nonhomogeneous clay wall tiles, mortar components and differences in manufac- turing methods (water-cement ratio, degree of filling the joints, their width etc.).

The long-term compressive strains in 19-cm.-thick (7-1/2″) clay tile wall panels were, on an average, after 1 year 52 percent higher and after 2 years 110 percent higher than the short-term strains at stresses ranging from 0 to 16.9 to 19.5 kp. per sq. cm. (240 to 277 psi) respectively. The long-term relative compression strains after 2 years were on an average ϵ_{lt} = 0.18 percent.

In the 33-cm-thick clay tile wall panels, the long-term compressive strains at stresses ranging from 0 to 12 or 13 kp. per sq. cm. (171 to 185 psi) respectively, were found to be higher after 1 year by 64 percent and after 2 years by 109 percent compared with the short-term ones. The long-term relative compressive strain after 2 years was on an average ϵ_{lt} = 0.18 percent.

The results of measuring changes in the overall height of the interior wall, after having completed the erection of the principal load-bearing structures, are shown in Figure 29-6.

The values measured directly were adjusted to correspond to the temperature of the first measurement. In this manner results, plotted in Figure 29-6 by the dashed line, were obtained. The maximum shortening of the wall height was 4.5 mm (1-3/4″). In addition, the dot-and-dashed line in Figure 29-6 indicates the shortening of the wall height as computed from strain gage measurements of relative strains in the panels. The coincidence of results obtained is relatively good.

Changes of Compressive Strains in the Interior Load-Bearing Cross Wall

The changes of compressive strains along the length of the interior load-bearing wall, as found on performing four measurements, are given in Figure 29-7. In the lower part of Figure 29-7, the changes of the relative compressive strains according to the design, are indicated, assuming that each panel or each part thereof next to the openings carries vertical loads merely from the appropriate vertical strip limited by their edges. For this reason, the adjoining panels fail to cooperate. This is, generally speaking, a correct procedure, since the panels are interconnected merely by horizontal reinforcement on the floor level. In general, this presumption is substantiated by changes of compressive strains experi mentally established. However, far more conclusive is the established fact that cracks appeared in vertical joints within approximately one year after the assembly of the building had been commenced. The appearance of these cracks in the interior wall is due to the different magnitudes of compression in the adjoining panels (for example, the difference in compression between storey-high clay tile wall panels was, according to results obtained by both computing and testing, of the order of 0.05 – 0.10 mm, 0.02″ – 0.04″), rather than gaping of joints (the maximum measured value of gaping was 0.03 mm, 0.01″).

In the exterior wall a different situation prevailed since in this wall the temperature variation had a more expressive effect and the experimental values of joint gaps were higher.

Conclusion

This chapter comprises the results of investigation on the structural performance of single-wythe load-bearing clay tile wall panels which have one wythe of structural wall tiles bonded together with lime-cement or cement mortar (Figure 29-7). The properties of these clay tile wall panels were investigated and the results are necessary for designing and assembling the panels. The loading tests of the specimens that were made as cut-outs of actual wall panels and the loading tests of the masonry piers were the basis of these investigations. The test specimens and the piers were made by using three different types of vertically cored structural clay wall tiles and two different types of cement mortar (Table 29-1). The survey of the tests is given in the Table 29-2, the main results of the tests in the Tables 29-3 and 29-5 and in Figures 29-2 and 29-3. It was found that it is possible to use in the design such values of the ultimate compressive strength of the single-wythe clay tile wall panels that are higher than those of the masonry piers and walls made of the brick and mortar of the same strength. (Table 29-5).

The experimental investigation on structural performance of clay tile wall panels, stressed by long-term loads, was made on the load-bearing exterior and interior walls of the eight-storey high precast residential building during two years (Figure 29-4). The relation between the long-term stresses and the strains both of the panels and of the building-high walls were found (Figures 29-5 and 29-6). The changes of the strains along the length of the interior load-bearing wall are given in Figure 29-7. It is supposed to perform the investigation on the clay tile wall panels in the next years.

Definition of Algebraic Symbols

f'_m Ultimate compressive strength of clay masonry, kp. per sq. cm.

f'_u Ultimate compressive strength of units (bricks, structural clay tiles), kp. per sq. cm.

f'_{mr} Ultimate compressive strength of mortar, kp. per sq. cm.

f'_m Mean ultimate compressive strength of clay masonry, kp. per sq. cm.

min f'_m Lowest ultimate compressive strength of clay masonry, kp. per sq. cm.

S Standard deviation

k Coefficient of homogenity

ϵ Compressive strain, %

a Strain factor

E Tangent modulus of elasticity of masonry, kp. per sq. cm.

References

1. *Czechoslovak Standard Building Code Requirements for Design of Concrete Structures,* ČSN 73 2001, Prague, 1955.
2. *Czechoslovak Standard Building Code Requirements for Design of Masonry Structures,* ČSN 73 1331, Prague, 1958.
3. Novák, J., "State in Design of Clay Tile Material Versions", *Stavivo* V. 42, No. 8, 1964, pp. 300–304.
4. Plummer, Harry C., *Brick and Tile Engineering,* SCPI, Washington, 1962.
5. Pume, D., *Buckling of Masonry Piers and Walls,* Publ. by Building Research Institute, Prague, 1962.
6. Pume, D., "Bearing Capacity of Vibrated Masonry of Clay Tile Walls", *Stavební výzkum,* No. 6, 1963, pp. 1–15.
7. Pume, D., "Bearing Capacity of Clay Tile Wall Elements", *Baustoffindustris,* No. 2, 1967, pp. 55–57.
8. *Tentative Regulations on Design and Testing of Clay Tile Wall Precast Elements,* Publ. by Building Research Institute, Prague, 1962.

30. Funicular brick shell roofs for industrial buildings.

Prof. G. S. Ramaswamy, Director, Structural Engineering Research Center, Roorkee, India

The Funicular Concept

The normal sequence followed in designing shell roofs demands that the first step is the selection of the shape or geometry of the shell surface. Then, the stresses in the shell surface under loads are determined. In selecting shell shapes, no deliberate effort is made to ensure a favourable state of stress in the material selected for building the shell. Mathematical convenience seems to be the only consideration influencing the choice of shapes. There are many advantages to be gained by reversing this traditional sequence; or, in other words, we may assume a desired state of stress in the material after carefully examining its strong and weak points and then proceed to find a shape in which the chosen stress state will prevail under a specified loading condition. Shapes so found are called funicular shapes.

We may illustrate this concept with reference to brick masonry. Our effort in building with brick masonry will naturally be directed towards fully exploiting its strong point, its compressive strength. Because tensile strength is its weak point, it is necessary to ensure, at the same time, that the structure develops little or no tension. These two desirable objectives are simultaneously realized by choosing a state of pure compression unaccompanied by shear in the shell roof. An element taken out of such a shell and its plan projection are shown in Figure 30-1. The following well-known relations exist between the real stress resultants N_x, N_y, and N_{xy} and the pseudo stress resultants N_x, N_y, and N_{xy} and between the real loads F_x, F_y, and F_z and the pseudo loads X, Y, and Z.

$$N_x = \overline{N}_x \sqrt{\frac{1+q^2}{1+p^2}} \qquad (30\text{-}1a)$$

$$N_y = \overline{N}_y \sqrt{\frac{1+p^2}{1+q^2}} \qquad (30\text{-}1b)$$

$$N_{xy} = \overline{N}_{xy} \qquad (30\text{-}1c)$$

and

$$X = F_x \sqrt{1+p^2+q^2} \qquad (30\text{-}2a)$$

$$Y = F_y \sqrt{1+p^2+q^2} \qquad (30\text{-}2b)$$

$$Z = F_x \sqrt{1+p^2+q^2} \qquad (30\text{-}2c)$$

where:

$$p = \frac{\delta z}{\delta x} \text{ and } q = \frac{\delta z}{\delta y}$$

We may write down the equation of equilibrium for the element in the z direction as:

$$\overline{N}_x \frac{\delta^2 z}{\delta x^2} + 2\,\overline{N}_{xy} \frac{\delta^2 z}{\delta x \delta y} + \overline{N}_y \frac{\delta^2 z}{\delta y^2}$$
$$= pX + qY - Z \qquad (30\text{-}3)$$

Most shell roofs in practice carry only vertical loads. For this condition of loading X = Y = 0, and Equation 30-3 takes the form:

$$\overline{N}_x \frac{\delta^2 z}{\delta x^2} + 2\,\overline{N}_{xy} \frac{\delta^2 z}{\delta x \delta y} + \overline{N}_y \frac{\delta^2 x}{\delta y^2} = -Z \qquad (30\text{-}4)$$

Let the vertical load acting on the shell be g per unit area. Inserting this value in equation 30-4, we get:

$$\overline{N}_x \frac{\delta^2 z}{\delta x^2} + 2\overline{N}_{xy} \frac{\delta^2 z}{\delta x \delta y} + \overline{N}_y \frac{\delta^2 z}{\delta y^2}$$

$$= - g\sqrt{1 + p^2 + q^2} \qquad (30\text{-}5)$$

In practice, shallow shells are generally favoured for roofing applications. For such shell roofs, p^2 and q^2 are small in comparison with unity, and one may write:

$$\overline{N}_x \frac{\delta^2 z}{\delta x^2} + 2\overline{N}_{xy} \frac{\delta^2 z}{\delta x \delta y} + N_y \frac{\delta^2 z}{\delta x^2} = - g \qquad (30\text{-}6)$$

At this stage let us specify the desired stress state. As already explained, it is desirable to have a pure compression state in the masonry unaccompanied by shear. Shear stresses should be obviated as they cause tension. For optimum utilization of the compressive strength of the material $\overline{N}_x$ and $\overline{N}_y$ must be equal. These conditions may be formulated as follows:

$$\overline{N}_x = \overline{N}_y = - N \qquad (30\text{-}7)$$

where N is the magnitude of the desired compression in the masonry, and:

$$\overline{N}_{xy} = 0 \qquad (30\text{-}8)$$

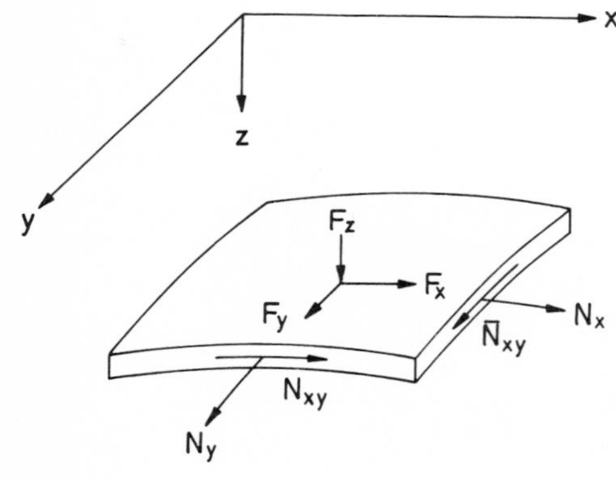

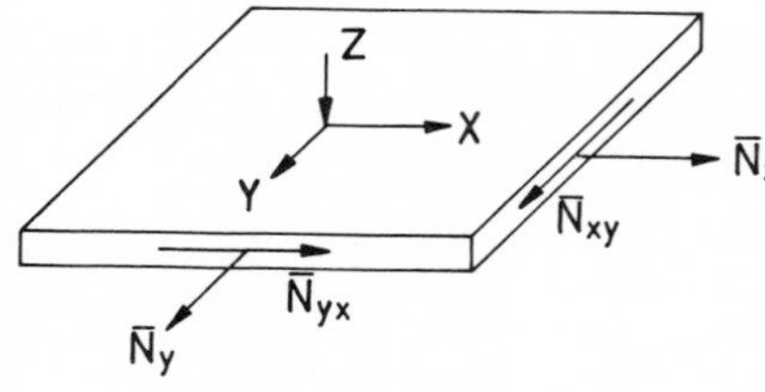

$\overline{N}_{xy} = \overline{N}_{yx}$

$N_{xy} = N_{yx}$

Figure 30-1.

Inserting these conditions in Equation 30-6, we get,

$$\frac{\delta^2 z}{\delta x^2} + \frac{\delta^2 z}{\delta y^2} = \frac{g}{N} \qquad (30\text{-}9)$$

Equation 30-9 defines the desired shape of the funicular surface. This relation may be generalized to make it independent of the coordinate system employed by recasting Equation 30-9 in vectorial form as:

$$\nabla_z^2 = \frac{g}{N} \qquad (30\text{-}10)$$

It must be distinctly understood that a shell surface can be made funicular only for one specified loading condition. In our case, vertical loading was selected, because the dominant load to which a shell roof is normally subjected is vertical. However, experience gained with numerous funicular shells already built shows that, although their shape is selected for optimum performance under vertical loads, they behave very well under other loads.

Analytical Methods for Finding Funicular Shapes

Equation 30-10 is the well-known Poisson's differential equation of mathematical physics. It may also be noted that it is the equation which governs the height z of the Prandtl[1] membrane in the Membrane Analogy for Torsion. Many available results relating to torsion of prismatic bars of various cross sections[2] may, therefore, be drawn on to find funicular shell shapes corresponding to various ground plans. Figure 30-2 gives equations of funicular surfaces over some of the usual ground plans. The ordinates of a funicular surface over a given ground plan can also be computed accurately at desired intervals by manual methods of computation such as Relaxation. Alternatively, by employing numerical methods, the Poisson's equation can be solved on an electronic digital computer to arrive at ordinates of the surface accurately.

Experimental Methods of Generating Funicular Shapes

A simple method of generating funicular shapes successfully is to make a wooden mould whose ground plan is similar to that of the structure which is to be roofed over by a funicular shell. A flexible fabric, stretched taut across the mould, is loaded with wet plaster of paris. The fabric is now allowed to sag and the plaster to set. On inversion, the shape obtained is the required funicular surface. The ordinates of the prototype roof are easily obtained by multiplying the ordinates of the model by the scale factor. The model of a funicular shell roof over an oval ground plan, generated by this process, is shown in Figure 30-3.

A more sophisticated method is to blow up a rubber membrane over the desired ground plan and measure its ordinates.

It is also well-known that the Poisson's equation involved can be solved by the Electrical Analogy Method.

In building large funicular shell roofs, the author's experience dictates that ordinates need to be at 2′ intervals for accurate fabrication of forms.

Bending Analysis of Funicular Shells

Equation 30-10 defines the funicular surface only if a membrane stress state prevails. Secondary bending stresses do arise in the shell in the neighbourhood of the edge members. A study was recently made of a funicular shell using the shallow shell bending theory of Vlasov[3]. It was found that even after bending stresses are taken into account, the shell is more or less in a state of low compression throughout. The small tensile stresses that develop are well within the limits that unreinforced brick masonry can withstand without cracking.

Examples of Practical Application

The author has successfully built two types of funicular shells using brick masonry. The details of the first type are given in Figure 30-4. Several shells of this type have been built for the National Design Institute, Ahmedabad, India. Figure 30-5 shows the finished view of one of the shells. The shells measuring 41′ x 41′ are supported on reinforced concrete edge beams 1′-2″ x 3′-6″ which, in turn, rest on reinforced concrete columns. The roof is 4-1/2″ thick and is built of bricks laid on edge. The joints which are 1/2″ and 1-1/2″ wide are filled with mortar. The brickwork is lightly reinforced by the provision of 3/8″-diameter reinforcement at 10-1/2″ in both directions. The joint width is entirely governed by the need to provide adequate concrete cover to the reinforcement to protect it from corrosion caused by efflorescence. The handmade bricks had an average compressive strength of 800 p.s.i. This quality of brick was considered quite adequate for the purpose as the

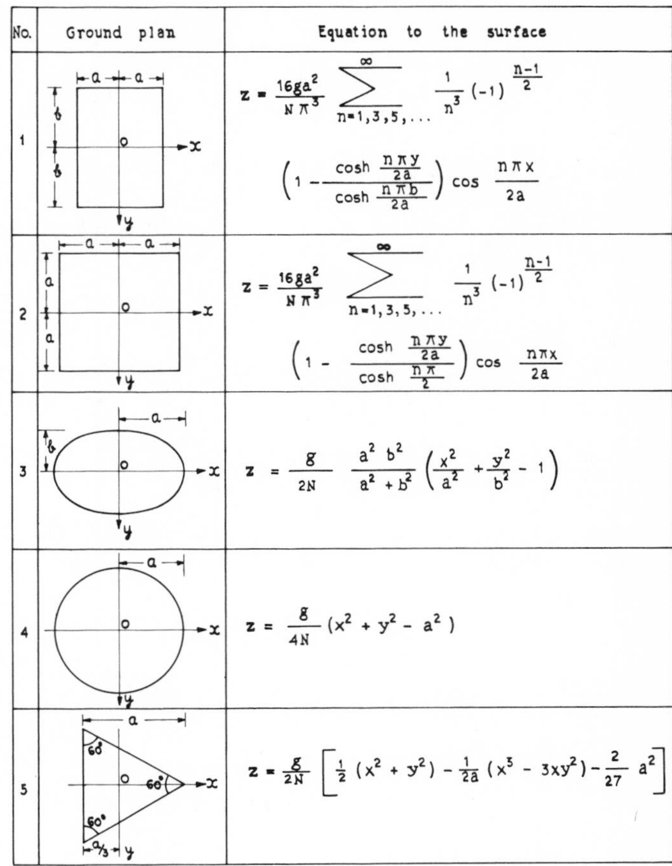

No.	Ground plan	Equation to the surface
1		$z = \frac{16ga^2}{N\pi^3} \sum_{n=1,3,5,\dots}^{\infty} \frac{1}{n^3}(-1)^{\frac{n-1}{2}} \left(1 - \frac{\cosh\frac{n\pi y}{2a}}{\cosh\frac{n\pi b}{2a}}\right) \cos\frac{n\pi x}{2a}$
2		$z = \frac{16ga^2}{N\pi^3} \sum_{n=1,3,5,\dots}^{\infty} \frac{1}{n^3}(-1)^{\frac{n-1}{2}} \left(1 - \frac{\cosh\frac{n\pi y}{2a}}{\cosh\frac{n\pi}{2}}\right) \cos\frac{n\pi x}{2a}$
3		$z = \frac{g}{2N} \frac{a^2 b^2}{a^2 + b^2} \left(\frac{x^2}{a^2} + \frac{y^2}{b^2} - 1\right)$
4		$z = \frac{g}{4N}(x^2 + y^2 - a^2)$
5		$z = \frac{g}{2N}\left[\frac{1}{2}(x^2 + y^2) - \frac{1}{2a}(x^3 - 3xy^2) - \frac{2}{27}a^2\right]$

Figure 30-2. Equations of funicular surfaces over some of the usual ground plans.

Figure 30-3. Model of a funicular shell roof over an oval ground plan.

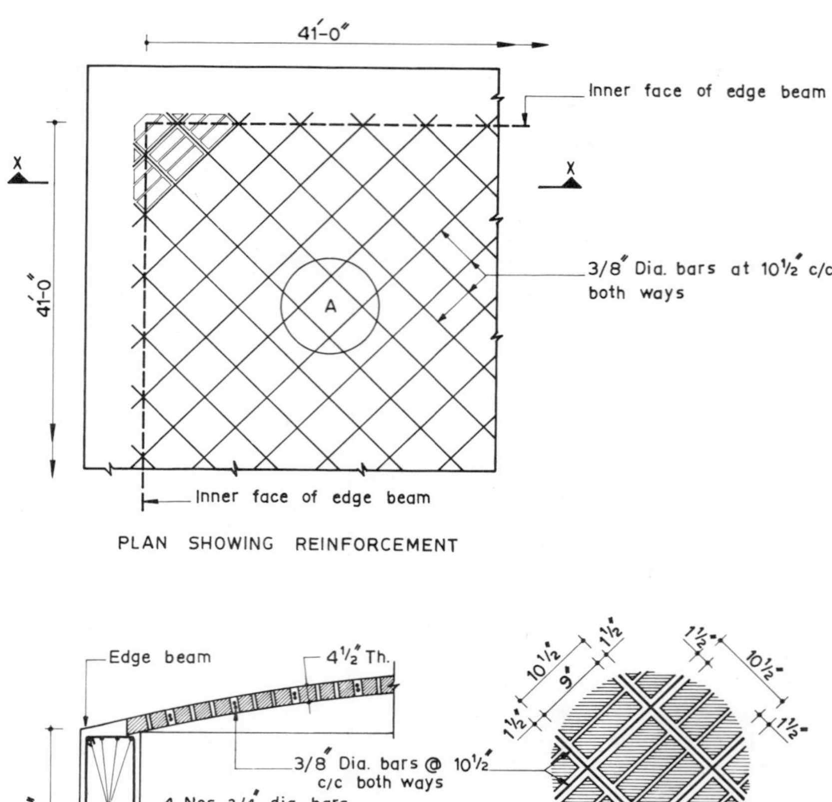

Figure 30-4. Funicular shell in reinforced brick work.

Figure 30-5. Finished view of funicular shell.

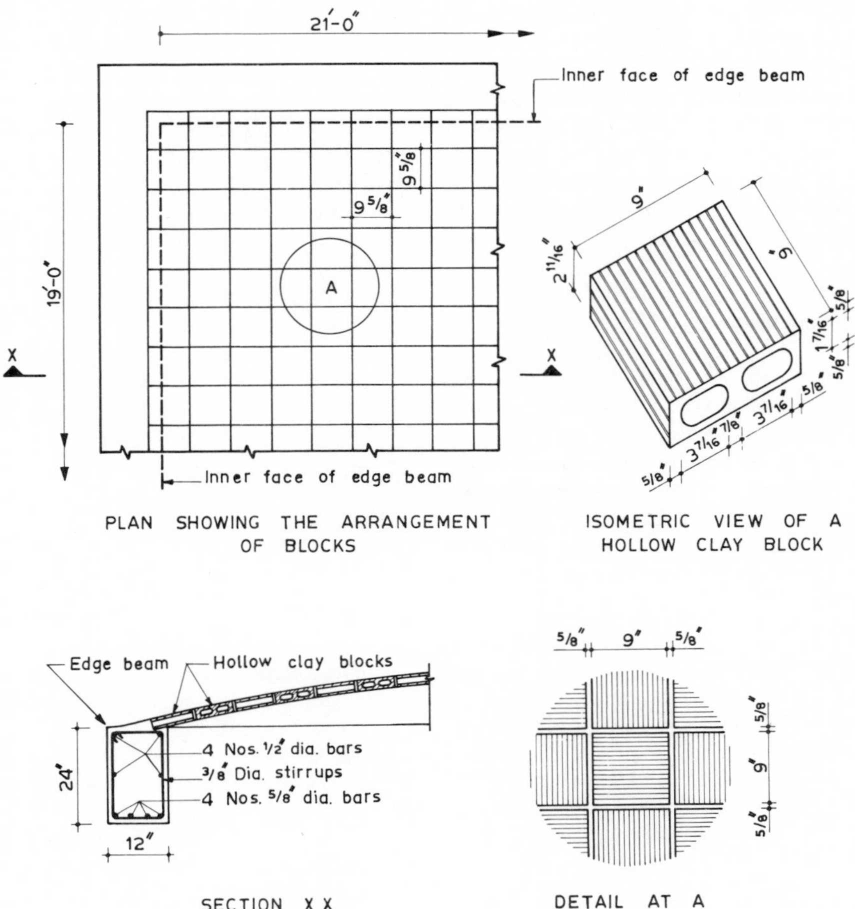

Figure 30-6. Unreinforced funicular shell built with hollow clay blocks.

Figure 30-7. Finished view of roof soffit.

compressive stresses that develop in the shell under a vertical load of 52.5 p.s.f. were of the order of only 175 p.s.i.

A different technique was employed for a masonry shell roof recently built at Roorkee, India. Measuring 22′ x 20′, it is built of extruded hollow clay blocks of the type shown in Figure 30-6. The 1:4 cement mortar joints between the blocks are only 5/8″ wide. The shell is supported on reinforced concrete edge beams which rest on columns. Details of this roof are given in Figure 30-6. A finished view of the roof soffit can be seen in Figure 30-7.

Conclusion

Brick funicular shell roofs of the type described in this chapter offer an economical means of roofing large column-free spaces required for factory buildings. They are especially suitable for wide application in the developing countries of the world where there is a pressing need to conserve the small supply of cement and steel. The brick funicular shell roofs developed by the author are an outgrowth of the extensive work carried out by him over the past ten years on reinforced concrete funicular shells.[4,5]

Nomenclature

x, y, z co-ordinates defining the surface of the shell

$z = f(x, y)$ Equation of the surface

$p = \frac{\delta z}{\delta x}$

$q = \frac{\delta z}{\delta y}$

$r = \frac{\delta^2 z}{\delta x^2}$

$s = \frac{\delta^2 z}{\delta x \delta y}$

$t = \frac{\delta^2 z}{\delta y^2}$

N_x Stress-resultant in the shell in the x direction

N_y Stress resultant in the shell in the y direction

N_{xy} Shear stress resultant

$\overline{N}_x$ Psuedo stress resultant in the x direction

$\overline{N}_y$ Psuedo stress-resultant in the y direction

$\overline{N}_{xy}$ Psuedo shear stress resultant

F_x External force acting on the shell element in the x direction

F_y External force acting on shell element in y direction

F_z External force acting on shell element in z direction

X Psuedo force in x direction

Y Psuedo force in y direction

Z Psuedo force in z direction

∇^2 Laplacian operator

g Vertical load acting on the shell per unit area

N Desired compressive stress in the shell

References

1. Timoshenko, S., and Goodier, J. N., "Theory of Elasticity," *Engineering Societies Monographs*, McGraw-Hill Book Co., 1951, pp. 268-269.
2. Timoshenko, S., and Goodier, J. N., "Theory of Elasticity," *Engineering Societies Monographs*, McGraw-Hill Book Co., 1951, pp. 259-285.
3. Vlasov, V. Z., "Generce Theory of Shells and its application in Engineering," TTF-99, NASA, 1964.
4. Ramaswamy, G. S., "Analysis, Design and Construction of a New Shell of Double Curvature," *Proceedings of the Symposium on Shell Research,* Delft, August 30-September 2, 1961.
5. Ramaswamy, G. S., Raman, N. V., and George, Zacharia, "A Funicular Shell for the Conference Hall of the Kanpur Municipal Corporation – Design and Construction," *Indian Concrete Journal,* Vol. 36, No:9, September, 1962.

31. Structural behavior of linear elastic walls having no tensile strength.

Svenn Risager, Danmarks Ingeniørakademi Bygningsafdelingen, Copenhagen, Denmark

Introduction

The bearing capacity of linear elastic walls having no tensile strength has been dealt with in the literature from different viewpoints. In 1933-34 and in 1944 respectively Kazinczy[1] and Nylander[2] determined the bearing capacity without taking into account that the wall becomes a variable system when the neutral axis falls within the cross section of the wall. In 1957 Angervo and Putkonen[3] advanced a procedure in which the influence of the variable system on the wall deflection, and thereby on the bearing capacity, is included.

Among the research workers who have since treated the problem of the simply supported, eccentrically loaded column of linear elastic material should be mentioned Sahlin[4] who determined the bearing capacity on the basis of the differential equations for the fundamental problem and Angervo[5] and Chapman and Slatford[6] who set up and solved the equation.

In a previous work, Poulsen and Risager[7], the author participated in analyzing the statical behaviour and the bearing capacity of the simply supported, eccentrically loaded column of linear elastic material without tensile strength on the basis of an estimated deflection curve.

The present chapter deals with the statical behaviour of linear elastic walls without tensile strength (brick walls), erected between floors which allow no side sway and with equal angle of rotation at both ends. For a given wall, i.e. a wall with known values of thickness, height, width, modulus of elasticity, compressive strength, and angle of rotation at the ends, the following values have been determined and illustrated graphically: bearing capacity, eccentricity of the compressive force at the ends of the wall, mode of failure (stress failure or buckling) and crack condition (uncracked or cracked cross section). The assumptions on which these determinations have been made are the same as in "The Bearing Capacity of Linear Elastic Brittle Columns,"[7]; but it is estimated that the deflection curve of the wall can be composed of parabolic arcs. Empirically, the approximation reached by assuming the deflection curve of a column to be parabolic will give results which come very close to the correct values. In solving a practical problem of this nature, there will always be a considerable element of uncertainty in determining the constants E and σ_{br}. Thus, the deviation from the assumed parabolic curve of deflection will be insignificant. However, the approximation is of decisive importance in giving a clear description of the statical behaviour, as a solution by means of differential equations gives only a mathematical answer and very little perception of the actual behaviour of the wall. In the treatment of the problem, proper consideration has been given to the fact that, when cracked, the wall constitutes a variable system, which influences the deflection curve and thereby the bearing capacity, etc.

Behaviour

The Equivalent Column

In Figure 31-1a a story is depicted as a frame with the height H consisting of two identical floors and walls loaded in such a way that the angles of rotation φ at wall ends are equal at top and base.

The left wall, which is subjected to the forces from the floor slabs equivalent to a compressive force P, acts at both ends with the eccentricity e, see Figure 31-1b. Thus, the weight of the wall itself is not taken into consideration. The horizontal components of P are exerted by the floor slabs.

Let us now compare the wall in Figure 31-1b with the system shown in Figure 31-1c, which can be regarded as two columns of equal length, simply supported, and centrally

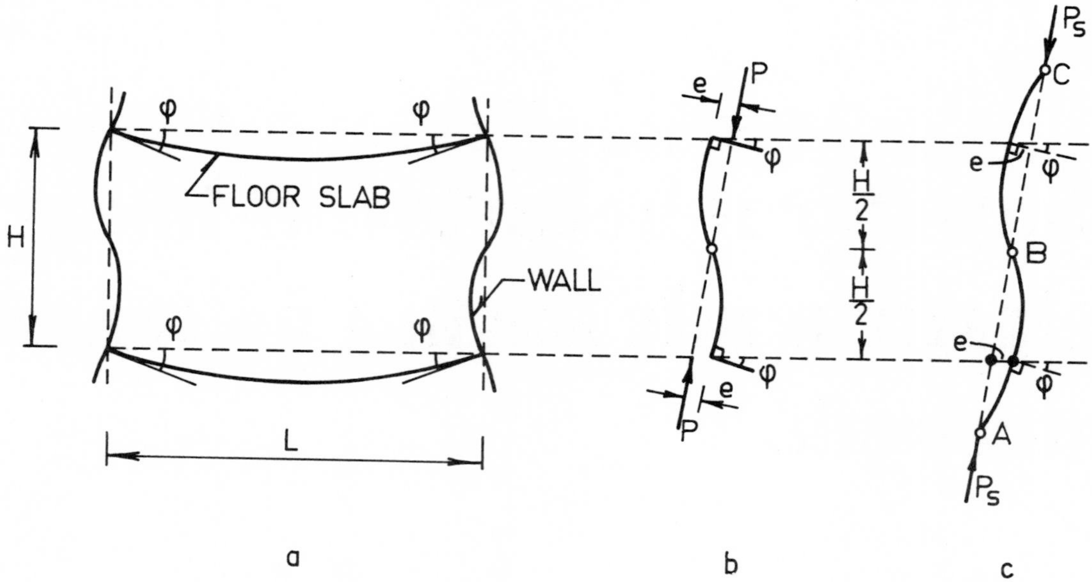

Figure 31-1.

loaded with the force P_s. The cross section and material of the columns are supposed to correspond to those of wall b, and the force P_s is assumed to be of a magnitude which just gives the columns c the deflection e at the distance ½H over and under the common point B. From a statical point of view wall, b and the part of the system c lying between the dotted lines are completely uniform systems. It must, therefore, hold that $P_s = P$, just as the free length of column must be dependent on H, φ, e and P. Thus, the following statment is valid:

From a statical point of view a given wall with a given load P, eccentricity e and angle of rotation at ends φ can be considered equivalent to a simply supported column of the same material and cross section and centrally loaded with the force P.

We shall call this column the equivalent column.

Bearing Capacity of the Wall

What happens to the wall when load P is increased and the angle of rotation φ at the ends at the same time is kept constant? Let us start with the case shown in Figure 31-2a, to which corresponds an equivalent column with the length $H_s >$ ½H. When P is increased, the wall tries to increase its deflection and thereby its angle of rotation φ at the ends.

As the ends of the wall are prevented from rotating, an external anticlockwise moment is created as a result of the reduction of the eccentricity e. Provided that the wall does not fail before, there will be a value of P at which the eccentricity e = 0. The length of the equivalent column will then be H_s = ½H, see Figure 31-2b. By regarding Figure 2c it will now be seen that the curve of wall deflection can be changed without changing the length of the equivalent column. This simply corresponds to a shift of the equivalent column in the direction of the acting force with a simultaneous increase of its deflection. Consequently, the chord force is unchanged or reduced so that the column becomes unstable.

In the following the equivalent column corresponding to a wall and its load will be used as basis for determining the bearing capacity, etc. of the wall.

Angle of Rotation at the Ends

Since φ denotes the angle of rotation at the ends of the wall, the effect of a mutual angle of rotation between floor and wall, if any, is a problem which can be investigated separately, and which has no influence on determining the bearing capacity of the wall made below.

Analysis

Geometry

As mentioned in the introduction, use is made of the approximation that the deflection curve is composed of parabolic arcs. Figure 31-3 shows a wall with the height H and the thickness t. The width of the wall is b. On the wall acts a load P, and the curves of deflection for uncracked and cracked cross sections respectively are shown. The corresponding equivalent columns have the length H_s.

For the equivalent column with the maximum deflection u_o we can now formulate the equations valid for a parabola with the deflection u and the inclination $\frac{du}{dx}$, see Figure 31-3.

$$u = 4u_o \frac{x}{H_s}\left(1 - \frac{x}{H_s}\right) \tag{31-1}$$

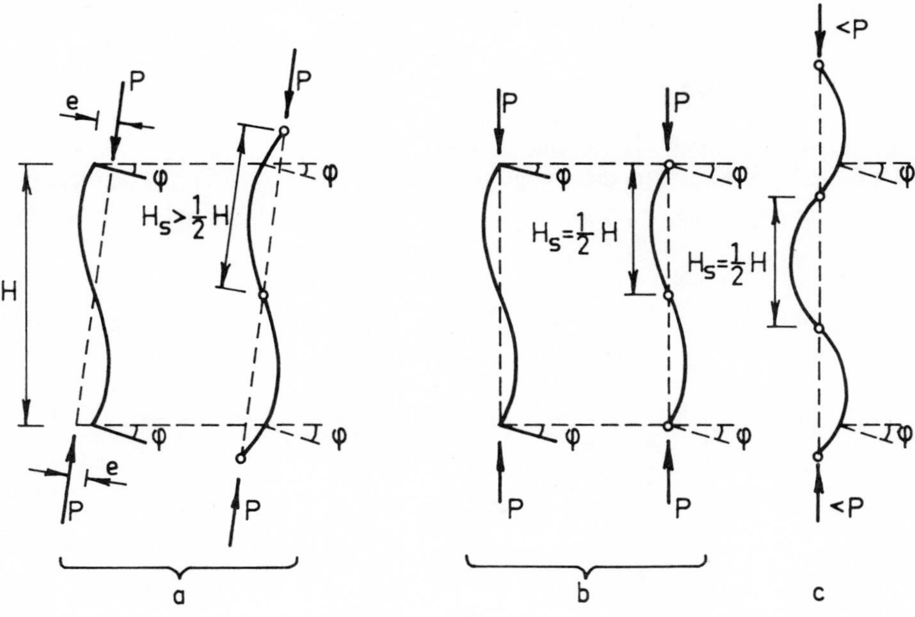

Figure 31-2.

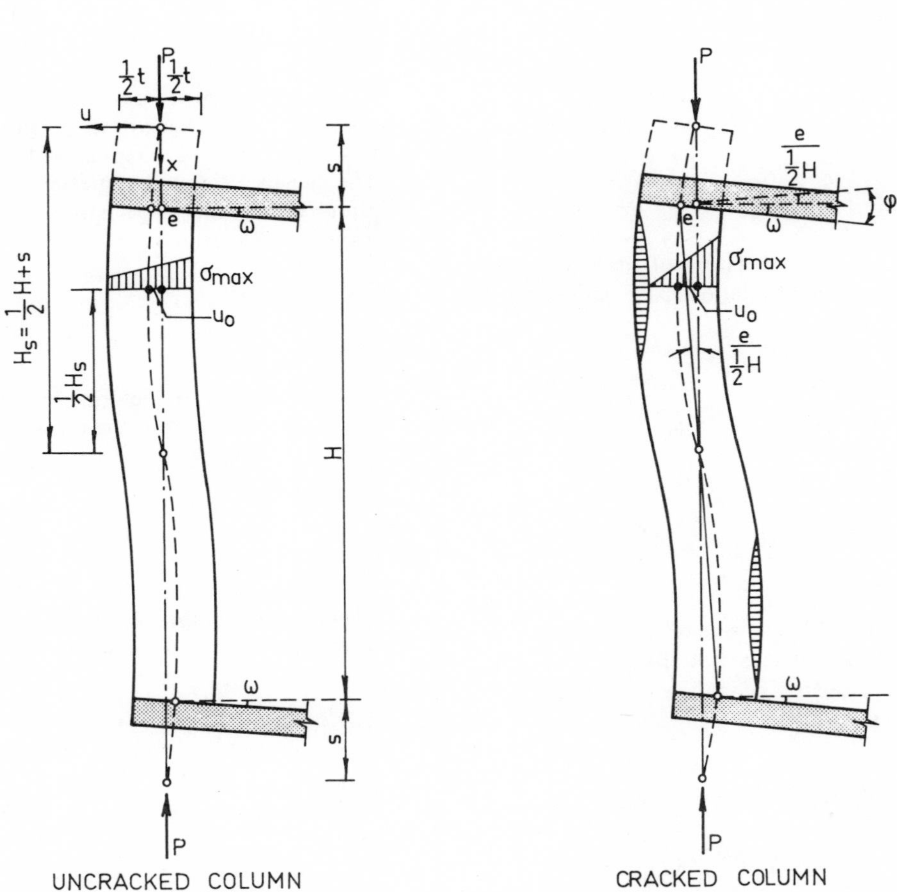

Figure 31-3.

$$\frac{du}{dx} = 4\,\frac{u_o}{H_s}\left(1 - 2\,\frac{x}{H_s}\right) \qquad (31\text{-}2)$$

We now get e, the eccentricity of the force, and ω, the rotation of the end of the wall relative to the compressive force line, as $e = u$ and $\omega = \frac{du}{dx}$ respectively for $x = s$

$$e = 4\,u_o\,\frac{s}{H_s}\left(1 - \frac{s}{H_s}\right) \qquad (31\text{-}3)$$

$$\omega = 4\,\frac{u_o}{H_s}\left(1 - 2\,\frac{s}{H_s}\right) \qquad (31\text{-}4)$$

For practical reasons we introduce the eccentricity dimensionless by:

$$\epsilon = \frac{e}{\frac{1}{2}t} \qquad (31\text{-}5)$$

and the angle of rotation by:

$$\Omega = \frac{H}{t}\,\omega \qquad (31\text{-}6a)$$

$$\Phi = \frac{H}{t}\,\varphi \qquad (31\text{-}6b)$$

where φ is the actual angle of rotation of the end of the wall, see Figure 31-3. By applying Equations 31-3 and 31-4 we then get:

$$\Omega = 2\,\frac{u_o}{\frac{1}{2}t}\,\frac{H}{H_s}\left(1 - 2\,\frac{s}{H_s}\right) \qquad (31\text{-}7)$$

$$\epsilon = 2\,\Omega\,\frac{s}{H}\cdot\frac{H_{s-s}}{H_s - 2s} \qquad (31\text{-}8)$$

Equations 31-7 and 31-8 are generally valid. For the case under consideration it is especially true that:

$$H_s = \tfrac{1}{2}H + s \qquad (31\text{-}9)$$

If this is substituted, we finally get:

$$\Omega = 4\,\frac{u_o}{\frac{1}{2}t}\,\frac{1 - 2\,\frac{s}{H}}{\left(1 + 2\,\frac{s}{H}\right)^2} \qquad (31\text{-}10)$$

$$\epsilon = 2\,\Omega\,\frac{\frac{s}{H}}{1 - 2\,\frac{s}{H}} \qquad (31\text{-}$$

From Figure 31-3 it will be seen that the angle of rotat at the ends of the wall φ can be expressed:

$$\varphi = \omega + \frac{e}{\frac{1}{2}H} \qquad (31\text{-}$$

or

$$\Phi = \Omega + \epsilon \qquad (31\text{-}$$

$$\Phi = \Omega\,\frac{1}{1 - 2\,\frac{s}{H}} = 4\,\frac{u_o}{\frac{1}{2}t}\,\frac{1}{\left(1 + 2\,\frac{s}{H}\right)^2} \qquad (31\text{-}$$

$$\epsilon = 2\,\Phi\,\frac{s}{H} \qquad (31\text{-}$$

Determination of the Bearing Capacity

A rectangular cross section of a linear elastic mate without tensile strength, the height of which is t and the wi b, is subjected to a compressive force P with the eccentricit The height of the compressed zone will then be 3(½t – after which the edge stress σ_{max} is determined by projection equation to be:

$$\sigma_{max} = \frac{2}{3}\,\frac{P}{b\,(\frac{1}{2}t - e)} \qquad (31\text{-}$$

The curvature is determined as the edge strain divided the compressed part of the cross section height and we get:

$$k = \frac{2}{9}\,\frac{P}{Eb(\frac{1}{2}t - e)^2} \qquad (31\text{-}$$

It proves convenient to introduce the term $P_{o.br} = bt\sigma$ whereby the compressive force can be expressed dimensionl by the symbol ν determined by:

$$\nu = \frac{P}{P_{o.br}} = \frac{P}{bt\sigma_{br}} \qquad (31\text{-}1$$

Furthermore the terms P_E and Ψ are introduced, defin by:

$$P_E = \pi^2\,\frac{EJ}{H^2} = \frac{\pi^2}{12}\,\frac{Ebt^3}{H^2} \qquad (31\text{-}1$$

$$\Psi = \frac{432}{5\pi^2}\frac{P_E}{P_{o.br}} = 7.2\left(\frac{t}{H}\right)^2 \frac{E}{\sigma_{br}} \qquad (31\text{-}20)$$

Distinction is made between uncracked and cracked cross section.

Uncracked Cross Section. The load on the equivalent column in the deflected position corresponding to Ω with the maximum deflection u_o at the middle is the chord force P determined by:

$$P = 9.6\,\frac{EJ}{H_s^2} \qquad (31\text{-}21)$$

Using P_E and s introduced by Equations 31-19 and 31-9, we get:

$$P = \frac{9.6}{\pi^2}\left(\frac{H}{H_s}\right)^2 P_E = \frac{192}{5\pi^2}\,\frac{P_E}{\left(1 + 2\,\frac{s}{H}\right)^2} \qquad (31\text{-}22)$$

From this can be found:

$$\nu = \frac{192}{5\pi^2}\,\frac{P_E}{P_{o.br}}\,\frac{1}{\left(1 + 2\,\frac{s}{H}\right)^2} \qquad (31\text{-}23)$$

or by using Ψ introduced by Equation 31-20:

$$\nu = \frac{4}{9}\,\Psi\,\frac{1}{\left(1 + 2\,\frac{s}{H}\right)^2} \qquad (31\text{-}24)$$

After this we apply Navier's formula for the maximum stress in the middle cross section of the column which, since $\sigma_{max} = \sigma_{br}$, gives:

$$\sigma_{br} = \frac{P}{bt}\left(1 + 3\,\frac{u_o}{½t}\right) \qquad (31\text{-}25)$$

When $\frac{u_o}{½t}$ is eliminated by the application of Equation 31-14, we get:

$$\nu = \frac{1}{1 + \frac{3}{4}\,\Phi\left(1 + 2\,\frac{s}{H}\right)^2} \qquad (31\text{-}26)$$

Now the two equations 31-24 and 31-26 give the bearing capacity, as $\frac{s}{H}$ can be eliminated. We find:

$$\nu = 1 - \frac{1}{3}\,\Phi\,\Psi \qquad (31\text{-}27)$$

The eccentricity can be expressed by ν and Φ. When Equation 31-26 is solved with regard to $\frac{s}{H}$, we get:

$$\frac{s}{H} = \frac{1}{3}\sqrt{\frac{3}{\Phi}\,\frac{1-\nu}{\nu}} - ½ \qquad (31\text{-}28)$$

which substituted in Equation 31-15 gives:

$$\epsilon = \frac{2}{3}\sqrt{3\,\Phi\,\frac{1-\nu}{\nu}} - \Phi \qquad (31\text{-}29)$$

By applying Equation 31-27 we get ϵ expressed by Ψ and Φ:

$$\epsilon = \frac{2}{3}\,\Phi\sqrt{3\,\frac{\Psi}{3 - \Phi\Psi}} - \Phi \qquad (31\text{-}30)$$

The crack criterion for the wall corresponds to $\nu = ½$, whereby Equation 31-27 gives:

$$\Psi = \frac{3}{2\,\Phi} \qquad (31\text{-}31)$$

As the wall becomes unstable for $\epsilon = 0$, note the section about the bearing capacity of the wall, we find the boundary validity of the formula for the bearing capacity by putting $\epsilon = 0$ in Equation 31-30, whereby the boundary condition is found to be:

$$\Psi = \frac{9}{4 + 3\,\Phi} \qquad (31\text{-}32)$$

As mentioned, instability sets in at $\epsilon = 0$, to which corresponds $s = 0$, note Figure 31-3. For the uncracked cross section Equation 31-24 is still valid, and with $s = 0$ it gives the critical load:

$$\nu = \frac{4}{9}\,\Psi \qquad (31\text{-}33)$$

The crack criterion is that $\frac{u_o}{½t} = \frac{1}{3}$. When this is substituted in Equation 31-14 and we put s = 0, we get:

$$\Phi = \frac{4}{3} \tag{31-34}$$

Cracked Cross Section. The load of the equivalent column corresponding to the considered deflected wall is determined by statical-geometrical analogy, whereby we find:

$$u_o = \frac{5}{48} k_o H_s^2 \tag{31-35}$$

Here, k_o is the curvature in the middle of the column, which for cracked cross section is determined by Equation 31-17.

$$k_o = \frac{2}{9} \frac{P}{Eb\,(½t - u_o)^2} \tag{31-36}$$

We get:

$$u_o = \frac{5}{48} \cdot \frac{2}{9} \frac{P}{EB\,(½t - u_o)^2} H_s^2 \tag{31-37}$$

which, after introduction of P_E and H_s from Equation 31-19 and Equation 31-9 respectively, can be arranged so that we get:

$$\frac{\frac{u_o}{½t}\left(1 - \frac{u_o}{½t}\right)^2}{\left(1 + 2\frac{s}{H}\right)^2} = \frac{5\pi^2}{1296} \frac{P}{P_E} \tag{31-38}$$

Here $\frac{s}{H}$ can be eliminated by means of Equation 31-14, and the result is:

$$\left(1 - \frac{u_o}{½t}\right)^2 = \frac{5\pi^2}{324} \frac{1}{\Phi} \frac{P}{P_E} \tag{31-39}$$

Now the condition of failure must be introduced. We get it by putting $\sigma_{max} = \sigma_{br}$ and $e = u_o$ in Equation 31-16, i.e.:

$$\sigma_{br} = \frac{4P}{3bt\left(1 - \frac{u_o}{½t}\right)} \tag{31-40}$$

which can be written:

$$\nu = \frac{3}{4}\left(1 - \frac{u_o}{½t}\right) \tag{31-41}$$

Eliminating $\frac{u_o}{½t}$ from Equation 31-39 and Equation 31-41 we get the formula of the bearing capacity

$$\nu = \frac{3}{4} \frac{1}{\Phi} \cdot \frac{1}{\Psi} \tag{31-42}$$

We get the eccentricity expressed by ν and Φ by putting $\frac{u_o}{½t}$ from Equation 31-14 in Equation 31-41 and solve the equation with regard to $\frac{s}{H}$. The result is:

$$\frac{s}{H} = \frac{1}{3}\sqrt{\frac{3}{\Phi}(3 - 4\nu)} - ½ \tag{31-43}$$

which substituted in Equation 31-15 gives:

$$\epsilon = \frac{2}{3}\sqrt{3\Phi(3 - 4\nu)} - \Phi \tag{31-44}$$

or expressed by Ψ and Φ alone:

$$\epsilon = 2\sqrt{\Phi - \frac{1}{\Psi}} - \Phi \tag{31-45}$$

The formula (Equation 31-42) for the bearing capacity is valid for the stable zone. The wall becomes unstable at $\epsilon = 0$, which substituted in Equation 31-45 gives the boundary validity of Equation 31-42. We find this to be:

$$\Psi = \frac{4}{\Phi(4 - \Phi)} \tag{31-46}$$

The bearing capacity in the unstable zone, where $\epsilon = 0$ and s = 0, is found from Equation 31-39 when we eliminate $\frac{u_o}{½t}$ by application of Equation 31-14. We then find the buckling load:

$$\nu = \frac{3}{64} \Phi\Psi(4 - \Phi)^2 \tag{31-47}$$

Graphic Illustration

The zones of validity for the four bearing capacity formulas and the eccentricity formula appear very clearly when they are

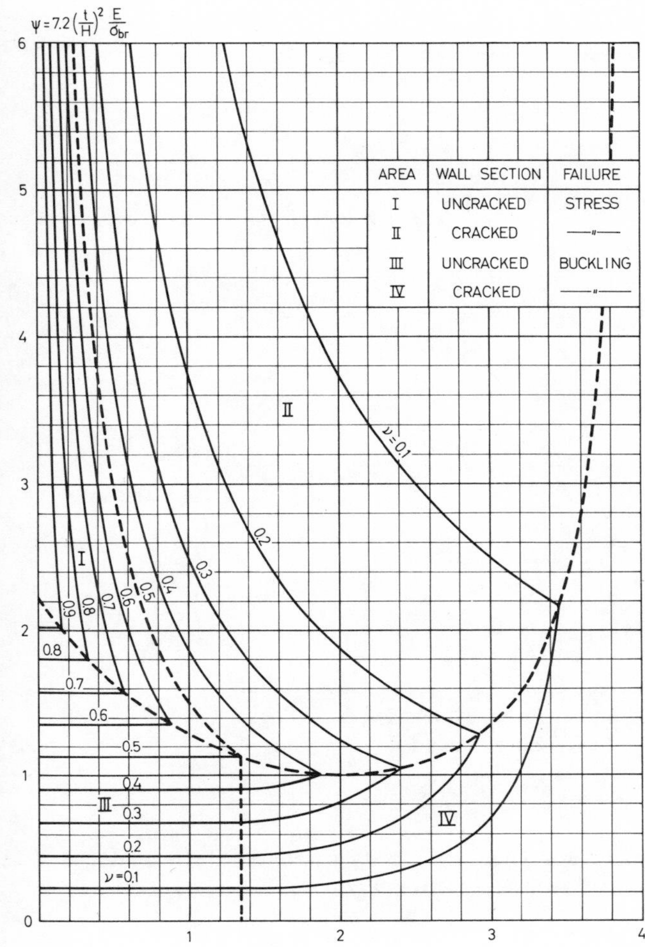

Figure 31-4. Curves for bearing capacity.

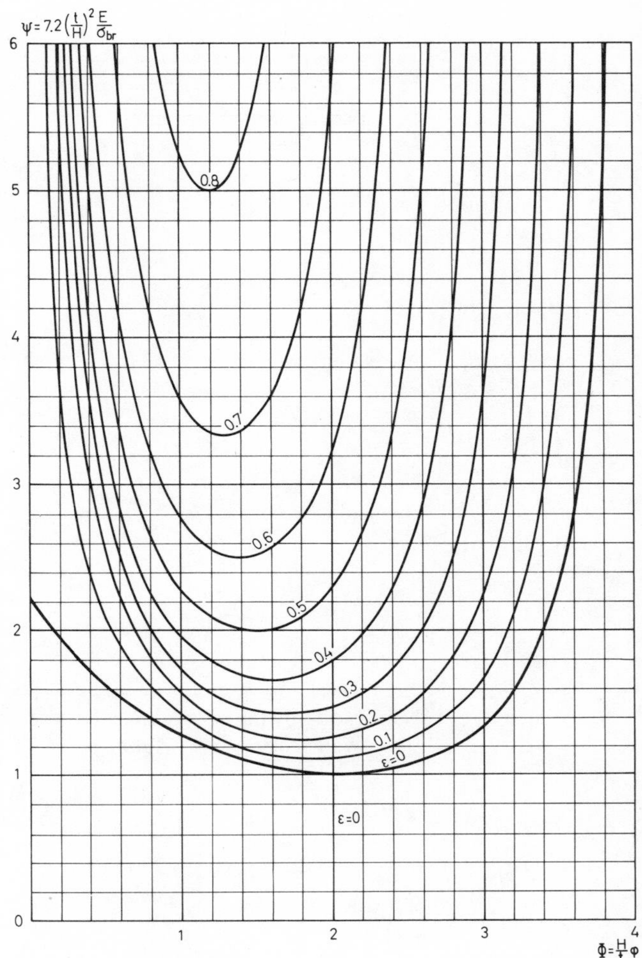

Figure 31-5. Curves for eccentricity of normal force at wall ends.

presented by a (Φ, Ψ) system of coordinates. Moreover, in this way all the characteristic properties of the wall are illustrated, so that for a given set of (Φ, Ψ) values the corresponding bearing capacity, eccentricity, crack condition, and mode of failure can be seen at a glance. In Figure 31-4 this presentation has been made, but for the sake of clarity the eccentricity has been shown in Figure 31-5.

Survey of Formulae

The Table 31-1 is a survey of the formulae for bearing capacity and eccentricity corresponding to the distribution of zones in Figure 31-4.

Example

A wall has the height H = 2.5 m and the thickness t = 12 cm. The material is linear elastic without tensile strength and with the modulus of elasticity E = 14.000 kg/cm^2. The compressive strength σ_{br} is 100 kg/cm^2. The wall is a structural member between two floors, and the angle of rotation at its ends is $\varphi = 0.067$ radian. The following are to be determined: bearing capacity, crack condition, mode of failure, eccentricity, and moment of eccentricity of the wall.

On the basis of the values given we find:

$$\Psi = 7.2 \left(\frac{t}{H}\right)^2 \frac{E}{\sigma_{br}} = 7.2 \left(\frac{12}{250}\right)^2 \frac{14000}{100} = 2.32$$

$$\Phi = \varphi \frac{H}{t} = 0.067 \frac{250}{12} = 1.40$$

$$P_{o.br} = 100 \cdot 12 \cdot 0.1 = 120 \text{ t/m}$$

In Figures 31-4 and 31-5 we mark the point (1.40, 2.32), and we can now read that $\nu = 0.23$ and $\epsilon = 0.57$. From this we can determine:

Table 31-1

Zone	Bearing Capacity	Eccentricity
I	$\nu = 1 - \frac{1}{3}\Phi\Psi$	$\epsilon = \frac{2}{3}\Phi\sqrt{\frac{3\Psi}{3-\Phi\Psi}} - \Phi$
II	$\nu = \frac{3}{4}\frac{1}{\Phi}\cdot\frac{1}{\Psi}$	$\epsilon = 2\sqrt{\Phi - \frac{1}{\Psi}} - \Phi$
III	$\nu = \frac{4}{9}\Psi$	$\epsilon = 0$
IV	$\nu = \frac{3}{64}\Phi\Psi(4-\Phi)^2$	$\epsilon = 0$

Mode of failure: Zones I and II: Stress failure. Zones III and IV: Buckling.
Wall section: Zones I and III: Uncracked. Zones II and IV: Cracked.

$$P_{br} = \nu \cdot P_{o.br} = 0.23 \cdot 120 = 27.6 \text{ t/m}$$

$$e = \tfrac{1}{2}t \cdot \epsilon = \tfrac{1}{2} \cdot 12 \cdot 0.57 = 3.42 \text{ cm}$$

$$M = P_{br} \cdot e = 27.6 \cdot 0.0342 = 0.94 \text{ tm/m}$$

Furthermore, it will be seen from Figure 31-4 that the wall is in zone II, i.e. that it is cracked, and that the mode of failure is stress failure.

Destruction Tests for Brick Walls

Preliminary model tests in the scale 1:4 were carried out at Danmarks Ingeniørakademi in the spring of 1967 to begin verifying the theoretical investigation described. They were applied to walls with no angle of rotation at base. Six frames were tested, the outer dimensions of which were height 70 cm and length 120 cm. The width of the walls was 33 cm and thickness 3 cm. The test arrangement is shown in Figure 31-6.

Because of the preliminary character of the tests, no further details will be furnished. However, preparations have been made for large scale tests based on the experience already gained from the preliminary tests.

Notation

b	Width of cross section
e	Eccentricity of compressive force
E	Modulus of elasticity
H	Height of wall
H_s	Length of equivalent column
J	Moment of inertia
k	Curvature of wall
P	Compressive force
P_{br}	Bearing capacity of wall
P_E	Euler critical load $\pi^2 \frac{EJ}{H^2}$
$P_{o.br}$	Ultimate load of wall section $bt\sigma_{br}$
s	Distance from end of wall to end of equivalent column see Figure 30-3.
t	Thickness of wall
u	Deflection of equivalent column

Figure 31-6. Test arrangement.

ϵ $\quad \dfrac{e}{\frac{1}{2}t}$

ν $\quad \dfrac{P_{br}}{P_{o.br}}$

σ Compressive stress

σ_{br} Compressive strength

φ Angle of rotation of wall sections at ends

Φ $\quad \dfrac{H}{t}\varphi$

Ψ $\quad \dfrac{432}{5\pi^2}\dfrac{P_E}{P_{o.br}} = 7.2\left(\dfrac{t}{H}\right)^2 \dfrac{E}{\sigma_{br}}$

ω Angle of rotation of wall sections at ends relative to compressive force line, see Figure 31-3

Ω $\quad \dfrac{H}{t}$

References

1. Kazinczy, G. v., "Die Bemessung unvollkommen eingespannter Stahl "I"–Deckenträger unter Berücksichtigung der plastischen Formänderungen," *IABS,* Zürick 1933-34.
2. Nylander, H., "Undersökning av bärkraften hos murade cementstensväggar," (Investigation of Load-Carrying Capacity of Cement Block Masonry Walls). *BETONG,* Häfte 3, Stockholm 1944.
3. Angervo, K., and Putkonen, A. I., "Erweiterung der Theorie der Biegung eines Pfeilers ohne Zugfestigkeit and ihre Anwendung zur Berechnung von Rahmentragwerken mit unbewehrten Stielen," Publikation 34, Staatliche Technische Forschungsanstalt, Helsinki, Finnland, 1957.
4. Sahlin, S., "Structural Interaction of Walls and Floor Slabs," Institutionen För Byggnadsstatik, KTH, Meddelanden nr. 33, Stockholm, 1959.
5. Angervo., K., "Über die Knickung und Tragfähigkeit eines exzentrisch gedruckten Pfeilers ohne Zugfestigkeit," Staatliche technische Forschungsanstalt, Publikation 26, Helsinki, Finnland, 1954.
6. Chapman, J. C., and Slatford, J., "The Elastic Buckling of Brittle Columns," Paper No. 6147, *Proc. Instn. Civ. Engrs.,* Vol. 6, January, 1957.
7. Poulsen, E. and Risager, S., "The Bearing Capacity of Linear Elastic Brittle Columns," Bygningsstatiske Meddelelser, Vol. 36, No. 3, Copenhagen, 1965.

32. Interaction of brick masonry walls and concrete slabs.

Sven Sahlin, Royal Institute of Technology, Stockholm, Sweden

Principle of Calculating the Load-Carrying Capacity of a Wall

In many buildings the load-carrying system consists of brick masonry walls and cast in situ (or prefabricated) concrete slabs. The joints will then be stiff enough to cause frame action so that the force resultant in the wall acts eccentrically. The eccentricity affects the wall's load-carrying capacity. A high eccentricity gives a low ultimate load.

A fundamental point in the theory of interaction of walls and slabs is the joint behaviour. The relationship between the moment and the angle of rotation of the joints must be established by tests. With the aid of full scale tests the author[2] has proposed an approximate relationship (see Figure 32-1).

Applying this relationship, and taking into account that the wall has practically no tensile strength and thus has a reduced stiffness at large eccentricities, the writer deduced a theory for calculating the load-carrying capacity of masonry walls [1,2].

The theory takes into account the frame-action of the joined slabs and floors and the reduction in stiffness of cracked parts of the wall as well as the eventual yielding in the joints. Equations for calculation of the end rotation of the wall, the slab, and the joint were established. The continuity at the joints requires that the angle of rotation of the wall end plus the rotation in the joint itself equals the end rotation of the slab:

$$\varphi_h = \varphi_v + \theta \tag{32-1}$$

This equation theoretically enables us to calculate the eccentricity e which is the only unknown variable in the angles given in Equation 31-1. After e has been calculated, by trial-and-error or by direct elimination, the edge stresses can be calculated. As the load increases, the stress finally reaches the strength of the material and the ultimate load is reached if the ultimate value of $\theta = \theta_B$ has not been reached before.

Influence of Openings in a Wall

In calculating an estimate of the load-bearing capacity of a wall, the stiffness of the wall has to be determined. If the wall has openings for windows, the effective stiffness is affected,

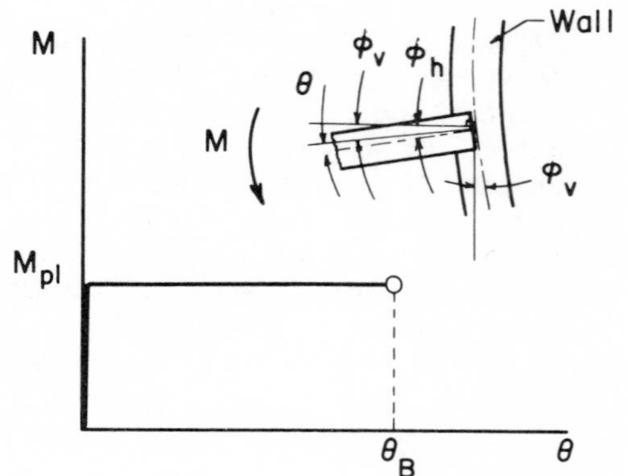

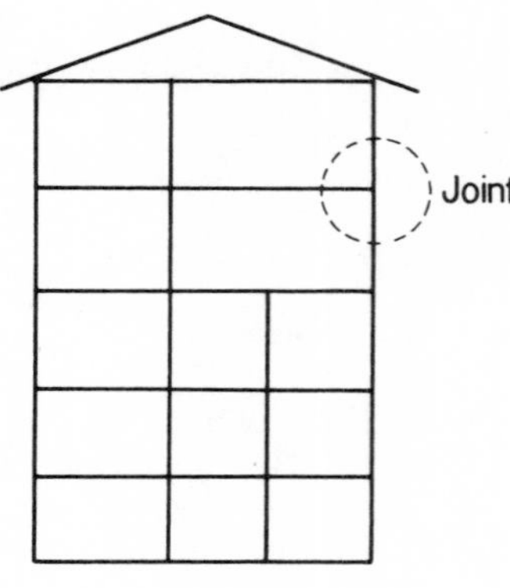

Figure 32-1. Joint type and idealized relationship between applied moment, M, and angle of rotation, Θ, in a joint.

and it is suggested that an average stiffness be chosen. In case of doubt, a higher figure should be taken because an overestimate of the wall stiffness results in a higher calculated figure for the eccentricity and thus gives a result on the safe side.

Influence of Cross Walls

If there is a wall crossing or ending at the actual wall, it strengthens the wall considerably if there is a risk of buckling, and the beneficial effect can be estimated according to equations deduced for thin-walled box beams or stiffened metal sheets. See Figure 32-2

Restraining Effect from Concrete Slab

Tests by the author[1] have shown that the slab considerably delays the cracking of the upper end of the wall where the eccentricity is large and the wall is subject to failure. The cracking zone is forced downward from the slab, and the wall fails in a zone two or three bricks below the slab, Figure 32-3. This effect can be taken into account by reducing the effective maximum eccentricity of the load to the value it has two or three bricks below the slab.

Tests on Masonry Walls with Built-In Slab End

In preparing the new Swedish building codes, BABS, of which rules for masonry walls are a part, tests of joints between masonry walls and concrete slabs have been carried out.

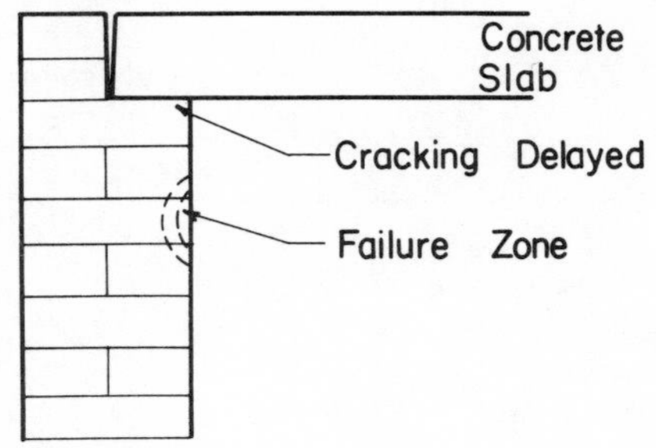

Figure 32-3. Restraining effect from concrete slab on the cracking behavior and the failure of a wall.

This was done to establish moment-angle of rotation relationship for some types of joints which were not tested previously. The tests were initiated and planned by the committee, established by the National Board for Building and Planning, to devise codes for masonry walls. The author is a member of this committee. The testing was financed by the Brick Manufacturer and the Light Weight Concrete Manufacturer in Sweden. The tests and their results are described in this section.

To study joints of the types shown in Figure 32-1 tests of the types shown in Figure 32-4 were carried out. In addition, control tests on plain bricks and blocks, mortar, and centrally loaded columns were carried out. The chosen height of the test specimens was as small as possible without interferring too much (compared with actual conditions) with the stress field around the slab end. The main dimensions as well as the

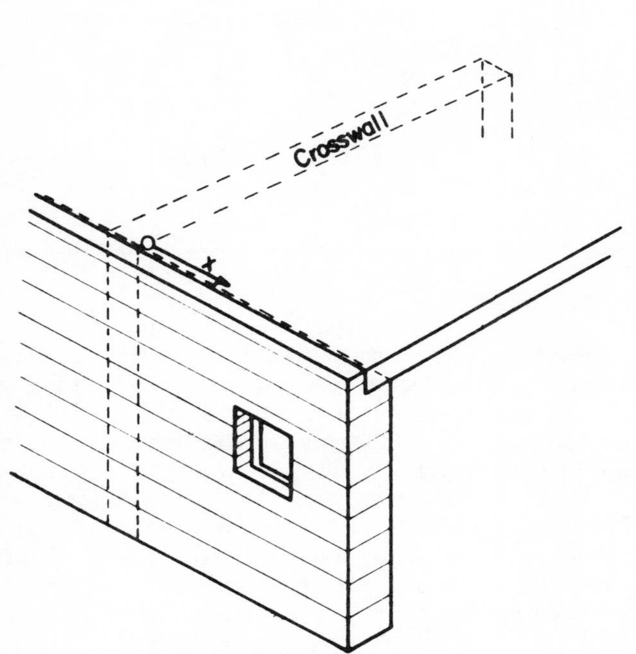

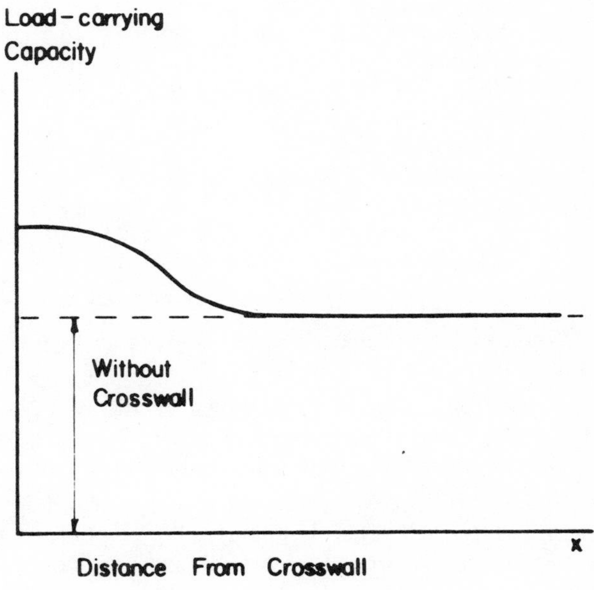

Figure 32-2. Restraining effect from crosswalls on the buckling load of a wall.

Table 32-1
Dimensions and Types of Test Specimens (Metric)

	Ta	Ta II	Tb	Tc	Td	La	La II	Lb	Lc	Pa	Ba
Type	B	B	C	A	A	A	A	A	A	A	C
a cm	147	147	78	146	147	175	176	138	136	178	91
b cm	16	16	16	16	16	16	16	16	15	16	16
c cm	12	12	12	12	6	15	15	15	15	15	15
d cm	12.5	12.5	12.5	25	25	25	25	25	25	25	20
Length of wall cm	52.5	52	51.5	52	52.5	50	50	50	50	50	60
Type of joint 1)	M	M	V	M	M	M	M	M	M	M	V
Mortar 2)	C	C	C	B	C	C	C	Br	Br	C	B
Material in Blocks or Bricks 3)	B1.6/300	B1.6/300	B1.6/300	B1.6/300	B1.6/300 W	L0.5/30	L0.5/30	L0.5/30	L0.5/30	Pa65/30	BH

Table 32-1a
Dimensions and Types of Test Specimens (U.S. Customary Units)

	Ta	Ta II	Tb	Tc	Td	La	La II	Lb	Lc	Pa	Ba
Type	B	B	C	A	A	A	A	A	A	A	C
a inches	58	58	31	57.5	58	57	57.5	54.2	53.5	70	36
b inches	6.3	6.3	6.3	6.3	6.3	6.3	6.3	6.3	5.9	6.3	6.3
c inches	4.7	4.7	4.7	4.7	2.36	5.9	5.9	5.9	5.9	5.9	5.9
d inches	5	5	5	10	10	10	10	10	10	10	8
Length of wall inches	20.7	20.5	20.3	20.5	20.7	19.7	19.7	19.7	19.7	19.7	23.6
Type of Joint 1)	M	M	V	M	M	M	M	M	M	M	V
Mortar 2)	C	C	C	B	C	C	C	Br	Br	C	B
Material in Blocks or Bricks 3)	B 100/4250	B 100/4250	B 100/4250	B 100/4250 W	B 100/4250	L 31/425	L 31/425	L 31/425	L 31/425	Pa 40/425	GH

characterisitics for the materials are indicated in Figure 32-4 and the accompaning Table 32-1.

The loads were applied as is shown in Figure 32-5 and Table 32-2. Thus, the tests were made on a statically determinate system contrary to many real building systems.

However, the behavior of the test specimen was judged to simulate reality well. This is supported by comparison with statically indeterminate tests carried out earlier by the author[1].

The test setup simulating the uppermost slab was statically indeterminate and is principally shown in Figure 32-6. The force-distribution was measured with the help of strain-gauges applied on the steel-beam which simulated the slab.

Test Results

The relationship between the moment and the angle of rotation in the joints was measured and is shown in Figures 32-7–32-9. The test results are shown in Figure 32-7 for 12 cm walls, in Figure 32-8 for topmost slab type joints, and in Figure 32-9 for the rest of the slabs not reaching through the walls.

As can be seen from Figure 32-7 the plastification action (or angle of joint rotation) starts very early and does not extend very far. This resulted partly because it became impossible to measure the true angle of rotation since the device for reading the angle was extended only to the adjacent bricks above and below the slab, and the main deformation took place between the first and second brick under the slab end.

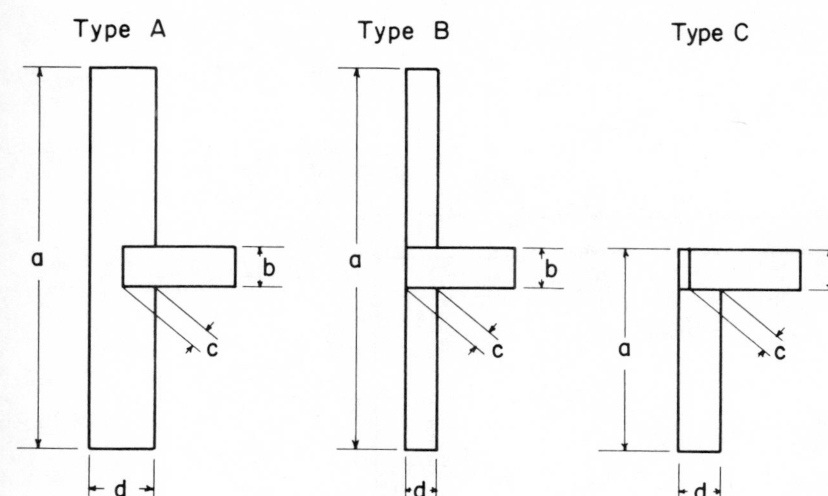

Figure 32-4. Types of tested joints (see Table 32-1).

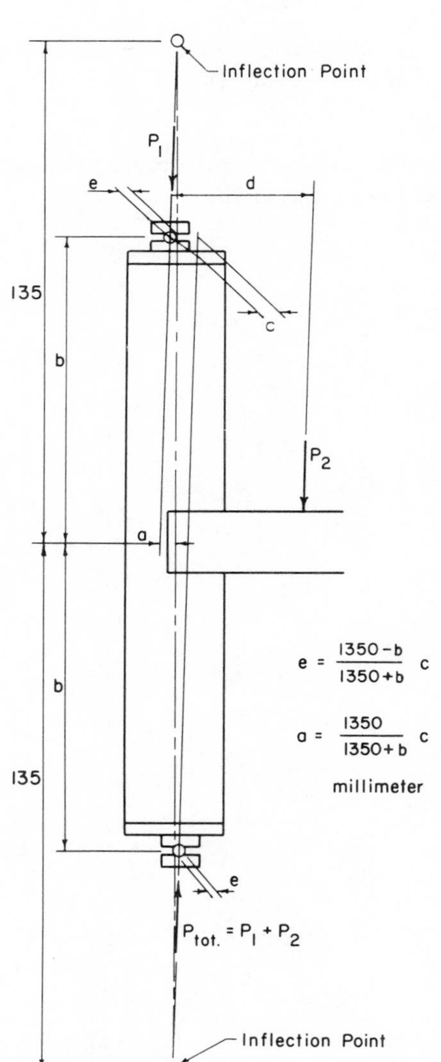

Figure 32-5. Principles of applying loads on the test specimens.

Table 32-2
Locations of Points of Application of Forces in Test Set Up

	a cm	b cm	c cm	d cm	e cm	P_1/P_2
Ta I	4.0	88	6.6	20	1.4	2
Ta II	4.0	88	6.6	20	1.4	2
Tc	4.3	85	7.0	35	1.6	4
Td	4.3	87	7.0	35	1.5	4
La I	4.0	100	7.0	35	1.0	4
La II	4.0	100	7.0	35	1.0	4
Lb	4.3	84	7.0	35	1.6	4
Lc	4.3	82	7.0	35	1.6	4
Pa	4.0	100	7.0	35	1.0	4

The attic type joint showed more measured plastic deformation (note Figure 32-8) and better similarity with the proposed approximate moment-rotation relationship (see Figure 32-1). The test results in Figure 32-9 show that most of the joints were relatively stiff until the maximum moment (point 1) was reached. After this point, the deformations rapidly increased with constant or slightly decreasing moment. Point 2 on the curves denotes the maximum angle of rotation, read, at most instances, at the load-step before failure.

This measured maximum angle of rotation has been considered as the maximum plastic rotation of the joint at that specific load. In other words, for the load at point 2 the joint cannot withstand larger rotation without failure.

The load at point 2 has been divided by the load which a similar column would carry if centrally loaded. The ratio is denoted κ (kappa). The load-carrying capacity for a centrally loaded wall has been taken from the tests shown in Table 32-3.

The calculated values κ has been plotted against the measured maximum angle of rotation θ in Figures 32-10 to 32-12. It is clearly seen from Figure 32-10 that a higher load is detrimental to the rotation capacity of the joint. This effect is also expected since $\kappa = 1$ means that the load is equal to the failure load for a centrally loaded column. Then the slightest

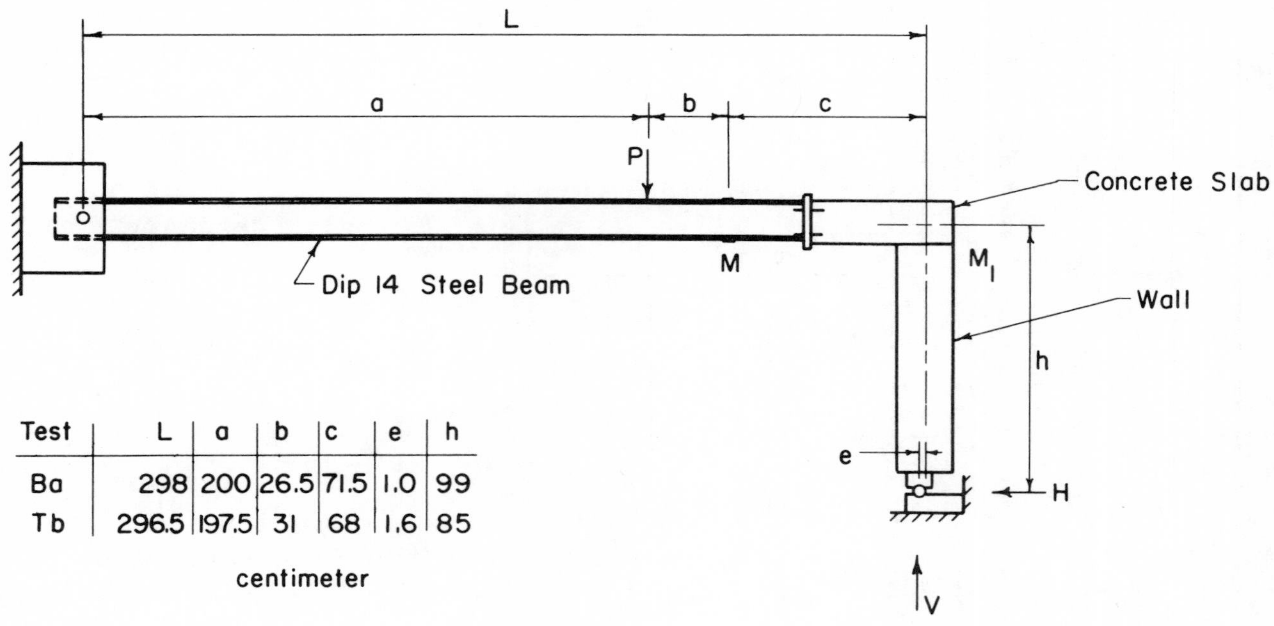

Test	L	a	b	c	e	h
Ba	298	200	26.5	71.5	1.0	99
Tb	296.5	197.5	31	68	1.6	85

Figure 32-6. Test set up for testing Type C joints. (See Figure 32-4.) M marks location of strain-gages for measuring of moment distribution in the test specimen. M_1 marks the location of section where maximum moment in the wall occurs.

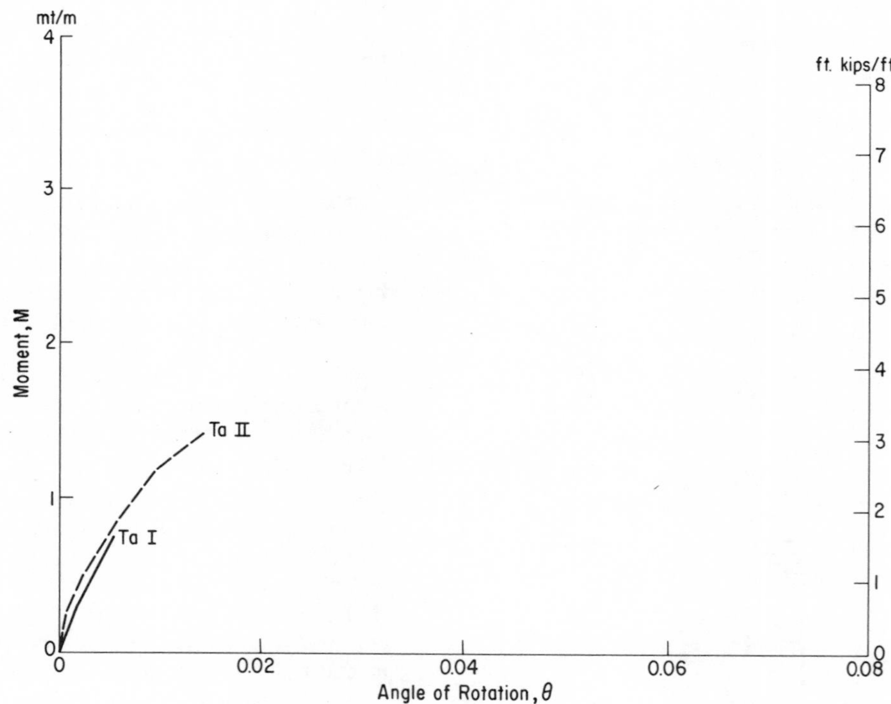

Figure 32-7. Relationship between applied moment and angle of rotation of joints of Type B. (See Figure 32-4.)

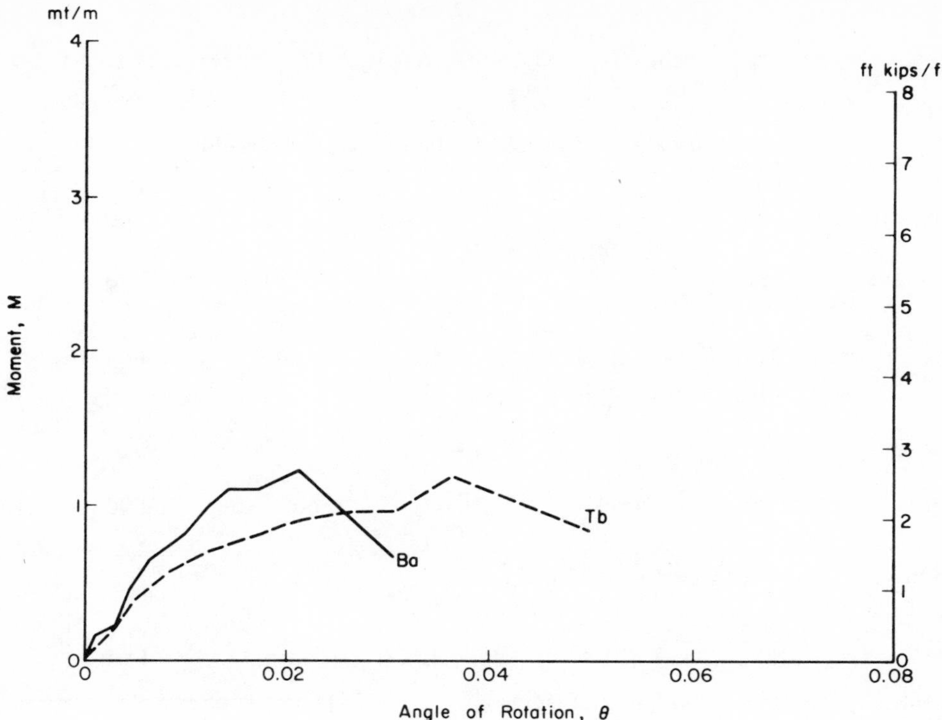

Figure 32-8. Relationship between applied moment and angle of rotation of joints of Type C. (See Figure 32-4.)

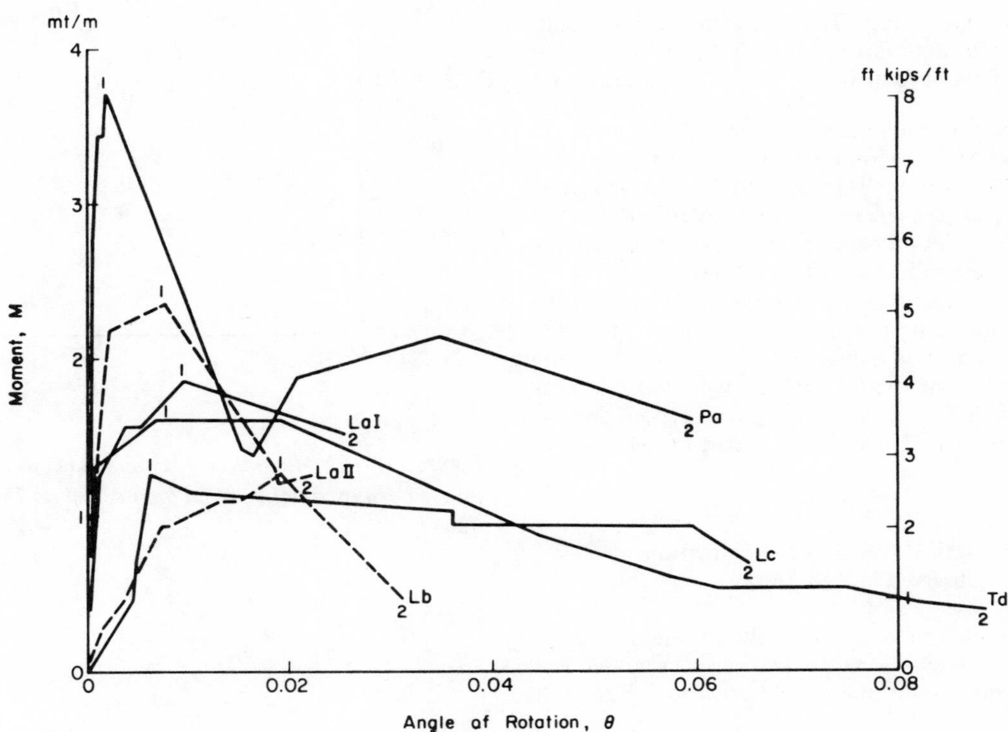

Figure 32-9. Relationship between applied moment and angle of rotation of joints of Type A. (See Figure 32-4.)

Table 32-3
Dimensions and Test Results for Centrally Loaded Columns

	T I	T II	L I	L II	P I	B I
Height approx. cm	100	100	100	100	100	100
Thickness cm	12	25	25	25	25	20
Length approx. cm	50	50	50	50	50	50
Mortar	C	B	C	Br	C	B
Material in Blocks and Bricks	$\frac{B1.6}{300}$	$\frac{B1.6}{300}$ W	$\frac{L0.5}{30}$	$\frac{L0.5}{30}$	$\frac{P0.65}{30}$	BH
Strength kg/cm^2	75	118	22.5	21.5	30	47.5
Modulus of elasticity approx. kg/cm^2	25000	70000	10000	6000	25000	150000

1 cm = 0.394 in. 1 kg/cm^2 = 14.22 lb/sq in.
Compare also Table 32-1

rotation causes an eccentricity which causes failure. In Figures 32-11 and 32-12 the same effect cannot be seen because the number of tests are to small. For the tests in Figure 32-11, the main rotation took place below the device which measured the rotation. Figure 32-10 has the test results with slab end not reaching through the wall, Figure 32-11 with slab ends reaching through the wall, and Figure 32-12 with specimens simulating the attic type joint. The above mentioned results have been condensed and represented in Table 32-4 with the main dimensions of the specimens and the main test results for easier reference.

The main use of the results is to give an estimate of M_{p1}: the moment up to which the joint mainly acts elastically, or as a rigid connection between the wall and the slab. Furthermore, if the moment M_{p1} is reached and the joint therefore starts to yield the maximum rotation capacity of the joint, θ_B can be estimated with the data provided in Table 32-4.

In addition to the results found in Table 32-4, some results from earlier full-scale frame tests by the author are quoted in Table 32-5. These results were obtained from tests on symmetric H-shaped frames with 2 or 4 m single span, with the type of joint shown in Figure 32-4 and marked type A. Mortar of type KC 2:1:15 means 2 parts lime, 1 part cement and 15 parts sand by weight.

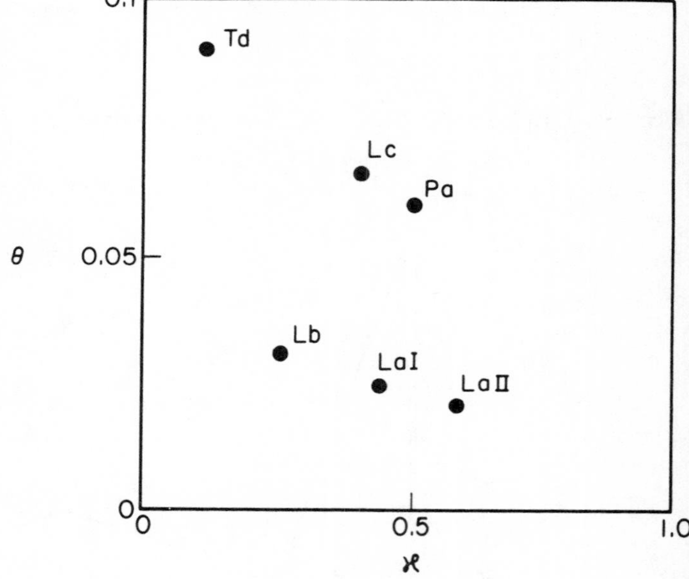

Figure 32-10. Maximum plastic rotation capacity of joints plotted against relative axial load κ. Joints Type A. (See Figure 32-4.)

Some Theoretical Aspects of Deformations Observed in Wall Tests

Two assumed forms of deflected walls in Figure 32-13a and b were studied. The following equations can be deduced by studying the equilibrium and the deformations of the wall parts in Figures 32-13a.

$$P_1 (e + y) - k_1\theta_1 = 0 \qquad (32\text{-}2)$$

$$\frac{\theta_1}{2} = \frac{y}{k/2} \qquad (32\text{-}3)$$

i.e.

$$y_1 = \frac{P_1 e}{\frac{4k_1}{h} - P_1} \qquad (32\text{-}4)$$

The following equations are obtained from Figures 32-13b.

$$P_2 (e + y) - k_2\theta_2 = 0 \qquad (32\text{-}5)$$

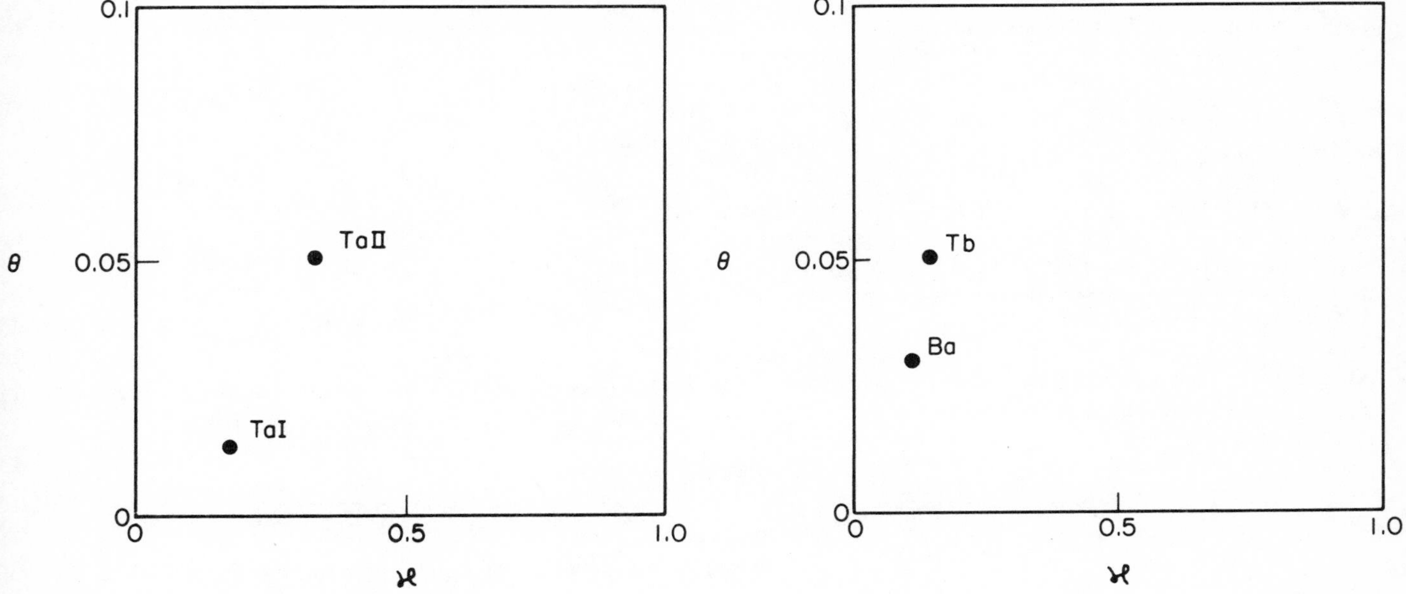

Figure 32-11. Maximum plastic rotation capacity of joints plotted against relative axial load κ. Joints Type B. (See Figure 32-4.)

Figure 32-12. Maximum plastic rotation capacity of joints plotted against relative axial load κ. Joints of Type C. (See Figure 32-4.)

Table 32-4
Summary of Test Results

1	2	3	4	5	6	7	8	9	10	11	12	13	14
Type (See Figure 32-4)	Speci-men	Thick-ness d cm	Built in length c cm	Ultimate Strength central load kp/cm²	Max obs stress σ max kp/cm²	Stress at failure σ_B kp/cm²	Max abs moment M^{max} t	Moment at max θ_B t	Max Relative load κ_{max}	Ult. rel. load κ_B	Ult. angle of rotation θ_B	Ult. load for centrally loaded column p_c t/m	Plastification Moment divided by p_c $\frac{M_{Dl}}{p_c}$
A	Pa	25	15	30.0	24.0	15.2	3.6	1.62	0.80	0.51	0.06	75	2.17
A	Lc	25	15	21.5	9.1	9.1	1.25	0.68	0.42	0.42	0.066	54	1.26
A	Lb	25	15	21.5	9.0	5.6	1.25	0.45	0.42	0.26	0.031	54	0.84
A	La I	25	15	22.5	12.0	10.0	1.8	1.52	0.53	0.45	0.025	56	2.7
A	La II	25	15	22.5	14.2	13.6	2.3	1.25	0.63	0.60	0.021	56	2.22
A	Td	25	6	75	9.6	9.1	1.60	0.38	0.13	0.12	0.09	190	0.2
A	Tc	25	12	118	43.8		7.08		0.37			295	
B	Ta I	12	12	75	11.4	13.7	0.75		0.152	0.182	0.0136	90	
B	Ta II	12	12	75	20.7	25.3	1.38		0.275	0.34	0.052	90	
C	Ba	20	15	47.5	5.1	5.6	1	0.55	0.108	0.118	0.03	95	0.58
C	Tb	12	12	75	11.0	11.0	0.9	0.72	0.147	0.147	0.05	90	0.80

P_c = The ultimate load for a centrally loaded column, as calculated from the ultimate stress (strength) found in control tests multiplied by the area of the actual column.

κ = The actual ultimate load divided by P_c.

1 t/m = 690 lb/ft

Table 32-5
Summary of Test Results from Earlier Test

Type of Joint	Type of Mortar	M_{p1} Average Mpm/m	M_{p1} Standard Deviation Mpm/m	$\frac{M_{p1}}{P_c}$ cm	Number of Observations
A	KC 2:1:15	2.5	1.1	1.1	4
B	K 1:5	2.1	0.6	2.1	8
B	KC 2:1:15	4.7	1.4	2.7	6

1 Mpm/m = 2.205 ft kips/ft
1 cm = 0.394 in.
KC 2:1:15 = 2 parts lime, 1 part cement, 15 parts sand.
K 1:5 = 1 part lime, 5 parts sand.

$$\theta_2 = \frac{y}{h/3} \tag{32-6}$$

$$y_2 = \frac{P_2 e}{\frac{3k_2}{h} - P_2} \tag{32-7}$$

If one finds in a test that the failure load is P_B and the deflection at this load is y_B, then the moment is:

$$M_B = P_B (e + y_B) \tag{32-8}$$

and the stress distribution must be such as to balance P_B and M_B. From these facts the following equations can be established.

$$y_1 = \frac{P_1 e}{\frac{4k_1}{h} - P_1} = y_2 = \frac{P_2 e}{\frac{3k_2}{h} - P_2} \tag{32-9}$$

and:

$$P_1 = P_2 = P_B \tag{32-10}$$

Hence

$$3k_2 = 4k_1 \tag{32-11}$$

Suppose the wall is a part of the (building) frame as shown in Figure 32-14. The end rotation of the slab:

$$\varphi_h = \frac{2Pl^2}{16EI} - \frac{Pel}{2EI} \tag{32-12}$$

An equation of equilibrium for the upper half of the walls gives

$$P(e + y) - 2\varphi_v k_1 = 0 \tag{32-13}$$

The deflection y can be expressed as

$$y = \frac{h}{2} \varphi_v \tag{32-14}$$

Inserting Equation 32-14 in Equation 32-13 and making the end rotations equal results in the following equation.

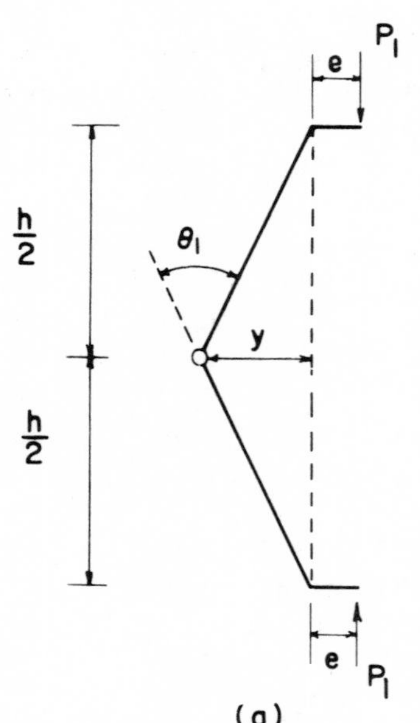

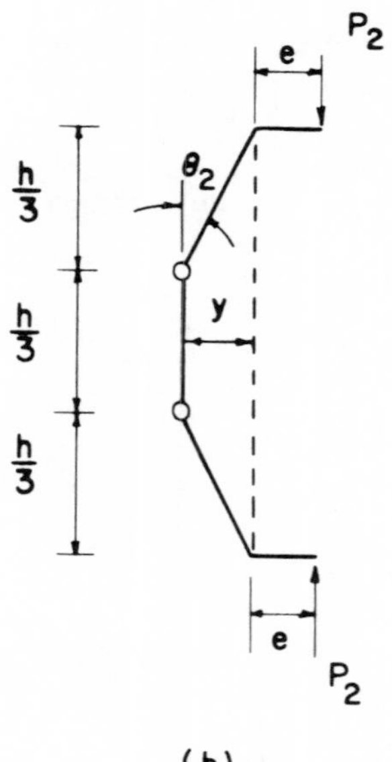

Figure 32-13. Two extreme cases of configuration of the deflection curve of a wall, a) with the deformations concentrated at midheight and b) with no curvature at midheight.

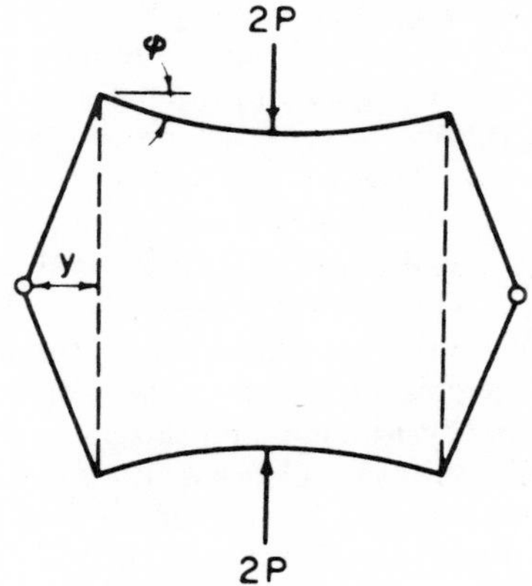

Figure 32-14. Frame consisting of two walls of the type shown in Figure 32-13a and two slabs.

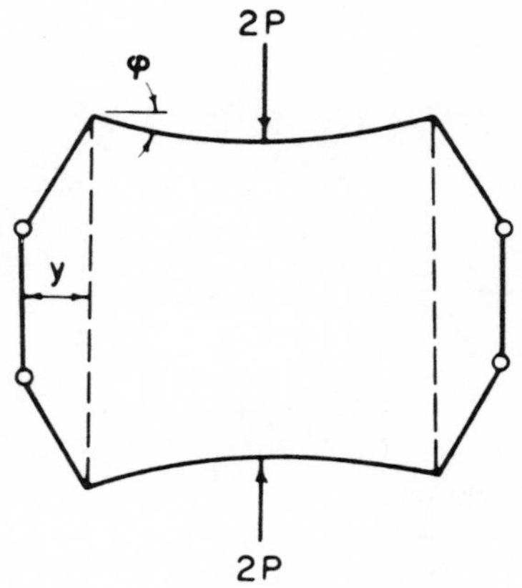

Figure 32-15. Frame consisting of two walls of the type shown in Figure 32-13b and two slabs.

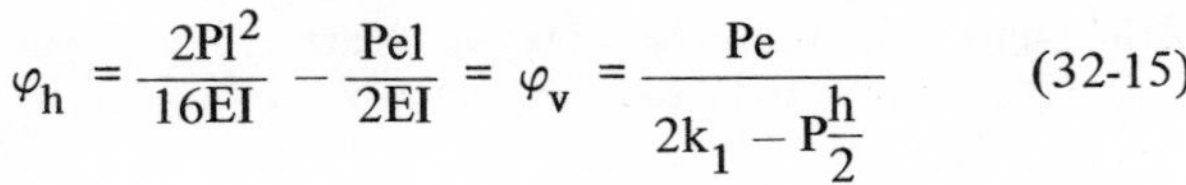

$$\varphi_h = \frac{2Pl^2}{16EI} - \frac{Pel}{2EI} = \varphi_v = \frac{Pe}{2k_1 - P\frac{h}{2}} \quad (32\text{-}15)$$

By calculating e from the Equation 32-15 and taking into consideration that:

$$y = \varphi_v \frac{h}{2} \quad (32\text{-}16)$$

The maximum eccentricity in the wall:

$$e_{ml} = e + y \quad (32\text{-}17)$$

is obtained.

After some derivations the following expression for the maximum eccentricity in the wall is obtained:

$$\frac{e_{ml}}{l} = \frac{1}{4 + \frac{4EI}{k_1 l} - \frac{Ph}{k_1}} \quad (32\text{-}18)$$

From Equation 32-4 it is seen that the buckling load for a pin-ended wall of this model type is:

$$P_{El} = \frac{4k_1}{h} \quad (32\text{-}19)$$

Equation 32-18 can then be rewritten:

$$\frac{e_{ml}}{l} = \frac{1}{4\left(1 + \frac{4EI}{lhP_{El}} - \frac{P}{P_{El}}\right)} \quad (32\text{-}20)$$

For an actual wall:

$$P_E = \frac{\pi^2 E_v I_v}{h^2} \quad (32\text{-}21)$$

and the quotient:

$$\frac{4EI}{lhP_{El}} = \frac{4EIh^2}{lh\pi^2 E_v I_v} \quad (32\text{-}22)$$

For simplicity, this ratio is set to 1 which is within practical limits.

Hence:

$$\frac{e_{ml}}{l} = \frac{1}{4\left(1 + 1 - \frac{P}{P_E}\right)} = \frac{1}{4\left(2 - \frac{P}{P_E}\right)} \quad (32\text{-}23)$$

The three-part wall is now studied. The end rotation of the end of the slab can be taken from Equation 32-12. The equilibrium of the upper third of the wall requires:

$$P(e + y) - \varphi_v k_2 = 0 \quad (32\text{-}24)$$

the deflection is:

$$y = \frac{h}{3} \varphi_v \quad (32\text{-}25)$$

Inserting and making the rotations equal:

$$\varphi_h = \varphi_v \quad (32\text{-}26)$$

gives:

$$\varphi_h = \frac{2Pl^2}{16EI} - \frac{Pel}{2EI} = \varphi_v = \frac{Pe}{k_2 - \frac{Ph}{3}} \quad (32\text{-}27)$$

Furthermore:

$$y = \varphi_v \frac{h}{3} \quad (32\text{-}28)$$

After some derivations:

$$\frac{e_{m2}}{l} = \frac{1}{4 + \frac{8EI}{k_2 l} - \frac{4}{3}\frac{Ph}{k_2}} \quad (32\text{-}29)$$

is obtained. With the help of Equation 32-7 a relationship between the eccentricity e_{m2} and the relative load P/P_{E2} is obtained:

$$\frac{e_{m2}}{l} = \frac{1}{4\left(1 + \frac{6EI}{lhP_{E2}} - \frac{P}{P_{E2}}\right)} \quad (32\text{-}30)$$

let:

$$P_{E2} = P_E = \frac{\pi^2 E_v I_v}{h^2} \quad (32\text{-}31)$$

and thus:

$$\frac{e_{m2}}{l} = \frac{1}{4\left(1 + \frac{6EIh^2}{lh\pi^2 E_v I_v} - \frac{P}{P_E}\right)} \quad (32\text{-}32)$$

and if as above:

$$\frac{4EIh^2}{lh\pi^2 E_v I_v} = 1$$

the following equation is obtained:

$$\frac{e_{m2}}{l} = \frac{1}{4\left(1 + 1.5 - \frac{P}{P_E}\right)} = \frac{1}{4\left(2.5 - \frac{P}{P_E}\right)} \quad (32\text{-}33)$$

From Equations 32-23 and 32-33 the relative eccentricities have been calculated and represented in Figure 32-16. Clearly, the shape of the deflected column greatly influences the eccentricity at the midheight of the wall.

The above examples show the importance of observing the angle of rotation of the wall ends. The author believes that more attention should be paid to this deformation than to the mid-height deflections usually determined and reported in tests on masonry walls. Of course when the joints are plastified the differences in end rotations are less significant

With reliable detailed expressions for the rotation of the wall end and the joints, the Equation 32-1 can be used for calculating the eccentricity of the resultant force in all sections of the wall, thereby providing means for calculating the load-carrying capacity with good precision.

The principal results of such calculations are already known from the theory outlined by the author[1]. In Figure 32-17 results of this theory are shown; n is the number of the wall numbered from the uppermost story down; κ is the relative strength of the wall i.e. the load-carrying capacity of the wall at the actual eccentricity divided by the strength of a similar centrally loaded wall.

Acknowledgement

The tests reported herein were supported by the Swedish Brick and Tile Manufacturers Association, The Light Weight Cellular Concrete Inc., and the Swedish Leca Inc.

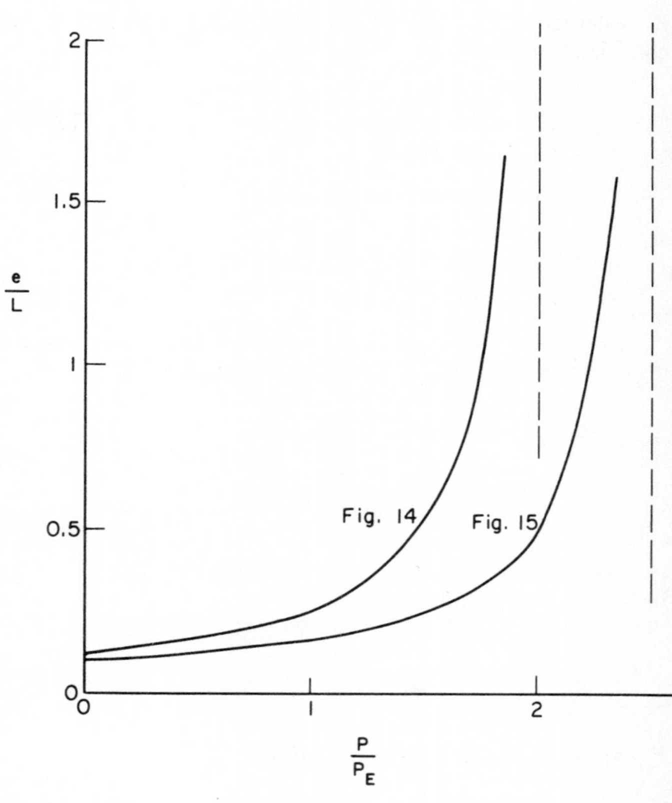

Figure 32-16. Calculated eccentricities at midheight of the walls shown in Figures 32-14 and 32-15 as function of the relative load P/P_E.

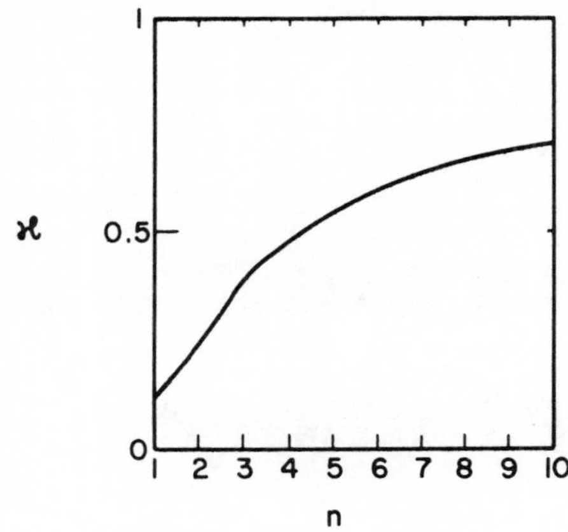

Figure 32-17. The relative load-carrying capacity, κ, of a wall as function of the location, n, of the wall. n = 1 refers to wall No. 1 which is the wall in the uppermost story of a building. n = 2 refers to the second wall from above, etc.

The test program was outlined by the committee, established by the National Board for Building and Planning, to devise codes for masonry walls. The author is a member of this committee.

The tests were carried out by the National Institute for Materials Testing in the Laboratories of the Civil Engineering Department, Royal Inst. Techn., Stockholm.

The manuscript was prepared at the Civil Engineering Department of the University of Illinois.

Notations

φ_h Angle of rotation of end of horizontal member
φ_v Angle of rotation of end of vertical member
θ Angle of rotation of joint.
κ The actual ultimate load divided by P_c
P_c The ultimate load for a centrally loaded column as calculated from the ultimate stress (strength) found in control tests multiplied by the area of the actual column
P Force on wall or slab
e Eccentricity of force
y Deflection of wall
k Spring constant
h Height of wall
E Modulus of elasticity
I Moment of inertia for cross section
l Span length

Subscripts

1 Member 1
2 Member 2
B Failure
m Maximum
v Vertical
h Horizontal
E Euler

References

1. Sahlin, S., "Structural Interaction of Walls and Floor Slabs", Bulletin No. 33, the Division of Building Statics and Structural Engineering, Roy. Inst. of Technology, Stockholm, 1959 (Also Report No. 35 from the National Swedish Council for Building Research Stockholm 1959.).
2. Sahlin, S., "Design Methods for Walls with Special Reference to the Load-Carrying Capacity" National Swedish Council for Building Research, Stockholm, 1966.

33. Interaction of brickwork walls and concrete floors under lateral load.

A. J. M. Soane, Bingham Blades and Partners, Consulting Structural Engineers, Liverpool, England

Introduction

This chapter attempts to describe how frameless blocks of apartments or hostels built with brickwork walls and concrete floors may be analysed under action of static lateral loading. For buildings with normal aspect ratios wind forces become significant if there are more than about ten storeys. Since the walls form stiff elements while the slabs are relatively flexible, it has been frequently assumed that each wall, or wall unit combined from several walls, acts as a full height cantilever carrying wind moment in proportion to its moment of inertia. The floors thus act as pin-ended struts carrying compressive forces only.

Hence:

$$\frac{M_{jo}}{M_o} = \frac{I_j}{I_j} \qquad (33\text{-}1)$$

where:

M_{jo} Cantilever moment on Wall J
M_o External bending monent
I_j Moment of inertia of wall J

Model tests have shown that this belief is very conservative[1] and that such systems act compositely. The end fixity of the floors, which are sandwiched between heavily loaded walls, is sufficient to reduce the cantilever moments in the walls since shear forces, carried in the slabs, are applied as axial forces to the wall units and thereby create couples in connected walls to assist in resisting lateral loads. Wall stresses and deflections are therefore smaller than the values calculated from pure cantilever action. This type of behaviour is a feature of conventional interconnected shear walls.

Such structural walls have been used extensively in recent years to provide lateral stiffness in tall buildings. The walls are normally constructed from reinforced concrete and, although their primary purpose is to stiffen a frame they function most economically when they also carry approximately 25 percent of the total vertical load. This percentage is sufficient to minimise the need for tensile reinforcement while a greater percentage might necessitate the use of compressive reinforcement. In theory, the most efficient shear wall is as wide as the building containing it, providing that the wall is restrained sufficiently by floors to prevent buckling. But, in general, several openings are required so that the system consists of shear walls, or wall assemblies, which are connected by beams or slabs at each storey level.

Load-bearing brick apartment blocks are composed of a particular type of shear wall and slab structure in which the walls perform several simultaneous functions, namely:

1. The walls carry all vertical loads.
2. The walls provide environmental insulation.
3. The walls carry all lateral loads.

Since the walls carry all vertical loads rather than the 25 percent recommended for concrete structures, the design criterion for unreinforced brickwork is that precompression from dead load only must exceed any tension in the brickwork due to lateral loading. Similarly, the total compression from dead loads, the worst condition from superimposed loads, and lateral load, shall not exceed the permitted compressive stress in the brickwork. The British Code of Practice (C.P. 111:1964) allows compressive stress increases of up to 25 percent provided that such increases are due solely to wind load.

The layout of walls is largely dictated by architectural requirements so the task of the designer is normally to ascertain whether the above criteria are maintained, and if not, to modify wall thicknesses and/or brickwork strengths while retaining the basic plan.

Complex wall units interconnected by floor slabs cannot be analysed directly by any existing techniques. However, there are several methods for investigating simpler shear wall problems, and it will be of interest to consider these before discussing how to deal with brickwork structures.

Current Techniques of Shear Wall Analysis

Most published works on shear walls describe plane walls of uniform section joined by beams at each floor level. The analysis of such a coupled wall system can be simplified if each row of discrete beams is replaced by a continuous elastic medium. With this substitution, the redundants can be expressed in terms of "shear connection" equations whose solution depends on finding unknown boundary conditions. Methods of solution for two or three wall systems have been presented by Beck[2], Eriksson[3], Rosman[4] and others. The simplest examples, with two symmetrical walls, can readily be analysed with the aid of a series of graphs for stress and deflection parameters which have recently been published by Coull and Choudhury[5]. If there are more than three walls, hand calculations becomes very tedious, but digital programs for the continuous medium process are available. The bibliography of the Symposium on Tall Buildings[6] may be consulted for references. Electronic analog computers have also been used[7], and they prove very satisfactory for multi-wall structures.

A second method of approach is to consider the conditions at each wall-beam joint and set up either a stiffness or a flexibility matrix. These are always solved on a digital computer and, again, Reference 6 gives further details of what may be termed "wide frame" techniques.

Thirdly, it is possible to use finite elements. Although these can give results of any required accuracy, a very fine mesh is required to produce results which compare favorably with those given by either the shear connection or wide frame methods. Finite element techniques, therefore, have the disadvantage that large capacity computers are required.

When dealing with brickwork structures, several approximations have to be made so that a high degree of analytical sophistication is not necessary. It will, therefore, be assumed that an existing shear wall program will be used, and the next sections will describe how to modify the geometric properties of slab and wall assemblies when preparing input data.

Effective Width of Flanges

The walls in a load-bearing brick structure are frequently combined to form wall units. Each unit consists of two or more walls orientated at right angles as webs and flanges. Whether a wall acts as a web or a flange depends on the direction of loading under consideration, but the shapes of these units may not have the proportions usually associated with beam sections. In particular, the flanges may be very wide when compared with the length of the web. For vertical loading, there is usually no restriction as to flange length, and, indeed, the longer a flange the greater its effectiveness when acting as a web in its own plane.

For loading at right angles to this plane, there is an effective length, which may be less than the actual length. This must be used in calculating the area and inertia of the unit as a vertical beam. Stress function solutions are available for wide flange T-beams on continuous simple supports to show how bending stresses decline along the flanges. Using these functions, Timoshenko[8] has derived a formula for effective flange widths as shown in Table 33-1. Slightly different formulae are given in The British Code of Practice on reinforced concrete (C.P. 114:1958) for T- and L-beams in terms of their spans and web and flange thickness. The concrete beam sections considered do, however, have much greater slenderness ratios than those of typical brick wall units, so these values are probably conservative. This was the case for a Perspex model of one of the University of Essex tower blocks 1, so somewhat larger effective widths have been suggested in the table below.

If the storey height is a typical 8′4″ and the wall thicknesses range from 4″ to 9″, then method 3 gives the largest effective widths for the upper storeys and method 5 gives the largest for the lower storeys.

Effective Width of Slabs

Conventional methods of shear wall analysis have been derived for application to two dimensional cases in which the walls are coupled by beams of the same wall width. Brickwork wall units, however, are normally connected by concrete floor slabs. These are of two basic types; firstly, in situ floors

Table 33-1*
Effective Flange Widths

Source	T-beam	L-beam
1. Timoshenko	$0.363d \quad t_w$	
2. C.P. 114	$0.33d + t_w$	$0.17d + t_w$
3. C.P. 114	$12t_f + t_w$	$4t_f + t_w$
4. Values suggested	$14t_f + t_w$	$7t_f + t_w$
5. S.C.P.I.	$12t_f + 0.16nd$	$6t_f + 0.062nd$

*d Storey height
t_w Web thickness
t_f Flange thickness
n Number of storeys above the section in question

spanning in two directions as flat plates and, secondly, precast unit floors spanning in one direction only. The first type may be subdivided into floors cast onto temporary shuttering and composite floors cast on thin precast slabs which act as permanent shuttering. If the floors are of precast unit beams, with or without filler blocks, these must bear on lintels over any openings perpendicular to the direction of the span. Thus, the lintels act as the only connections capable of taking shear due to lateral loads and less interaction will occur than with a flat plate in situ floor.

The width of the slabs will be greater than the width of the wall units, but only part of the slab will act as an equivalent connecting beam. The problem was considered by Khan and Sbarounis[9] in the analysis of column and slab structures. They divided a typical element of slab into a grid of intersecting beams and, with assumed boundary conditions, the system was investigated for an applied column moment at the centre. The effects of bending and torsional stiffnesses of the beams were included, and effective slab widths were calculated for a variety of cases. The theoretical results were checked with experiments on an isolated section of plate, but its boundaries were discontinuous so that conditions were more severe than would occur in the internal bay of a cellular structure.

To determine the effective slab width for a particular column and slab structure, a model test was carried out by the author. The model, made by Perspex, was square in plan with four bays each way and four storeys. Lateral loading was applied at the panel points by dead weights, and a number of stress and deflection measurements were taken. These included readings from a grid of strain gauges arranged around one of the internal columns.

From the experimental data two "a posteriori" methods were used to find the effective slab width. Firstly, the structure was analysed with a general frame program for various slab widths acting as beams. Theoretical column moments and deflections were then compared with measured values and the optimum fit was obtained with a ratio of $1_e/1 = 0.5$. The bay width, represented by 1 and 1_e, is the effective slab width (see Figure 33-2). Secondly, a strain energy method was used to evaluate the moment carried in the slabs by

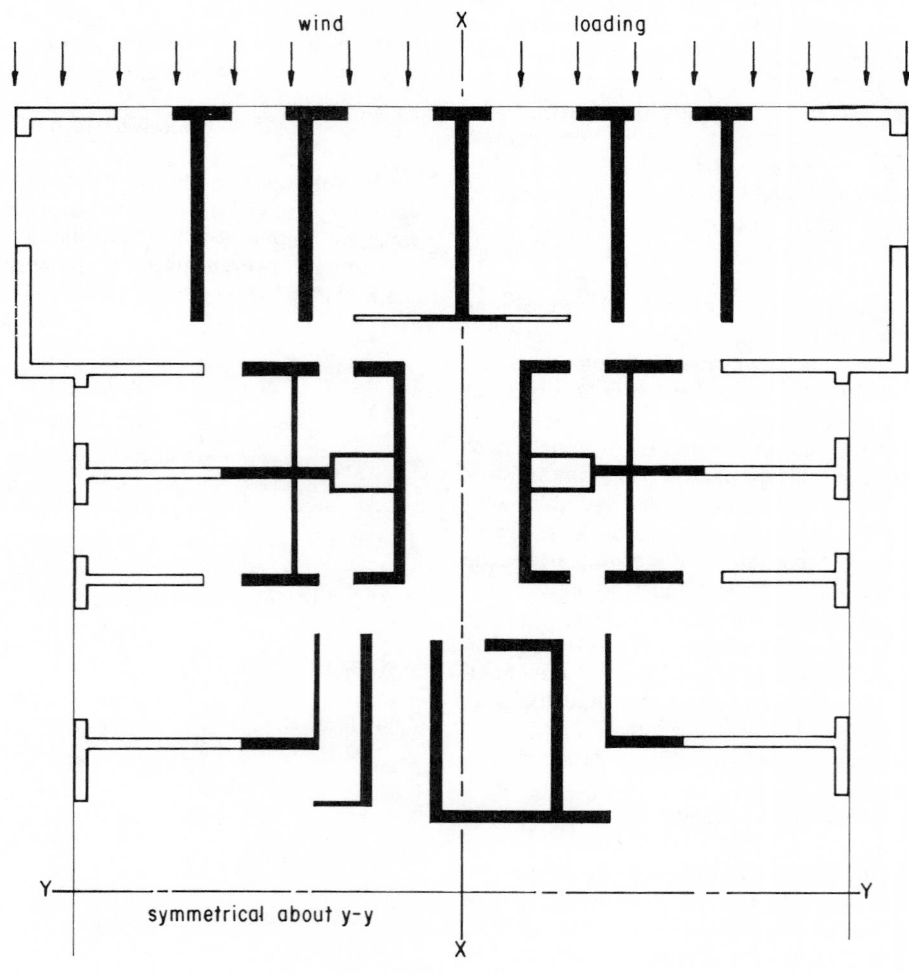

Figure 33-1. Plan of typical block.

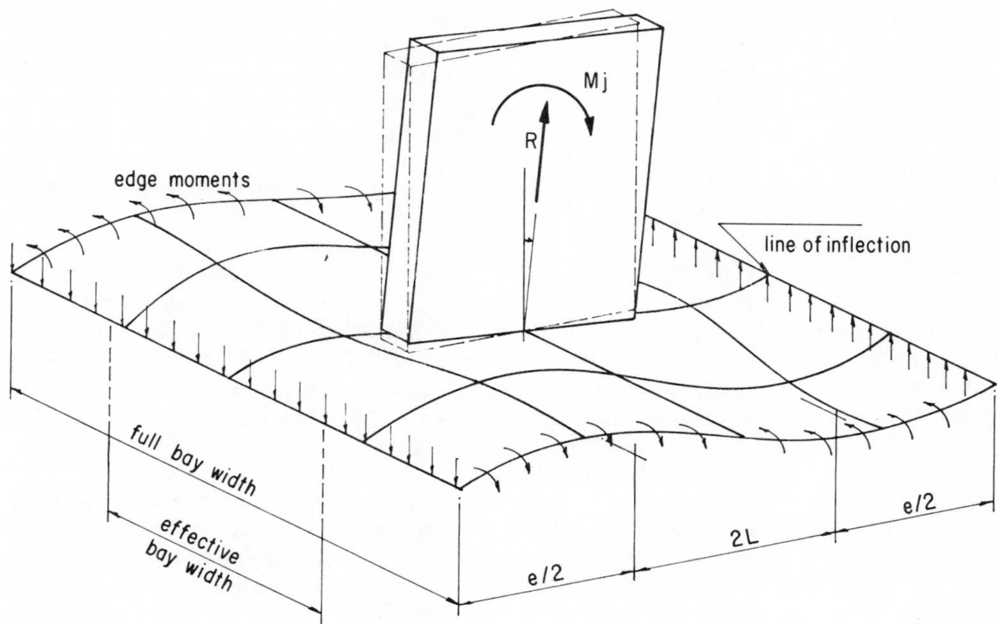

Figure 33-2. Free body diagram of wall and slab element.

Table 33-2
Effective Slab Widths for Column and Slab Model

Method	l_e/l
1. Equivalent frame	0.5
2. Strain energy in slabs	0.622
3. Khan and Sbarounis	0.395

performing a graphical integration of the strain profiles on a full bay width.

Results are given in Table 33-2, and, in the absence of more specific data, the equivalent width of a slab between parallel walls in a regular structure will be taken as half of the bay width. The complex shapes of wall units, and the presence of holes in the slabs will frequently preclude any ready definition of bay widths. Furthermore, the effective widths will depend to some extent on the relative thicknesses of the walls and slabs; further work on this topic is necessary. A fruitful approach might be the use of finite element techniques.

Conditions at Slab-Wall Junction

A reinforced-concrete shear wall system is classed as being constructed from a homogeneous and isotropic material. The beams have fixed ends and the position of fixity is normally taken at the wall face, although local elastic deformations must rotate this face and displace the point of fixity inside the wall. Michael[10] has examined these deformations. By treating the wall as a semi-infinite plate subject to local shear and moment, he has demonstrated that the effect is to reduce the efficiency of coupled walls, the reductions being greatest for short walls connected by flexible beams. A similar condition exists in the structures discussed here, but, since brick walls and concrete slabs do not form a homogeneous medium, the problem must be approached differently.

Consider the section shown in Figure 33-3 where one half of a slab is sandwiched between two walls, the slab and wall both being of unit thickness. Due to composite action, the slab will have a point of inflection at its mid-point, and it will be loaded there with a vertical shear force. Assuming no other forces have any effect at the wall slab junction, the system is analagous to a pile partially embedded in a cohesionless soil and subject to a point load at its free end. If the origin is taken at the junction of the walls and slab the behaviour of the slab can be represented by Equation 33-2:

$$E_s I_s \frac{d^4y}{dx^4} = ky \qquad (33\text{-}2)$$

where:

I_s Moment of inertia of the unit thickness slab section
k "Foundation modulus"
x Co-ordinate of length
y Co-ordinate of deflection

The foundation modulus, k, is defined as the force on a unit area which will cause unit deflection. From full-scale tests on single wall panels by Bradshaw and Hendry[11], a typical value of k is found to be 25×10^3 lb./in^2.

Let 2L denote the web length of a typical internal wall unit and let:

$$\lambda = \sqrt[4]{\frac{k}{E_s I_s}} \qquad (33\text{-}3)$$

then L gives a measure of the stiffness of the embedded slab and, according to Hetényi[12], $\lambda L > \pi$ classifies a long beam in which the actual value of L will have a negligible effect on conditions at the origin. In a case where $E_s = 4 \times 10^6$ lb./in^2, $I_s = 18$ in^4 (6″ slab), $k = 25 \times 10^3$ lb./in^2 and L = 36 in, then $\lambda L = 4.91$. For normal structures, L will always exceed π so the solution of Equation 33-3 will not be significantly influenced by boundary values at the end remote from the origin.

Equation 33-2 is of the fourth order so, with mixed boundary conditions, two known values at each end are sufficient to obtain the solution. This solution (which can be evaluated by either analog or digital computer), analysed in this case with a digital program evolved by Dr. I. F. Christie and Mr. J. W. Searl, Department of Engineering, University of Edinburgh, includes the slope $\left(\frac{dy}{dx}\right)$ and the deflection (y) at the origin. Knowing these values, it is possible to determine the point inside the wall at which the slab is fixed. The effective span of the slab is therefore greater than e, the clear distance between the walls, and can be represented by e + 2Δ as shown in Figure 33-3.

Figure 33-4 shows the variation of Δ for a range of slab thicknesses and a particular set of elastic and geometric constants. Obviously, many such relationships could be computed, but until experiment verification is available, it is intended simply to put forward these values as a guide to the probable effects. It may be noted that a first approximation is given by Δ = h.

Analysis of 15 Storey Structure

The techniques described in the previous sections will now be applied to a proposed fifteen storey apartment block with the plan form shown in Figure 33-1. The walls are nominally 4½″ and 9″ thick, but for calculation, the actual thicknesses of 4.125″ and 8.675″ were used. The floors are 6″-thick in situ slabs. Starting with the basic geometric sizes, the necessary steps in preparing input data for loading parallel to the X - X axis are:

1. Select the wall units which are capable of resisting lateral load, omitting the outer walls parallel to X - X. It may be argued that these form a stiff facade, particularly if the window openings are small, but they are not connected as compositely by the floors as the internal units and are hence neglected.
2. From item 4 in Table 33-1 calculate the effective lengths of any flanges. These are shown as shaded in Figure 33-2.
3. Consider the wall units in each row, parallel to the Y - Y axis, as an equivalent single wall and calculate its area, the position of its centroid, and the moment of inertia about this centroid.
4. Take one half of the bay width between each pair of web walls as the effective slab width i.e. $l_e/l = 0.5$ from Table 33-2. If the bay widths differ between adjacent rows of wall units then the mean value should be used. From this effective

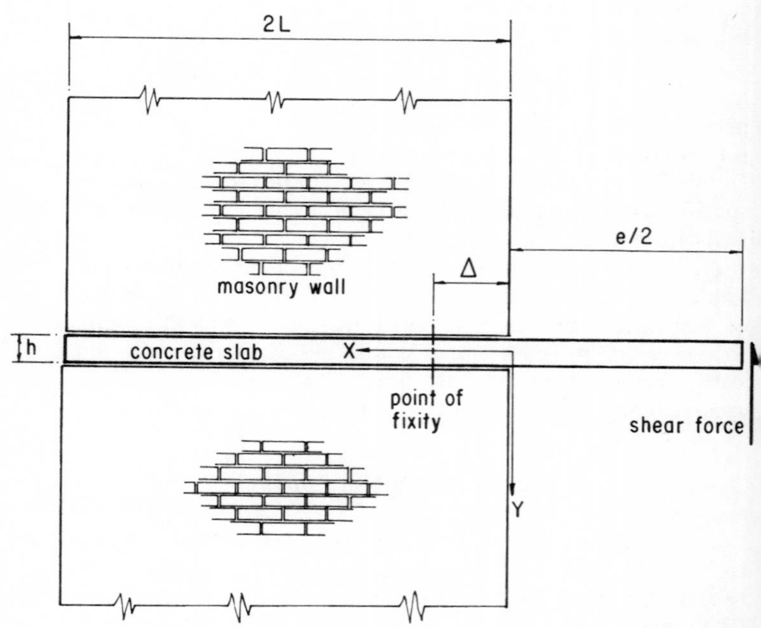

Figure 33-3. Section through wall-slab junction.

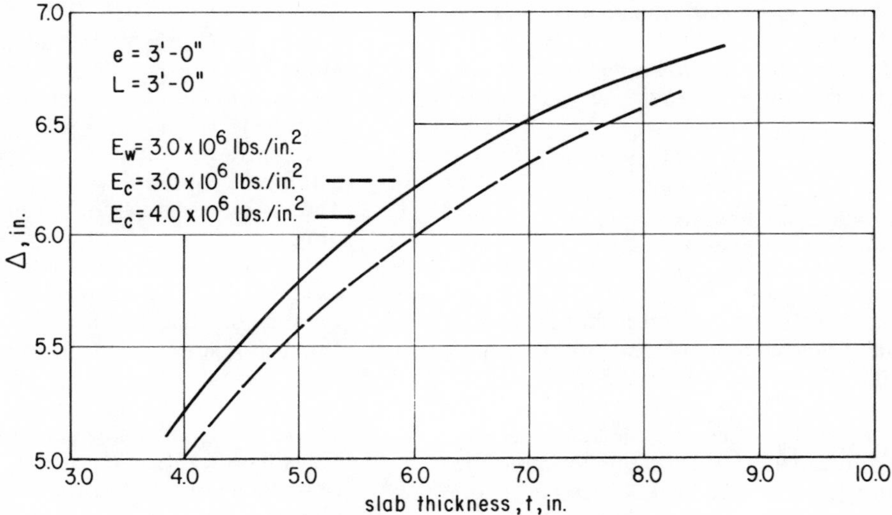

Figure 33-4. Effective slab spans.

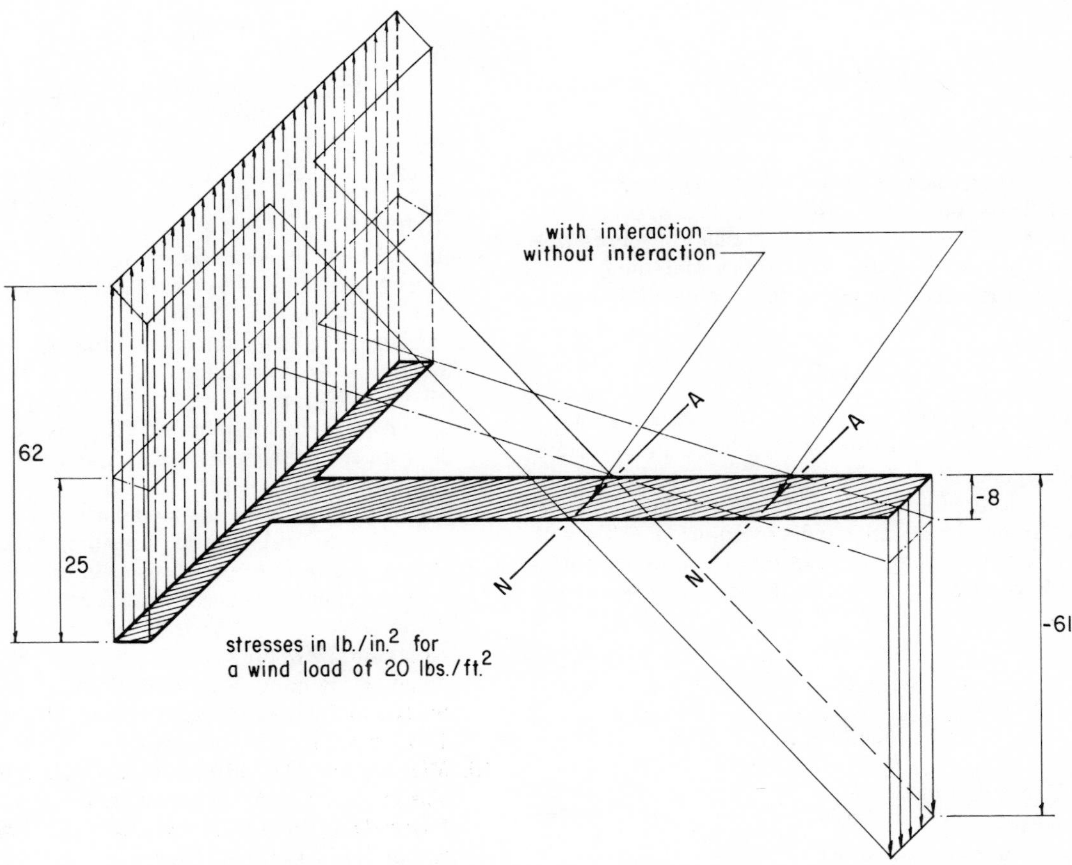

Figure 33-5. Stress distribution in typical unit at foundation level.

width calculate the area ($1_e \cdot h$) and moment of inertia ($1_e \cdot h^3/12$) of the slab section.

5. Select the appropriate value of Δ in Figure 33-4 and hence obtain the effective spans (e + 2 Δ) between each row of wall units.

6. Estimate the elastic moduli of the type of brickwork and concrete to be used. In this case:

$$E_w = 2 \times 10^6 \text{ lb./in}^2$$
$$E_s = 4 \times 10^6 \text{ lb./in}^2$$
$$G_s = 1.7 \times 10^6 \text{ lb./in}^2$$

The ratio of E_s to E_w affects the stress distribution in the members, but a number of computer runs for a typical example showed that the effect was small for $2.5 > E_s/E_w > 1.5$.

7. Express the design wind pressure on the gable perpendicular to X - X as a vertical line load. In this example the pressure of 20 lb./ft^2 is equivalent to a load of 1,260 lb./ft for the 125 ft high structure.

The data from items 1 - 7 was presented to a commercially available computer program held by the Cement and Concrete Association, Wexham Springs, Slough, Bucks., England, for plane shear walls and the results included the forces in all equivalent walls and slabs, and the deflection of the structure. The wall stresses shown in Figure 33-5 at foundation level were found from Equation 33-4.

$$\sigma = \frac{R_j}{A_j} \pm \frac{M_j \bar{y}}{I_j} \tag{33-4}$$

The stresses which would occur if the same wall units acted as independent cantilevers are up to 340 percent higher than those obtained from composite action so savings in brickwork strengths can be affected with fuller analysis. For this structure the plan form is quite satisfactory and there is no possibility of tension occurring under the combined action of dead and lateral load.

Conclusions

It must be emphasised that there is no exact technique available for the analysis of complex brickwork and concrete structures under lateral load. Plane shear wall programs are available, and by following the methods outlined, it is possible to use these to obtain an approximate solution. This will generally be of sufficient accuracy to provide a guide, but if the structure is particularly unusual, it may be advisable to conduct a model test.

Notation

Symbol	Significance
A_j	Area of Jth wall unit
d	Storey height
e	Clear span between wall units
E_s	Modulus of elasticity of floor slabs
E_w	Modulus of elasticity of brickwork
G_s	Modulus of rigidity of floor slabs
h	Thickness of floor slabs
I_j	Moment of inertia of Jth wall unit about its centroid
I_s	Moment of inertia of unit width of slab ($h^3/12$)
k	"Foundation modulus", see text for definition
L	Half the length of a web wall
l	The centre to centre distance between two parallel walls acting as the webs of wall units (i.e. the bay width)
l_e	The effective slab width which will act as an equivalent beam
M_j	Net bending moment on the Jth wall unit
M_{jo}	Cantilever bending moment on the Jth wall unit
M_o	External bending moment
n	Number of storeys above the section in question
R'd	Shear force in a connecting slab
R_j	Axial force in Jth wall unit
t_f	Thickness of wall acting as flange
t_w	Thickness of wall acting as web
x	Co-ordinate of length (see Fig. 33-3)
y	Co-ordinate of deflection (see Fig. 33-3)
$\bar{y}$	Distance from wall edge to centroid
Δ	Distance from edge of wall at which slab is considered fixed
λ	Stiffness parameter (see text)
σ	Stress in wall

References

1. Soane, A. J. M., "Model analysis of Essex University tower block," Research Note 1,(1), Clay Products Technical Bureau, 1967.
2. Beck, H., "Contribution to the analysis of coupled shear walls," *J. Am. Concr. Inst.*, 5, (59), 1962, pp. 1055 – 1070.
3. Eriksson, O., "Analysis of wind bracing walls in multi-storey housing," *Ingenioren,* (International Edition), 5, (4), 1961, pp. 115 –124.
4. Rosman, R., "An approximate method of analysis of walls of multi-storey buildings," *Civ. Engrg publ. wks Rev.*, 59, (690), 1964, pp.
5. Coull, A., and Choudhury, J. R., "Stresses and deflections in coupled shear walls," *A.C.I. Journal,* March 1967, pp. 65 – 72.
6. *Proceedings of the Symposium on Tall Buildings,* University of Southhampton, Pergamon Press, London, 1967.
7. Soane, A.J.M., "The analysis of interconnected shear walls by analogue computation," *ibid,* pp. 207 – 222.
8. Timoshenko, S., *Strength of Materials,* Part II, Van Nostrand, New York, 1956, pp. 64 – 68.
9. Khan, F. R., and Sbarounis, J. A., "Interaction of shear walls and frames," *Proc. Am. Soc. Div. Engrs.*, 88, (ST6), 1962, pp. 285 –335.
10. Michael, D., "The effect of local wall deformations on the elastic interaction of cross walls coupled by beams," *Proceedings of the Symposium on Tall Buildings,* Pergamon Press, London, 1967.
11. Bradshaw, R., and Hendry, A. W., Private communication.
12. Hetényi, M., *Beams on Elastic Foundations,* Ann Arbor, University of Michigan Press, 1946.

34. Current post-tensioned and prestressed brickwork and ceramics in Great Britain.

Kenneth Thomas, Clay Products Technical Bureau of Great Britain, Ltd., London, England

This chapter presents a summary of some recent work in Great Britain on post-stressed and pre-stressed brickwork and ceramics.

The investigation described each relate to beam construction, and although the three projects were sponsored by separate bodies, liaison existed through the Clay Products Technical Bureau of Great Britain. As a direct result of the work described, a British Patent has been registered for a ceramic flooring system.

This chapter is in three parts. Section 1 describes work carried out by the author; sections 2 and 3 relate the results of work by Dr. J. M. Plowman and Mr. L. S. Ng respectively, the author providing the commentary.

History of Work in the United Kingdom

Post-stressing and pre-stressing techniques are usually associated with concrete construction, yet records show that post-stressed brickwork was successfully employed over 140 years ago for part of the Thames Tunnel Project[1].

In 1825 Marc Isambard Brunel's plan for tunnelling under the River Thames was carried out, his scheme being based on the sinking of a caisson on either side of the Thames and tunnelling between shafts. The caissons were, it is believed, not only the first attempts to reinforce brickwork but also the birth of the technique known as post-stressing.

The caissons consisted of two vertical brick tubes 50 ft. diameter and 70 ft. high. The 30-in-thick walls were reinforced vertically with 1-in-diameter wrought iron bolts built into the brickwork and fastened to wooden curbs at the top and bottom with nuts at the threaded ends of the bolts. Horizontal reinforcement consisted of iron hoops 9 in. wide and 1/2 in. thick.

Building of the shaft was completed above ground with temporary piles supporting the structure which ultimately weighed 910 tons. After completion of the brickwork and tensioning of the wrought iron rods, the piles were gradually removed. Sinking of the shaft was engineered by loosening the earth within the brickwork enclosure and removing it by means of a windlass and buckets, the shaft descending under its own weight. During the operation of sinking the shaft, the whole structure was severely tested due to uneven strata; an alarming surge took place and the tower suddenly dropped seven inches at one side and only three and a half inches on the opposite. Throughout the whole operation, the structure behaved as a composite unit, and work was completed without injury to the brickwork. The structure remains to this day, an outstanding example of reinforced and post-stressed brickwork.

Since the pioneer work of Brunel, developments in post-stressed and pre-stressed ceramics have been rather disappointing, no doubt due to the extensive use of reinforced and pre-stressed concrete. Current developments suggest a renewed interest in this form of construction.

Many types of stressed ceramic construction have been suggested, particularly in the form of beams and planks for prefabricated flooring systems, but perhaps the more interesting uses and suggestions relate to walls.

In Darlington, County Durham, 11-in-cavity walls have been constructed approximately 24 feet high and 30 feet long with post-stressing rods in the cavity. This form of building permitted slender construction which would otherwise not have been possible without additional structural members; thus the wall gave greater architectural freedom without additional cost. The building is described in more detail elsewhere[2].

Tests have recently been carried out on simulated cross-wall projections using reinforced concrete floor slabs compositely with reinforced brick walls. In one instance, post-stressing steel was used vertically to restrain cracking. Details of these tests are described elsewhere[3,4].

Other work of interest in this field concerns pre-stressing of brickwork shear walls and walls on reactive soils[5,6].

SECTION I

Testing

Post-Stressed Brickwork Beams–Belfast College of Technology, Summer 1963

During the Summer of 1965, the author was responsible for testing two post-stressed brickwork beams, to determine the possibilities of resting a suspended floor on beams constructed in this manner.

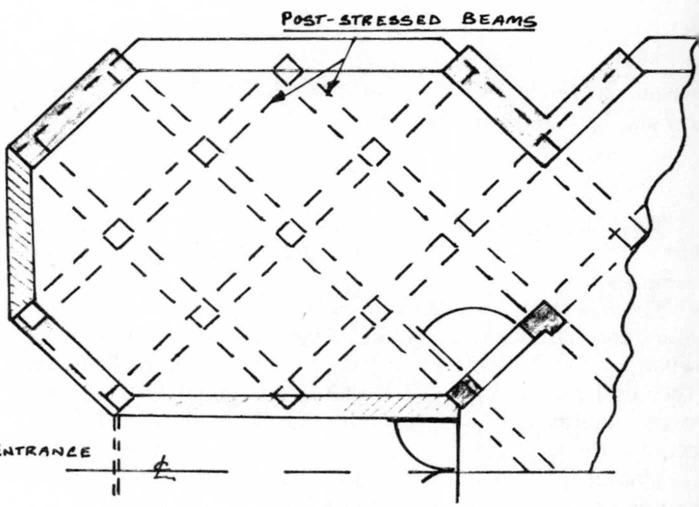

Figure 34-1. Floor plan (1st. project).

It was appreciated by the architect and consulting engineer* that this form of construction, using standard perforated wire-cut bricks, was unlikely to provide an economically viable method of supporting a suspended floor, but as the client was a brick manufacturer interested in brickwork as a structural material, it was decided to prepare a preliminary design and initiate a small testing programme.

The supporting structure for the suspended floor was intended to be a diagrid of 9-in. wide x 18-in-deep brick members with 9-in x 9-in x 18-in deep pre-cast concrete junction pieces (to facilitate post-stressing cables in two directions). See Figure 34-1. The diagrid system should be constructed on scaffolding and post-stressing cables threaded through holes in the brickwork to anchor blocks, and then th whole framework post-stressed in situ. All beams were to hav been supported on 9-in. loadbearing panels of brickwork an the 3-in. pre-cast concrete floor slab units laid over each squa of the diagrid system after post-stressing. Internally, it wa proposed to express the coffered ceiling structure and to hav the concrete squares lined in an accoustically absorben material. Unfortunately, the design was not built, but th enthusiasm initiated in Belfast for this form of constructio was not lost; indeed, it gained momentum.

Structural Tests

Beam No. 1. The beam was composed of perforated bricks an constructed on a timber plank, laying all units as "soldiers with mortar joints. Placing of bricks in this manner is a slo and tedious business but was considered preferable to buildir short lengths vertically and risking damage due to handling. T prevent mortar penetration into the lower perforation a simp "pull though" was devised by the bricklayer and consisted of rubber washer secured to a length of galvanized wire. Th elementary device proved extremely effective. Bricks used fo the beam were wire-cut rustics having an average compressiv strength of not less than 4,000 lb/in^2 and dimensio approximately as indicated in Figure 34-2. Mortar consisted o a 1:3 mix (by volume), of masonry cement/sand.

End anchorages were made up of a standard cast-iro distribution block, the reinforcement consisting of a simpl spiral and light cage. Concrete was 1:2:4 mi (cement-sand-aggregate by volume), the cement bein "Fondu".

After constructing the brick soldier section beam i position on a flat bed, the brickwork was covered and kep permanently damp until testing of the beam took place. Afte 28 days the concrete anchor blocks were fitted to the bea

*Architects: R. J. McKinstry, Belfast, Consulting Engineers: Kirk, McClure and Morton, Belfast.

ends, and a thin layer of mortar used to ensure that local high-point loading would not cause premature failure of the beam adjacent to the anchorage.

Six 0.276 (7 m.m.) high-tensile steel stressing wires were then threaded through the lower of the three holes in the perforated bricks and the anchorage block and a light stress applied to facilitate handling of the beam prior to testing. The stressing of wires was carried out using the P.S.C. mono wire system.†

The test rig and ancillary equipment consisted of the following:

1. Rolled steel joist overhead beam supported on brick piers.
2. Mild steel hanger flat bars with bossed holes at 6 in. centres.
3. Supporting steel rods with split pin fasteners.
4. Mild steel distribution saddles for points of support.

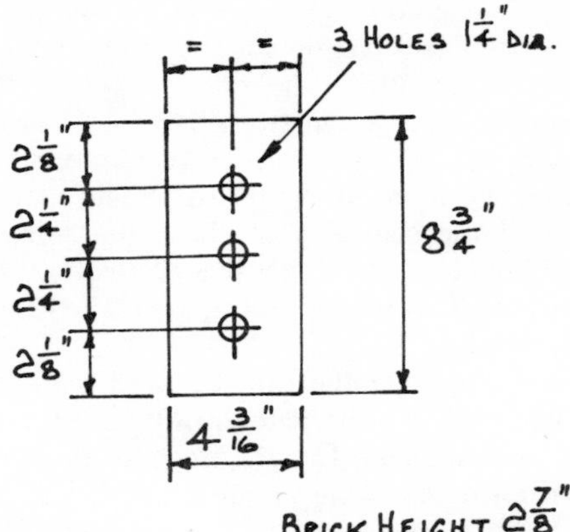

Figure 34-2. Cross section of brick for beams 1 and 2 (1st project).

Figure 34-3. Test rig fully assembled supporting 8′ 3″ span beam (1st project).

5. 15-ton hydraulic jack.
6. Load cell with gauge attached (20,000 lb/in^2 capacity).

Figure 34-3 shows the test rig fully assembled, the beam in position and a final force of 15,000 lb. applied to the cable. During the stressing process, it was necessary to apply a small force to each wire in turn rather than the full force of 2,500 lb., as rotation of the concrete anchor block due to full stress on the adjacent wire tended to dislodge other wires from the distribution block.

When the test rig was initially considered, it was intended that each beam should be subjected to equal vertical load at third points of the span, but because only one jack and load cell was available at that time, it was decided to apply a central point load, jacking the brick beam against the overhead steel member.

Final stressing of the beam and testing took place within a matter of hours. Due to the experimental nature of the work it was decided not to grout the cable in position. Ideally, the hole for the post-stressing cable should have been within the "middle third" of the beam depth, thus ensuring that the whole of the beam cross section was in compression. For this pilot investigation, the brick company's standard brick with a three-hole perforation pattern was used, the centre of the bottom hole being 2-1/4 in. from the beams's neutral axis and thus outside the middle third.

After final stressing of the post-stressing wires, the beam was carefully positioned with supports at 8-ft. 3-in. centres and the hydraulic jack and load cell placed in the centre of the

†P.S.C. Mono Wire System supplied by P.S.C. Equipment Limited, Ridge Way, Iver, Bucks.

beam. Load was gradually applied at the mid point at the span by the hydraulic jack. As no adverse effects were apparent at a load of 4,045 lb. (1.75 the design load of the beam, the maximum estimated design stress based on nominal dimension being 750 lb./in^2) it was decided to remove the central load and increase the force in the post-stressing cable to 24,000 lb. On release of the central point load, the deflection returned approximately to zero. The load/deflection graph (Figure 34-4) indicates that after initial stiffness the beam had a direct elastic relationship.

Prior to reapplying the central point load, the beam was partially wrapped in polythene sheeting as a safety precaution. The load was applied for the second time with the load deflection curve following an almost identical path to Figure 34-4 but when a load of 3,850 lb. was approached, the beam failed. Figures 34-5 and 34-6. This failure was considered to be due to the principal tensile stress close to support being greater than the resistance of the fired clay.

Beam No. 2. This beam was composed of 8-3/4 in. x 4-3/16 in. x 2-7/8 in. bricks as for beam No. 1 but was formed into a cross section nominally 18 in. deep by 9 in. wide. Figure 34-7. The total length of the beam was 20 ft. The beam was constructed in a similar manner to its predecessor but provision made for two post-stressing cables. Figure 34-7. End anchorages were precast concrete blocks similar in design to the first beam, but having twin cast iron distribution blocks, see Figures 34-8 and 34-9. Beam No. 2 was constructed at the same time as beam No. 1, and the same materials used for each. Testing again took place at 28 days. Numerous difficulties were encountered due to each cable consisting of six strands. Blockages occurred despite the "pull through", and to thread the cables eventually four courses of brickwork had to be removed before the test could proceed.

This beam was stressed on the horizontal plank bed, starting on cable 1 and stressing one wire then stressing one wire in cable 2, but before the stressing was complete, cracking started in the beam immediately behind the anchorage. (Figure 34-9). Failure was again considered to be due to the principal tensile stress adjacent to the support being greater than the resistance of the fired clay.

Conclusions

Both beams failed due to excessive tensile stresses. In beam No. 1, the principal tensile stress at failure was estimated at 120 lb/in.^{2} and beam No. 2, 90 lb/in^2. These values, however, assume the joints to have the same properties as the ceramic and are therefore somewhat conservative. If this form of construction were to be adopted, it is considered that the principal tensile stresses should be no greater than perhaps 60 lb/in^2. To achieve a smaller stress adjacent to the anchorages either (a) a larger cross-sectional area is necessary, (b) units having a higher tensile strength are required, or (c) reinforcement should be introduced into the bed joints to reduce the lateral strain of the mortar. This would increase the compressive strength of the beams in the length[7,8].

Alternatively, the use of self-supporting slabs of post-stressed ceramic would disperse the forces over a larger area. New units would need to be developed for this.

SECTION II

Testing

Post-Stressed Brickwork Beams Sponsored By the Clay Pro ducts Technical Bureau of Great Britain, Testing Carried Out By Dr. J. M. Plowman – Spring 1965.**

The Clay Products Technical Bureau of Great Britain wer consulted regarding the Belfast project and as a direct resul decided to sponsor a similar research programme. The decided to investigate whether ceramics were suitable fo post-stressing and if they could be used for floors etc.

For this pilot investigation, there was no need to go to th expense of designing and making special units which migh need modifying during the tests. Therefore, standard siz bricks were adopted with holes at the third points. Althoug the brick size was standard, the hole positions were no standard and it was necessary to drill or punch solid brick whilst still in the green state, in some instances.

For this project, all beams were fabricated by laying th bricks as "soldiers" with mortar joints. By placing the stressin wires at the lower third point, the whole cross section of th beam was in compression whilst under axial stress. In view o this arrangement, it was unnecessary to provide secondar steel to withstand handling stresses.

Laying of the bricks took a considerable time because th basic unit was only 2-5/8 in long so that there were over fort joints to make a span of 10 ft. The beams did not have th holes grouted.

Tests

Figure 34-10 shows a beam in the test rig. All beams teste were identical in dimensions (4-1/8 in. wide x 8-5/8 in. deep x

**J. M. Plowman, Consulting Engineer, Hatfield, Hertfordshire.

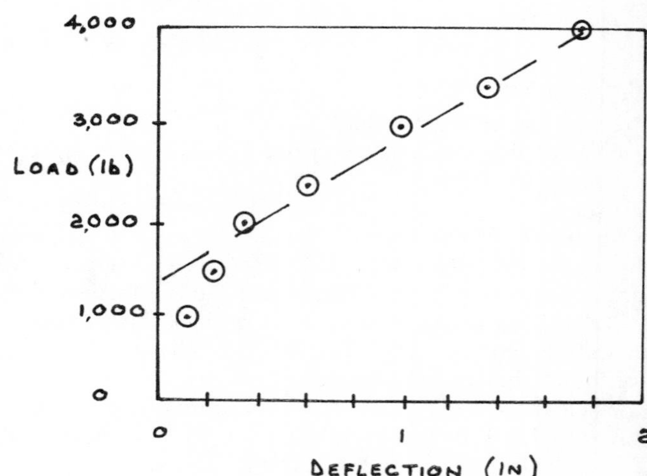

Figure 34-4. Load/deflection graph for beam 1 (1st project).

Figure 34-5. Failure of 8′ 3″ span beam view adjacent to support (1st project).

Figure 34-6. Failure of 8′ 3″ span beam view from end of beam (1st project).

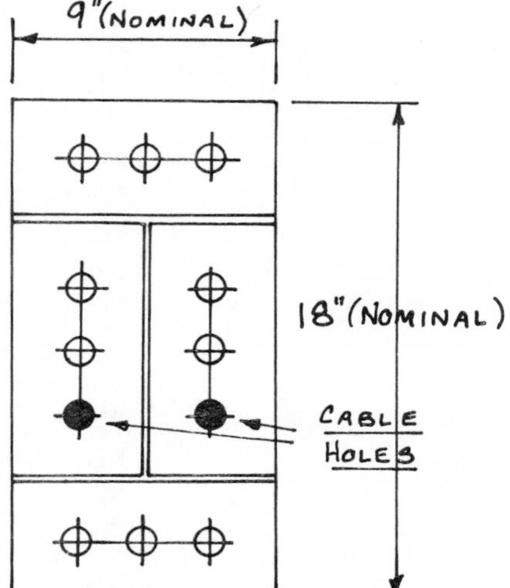

Figure 34-7. Cross section of beam 2 (1st project).

Figure 34-8. 20′ beam on supporting form prior to final stressing (1st project).

Figure 34-9. 20′ beam showing end anchorage and method of failure (1st project).

10 ft. long, centres of supports). The method of applying the central point load was similar to the Belfast project, although a 20-ton proving ring was used in this series of experiments instead of a load cell for recording the applied load.

The large forces from the anchorages were concentrated on a small area due to the design of the patent cast-iron anchor plates, and a concrete distribution block was therefore provided at each end of the beams. A 1:1½:2½ concrete mix was adopted for the blocks using high alumina cement with a 3/4 in. maximum sized aggregate, giving a 28-day cube strength of 7,300 lb/in^2.

All beams were constructed on level supporting forms to ensure absolute straightness, the sequence being as follows:

1. Bricks laid as soldiers using mortar as in Figure 34-10, each brick being dipped in water for approximately 1/2 minute before placing. Jointing was carried out concurrently with placing. Tables 34-1, 34-2 and 34-3 give properties of the bricks and mortar used.
2. Mild steel bars 3/8 in. diameter were passed through the two lines of holes at the third points. Nuts on the ends were

Figure 34-10. Test rig fully assembled supporting 10′ span beam (2nd project).

Table 34-1
Crushing Strength of Bricks

Brick A	Brick Ba
7,910 lb./in.^{2} (Av.) Standard Deviation 1034	5,170 lb./in.^{2} (Av.) Standard Deviation 367
Brick Bb	**Brick C**
4,830 lb./in.^{2} (Av.) Standard Deviation 692	3,840 lb./in.^{2} (Av.) Standard Deviation 526

Table 34-2
Water Absorption Tests (24 hrs.)

Brick A	Brick Ba	Brick Bb	Brick C
Av. 11.4%	Av. 11.45%	Av. 9.72%	Av. 9.7%
Density			
138 lb/ft^3	126 lb/ft^3	128 lb/ft^3	122 lb/ft^3

Table 34-3
Mortar Cube Strengths and Sieve Analysis of Sand

Mortar Mix (By Weight)
1 : 0-11 : 3 Portland Cement : Lime : Sand

Beam No.	Average Cube Strength (4^{in})
1	3270 lb./in.^{2}
2	3600
3	3520
4	3150
5	3150
6	2420
7	2700
8	3120
9	2690
10	2810
11	2690
12	2690
13	2810

Grading of Sand

Sieve Size	3/16 in.	7	14	25	52	100
% Passing	99	96	93	81	27	8

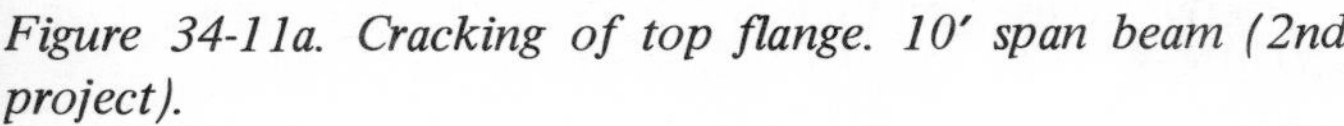

Figure 34-11a. Cracking of top flange. 10′ span beam (2nd project).

Figure 34-11b. Spalling of top flange. 10′ span beam (2nd project).

tightened on to washers bearing on the end bricks. Thus, the joints between the soldiers were kept in compression.

3. After 24 hours the nuts on the bars were tightened further.

4. At 27 days the 3/8 in.-diameter bars were removed and the required number of 0.276 (7 m.m.) diameter high tensile wires threaded through the lower of the series of holes.

5. The concrete distribution blocks were threaded on to the wires and bedded in high alumina mortar against the end soldiers.

6. After the mortar had stiffened the wires were stressed to give an end force of 1,000 lb.

7. At 28 days the end force was increased to 3,000 lb. and the beam placed in the test rig. Figure 34-10.

8. After placing in the test rig, the wires were further stressed to the desired value. Table 34-4.

9. The beam was tested to failure (Figures 34-11a and 34-11b) by loading at the mid point, measuring deflections at suitable increments of load.

10. After failure in some instances, four soldiers mortared together were salvaged from the undamaged portions of each beam. These specimens were tested in a 200-ton press applying the load through a ball joint, the axis of which passed through the one-third point of the specimen, thus, partly simulating the action of the high tensile stressing wires. Failing loads of such columns are given in Table 34-5.

Table 34-4
Pre-stressing Stresses

Beam No	Top	Bottom	Bottom Brick Str.	Bottom Calculated Bwk. Str.
1				
2	28 lb/in^2	215 lb/in^2	0.043	0.12
3	35	267	0.033	0.16
4				
5	56	430	0.086	0.25
6	63	480	0.096	0.28
7	59	455	0.091	0.26
8	111	855	0.107	0.36
9	125	930	0.120	0.40
10	146	1120	0.140	0.46
11	48	370	0.097	0.26
12	67	515	0.151	0.36
13	104	800	0.210	0.55

Results

Due to difficulties in obtaining bricks of the specified strength for the tests, the four batches did not become available in the sequence required. Therefore, tests could not follow logically (without undue delay) from low stressed, low strength to high stressed, high strength bricks. The results are reported in chronological order.

Beam I Brick Ba. This beam was used as a "guinea pig" to develop techniques for laying the soldiers and keeping the holes for the wire free of mortar.

Beam II Brick Ba. Post-stressing force 4,000 lb. At a load of 500 lb. the centre joint in the beam opened, followed by the adjacent one at 600 lb. At 1,100 lb. several joints opened, the position of these joints being determined by the friction of the brick and mortar on the wire. The deflection at this load was 1.95 in. At a load of 1,290 lb. the deflection was 3.1 in. and the brickwork under the load distributing plate started to spall. No increase in load could be supported. Although the deflection was increased to 6 in. little crushing of the brickwork occurred.

Beam III Brick Ba. Post-stressing force 5,000 lb. At a load of 650 lb. several central joints opened. A load of 1,500 lb. caused local crushing and a deflection of approximately 6 in. After removal of the load, the residual deflection was approximately 1/4 in. The loading was then moved close to a support to test the beam's shear strength. At a load of 2,100 lb. joints opened as the beam bent. At twice this load, brickwork to the midspan side of the load failed in flexural compression. There was no shear failure.

Beam IV Brick Ba. At a post-stressing force of 5,000 lb. one of the patent cast iron anchor plates collapsed resulting in the destruction of the beam.

Beam V Brick Ba. Post-stressing force of 8,000 lb. Failure occurred at a load of 1,760 lb. due to excessive flexural compression of the brickwork.

Beam VI Brick Bb. Post-stressing force 9,000 lb. Failure occurred at a load of 1,720 lb. due to excessive flexural compression of the brickwork with a final deflection of approximately 1-1/2 in.

Beam VII Brick Bb. Post-stressing force 8,500 lb. Failure occurred at a load of 1,880 lb. due to fracture of the stressing wire close to one anchor grip. Maximum deflection approximately 4-1/4 in.

Beam VIII Brick A. Post-stressing force 16,000 lb. When the stressing force reached 11,500 lb., the first brick developed a horizontal tensile crack along the axis of the wires. This crack spread through the mortar joint into the distribution block outside the reinforcement cage.

On removal of the stressing force, the beam was found to be little damaged and by removing the first six soldiers at the damaged end it was possible to add a new distribution block and make a shorter beam. Expanded aluminum mesh was inserted into the joints between blocks and soldiers at each

Table 34-5
Column Failing Loads and Brick/Pier Strength Ratio

Beam No.	Column Failing Load	Calculated Max Strength Strength of Brick
1		
2		
3	51,000 lb.	0.6
4		
5	125,000	1.46
6	100,000	1.25
7	80,000	1.00
8		
9		
10	80,000	0.61
11	40,000	0.63
12	55,000	0.87
13	61,000	0.97

end. Failure of the beam was due to excessive flexural compression of the brickwork. The results have been corrected to allow for the reduction in span and can thus be compared directly in the graphs with all the other beams, see Figure 34-12a, b, and c.

Beam IX Brick A. Post-stressing force 18,000 lb. Failure occurred at a load of 3,400 lb. due to excessive flexural compression of the brickwork. One of the cast iron anchor plates was cracked by this load. Expanded metal reinforcements as in Beam VIII was used in the joints between brickwork and distribution blocks.

Beam X Brick A. Post-stressing force 21,000 lb. This beam failed under a load of 3,650 lb. due to excessive flexural compression in the brickwork at midspan. Expanded metal reinforcement was used in the joints as for Beam VIII.

Beam XI Brick C. Post-stressing force 6,900 lb. This beam reached a point where the deflection increased greatly without any measurable increase in the load of 1,400 lb.

Beam XII Brick C. Post-stressing force 9,600 lb. This beam was loaded to 11,700 lb. and then unloaded. The residual deflection was 0.013 in. after deflection under load of 0.184 in. Loading was then continued to 2,100 lb., the deflection being 1.358 in. On release the residual deflection was 0.125 in. In this beam, partial failure occurred at 1,650 lb. by a horizontal crack forming at about 3 in. from the top of the second "soldier" from the load point. On increasing the load to 21,000 lb., this crack extended to the third soldier following a direction inclined towards the central axis of the beam. The crack did not extend beyond these two "soldiers" and closed up almost completely on removal of the load (Figure 34-11a.)

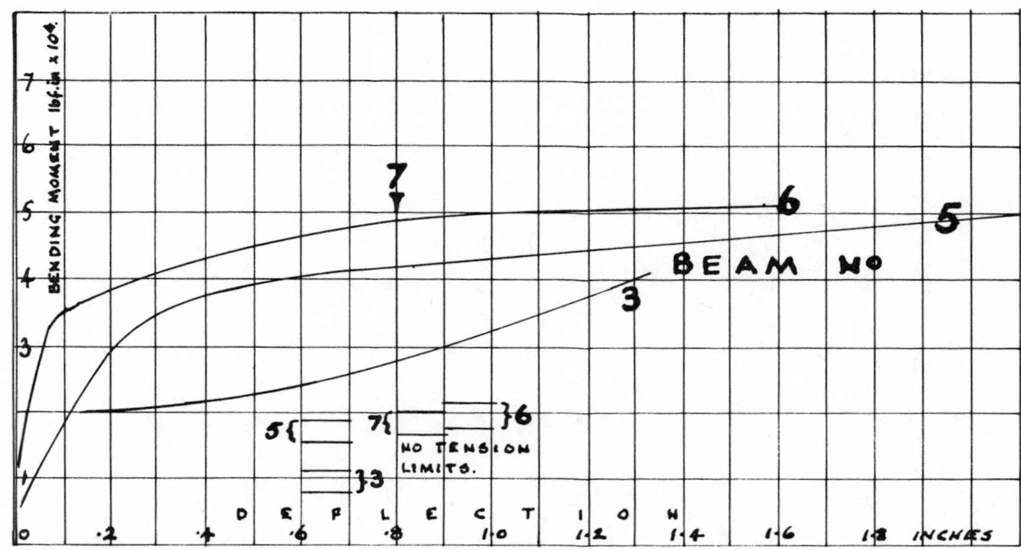

Figure 34-12a. Bending moment/deflection graph beams 3, 5, 6, and 7 (2nd project).

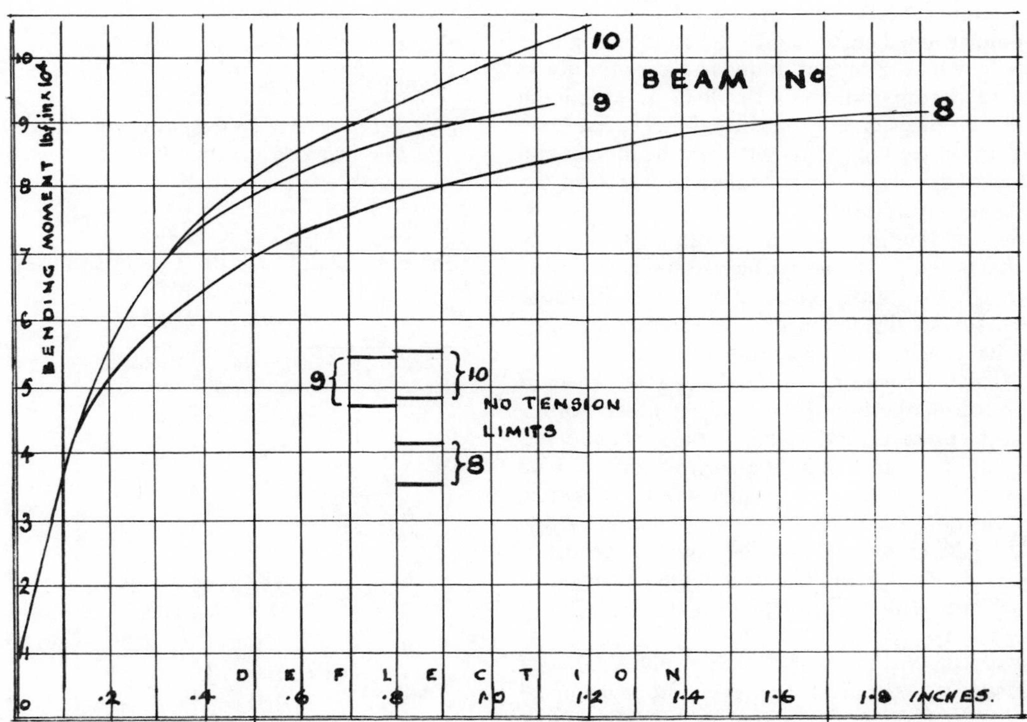

Figure 34-12b. Bending moment/deflection graph beams 8, 9, and 10 (2nd project).

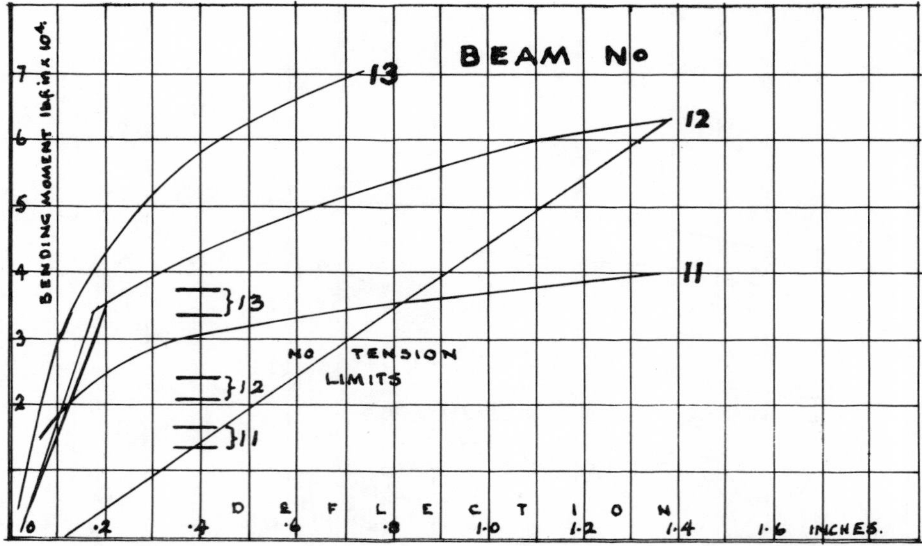

Figure 34-12c. Bending moment/deflection graph beams 11, 12, and 13 (2nd project).

Beam XIII Brick C. Post-stressing force 15,000 lb. This beam failed in the normal way by crushing the top 1 in. of a "soldier" adjacent to the load point. Failure occurred at a load of 2,700 lb. (Figure 34-11b).

The bending moment/deflection graphs, (Figure 34-12a, 34-12b, 34-12c) are grouped according to the basic strength of the ceramic used. It will be seen that there is a discontinuity in each of the curves corresponding to the load at which the beams cracked in the lower or tension zone. In all cases, these cracks took the form of a bond failure between the mortar and the ceramic. Because of the necessary tolerance between the diameter of the holes in the ceramic and the size of the wires, the actual position of the wires at failure cannot be exactly known. When a beam bends the wires, being free in the holes, will tend to touch the upper boundary of the holes at mid-span. This will reduce the eccentricity of the post-stressing force, and thus its efficiency in resisting the applied loads. Using these two limiting positions for the wires, (the centre of the holes and the top of the holes) the loads at which normal pre-stressing theory predicts zero tension have been determined. Thus, for any one beam there is a narrow range of load over which tension may develop depending upon the actual position of the wires. These bands have been plotted on the graphs, Figures 34-12a, b, and c. It will be noted that most of the discontinuities in the curves occur at higher loads than marked for no tension, thus indicating that the mortar joints have some tensile strength.

The design load for post-stressed ceramic units should, at this stage of knowledge, be that at which zero stress occurs at the soffit of the beam. Basing calculations on this assumption, the loads for the two possible positions of the wires in each of the beams have been obtained and these are listed with the "factors of safety" in Table 34-6.

The tests on the four courses of ceramic in the form of column eccentrically loaded were intended to determine th type of likely failure rather than give accurate values. Result obtained are listed in Table 34-5. In all cases the failure was b splitting parallel to the line of action of the load. Figure 34-13a and b show a typical case.

Author's Comments

1. Ceramics can be post-stressed satisfactorily.
2. Post-stressed ceramic beams behave in a manner simila to concrete beams.

Table 34-6
Factors of Safety for the Two Positions of No Tension Load

$$\text{Factor of Safety} = \frac{\text{Failing Load}}{\text{No Tension Load}}$$

Beam No	Lower No Tension Load	Factor of Safety	Upper No Tension Load	Factor of Safety
1				
2	190 lb.	6.7	230 lb.	5.5
3	280	5.5	230	4.6
4				
5	530	3.3	620	2.9
6	610	2.8	720	2.4
7	580	3.2	670	2.8
8	1200	3.1	1380	2.7
9	1360	2.5	1580	2.0
10	1620	2.4	1860	2.2
11	440	3.2	520	2.7
12	670	3.2	780	2.7
13	1110	2.4	1280	2.1

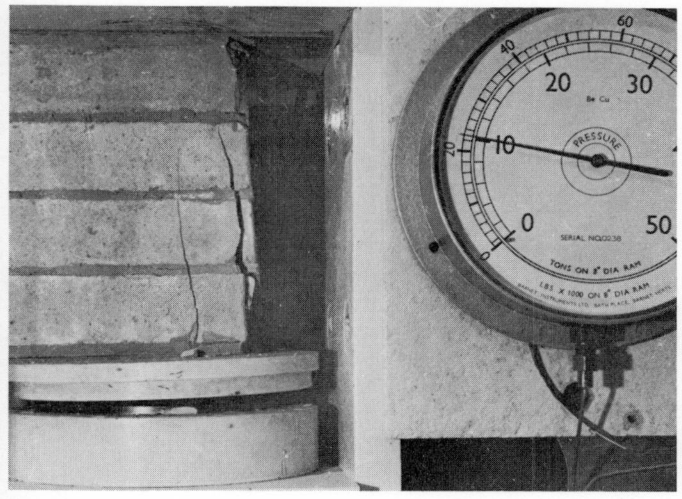

Figure 34-13a. Failure of brickwork column in 200 ton testing machine (2nd project).

Figure 34-13b. Failure of brickwork column in 200 ton testing machine (2nd project).

3. Shear failure is not a major concern.
4. Some shear reinforcement may be required adjacent to the anchorages in some cases.
5. As with concrete, the recovery to deflected beams on removal of load is good.
6. Failure of ceramic beams in compression is by slow crushing of the material, whilst supporting the load with increasing deflection.
7. Failure by steel failure is as with concrete, sudden and complete.
8. Local tensile failure is always in the bond between mortar and ceramic.

Discussion

There seems no technical reason why post-stressed ceramic units should not be used for beams and floor slabs which will compete economically with concrete or any other material.

Further tests are of course, required to develop suitably shaped units. The major problems in the development of such beams and slabs are:

1. Reduction of number of joints by making longer ceramic units.
2. Jointing material of high tensile bond strength easily applied.
3. Grouting with portland cement or other adhesive of wires to ceramics.
4. Long-term behaviour.
5. Development of suitable anchorage units.

With regard to Item 4 it is thought that creep and shrinkage, both properties which are a cause of concern in concrete floors, will be very much less with ceramics.

SECTION III

Laboratory Investigation into Extruded Clay Block Flooring System

This investigation was carried out by L. S. Ng, a fourth year degree student in the Civil Engineering Department of Sunderland Technical College during the 1965-1966 academic year.

The objects of the project were (a) to determine the physical properties of the extruded clay units, such as crushing strength, modulus of rupture and creep; (b) to test the bond strength of the jointing material and (c) to find the ultimate load on a pre-stressed ceramic beam and compare it with the theoretical ultimate load. Hollow clay blocks used for all the tests were as illustrated in Figure 34-14b.

As hollow clay blocks are cheap and light compared with other building materials a new ceramic flooring system might result from this investigation. The student's employers†† were also interested in such a system and suggested the project.

As difficulties had been experienced by the author and Dr. Plowman in their investigations using traditional mortars, it was decided to bond the ceramic units with thin joints using epoxy resin as the bonding agent. By so doing, it was hoped that the mortar would exhibit a much smaller lateral strain and, hence, delay tensile splitting of the ceramic, thus permitting much larger forces to be applied along the beam axis.

It is not possible to record in this chapter the full details of all preliminary testing. The results are summarised as follows:

††Messrs. Steen Sehested and Partners, later Peter Heath and Partners.

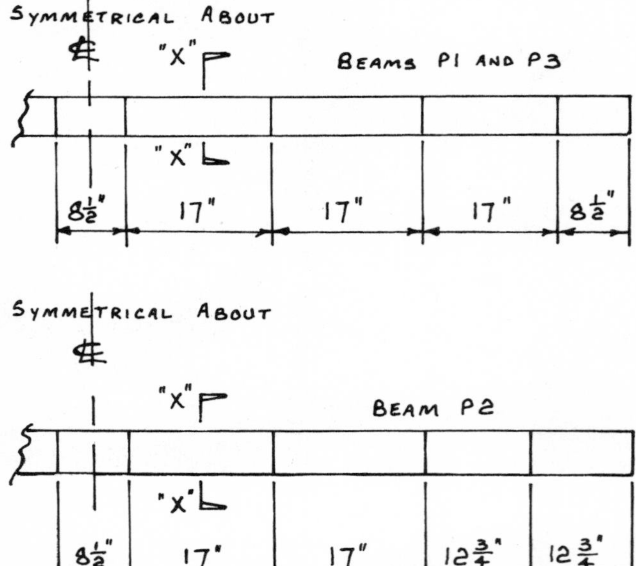

Figure 34-14a. Arrangement of beams P1, P2, and P3 (3rd project).

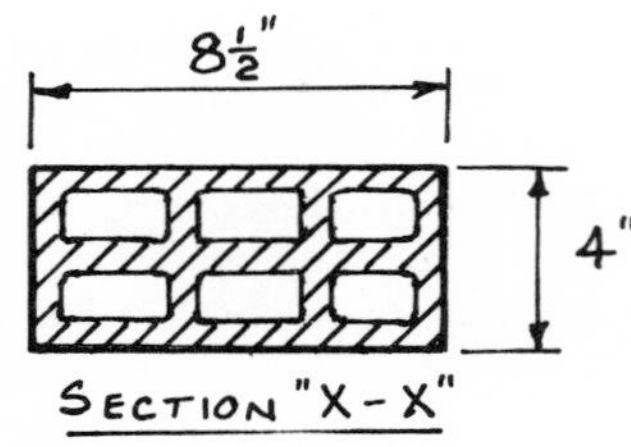

Figure 34-14b. Cross section of block (3rd project).

Compressive Strength (Individual Blocks Crushed)

Batch No. 1 Average compressive strength of 5 blocks tested between 3/8 in. thickness plywood (3 ply) = 6,425 lb./in^2.

Batch No. 2 Average compressive strength of 4 blocks tested between 1/8 in. thickness plywood (3 ply) = 6,750 lb./in^2.

Young's Modulus of Elasticity (E) (Individual Blocks Tested Statically – Direct Load)

The average value of E (five blocks) was found to equal 6.32 x 10^6 lb./in^2 measured over a 6 in. gauge length within the stress range 0 to 1,830 lb./in^2.

Shear Strength (Small Beams 10 in. between supports – made up of 3 Blocks)

The average shear strength based on 3 tests was 137 lb./in^2.

Modulus of Rupture (Small Beams)

The modulus of rupture varied from 341 lb./in^2 to 677 lb./in^2 over 12 tests on beams of 16-in. and 30-in. span.

Two of the beams tested failed in shear at 63 and 80 lb./in^2 which is considerably lower than the values obtained in the previous tests.

Creep Test (Individual Block)

Results were recorded over a 50 day period with an applied load of 10,000 lb. Creep calculations are based on a 6-in. gauge length; compensation for temperature and moisture movement being measured on an unrestrained block. Creep at an age of 50 days was 7.42 x 10^{-5} in/in.

Loading Tests on Pre-Stressed Beams

Loading tests were carried out to examine the behaviour of three pre-stressed ceramic beams spanning 10 ft. with concentrated loading at third points. The beams were formed by jointing extruded hollow clay blocks together with epoxy resin. Each beam was pre-stressed with two 0.20-in.-diameter pre-stressing wires and grouted with 1:1 cement/sand.

Fabrication

The hollow clay blocks used in this series of tests were of three different lengths, i.e. 8-1/2 in., 12-3/4 in. and 17 in. The arrangement of the blocks was as shown in Figure 34-14a.

Assembly of the beams was carried out on a sloping jig, the mix proportions of the mortar (by weight) being 100 parts epoxy resin: 60 parts hardener: 40 parts powdered china clay passing B.S. sieve No. 120.

Each beam was pre-stressed with two 0.20-in.-diameter bright plain wires with an ultimate tensile strength between 100 to 110 lb./in^2. The total pre-stressing force for beams P1 and P2 was 8,000 lb. and for beam P3, 10,000 lb. Anchor plates were 3/4-in-thick and their detail as shown in Figure 34-15. An epoxy resin joint was used between the anchor plate and end block to take up the uneven surface of the block. At the dead end of each wire, a steel collar was fitted with an electrical strain gauge placed between the anchor plate and the permanent anchor sleeve to measure the change in tension in the wire, see Figures 34-16a and b. There were also four electrical strain gauges stuck at the midspan of each beam to measure the strain distribution. Figure 34-17. After pre-stressing, all beams were grouted with 1:1 cement/sand.

Method of Pre-stressing

The wires were pre-stressed using Gifford Udall's system*** of stressing short wires, each wire being jacked individually. Initially wires were jacked to the required value and then

***Gifford Udall's System – This system is no longer available in the U.K.

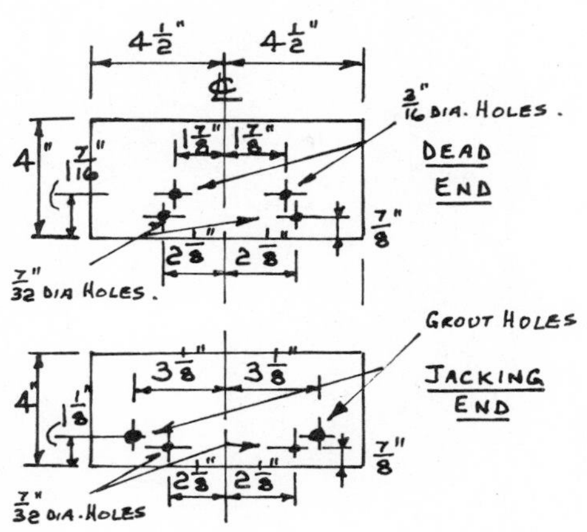

Figure 34-15. Anchor plates for beams P1, P2, and P3 (3rd project).

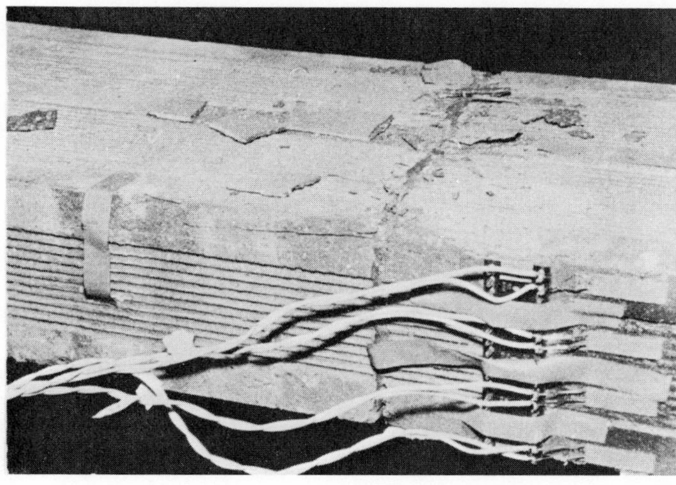

Figure 34-17. Electrical strain gauges at midspan (3rd project).

Figure 34-16a. End anchorage at jacking end (3rd project).

Figure 34-16b. End anchorage at dead end (3rd project).

released to ensure that the wedges had achieved a firm grip on the wire. Each wire was then rejacked until there was about 1/8-in. gap between the anchor sleeve and the anchor plate. A horseshoe washer, 1/8-in. thick, was then dropped in the gap before the load was finally released.

Method of Test

All beams were tested to failure with a four point loading system, Figure 34-18, the two applied point loads being at the third points.

Loading was applied and increased until approximately twice the design load was reached, the loading then being released to determine the recovery. Beams were then reloaded to failure. Dial gauges were placed at midspan to measure deflections and readings taken during testing. At the end of each test, the actual position of the pre-stressing wires, near the midspan were measured.

Results

Beam P1. Beam P1 was pre-stressed and grouted six days after assembly and jointing. Testing took place the following day. The total pre-stressing force was 8,000 lb.

At a total applied load of approximately 1,200 lb. (2.3 times the original design load), a visible crack was observed at the resin joint near to midspan. At this point the deflection was 0.73 in. The load/deflection curve (Figure 34-19) shows a large increase in deflection at approximately 1,080 lb. The actual crack probably occurred at this load. After reaching 1,357 lb. the load was reduced to 562 lb. and the recovery was 93.4 percent. Load was reapplied, but the beam deflected very rapidly without gaining much load. This was probably due to the beam no longer being capable of taking tension after cracking. Due to excessive deflection, the bottom flange of the upper steel beam was touching the top face of the clay beam

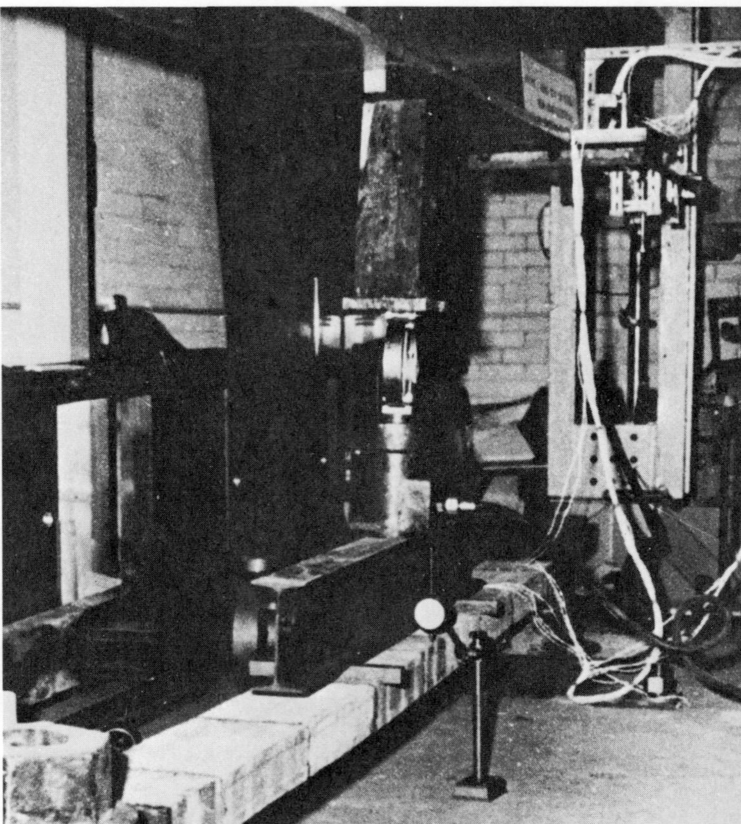

Figure 34-18. Test rig assembly with third point loading (3rd project).

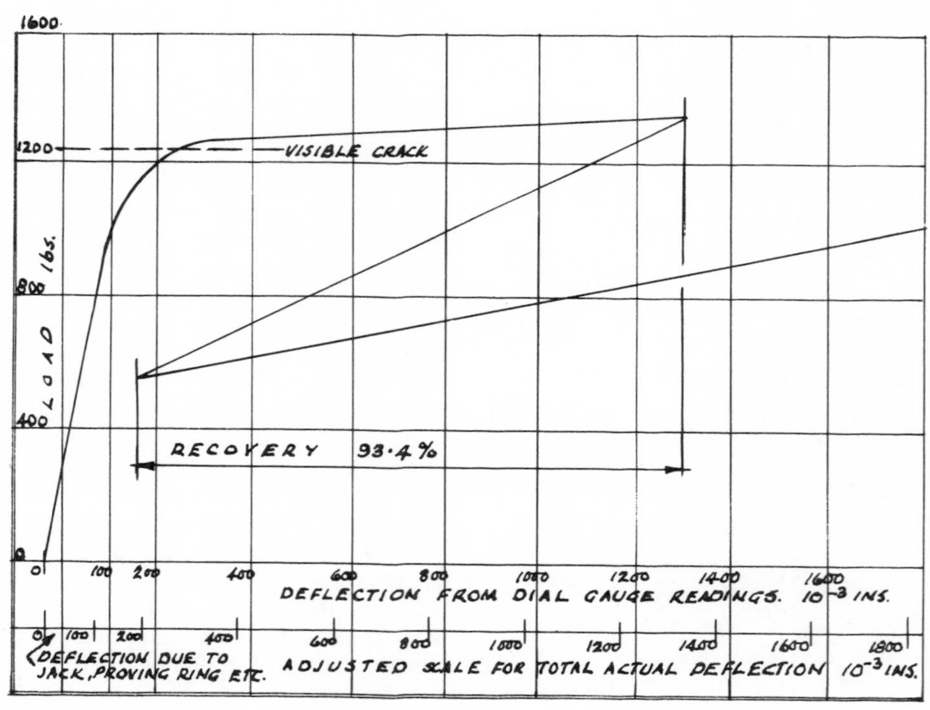

Figure 34-19. Load/deflection curve for beam P1 (3rd project).

Figure 34-20. Failure of beam P3 showing crack in bottom of beam (3rd project).

Figure 34-21. Failure of beam P3 showing spalling of beam top (3rd project).

and, therefore, loading was discontinued at approximately 1,300 lb. At this load, the opening in the resin joint was about 1/2 in. and also some crushing of the ceramic occurred in the compression zone. The pattern of failure was as shown in Figure 34-17. Maximum total load applied to the beam was 1,357 lb. After the test, the beam was loaded to collapse by applying a central point load. Collapse of the beam was due to partial crushing of the ceramic. When the load was removed completely, the beam recovered quite considerably due to the tension in the pre-stressing wire and, on inspection, it was noted that the grout in the duct was still soft and the pre-stressing wires had lifted to the top of the duct due to the deflection of the beam. Thus, this beam could be considered as ungrouted.

At an applied load of 1,080 lb. the deflection at midspan increased rapidly though no cracking was observed. From the strain diagram at this load, assuming an E value of 6.32×10^6 lb./in^2, the maximum compressive stress at the top fibre was 1,360 lb./in^2 and the maximum tensile stress at the bottom fibre was 815 lb./in^2. These values do not take into account creep or moisture and temperature movements.

Beam P2. Beam P2 was pre-stressed and grouted three days after assembly and jointing. Testing took place after a further seven days. The total pre-stressing force was 8,000 lb.

Loading was applied in approximately 100-lb. increments to 878 lb. and then reduced to 604 lb., recovery being 94.6 percent. Loading was then increased to collapse. At the end of the test, the actual position of pre-stressing wires at midspan was measured and their eccentricity found to be approximately 0.775 in. instead of the intended eccentricity of 1.085 in. This was because part of the resin joint had squeezed into the duct during gluing of the beam. The safe allowable applied load based on an eccentricity of 0.775 in. was 380 lb.

The first crack was observed at a total load of 1,144 lb. and occurred at the resin joint. As the load increased to approximately 1,307 lb. the second crack was seen and the load dropped to 1,162 lb. This crack developed into horizontal cracks in the compression zone and crack three followed. The beam failed by excessive cracking along the joints and finally collapsed by crushing of the ceramic at a total applied load of 1,639 lb. A Load Factor of 4.3 was calculated based on an allowable applied load of 380 lb. the deflection just prior to collapse being approximately 4 in.

The maximum load before cracking was taken as 1,062 lb. After this load, deflection began to increase rapidly. From the strain diagram at this load, and assuming $E = 6.32 \times 10^6$ lb./in^2, the maximum compressive stress was 905 lb./in^2 and the maximum tensile stress was 732 lb./in^2.

Average losses of pre-stress at transfer and working loads was 2.5 percent and 10 percent respectively. The losses were taken from the percentage change of strain gauge at the end of the wires, and did not take into account the frictional force between the grout and the wires.

Beam P3. Beam P3 was pre-stressed and grouted seven days after assembly and jointing. Testing took place after a further three days. The pre-stressing force was 10,000 lb.

Loading was applied up to 970 lb. and then reduced to 604 lb. recovery being 88 percent. Loading was again increased until collapse occurred at 1,579 lb. The average eccentricity of pre-stressing wires at midspan was measured after the test and found to be 0.825 in. A safe allowable applied load based on this eccentricity was 536 lb. giving a load factor of 2.95.

At a load of 1,185 lb. a visible crack was observed at the bottom of the block, Figure 34-20. As the load increased, the crack opened and the top of the block began to spall away. At 1,428 lb. the continuous deflection made it difficult to maintain a steady load. At 1,447 lb. another crack appeared along the resin joint. The maximum load reached was 1,579 lb. then the beam collapsed suddenly with the top portion of the block completely disintegrating, see Figure 34-21.

One would have expected the beam to carry a higher load than Beams P1 and P2, since it had a higher pre-stressing force. However, its collapse load and cracking loads were approximately the same as for Beam P2. Also this was the only beam which cracked at the block instead of at the joint. Therefore, the cause of failure may have been due to a particular weak block but further testing is obviously necessary to verify this. The relationship between applied load and deflection was recorded and up to 1,000 lb. the relationship was linear but just before any visible crack was observed the deflection increased rapidly. At the allowable applied load of 536 lb. the deflection was approximately 0.49 in., i.e. span/2,400 and at twice the allowable applied load of 1,072 lb. the deflection was 0.13 in., i.e. span/425.

The maximum load before cracking was taken as 970 lb. From the strain diagram at this load and assuming $E = 6.32 \times 10^6$ lb./in^2, the maximum compressive stress at the top fibre was 1,450 lb./in^2 and the maximum tensile stress at the bottom was 753 lb./in^2.

The average loss of pre-stress at transfer was 2.05 percent which was less than beam P1, 4.9 percent and P2, 2.5 percent. This decreasing loss of pre-stress at transfer was probably due to improvement in the technique of pre-stressing. It is not possible to record the loss of pre-stress at the working load due to a failure in the electricity supply at that time.

Author's Comments

1. The average crushing strength of the extruded clay blocks was 6,425 lb./in.^{2} for batch No. 1 and 6,750 lb./in.^{2} for batch No. 2.

2. The stress/strain curve during loading and unloading is not the same, there is a hysteresis. If the average values of loading and unloading curves are taken, then the stress/strain relationship is linear up to a stress of 1,835 lb./in^2. (No test was carried out above this value.) The modulus of elasticity $E = 6.32 \times 10^6$ lb./in^2.

3. Due to the brittleness of the material the failure in compression is sudden and without warning.

4. From the shear tests, the shear stress at failure was 137 lb./in^2. This value is quite low and should be considered carefully during design.

5. The modulus of rupture from the flexural tests varies from 341 lb./in^2 to 677 lb./in^2. Variation is mainly due to the location of the resin joint which is weaker than the parent material.

6. The creep observed at an age of 50 days was 7.42×10^{-5} in./in.

7. In the majority of beams tested, failure occurred along the resin joints, indicating that the resin joint is not as strong as the parent material. It is considered that the joint weakness may be due to it being too thick.

8. To increase the joint strength, it is recommended that the ends of blocks should be ground.

9. Since the ends of the blocks are not square, the beam formed by jointing these blocks together will not be straight. This difficulty can also be overcome by grinding the ends.

10. The recovery of pre-stressed beams was found to be very good. When the load had been reduced after reaching about twice the safe applied load, the recovery was approximately 90 percent. The average Load Factor at collapse was approximately 3.5.

11. From strain gauge measurements on the pre-stressed beams, it was noted that the clay blocks were able to take a tensile strain of approximately 12×10^{-5} in./in. before cracking. Assuming an E value of 6.32×10^6 lb./in.^{2} the tensile stress is approximately 763 lb./in^2.

Discussion

Extruded ceramic blocks can be satisfactorily pre-stressed. There seems no major technical reason why pre-stressed extruded ceramic blocks should not provide a satisfactory and economical flooring system, though there are still some problems:

1. The ends of the blocks may have to be ground smooth to obtain a strong resin joint. The cost involved will undoubtedly be the deciding factor.

2. Long ceramic blocks will reduce the number of joints, thus saving jointing material and labour and also reducing the tendency for failure where joints would otherwise have occurred. However, long extruded ceramic blocks are difficult to manufacture and tend to warp during firing.

3. Long-term behaviour is still not fully understood.

If a pre-stressed ceramic flooring system is to be developed, further investigations are necessary and the following suggestions may be worthy of consideration.

a. To improve the strength of the joints, grinding the ends of the blocks may be necessary or alternatively another jointing material investigated.

b. The performance of various geometrical shapes should be investigated.

c. Long-term tests should be carried out on loaded beams.

d. Since such beams are intended to be laid side by side and inter-locked to act as a single floor, behaviour in the lateral direction under load should also be investigated.

As a direct result of the investigation at Sunderland a British patent* has been taken out on a pre-stressed ceramic flooring system, the cross-section of which is illustrated in Figure 34-22.

The Future

As described, great interest has been shown in this form of construction and undoubtedly further developments will take place.

Pre-fabrication offers a challenge to the ceramic industry and one method of permanently assembling small components is to pre-stress.

In the realm of traditional brickwork, temporary external post-stressing techniques could be developed to facilitate erection of large panels which, when in position, could be released from pre-compression, thereafter functioning as traditional panels.

It is not always appreciated by designers that some fired clay products can offer compressive strength far in excess of many concretes and with the advent of cheaper high-strength mortars and post or pre-stressed methods, yet another structural material will be available.

References

1. "Reinforced Brick Masonry", Bulletin No. 5, National Brick Manufacturers Research Foundation, February 1932.

*Patent Specification No. Hd – 34864 – "Improvements in or Relating to Flooring and Like Structures"

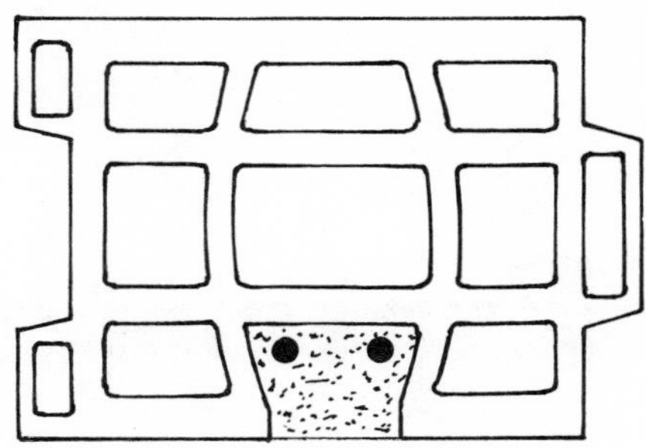

Figure 34-22. Cross section of new ceramic block (3rd project).

2. Neill, J. A., "Post-tensioned Brickwork and its use in the construction of a factory at Darlington", *C.P.T.B. Technical Note,* Vol. 1, No. 9. May 1966.
3. Foster, D., "Reinforced Brickwork Box Beams", S.C.P. 3, Structural Clay Products Limited, October 1966.
4. Plowman, J. M., Sutherland, R. J. M., and Couzens, M. L., "The Testing of Reinforced Brickwork and Concrete Slabs Forming Box Beams", *The Structural Engineer,* Vol. 45, No. 11, November 1967.
5. Henkley, A. T., "Test of one-storey Pre-stressed Brickwork Shear Walls", *New Zealand Engineering,* 21 (6) June 1966.
6. Tasker, H. E., "Recommendations for the use of Pre-stressed Brick or Block Walls on Reactive Soils", Technical Record 52:75:349, Department of Works, Commonwealth Experimental Building Section.
7. Prasan, S., Hendry, A. W., and Bradshaw, R. E., "Crushing Tests of Storey-Height Panels 4-1/2 inches Thick", *Proceedings of the British Ceramic Society,* Issue No. 4, July 1965.
8. Thomas, K., "Laterally Reinforced Brickwork", (Some notes on current practice in Eastern Europe.) *C.P.T.B. Technical Note,* Volume 2, No. 1. July 1967.

35. Experimental determination of eccentricity of floor loads applied to a bearing wall.*

David Watstein and P. V. Johnson, Structural Clay Products Institute, McLean, Virginia

Introduction

Since exterior bearing walls are designed as eccentrically loaded compression members, it is important to know what the eccentricities of the applied floor loads are for different bearing materials and different conditions of contact between the supporting structure and the floor beams. Some recently completed exploratory studies by the Structural Clay Products Institute Research Fellowship at NBS indicated that it is feasible to measure the eccentricities of applied loads using a specially designed, stress-sensitive compressive strut calibrated under loads of known eccentricities. The strut was assumed to simulate a load-bearing wall of brick masonry even though the boundary conditions and the elastic properties of the strut were different from those encountered in an actual masonry structure.

The exploratory study included investigating such parameters as thickness and rigidity of bearing materials, intimacy of contact between the supporting structure and the flexural members, and effect of bond with the bedding material on the eccentricity of the floor loads.

The feasibility of measuring the eccentricity of the force supporting a masonry wall subjected to an eccentrically applied load was also explored.

Description of the Compressive Steel Reaction Strut for Measurement of Eccentricities, and Its Calibration

The compressive steel reaction strut was a rectangular steel tube 4 by 8 inches in cross section, having a 0.187-inch-thick wall. The strut was 18 inches high and had a 3/8-inch welded steel plate insert at the top providing a closed end. The strut was capped with a 1- by 4- by 8-inch cold rolled steel plate bonded to the top welded plate insert with epoxy cement. The whole assembly was then capped with a solid extruded clay brick which served to receive the load simulating the bearing conditions at the top of a brick wall. The open bottom end was machined normal to the axis of the strut and was supported on a machined steel plate 4 inches thick.

The dimensions of the capping brick were 2-1/4 by 3-9/16 by 7-7/8 inches and, hence, the brick did not cover the 1-inch steel cap completely. The brick was set flush with one side of the strut (designated as side H) and was centered with respect to the 4-inch dimension of the strut as shown in Figure 35-1.

The strut was instrumented with bonded wire strain gages at two different levels. The location of the gages is indicated in Figure 35-1.

During calibration, load P was applied to the strut through a hardened steel knife edge seated in a suitable V block. Thus, the eccentricity of the applied load could be measured with a steel scale with an accuracy of about 1/32 inch.

Let σ_{max} and σ_{min} be respectively the stresses on the side of the applied load and the opposite side; then the following expressions can be written:

$$\sigma_{max} = \frac{P}{A} + \frac{Pec}{Ar^2} = \frac{P}{A}\left[1 + \frac{ec}{r^2}\right] \qquad (35\text{-}1)$$

and:

$$\sigma_{min} = \frac{P}{A} - \frac{Pec}{Ar^2} = \frac{P}{A}\left[1 - \frac{ec}{r^2}\right] \qquad (35\text{-}2)$$

where:

A The cross section area of the strut, in.^{2}

c Distance from the neutral axis to the outermost fiber in.

*Contribution of National Bureau of Standards, not subject to copyright.

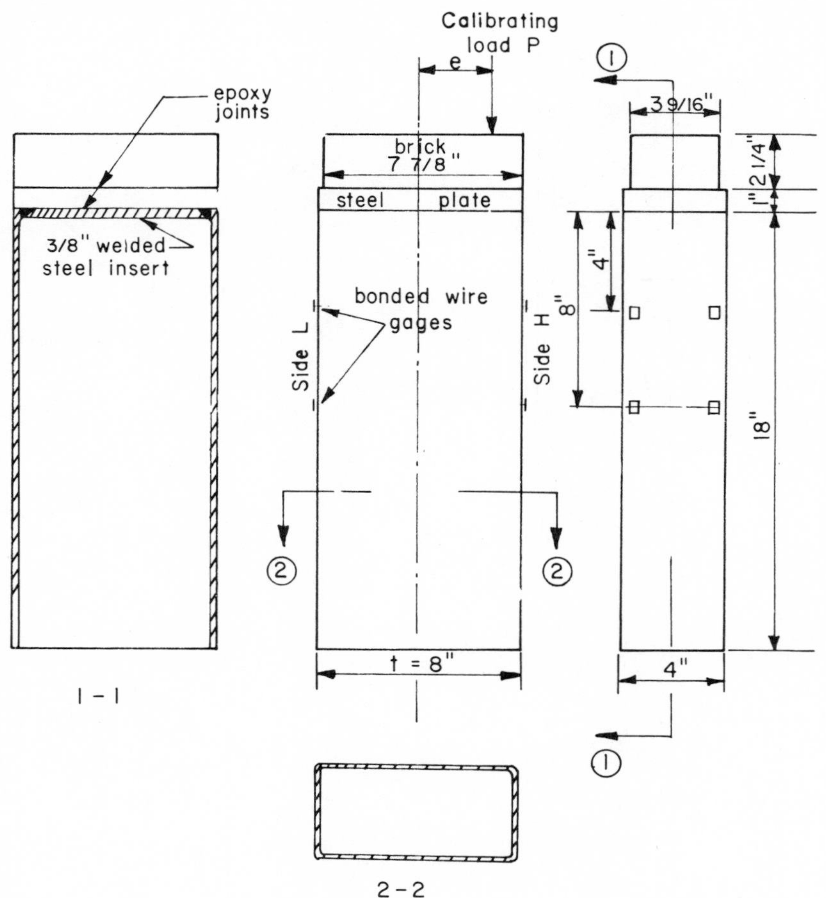

Figure 35-1. Schematic drawing of instrumented reaction strut for measurement of eccentricity of load.

r Radius of gyration, in. (Ar^2 = moment of inertia of the section.)
e Eccentricity of applied load, in.

Adding Equations 35-1 and 35-2:

$$\sigma_{max} + \sigma_{min} = \frac{2P}{A} \quad (35\text{-}3)$$

Subtracting Equation 35-2 from Equation 35-1:

$$\sigma_{max} - \sigma_{min} = \frac{2\,Pec}{Ar^2} \quad (35\text{-}4)$$

Dividing Equation 35-4 by 35-3:

$$\frac{\sigma_{max} - \sigma_{min}}{\sigma_{max} + \sigma_{min}} = \frac{ec}{r^2} \quad (35\text{-}5)$$

and solving for e:

$$e = \frac{r^2}{c}\left[\frac{\sigma_{max} - \sigma_{min}}{\sigma_{max} + \sigma_{min}}\right]$$

Assuming that the stresses σ_{max} and σ_{min} are within the elastic limit, the eccentricity e in terms of strains ϵ_{max} and ϵ_{min} is given by:

$$e = \frac{r^2}{c}\left[\frac{\epsilon_{max} - \epsilon_{min}}{\epsilon_{max} + \epsilon_{min}}\right] \quad (35\text{-}6)$$

For the reaction strut used in these tests, $r^2/c = 2.06$, and Equation 35-6 becomes:

$$e = 2.06\,\frac{(\epsilon_{max} - \epsilon_{min})}{(\epsilon_{max} + \epsilon_{min})} \quad (35\text{-}7)$$

where e is given in inches.

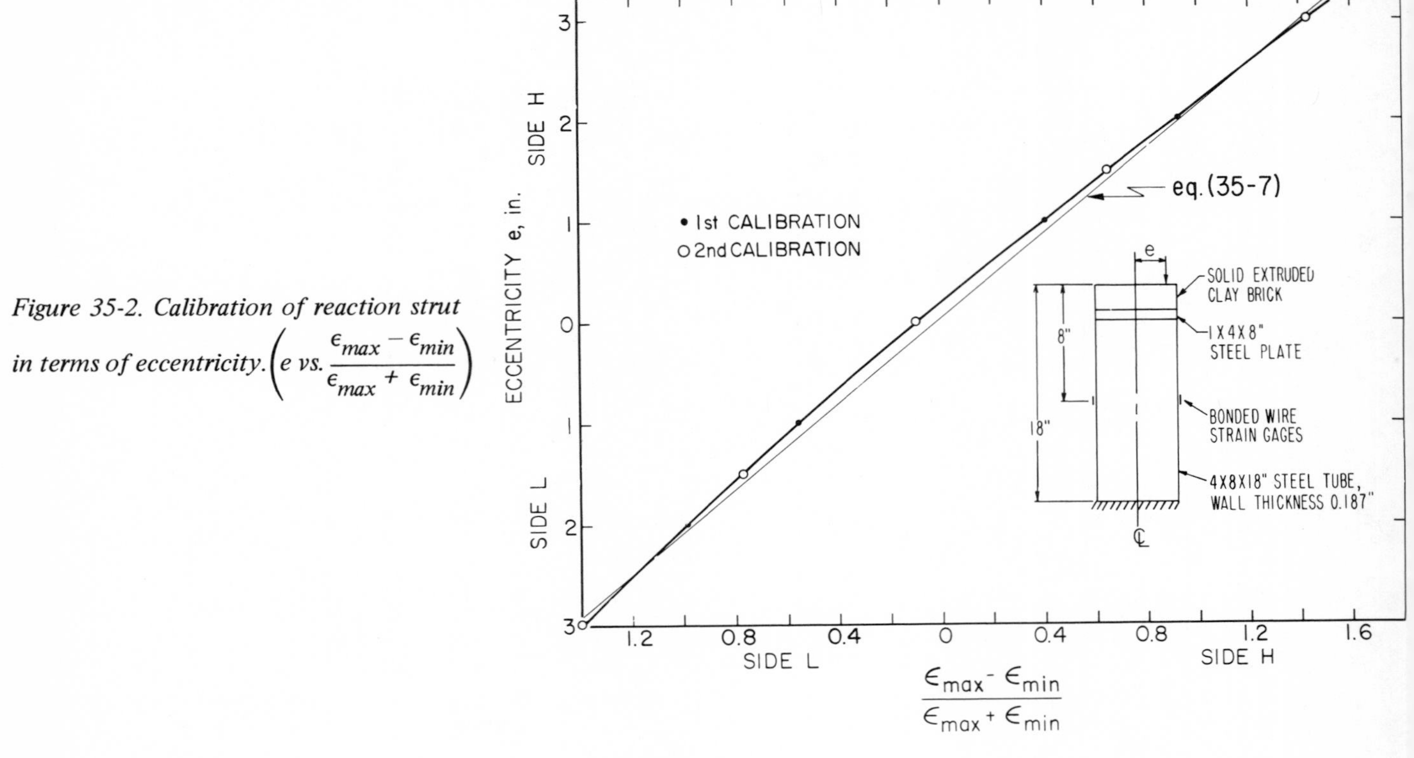

Figure 35-2. Calibration of reaction strut in terms of eccentricity. $\left(e \text{ vs. } \frac{\epsilon_{max} - \epsilon_{min}}{\epsilon_{max} + \epsilon_{min}}\right)$

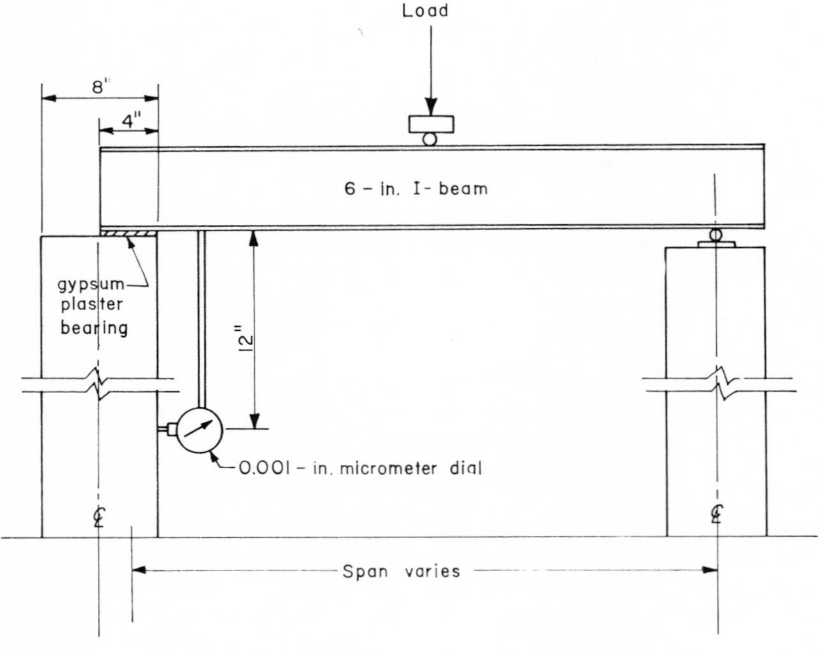

Figure 35-3. Schematic diagram of test set-up for an I-beam bedded in gypsum plaster.

The theoretical relationship given by Equation 35-7 and the experimental curve determined in two separate laboratory set-ups are compared in Figure 35-2. The experimental values of eccentricity e were varied over a range of 3 inches on each side of the center line of the strut. It should be added that the strain values given in Figure 35-2 were those obtained from the lower set of strain gages, since they yielded a more consistent relationship than the top gages.

The departure of the calibration curve from the straight line predicted by Equation 35-7 may possibly be accounted for by the non-homogeneous nature of the welded steel tube used in fabricating the strut, and the possible presence of slight

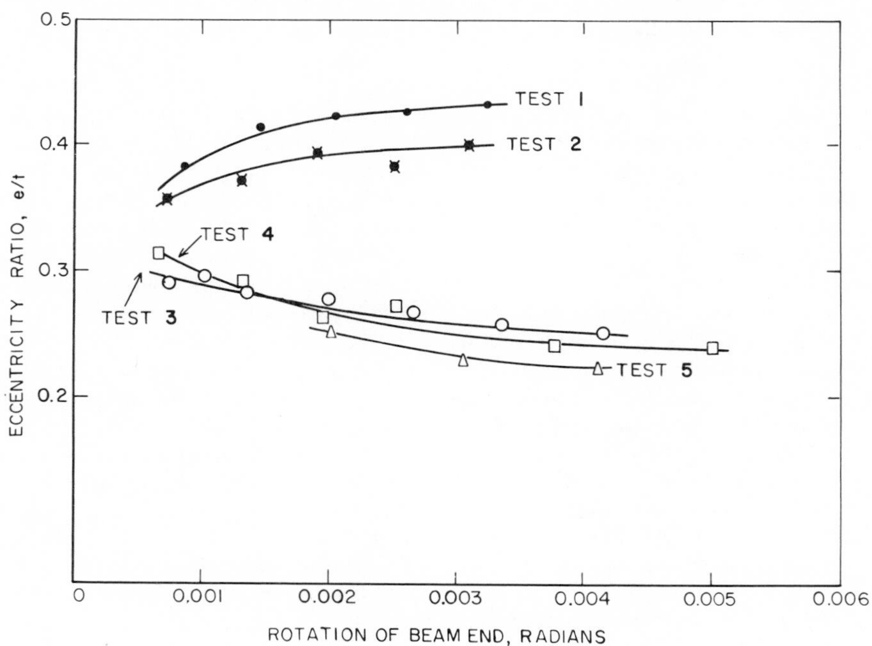

Figure 35-4. Eccentricity of reaction for an I-beam bedded in gypsum plaster. Tests 1 and 2–unbonded plaster. Tests 3, 4, and 5–bonded plaster, spans 24, 36, and 48 in. respectively.

irregularities commonly found in thin-walled extruded steel shapes. In future work, it is intended to fabricate a strut of greater strain sensitivity and have it relatively free from the deficiencies which might have caused the deviation from theoretical relationship shown in Figure 35-2.

Eccentricity of Reaction of an I-Beam Bedded in Gypsum Plaster

One series of five tests was carried out with an I-beam 6 inches deep and a flange 3-1/2 inches wide bedded in high strength gypsum plaster. As in all determinations of eccentricity described in this chapter, the end of the I-beam extended to the center line of the supporting strut. The arrangement of supports and the load are shown in Figure 35-3, along with the device for measuring the rotation of the beam end at the strut. This measurement was an approximation based on the assumption that the strut did not depart from its initial vertical position, and that the vertical displacement of the point at which the micrometer dial assembly was attached to the I-beam was negligible.

In Tests 1 and 2, the I-beam was bedded in unbonded plaster. The bond between the plaster and the bearing surfaces was destroyed by confining the plaster putty between two sheets of polyethylene. The variation of the eccentricity ratio with the rotation of the beam end is illustrated in Figure 35-4. It is noted that at small rotations of the beam supported on the strut simulating a wall, the eccentricity ratio e/t* was about 0.35, or nearly the value usually assumed in design of masonry walls. The eccentricity ratio increased with the beam rotation and tended to reach a constant value at large rotations. For Tests 1 and 2, the maximum values of e/t were 0.43 and 0.40 respectively, with an average of 0.415. The maximum center load applied in these tests was 25 kips and the beam span was 44 inches.

In Tests 3, 4, and 5 the I-beam was bedded in bonded plaster and the span lengths were 24, 36, and 48 inches respectively. It is interesting to compare in Figure 35-4 the effect of bonded and unbonded plaster bearings on the behavior of the I-beam. The unbonded I-beam showed an increase in the eccentricity ratio with load, while that for the bonded I-beam showed the opposite. The value of e/t for the bonded I-beam was about 0.32 for low loads and decreased with the rotation of the beam; the eccentricity ratio tended to reach a constant value as the rotation increased. The average e/t for the three tests at the maximum recorded rotation was about 0.24, and represents a reduction of 42 percent as compared with the eccentricity ratio for unbonded plaster.

Although the use of high strength gypsum plaster is not practical as a permanent bedding material for floor beams, its effect as a bonding bearing material was investigated as one phase of the broad problem of load transfer to masonry walls. It is possible that some other more permanent bedding material can be found which would have the same favorable effect on the eccentricity ratio as the high strength gypsum plaster.

*t is defined as the overall thickness of the strut.

Eccentricity of Reaction of an I-Beam Supported on Neoprene Rubber

Five tests were performed to determine the eccentricity ratio for the previously described I-beam supported on a neoprene rubber pad. The hardness of the rubber as given by Shore A. Durometer was 65 (instantaneous value). The rubber sheets were 1/16 inch thick and they were stacked to give thicknesses of 1/8- and 1/4-inch.

The test set-up used in the tests with a rubber bearing material was similar to that shown in Figure 35-3, except that the rotation of the beam end was measured with two micrometer dial gages; one of these was clamped to the web of the I-beam and measured the movement of the end of the beam with respect to the bearing surface of the strut, while the second one was attached to the side of the strut and its stem was in contact with the underside of the flange of the I-beam.

In tests 6 and 7, the I-beam was supported on a 1-8-inch-thick neoprene pad over its entire 4-inch bearing length. The rubber pad was coated with gypsum plaster putty on both bearing surfaces to assure intimate contact over its entire area.

The values of e/t obtained in Tests 6 and 7 are shown in Figure 35-5. It is noted that e/t increased with the beam end rotation as would be expected in an unbonded bearing which leaves the beam end free to rotate without any restraint from the supporting wall. The average value of e/t ranged from 0.27 initially to 0.30 at the maximum rotation. The beam span used in these tests was 44 inches and the maximum applied load was 30 kips.

Tests 6 and 7 were two independent determinations representing, as nearly as possible, identical support conditions. It is important to note that in spite of all efforts to secure uniform and intimate contact with the rubber bearing pad, the two determinations of e/t varied from 0.28 to 0.31 at the maximum rotation. Perhaps this variability even between two supposedly identical tests will account for the very large difference in e/t values between Test 10 and Tests 6 and 7. In Test 10 the carefully leveled I-beam was set directly on a rubber pad 1/8 inch thick; however, it was noted that the contact with the rubber pad was not intimate, and that daylight could be seen under the outer corners of the I-beam flange. In this instance a large rotation was observed at an extremely small load. In this test, the value of e/t was initially 0.45 and it tended to become nearly constant at 0.40 for the maximum rotation of the beam end. The span length in this test was 44 inches and the maximum applied load was 30 kips. This comparison of otherwise identical tests (Tests 6, 7, and 10) points up the importance of attaining intimate contact with rubber pads of limited thickness and large bearing area. It can be seen that the e/t ratio of 0.40 for Test 10 was about the same as for unbonded plaster bearing pads in Figure 35-4.

In Tests 8 and 9 the length of the bearing pad was reduced to 2 inches at the extreme end of the beam. As would be expected, the confinement of the bearing reduced the e/t ratio considerably. For Test 8, with a 1/8-inch-thick capped bearing

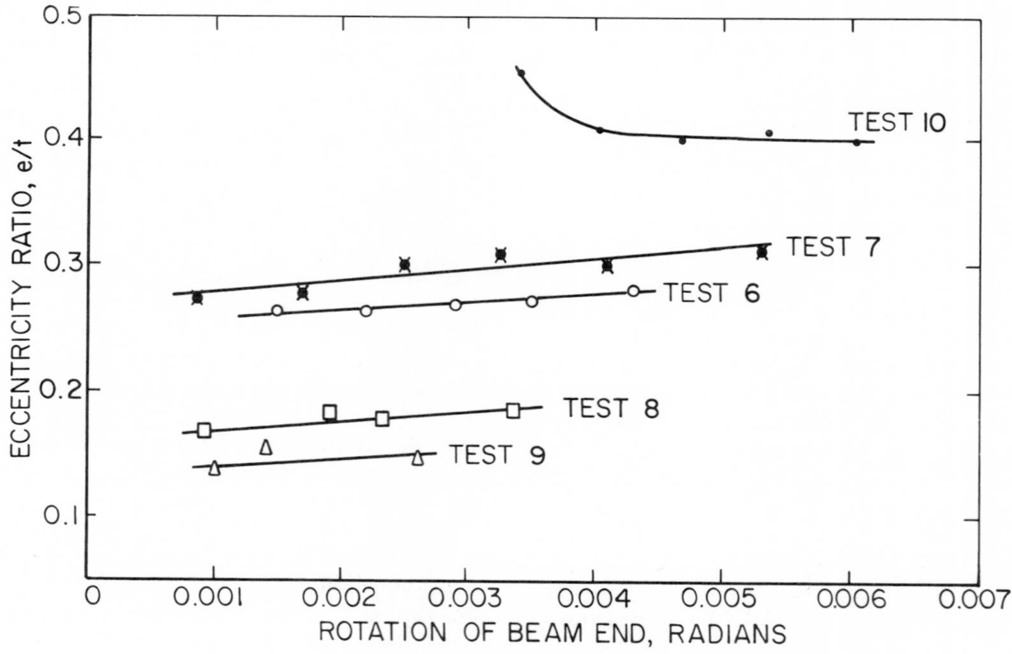

Figure 35-5. Eccentricity of reaction for an I-beam supported on neoprene rubber pads. Tests 6 and 7–1/8" rubber pad, 4" long, coated with plaster. Test 8–1/8" rubber pad, 2" long, coated with plaster. Test 9–1/4" pad, 2" long, no plaster. Test 10–same as 6 and 7, but no plaster coating.

Figure 35-6. Overall view of test set-up to determine the eccentricity of supporting force at the base of an eccentrically loaded bearing wall.

pad, e/t ranged from an initial value of 0.17 to 0.185 at the maximum end rotation. For Test 9 in which the rubber pad thickness was increased to 1/4 inch and no plaster capping, the e/t ratio was further reduced to yield a maximum of about 0.15. It is noted that in this test the minimum value of e/t was 0.135, as compared with a theoretical value of 0.125. This theoretical value would be expected from the assumption that the centroid of the bearing stresses lies at the midpoint of a uniformly compressed pad.

Eccentricity of Supporting Force at the Base of a Bearing Wall Subjected to an Eccentrically Applied Load

Two exploratory tests were performed to investigate the feasibility of measuring the eccentricity of the supporting force at the base of a wall subjected to an eccentrically applied load. An overall view and a close-up of the loading fixture are shown in Figures 35-6 and 35-7.

The wall used in these tests was essentially a pier 3-9/16 by 7-7/8 inches in cross section built of solid extruded clay brick laid in stacked bond with extremely thin joints of high-strength gypsum plaster. The strut was used as a base for this assembly, as shown in Figure 35-6. The wall was built in two stages—the first was 24 inches high and the second was 48 inches high; both dimensions are nominal. The wall was subjected to two loads at each height, a centrally applied load, and an eccentric load applied on side H (see Figure 35-1) 2.5 inches from the center line of the pier.† The values of eccentricity of applied loads and the measured values of eccentricity of reactions at the base of the wall are given in Table 35-1 for both the 24- and 48-inch high wall.

It can be seen from the data in Table 35-1 that the calibrated reaction strut can be used to measure the eccentricity of the reaction at the base of a bearing wall. The effect of the wall height on the possible decrease of eccentricity at the base will be explored further in future tests using a calibrated reaction strut of sufficient capacity to accommodate a larger wall specimen.

Summary

The following comments appropriately summarize the work reported herein:

1. A test procedure was developed by means of which the eccentricity of loads applied to a strut assumed to simulate a bearing wall could be measured. The device also was suitable

†The center line of the pier was taken as the center line of the compressive strut.

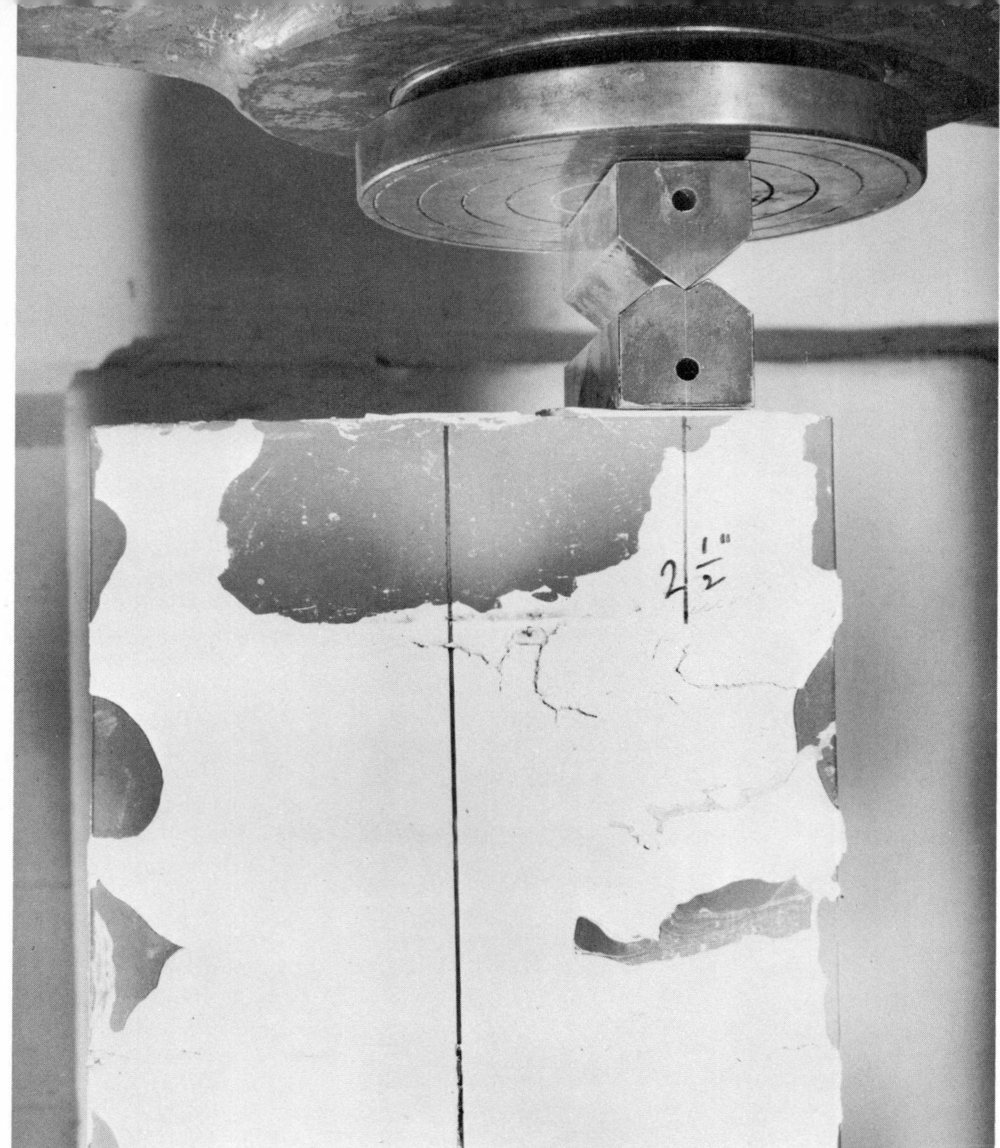

Figure 35-7. Close-up of eccentrically loaded wall showing the loading knife edge.

Table 35-1
Measured Eccentricities of Reaction at the Base of Wall Subjected to a Load of Known Eccentricity

Wall Height	Eccentricity of Applied Load	Applied Load	Measured Strains on strut		$\frac{e\ max - e\ min}{e\ max + e\ min}$	Measured eccentricty at base of wall (from Fig. 2)
			e max	e min		
in.	in.	kips	10^{-6}	10^{-6}		in.
24	0	15	112	112	0	0.15
24	0	20	151	149	0.007	0.16
24	2.5	10	155	-10*	1.14	2.45
48	0	10	69	77	-0.05	0.06
48	0	20	148	159	-0.04	0.06
48	2.5	5	83	0	1.00	2.20
48	2.5	10	157	2	0.97	2.14

*Tensile strain

for measuring the eccentricity of the supporting force at the base of a bearing wall subjected to an eccentric load.

2. Both rigid and resilient bearing materials, such as gypsum plaster and neoprene rubber, were used to support an I-beam as a floor member.

3. For an unbonded plaster bearing, the observed eccentricity ratio increased with rotation of the beam end to a maximum value of about 0.42. For the bonded plaster bearing, this ratio decreased with rotation to an average value of 0.24 at the maximum load.

4. Intimacy of contact was essential for achieving a favorable distribution of bearing stresses with a neoprene rubber pad. Lack of intimate and complete contact between the I-beam and the rubber pad resulted in an eccentricity ratio of about 0.40; this value was reduced to 0.29 by bedding the rubber pad in plaster. A 50 percent reduction of the bearing length of the pad and its confinement to the extreme end of the beam further reduced the eccentricity ratio to a minimum value of 0.135.

5. The eccentricity ratio was not found to be sensitive to substantial increases in the rotation of the beam end in the loading range producing rotations on the order of 0.004 – 0.005 radians.

6. Because of the limited sensitivity of the eccentricity measuring device, the values of eccentricity ratio observed for low loads and extremely small rotations were not considered sufficiently accurate for presentation.

7. Because of the limitation of the span lengths and flexural rigidities of the floor beam and the reaction strut used in these tests, the eccentricity ratios reported herein may not be applicable to spans and rigidities of widely different values. It is considered that additional experimental work with greater range of parameters is needed.

8. To achieve a greater degree of similitude between the eccentricity measuring device and an actual masonry wall, the boundary conditions with respect to sidesway at the top and restraint at the base of the strut will need to be observed during both calibration and the measurement of eccentricities.

36. Effect of manufacturing and construction variables on durability and compressive strength of brick masonry.

J. W. Howard, Clay Products Association of the Southwest, R. B. Hockaday, Acme Brick Company, and Wm. K. Soderstrum, Structural Clay Products Research Foundation

The following discussion among the three authors is an attempt to examine the triaxial innerfaces of structural engineering, ceramic engineering, and production research.

Mr. Howard: To guide us in this discussion we shall limit ourselves to brick, made from burned clay or shale, and to two properties of brick: compressive strength and durability. These two properties are of great importance when brick is to be used in a load-bearing brick masonry structure. The structural engineer must be assured of a given level of strength in brick masonry as well as durability of the assemblage. The structural engineer, utilizing a brick masonry structural system, must be convinced by the manufacturer and product research engineer that the brick are produced with consistent quality materials.

Mr. Hockaday: I think we can do just that. When you understand the manufacturing process you will see how it is possible to produce a brick of consistent strength and durability.

Mr. Soderstrum: Mr. Howard, you say it is important that you know the compressive strength of brick. To what extent does the brick strength affect the strength of brick masonry?

Mr. Howard: Mr. Grimm[1] suggests that the ultimate strength of brick masonry is dependent upon variables defined by the following equation:

$$f_m' = .087\ \omega\delta\epsilon \left\{4590 + f_b' \left[1 + 1.29\ \alpha\beta\gamma\ (1 + 1.46 \text{ Log } C/L)\right]\right\}$$

where:

f_m' = ultimate compressive strength of the brick masonry, psi:

ω is the workmanship coefficient, dimensionless. Equal to 1 for inspected workmanship and equal to .67 for commercial workmanship.

δ = $.0178\ \{57.3 - [(h_s/t_s) - 6]^2\}$, slenderness coefficient, dimensionless h_s/t_s is the ratio of height to the least lateral dimension (thickness) of the brick masonry test specimen, where:

$$5 > (h_s / t_s) > 2$$

ϵ $1.23\ (1.19 - t_j)$, joint thickness coefficient, dimensionless.

t_j Mortar bed joint thickness in inches, where:

$$.75 > t_j > .25.$$

f_b' = compressive strength of brick, psi.

α = $.3\ (1 + 1.59 \text{ Log } d)$, specimen age coefficient, dimensionless.

d is the age of the brick masonry test specimen in days where:

$$d \leqq 28$$

β = $15.67/7^{1.3\ (W/C)}$, water-cement coefficient, dimensionless.

W/C is the ratio of water to cement by weight in the mortar, where:

$$.7 > (W/C) > .4$$

γ = .021 (57.3 – A), air content coefficient, dimensionless.
A is the percent air by volume in the mortar, where:

$$30 \geqq A$$

C/L is the volumetric ration of Type I portland cement to Type S hydrated line, where:

$$4 > (C/L) > 1$$

in mortar conforming to ASTM C 270.

The low and high probable extreme of each variable is:
ω = 1 and .667
δ = 1 where h/t = 5. Keep this constant.
ϵ = .54 to 1.16 (3/4" to 1/4" joint thicknesses)
f_b' = 4,000 to 15,000 psi
α = 1 where d = 28 days. Keep this constant.
β = 2.30 to .79 where W/C = .45 to .70
γ = 1.20 to .68 where A = 0% to 25% air entrainment
C/L = 1 to 4

The substitution of the low and high probable extreme value for each variable into Grimm's equation gives an average value of f_m' of 2425 psi. The normal value for each variable, which produces this average compressive strength, has been constant while one variable varies.

Example:
ω = 1

$$f_m' = \frac{.087 \times 1 \times 1 \times 1}{\{4590 + 8{,}000[1 + 1.29 \times 1 \times 1 \times 1(1 + 1.46 \text{ Log } 1/½)]\}}$$

f_m' = 2386 psi
ω = .667

$$f_m' = \frac{.087 \times .667 \times 1 \times 1}{\{4590 + 8{,}000[1 + 1.29 \times 1 \times 1 \times 1(1 + 1.46 \text{ Log } 1/½)]\}}$$

f_m' = 1590 psi

The effect on f_m' of any one variable can be computed. Assuming an allowable tolerance of ± 10 percent from the average value produced from all extremes represents the first order of significance. This significant deviation is 10 percent x 2425 psi or 242 psi. A significant index for any one variable can be computed as follows:

Example:
ω = 1 f_m' = 2386 psi
ω = .667 f_m' = 1590 psi
2386 – 1590 = 796
796/242 = 3.3

and compared to the significant index for the other variable. Table 36-1 gives these significant indexes for the variables selected here for analysis.

Table 36-1
Construction Variables and Their Effect on Ultimate Strength of Brick Masonry

Variable	Significant Index	
	Individual	Group
Mortar		17.2
Air content	2.7	
Cement-Lime ratio	3.3	
Water-Cement ratio	8.1	
Mason		7.9
Workmanship	3.3	
Joint Thickness	6.1	
Brick		11.4
Compressive Strength	11.4	

If a variable were to have a significant index of less than one, it would be significant. Interesting comparisions can be made of the variables of these groups, e.g., mortar, mason, and brick. The index for mortar of 17.2 is misleading in that the water-cement ratio is the big factor and is affected by the initial absorption rate of the brick and the mason's subjective evaluation of workability.

The two most important individual factors affecting masonry strength are the factors which deal with the properties of the units themselves, the compressive strength, and the initial rate of absorption.

Mr. Hockaday: This is very interesting, but you have used extreme values for each variable. What happens on the job site where the values may vary only slightly?

Mr. Howard: If we apply this same methodology as before with the exception of limits of the variables, in an example, of 8,000 psi brick and ASTM C270 type S mortar, the probable high and low range of variables are shown in Table 36-2.

These values are substituted into Grimm's equation and a significant index for each variable is shown in Table 36-3.

Considering the accuracy of the equation and the choice of variation of each variable, it is evident that workmanship, brick, and mortar have about equal effect on compressive strength of masonry in a particular project.

If one looks at individual variables and their significant index numbers, it becomes evident that workmanship is of great importance. Workmanship, as defined by Grimm's equation, is simply the degree to which the mason completely fills the mortar joints. The coefficient is 1 for completely filled joints and .667 for deeply furrowed bed joints and very little mortar in head joints.

High-quality brick masonry is obtained when the mortar design is compatible with the brick to be used and the mason assembles these two by filling all joints.

Table 36-2
Probable Range of Variables in Brick Masonry for 8,000 psi Brick and Type S Mortar

	Variable	Values		
		Low	Avg.	High
ω	Workmanship coefficient	.667	.834	1
δ	h/t ratio, keep this constant		1	
ϵ	Joint thickness coefficient*	.89	1	1.12
f'_b	Compressive strength†	7100	8000	8900
a	Specimen age coefficient (constant)		1	
β	Water-Cement coefficient	.79	1	1.21
γ	(5% to 25% air entrainment)	.68	1	1.10
C/L	Cement to lime ratio	1.33	1.6	2

* ASTM C216-65
"Facing Brick (Solid Masonry Units Made from Clay or Shale)", Table IV type FBS Brick, Maximum permissible variation at 3/32" for dimensions of brick 3" and under.

† "National Testing Program" Progress Report No. 1, October 1964, Structural Clay Products Research Foundation. Coefficient of variation is 11.3 percent ±.

Table 36-3
Construction Variables for 8,000 psi Brick and Type S Mortar and Their Effect on Ultimate Strength of the Brick Masonry

Variable	Significant Index	
	Individual	Group
Workmanship	4	4
Brick		4.25
Compressive strength	1.91	
Joint thickness	2.28	
Mortar		5.1
Water-cement ratio	2.18	
Air content	2.18	
Cement-lime ratio	1.01	

In this discussion, we are dealing with compressive strength and durability. Can you, Mr. Hockaday, produce brick with high compressive strength and high durability at the same time?

Mr. Hockaday: You have mentioned the variables which affect the strength of a brick wall. Let me mention the variables which affect the strength of a brick in the manufacturing process.

1. Clay or shale. This is the primary source of strength. Clays and shales vary from different parts of the country as well as in any one pit.

2. Grog (ground burned clay). The addition of grog can increase strength to a point, then it becomes detrimental. Grog breaks up laminations and affects some interlocking ties and the clay body. It is also used to prevent cracking in drying.

3. Water. The lack of water would result in insufficient bond of the clay particles, while too much water results in laminations, high porosity, drying problems, and insufficient bond.

4. Grinding. The finer you grind the clay the higher the strength.

5. Particle size. The distribution of particle size adds to the mechanical interlocking which increases strength.

6. Extrusion. The stiff column gives higher strength and a dense brick. It should be noted that if the brick is too dense it will have a low initial absorption rate and become a floater (mason's name for a brick which floats on the mortar when laid. It will not stay in place).

7. Vacuum. A high vacuum removes air from the clay and reduces lamination. The vacuum also affects the density of the brick.

8. Drying. If the brick is dried too rapidly and cracks, the strength is lowered.

9. Burning. In burning, both time and temperature is important. You must get complete crystal growth with some glass formed. Crystal growth affects ceramic and mechanical bond while glass acts as a glue or ceramic bond.

These are the variables that affect the strength of brick. To explain the relationship between variables, I will ask Mr. Soderstrum to relate some of the results of his factorial experiments at Structural Clay Products Research Foundation.

Mr. Soderstrum: This factorial experiment for which testing has been completed but analysis is not yet complete was an attempt to establish a relationship between resistance to freeze-thaw, as measured on our experimental freeze-thaw plates, and the physical properties of brick. While some relationships have been established in the past, the absence of levels of certain properties made it difficult to have good statistical correlation. It was decided to conduct an experiment which used a high and low level on such variables as clay, particle size distribution, grog content, water content, water temperature, vacuum, firing rate, and firing temperature. As an example of high and low levels of each variable, the vacuum used was 0 to 20 in Hg. This experiment will give us the relationship between the controlled variables and such observed variables as machine amperage, extrusion rate, column consistency, column temperature, drying shrinkage, weight loss on drying, firing shrinkage, total shrinkage, loss on ignition, dry modulus of rupture, 24-hour cold absorption, 5-hour boil absorption, modulus of rupture (flat and on edge), compressive strength (flat, on edge, and on end), pore size distribution, sonic modulus, and freeze-thaw resistance.

The data have been analyzed for compressive strength with the units tested flat (the normal way of testing) and for first sign of failure on our experimental freeze-thaw plates.

The average compressive strength for all 256 specimens was 10,851 psi. It is my feeling that, if the average of all units made from one level of a variable did not vary from the average of all units made from the other level of the same variable by more than 10 percent of the average value, or 1058 psi, the variable had no significant effect on strength. To get a significant index number, therefore, divide the difference in the averages by 1058 psi. Thus, a variable has no significant effect unless this number is greater than 1.0. The average number of cycles on freeze-thaw was 671. The significant index number was, therefore, obtained by dividing the difference by 67.

The analysis of the variables by themselves are quite simple. Table 36-4 gives the variables in order of increasing importance along with their practical significance index.

This table indicates that for each of the properties studied, four variables are significant and four are not.

In addition, I studied all of the two-way interactions. This gets very complicated, and a detailed explanation would not be of great interest to structural engineers. Some variables become important when certain other ones are held constant. I have attempted to analyze these and find the best combinations.

For obtaining the highest compressive strength, we obviously need the higher firing temperature first since this is the most significant variable.

The next most significant variable is vacuum. Here we get an interaction between vacuum and temperature. At the higher temperature, vacuum becomes more significant having a significance number of 1.841 at the higher temperature as compared to 0.749 at the lower temperature. We, therefore, should use vacuum to achieve better strength.

To get a more complete picture from here on, we should go into three or more way interactions. I did not do this,

Table 36-4
Manufacturing Variables and Their Effect on Brick

Variable	Significant Index
Strength	
Clay Type	0.079
Water Temperature	0.182
Grog Content	0.494
Particle Size	0.498
Firing Rate	1.027
Water Content	1.042
Vacuum	1.841
Firing Temperature	3.705
Freeze-Thaw Resistance	
Vacuum	0.119
Water Temperature	0.238
Grog Content	0.432
Water Content	0.923
Particle Size	1.013
Clay Type	1.578
Firing Rate	1.891
Firing Temperature	8.815

however, since it becomes very involved. Since the firing temperature is the overriding variable, I did look for interactions there, however.

The effect of the water content is reduced at the higher temperature. Its significance number drops to 0.922. This still indicates that a lower water content is desirable.

The firing rate loses much of its significance at the higher temperature. Its number of 0.492 indicates a slight edge for faster firing.

The particle size gains in importance at the higher temperature. Its number rising to 1.281 indicates that more fines added improves the strength.

Water temperature and grog content remain unimportant. The clay type has little effect at the higher temperature, but looking at it the other way around, the clay type G is more responsive to temperature (4.575) than clay type O (2.831).

Therefore, to obtain maximum strength with a given clay, increase the amount of fines, use low water content for extruding, use vacuum, perhaps fire fast, and definitely fire to as high a temperature as possible. The eight specimens having these levels of variables averaged 16,590 psi.

For freeze-thaw resistance, we again need high temperature firing first. At the higher temperature, the firing rate becomes even more important. The number at the higher temperature is 3.460 vs. 0.313 at the lower temperature. Contrary to that indicated for strength, the slower rate is better here.

The clay type is still significant here. The higher temperature reduces its significance number only to 1.444. Therefore, the selection of the right clay is important.

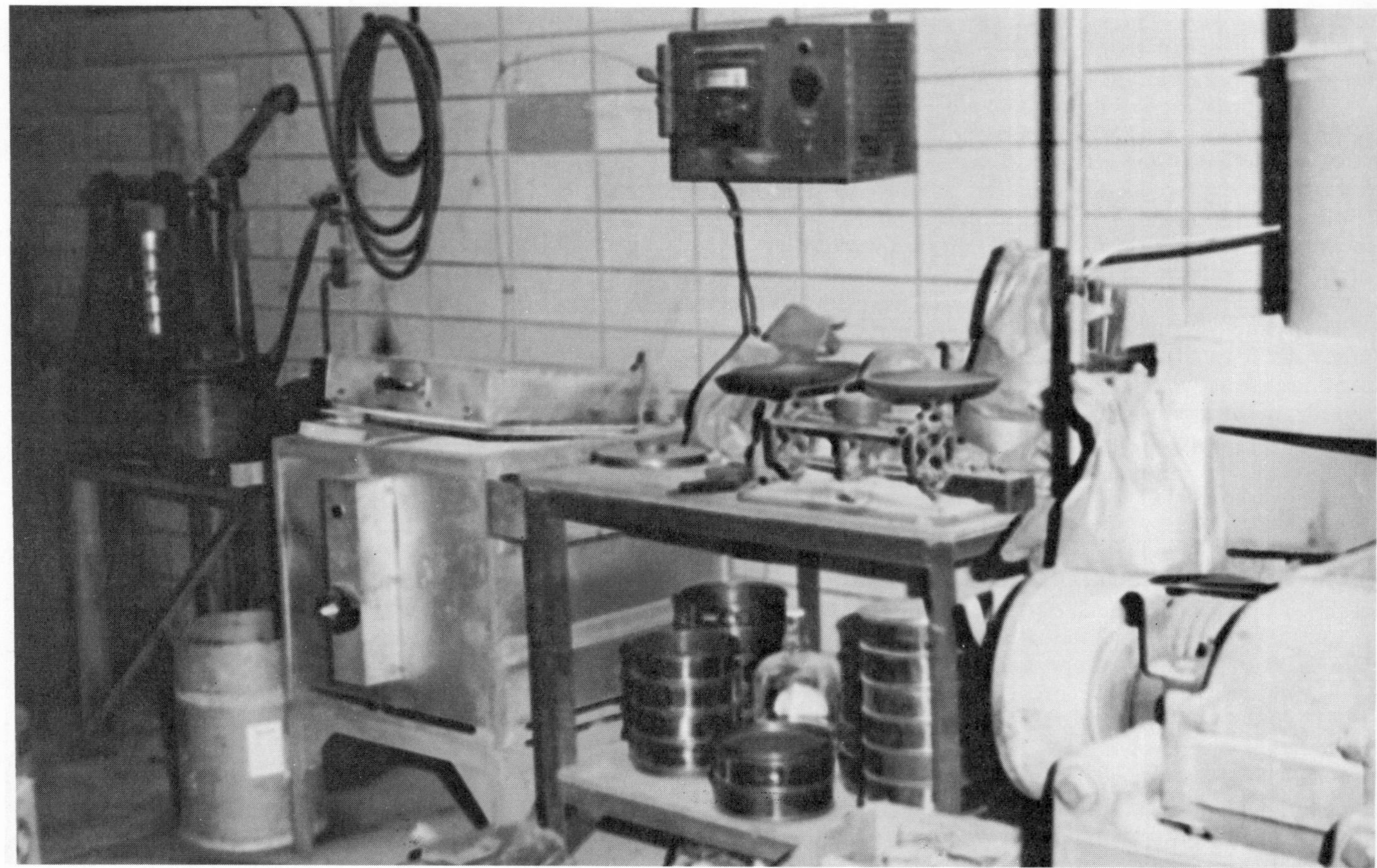

Figure 36-1. Quality control begins in the laboratory. Screen analyses, firing rates, and temperatures are investigated.

The particle size becomes more important at the higher temperature. At the higher temperature, the significance number jumps to 1.831. Here, again, more fines help.

The water content also becomes more important at the higher firing temperature. The significance number jumps to 1.742. Again, the lower water content is desirable.

The water temperature does not assume any importance at the higher firing temperature. Vacuum becomes more important at the higher temperature. Its significance number rises to 1.027.

Grog has no interaction with higher temperature.

Thus, it would appear that the same things that affect strength affect freeze-thaw resistance. Clay type is more important to freeze-thaw resistance. The firing rate, while not significant to strength at the higher temperature, indicates that the fast fire may be better. The firing rate has a strong influence on freeze-thaw resistance, however, and the slower rate is better. Therefore, the slower rate probably should be used.

The eight units made under these conditions withstand an average of 1418 cycles of freezing and thawing before first sign of failure.

Mr. Hockaday: In this experiment, you made sure that no laminations were present. We have found that even a high strength brick will fail the freeze-thaw test if laminations are present. Examples of this are:

1. A midwest brick company marketed brick with 15,000 psi strength. The brick had a considerable number of freeze-thaw failures. Failure was due primarily to lamination.
2. Hudson River brick will not pass A.S.T.M. Specifications, but has good record in durability. Doubtlessly, good pore structure is the explanation.
3. Clays in the Ohio-Pennsylvania area appear to be the same, but their durability records differ.
4. Soft mud brick low in strength and high in water absorption do not fail in service, doubtlessly because of good pore structure.
5. Some typical test results are shown in Table 36-5.

From the data in Table 36-5, there is no assurance that failure will not occur, even if brick do pass ASTM C216 Specifications. It is very important, therefore, that the architect or engineer specify brick manufactured by a reliable

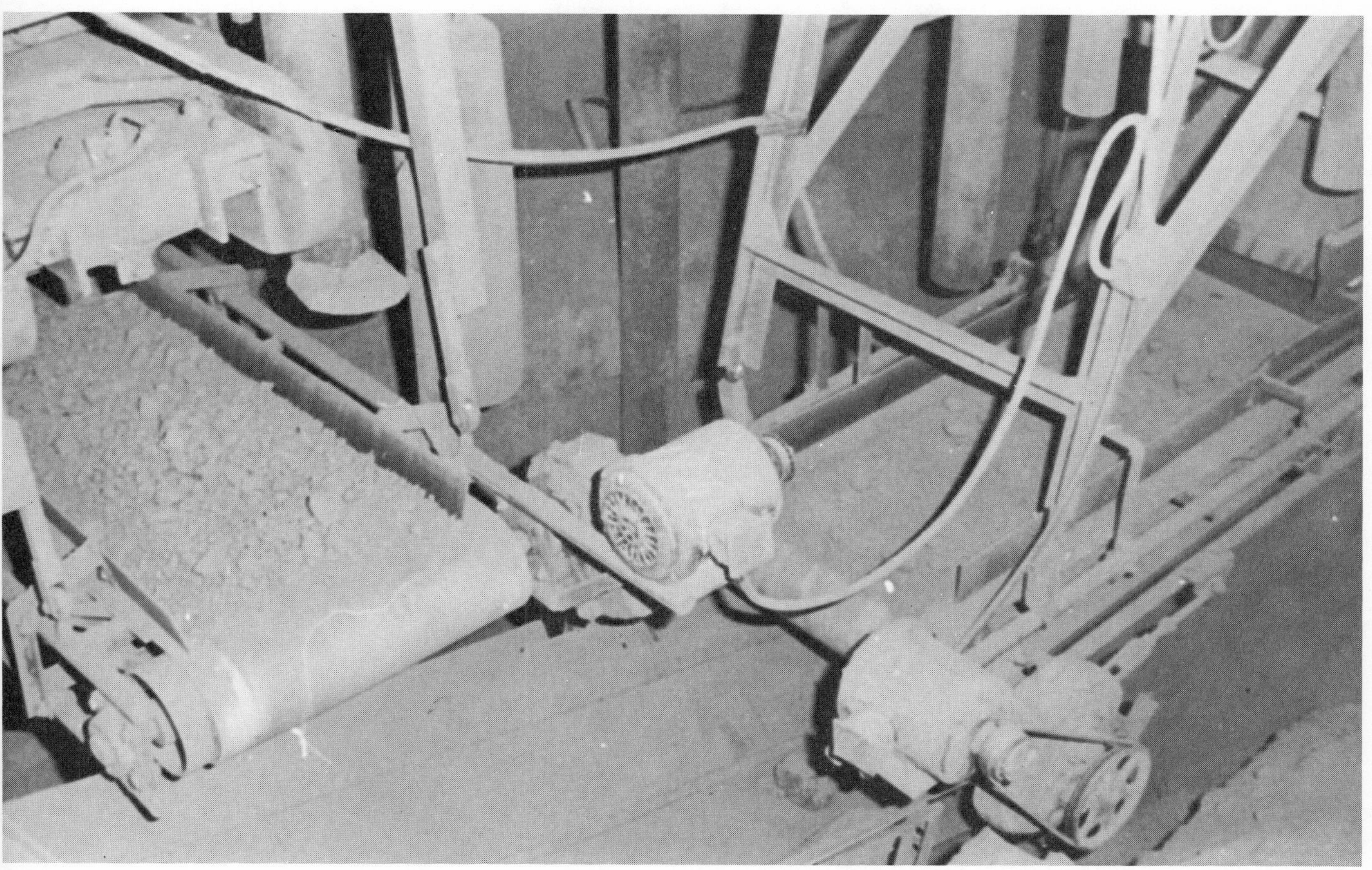

Figure 36-2. After a mix has been established in the lab, production runs are mixed by means of electronic devices which control the flow rate of each type of clay.

Table 36-5
Physical Properties of Brick

24 Hr. Abs. %	5 Hr. Boil %	C/B Ratio	Comp Strength Psi	51 Cycles Freeze-Thaw Test	ASTM C 216 Grade		
					Strength*	C/B Ratio and 5 hr. Boil**	Freeze-Thaw***
11.7	13.7	.85	7,590	Passed		MW	
10.1	13.0	.78	8,660	Failed @ 50 cy	SW		
10.6	13.3	.80	7,510	Passed		MW	
12.5	13.9	.90	8,640	Failed @ 26 cy	SW		
11.9	13.3	.89	10,450	Failed @ 40 cy	SW		
10.8	12.5	.86	8,000	Passed		MW	
10.1	11.3	.89	5,875	Passed			SW

* If the average compressive strength is greater than 8,000 psi the C/B (saturation coefficient) ratio is waived.

** Meets the requirements for C/B ratio and 5-hour boiling

*** Freeze-thaw test required only if brick fail to meet requirements of 1 or 2 above.

company in whom he has considerable confidence. Buying brick under an ASTM Specification is not quite like buying a pig in a poke, but there are some similarities. Much more research is needed. In the interim ASTM Specifications should be used. I do think that strength, absorption, pore structure, and lamination free properties all related properly will give a durable brick.

Mr. Howard: This discussion on manufacturing is very interesting. This makes for a better understanding of the manufacturing variables and how they affect the strength and durability of brick. The question still remains how can a constant level of strength be assured in a durable brick?

Mr. Hockaday: In review, the factors which are of primary importance in strength and durability are:

Strength:	Durability:
1. Firing temperature	1. Firing temperature
2. Vacuum	2. Firing rate
3. Water content	3. Clay type
4. Firing rate	4. Particle size

Quality control begins in the laboratory and continues through the production stage (see Figures 36-1 and 36-2).

As can be seen with such sophisticated (and expensive equipment, it is not difficult to control the principal variables

The type of clay is ascertained from ceramic analysis; the vibrating screens insure proper particle size; constant flow of clay and water insures constant water content; vacuum i subject to constant check; and firing rate and temperature are controlled and recorded. With experience to back this up, a reputable manufacturer can assure production of strong and durable brick.

Mr. Howard: An understanding of the variables which affect the strength of brick masonry as well as the variables which affect the strength and durability of brick through the manufacturing processes gives an appreciation for the problems relating to manufacturing as well as an understanding and appreciation of the problems of engineering application.

Reference

1. Grimm, Clayford T., P. E., Executive Director, Clay Products Association of the Southwest, Private communication, Austin, Texas.

Part 5: Design methodology

37. Assessment of British design methods of calculated brickwork.

R. E. Bradshaw, School of Architecture, Leeds, England, and D. Foster, Structural Clay Products, Ltd., Potters Bar, Herts., England

Introduction

The purpose of this chapter is to describe the background to the British Standard Code of Practice CP111 1964 "Structural Recommendations for Load-bearing Walls" (hereafter referred to as "the Code") and its use as a guide to the design of calculated load-bearing brickwork. The term "calculated" is used in the U.K. to distinguish between "engineered" and "non-engineered" brick masonry, because the latter is still permitted (although now only for buildings of a height of 40 ft. 0 in. or less) in the current British National Building Regulations.

Although structure is the primary consideration, other functions of the wall will be discussed where they affect the structural decision. Continual reference is made to the Code throughout this chapter, highlighting areas in which, in the author's view, it needs expansion or modification. It is assumed that a copy of the Code is available to the reader but certain sections of it are reproduced for easy reference.

History of the Code

The first issue of the Code appeared in 1948. The permissible stresses it embodied derived from extensive testing[1,2] over a twenty-five year period at one laboratory, the Building Research Station. The bulk of this work consisted of compressive tests on columns of brickwork, in all of which workmanship was of a consistently high quality. The results established the effect of the strength of brick and mortar, slenderness, and eccentricity of load on the strength of the composite material.

It became apparent about 1960 largely as a result of work in Switzerland[3] and U.S.A.[4] earlier in the decade 1950-1960 that this 1948 issue of the Code leaned heavily on safety, and consequently the Code was extremely conservative, giving load factors ranging from 6 to 27. The reasons for this conservatism are easily found.

First, the Code was (and still is) of an umbrella nature, embracing a wide range of bricks and blocks of different materials, of different size and type of manufacture, and of strengths from 400 – 10,000 lb./in.^{2}, many of which perform in distinctly different ways. For example:

1. strong units in strong mortar suffer far less from the effect of eccentricity of load and slenderness than do weak units in weak mortar;
2. strength ratios–strength of wall to strength of unit–vary considerably over the range of unit strength;
3. the performance of masonry columns was used, although not directly, as a basis for the design of walls; yet, the few wall tests done at that time had shown a marked superiority in terms of permissible stress;
4. no account was taken of the degree of restraint provided by the floor slab–in other words hinged rather than fixed or partially fixed junctions were assumed.

Second, and perhaps more important, was the general assumption that the Code would be used only for relatively low structures. The four storey building was the thought in the minds of the committee.

It is, of course, easy to write about what ought to have been done in 1948. It is less easy to take account of all the factors described above and produce a document which is realistic in terms of permissible stress yet comprehensive, fair, safe, and also simple to use. The 1964 edition of the Code, giving much increased permissible stresses, achieved some of these aims, but it does not by any means correct all the deficiencies of the '48 issue. For example, single leaf, 4-1/2-in. unbonded walls still have load factors ranging up to 14, even though it was known from Swiss work that for axial loading conditions their ultimate strength is considerably in excess of that of bonded (9-in.) walls. In that country there is a single load factor of 5 for all types of wall[5] and for all slenderness ratios, and recent work in the U.K. has confirmed this higher performance of thin unbonded walls[6,7].

The 1964 issue achieved its enhanced permissible stresses by considerably modifying the penalties for slenderness (the reduction factors) rather than by modifying the basic stresses corresponding to members of unit slenderness. It also incorporated guidance on the effects of eccentricity by giving reduction factors for combinations of degrees of eccentricity (expressed as a proportion of the thickness) and for slenderness.

Guidance on stability as opposed to strength is lacking almost as much in the '64 as in the '48 issue, despite the knowledge that high buildings were likely to be built using it as a basis. Indeed, one addition (Clause 304(ii)) relating to notional forces for the design of connections between walls and their lateral supports, caused more confusion than enlightenment in this respect. Fortunately, this clause will be modified considerably in the coming revision. Further consideration of this and other portions of the Code is given below.

The Code is currently being revised. It is conjectured, inter alia, that the maximum permissible slenderness ratio will be increased from 18 to 24 or 27; that clearer guidance, in terms of basic compressive stresses, will be given on the use of units of different height/width ratios; that for the first time mortar compressive strength tests will be required; and that recognition will be given to quality control of brick manufacture by enhanced allowable basic stress where such units are used.

Use of Code

Basic Permissible Stress

The basic permissible design stress for a given brick crushing strength and a given mortar mix (strength not specified) is given in Table 37-1, and this basic stress is multiplied by a reduction factor for slenderness when the slenderness ratio (see below) is greater than 6.

Table 37-1
Basic Compressive Stresses for Brickwork or Blockwork Members

Description of mortar	Mix (parts by volume)			Hardening time after completion of work†	Basic stress in lb./in.^{2} corresponding to units whose crushing strength (in lb./in.^{2}) ‡is:								
	Cement	Lime	Sand		400	1000	1500	3000	4000	5000	7500	10,000	14,000 or greater
				days									
Cement	1	0-¼*	3	7	40	100	150	240	300	360	510	660	850
	1	½	4½	14	40	100	140	210	250	300	410	520	650
Cement-lime	1	1	6	14	40	100	140	190	230	270	360	450	550
Cement with plasticizer §	1	–	6										
Masonry cement ‖	–	–	–										
Cement-lime	1	2	9	14	40	80	120	170	210	240	300	360	450
Cement with plasticizer §	1	–	8										
Masonry cement ‖	–	–	–										
Cement-lime	1	3	12	14	30	70	100	140	170	200	250	300	350
Hydraulic lime	–	1	2	14	30	70	100	140	170	200	250	300	350
Non-hydraulic	–	1	3	28¶	30	60	80	100	110	120	150	170	200

* The inclusion of lime in cement mortars is optional.

† These periods should be increased by the full amount of any time during which the air temperature remains below 40°F, plus half the amount of any time during which the temperature is between 40° and 50°F.

‡ Linear interpolation is permissible for units whose crushing strengths are intermediate between those given in the table.

§ Plasticizers must be used according to manufacturers' instructions.

‖ Masonry cement mortars must be used according to manufacturers' instructions, and mix proportions of masonry cement to sand should be such as to give comparable mortar crushing strengths with the cement : lime : sand mix of the grade.

¶ A longer period should ensue where hardening conditions are not very favourable.

Vertical Loading

Axial Loads. For axial loads, the only factors used to determine the permissible design strength of the brickwork are the compressive strength of the brick, the mortar mix, and the slenderness ratio of the member under load. For axial loading this process gives load factors which range between 4 and 7 for 9-in.-thick walls of normal storey height, and between 6 and 14 for 4-1/2-in.-thick walls, assuming a reasonable standard of workmanship[6,7,8]. As mentioned earlier, the load factors of 4-1/2-in.-thick walls appear unnecessarily high and a value of 5 or 6 would be more appropriate.

Little information is available on loading tests on cavity walls. It might be expected that the strength would be the addition of the two leaves built and tested separately, but oddly enough the few tests which have been done show that the strength is less[9].

Eccentric Loads. The assessment of the amount of loading eccentricity at a wall/slab junction is complex and is influenced by the degree of fixity at the junction as well as by the floor loading and relative stiffnesses of the slab and walls. No guidance is given in the Code, and it is usual to consider all walls as being axially loaded when the floor slab is stiff and passes over the full width of the wall. The decision rests with the designer and depends, obviously, on his assessment of slab stiffness. Some designers assume eccentricity of t/6 where a wall is loaded from one side only. In those instances where the eccentricity can be assessed with some degree of accuracy, the appropriate stress reduction factor for combined slenderness and eccentricity may be obtained from Table 37-2. For eccentricities of up to t/6 the resulting reduction in permissible load, after allowing the 25 percent increase in maximum compressive edge stress, is similar to that in the Swiss regulations[5]. For eccentricities greater than t/6, however, the reduction in load for eccentricity is considerably less than the Swiss. Where properly tied cavity walls are eccentrically loaded, it is normally assumed that any bending moment will be distributed between the two leaves in proportion to their stiffnesses.

Table 37-2*
Reduction Factors for Slenderness

Slenderness ratio	Reduction factor			
	Axially loaded	Eccentricity of vertical loading as a proportion of the thickness of the member		
		1/8	1/3	1/2
6	1.00	1.00	0.98	0.97
8	0.92	0.92	0.87	0.85
10	0.84	0.82	0.76	0.73
12	0.76	0.72	0.65	0.60
14	0.67	0.62	0.54	0.48
16	0.58	0.52	0.42	0.35
18	0.50	0.42	0.30	0.23
21	0.47	0.38	0.25	0.17
24	0.44	0.34	0.19	0.11

Linear interpolation between values for the reduction factor is permissible.

Concentrated Loads. The design stress for bearings at beam, window lintel, and cantilever supports is normally 50 percent greater than the permissible compressive stress in the wall. This simplified approach is well established and generally satisfactory, but it takes no account of the increased edge stresses when medium and large-span beams or cantilevers deflect under load.

Slenderness Ratio. The slenderness ratio is taken as the ratio of effective height to effective thickness, both of which are described below. Extensive tests on piers have shown, as mentioned earlier, that the reduction in strength associated with increase in slenderness ratio is greatest when weak bricks and mortar are used, and least when strong materials are used. No account of this is taken in the '64 Code, and only one set of reduction factors for slenderness ratio is used, based on the average curve (Figure 37-1).

The difference in load factor that might be expected between strong brickwork and weak brickwork has been narrowed by adjustments to the basic permissible stresses, but this difference in load factor still exists and, moreover, increases as the slenderness ratio increases. When the load is applied eccentrically, there is a further reduction in strength, increasing with increase in slenderness ratio and eccentricity and also as the brick and mortar strength decreases.

Few tests on walls (as opposed to columns) have been reported in U.K. to investigate the effects of slenderness and eccentricity, and even fewer tests have been on walls between realistic end conditions that would normally be met in an actual building.*

The few tests that have been made indicate that for axial loading there is little, if any, reduction in strength for S.R. up to 18 and that the present limit for slenderness ratio of 18 might well be increased.

It has also been shown that the effects of eccentricity are less when the wall is restrained between r.c. slabs[6,7]

In cases where a wall is stiffened by intersecting walls, the Code allows an increase in permissible design stress when the horizontal distance between restraints is less than the effective height, and here the horizontal distance may be used to determine the slenderness ratio.

Clearly, increased stresses should be allowed where a panel is supported on all four sides, and Haller[3] recommends that then the permissible design stresses should be:

* Tables 37-1 and 37-2 are reproduced by permission of the British Standards Institution, 2 Park Street, London, W.1.

* It is known that in the U.S.A. an extensive investigation on wall columns has been made by C.B. Monk, Jr.

$$Pcc = Psr + (P6 - Psr) F$$

where:

Pcc = revised permissible compressive stress in brickwork.

Psr = permissible compressive brickwork stress in wall when the slenderness ratio is based on effective height,

P6 = basic permissible stress in brickwork having a slenderness ratio of 6 or less (from Table 37-1),

F = reduction factor from Figure 37-2.

An upper limit for the value of F is suggested by the authors.

Effective Thickness. For solid walls the effective thickness is taken as the actual thickness of the wall, and for cavity walls as 2/3 $(t_1 + t_2)$ where t_1 and t_2 are the thicknesses of the two leaves. This closely approximates the actual values for the most common cavity walls, viz:- 4-1/2 + 4-1/2 in. leaves and 4-1/2 + 9 in. leaves.

No allowance is made, however, for the greater stiffness of high strength materials and no account is taken of any difference in strength of the two leaves of a cavity wall.

Effective Height. As mentioned, the general relationship between slenderness ratio and strength reduction (Figure 37-1) was derived solely from tests on piers, and this probably accounts for the rule that the effective height of a pier is the actual height whereas that of a wall is 3/4 actual height, thus making some arbitrary allowance for its increased stiffness.

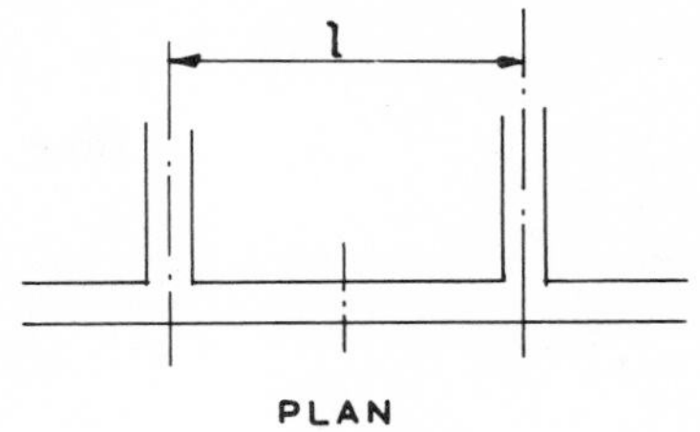

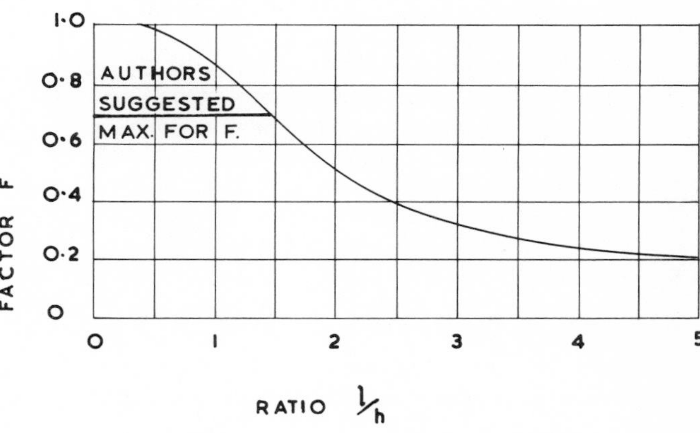

Figure 37-2. Slenderness reduction factors for walls stiffened by intersection walls. (After Haller).

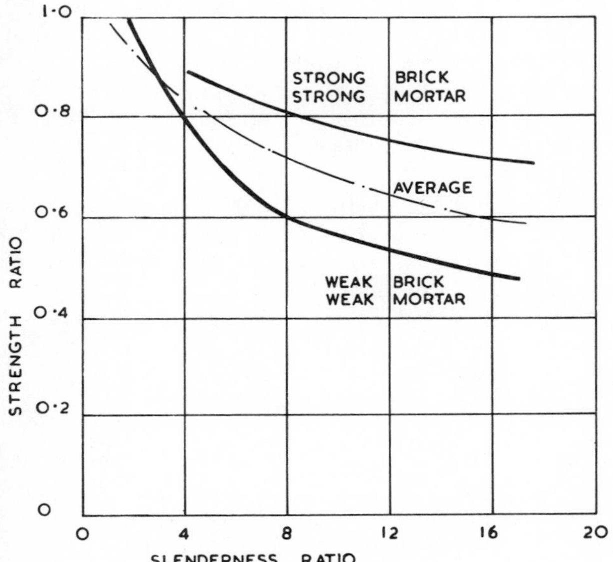

Figure 37-1. Strengths of axially loaded piers of various slenderness ratios, as a proportion of the strength of a pier of slenderness ratio of unity. (After Thomas).

Small Area Reduction. Where the cross-sectional area of a wall or column does not exceed 500 in.^{2} the basic stress must be multiplied by a reduction factor equal to 0.75 + A/2000 where A is the area (in square inches) of the horizontal cross section of the wall or column.

This is based on the argument that statistically there is a greater chance of failure of a small cross section if weak units are built in, and while the logic of this assumption cannot be denied, it could be argued that the load factors built into the Code would alone safely cope with such a condition without this further penalty.

Top and Bottom 1/8th. The reduction factor for slenderness ratios need not be used for sections within one-eighth of the height of the member above or below the position of the lateral supports.

This clause may be applied when a wall supports a concentrated load at or near floor level. In such a case, the permissible design stress at the bearing is 50 percent greater than the basic stress, and no reduction for slenderness ratio needs to be made. However, a stress check should also be made near the bottom of the wall, taking into account the slenderness ratio reduction factor and allowing for the spread of the concentrated load at 45° (Figure 37-3).

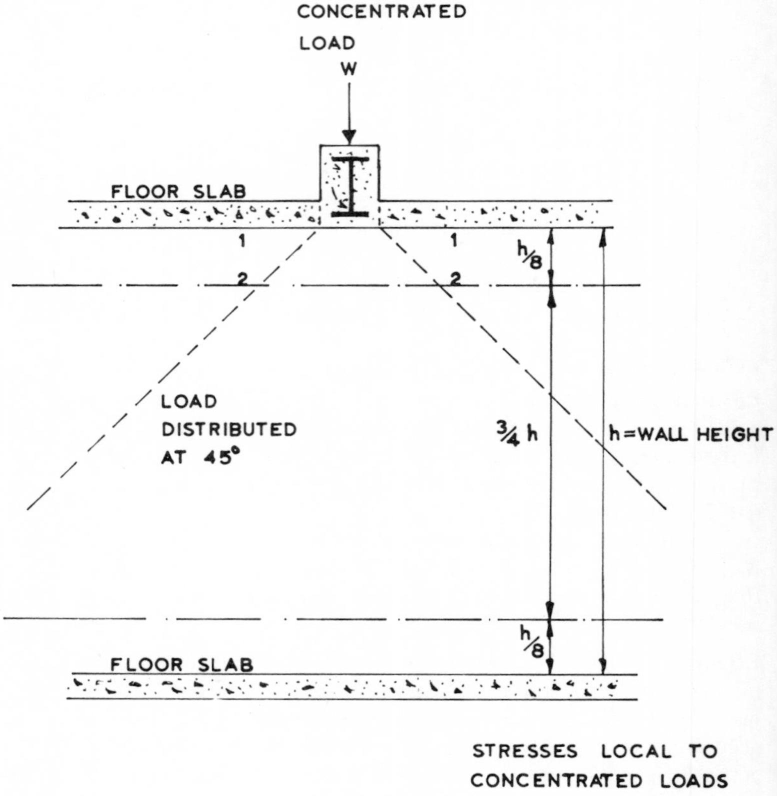

Figure 37-3. Permissible design stresses local to concentrated loads. Notes: Permanent design stress at 1–1 = Basic stress (Table 37-1) + 50%. Permanent design stress at 2–2 = Basic stress (Table 37-1) x R.F. for S.R.

Lateral Loading

Stability. It was noted in the "History of the Code" that guidance on stability is lacking in the Code. In addition to ability to resist wind pressure or drag, the building must also be capable of resisting lateral forces arising from dynamic effects or from out of balance due to lack of plumb or settlement. Since the magnitude of these forces is not readily determined, it is usual to make them an arbitrary percentage of the total vertical load. The difficulty, of course, is to decide what percentage. Various notions have been put forward during discussions on the revision of the '64 issue and it is possible that a figure of something like 1/2 percent to 1 percent may be adopted.

This proposal must not be considered to replace the present Clause 304a(ii). It is the intention of that Clause to ensure that where lateral forces arise from out of plumb conditions then the "connection" between the member concerned, e.g. a wall, and the element of structure providing it with lateral support, e.g. a floor, should be capable of resisting a force the magnitude of which is 2-1/2% of the vertical load the wall is carrying at that point. As already mentioned, this clause has caused some confusion.

Eccentricity of Loading. As noted earlier, the '64 issue includes (Table 37-2) stress reduction factors for various combinations of slenderness and eccentricity of load.

Confusion has arisen here also because of lack of explanatory detail or diagrams. Some users have not appreciated that reduction factors apply only to the maximum stress on the compressive edge and that due to the change in shape of the stress block (from rectangular to trapezoidal or triangular depending on the degree of eccentricity) the reduction of total load is much more than it appears to be from the difference in reduction factors.

This confusion is likely to be resolved in the revision by including a table of load reduction factors, which will show at a glance how the load capacity of a given member is reduced by eccentricity of the applied load.

It should be noted that, in common with structural codes in other materials, an increase of 25 percent in the maximum stress is allowed over the basic stress when designing for the effect of eccentric and lateral loads.

Permissible Tensile Stresses. In considering lateral loading on shear walls and wind panels, the designer is also concerned with the permissible tensile stress in two directions, i.e. at right angles to the bed joints and perpend joints. The '64 Code allows, respectively, permissible stresses of 10 and 20 lb./in.^{2} (pounds force per square inch). The difference arises from the fact that the first is almost pure tensile bond stress whereas the latter is part shear. In comparison with other national Codes (such as the S.C.P.I. recommended Code), the British '64 Code appears to be unduly conservative, but, in reality, it is

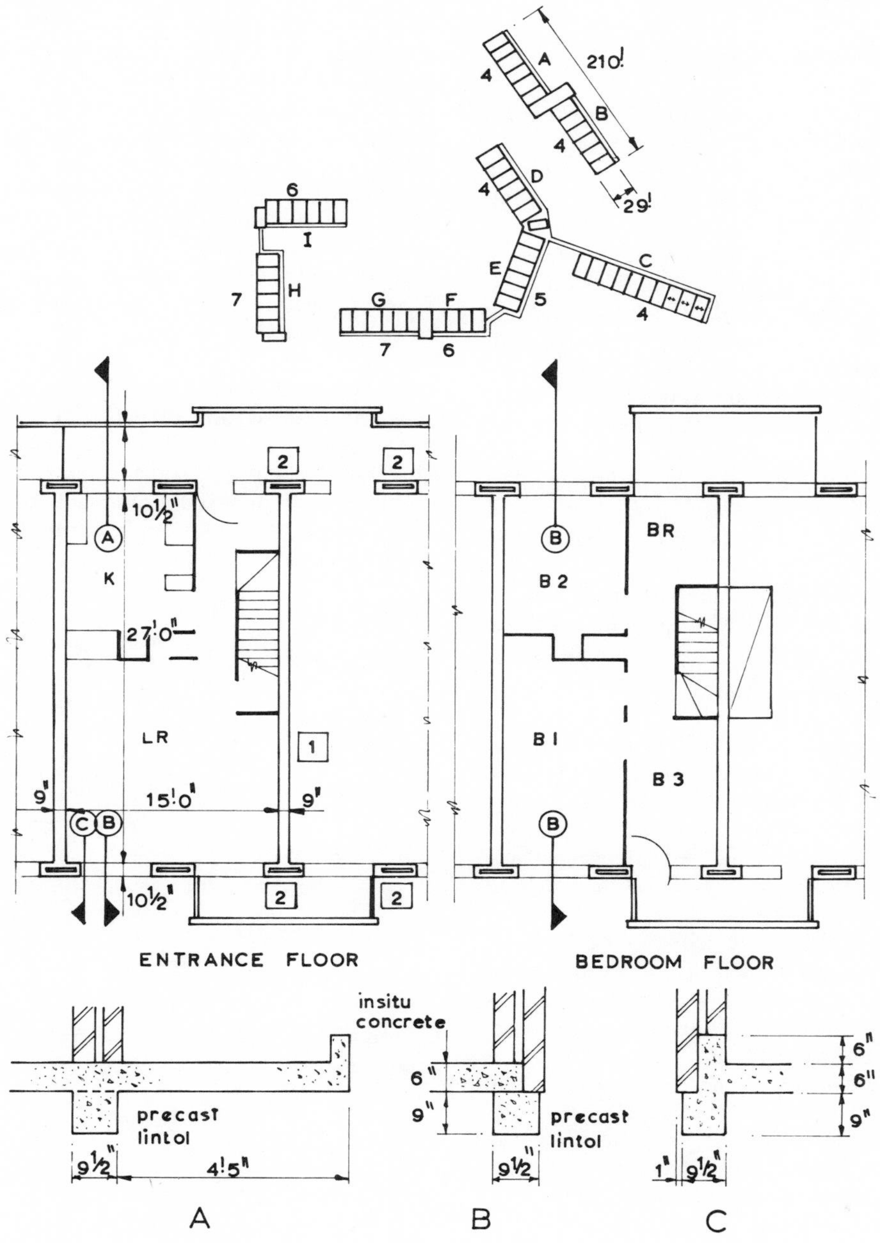

Figure 37-4. Norwich. Typical crosswall with access balconies. Note: □ *= brickwork strength (see Table 37-3).*

probably unsafe in these respects. In the author's experience, based on simple site tests, rarely can a tensile stress of 10 lb./in.^{2} be guaranteed. A load factor of three would require an actual tensile bond strength of 30 lb./in.^{2}, and it is doubtful if this is often achieved.

It is, of course, possible to accept a degree of cracking and then design on the basis of the cracked section. Some British designers do this when considering the stress due to combinations of vertical and lateral loads on shear walls.

Permissible Shear Stress. The Code (Clause 317) recommends an upper limit of 30 lb./in.^{2} as the permissible shear stress in the plane of the wall when this is calculated on the area of horizontal joint. Recent work has shown that this is also conservative, and that the upper limit should be increased to about 80 lb./in.^{2} where the precompression due to dead load is 360 lb./in.^{2} varying linearly to 15 lb./in.^{2} where precompression is zero. These or similar figures are likely to be adopted in the coming revision of the Code.

The Building as a Whole

Plan Types Suitable for Calculated Brickwork

Obviously, buildings suitable for calculated brickwork are those where the requirements of the plan repeat on each floor, thus enabling bearing walls and shear walls to continue uninterrupted in one vertical plane from foundation to roof. In the United Kingdom these can be broadly classified as crosswall structures (Figure 37-4) and tower structures (Figure 37-5).

Crosswall structures are characterised by a regular spacing of party walls between rows of superimposed dwellings, with either balcony access or central corridor depending on whether the building is one or two dwellings wide. (Figure 37-6.) These buildings are also usually long in relation to their height and width.

Tower structures are characterised by a plan arrangement in which (usually) four dwellings are placed around a central staircase and lift lobby, and in which height is greater than width or length.

There are, of course, variations on these two main themes, but these simple definitions will suffice for present purposes.

Location of Bearing Walls and Shear Walls

In the crosswall types, the functional requirements of division between dwellings and resistance to vertical and lateral loads coincide. From this standpoint, they obviously give a most economical arrangement. Resistance to wind loading in the longitudinal direction is provided by the buttressing effect of staircase towers, or by a multiplicity of internal division walls running in that direction,or by facade walls, if the latter are of brickwork. In towers this coincidence of bearing and shear walls with the requirements of plan also occurs but is not nearly so clearly defined. Division walls between dwellings may or may not be the main load-bearing agents, and they may also be much shorter than the walls or wall complexes surrounding lift shafts and staircases. These,being stiffer, will attract more of the lateral load due to wind yet almost always have less precompression due to weight from floors simply because the rooms, e.g. bathrooms and closets, around these central areas are smaller than those with outside walls.

Such anomalies can be reduced or avoided by careful collaboration between architect and engineer in the early stages of planning, but this happens all too rarely. The use of two-way floor spans can also distribute the precompression more evenly, but often this implies taking load onto outer walls which may be heavily pierced by window openings.

Effect of Structure on External Design

This leads to a consideration of the effect of structure on external design, or vice versa, depending on reader's point of view. The following are a few of the problems encountered.

Balconies. Balconies are one of the strongest architectural elements, but the additional load from a balcony may require either a local increase in the thickness of a facade wall or a locally higher strength brick. (See Figure 37-6.) Experience has shown that it is better to avoid too many different brick mortar combinations on any one floor, if possible, because of reducing the chance of errors on the site. But, it is recognised that one cannot always achieve this degree of simplicity, and balconies and similar features must be catered for. In the long run, the wider adoption of calculated brickwork will depend as much on the increasing ability of the engineer to provide freedom for the architect as it will on the already established fact of reduced cost. Much more advanced techniques allowing cantilevering of substantial sections of facades, are being developed[10].

External Cavity Walls. Cavity walls are essential in the United Kingdom climate, and bricks to build them are available in a wide range of prices, colours and strengths. The combination of these facts poses some interesting and possibly unique problems in comparison with the situation in other countries where the range of bricks is perhaps not so great or where facing bricks are not used.

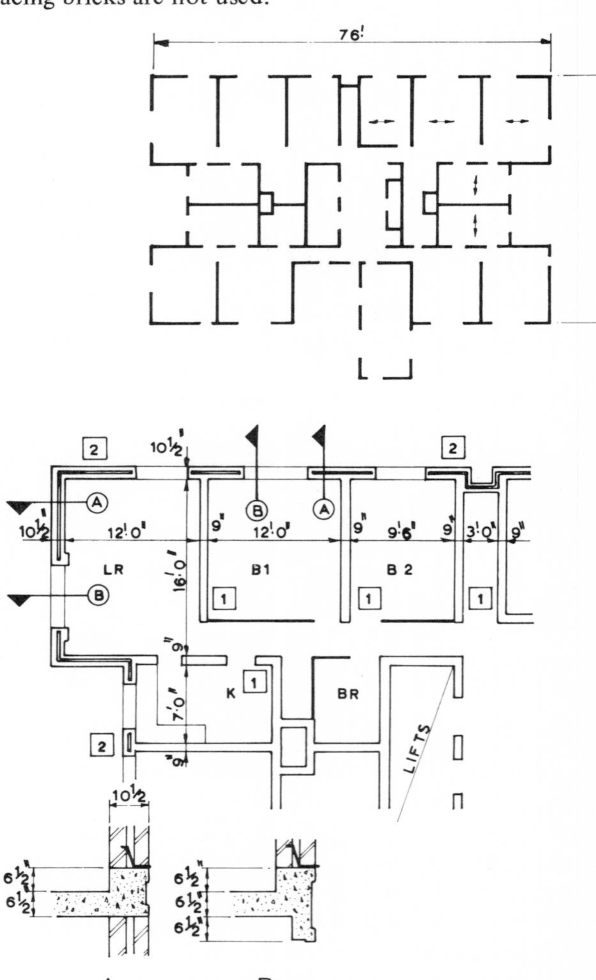

Figure 37-5. Oldham. Typical tower block. Note: □ brickwork strength (see Table 37-3).

First, there is the question of whether to carry the floor load on only the inner leaf or on both leaves of the wall. If the former method is adopted, then the Code (Clause 308a) allows alternative methods of determining the strength of brickwork. Either the inner leaf can be considered as unattached to the outer, in which case the strength is determined on the basis of the slenderness of that leaf alone, or the inner can be considered as stiffened by the outer, which is then judged to increase the effective thickness, and hence reduce the slenderness. Usually, the latter method is adopted.

One must then consider the likely differential movement between the inner and the outer leaf (because the inner is firmly restrained between the floors whereas the outer is not) and the support of the outer leaf.

The Code (Clause 308f) recommends support at least every third storey or every thirty feet of height, whichever is the less, implying thereby that the floor slab is projected through both leaves at these intervals and that the outer leaf is built solidly up to it on its underside.This method has been adopted on the Norwich and Derby schemes. Clearly, such support and restraint is best effected by projecting the slab completely to the outer face, thus showing bands of concrete in the brickwork, but, often, architectural requirements demand an uninterrupted brick face. Brick slips or tiles 1 in. thick are then used to mask the edge of the slab, to which they are loaded (Figure 37-7).

Although this device has so far proved to be satisfactory, it nevertheless is open to some criticism. There may be, for example, some transfer of load from inner to outer leaf because the inner leaf is subjected to greater strain. This is especially likely to occur if the outer leaf is built of brick with a greater E value than the inner, as it well might be if the architect and engineer have chosen it solely on the basis of colour, texture, or even durability. This issue becomes even more complicated when it is realised that the strength of brick used for the inner leaf will vary from top to bottom of the building on the grounds of cost, whereas the outer will almost invariably be of one colour and, hence, of one type and one strength for the whole height of the building.

One solution to this problem is to ensure the use of a softer mortar between the underside of the projecting slab and the top of the lift of the outer leaf. Alternatively, some form of pressure absorbing membrane such as a layer of damp proof course might be used. Indeed, since the cavity is interrupted vertically by the slab, it is usual to incorporate a horizontal d.p.c. flashing sloping to the exterior to ensure drainage of any rain water which penetrates the outer leaf and runs down its inside face. Thus, some relief of pressure due to differential movement is provided fortuitously (Figure 37-6).

Where the cavity wall is deemed to carry its load on both leaves, then both are automically restrained at each floor level. But, the problems outlined above, particularly that of differential strain, still exist, and the designers still have to choose between expressing the slabs or using brick tiles to mask them.

Occasionally, the architect prefers to emphasize the expression of the slab by increasing its thickness in the wall, thus forming a ring beam. This was done at Oldham where it can be seen that, in addition, the beam was recessed one inch on the outer face to relieve the somewhat stark effect of a four-course depth of concrete. (Figure 37-5.) It is difficult, due to lack of research on this point, to decide just what proportion of load is carried by each leaf and also the degree of eccentricity of load and hence the bending moment on each leaf in the wall due to loading from the floor on one side of it. Grimm[11] has given guidance on these aspects of design, but it is clear that much remains to be done. At the time of writing, the degree of eccentricity has to be assumed by the U.K. designer and depends on such obvious factors as the type and stiffness of the floor construction, whether it is in situ or precast, and whether any attempt is made to provide extra resistance to local crushing (by means, say of bearing plates or beams) at the edge of the wall.

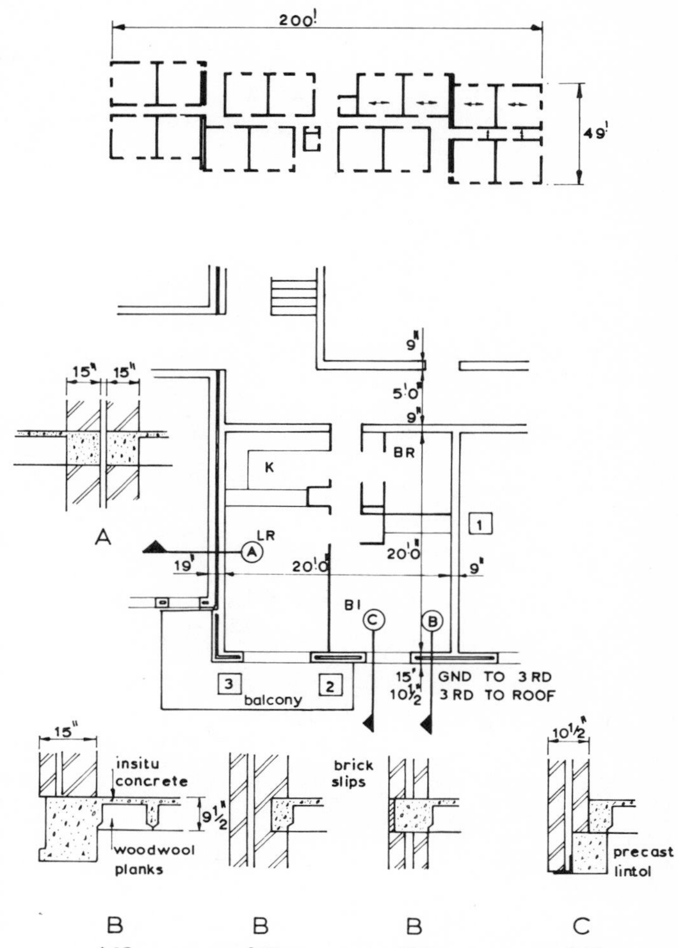

Figure 37-6. Derby. Typical crosswall with central corridor. Note: □ = brickwork strength (see Table 37-3).

Window Openings. The primary structural effect of openings is, of course, to reduce the wall area capable of carrying load. Thus, the amount of opening in relation to solid may well determine whether an external wall can be used as an agent for

Table 37-3

Scheme	Oldham (Fig. 37-5)		Norwich (Fig. 37-4)		Derby (Fig. 37-3)		
	Brickwork grade		Brickwork grade		Brickwork grade		
Storey	1	2	1	2	1	2	3
12 – 13	as below	as below					
11 – 12							
10 – 11							
9 – 10							
8 – 9							
7 – 8	9/3/3	10½/3/3					
6 – 7	9/5/3	10½/5/3	as below	as below	as below	as below	as below
5 – 6	9/5/3	10½/5/3					
4 – 5	9/5/1	10½/5/1					
3 – 4	9/5/1	10½/5/1				10½/3/3	10½/3/3
2 – 3	9/5/1	10½/5/1	9/3/3			15/3/3	15/3/3
1 – 2	9/7/1	10½/7/1	9/4/3		9/3/3	15/3/3	15/3/3
Gr'nd-1	9/7/1	10½/7/1	9/4/3	10½/3.5/3	9/3/2	15/4/1	15/7.5/1

1st figure denotes wall thickness – 9in. solid; 10½ in. and 15 in. cavity. 2nd figure denotes brick strength in 1000lb/in^2 – 3 = 3000lbf/in^2;

7.5 = 7,500lbf/in^2.

3rd figure denotes mortar mix – 1 = 1:¼:3; 2 = 1:½:4½; 3 = 1:1:6 all cement: lime: sand nominal volume mixes.

Thus 9/7/1 denotes 9 in. solid wall of bricks having a crushing strength of 7,000lb/in^2 laid in a 1:¼:3 mortar.

carrying floor loads or whether it is simply used to support its own weight. It will also affect a decision on the use or otherwise of two way slabs.

Secondly, the amount of opening will determine what length of a facade wall can act as a shear wall. For example, if the area of openings is dominated by the area of solid and the openings themselves have substantial areas of walling above and below them, then shear wall action is possible over the whole length. If, on the other hand, the windows are full storey-height and separated only by the slabs, then the wall must be considered as a series of connected but individual cantilevers. The degree of interaction is then dependent on the shear and bending strength of the connecting slabs and clearly the deeper the slab (or ring beam) the more effective is this action. The same problem occurs in the effect of crosswalls pierced by corridor openings, the action of which has been considered by Soane[12].

It can be seen then, from this discussion, that architecture and structure perhaps needs closer integration in a calculated brickwork building than in, say, a framed structure and that research needs to be undertaken to establish more accurately the behaviour of brickwork structure. The closer the understanding achieved in this respect, the greater the freedom which will be afforded to the architect, and hence, the greater the use of calculated brickwork.

Figure 37-7. Brick slips. Derby.

Constructional Problems

The following notes deal very briefly with a few of the problems met in practical building. Reference should be made to the Model Specification recently issued in the U.K.[13]

Provision for Services

Is is now well established that chasing and cutting of walls for services must be kept to a minimum and then only allowed with special tools and under strict supervision. This prohibition entails much more careful planning, and the provision by the architect of a detailed drawing of holes and duct layouts.

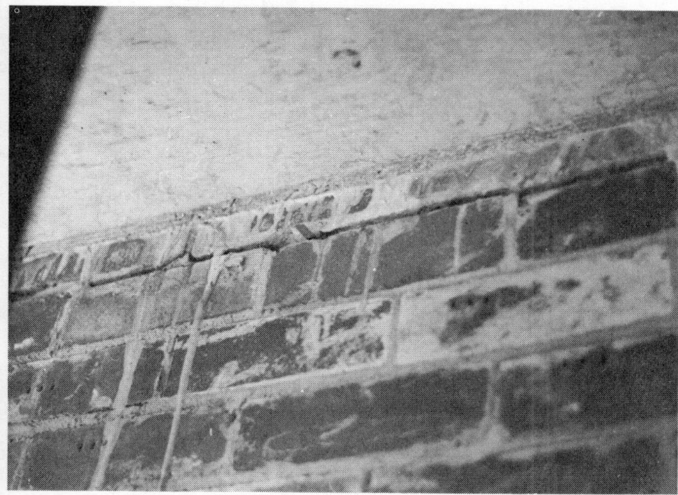

Figure 37-8. Damage to top courses by floor shuttering (Oldham).

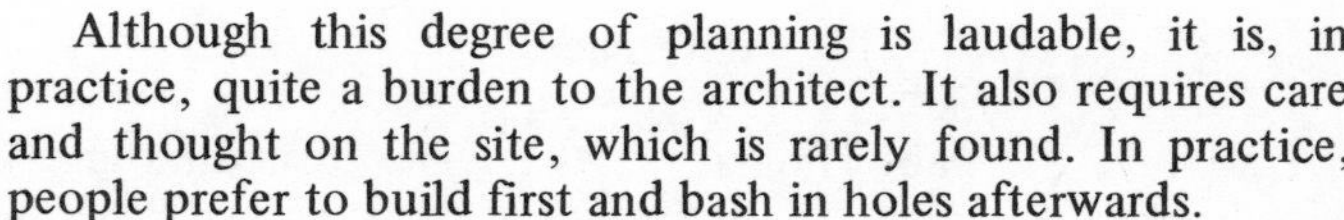

Although this degree of planning is laudable, it is, in practice, quite a burden to the architect. It also requires care and thought on the site, which is rarely found. In practice, people prefer to build first and bash in holes afterwards.

Damage by Floor Shuttering

Damage to newly built walls by careless positioning of temporary floor timbering (used to provide support for cast in plan slabs) is perhaps one of the most serious problems of calculated brickwork because it usually does not become evident until the timber supports are removed, by which time a complete further storey may have been erected. (Figure 37-8.) The designer is faced with the alternative either of instructing that portions of the work be pulled down and rebuilt or of devising remedial measures. The latter are perhaps preferable but not always easy to accomplish.

Brickwork/Mortar Combinations

Economy demands the use of the cheapest brick and wide range of strengths available in U.K. can give rise to many combinations on a job. Some idea of the range for the three jobs mentioned in these notes is set out in Table 37-3.

Conclusions

It is obvious, even from this chapter that the design of structural masonry in the U.K. is far from being an exact science and that there is room for great improvement. Above all, information on the behaviour of the whole masonry structure rather than its parts is required. More research is the keynote.

This situation in the United Kingdom seems to be reflected in the current Codes of other countries, but it is expected that the next decade will see great advances.

Figure 37-9. Norwich. General view.

Figure 37-10. Oldham. General view.

References

1. Davey, N. and Thomas F. G., "The structural use of brickwork", *Proc. I.C.E. Structural and Building*, Paper No. 24, 1950. pp. 3-66.
2. Thomas, F. G., "The Strength of Brickwork", *Structural Engineer* Vol. 31, No. 2, Feb. 1953, pp. 35-46.
3. Haller, P., "The properties of loadbearing brickwork in perforated fired brick for multi-storey buildings", Schweizerische Bauzeitung, 1958, (Translated from German by G.L. Cairns, Building Research Station Library Communication 870.).
4. Davidson, R. L. and Monk, C. B., "Thin walls are the only support in a design for multi-storey buildings", *Architectural Record,* June 1952, pp. 208-216.
5. "Normen fur die Berechnung und Ausfuhrung von Mauerwerk aus kunstlichen und naturlichen bausteinen", Technische Normen No. 113, S.I.A. Schweizerishen Igenieur-und Architekten-Verien, Oct. 1963.
6. Prasan, S., Hendry, A. W., and Bradshaw, R. E., "Crushing tests of storey height panels 4-1/2 in. thick", *Proc. Brit. Ceram. Soc.*, July 1965, pp. 67-80.
7. Bradshaw, R. E. and Hendry, A. W., "Crushing tests o storey height panels 4-1/2 in. thick - Further results", *Proc Brit. Ceram. Soc.* (in press)
8. Simms, L. G., "The strength of walls built in the laboratory with some types of clay bricks and blocks", *Proc. Brit Ceram. Soc.*, July 1965, pp. 81-92.
9. Bradshaw, R. E. and Hendry, A. W., "Preliminary tests on storey height cavity walls" Chapter 15, *Designing, Engineering, and Constructing with Masonry Products,* Gul Publishing Co., Houston, Texas, 1969.
10. Sutherland, R. J. M., "Reinforced brickwork box beams" Report S.C.P.3. Structural Clay Products Ltd., Octobe 1966.
11. Grimm, C. T., "Preliminary structural design of unreinforced loadbearing brick walls", Clay Products Associatio of the Southwest, Austin, Texas, Jan. 1966.
12. Soane, A. J. M., "Model Analysis of Essex University Towe Block", Clay Products Technical Bureau Research Note Vol. 1, No. 1, Jan. 1967.
13. "Model Specification for Loadbearing Clay Brickwork" Special Publication No. 56., British Ceramic Researcl Association.

38. Design and construction of slender wall brickwork buildings.

W. G. Curtin and A. W. Hendry, W. G. Curtin and Partners, Liverpool, England

Introduction

Our office, up to a few years ago, did not consider brickwork as a structural material, but rather as an obsolete material used by the early Victorian engineers because they had nothing better. Our first use of load-bearing brickwork happened more by accident than design. We were appointed consultants to a large secondary school for which we designed a reinforced concrete frame and used 9″ brick partition walls between the classrooms for acoustic and other reasons. The classroom block was three storeys high, rectangular in plan with a central corridor along the main axis. Classrooms opened off the corridor and were separated by 9″ brick cross walls. We checked the load-bearing capacity of the walls and found, to our surprise, that we did not need the reinforced concrete frame. We were at first sceptical of our calculations since the stress in the walls was about ten times the stress in the normal two storey house, which in England frequently have 9″ brick walls. However, a detailed check of the calculation showed that the walls were adequate, and we decided to construct the school without the frame, thus saving over 8 percent of the cost of the school. During construction, we were surprised to find that far from being a slow method of erection, the brick structure was actually a little faster than concrete construction. This happy experience led us to adopt brickwork as the structural material and the cross-wall as the structural system for several large schools.

Most of these schools were three storeys high with cross-walls at 20 ft.-25 ft. centres with floor live loads of 60 lb. per sq. ft. and own weight of 80 – 90 lb. per sq. ft.

In 1961, the architect for a women's residence hall at the University College, Bangor, North Wales, approached us through the Clay Products Technical Bureau to discuss the feasibility of constructing a six storey building in 9″ brick cross-walls. Details of the building are shown in Figures 38-1 and 38-2 from which it will be seen that the walls were at 10 ft. centres. As the total floor live and dead loading would be about 100 lb. per sq. ft., we knew that this would be feasible and might reduce the thickness of the upper storey walls to 4-1/2″. Detailed calculations based on the British Standard Code of Practice C.P. 111 (1948), current at that time but now superseded, showed that the walls could be 4-1/2″ from foundation to roof. Though the calculations were relatively simple and within the provisions of the code, we had no experience of using such a slender wall. Furthermore, the research work carried out by the Building Research Station, on which the Code was based, had been carried out on 9″ and 13-1/2″ walls and piers. We had no certainty that the results of tests on 9″ and 13-1/2″ walls would be applicable to 4-1/2″ walls, so it was decided to confirm (or otherwise) the validity of the calculations by carrying out a series of tests on 4-1/2″ walls. The results of these tests are summarized under Research Testing.

These results confirmed that the scheme was feasible and that the load factor under laboratory conditions was generally in the range 15 – 25. (The new code of practice allows higher working stresses, and the load factor is now therefore reduced). This factor of safety would not necessarily be obtained on site since workmanship and materials could not be so closely supervised.

Though it was obvious that the individual walls were safe, we had to consider the problems of overall stability under the action of wind forces. A series of cross-walls, acting alone, could suffer a 'house of cards' collapse. It was thought, correctly as later research showed, that the provision of walls at right angles to the cross-walls, i.e. external and corridor walls, would be more than adequate to prevent this. The effect

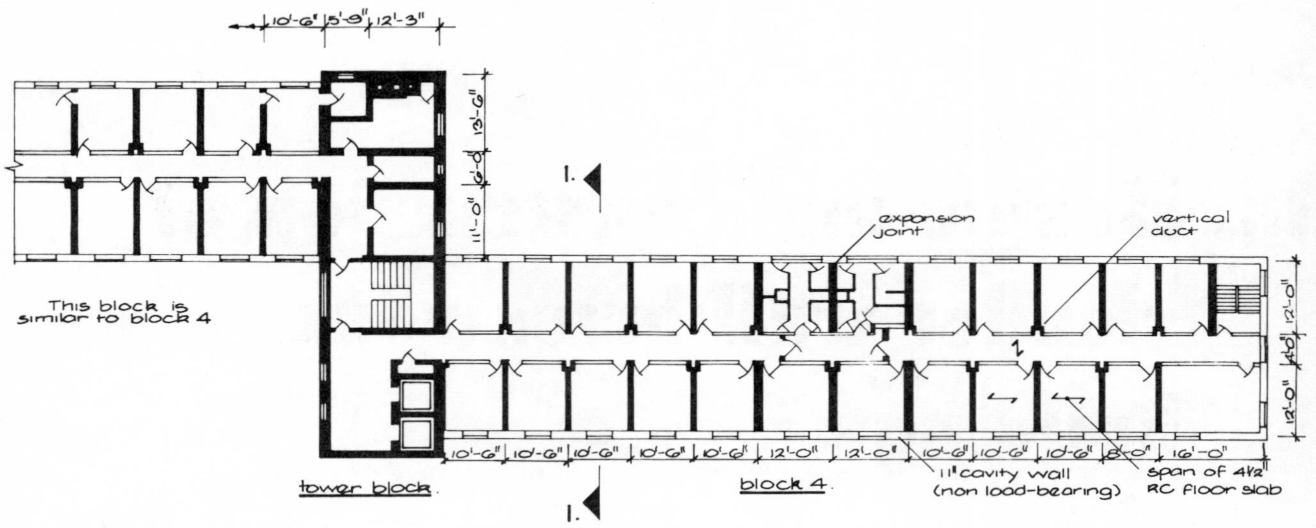

Figure 38-1. Typical floor plan. University College, Bangor. Note: The load-bearing crosswalls are shown solid.

of wind forces acting parallel to the cross-walls was not quite so simple. If the two cross-walls connected by the corridor slab were considered to act as a single structural entity similar to Vierendel girder, the wind stresses were insignificant. Since the corridor slab would form a very slender strut between the girder booms, the cross walls were then considered to act as separate cantilevers. Under this assumption the wind stresses, though now significant, were still tolerable. We believed that the actual wind stresses would be somewhere between the two calculated stresses. This problem has since been developed extensively under the heading of shear wall theory by many reasearch workers[1]. The behaviour of interconnected shear walls has been considerably elucidated, but the applicability of elastic theory to brickwork structures still requires further study[2].

Research

Tests on 4-1/2"-thick storey-height brickwork panels were initiated in designing Bangor University College Hostel in 1961. These initial tests have been described in detail elsewhere[5], but a summary of the results and of those obtained from a second series of tests[6] are given in Tables 38-1 and 38-2. These indicate the range of variables considered. All the tests were carried out in a specially designed loading frame in which the wall panels were loaded between sections of 4"-thick reinforced concrete slabs to give realistic end conditions and to permit investigation of the effect of bending moments introduced into the wall by loading on the floor slabs.

The conclusions from these tests may be summarised as follows:

1. The typical wall failure mode was by transverse splitting although in eccentrically loaded walls; spalling of the brickwork at the top of the wall was also observed.
2. Load factors on the British Standard Code of Practice C.P. 111 were high, even on the revised (1964) version. There would appear to be scope for some increase of permissible stresses, especially for eccentrically loaded walls.
3. The current limit for the height/thickness ratio of 18 could be safely increased, possibly to 24.
4. The effect of bending moments introduced into the wall panels by loading of the floor slabs on alternate sides of the wall appears to be insignificant.
5. Considerable increases in the strength of brickwork were achieved by placing light reinforcement in the horizontal joints, but further work is necessary to formulate design recommendations.

Tests on Scale-Model Structures

Lateral Resistance of Cross-wall. Following on this work, it was considered desirable to study the lateral resistance of cross-wall structures. As this required studying the interaction between the various elements of the structure, a model technique was developed, using 1/6th scale brickwork[7]. In preliminary experiments, tests on piers and walls, originally carried out at full-scale at the Building Research Station and elsewhere, were repeated at 1/6th scale. These tests confirmed that it was possible to reproduce on model scale the failure mode of full-sized brickwork elements and to estimate their strength from the small-scale tests, taking into account brick strength, mortar strength, and other relevant variables. Having thus established the validity of the model method, tests were conducted to study the strength of brickwork shear panels under varying amounts of precompression; the results of these tests are being reported in another chapter of this book.[8]

Strength and Rigidity of Multi-storey Cross-Wall Construction The next stage was to study on model scale the strength and rigidity of a section of multi-storey, cross-wall construction. One of the test structures after failure is shown in Figure 38-3. The structure was subjected to lateral loading by hydraulic jacks at each storey height; deflections were measured and eventually the structure was loaded to failure in the direction of the longitudinal shear walls. The ultimate load behaviour was consistent with the previous work done on the shear panels, but it was found that existing shear wall theories did not give an accurate indication of deflections when applied to this structure. A simplified theory based on calculation of shear deflections from storey to storey, however, gives promising results and is being studied further.

Tests on Full-Scale Structures

The final phase of the work on slender cross-wall structures is to be a series of tests on full-scale structures. This will repeat some model work and is intended to give a final check on its validity. These tests will be carried out in a quarry so that lateral loads can be applied by jacking against the rock face.

Calculations

The design calculations for this contract, as for most other brick contracts, were relatively simple. But, as with most brickwork calculations, there can be a bewildering choice of brick strengths and mortar mixes. The brick and mortar strengths can be reduced as the structure rises, but this leads to buying in small quantities and increases supervision difficulties. It is common procedure in our practice and most others in England to have two or three brick and mortar strengths. The bricks, selected were 7,500-lb.-per-sq.-in. crushing strength brick (a second class engineering brick) from foundation to third floor and 5,000-lb.-per-sq.-in. (a good 'common' brick) from there to the roof. The mortar mixes were 1:0:3 for foundation to second floor, 1:1:6 second to third floor and 1:2:9 from there to the roof. These strengths have been reduced on subsequent contracts following the introduction of the 1964 code.

As a check on the validity of the calculations, strain gauges were fixed to a ground floor wall, and recordings were taken as the building rose and was loaded. The results of this investigation showed that at most points, the measured strains were proportional to the calculated stresses[3].

In addition to tests on design, we wanted to carry out some form of quality control as construction proceeded. At that time, the only test was for the crushing strength of bricks, and a mortar test cube was being discussed by a committee of the British Standards Institution. We were concerned with the interaction of the mortar and brick and the influence of workmanship. We proposed the use of 9" brick and mortar cubes to be made by the bricklayer from the bricks and mortar he was using for the walls.

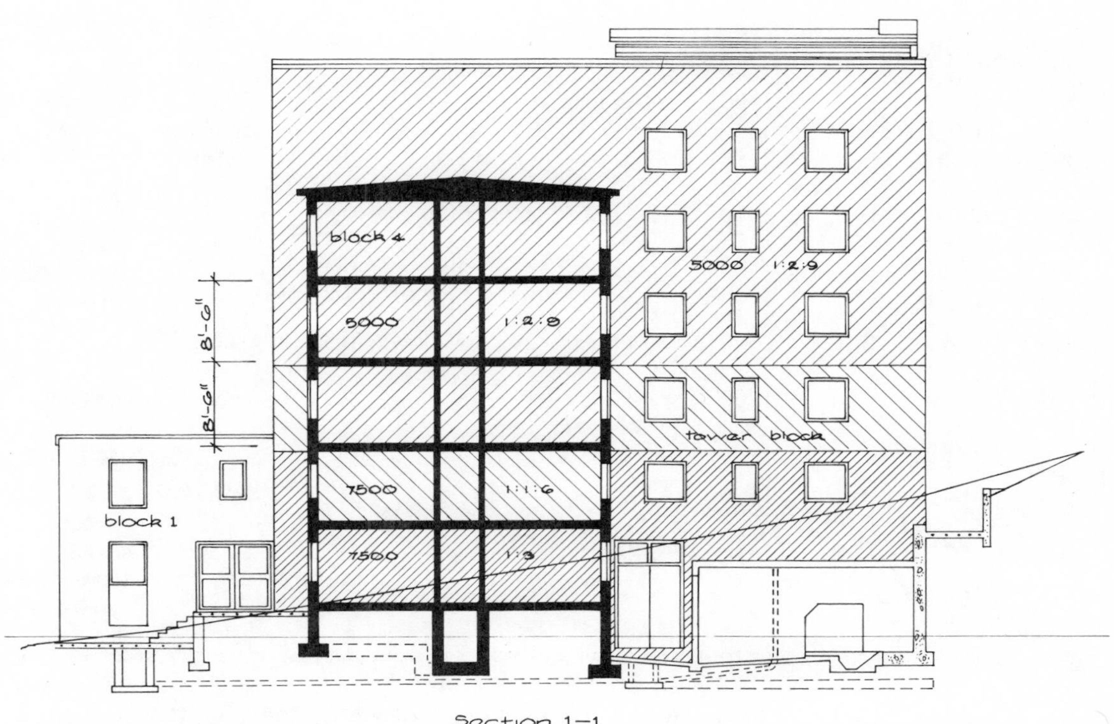

Figure 38-2. Sectional elevation. University College, Bangor.

Table 38-1
Summary of Test Results on 4½″ Storey-Height Wall Panels (After S. Prasan and R.E. Bradshaw)
Width of panels: 36.″ Height of panels: 8′-4″.
First Series

Wall No.	Brick Strength lb/in 2	Mortar Strength lb/in2	Ultimate Load tons	Average compressive stress lb/in2	Perm. Design Stress (C.P. 111 1964) lb/in 2	Load Factor	Strength Ratio brickwork/brick	Loading	Mode of Failure	Remarks
1	5640	1166 (1:1:6)	60	915	141	6.5	0.16	Axial	transverse splitting	5/8″ joints bad workmanship
2	5640	945 (1:1:6)	134	2040	141	14.5	0.36	”	”	
4	5640	80 (1:1:6)	44	660	141	4.7	0.12	”	buckling	very weak mortar
5	5640	1960 (1:1:6)	137	2080	199	10.4	0.37	”	transverse splitting	
7	7500	945 (1:1:6)	170	2580	180	18.3	0.34	”	”	
8	7500	630 (1:1:6)	142	2150	180	11.9	0.29	”	”	
3	5640	1201 (1:1:6)	145	2205	141	15.6	0.35	Axial + 30 lb/ft^2 super	”	vertical chase 3′6″ × 3/4″ × 1/2″ deep.
6	5640	2041 (1:0:3)	128	1946 ave.	199	13.8	0.34	Axial + 80 lb/ft^2 super	”	
10A	5640	1350 (1:0:3)	204	3100	199		0.55	Axial	none	reinforced 1 in 1
10B	5640	1350 (1:0:3)	204^T	3100 ave.	145 max. 86 ave.		0.55	Sway* ½″ reloaded	crushing at top	reinforced 1 in 1
11	4923	2240 (1:0:1)	141	2138	178	12.0	0.43	Axial		reinforced 1 in 4
12	4923	2380 (1:0:2)	192	2910	178	16.3	0.59	”		reinforced 1 in 3
13	4923	980 (1:0:3)	104	1580	178	8.9	0.32	”	transverse splitting	reinforced 1 in 5
14	5640	840 (1:0:3)	140	2128	249 max.	14.7	0.38	Ecc. ½″		
15	5640	945 (1:0:3)	116	1700 ave.	249 max.⊕ 97 ave+	18.2	0.31	Ecc. 1″	crushing at top before splitting	
16	5640	945 (1:0:3)	100	1520	249⊕ 119 ave+	12.8	0.27	Sway* ¾″	crushing at top	
17	5640	975 (1:0:3)	124	1886 ave.	249 max.⊕ 134 ave+	14.1	0.33	Sway* ⅝″	crushing at top before splitting	

† These are maximum permissible edge stresses and include the 25 percent increase for bending stresses allowed by C.P.111, 1964.

\+ The average values have been calculated by dividing the total safe load by the wall area. The total safe load has been determined by assuming that the maximum edge stress is the value marked ⊕ and that the wall has no tensile resistance.

* The calculations for permissible stresses for walls subjected to sway are based on an eccentric load equal to the sway.

Table 38-2
Summary of Test Results on 4½″ Storey-Height Wall Panels (After R. Bradshaw)
Width of panels: 36″. Height of panels: 8′4″.
Second Series

Wall No.	Brick Strength lb/in²	Mortar Strength lb/in²	Ultimate load tons	Average compressive stress lb/in²	Permissible design stress (C.P. 111 1964) lb/in²	Load factor	Duration of Loading minutes	Strength ratio brickwork/brick	Loading	Age days	Remarks
1	4825	660	53.6	835	132	6.3	90 (9)	0.17	Axial (t/22)	38	1:1:6 mortar/cement/ lime/sand
2 (2/1)	6235	2015	120	1630	217	7.5	90 to 92 tons (12) 90 to 120 tons (18)	0.26	Axial (t/17)	46	
3 (1/1)	6235	1585	114.5	1790	217	8.2	105 to 114.5 tons (17)	0.29	Axial (t/55)	18	Joint thick-ness: 3/16 in.
4 (3/1)	6235	1540	135	2110	217	9.7	90 to 135 tons (23) 15 to 135	0.34	Axial (t/40)	18	
5 (3/1)	6235	2450	157	2450	217	11.3	30 (82)	0.39	Axial (t/62)	78	
6 (3/1/w)	6235	865	150	2330	217	10.7	30 to 90 tons (48) 8 to 150 tons	0.37	Axial (t/67)	2	
7 (3/1/w)	6235	2335	172	2670	217	12.3	20 to 22.5 tons (17) 60 to 172 tons (44)	0.43	Axial (t/24)	18	
8 (3/1)	6235	700	149.5	2320	217	10.7	60 (39)	0.37	Axial (t/29)	7	Reinforced every second course
9	6855	1400 3070	200	3100	235	14.3	30 to 150 tons (39) 30 to 188 tons (97) 20 to 200 tons (155)	0.45	Axial	148	Reinforced every second course
10 (3/1/w)	6235	1100	132	2060	120	17.2	30 (69)	0.33	ecc. ¾″ (t/5.5- t/7.8)	6	
11	6235	630	117	1825	120	15.2	30 (61)	0.29	ecc. ¾″ (t/5.5- t/3.6)	5	
12 (3/2)	6235	765	120	1630	120	13.6	35 (47)	0.26	¾″ off plumb	7	
13 (3/2)	6855	695	131	2035	129	15.7	35 (58)	0.30	¾″ off plumb	8	
14 (3/3/w)	3710	805	81.5	1265	77	16.4	30 (42)	0.34	¾″ off plumb	19	
15 (3/2)	3710	770	70	1085	140	7.7	25 (43)	0.29	Axial	7	
16 (3/2/w)	3710	940	67	1040	140	7.4	30 (35)	0.28	Axial	13	Mortar at 17 days

The results of the crushing tests on site cubes were compared with those obtained from tests on similar cubes made under laboratory conditions, but as this was the first time 9" brickwork cubes had been used, we had no yardstick against which to compare our results and rather arbitrary acceptance criteria had to be specified. This situation will soon be changed, however, since the British Ceramic Research Association, Structural Clay Products Ltd. and others in Britian are carrying out cube testing programmes to establish the correlation between the cube strength and the wall strength. It is possible that this test may become standard practice in Britain in the near future[4].

At Bangor, cube testing had a useful side effect on the site since it had a psychological effect on the men. We experienced a little difficulty with the bricklayers at the beginning of the contract since their work, though acceptable by normal brick building standards, was not acceptable by engineering standards. After some discussion with the men (when they were shown photographs of the research work etc.), work improved considerably and the men worked well and enthusiastically. As a result of this experience, we were satisfied that these measures together with regular supervision ensured a high standard of workmanship.

Figure 38-3. Test on a 1/6th scale model crosswall structure

Construction

In addition to the normal problems of design and construction, we were faced with several detailing problems. Provision for expansion was made by isolating each block and also providing an expansion joint across the centre of each block. We still have no data on expansion joint requirements but would on most jobs provide expansion joints at about 75 ft. centres.

Close liason was necessary with the services engineers, and they had to accept the discipline of detailed planning of services before construction began because we would not permit the bashing of holes through the slender walls. Provision for services was made by forming vertical ducts at the junction of cross and corridor walls. Pre-formed holes were left in the walls, and reinforcement was embedded in the brickwork around the holes to distribute the stresses. No chasing of the brickwork was permitted, and, because this prevented using normal electrical conduits, plastic coated cables were stuck to the walls and plastered over.

The architect, fortunately, realised there was a planning discipline in cross-wall construction in that the walls should remain in the same plane from foundation to roof. We have not always been so fortunate and where architects have not accepted such discipline there has been a resultant increase in structural cost and construction time.

As engineers, we are naturally interested in the architectural expression of the structural form. In the past, this has been achieved by projecting the walls and slab beyond the face of a curtain wall – this tends to be expensive and on this contract the face wall was an 11" cavity brick wall. This forms an economical cladding to the structure which is virtually maintenance free and gives a good internal environment. Where the cross-wall has been projected beyond the curtain wall, there is liable to be damp penetration through the wall. The provision of a vertical damp proof course is unlikely to be satisfactory since the brickwork projecting externally beyond the damp proof course is liable to peel off. This problem has been solved on another contract by building the wall projection in engineering brick which is practically impervious.

Our experience on the Bangor contract confirmed our view that slender brick wall construction is economical, simple, and quick to construct and gives adequate performance for residential buildings. We have since used this form of construction (4-1/2" cross-walls) for student hostels at Aberystwyth and Oxford Universities, at Leeds, Chester, and Rugby teacher training colleges and at Wrexham Technical College. We have also continued to use the 9" cross-wall on numerous school buildings where larger floor spans are involved.

References

1. Coull, A., and Smith, E. Stafford, "Tall Buildings" Pergamon Press, 1967.

2. Sinha, B. P., "Model Studies Related to Load-Bearing Brickwork". Ph.D. Thesis, University of Edinburgh, 1967.
3. Stockbridge, J. G., "A Study of High-Rise Load-Bearing Brickwork in Britian", M. Arch. Thesis, University of Edinburgh, 1967.
4. "Model Specification for Load-Bearing Brickwork". The British Ceramic Research Association, Spec. Publ. 56, 1967.
5. Prasan, S., Hendry, A. W., and Bradshaw, R. E., "Crushing Tests on Storey-Height Walls 4-1/2" Thick", *Proc. British Ceramic Soc.*, No. 4., 1967. pp. 67-80.
6. Bradshaw, R. E. and Hendry, A. W., "Crushing Tests on Storey-Height Walls 4-1/2" Thick: Further Results", *Proc. British Ceramic Society,* In Press, 1967.
7. Murthy, C. K., and Hendry, A. W., "Model Experiments in Load-Bearing Brickwork". Building Science, Vol. 1. No. 4., 1966 pp. 289-299.
8. Sinha, B. P. and Hendry, A. W., "Racking Tests on Storey-Height Shear-Wall Structures"., chapter 23, *Designing, Engineering, and Constructing with Masonry Products,* Gulf Publishing Co., Houston, Texas, 1969.

39. Engineering evaluation for East Liberty Plaza.

R. M. Gensert and U. Kirsis, R. M. Gensert Associates, Cleveland, Ohio

Introduction

The East Liberty Plaza will be a 20 story masonry wall bearing apartment building for the low income level. (Location: Pittsburgh, Pennsylvania; Architect: Tasso Katselas) It will be situated near the Pennley Park project that contains 15 masonry wall-bearing buildings ranging from four to nine stories. These buildings proved to be more economical than steel or concrete framed buildings, using masonry walls as dividers between suites and corridors.

This 20 story building was designed in accordance with the City of Pittsburgh and State of Pennsylvania building codes. These codes embrace in part the American Standards Association code and some of the more liberal suggestions from the publications of the Structural Clay Products Institute. Although Pittsburgh is located in Zone I for earthquake analysis, the intensity of seismic forces in Zone I does not control design if the structure has inherent tensile resistance. However, it was the opinion of the Federal Housing Authority technical staff as well as the design engineers that a building of this height and type of construction should have some basis for the determination of ductility.

This chapter evaluates and gives the criteria that were developed for this building project with the cooperation of Mr. Dressel, Structural Engineer with the Federal Housing Authority in Washington, D. C.

Factors Considered in Planning the Building

The effect of wind forces in the transverse direction of the building (Figure 39-1) is more critical than in the longitudinal direction (Figure 39-2) since a larger surface area is exposed to

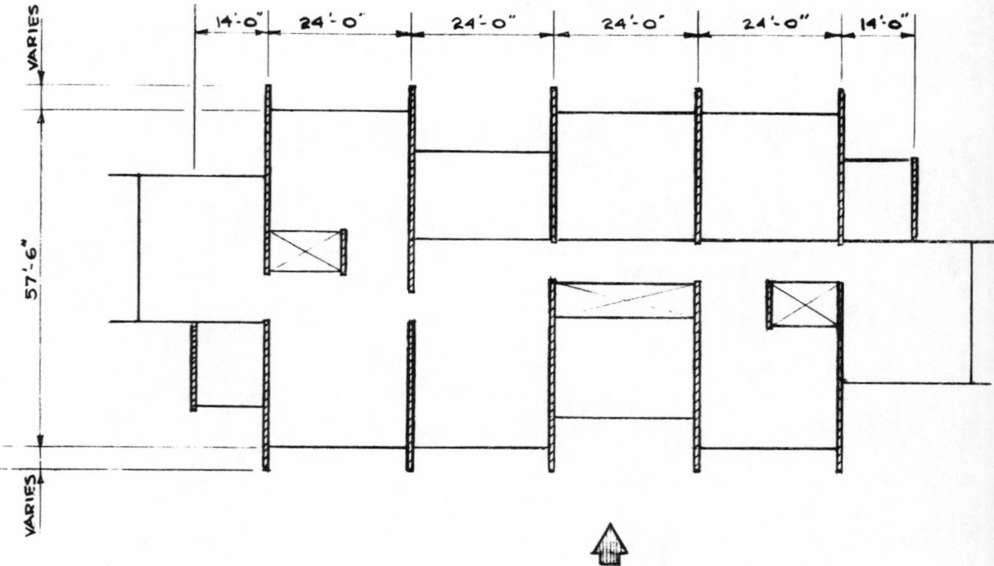

Figure 39-1. Plan of transverse walls.

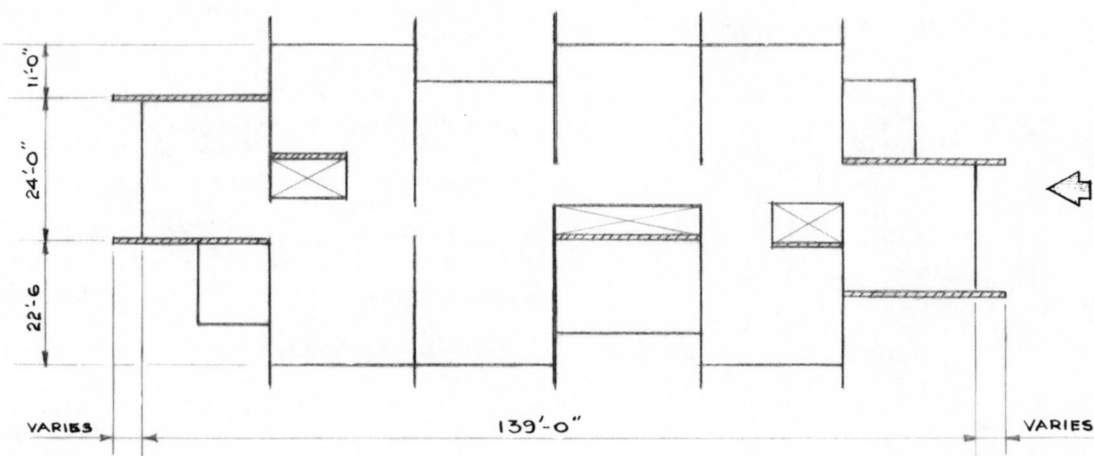

Figure 39-2. Plan of longitudinal walls.

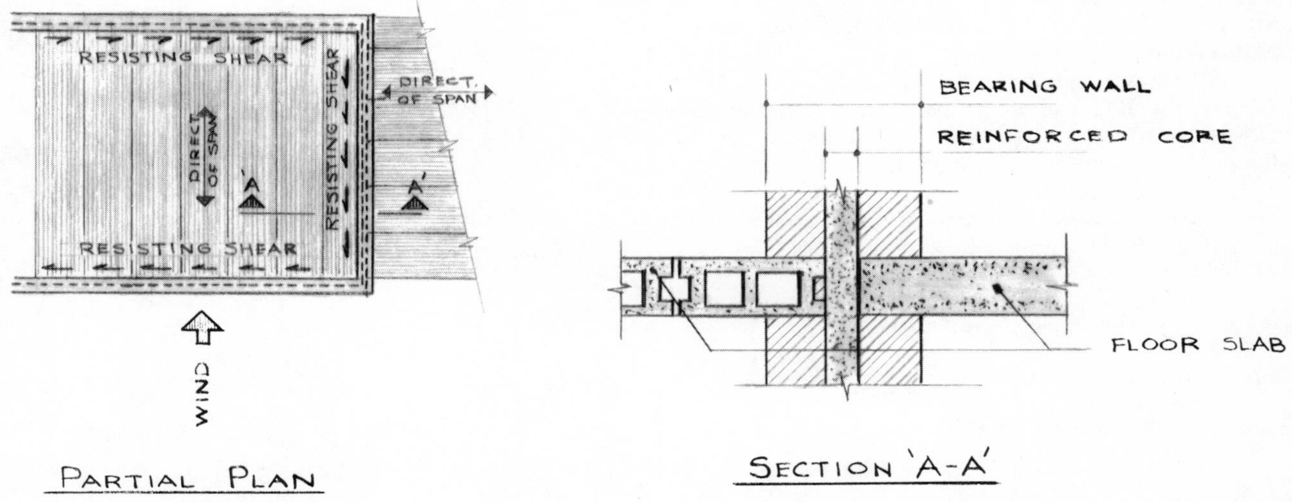

Figure 39-3. Partial floor plan and section through floor and slab.

the wind. Since seismic loads are affected by the building mass only, the total seismic load is equal in both directions. The arrangement of walls in the transverse direction was controlled by wind forces, and those in the longitudinal direction by seismic loads.

Lateral Stability when Load and Wall are Eccentric

Where the end of a building is open, it is necessary to distribute the wind loads to shear walls by means of the entire floor slab acting as a diaphragm. (Figure 39-3, Plan) To develop the shear resistance between diaphragm and walls, the floor should engage the wall even when the slab spans parallel to the wall (Figure 39-3, Section).

Lateral Stability when Wall is Parallel to the Span of the Slab

The entire slab acting as a diaphragm transfers lateral forces to the wall. The slab must engage the wall to accomplish this transfer (Figure 39-4).

Lateral Forces – Wind and Seismic Loading

Since allowable tension and shear stresses are small, the walls should be arranged so that the compressive forces due to the dead load of the floor and walls balance the tension forces due to lateral loads (Figure 39-5).

The dead load should also be sufficiently large to provide a resisting force, based on the coefficient of friction between

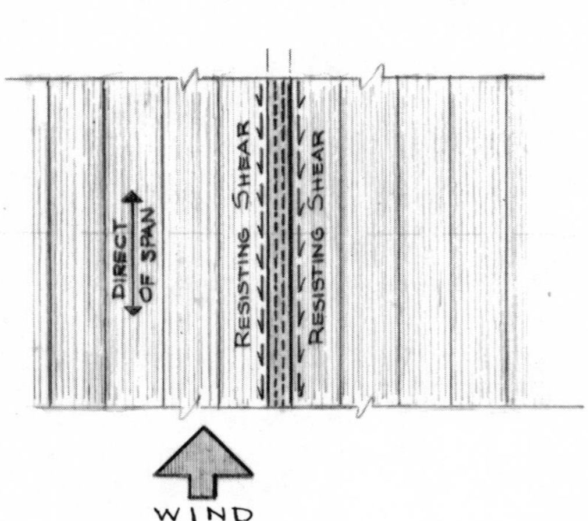

Figure 39-4. Partial plan at shear wall.

masonry units, greater than the applied shear stresses. This action is similar to the behavior of several precast units post-tensioned together (Figure 39-6).

In the transverse direction, the cross walls of the East Liberty Building had to be battered within their plane to satisfy overturning and tensile requirements due to wind forces. This was not a requirement for seismic loads.

In the longitudinal direction, to satisfy the seismic load requirements, the end walls had to be battered and additional longitudinal interior walls were also introduced.

Maximum and Minimum Stresses Due to Gravity and Lateral Forces

Wind force used = 30 psf. for the upper 85 feet of the building; 20 psf. below this level.

Seismic loads were based on the Uniform Building Code, 1967 edition, requirements for Zone I[2]

Total Shear V = Z K C W[1]

z = 1/4; K = 1.33; C = 1.20; W = Dead load of building.

Of the total shear, 10 percent was placed at the top story and the remainder distributed in a triangular pattern.

Allowable Stresses

Allowable stresses are based on Recommended Building Code Requirements for Engineered Brick Masonry by Structural Clay Products Institute.[1]

Allowable compressive stress computed from the following equation.

$$f = 0.25\, f'_m\ 1 - h/40t$$

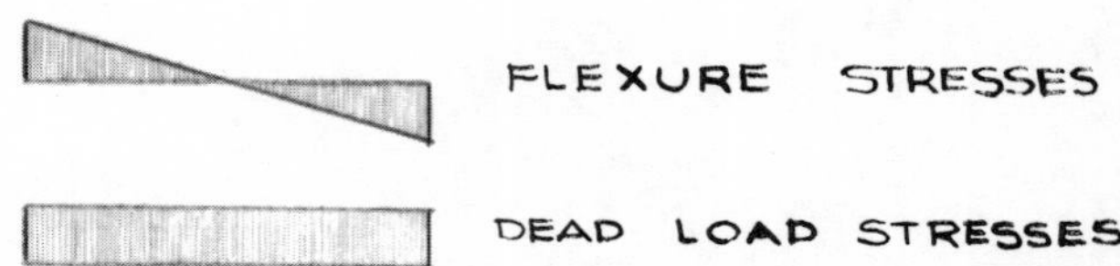

Figure 39-5. Vertical stress diagram.

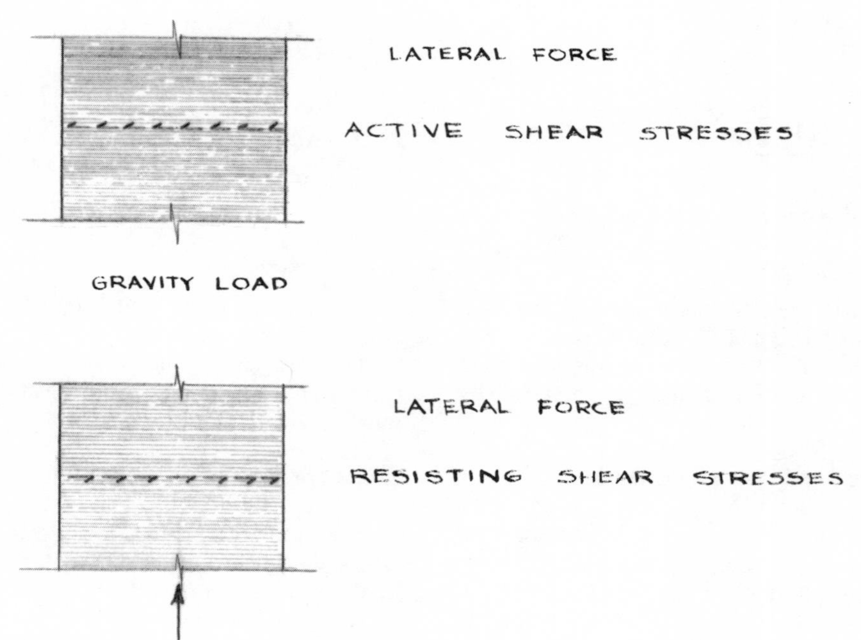

Figure 39-6. Shear stress diagram.

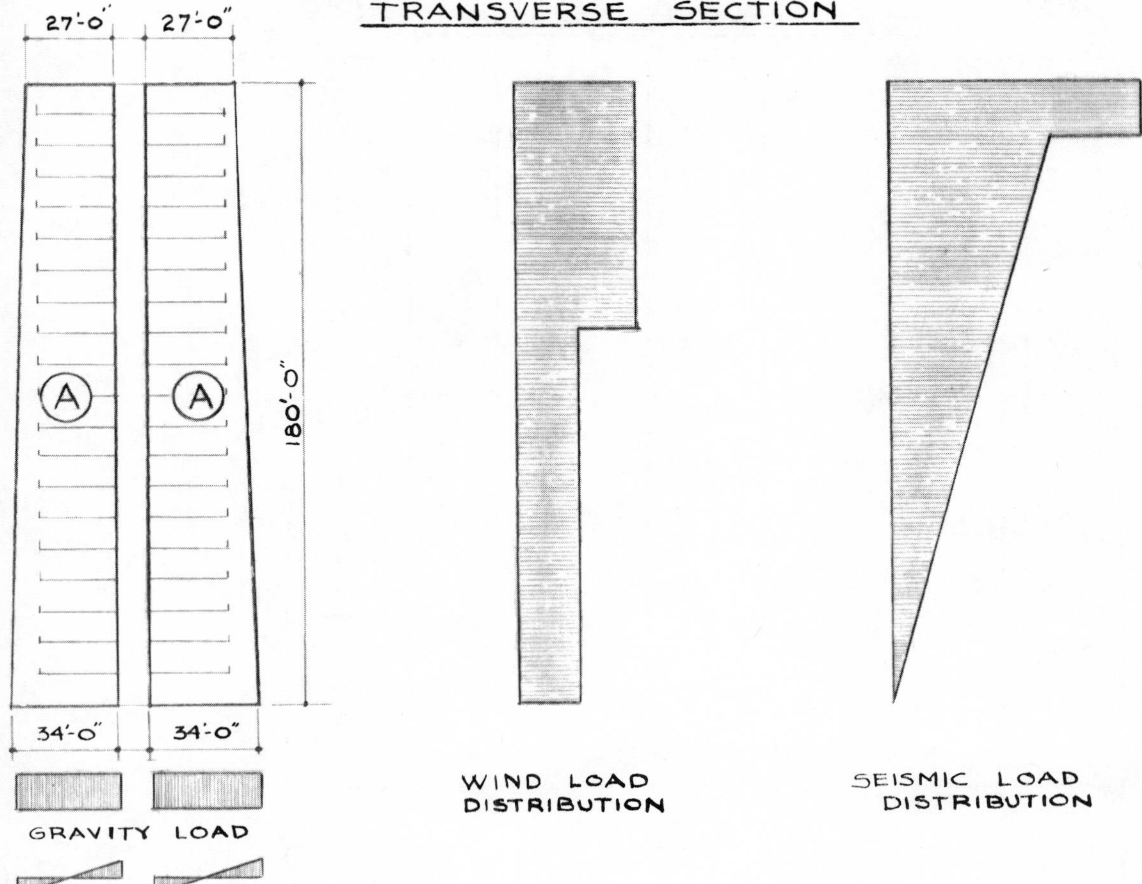

Figure 39-7. Lateral load distribution and stress diagrams transverse section. Overturning factors and stresses due to wind and seismic loads. See Table 39-1 for wind and seismic load distribution.

Table 39-1
Table for Wall Stresses

Wall	Gravity Load L.L. + D.L.	Gravity Load D.L.	Wind Load	Seismic Load	Combined Gravity & Wind		Combined Gravity & Seismic		Factor of Safety Against Overturning	
					Max.	Min.	Max.	Min.	Max.	Min.
A	570 psi	400 psi	±270 psi	±160 psi	840 psi	130 psi	730 psi	240 psi	4.50	7.70
B	270 psi	200 psi	±150 psi	±190 psi	420 psi	50 psi	460 psi	10 psi	2.40	1.80
C	580 psi	300 psi	±170 psi	±220 psi	750 psi	130 psi	800 psi	80 psi	2.40	1.80
D	360 psi	260 psi	±110 psi	±150 psi	470 psi	150 psi	510 psi	110 psi	2.40	1.80

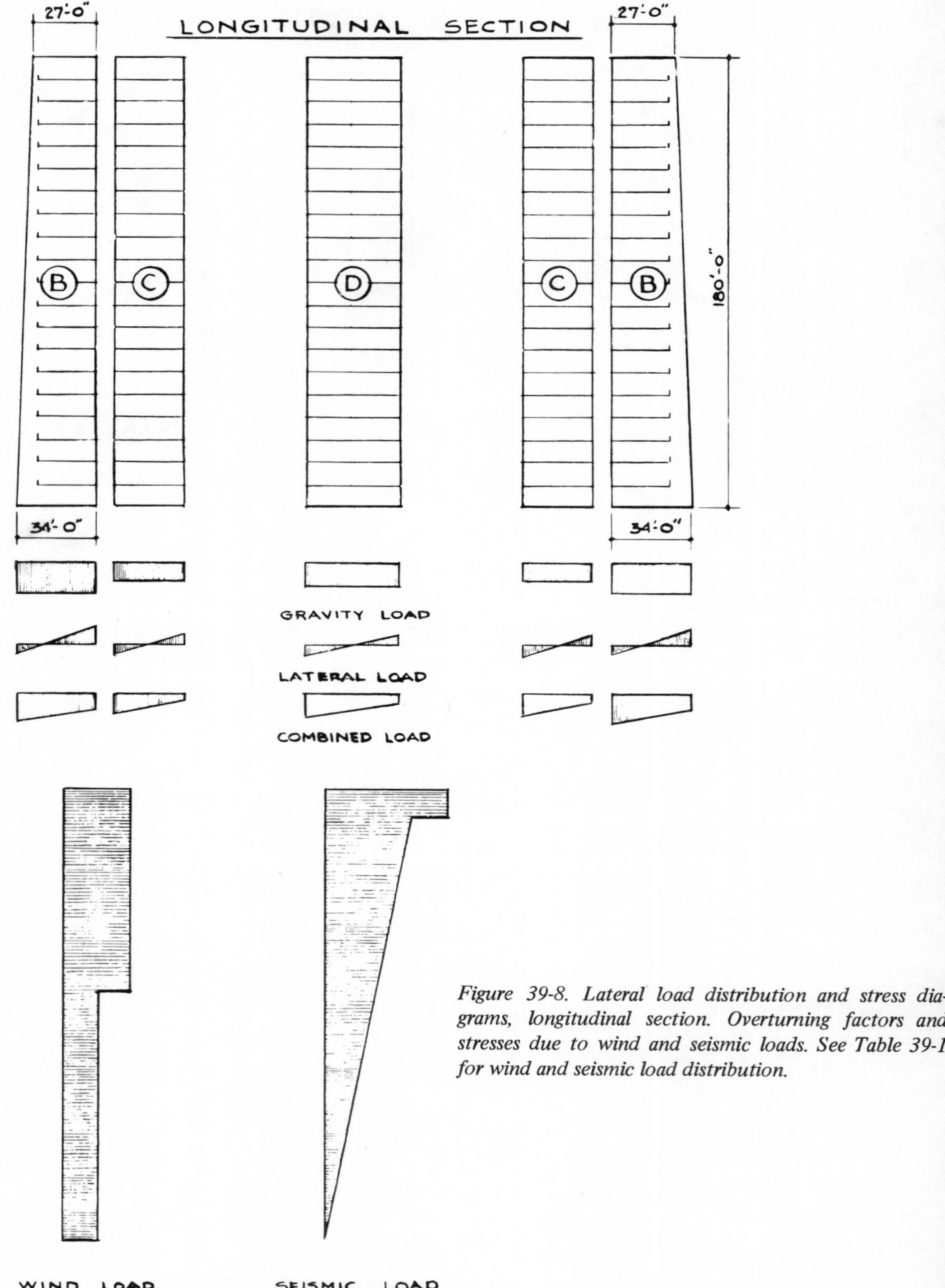

Figure 39-8. Lateral load distribution and stress diagrams, longitudinal section. Overturning factors and stresses due to wind and seismic loads. See Table 39-1 for wind and seismic load distribution.

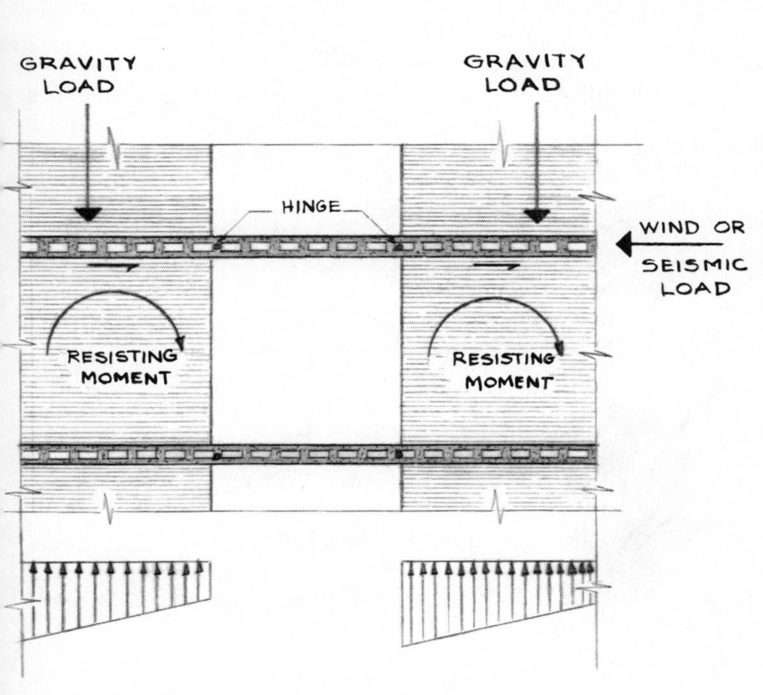

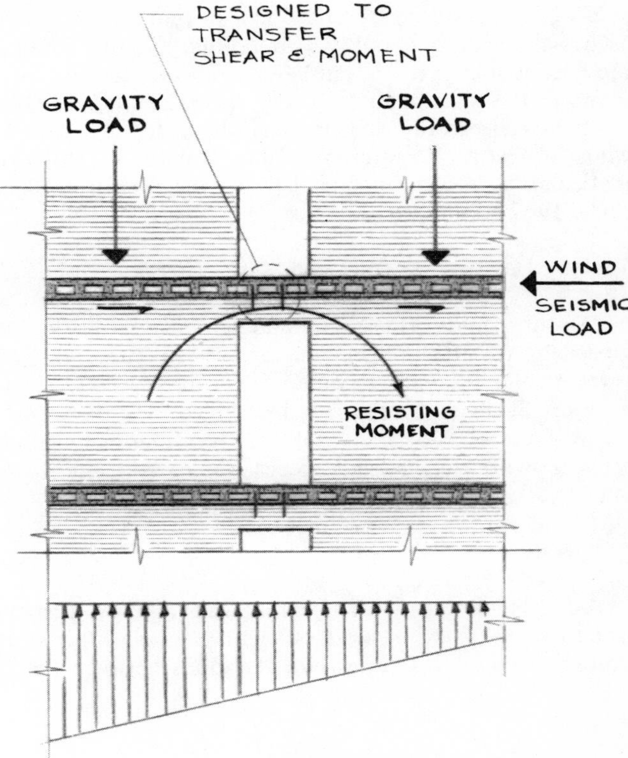

Figure 39-9. Opening at corridors.

Figure 39-10. Opening at doors through shear walls.

where:
h = effective unsupported wall height
t = thickness of wall[2]

The prism test method will be used to determine f'_m. This test sample will have a height to thickness ratio of 5, and all materials and bonding arrangements will be the same as those proposed for the actual building construction.

Type M mortar conforming to Standard Specifications for Mortar and Grout for Reinforced Masonry, C-476-63, and consisting of mixture of Portland cement and aggregate will be used.

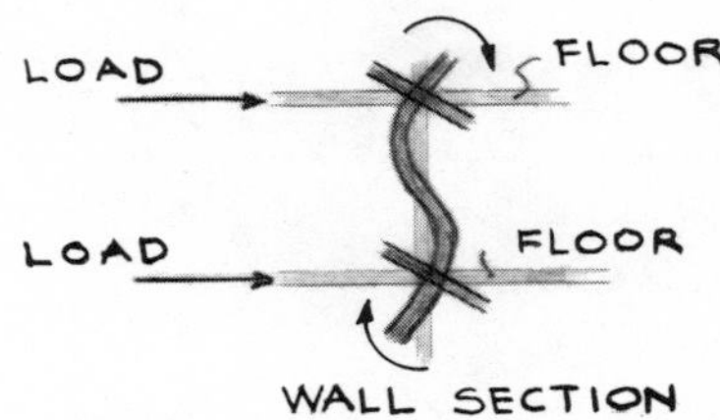

Figure 39-11. Flexural resistance of walls.

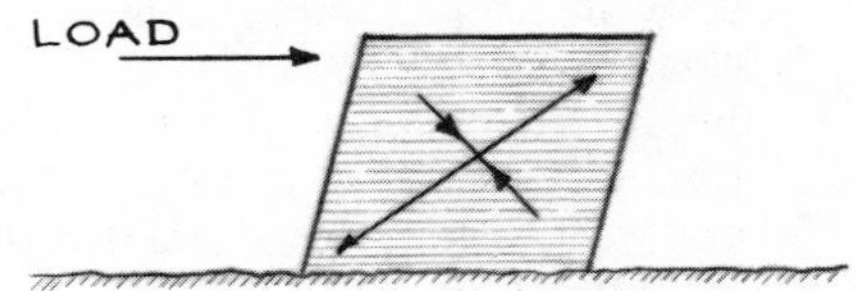

Figure 39-12. Shear resistance of walls.

Design of Shear Walls

Since openings in shear walls at corridors (Figure 39-9) were wide and extended to the underside of the floor slabs, sufficient ties could not be developed to have a coupled shear wall action and walls were designed as individual units. At door openings (Figure 39-10) the section of wall above the opening was designed to transfer shear and moment from one wall to the other and so the wall was designed as one unit.

Reinforcing for Ductility

Since this type of structure resists all lateral forces by its shearing action, (Figure 39-12) it is classified as a rigid rather than a flexible structure. This means that bending resistance transverse to the walls (Figure 39-11) is not critical, and thus transverse ductility is not necessary.

Portal action does not occur since distortion from shear resistance is considerably less than distortion from flexural resistance, and so walls cannot flex when shear panels restrain them. Nevertheless, the nominal reinforcing in the walls will offer this ductility even though it is not required.

Flexural resistance of lateral loads occurs in the plane of each wall, and so ductility is important for this action. To provide elasticity for a cantilever, it becomes necessary to reinforce the edges of all walls (Figures 39-13 and 39-14).

Reinforcing in the walls for ductility is figured as a couple whose force is 25 percent of the total seismic force in a particular wall as recommended by the Uniform Building Code, 1967 edition.[2]

Masonry Details

Masonry units for this building will be bricks made especially for the project. (Figure 39-15) They will be 75 percent solid and will measure 5-5/8″ wide by 2-1/2″ high by 8″ long. Shells and webs shall be bedded in mortar. All cells below grade shall be filled with mortar. Interior longitudinal walls resisting only seismic forces will be concrete masonry units with an ultimate strength of 4000 psi.

Temperature

A tall building with load-bearing walls arranged perpendicular to its perimeter is more efficient than any other type of exposed structure. Temperature variations between that part of the wall exposed to the interior and that part held at a constant temperature inside the building are gradual. These gradual variations in the temperature gradient will not overstress the wall.

For a 100° change in temperature, the shear stress in the wall = 7.2 psi. (Figure 39-17)

Contrary to this, a tall building with load-bearing walls around the perimeter but connected to interior bearing walls by means of shear walls will suffer marked differences in temperature. These differences lead to internal stresses near the junction of interior and exterior walls. (Figure 39-18)

For a 100° change in temperature, the shear stress in the wall = 100 psi.

Floor Slabs

Cast in place, concrete floor slabs offer a monolithic diaphragm; however, the shrinkage of a concrete floor will induce bending and shear stresses into a supporting masonry wall. (Figures 39-19 and 39-20)

When tied together, precast concrete floor slabs will offer a rigid diaphragm without the shrinkage problem. The resisting forces necessary to develop diaphragm action are very small, and so intermittent connections such as welded steel plate anchors is all that is required. Should the precast elements be narrow units, such as 16″ or 24″ wide, the cost of anchoring would be high. A more convenient solution in this case would be introducing a reinforced bonded topping. Since this reinforcing acts as a tension tie and not as flexural reinforcing, its position at the top of all slabs is not a disadvantage. Criteria for minimum A_s in topping is 0.2 percent of slab action. (FHA requirement–Figure 39-21.)

In the Pittsburgh area, it is often more economical to resort to a precast floor slab made from hollow concrete block units held together by the bottom reinforcing steel that is grouted into adjacent block units. For this project, the large spans and seismic considerations required that all slabs shall be prestressed in the direction of span to eliminate tensile stresses in the slabs as well as to join individual block units that make up each slab.

The ends of all slabs shall be solid to provide load transfer within the walls and to develop their own shear resistance.

Abutting slabs shall be reinforced at all bearing walls for negative moments due to live loads.

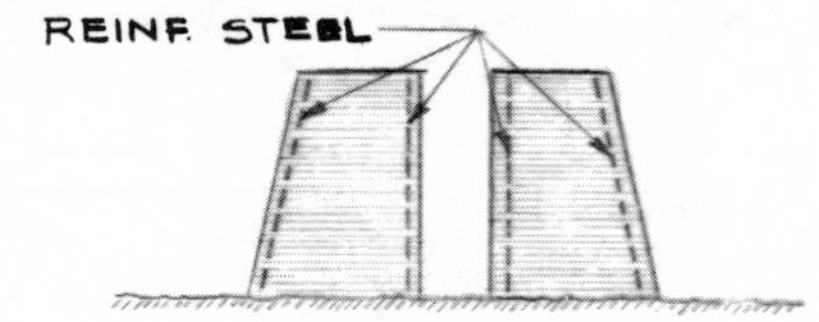

Figure 39-13. Crosswalls.

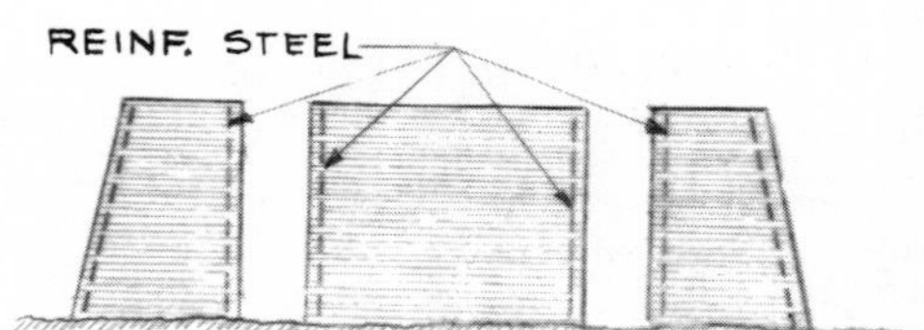

Figure 39-14. End walls and corridor walls.

In the case of diaphragm action, wind shears parallel to the span of the precast slabs produce shear stresses between 1 and 2 psi.

Investigation of Wall Eccentricities

Specification for wall-bearing structures designed by our office set tolerances for out of plumb as follows: Maximum eccentricity in any one story = 1/2″. Maximum eccentricity in total building height = 1/2″ for building height of 5 stories or less; 3/4″ for 10 stories or less; and 1″ for a building over 10 stories high.

Although allowable stresses have been based on tests with an eccentricity 1/3 the wall width, it was decided to investigate the effects of a 1″ eccentricity in an end wall and an interior wall as indicated in Figures 39-22 and 39-23. Stresses due to this eccentricity are small compared to total stress. The possibility of some small tension stresses at upper floors should be investigated since compressive stresses from dead load may not overcome tension stresses from bending.

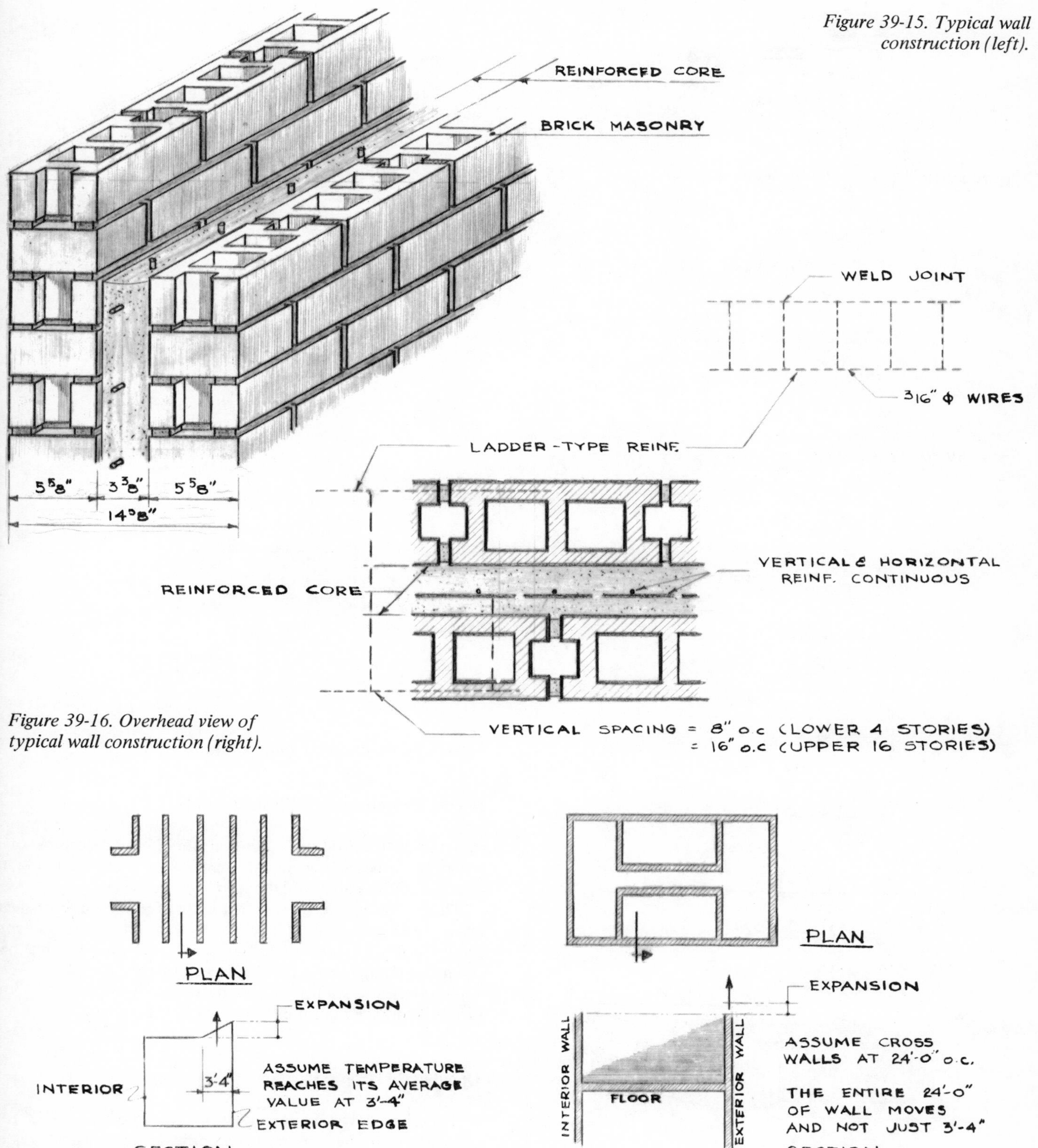

Figure 39-15. Typical wall construction (left).

Figure 39-16. Overhead view of typical wall construction (right).

Figure 39-17. Plan and section of walls.

Figure 39-18. Plan and section of walls.

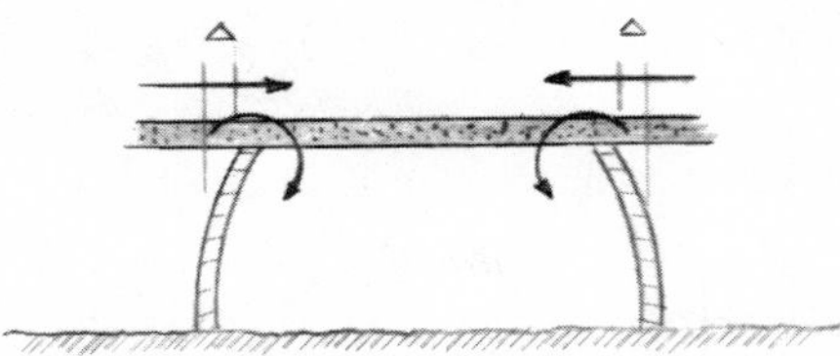

Figure 39-19. Walls in section, bending stresses.

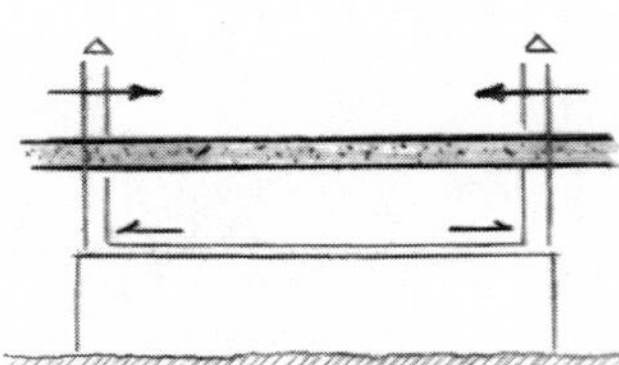

Figure 39-20. Walls in elevation, shear stresses.

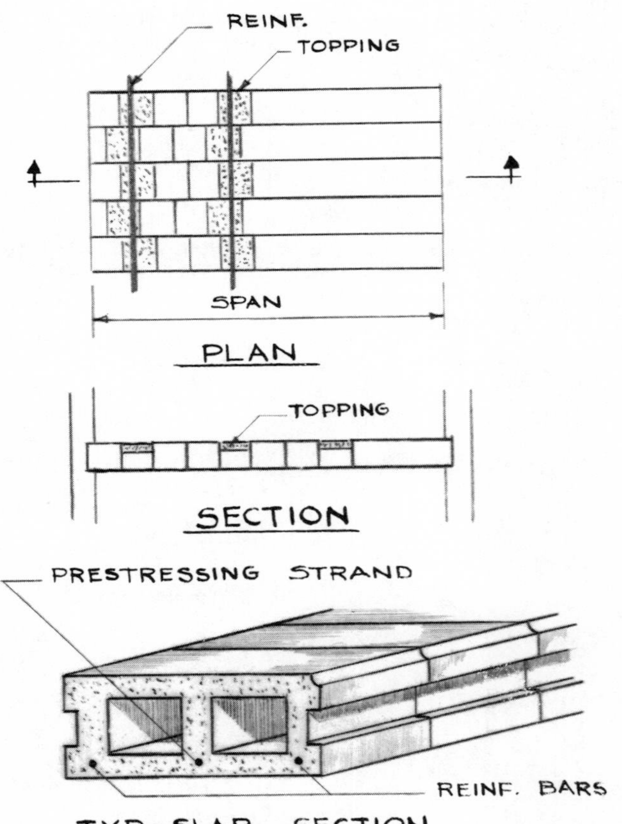

Figure 39-21. Floor slab details.

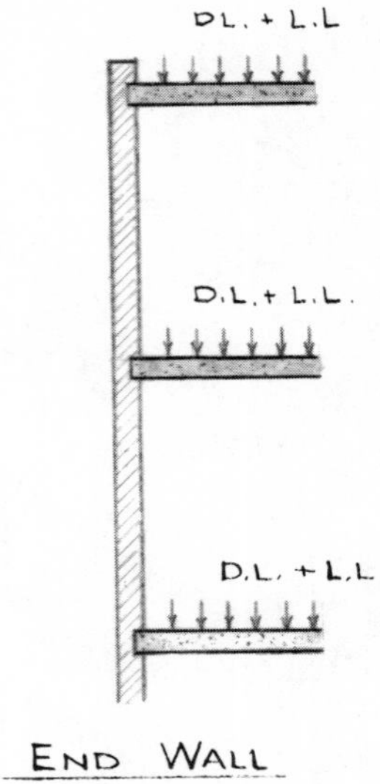

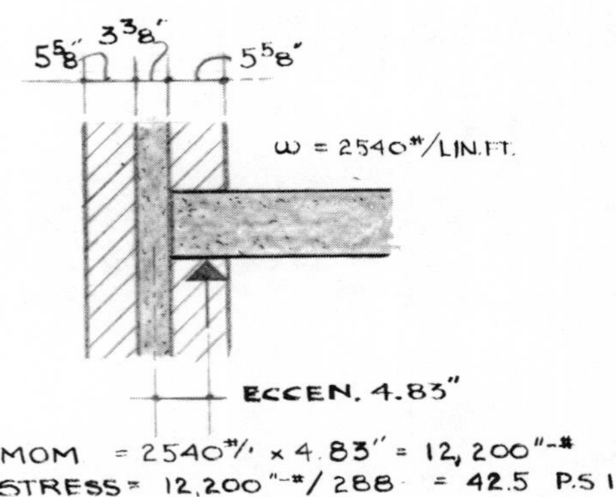

Figure 39-22. Eccentric loading on end walls.

Stress Concentrations at Bearing Points.

Stress concentrations occur at the interior corners of a north in a bearing wall that receives a floor slab due to rotation of the slab as it deflects. (Figure 39-24)

These stresses can be satisfied by reinforcing three adjacent brick joints just above and below the slab. The reinforced core should not be interrupted, and a 1/8" asbestos bearing pad should be placed under the slab at its bearing.

Photo elastic studies of bearing stresses were made for the earlier Pennley Park buildings shown in Figure 39-25.[5]

Openings in Walls

Large openings in bearing walls will produce stress concentrations at the corners of window or door heads. (Figure 39-26) To accomodate these stresses, #2 reinforcing wires are placed at the upper corners in the grouted core of the wall and lintels are given additional bearing.

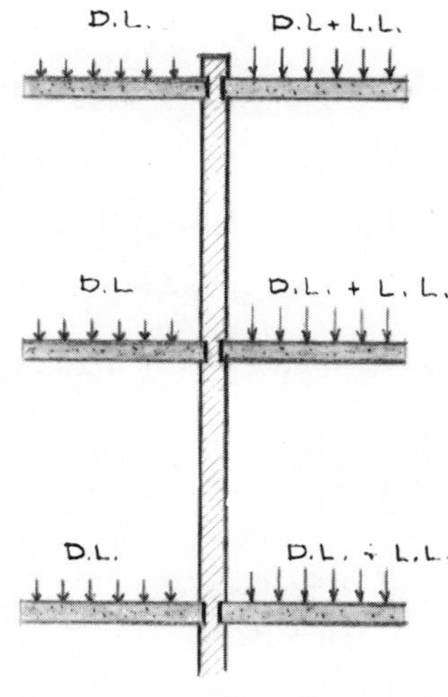

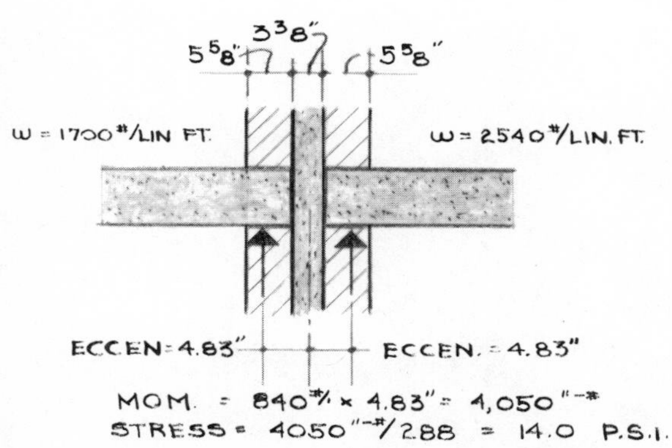

Figure 39-23. Eccentric loading on interior walls.

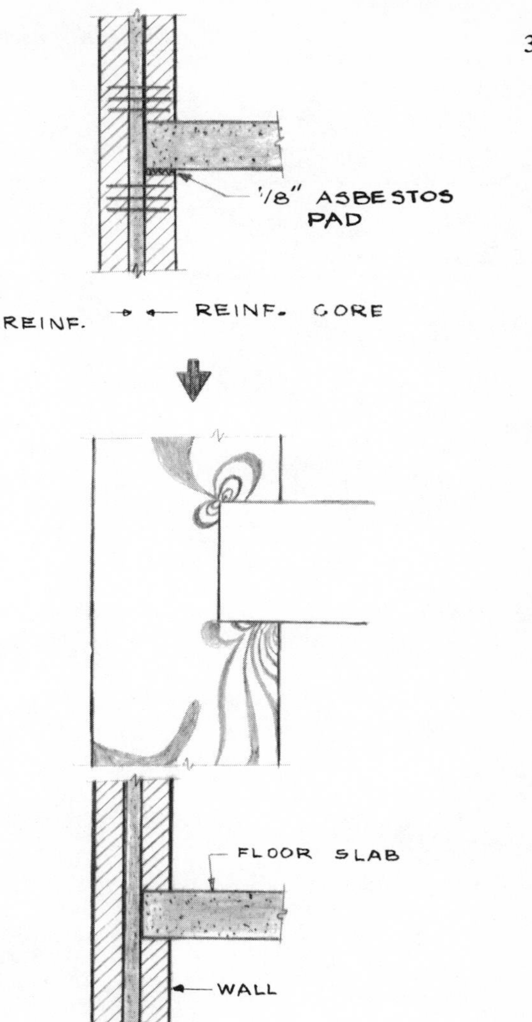

Figure 39-24. Stress concentrations at bearing points, East Liberty Plaza.

Figure 39-25. Pennley Park Apartment.

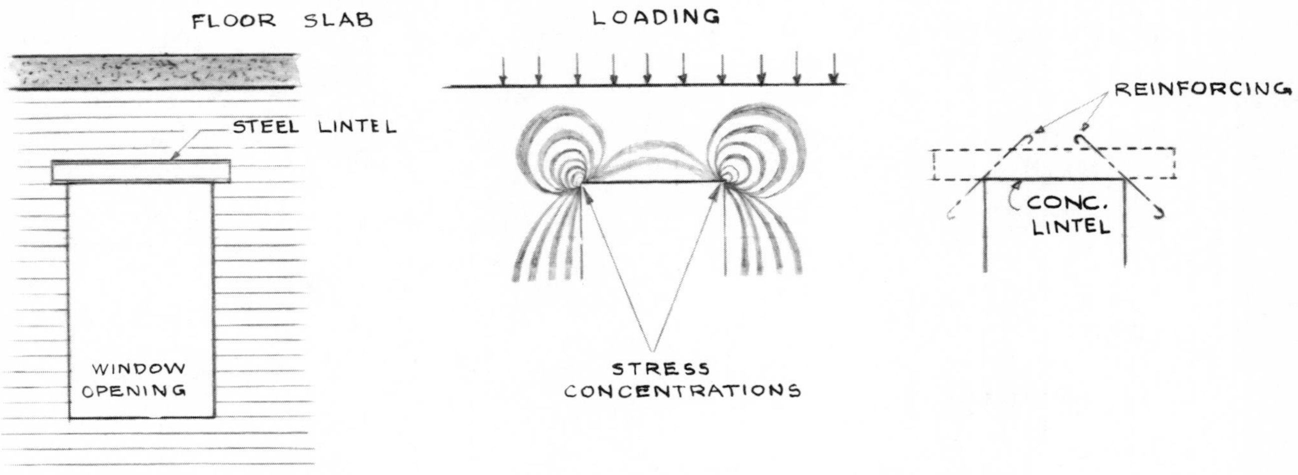

Figure 39-26. Stress concentrations at openings.

Figure 39-27. Western Reserve University dormitory.

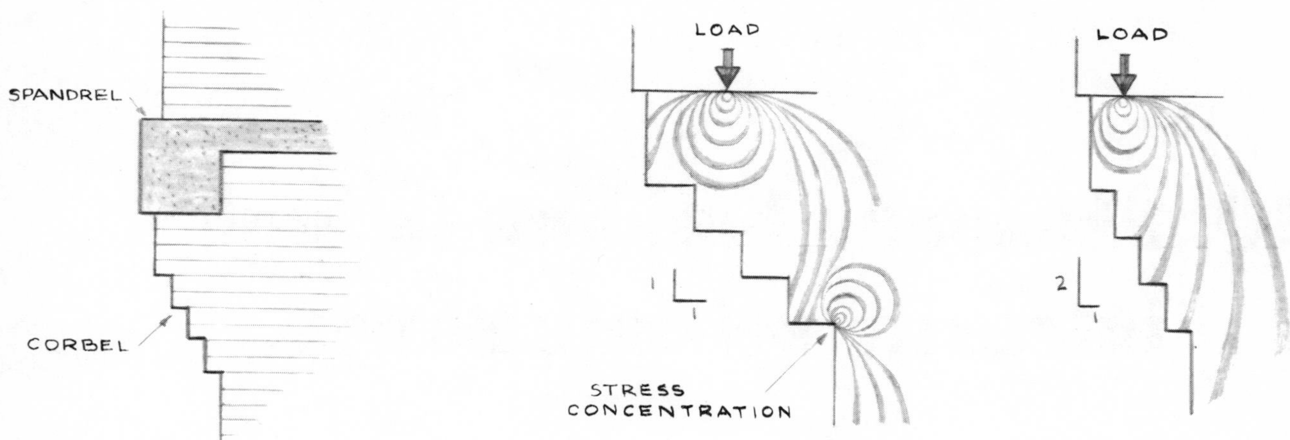

Figure 39-28. Stress concentrations at wall corbels, East Liberty Plaza.

Figure 39-29. St. Vincent Monastery.

Figure 39-27 shows the dormitory building for Western Reserve University where some lintels required extra wall reinforcing and embedment.[5]

Wall Corbels

A corbel in the plane of a wall will transfer pure compressive loads when its profile is on a slope of 2:1 or steeper. A slope of 1:1 will cause bending stresses in the corbel with a high concentrated stress at the reentrant angle. (Figure 39-28)

Studies for this particular detail were made earlier for the St. Vincent Monastery shown in Figure 39-29.[5]

References

1. "Recommended Building Code Requirements for Engineered Brick Masonry," Structural Clay Products Institute, May 1966.
2. *Uniform Building Code,* International Conference of Building Officials, California, 1967 Edition.
3. Plummer, Harry C., *Brick and Tile Engineering,* SCPI, Washington, D.C., 1950.
4. "Minimum Standards for Multi-Family Housing," U.S. Department of Housing and Urban Development, Federal Housing Administration, Washington, D.C., May 1968.
5. Gensert, R. M. and Kirsis, U., Model Studies, unpublished.

40. Masonry building in high intensity seismic zones.

I. L. Holmes, Holmes & Wood, Christchurch, New Zealand

History of New Zealand Earthquake Activity

In 140 years of organised European settlement, New Zealand has experienced 17 destructive earthquakes, that is earthquakes of magnitude 7 or greater on the Richter scale. In 1848 and 1855, destructive earthquakes caused major damage and land upheaval at the site of Wellington, a city now of 350,000 people.

In 1848, the population was only a few hundred and buildings were modest. Nevertheless, a contemporary account[1] stated, "Most of the large brick stores and dwellings together with many of the solid clay buildings, received a severe shock, and chimneys were levelled to the roof in about two fifths of the houses in town. The Wesleyan Chapel, the gaol, and other public buildings were seriously damaged." A man and two of his children were buried beneath falling bricks and killed. For many years, from this time brick was avoided for buildings in Wellington.

In 1855, an earthquake of reported felt intensity MM.11 hit Wellington; and the land was permanently raised 5 ft. to 6 ft. Only one man was killed in this earthquake. The policy, following the 1848 earthquake, of building largely in timber had paid off. The lesson, however, was slowly forgotten.

It was not until 1929 that another earthquake in New Zealand caused loss of lives. In that year, the Murchison earthquake of magnitude 7 resulted in major changes to the countryside and killed 17 people. Less than two years later, in February 1931, an earthquake of magnitude 7-3/4 at Napier caused 256 deaths.

Between 1855 and 1929, earthquakes of magnitude 7 or greater had occurred at regular intervals, nine altogether. But none of these had an epicentre sufficiently close to a populated area to cause major damage or death. The people of New Zealand got used to the regular tremblings of their "shaky islands" and gave no particular thought to the earthquake design of their buildings.

But the earthquakes of 1929 and 1931 taught new lessons. The earthquake of 1931, in particular, showed those concerned with building that the simple load-bearing structures, traditional in Europe, were inadequate to resist earthquake shock. There were many brick buildings in Napier in 1931, and these were largely responsible for the loss of life. Not only were they inadequate in their design, but also in many cases they exhibited inadequate workmanship and poor supervision of construction.

Immediately after the Napier earthquake, the New Zealand Institute of Architects appointed a Committee to recommend new building regulations[2]. As a result, the larger local authorities introduced immediate changes to their building bylaws, and, in 1935, a New Zealand Standard Model Building Bylaw was published. The high seismic risk in New Zealand was acknowledged, and rational design for earthquake was introduced for the first time.

New Zealand Design Rules for Masonry

Under the New Zealand Municipal Corporations Act, each local authority is responsible for promulgating its own building bylaws. Generally, all local authorities, cities, boroughs, and counties adopt the Model Building Bylaws produced as N.Z.S.S. 1900 by the New Zealand Standards Association. Some authorities do make local amendments, and many are slow to adopt the latest revisions. In general, however designers throughout the country work to the latest editions of N.Z.S.S. 1900.

The parts of N.Z.S.S. 1900 particularly relevant to masonry design are (1) Chapter 8 "Basic design loads", (2) Chapter 6.2 "Construction requirements for buildings not requiring specific design : Masonry" and (3) Chapter 9.2 "Design and construction, Masonry".

Chapter 8 was considerably changed in a December 1965 revision. For the first time, the country was divided into seismic intensity zones. The zones are based on geological history and on the pattern of recorded earthquakes over 120 years.

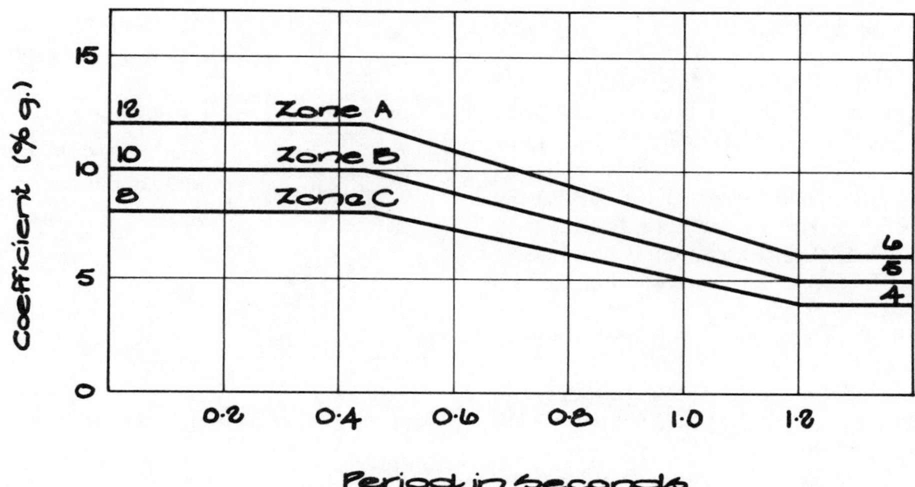

Figure 40-1. Basic seismic coefficients from N.Z.S.S., 1900, Chapter 8, 1965.

The earthquake design forces are high. In relation to the appropriate design stresses and design loads, they are higher than corresponding earthquake forces in United States codes, although lower than those in Japanese codes[3]. In Zone A, for private buildings of period up to 0.44 sec. the base shear is 0.12 W, where W includes one third of the design live load. For periods between 0.44 sec. and 1.2 sec. the base shear reduces from 0.12 W to 0.06 W in a straight line relationship, and is constant at 0.06 W for higher periods. For Zone B and Zone C the base shears are 0.10 W to 0.05 W, and 0.08 W to 0.04 W, respectively (Figure 40-1). Public buildings and places of assembly or restraint are designed to higher base shears. Design stresses corresponding to these earthquake design forces are, in general, 33 percent higher than normal working stresses based on elastic design.

The assumption behind the earthquake design forces is an El Centro type earthquake acting on a structure with adequate ductility and damping characteristics. In Zone A, a building designed to N.Z.S.S. 1900 can be expected to behave satisfactorily in an earthquake of intensity MM.9[3]. The amount of secondary damage suffered will depend on the extent of excursions into the plastic range and on the degree of protection for nonstructural components.

Chapter 8 "Loads" has specific restrictions on masonry. Except for single or double unit dwellings, unreinforced masonry is not permitted at all in Zone A. In Zones B and C, it is permitted only for infill panels and partitions, and, to a limited extent, for load-bearing buildings of one and two storeys.

The design coefficients for earthquake load normal to the face of walls, infill panels, and partitions are double the appropriate coefficients for base shear. Together with the low permissible stresses for unreinforced masonry this imposes a further restriction on unreinforced masonry in Zones B and C.

Chapters 6.2 and 9.2 "Masonry" were published in their present form in July 1959. Both chapters contain identical requirements for materials, construction, and workmanship. Chapter 6.2 is limited to small one-storey buildings or to dwellings of limited size. It gives design rules in terms of wall lengths and heights related to bond beam sizes and reinforcement. These rules are based on the principle that every wall is supported by other walls at right angles by horizontally spanning bond beams. Rules are given for unreinforced and for reinforced masonry walls.

Chapter 9.2 is based on an elastic analysis and allowable working stresses. Allowable stresses are given for unreinforced and for reinforced masonry and for masonry with and without continuous inspection (Table 40-1). Allowable stresses are similar to those published in the United States. Chapter 9.2 requires the elastic analysis to take into account all elements in a structure that are affected by the loading, whether they are considered part of the basic structure or not. This means, for instance, that the stresses occurring in masonry panels in a framed building must be analysed and not permitted to exceed the allowable stresses. The effect of this last requirement on a revival of load-bearing masonry wall construction will be mentioned later in the chapter.

Practically all industrial and commercial buildings in New Zealand that incorporate masonry are, or should be, designed to these Chapters of N.Z.S.S. 1900. Much rule-of-thumb designing of masonry continued even after the July 1959 edition of Chapter 9.2. This, however, should largely cease as the full significance of the December 1965 edition of Chapter 8 becomes appreciated.

Masonry Development in New Zealand

Prior to the Napier earthquake of 1931 many buildings in New Zealand were built of load-bearing masonry. Some were of stone, but most were of brick, designed by rule-of-thumb methods common in Europe at that time.

Observations of the effects of the Napier earthquake caused a shift of interest from load-bearing to framed buildings. Buildings "of good reinforced concrete frame and steel frame construction resisted the shock with remarkable success," although they were not specifically designed for earthquake forces, reported the N.Z.I.A. Committee*. In future, they decided, no buildings such as theatres, churches, hospitals or schools should be built of bearing wall construction, and no building of more than two storeys†. As well as these general restrictions, they gave detailed recommendations for the better construction of brickwork.

The recommendations of the N.Z.I.A. Committee were soon adopted and made into bylaws by the Wellington City Council in Bylaw Amendment No. 3 (Building) 1934. A design horizontal force of 0.10 W was specified, and several buildings of special concern to the public were restricted from being constructed "otherwise than with a structural frame of steel or reinforced concrete". All masonry bearing walls were restricted to 25 ft. height unless the floors were in reinforced concrete, when they were restricted to three storeys or 40 ft. They were to be secured with reinforced concrete bands at floor and roof levels and tied across the building or braced with cross walls. Parapets were to be backed with reinforced concrete. Brickwork was to be laid with attention to mortar bond, and with mesh reinforcement in every fourth course.

From this time on, particularly in the more active seismic areas, most buildings of more than one storey were built in reinforced concrete or structural steel. They were designed for the earthquake force of 0.10 W as frames, and walls were infilled as panels of brick or reinforced concrete.

The design rules were consolidated in the 1935 first edition of the Standard Model Building Bylaw, known then as N.Z.S.S. 95, Parts I to X. The parts were revised and reissued at regular intervals. This Standard Model Building Bylaw was consolidated and reissued as N.Z.S.S. 1900 in 1964.

Revisions of Model Building Bylaw illustrate the development in design thinking as the earthquake behaviour of buildings became better understood.

The December 1939 revision included a section, Part VI, on panel walls. Panels, either of brick or concrete, were classified as non-rigid or rigid according to their thickness and stiffness. If a panel was "rigid" its effect on the distribution of forces on the structure had to be considered, but unless it was reinforced as a structural panel it could not contribute to the design resistance. It took several years for the logic of this revision to be generally appreciated by designers. Almost until 1959 the non-rigid panel of concrete or brick, in an earthquake resisting frame, was most commonly used. Very few designers went to the trouble to use the concept of a structural panel. The requirements for a structural panel in masonry were rigorous, requiring slotted bricks and rust-resisting reinforcement. The alternative cavity brick panel of two 4-1/4" leaves which was classed as non-rigid was much more attractive and almost universally used.

A revision of July 1959 reintroduced the concept of load-bearing masonry, but this time replacing the old rule-of-thumb methods of design with rational design by elastic analysis. This revision, first issued as a revision of N.Z.S.S. 95, Part X "Masonry Construction," was reissued without change as Chapters 6.2 and 9.2 of the consolidated N.Z.S.S. 1900, the current Bylaw.

Table 40-1
Allowable Stresses from N.Z.S.S. 1900, Chapter 9.2: 1964

Unreinforced Masonry						
Material Grade of Unit	Allowable stress in lbs./sq. in.					
	With cont. inspect			Without cont. inspect.		
	comp.	tens.	shear	comp.	tens.	shear
Plain masonry:						
Brick & solid block	150	10	10	75	5	5
Hollow masonry	60	10	10	40	5	5
Cavity wall:						
Solid	100	8	8	70	4	4
Hollow	50	8	8	30	4	4
Natural stone	100	4	4	80	2	2

Reinforced Masonry						
Material Grade of Unit	Allowable stress in lbs./sq. in.					
	With cont. inspect			Without cont. inspect		
	Axial Comp.	Flex. Comp.	Shear*	Axial Comp.	Flex. Comp.	Shear*
Grouted solid:						
2,500 plus	300	500	60	150	250	30
1,500 to 2,500	150	250	30	150	150	15
Filled cell	250	400	50	125	200	20
Bond:						
Smooth bars			60			30
Preformed bars			120			90

*All tensile components of shear to be carried by reinforcement

The Masonry Structure and Earthquake

The Bylaw revision, Part X, "Masonry Construction" of 1959 altered entirely the earlier conception of non-rigid, rigid, and structural panels. With this revision all panels were structural and the stresses in them had to be analysed. No

*Provisional Report on Modification of Existing Structural Systems to Provide Greater Resistance to Earthquake Shocks," New Zealand Institute of Architects, Wellington, August 1931; pp 3-4.

†*Ibid*, p. 11.

longer could the frame be designed simply as a frame. Moreover, neither the effect of partitions and wall panels on its behaviour in an earthquake, nor the effect of the swaying frame on the brittle partitions and panels could be ignored.

Designers found the new allowable stresses for unreinforced masonry limiting. At the same time earthquake theory was teaching the lesson of ductility and the value of reinforcing for prolonging the load-deflection curve. Reinforced masonry, even for panels, seemed inevitable.

Once the masonry was reinforced, it became apparent that the masonry was doing the earthquake resisting job, and not the frame. It was a short step to omit the frame altogether and return to load-bearing wall construction.

Not all engineers in New Zealand are ready to abandon the frame in multi-storey construction. Arguments revolving round energy absorption, plastic yield, and frequency response are still hotly pursued. But most designers will admit that, if a building has walls, the walls will determine its rigidity, and the plasticity and longer period of the frame will only be effective after the walls have been damaged. The damage to the walls of a load-bearing structure, adequately reinforced to permit some degree of ductility, would be no greater and should be less. What the load-bearing wall loses in ductility and as the result of a low natural frequency, it regains in higher damping and greater mass.

If the same quality of design, detailing, workmanship, and materials can be put into load-bearing masonry construction that has previously been put into reinforced concrete and structural steel, the only limit to its use in multi-storey building is that imposed by the allowable working stresses. This is the author's philosophy. It has resulted in several multi-storey buildings being designed and built for all three Zones of New Zealand. The highest of these is a nine storey block, Millbrook Apartments, which is described later.

One major authority, New Zealand Ministry of Works, does not at present share this confidence in load-bearing masonry. Their controlling document, P.W.81/10/1, "Design of Public Buildings," May 1966, limits reinforced masonry construction to two storeys in Zone A and to three storeys in Zones B and C. Wall thickness and reinforcing is also arbitrarily controlled according to Zone. On special dispensation, Ministry of Works engineers have permitted four storey construction in Zones B and C, and they anticipate further liberalization as experience with reinforced masonry is acquired.

The confidence with which reinforced masonry is used by designers in high seismic areas is related to their confidence in their design methods, in their detailing for ductility, in the quality of the available materials, and in the quality of the supervision and workmanship.

Construction

Brick Masonry Construction

The masonry design work carried out by the author's firm to date has been almost entirely in reinforced concrete block. Despite publicity and a number of early examples[4], reinforced brick masonry has not developed in New Zealand as quickly as reinforced concrete block.

The popularity of the weather-resistant cavity wall coupled with the difficulty of reinforced brickwork in thin-wall thicknesses accounts for this. A 3-5/8"-wide concrete block can be reinforced and used as the outer or inner leaf in cavity wall construction; a 4-1/2"-wide brick leaf cannot be reinforced with the bricks available. A 5-5/8" block or 7-5/8" block can be reinforced to give a very substantial load-bearing wall; with standard bricks the minimum width of wall that can be reinforced is 10", using two 4-1/4" wythes and a 1-1/2" grout space.

Recently 3"-wide bricks have become available. They have been widely used in the last 18 months, particularly in the Auckland area, for 8"-wide reinforced brick walls in buildings up to five or six storeys high. These walls rely on quality of workmanship and of detailing for weather exclusion.

Concrete Masonry Construction

Hollow concrete block masonry was introduced in New Zealand in 1951, and by 1955 it was fairly widely used. Some designers saw in it a ready opportunity for building reinforced masonry. The author's first designs using load-bearing reinforced concrete block masonry were built in 1958. The design methods and construction techniques were described in a paper presented to the New Zealand Institution of Engineers in January 1961[5]. The buildings described in that paper were two storey or three storey. In 1961, a four-storey classroom block was built to the author's design, and in 1963 and 1964 two six-storey blocks of flats. These buildings are described in a paper presented in February 1965[6]. In this chapter two typical recent buildings are described, a nine-storey block of flats and a three-storey residential college. All these buildings are load-bearing masonry buildings conforming strictly to N.Z.S.S. 1900.

Until 1961 the only concrete blocks available were standard hollow blocks, with two cores, that had to be lifted over the reinforcing rods after the first courses had been laid and filled. Filling was done manually, after each sequent three or four courses were laid, using a pea gravel concrete. In 1961 open-end blocks, for laying up to the vertical reinforcing, were developed. By 1964 a range of open-end blocks, bondbeam blocks, and closers that would readily accommodate vertical and horizontal reinforcing were available. These are illustrated in the paper of February 1965[6]. The style of bond beam block has since been modified to a knock-in type. A great deal of block cutting, using the carborundum saw, is now done, usually on the site. This improves the precision of laying and also ensures a good architectural result.

Reinforcing is invariably deformed bars; and where there is likely to be dampness, as in the outer leaf of cavity walls, this is hot dip galvanised. Reinforcement is used vertically only in low stressed walls; and vertically and horizontally in high stressed walls. Reinforcement is spaced at 16" to 32" centres (Figures 40-2 and 40-3).

A popular form of construction in New Zealand is the cavity wall. It has valuable properties for excluding weather,

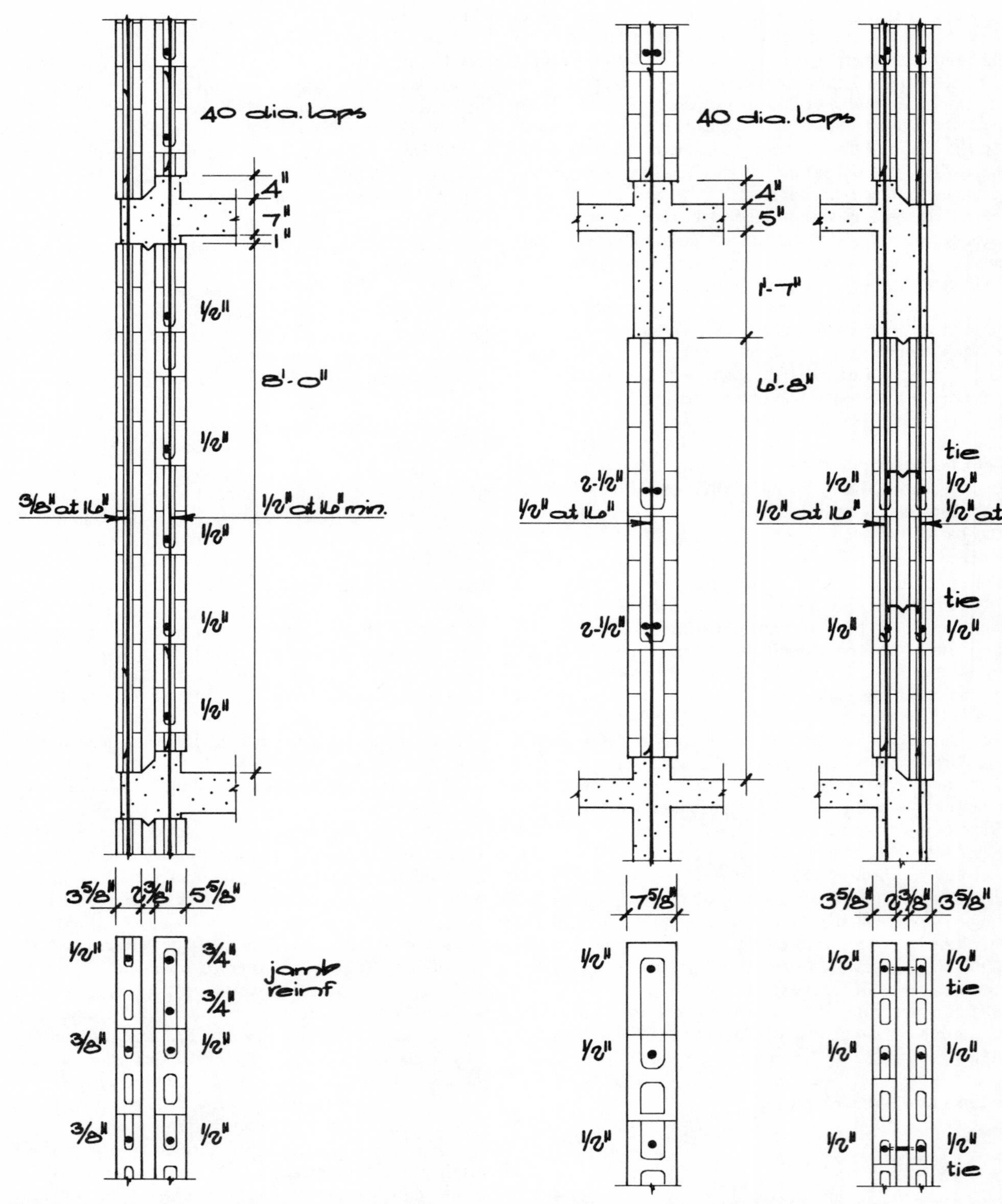

Figure 40-2. Detail of typical wall, Millbrook Apartments.

Figure 40-3. Detail of typical walls, Christchurch College.

Figure 40-4. Cavity wall detail.

thermal insulation, and sound insulation. Traditionally, it is built with wire ties between the leaves. In concrete block construction, the wire tie has been replaced by a heavy-duty cramp in galvanised or stainless steel strip (Figure 40-4). Where ties are not needed to improve the slenderness ratio of the individual leaf, and both leaves are reinforced, they can be omitted altogether to the advantage of the weather-excluding properties of the wall (Figure 40-2).

Difficulty is still experienced in maintaining a good quality laying mortar. This is because the sources of supply of the sand are not well controlled. However, compression tests are always made and a minimum strength of 1,800 lb./sq. in. at 28 days is required. Filling concrete is generally a 3/16" maximum aggregate mix with 650 lb. cement/cu. yd. This, with a high slump, gives a minimum strength of 2,500 lb/sq. in. at 28 days. It is delivered by pump or by gravity hose from a crane-hoisted skip. It is easier and more reliable to fill all voids rather than only those containing reinforcement, and a full storey height is often filled at one time.

Supervision is closely maintained to ensure clean voids, correctly placed reinforcement, and complete filling. Concrete block quality is closely controlled by specification, N.Z.S.S. 595 : 1952.

Masonry in the Western Pacific

The whole chain of islands forming the Solomons and the New Hebrides has a record of seismic activity, and the activity is distributed fairly uniformly along the centre line of the chain. Records of seismic activity exist since 1910 and have been more detailed in recent years. On the seismicity map for 1963-1966[7] earthquakes of shallow (up to 50 Km.) and intermediate (50 Km. to 290 Km.) focal depth are scattered uniformly down the chain. From Bougainville, latitude 6°S, to Hunter Island, latitude 22°S there are 19 earthquakes of magnitude greater than 6.0 in this period. Six of these are in the Solomons group, three in the Santa Cruz group, and ten in the New Hebrides group.

The record of building damage resulting from earthquakes is not considerable because of the relatively few substantial buildings in the area. However, since 1945 building activity has been on the increase and buildings of concrete masonry are becoming common, and they are being built up to three storeys high.

There are no existing regulations for earthquake resistant design in either the Solomons or the New Hebrides. For the design work carried out by the author's firm the New Zealand design rules, N.Z.S.S. 1900, have been used. This work commenced in May 1964 and has included buildings for schools, hospitals, government offices, shops and commercial premises, and hotel. Many buildings are single storey, but some are two storeys and one is three storeys.

After considering the apparent seismicity of the area and the nature of the communities for which the designs were being made, the requirements appropriate to Zone B in N.Z.S.S. 1900 were adopted. This meant a base shear of 0.10 W for most buildings, and restrictions on using unreinforced masonry except for single storey buildings.

Concrete blocks are locally made in the New Hebrides and the Solomons, and are very widely used for construction. The blocks in the New Hebrides are 40 cm. (16 in.) long, 20 cm. (8 in.) high and 5 cm. (2 in.) to 20 cm. (8 in.) thick. They are generally two-core hollow blocks of variable strength quality. The blocks in the Solomons are 18 in. long, 6 in. high and 3 in., 6 in. and 9 in. wide. The 3 in. blocks are solid and the 6 in. and 9 in. are two-core hollow. The strength quality of the block is closely controlled by the local Works Department.

In both the New Hebrides and the Solomons, the general practice has been for concrete blocks to be laid unreinforced except for a light wire mesh or two 1/4" rods in every second or third horizontal joint. In the New Hebrides, and to some extent in the Solomons, the unreinforced blockwork is often stiffened by a reinforced concrete frame, generally poured after the blockwork is laid. This takes the form of columns at wall ends and wall junctions and also at intermediate points of long walls. The reinforcement from the columns, generally four 1/2" bars, turns into wall capping beams, reinforced with two 1/2" bars. The wire mesh laid in the horizontal joints is carried into the concrete columns.

This was the system used in the first buildings designed by the author's firm. Observations of this kind of construction after a series of earthquakes near Santo in August 1965 showed that there is a tendency for unreinforced masonry to fall out of the surrounding frame. This was particularly true in some buildings under construction at Lakatoro on Malekula, where an intensity of MM.8 was recorded.

The same phenomenon has been observed after earthquakes in other countries. Masonry walls seem to suffer as much from earthquake forces at right angles to their own plane as from raking forces. For this reason, the author now advocates uniformly spaced vertical reinforcement in the blockwork, and all the work done in the islands by his firm is currently detailed this way. Some recent buildings designed by the Public Works Department in the Solomons have also used vertical reinforcement.

The vertical reinforcement is anchored to the floor slab and into reinforced horizontal bands at intermediate floors and the roof. The intermediate floor for two storey buildings can be in timber, with the timber well-tied to the horizontal wall bands by straps and bolts. For three storey buildings, the floors are usually of reinforced concrete.

The cost of this vertical reinforcing is little different from the cost of the reinforced concrete surrounding frame. At present, the blocks are lifted over the reinforcing rods as they were in New Zealand prior to 1961. It is hoped that before long an open-end block will be made. The local block making machines are mostly hand operated, and the facilities for producing a variety of block types are not as good as with automatic machines.

Partial Reinforcement

The New Zealand design rules, N.Z.S.S. 1900, define "unreinforced masonry" and "reinforced masonry".

Reinforced masonry is to have not less than one 1/2" rod at all corners, at all wall ends, and on all sides of openings (clause 9.2.13); it is to have vertical reinforcing at not more than 40" centres, and horizontal reinforcing at not more than 32" centres or concentrated at tops and bottoms of openings and in continuous wall beams (clause 9.2.14).

Unreinforced masonry is to have wall beams at floor and roof levels of reinforced masonry or reinforced concrete (clause 9.2.17).

The author's experience in the New Hebrides and Solomons leads to the belief that the requirement for reinforcement at corners, wall ends, and openings (clause 9.2.13) would be better applied also to unreinforced masonry. This view is supported by a paper by Krishna and Chandra presented to the Third World Earthquake Conference[8]. The paper describes a series of tests on a model brick house with different arrangements of reinforcing. It is clearly demonstrated that vertical reinforcement in the corners and jambs increases the strength and ductility of the structure considerably.

A series of raking tests on 8 ft. x 8 ft. x 5-5/8 ins. masonry walls carried out in Christchurch over the past three years also show the importance of perimeter reinforcement. These tests are described in another chapter of this book[9]. Several similar walls were constructed with different amount and different arrangements of reinforcement. They were tested by raking and with a restraint against overturning so as to produce shear rather than bending stresses. The test results demonstrate that, for this size panel, perimeter rods are equally as effective as uniformly spaced vertical rods in resisting the shear loads.

Elastic analysis calculations for wall panels show that earthquake loads in the plane of the wall generally produce perimeter tensions due to bending considerably in excess of the shear tensions. Calculations for the author's first designs led to detailing with perimeter reinforcement as an intermediate stage between unreinforced and fully reinforced walls**.

The author believes that in seismic areas all so-called unreinforced masonry should be required to have a minimum reinforcement of rods at all corners, at wall ends, and around openings, as well as at floor and roof levels. The reinforcement should be placed in the masonry wherever possible rather than in surrounding concrete frames. In the paper of 1961 this was referred to as "partial reinforcement."†† The author must admit to having modified his views since 1961, in that he was prepared then to accept masonry without any reinforcing at all if the calculated stresses were low. For low stress and low cost work in seismic areas, reinforced masonry should be replaced not by unreinforced masonry but by partially reinforced masonry.

From this discussion it appears that the usual distinction between unreinforced and reinforced masonry would be better replaced by two classes of reinforced masonry : partially reinforced and fully reinforced. The present allowable stresses for unreinforced would then apply to partially reinforced, with the addition that the perimeter reinforcement could be designed to take tension. The term unreinforced masonry would then apply to masonry which has no reinforcing and which is permitted in some circumstances.

Design Methods

The author's office designs all masonry buildings, even single storey houses, by elastic analysis. The method is basic structural design theory. In the design office, inevitably, tabulation methods and approximations that lead to short cuts are developed. The systems described in an earlier paper[5] are still used in the author's office.

For small buildings the principal approximation is to treat masonry panels as either fully fixed or free at its ends. With the low stresses involved, this approximation is not too critical. Centre of resistance of the structural system, resultant torsion, and loads and stresses in all panels are calculated on this basis. Bending tension reinforcement is concentrated at the edge of panels, the effective depth is taken as the width of the panel, a constant value is taken for the position of the neutral axis.

Generally there is sufficient stiffening at floor levels of two and three storey buildings to justify the assumption of full end fixity. Where this is not the case, and particularly in high buildings or end walls consisting of one panel only, a more strict analysis is made. The technique is identical with that used for designing reinforced concrete shear walls. The

**I. L. Holmes, "Load-bearing masonry design," *N. Z. Engineering*, Vol. 16, No. 1, January 1961, Section 4.

††*Ibid*, Section 2.4.

Figure 40-5. Millbrook Apartments.

Figure 40-6. Christchurch College.

composite pattern of cantilever moment for the full height of the building and of superimposed restraint moments at each floor level is determined. The bending stresses are then combined with direct load stresses. Where direct load stresses provide a relief of tension due to the earthquake design load, careful attention is given to balancing these two conditions so as to maintain adequate reinforcing for an earthquake overload into the plastic range.

The key to the design method with reinforced masonry for high buildings is the assumption that it can be designed according to the same rules as reinforced concrete. Detailing and construction techniques have been developed in New Zealand to the point where this assumption seems valid.

Where areas of high stress are encountered and it is preferable not to increase wall thicknesses, the author substitutes reinforced concrete for masonry for certain walls. The reinforced concrete and the masonry walls act together. Appropriate design adjustments are made for the different modulus of elasticity of each material. Also an attempt is made to achieve a balanced arrangement of reinforced concrete walls so that their different behaviour in the ductile range does not seriously affect the overall balance of the structure in a major earthquake.

Typical Buildings

Millbrook Apartments (Figures 40-2 and 40-5), architect D. E. Donnithorne, and Christchurch College (Figures 40-3 and 40-6), architects Warren and Mahoney are typical of recent load-bearing designs by the author's firm. Both buildings are designed for Zone B seismic coefficients.

External walls are cavity construction. The 5-5/8" inner leaf combined with a 3-5/8" outer leaf (Figure 40-2) is generally preferable to the two 3-5/8" leafs (Figure 40-3). The 5-5/8" leaf takes heavy reinforcing better and also it permits cavity ties to be omitted. Millbrook Apartments, which is nine storeys and has a large proportion of window opening, proved to be about the limit of design to N.Z.S.S. 1900. Reinforced concrete 6" load-bearing walls were used as party walls between apartments and for the ground floor garage walls.

Both buildings are finished externally and internally in white painted concrete masonry.

References

1. "The Wellington Independent," October 18, 1848.
2. "Provisional Report on Modification of Existing Structural Systems to Provide Greater Resistance to Earthquake Shocks," New Zealand Institute of Architects, Wellington, August 1931.
3. "Commentary on Chapter 8 of N.Z.S.S. 1900," Miscellaneous Publication MP 12:1965, New Zealand Standards Institute, December 1965.
4. "Reinforced Brickwork," Clay Products Bulletin, Publication Nos. 8-13, N.Z. Pottery and Ceramics Research Association (Inc.), 1957-59.
5. Holmes, I. L., "Load-bearing masonry design," *N. Z. Engineering,* Vol. 16, No. 1, January 1961, p. 23.
6. Holmes, I. L., "Concrete masonry buildings in New Zealand," *Proc. Third World Conference on Earthquake Engineering,* Vol. III, 1965, pp. IV-244.
7. "Seismicity of Melanesia: Earthquakes of magnitude 5 and greater 1963-1966," Map, supplied by Director of Geological Surveys, British Solomon Islands.
8. Krishna, J. and Chandra, B., "Strengthening of brick buildings against earthquake forces," *Proc. Third World Conference on Earthquake Engineering,* Vol. III, 1965, p. IV-324.
9. Scrivener, J. C., "Concrete masonry wall panel tests," International Conference on Masonry Structural Systems, 1967.

41. Building code requirements relating to load-bearing brick masonry.

James G. Gross and Robert D. Dikkers, Structural Clay Products Institute, McLean, Virginia

Introduction

This chapter compares the structural design requirements for load-bearing brick masonry in the standards and building codes adopted and used in Germany, Great Britain, Canada, Switzerland, and the United States of America. Although no attempt has been made to review all available standards and codes, the following are representative of those promulgated since 1960.

1. German Standard DIN 1053, November, 1962[1].
2. British Standard Code of Practice CP111:1964[2].
3. National Building Code of Canada, 1965[3].
4. Switzerland Technical Standard 113, 1965[4].
5. U.S.A., Structural Clay Products Institute Standard, May, 1966[5].

The standards and codes which were reviewed are more rational in their approach to structural design than are some standards[6] which establish empirical limitations on masonry wall thicknesses.

This chapter discusses non-reinforced brick masonry although requirements and recommendations pertaining to other types of masonry units and constructions have been reviewed [7,8]. The most pertinent information is that covered on brick masonry in the above standards.

Among the factors compared are the allowable stresses which are permitted for compression, flexure, and shear; the influence of eccentricity and slenderness; and the computation of allowable axial and eccentric loads. The authors did not attempt to justify the requirements nor criticize them; they simply compared the provisions of the various standards.

Comparing the requirements in the standards and codes listed above is complicated due to the different approaches used to consider the various design factors as well as differences which exist in the test methods and requirements for brick and mortar. With these limitations in mind, various direct comparisons have been attempted.

Allowable Stresses

Basic Compressive Stresses

In general, the codes and standards reviewed contain basic compressive stresses for use in computing allowable vertical loads on non-reinforced brick masonry walls and columns. These basic stresses are related to a particular slenderness ratio and axial loading and are dependent on (1) the ultimate compressive strength of the masonry units and (2) the type of mortar used. To determine allowable compressive stresses, the basic stresses must be further modified in accordance with the slenderness ratio of the particular member under consideration and the virtual eccentricity of the vertical and horizontal loads acting on the member. Other modifications to basic compressive stress requirements are also presented. Determination of allowable compressive loads as affected by stress distribution is discussed in a later section.

Germany. Basic compressive stresses in the German Standard (DIN 1053) for various unit strengths and mortar types are given in Table 41-1.

A 50 percent increase in the basic compressive stress is permitted under beam supports if the width of strip subject to stress is not more than one half the wall thickness.

Britain. The British Standard (CP 111:1964) contains basic compressive stresses which are given in Table 41-2. A 25

Table 41-1
Basic Compressive Stresses for Brick Masonry, psi *
(Germany DIN 1053-1962)

Compressive Strength of Units, psi	Mortar Mix (parts by volume)**	
	1PC:4S	1PC:2L:8S
5000	428	314
3560	314	228
2140	228	171
1420	171	128

* Stresses given are applicable to (1) stiffened walls with thicknesses not less than 9.5 in. and (2) piers and walls without stiffening having slenderness ratios not exceeding 10.
** PC = portland cement; L = hydrated lime; S = sand

Table 41-2
Basic Compressive Stresses for Brick Masonry, psi*
(Britain CP111:1964)

Compressive Strength of Units, psi**	Mortar Mix (parts by volume)		
	1PC:1/4L:3S	1PC:1/2L:4-1/2S	1PC:1L:6S
14,000	850	650	550
10,000	660	520	450
7,500	510	410	360
5,000	360	300	270
4,000	300	250	230
3,000	240	210	190
1,500	150	140	140
1,000	100	100	100
400	40	40	40

* Stresses are only applicable to members with slenderness ratios not exceeding 6 and cross-sectional areas greater than 500 sq. in.
** Linear interpolation is permissible.

percent increase in the basic stress is permitted where the additional stress is due solely to eccentricity of loading and/or lateral forces. A 50 percent increase is also permitted where additional stresses occur under concentrated loads.

Where the cross-sectional area of a wall or column does not exceed 500 sq. in., the basic compressive stress must be multiplied by a reduction factor equal to 0.75 + A/2000 where A is the cross-sectional area in square inches of the wall or column. (A column is defined as an isolated vertical load-bearing member whose width is not more than four times its thickness.)

Modifications to the basic compressive stresses are also included which account for the shape (ratio of height to thickness) of masonry units; see Table 41-3. Presently, however, modifications are not permitted for clay units with compressive strengths greater than 3000 psi.

Canada. Basic compressive stresses for brick masonry contained in the 1965 Canadian Code are given in Table 41-4. This code also permits a 50 percent increase in compressive stress under concentrated loads.

A reduction factor, identical to that in British Standard where the area of the member does not exceed 500 sq. in., is also included in this code.

Under the engineered masonry subsection of this code, special engineering or architectural supervision is required to insure that all construction, workmanship, and material requirements are satisfied.

Switzerland. Basic compressive stresses specified in the Swiss Standard (Technical Standard 113, 1965) are given in Table 41-5. As Table 41-5 indicates, these stresses not only depend on the compressive strength of the units and type of mortar, but they also are related to the wall type (single wythe or multiple wythes) and wall thickness.

United States of America. In the 1966 SCPI Standard, basic compressive stresses for both nonreinforced and reinforced brick masonry are based on the 28-day compressive strength of the masonry (f'_m). This compressive strength may be established by tests of prisms, which are required to be representative of the proposed construction, or it may be assumed on the basis of the brick compressive strength and type of mortar.

To obtain basic compressive stresses for walls and columns, the value of f'_m is divided by four and five, respectively, so the basic compressive stress becomes 0.25 f'_m for walls and 0.20 f'_m for columns; see Table 41-6. (A wall is defined as a vertical member whose horizontal dimension measured at right angles to the thickness exceeds three times its thickness. A column is defined as a vertical member whose horizontal dimension measured at right angles to the thickness does not exceed three times its thickness.)

When there is no engineering or architectural inspection to insure that the workmanship requirements of this standard are satisfied, basic compressive stresses must be reduced by one third.

This standard also permits higher stresses under concentrated loads. These stresses may be up to 50 percent greater than the basic compressive stresses where the area in bearing is less than one third of the total area.

Tensile and Shear Stresses

Germany. The German Standard permits tensile stress in bending in walls if they are properly bonded, the direction of stress is parallel to the bed joints, and the brick strength is not less than 2140 psi. These permissible tensile stresses are 28 psi for a 1PC:4S (parts by volume) mortar and 14 psi for a 1PC:2L:8S mortar. Tensile stresses in bending at right angles to the bed joints may only be taken into account in exceptional cases with the agreement of the building inspection authorities.

The shear stresses cannot exceed one tenth of the values given in Table 41-1 nor 14 psi for a 1PC:2L:8S mortar or 28 psi for a 1PC:4S mortar, whichever is less.

Britain. The British Standard indicates that "in general no reliance should be placed on tensile strength of brickwork" and "the designer should assume that part of the section will be inactive and the remainder will carry compressive stress only". However, it also indicates that "in some types of walls, tensile stresses in bending may be taken into account at the discretion of the designer". For mortar not weaker than a 1PC:1L:6S mix, the permissible tensile stress is 10 psi when the direction of stress is perpendicular to the bed joints and 20 psi when the direction of stress is parallel to the bed joints and the brick compressive strength exceeds 1500 psi.

The permissible shear stress, calculated on the area of the horizontal bed joint, is 15 psi for walls built with a 1PC:1L:6S (parts by volume) mortar; 20 psi where a 1PC:1/4L:3S or stronger mortar is used; or one third of the compressive stress produced by dead load at the level under consideration. The

Table 41-3
Modification Factor for Shape of Unit*
(Britain CP111:1964)

Ratio of height to thickness of unit	0.75	1.0	1.5	2.0 - 3.0
Factor	1.0	1.2	1.6	2.0

* For units with strength not exceeding 800 psi, the modified basic stress is equal to basic stress specified in Table 41-2 multiplied by the above factor.
For units with strength between 800 and 3000 psi, the modified basic stress may be obtained by linear interpolation between the modified basic stress for unit strength of 800 psi and the basic stress given in Table 41-2 for a unit strength of 3000 psi, or the basic stress, whichever is greater.

Table 41-4
Basic Compressive Stresses for Brick Masonry, psi*
(Canada - 1965)

Compressive Strength of Units, psi	Mortar Mix (parts by volume) 1PC:1/4L:3S	1PC:1/2L:4-1/2S	1PC:1L:6S
10,000 plus	650	585	455
8,000 to 10,000	520	455	390
4,500 to 8,000	325	292	260
2,500 to 4,500	228	208	182
1,500 to 2,500	163	150	130

* Stresses are only applicable to members with slenderness ratios not exceeding 10 and cross-sectional areas greater than 500 sq. in.

permissible stress is the greater of the two values specified for each mortar, but it must not exceed 30 psi.

Canada. The allowable flexural tensile and shear stresses for brick masonry in the Canadian Code vary from 10 psi to 20 psi depending on the type of mortar and the compressive strength of units.

The tensile stresses are subject to the same reduction factors as the compressive stresses (cross-sectional area less than 500 sq. in., slenderness, and eccentricity).

Switzerland. The allowable flexural tensile stresses parallel to the bed joints, f_t, and the allowable shearing stresses, v_s, for all wall types are computed in accordance with the formula contained in the Swiss Standard:

$$f_t \text{ and } v_s = \frac{f_m}{100}\left[\frac{f_g}{4.5} + 1\right] \text{ but not to exceed 56 psi,} \qquad (41\text{-}1)$$

where:

f_g = average compressive stress from dead load,
f_m = allowable average compressive stress for a slenderness ratio of 5 and axial loading.

Flexural tensile stresses perpendicular to the bed joints are not permitted.

United States of America. The allowable stresses for flexural tension and shear in nonreinforced brick masonry given in the SCPI Standard are as follows:

Flexural tension (perpendicular to bed joints):

36 psi (1PC:1/4L:3S or 1PC:1/2L:4-1/2S mortar, parts by volume)
28 psi (1PC:1L:6S)

Flexural tension (parallel to bed joints):

Twice the allowable values given for perpendicular to bed joints
Shear
50 psi (1PC:1/4L:3S or 1PC:1/2L:4-1/2S)
40 psi (1PC:1L:6S)

Similarly, for compressive stresses, these allowable stresses are reduced by one third when there is no engineering or architectural inspection to insure that the workmanship requirements are satisfied.

In shear walls where vertical and horizontal loads are acting parallel to the plane of the wall, no tension is permitted.

Slenderness and Eccentricity

Among the more important variables which affect the compressive strength of brick masonry walls and columns are the slenderness of the member and the manner and location in which the loads are applied to the member. These variables along with the basic compressive stresses and stress distribution ,are reviewed in this section. Reduction factors shown in Figures 41-1 through 41-5 provide for the effects of slenderness and eccentricity.

Table 41-5
Basic Compressive Stresses for Brick Masonry, psi*
(Switzerland, SIA113 - 1965)

Wall Type	Wall Thickness in.	Normal Quality Units (2150 psi)	High Quality Units (4275 psi)	Special Quality Units (5700 psi)
	Cement Mortar (1PC:3.2 - 3.7S, parts by weight)**			
Single Wythe	4.7	Not permitted	455	710
	5.9		384	625
	7.1; 9.8		342	568
Multiple Wythe	9.8; 11.8; 12.6; 14.9	Not permitted	256	484
	Cement-Lime Mortar (1PC:2.5L:12.8S, parts by weight)**			
Single Wythe	4.7; 5.9; 7.1; 9.8	171	256	Not permitted
Multiple Wythes	9.8	142	214	Not permitted
	11.8; 12.6; 14.9	128	185	

* Stresses are only applicable for members with slenderness ratios not exceeding 5.
** Required 28-day compressive strength (1.5 by 1.5 by 6-in. prism) = 2840 psi for cement mortar and 500 psi for cement-lime mortar.

Table 41-6
Basic Compressive Stresses for Brick Masonry, psi*
(USA, SCPI - 1966)

Compressive Strength of Units, psi **	Mortar Mix (parts by volume)		
	1PC:1/4L:3S	1PC:1/2L:4-1/2S	1PC:1L:6S
14,000 plus	1150	975	800
12,000	1000	850	700
10,000	850	725	600
8,000	700	600	500
6,000	550	475	400
4,000	400	350	300
2,000	200	225	200

* Stresses are only applicable for walls with slenderness ratios not exceeding 5. For columns, the above stresses must be reduced by 20 percent.
** Linear interpolation is permissible.

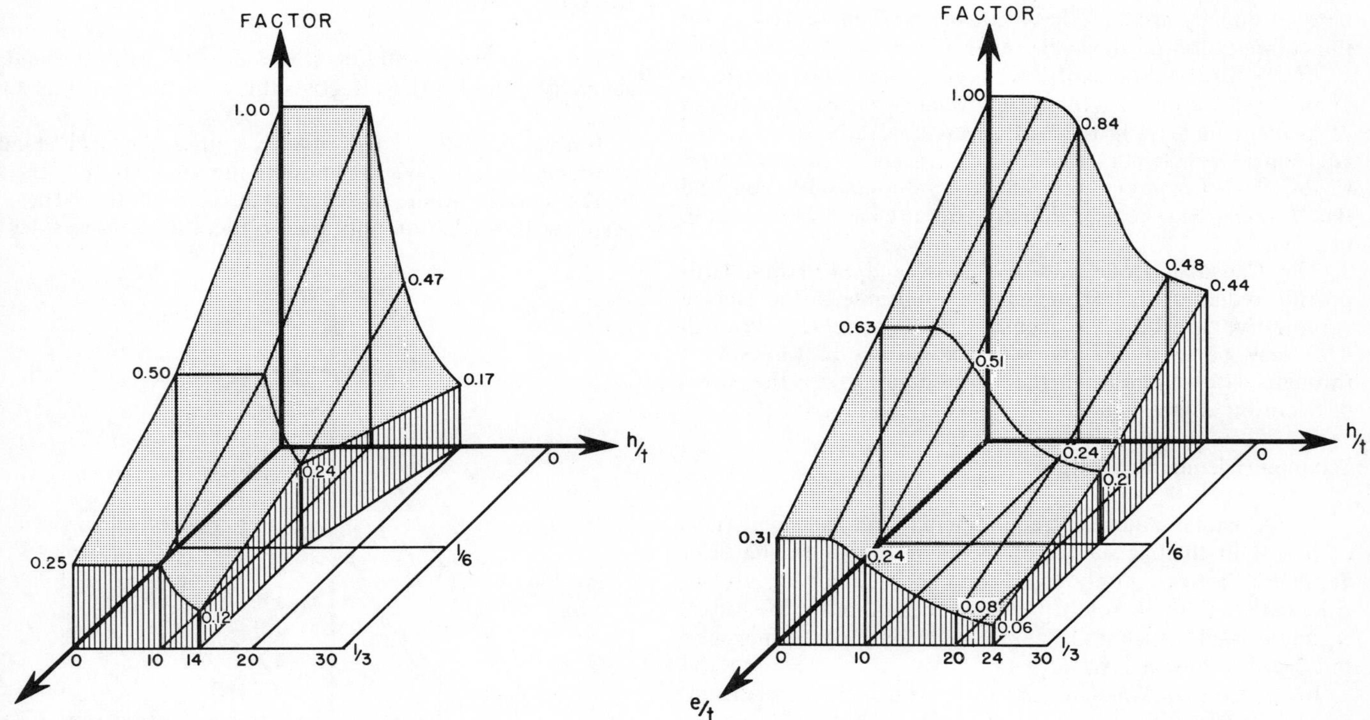

Figure 41-1. Reduction factors (Germany DIN 1053, 1962).

Figure 41-2. Reduction factors (Britain CP111, 1964).

Basic Compressive Stresses

Basic compressive stresses contained in the various standards and codes have previously been discussed (Tables 41-1 through 41-6). In the Swiss and SCPI Standards, the basic compressive stresses are applicable to a slenderness ratio (h/t) of 5. In the British Standard, the basic stress is applicable to an h/t of 6. In the German Standard, the basic stresses are applicable to (1) stiffened walls (discussed later) with thicknesses not less than 9.5 in. and (2) piers and walls without stiffening with h/t of 10. The basic compressive stresses given in Table 41-4 are based on the Canadian Code and are applicable to an h/t of 10. (Note: In the Canadian Code, basic compressive stresses are actually given for an h/t of 20, and stresses are increased for members with an h/t between 20 and 10. For comparison, the basic stresses in the Canadian Code have been appropriately increased so they are applicable to an h/t of 10.)

Stress Distribution

All the standards reviewed except the German Standard contain provisions and reduction factors permitting stresses for flexural compression greater than those permitted for axial compression up to e/t of 1/3.

In the German Standard, the basic compressive stresses are the maximum allowable stresses which apply for both concentrically loaded sections and eccentrically loaded sections. Since straight-line stress distribution is assumed and tensile stresses are neglected, this limits a member loaded with an eccentricity of 1/6 t to a maximum load of one half of the allowable axial load and a member loaded with an eccentricity of 1/3 t to a maximum load of one-fourth of the allowable axial load. Accordingly, Figure 41-1 shows reduction factors which can be used directly with the basic stresses given in Table 41-1 for the computation of allowable vertical loads, axial or eccentric.

In the British Standard, the basic compressive stresses in Table 41-2 are also maximum allowable stresses. However, a 25 percent increase in the basic stress is permitted where the additional stress is due to eccentric loads and/or lateral forces. Figure 41-2 has taken this increase into consideration and therefore can also be used directly with the basic stresses given in Table 41-2.

The Canadian Code and the Swiss and SCPI Standards provide reduction factors which are applicable to the average compressive stress in the member, so Figures 41-3 through 41-5 may be used directly with the stresses in Tables 41-4 through 41-6 without further consideration to the stress distribution in the member.

Maximum Slenderness Ratios

The Canadian and SCPI requirements limit the slenderness or height to thickness ratio of members to 30. In the SCPI Standard, however, only walls may have a h/t up to 30; columns are limited to a h/t of 25. The h/t limit in the British Standard is 24, which under some conditions may be increased to 32 as discussed below.

In the German Standard, the maximum slenderness ratio is 20 unless the eccentricity is 1/6 t or greater, in which case the h/t limit is 14.

The Swiss Standard reduces the maximum slenderness ratio, depending upon the eccentricity. With a concentric load, h/t may be as great as 55. With an eccentric load (e/t = 1/3), the limit for the same wall is 16. The Swiss Standard also varies the permissible slenderness depending upon the units and mortar used for the construction.

Effective Height and Length

In the Swiss, German, and SCPI Standards, slenderness ratio is defined as the ratio of the effective height of a member to its effective thickness. In the British and the Canadian Standards, it is defined as the ratio of the effective height or the effective length, whichever is less, to the effective thickness.

For nonreinforced members and for most end conditions, the various standards assume pinned or hinged end conditions so the effective height (or length) is taken as the actual height (or length) between supports. However, in the British Standard, walls which (1) receive the reaction of the floor or roof systems which span at right angles to the wall or (2) support concrete floors, irrespective of the floor span direction, may be considered to have an effective height of 3/4 of the actual height between supports.

The German, Canadian, and SCPI Standards require that the effective height be twice the actual height where the member (wall or column) is unsupported at the top. The British Standard has a similar requirement for columns; however, the effective height for walls is considered 1-1/2 times the actual height above the bottom support.

Effective Thickness

For solid walls without stiffening, the various standards generally consider the effective thickness as the actual thickness.

For cavity walls loaded on both wythes, the SCPI Standard considers the effective thickness as the square root of the sum of the squares of the actual thicknesses of both wythes. For cavity walls loaded on only one wythe, the effective thickness

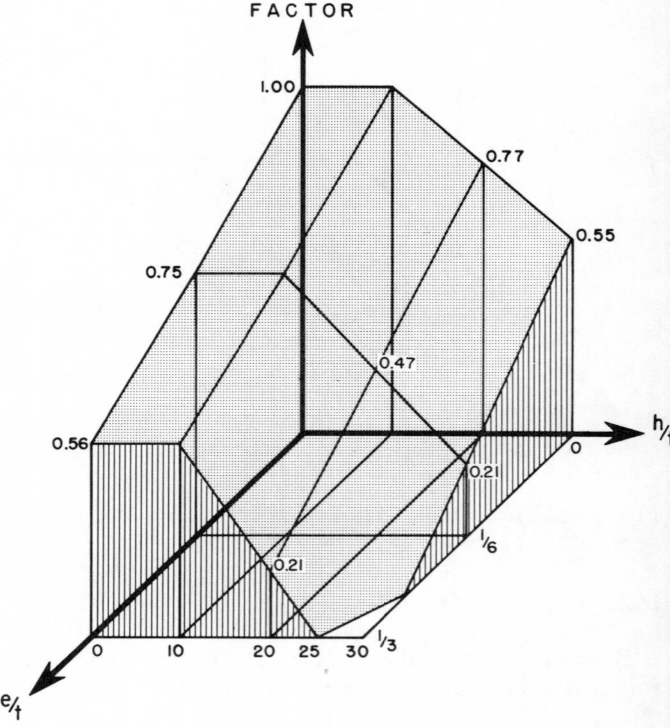

Figure 41-3. Reduction factors (Canada, 1965).

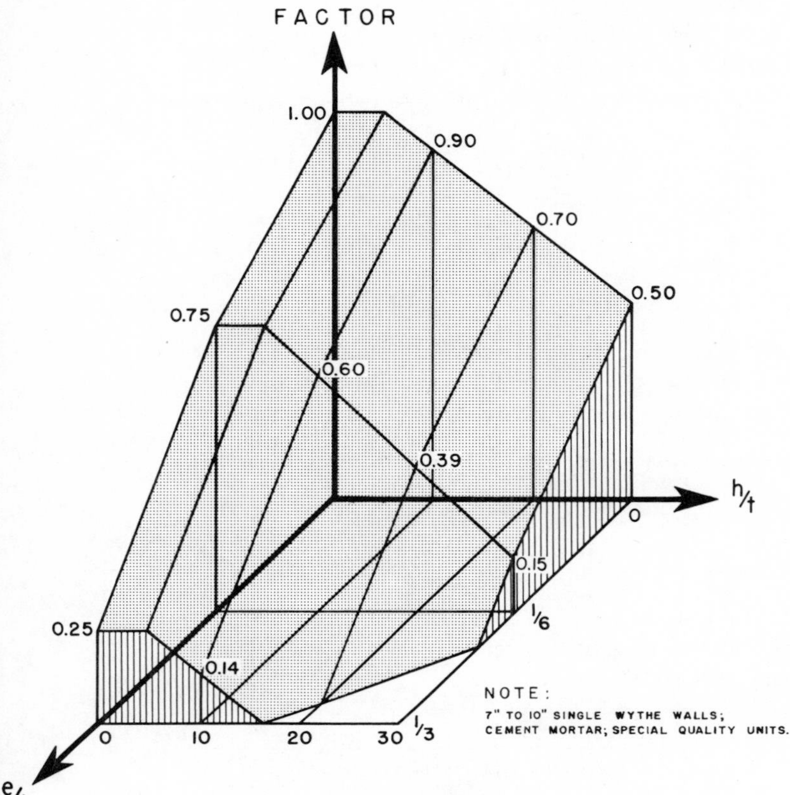

Figure 41-4. Reduction factors (Switzerland, SIA113, 1965).

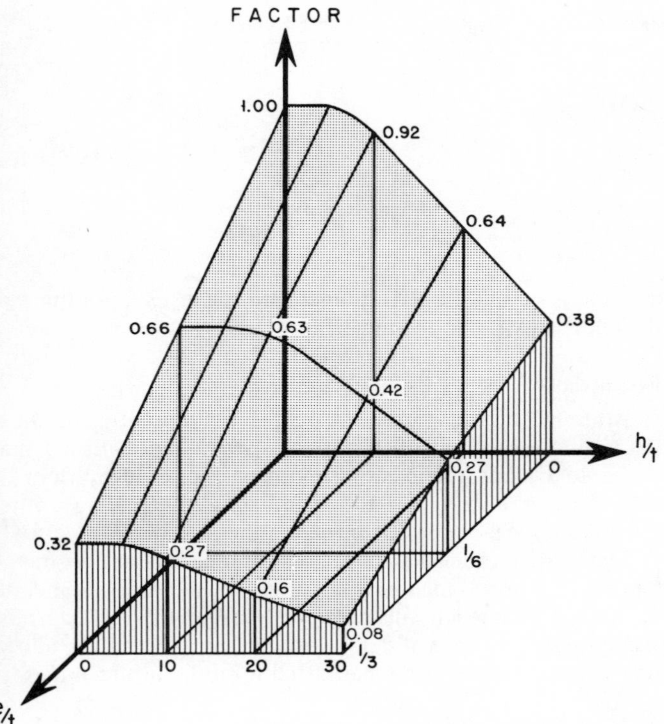

Figure 41-5. Reduction factors (USA, SCPI, 1966).

may be similarly computed, except the effective thickness cannot exceed 1.5 times the actual thickness of the loaded wythe.

The British Standard considers the effective thickness of cavity walls as 2/3 the sum of the actual thicknesses of both wythes. The Canadian Code has a similar requirement where both wythes are loaded. For load on only one wythe, the effective thickness is based on the actual thickness of the loaded wythe.

The German Standard provides that the interior wythe, which must be equal to or thicker than the exterior wythe, is the only wythe considered for strength and stability. The Swiss Standard assumes that each wythe of a cavity wall acts separately.

Stiffened Walls

The British, Canadian, and German Standards permit greater allowable compressive loads on walls which are stiffened. The SCPI Standard does not include specific provisions for stiffened walls.

In the British and Canadian Standards, the effective wall thickness may be increased up to two times the actual wall thickness, depending on the ratio of pilaster thickness (t_p) to wall thickness (t_w) and the ratio of pilaster spacing to pilaster width. Table 41-7 provides these stiffening coefficients. In the British Standard, intersecting walls are considered equivalent

Table 41-7
Stiffening Coefficients for Walls Stiffened by Pilasters
(Britain CP111:1964 and Canada-1965)

$\frac{\text{Pilaster Spacing (center to center)}}{\text{Pilaster Width}}$	Stiffening Coefficients*		
	For $\frac{T_p}{T_w} = 1$	For $\frac{T_p}{T_w} = 2$	For $\frac{T_p}{T_w} = 3$
6	1.0	1.4	2.0
8	1.0	1.3	1.7
10	1.0	1.2	1.4
15	1.0	1.1	1.2
20 or more	1.0	1.0	1.0

*Linear interpolation is permissible.

Table 41-8
Intersecting Walls Providing Stiffening
(Germany DIN 1053 - 1962)

Wall thicknesses and Mean Distances				
		Intersecting Wall Providing Stiffening		
Thickness of Loaded Wall	Height of Story	In the 1st to the 4th Story from Above Thickness	In the 5th and 6th Story from Above, Thickness	Mean Spacing
⩾4.5″ <6.9″	⩽10′-8″	⩾4.5″	⩾6.9″	⩽14′-9″
⩾6.9″ <9.5″	⩽10′-8″			⩽19′-8″
⩾9.5″ <11.8″	⩽11′-6″			⩽26′-3″
⩾11.8″	⩽16′-5″			⩽26′-3″

to a pilaster of width equal to the intersecting wall's thickness and of thickness equal to 3 times the stiffened wall's thickness.

The German Standard provides that for walls with a thickness of not less than 9.5 in. and stiffened according to the provisions in Table 41-8, a reduction factor based on a h/t of 10 may be used (see Figure 41-1). For walls less than 9.5 in. in thickness and stiffened in accordance with Table 41-8, a reduction factor based on a h/t of 12 may be used. For unstiffened walls, reduction factors based on the actual slenderness ratio of the walls must be used.

The Swiss Standard permits higher allowable stresses at intersections of walls in L, T or cross-shaped sections. The increased allowable stress is higher near the intersection and no increase is permitted at a distance more than 12 times the wall thickness away from the intersection.

Eccentricity

Although the standards are not specific in pointing out how the virtual eccentricity is to be calculated, some indicate that it should include the bending moment produced by floor or roof systems bearing on the member, as well as any other vertical and/or lateral loads acting on the member.

The German, Canadian, and Swiss Standards limit e/t to 1/3 for nonreinforced load-bearing walls. In the SCPI Standard, the virtual eccentricity may exceed 1/3t but the tensile stress, assuming linear stress distribution, can not exceed the allowable flexural tensile stress permitted for nonreinforced mason-

Table 41-9
Average Allowable Compressive Stresses for
Non-reinforced Brick Masonry, psi*
(6000 psi brick and 1 PC:1/2L:4 1/2S mortar)

Standard	Basic Compressive Stress, psi	h/t = 10			h/t = 15			h/t = 20		
		$\frac{e}{t} = 0$	$\frac{e}{t} = \frac{1}{6}$	$\frac{e}{t} = \frac{1}{3}$	$\frac{e}{t} = 0$	$\frac{e}{t} = \frac{1}{6}$	$\frac{e}{t} = \frac{1}{3}$	$\frac{e}{t} = 0$	$\frac{e}{t} = \frac{1}{6}$	$\frac{e}{t} = \frac{1}{3}$
Germany	428	428	214	107	180	0	0	73	0	0
Britian	344	289	175	83	217	124	52	165	83	28
Canada	292	292	219	163	257	178	111	225	137	61
Switzerland	568	511	340	80	455	284	11	398	222	0
USA	475	437	300	128	376	266	104	304	199	76

* Based on basic compressive stresses given in Tables 1, 2, 4 through 6 and reduction factors shown in Figs. 41-1 through 41-5.

ry. In the British Standard, reduction factors are given for e/t up to 1/2.

Summary

To summarize the structural design requirements for load-bearing nonreinforced brick masonry walls contained in various standards and codes, average allowable compressive stresses have been computed and are given in Table 41-9. As indicated, these stresses have been computed for brick with a compressive strength of 6000 psi and a 1PC:1/2L:4-1/2S mortar and are based on the basic compressive stresses given in Tables 41-1, 41-2, 41-4 through 41-6 and the reduction factors shown in Figures 41-1 through 41-5. When comparing these stresses, one should bear in mind the various limitations and differences in the standards reviewed as well as in other related standards for brick and mortar.

References

1. "Wall Masonry, Design and Execution", German Standard DIN 1053, November 1962.
2. "Structural Recommendations for Loadbearing Walls", *British Standard Code of Practice,* CP111:1964, The Council for Codes of Practice, British Standards Institution, March 1964 (as amended 29 March, 1966 and 22 May 1967).
3. "Detailed Structural Analysis for the Design of Loadbearing Masonry", Subsection 4.4.9, *National Building Code of Canada,* National Research Council, 1965.
4. "Standard for Calculation and Execution of Manufactured and Natural Bricks", Technical Standard 113, Swiss Engineers and Architects Society, 1965 Edition.
5. "Recommended Building Code Requirements for Engineered Brick Masonry", Structural Clay Products Institute, May, 1966.
6. "American Standard Building Code Requirements for Masonry", American Standard A41.1-1953, National Bureau of Standards Miscellaneous Publication 211, July 15, 1954.
7. Cassinello, Fernando, "Bearing Walls Made of Brick", Eduardo Torroja Institute, Madrid, Spain, 1964.
8. "Methods of Design of Masonry Walls–Bibliographical Study", *Transactions, International Building Council,* No. 68, June 1964.

42. Design of tall masonry buildings with complex layout.

Dr. P. T. Mikluchin, Toronto, Ontario, Canada

Introduction

Recent progress in designing and constructing modern masonry buildings, based on the results of extensive theoretical and experimental research, enabled leading architects and engineers to create a series of outstanding projects. Among these projects, tall masonry structures are of great interest. Such structures, varying in size, form, architectural, and structural aspects, have been erected in many parts of the world, especially in Europe, USA, Canada, and South America.

Within the last decade, buildings ranging from 12 to 18 storeys high were designed and built in plain and reinforced masonry[1]. Several 25-storey buildings in plain masonry were designed according to modern engineering methods and the latest recommendations of the new progressive Building Codes[2,3].

Investigations have shown that reinforced masonry makes it possible to design and construct buildings 30 to 35 storeys high.

Due to increase in height and complexity of the layout, bearing wall structures require more accurate methods of design.

Design

Structural Geometry

In this chapter we will consider one design method for tall buildings which can be applied to the structures with layouts similar to arrangements of bearing walls shown on Figures 42-1, 42-2, and 42-3.

High-rise buildings in the form of apartments, hotels, office buildings, and other structures of similar type can be designed by this method. This type building has certain features which, in principle, determine the essence of the design philosophy. In such buildings, horizontal structural elements of reinforced concrete floor slabs, which are supported on and tied to the vertical structural walls, restrain these walls from deformations in the horizontal plane.

In other words, the original contour of supporting walls remains unchanged after the system of external forces has been applied to the structure.

Realistic evaluation of the overall structural behaviour of such buildings indicates that the specific constructional features incorporated into a given building determine the general pattern of force distribution and character of deformations within the structure.

These factors singularly define the essence of mechanical and geometrical hypotheses which have to be used to mathematically formulate the structural analysis of such buildings.

Design Hypothesis

In tall bearing wall buildings these hypotheses can be formulated as follows:

1. Straight elements of a bearing wall normal to the middle surface before deformation remain straight after deformation and do not change length.
2. Normal stresses acting in planes parallel to the middle surface may be neglected in comparison with other stresses.
3. Middle surface of a bearing wall is inextensible in the transverse direction.

It is well-known that the set of similar hypotheses is used in the theory of cylindrical shells.

This theory in modified form can be used for determining all internal stresses, strains, and deformations in the shell-like structures due to the action of external forces applied to such structures.

Differential equations, in partial derivatives of the eighth order with respect to coordinate taken in the direction of the contour, and of the fourth order with respect to coordinate parallel to the direction of the generator, expressing the relationship between the external forces and internal stresses and strains, could be used for the solution of this problem.

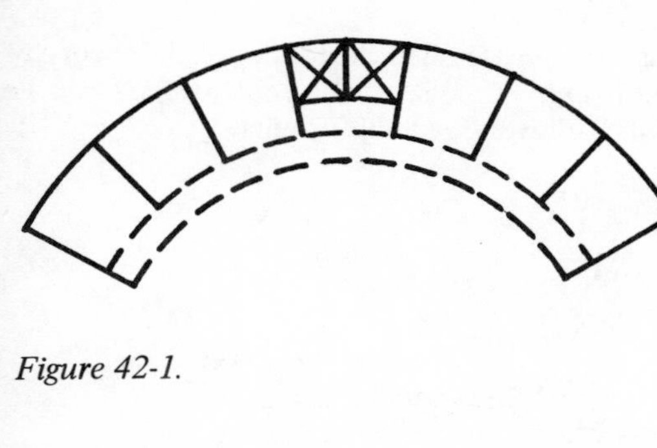

Figure 42-1.

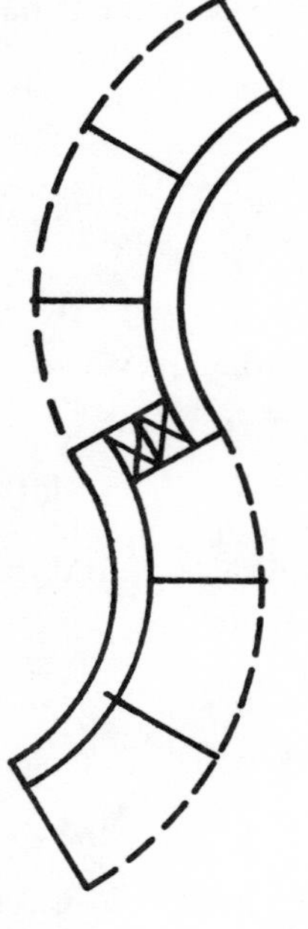

Figure 42-2.

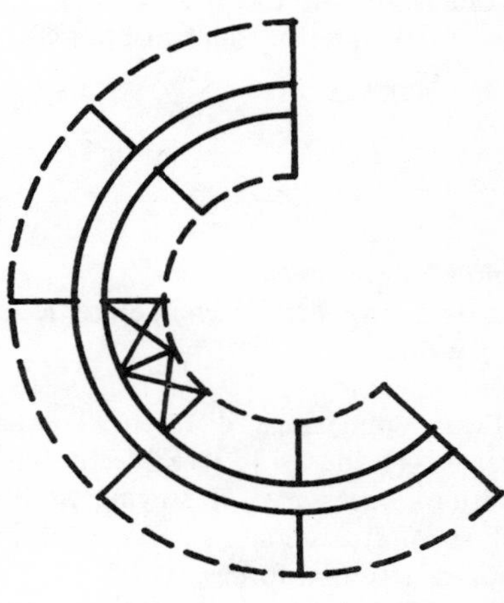

Figure 42-3.

Integrating the differential equations of equilibrium with the compatibility equations and the boundary conditions provides the solution.

The special stress function which satisfies differential equations and boundary conditions can also provide the answer. All stresses and strains necessary for the rational structural design may be expressed through the appropriately chosen stress function.

In addition to the aforementioned hypotheses, suppose we assume the nondeformability of an original contour of a shell due to horizontal rigid floor slabs. In this case, such structures, in form of vertical cylindrical shells with curved or polygonal contours, reinforced by horizontal reinforced concrete slabs or similar diaphragms, can be considered thin-walled space structures with rigid contours, and can be subjected essentially to normal and shear forces acting in the plane in such vertical walls.

Longitudinal bending and torsional moments, due to their small magnitudes, can be neglected. Such thin-walled space structures can be classified as orthotropic space systems because these walls possess different structural characteristics in vertical and horizontal directions.

Design Calculations

Design method of such structures will be used here for the structural analysis of two types of buildings.

The first type, which can be defined as open thin-walled structures, consists of a series of solid, continuous bearing walls (shown as solid lines in Figures 42-1, 42-2, 42-3) with open spaces between them (shown as dotted lines) e.g. glass curtain walls.

The second type, which can be defined as open thin-walled structures reinforced by spandrel beams, consists of a series of solid continuous bearing walls, similar to walls of the first type, connected by spandrel beams possessing definite strength and rigidity.

The first type (Figure 42-4) can be analyzed by the general theory of open thin-walled space structures[4,5,6].

Differential equations of the equilibrium of thin-walled structures of this type can be presented in the following form:

$$\nabla^4 M(z,s) + \frac{\gamma^2}{\gamma z^2} \sigma(z,s) \cdot h = P(z,s) \qquad (42\text{-}1)$$

here:

∇^4 differential operator of the 4th order with respect to s:

$$\nabla^4 = \frac{\gamma}{\gamma s^2} \left[R(s) \frac{\gamma^2}{\gamma s^2} \right] + \frac{\gamma}{\gamma s} \left[\frac{1}{R(s)} \cdot \frac{\gamma}{\gamma s} \right]$$

M(z,s) = transversal bending moment
z and s = coordinates of a point on the middle surface of the wall. z is directed along the generator, s is directed along the contour of the wall
R(s) = is the radius of the middle surface
σ (z,s) = normal stress
h thickness of the wall
P(z,s) = a given load function, expressed through the components P_z, P_s, P_n, of the vector of intensity of external forces acting on the wall

Equation 42-1 contains two unknown functions M(z, s) and σ (z, s). From considering the compatibility conditions of deformations of the wall's middle surface an additional differential equation can be obtained:

$$C \cdot \frac{\gamma^2 M(z,s)}{\gamma z^2} + \nabla^4 \sigma(z,s) = 0 \qquad (42\text{-}2)$$

where:

C is a geometrical characteristic of rigidity of the bearing walls.

Two symmetrical differential equations in partial derivatives (42-1) and (42-2) represent the fundamental system of equations necessary for solving problems connected with the analysis of stresses and strains in tall buildings subjected to the action of external forces.

Considering these assumptions, we can obtain from differential Equations 42-1 and 42-2, all necessary formulas for determining stresses and deformations in tall structures.

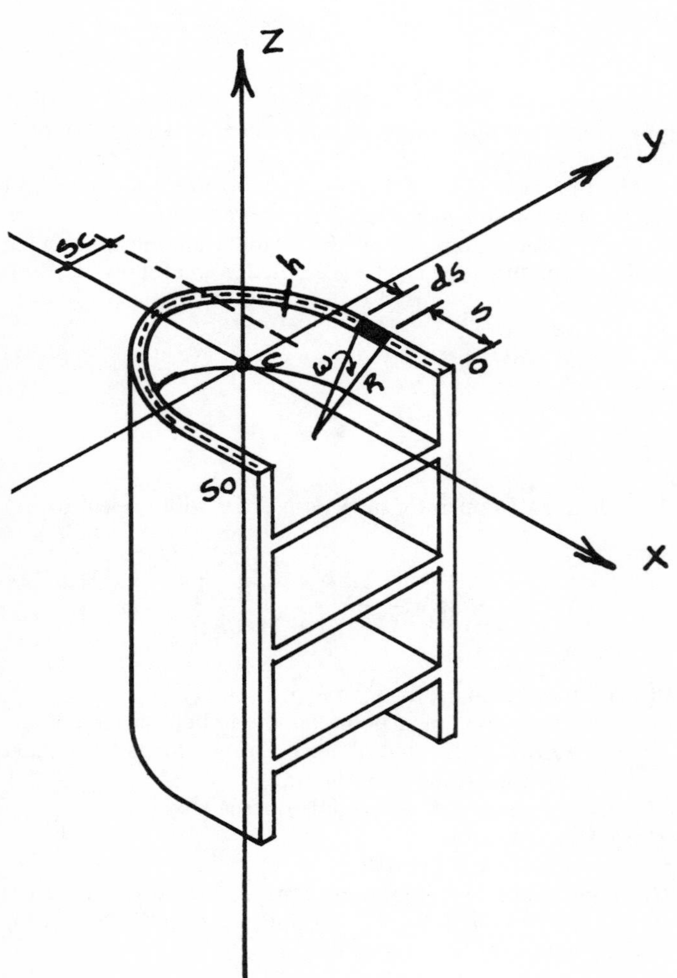

Figure 42-4.

Without going into any detailed exposition of the theory of thin-walled orthotropic systems, the normal stresses can be computed from the following general formula:

$$\sigma(z,s) = \frac{P(z,s)}{A} - \frac{M_y(z)}{I_y} \cdot x + \frac{M_x(z)}{I_x} \cdot y + \frac{M_w(z)}{I_w} \cdot W \qquad (42\text{-}3)$$

where:

- $P(z,s)$ = total normal force parallel to z-axis
- A = cross-sectional area of vertical walls
- $M_y(z)$ = bending moment with respect to y-axis
- I_y = moment of inertia with respect to y-axis
- $M_x(z)$ = bending moment with respect to x-axis
- I_x = moment of inertia with respect to x-axis
- x, y = Cartesian coordinates of the middle surface of the wall

$M_w(z)$ is a generalized force called a bimoment. This bimoment is an internal couple appearing due to the warping of the cross section and statically equivalent to zero.

The magnitude of the bimoment can be expressed through the normal stresses and sectorial coordinate in the following way:

$$M_w(z) = \int_A \sigma(z,s) \cdot w(s) \cdot dA \qquad (42\text{-}4)$$

The bimoment can be also expressed through the angle of rotation related to the shear centre and presented in the following way:

$$M_w(z) = -EI_w \cdot \theta''(z) \qquad (42\text{-}5)$$

I_w is a geometrical factor called sectorial moment of inertia determined by the formula:

$$I_w = \int_A w^2(s)\, dA \qquad (42\text{-}6)$$

w is a basic generalized sectorial coordinate representing a doubled area enclosed between the initial and moving radius-vectors and by the wall contour.

As far as the shear stresses are concerned, they could be determined from the following formula:

$$T(z,s) = \frac{V_x \cdot Q_{xi}}{I_x \cdot h} + \frac{V_y \cdot Q_{yi}}{I_y \cdot h_i} + \frac{M_w(z) \cdot Q_{wi}}{I_w \cdot h_i} + \frac{M_T \cdot h_i}{I_p} \qquad (42\text{-}7)$$

where:

- $V_x(z)$ — shear force in xoz plane in the direction of x-axis
- $V_y(z)$ — shear force in yoz plane in the direction of y-axis

$Q_{xi} = \int_o^i y \cdot dA$ first moment of area about x-axis

$Q_{yi} = \int_o^i x \cdot dA$ first moment of area about y-axis

$Q_{wi} = \int_o^i w \cdot dA$ sectorial first moment of area

h_i wall thickness at point i

$M_w(z)$ twisting moment, carried by warping torsion

$I_p = 1/3\Sigma \int_s h^3 ds$ torsional moment of inertia

$M_T(z)$ twisting moment, carried by pure torsion.

It must be pointed out that:

$$M_w + M_T = M_z$$

where M_z is total twisting moment about shear centre axis.

As far as the deformations of the whole thin-walled structure are concerned, they consist of:

1. Axial extension or compression due to vertical forces.
2. Bending in two principal planes due to horizontal or excentric vertical forces.
3. Rotation due to torsional forces acting on the wall.

To determine the magnitude of the angle of rotation the following differential equation can be used:

$$EI_w \frac{d^4\theta(z)}{dz^4} - GI_p \frac{d^2\theta(z)}{dz^2} = M(z) \qquad (42\text{-}8)$$

This equation, with corresponding boundary conditions, determines an angle of rotation $\theta(z)$ as a function of coordinate z.

In Equation (42-8) EJ_w is the sectorial rigidity, GJ_p is the pure torsional rigidity of the structure and $m(z) = -dM_z/d_z$ is the external torsional moment per unit length of the structure in longitudinal direction.

The general solution of this differential equation can be presented in the following way:

$$\theta(z) = C_1 + C_2 \cdot z + C_3 \cdot \sin h\,\lambda \cdot z + C_4 \cdot \cos h\,\lambda \cdot z + \bar{\theta}(z) \qquad (42\text{-}9)$$

here:

C_1, C_2, C_3, C_4, are the constants of integration,

$\bar{\theta}(z)$ - particular solution of the differential Equation (42-9)

$\lambda = \sqrt{\frac{GI_p}{EI_w}}$ - parameter.

Generally speaking, it means that the total displacement of any point of the structure must be calculated from four differential equations with corresponding boundary conditions.

The angle of rotation $\theta(z)$ is related to the shear centre, whose coordinates a_x and a_y may be found from the following formulas:

$$a_x = \frac{\int_s y(s) \cdot h \cdot w(s) \cdot ds}{\int_s y^2(s) \cdot h \cdot ds} \qquad (42\text{-}10)$$

$$a_y = -\frac{\int_s x(s) \cdot h \cdot w(s) \cdot ds}{\int_s x^2(s) \cdot h \cdot ds} \qquad (42\text{-}11)$$

The second type of tall buildings (Figure 42-5), can be analyzed as three-dimensional structural systems, occupying an

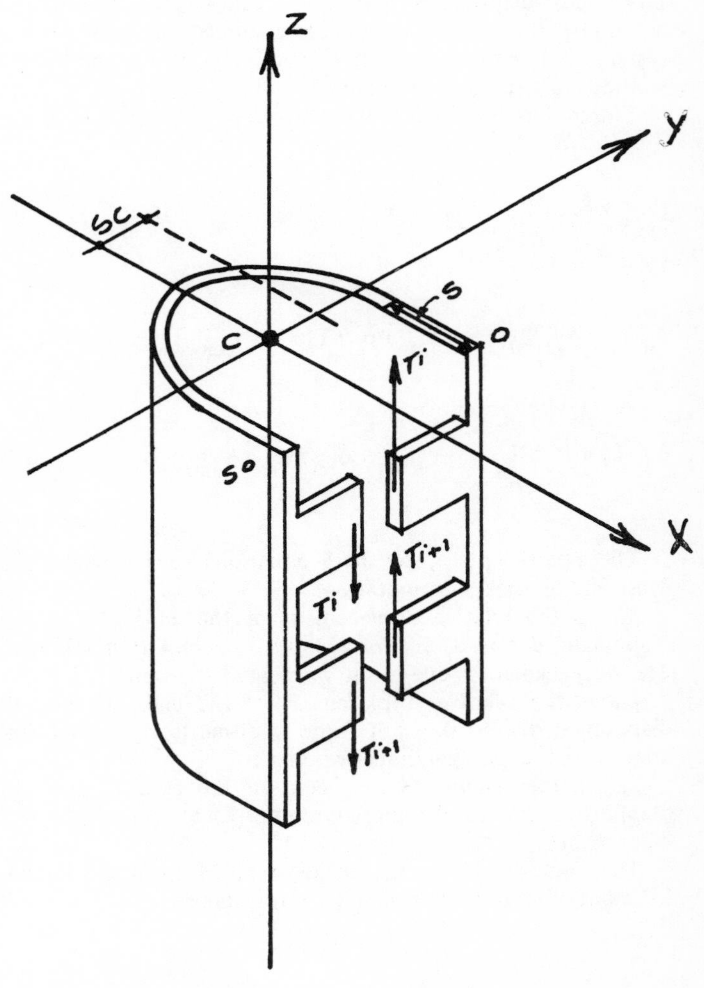

Figure 42-5.

intermediate place between thin-walled structural systems with the open contour and thin-walled structural systems with the closed contour.

The structural thin-walled systems, reinforced with spandrel beams, occurring very often in practice, can be analyzed on the basis of the following assumptions:

1. The contour of open thin-walled structure is rigid and shear deformations are neglected.
2. Spandrel beams are flexible in their plane and shear deformations are taken into consideration.

Such structural system can be considered as a space structure consisting of an open thin-walled structure connected with the Virendeel type vertical frames.

Since the spandrel beams or diaphragms are rigidly connected to solid bearing walls, which are subjected to the longitudinal warping, these diaphragms, in turn, will bend in the vertical plane.

Cutting these diaphragms in the centre, we will find a series of transversal forces $T_1 \ldots T_n$, acting at each end of the cut. These cut diaphragms behave as cantilevered beams. To determine the magnitude of these forces, we can write a system of n equations with n unknowns, using well-known methods of structural mechanics.

This system has the following form:

$$(\delta_{11} + \overline{\delta}_{11}) T_1 + \delta_{12} T_2 + \cdots \delta_{ln} T_n + \delta_{lp} = 0$$

. . . .

$$\delta_{il} T_1 + \delta_{i2} T_2 + \cdots (\delta_{ii} + \overline{\delta}_{ii}) T_i + \cdots + \delta_{in} \cdot T_n + \delta_{ip} = 0$$

. . . .

$$\delta_{nl} T_1 + \delta_{n2} T_2 + \cdots (\delta_{nn} + \overline{\delta}_{nn}) T_n + \delta_{np} = 0 \qquad (42\text{-}12)$$

The coefficients δ of these equations can be given the following physical interpretations:

δ_{ik} is the relative displacement of the ends of the i-th diaphragm, due to a unit force applied to the k-th diaphragm. This displacement is due to the warping of the walls.

$\overline{\delta}_{ii}$ is the relative displacement of the ends of the i-th diaphragm, due to the unit force resulting from the deformation of the diaphragm in its own plane.

δ_{ip} is the relative displacement of the ends of the i-th diaphragm, due to the given external force, applied to this diaphragm.

The coefficients $\overline{\delta}_{ii}$ can be determined from the known formulas of structural mechanics. For instance:

$$\overline{\delta}_{ii} = 2 \left(\int_0^{a/2} \frac{M ds}{EI} + C \int_0^{a/2} \frac{V^2 ds}{GA} \right) \qquad (42\text{-}13)$$

where:

- a the length of the diaphragm
- $I = \frac{hd^3}{12}$ the moment of inertia of the cross-sectional area of the diaphragm
- A the cross-sectional area of the diaphragm
- d the depth of the diaphragm
- C coefficient, depending on the geometric shape of the diaphragm

For a rectangular cross section of the diaphragm $\overline{\gamma}_{ii}$ can be written down in the following form:

$$\overline{\delta}_{ii} = \frac{a^3}{12EI} + \frac{C \cdot a}{G \cdot A}$$

Coefficients δ_{ip} representing the relative displacements in the direction of forces T_i due to the action of the external forces, can be found from the following equation:

$$\delta_{ip} = -\theta^1 (zi) \cdot c_o \qquad (42\text{-}14)$$

where:

- $\theta^1(z)$ the relative warping, which depends on the external load P and on the boundary conditions at the ends of the structure
- c_o a constant, depending on the geometry of the cross-section of the structure

The coefficients δ_{iu} representing the relative displacements at the centre of the i-th diaphragm in the direction of the acting forces T_i, due to a unit force applied to the k-th diaphragm, can be determined from the following formula:

$$\delta_{ik} = -\theta^1_{M_{wz}} (z) \cdot c_o \qquad (42\text{-}15)$$

where:

- $\theta^1_{M_{wz}}(z)$ the relative warping, due to the action of external bimoment produced by forces T_k
- c_o coefficient mentioned earlier

Solving the system of equations (42-12) we can find the values of the unknowns T_i.

Having determined these forces we can determine all stresses and deformations in any point of the structure.

Comments

Due to lack of space, we cannot go into a detailed presentation of the method described briefly and discuss all aspects of the design process.

It must be pointed out that this method was used for the design of two buildings in Toronto, Canada. Amount of design work does not differ, appreciably, from the conventional design methods of similar buildings.

Use of computers greatly reduces not only the design time, but also permits designer to evaluate the effect of changes in configurations of the building on the overall design and helps to quickly find an economical solution.

At the present time, this design method is being extended on the types of structures containing various combinations of thin-walled space structures with isolated walls and columns.

This method can also be successfully used for solving problems of vibrations and seismic design of tall buildings.

References

1. "Proceedings of the First National Bearing Wall Conference," SCPI, Washington, D.C., 1965.
2. Timoshenko, S. and Woinowsky-Krieger, S., "Theory of Plates and Shells," McGraw-Hill, New York, 1959.
3. "Structural Recommendations for Load Bearing Walls," British Standard Code of Practice CP111:1964.
   "Technical Standard 113," Swiss Engineers' and Architects' Society, 1965.
   "Recommended Building Code Requirements for Engineered Brick Masonry," SCPI, Washington, D.C., 1966.
   "National Building Code of Canada," Section 4.4, Ottawa, 1965.
4. Vlasov, V. Z., "Thin-Walled Elastic Beams," Jerusalem, 1961.
5. Billington, D. P., "Thin Shell Concrete Structures," McGraw-Hill, New York, 1965.
6. Timoshenko, S. and Gere, J., "Theory of Elastic Stability," McGraw-Hill, New York, 1961.

43. Modular coordination in the U.S.

Harry C. Plummer, Structural Clay Products Institute, McLean, Virginia

In the United Nations publication, "Modular Co-ordination in Building; Asia, Europe and the Americas"[1] the authors state,

> Modular co-ordination seems to have started in the United States of America already in the 1920's and 1930's. Since the first American Standards Association (ASA) standard for modular co-ordination was adopted in 1945, and the basic American work in the field, the "A62 Guide on Modular Co-ordination"[2], firmly establishing 4 inches as the size of the module, was published in 1946 by the Modular Service Association; adoption of modular construction principles, introduction of modular-sized building materials, and utilization of modular dimensioning have made considerable progress.

The first meeting on modular coordination was called by the American Standards Association in August 1938 to explore the possibility of setting up a project on modular coordination. Prior to that meeting, the heirs of Albert Farwell Bemis had incorporated the Modular Service Association. At the meeting Mr. Allan C. Bemis offered the services of Modular Service Association to the modular project if it were initiated. The unanimous recommendation of this conference to ASA was that a project on modular coordination be initiated, and I would like to review briefly the development of this project during the last 29 years.

Stage 1

Following the ASA industry conference in 1938, an ASA project for the Coordination of Dimensions of Building Materials and Equipment was initiated under Sectional Committee A62. The Modular Service Association provided secretarial and technical services to this committee, and in 1945 the American Standard Basis for Coordination of Dimensions of Building Materials and Equipment[3] was approved. This established the 4-inch module as the basis for coordination.

Also, in 1945, the American Standard "Basis for the Coordination of Masonry"[4] was approved, and in 1946 the American Standard Sizes of Clay and Concrete Masonry Units[5] was approved.

In 1946, the Modular Service Association published a guide for modular coordination which set forth the basic principles of modular coordination and included many modular details.

From 1938 until the end of 1946, the Modular Service Association was supported primarily by Allan Bemis and his associates. However, on January 1, 1947, these funds were no longer available, and the Producers' Council, one of the sponsors of ASA Project A62, negotiated a contract between the Office of Technical Services of the Department of Commerce and Modular Service Association to continue its work for another year.

Work started under this contract in February 1947, and the final report[6] was submitted in March 1948. During the period, the publication "Grid Lines"[7], which appeared for many years as a section of the American Institute of Architects' Bulletin, was initiated. The first issue was published in April 1947.

The report of the Modular Service Association to OTS contains many recommendations worthy of consideration today.

With the termination of the OTS contract in March 1948, Modular Service Association was also terminated, and this ended the first stage of the development of modular coordination.

Stage 2

Following the retirement of the Modular Service Association, the responsibility for further development of Project A62 fell upon the sponsors—at that time the American Institute of Architects and the Producers' Council. Neither was able to provide the financial support to the project that had formerly been available and, as a result, the interest in modular coordination reached an all-time low.

During this period, the Producers' Council sponsored a promotional program, and Gordon Lorimer made an extensive series of lectures to architectural and manufacturing groups throughout the country.

Through Leonard G. Haeger, Director of Research, the Housing and Home Finance Agency also contributed to the promotion of modular coordination during this period. In January 1949 HHFA contracted with the National Academy of Sciences for a survey by the Building Research Advisory Board to determine factors hindering more general acceptance of the modular principle in design and construction.

BRAB employed Arthur D. Little, Inc. to conduct this survey and submitted its report on June 30, 1949. This report[8] documents factors hindering more general acceptance of modular coordination, and the Building Research Advisory Board recommended steps HHFA might take to increase this acceptance. The No. 1 recommendation is headed "Cooperation" and I quote:

> Successful further development and promotion of modular coordination in the building industry should aid in providing better homes of lower cost and merits the closest cooperation of all elements of the building industry and the Government. Its accomplishment will require a great and long continued effort. This work has been privately supported for many years, during which substantial progress has been made, but at a very slow rate. Until adequate factual data have been assembled to convince the various sectors of the building industry of the importance of much greater activity than is now in prospect, substantial financial support will need to be provided by the Government if the project is to proceed at a healthy rate.

Other recommendations covered experimental work to document the savings resulting from modular coordination, technical services to assist architects in producing modular drawings and to aid manufacturers in developing modular sizes, and education directed to all segments of the construction industry and to the consumer.

This report also documented that modular coordination was definitely on the decline and, following the report, the Joint Committee of the AIA and PC, cosponsors of the project, called a meeting of industry representatives to discuss means of reactivating modular coordination. As a result of this meeting, industry, particularly trade associations, agreed to finance an Office of Secretary for Modular Coordination in the American Institute of Architects.

In May 1950, W. G. Demarest was employed for this position.

Stage 3

Bill Demarest's activities were primarily of a promotional nature. He addressed architects' meetings throughout the country, he talked to contractors and building material manufacturers; and he collaborated with the Building Research Institute in organizing a research correlation conference on modular coordination which was held in December 1954. The conference sponsors were the American Institute of Architects, American Standards Association, Associated General Contractors of America, the Association of Collegiate Schools of Architecture, Building Research Advisory Board, Chamber of Commerce of the United States, National Association of Home Builders, and the Producers' Council.

This conference was the first time that all of these segments of the construction industry had ever met together to consider modular coordination.

From the standpoint of the clay products industry, many important facts were disclosed. Mr. J. P. Caldwell, Vice President and Director of the J. A. Jones Construction Company, Charlotte, N. C., stated that his company had built two hospitals simultaneously in nearby towns. One, designed by Charles H. Hartmann of High Point, N. C., was completely modular. On the other hospital no attempt was made to use modular measure and the dimensions were naturally worked out in inches and odd fractions.

He stated that his costs showed approximately $42 labor per thousand for the face brick on the High Point Hospital (modular) against approximately $81 per thousand for hospital No. 2. Mr. James E. Coombs, President, Baker & Coombs, General Contractors, Morgantown, West Virginia, stated at this conference that, based on his company's experience on six large modular structures, savings in masonry labor were from 7 to 10 percent.

In 1956, Bill Demarest resigned as Secretray for Modular Coordination of the AIA, and in 1957 the Modular Building Standards Association was organized.

Stage 4

The Modular Building Standards Association was a membership organization; the funds derived from membership dues were used to promote use of modular measure.

The United Nations publication, previously referred to[1], stated, "Thus, in the United States of America, the emphasis has been on convincing and converting architects, builders and manufacturers to the practice of modular coordination, while less emphasis has been put on developing the theories of modular coordination, questions of tolerances, preferred sizes, multimodes, etc."

This statement was essentially true in 1957 when the Modular Building Standards Association was organized.

MBSA, a non-profit corporation, was formed in 1957 to develop the educative tools for wider understanding and use of the system of Modular Measure in the building industry. The "Selected List of Publications Pertaining to Modular Practices"[9] forms a notable library of information generated and distributed by MBSA.

MBSA teaching and drafting workships were conducted in many parts of the country. Concurrent with all the editorial and promotional activity, a lively service correspondence was carried on in this country and abroad with literally thousands of persons and organizations interested in the values of modular measure. Not the least of the accomplishments was the publishing of the book, *Modular Practice*[10] by John Wiley and Sons.

This latter publication, published in February 1962, shows various grids and preferred numbers so that this project is now concerning itself with these problems. However, in January 1964, C. E. Silling, President of MBSA, wrote, "With regret, we now report that even the recited meager operating funds we require are at an end, and we must stop short of our ultimate goals, at least for the time being. If we lack adequate funds to continue the broad levels of work outlined above, we also deem it inappropriate to continue billing membership fees, this latter never being a robust support for our budgetary necessities."

Shortly after this time, Project A62 of the American Standards Association was discontinued.

Stage 5

In the spring of 1965, the National Bureau of Standards decided to evaluate the activity relating to the modular concept. The need for this evaluation was evident from the increase in large and premanufactured building components in building construction. Following this evaluation, the Institute for Applied Technology of the National Bureau of Standards wrote the American Standards Association expressing the Institute's interest in seeing the establishment of a project dealing with the coordination of building components and systems and offering NBS assistance in initiating and sponsoring a project in this area if requested.

The Executive Committee of the ASA Construction Standards Board considered the NBS proposal and voted to request NBS to organize "an exploratory committee, consisting of individuals concerned with premanufactured building component coordination projects, to make a survey to determine the need, interest, and value of such a project and submit any recommendations they may have to the Construction Standard Board."

On May 1966, the Construction Standards Board by letter ballot approved the reactivation of the A62 project under the sponsorship of the National Bureau of Standards, with the title A62, Precoordination of Building Components and Building Systems.

The National Bureau of Standards, as sponsor, then named Jack E. Gaston, Armstrong Cork Co., as Chairman and Russell W. Smith, NBS, as Vice Chairman and Secretary.

Mr. Gaston named four subcommittee chairmen: Burr Bennett, Portland Cement Association, Chairman, Systems, Programming and Planning Subcommittee; Robert LaCrosse, Chairman, Components, Programming and Planning Subcommittee; James Gross, Chairman, Elements, Programming and Planning Subcommittee; Roy Murphy, Chairman, Special Projects Subcommittee. This Executive Committee of A62 held their first meeting on January 24, 1967. Since that time, the sub-committees have set up technical committees for the following purposes:

1. to develop a standard establishing an overall dimensioning disciple and preferred sizes for modular systems and components thereof,
2. to develop a standard establishing criteria for classifying components according to the functions they perform in the modular system,
3. to develop a standard establishing criteria for classifying modular building systems according to type and placement on the modular grid, and
4. to draft a revision of A62.1.

Each technical committee has had one or more meetings and is working on the assigned project as of this date.

European Practice

The authors of *Modular Practice* make the following statements regarding the growth of modular coordination in the United States and Europe.

> Since the publication of Bemis' book,[11] the growth of understanding, acceptance and use of the principles of modular coordination has been slow but steady in the United States. In Europe, the decade of the 1950's was a period of increasing modular awareness with a strong positive approach contributed by the European Productivity Agency of the Organization for European Economic Cooperation. In 1953 and 1954, the EPA started a modular project in which eleven nations were to participate. These were Austria, Belgium, Denmark, France, Germany, Greece, Italy, the Netherlands, Norway, Sweden, and the United Kingdom. Canada and the United States and later Iceland, Turkey, and Yugoslavia joined the EPA project as observers.

"Modular Co-ordination in Building; Asia, Europe and the Americas[1]" summarizes the work in this field as of 1966. Some of the European countries that make modular coördination compulsory have progressed to a greater extent than those in which the acceptance of modular coordination is totally voluntary, such as in the United States.

References

1. "Modular Co-ordination in Building, Asia, Europe and the Americas," United Nations Publication, 66.IV.4, New York, 1966.
2. Adams, Myron W., and Bradley, Prentice, "A62 Guide for Modular Coordination," Modular Service Association, Boston, Mass., 1946, out of print.
3. "Basis for the Coordination of Dimensions of Building Materials and Equipment," A62.1-1945, USA Standards Institute, 1945.
4. "Basis for the Coordination of Masonry," A62.2-1945, USA Standards Institute, 1945.
5. "Sizes of Clay and Concrete Modular Masonry Units," A62.2-1946, USA Standards Institute, 1946.
6. "Dimensional Coordination of Buildings, and Materials and Equipment, on the Modular System," Final Report of Modular Service Association, to Office of Technical Services, Department of Commerce, Cac-47-3, March 1946.
7. "Grid Lines," *Bulletin*, American Institute of Architects, 1947, out of print.
8. "Report on Survey of Factors Hindering More General Acceptance of the Modular Principle in Design and; Construction to Housing and Home Finance Agency," Executive Committee, Building Research Advisory Board, June 1949.
9. "Selected List of Publications Pertaining to Modular Practices." Modular Building Standards Association, 1961.
10. *Modular Practice,* John Wiley & Sons, Inc., 1962.
11. Bemis, Albert Farwell, "Rational Design," *The Evolving House,* Vol. III 1936.

44. Design engineer's approach to masonry construction.

R. J. M. Sutherland, Harris and Sutherland, London, England

Introduction

This chapter, unashamedly related to personal experience, describes the developing use of brickwork in a particular design office in Britain. It shows how brick compares with other materials here, what general designers still need to know about its behaviour, and why and where we should use it.

To most British engineers brickwork, like timber, is hardly a structural material at all. However, it has lately become accepted in Britain as a major structural element by a handful of design firms and is now being used for quite tall buildings. If this trend continues, in a few years high performance brickwork may be understood and used as universally as reinforced concrete is today.

Our first experiences with brickwork were on several low-rise (up to 6 story) buildings where, for economic reasons, we were forced to change the architect's schemes conceived in exposed precast concrete to brick wall ones. In the process, we found that savings from the bearing walls made it possible to pay for moulded and expensively finished concrete cladding; thus the greater part of the original aesthetic concept was maintained at much lower cost.

Another early experience arose out of the University Grants Committee's invitation to take part in a practical development exercise in student housing. Here, the economy of brickwork became even more obvious. The resulting buildings, using mainly 4-1/8"-thick cross-walls in low-strength bricks, was economical enough to justify the Committee fixing low cost limits which have since proved a rod for our own backs as well as those of other designers.

The first real structural challenge (in 1963) was presented by the need for student accommodation at the new University of Essex. Here, the architect's* development plan included a series of over 20 slim residential towers, each fourteen storeys high[1]. Our earlier experiences led us to believe that the economy of brickwork on previous lower buildings with similar sized rooms would also apply at these heights. Events have shown this to be correct, but it was only gradually, and when fully committed to using brick walls, that the gaps in our knowledge of the material and the weaknesses of accepted design techniques became apparent. I now propose to discuss these, using the progressive development of the Essex tower designs as the main example.

*Kenneth Capon of Architects' Co-Partnership.

Economics

Where heavy walls are needed for sound insulation, the separate frame can do little but add to the cost of the overall structure. Our experience shows that, where the layout permits, it is almost always more economical to use the walls structurally. The real problem is whether to use brick or concrete.

A histogram prepared from data supplied by the Quantity Surveyors, Monk and Dunston (Figure 44-1) shows prices per square foot for in situ concrete and brick walls from ten actual contracts of comparable value. These prices are for rough walls suitable for plastering, and they have all been adjusted for one time (Autumn 1965).

Using bricks at 130/-per 1000†, which are readily available with strengths of 3000 to 4000 lb./in.^{2}, the average cost of an 8-5/8" brick wall is little over half that of a 6" concrete one**, and there is no sign of overlapping price ranges. With stronger bricks at 300/-per 1000, brickwork still wins, but overlapping is imminent. With bricks at 600/-per 1000 (rarely needed for strength alone), brickwork shows no economic advantage over concrete. Thus, it is particularly important to use the cheapest brick which will carry the load.

Once fair faced surfaces are demanded, suitable for use with paint but no plaster, the odds tend to swing still more in

† These bricks prices are for bricks 8-5/8" x 4-1/8" x 2-5/8".

** i.e., with comparable sound insulation.

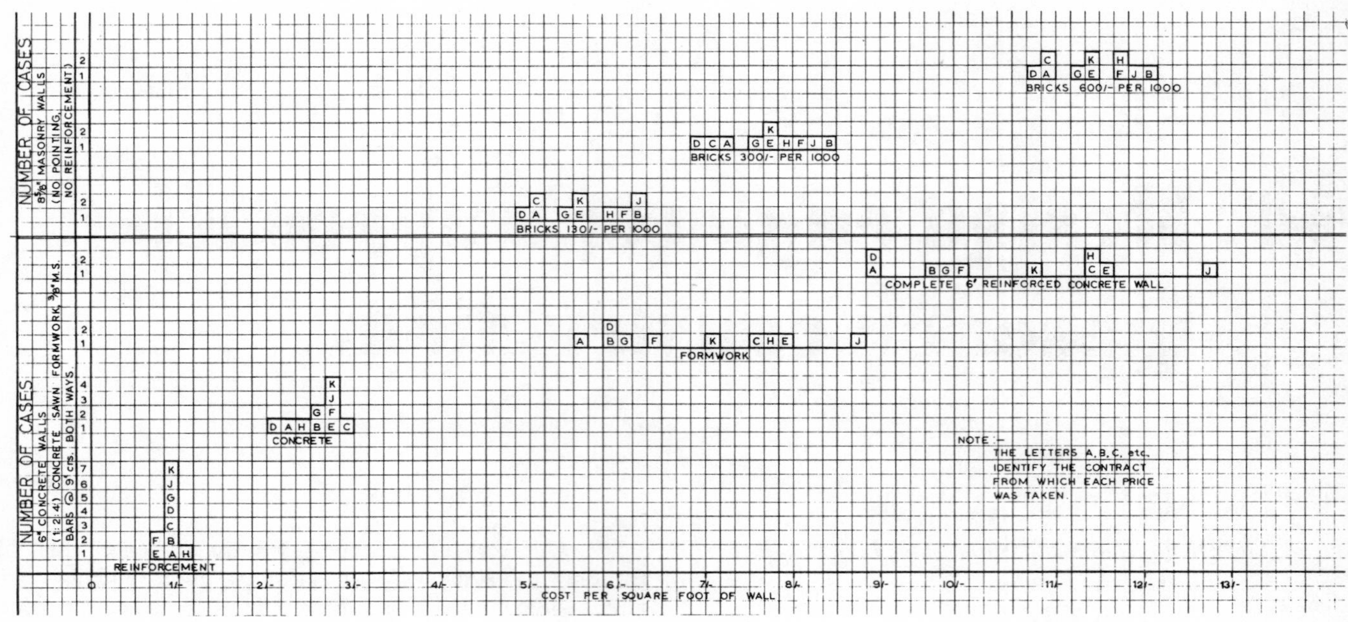

Figure 44-1. Histogram showing relative costs of masonry and concrete load-bearing walls.

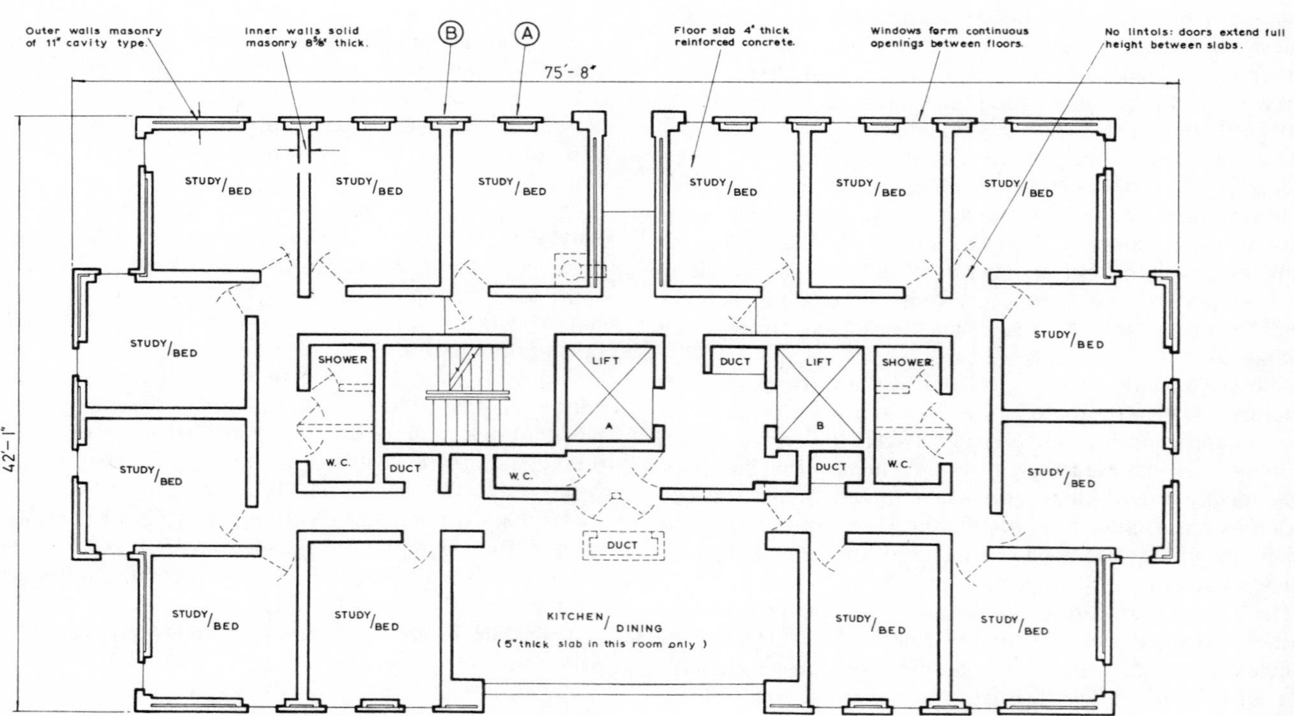

Figure 44-2. Essex University: Typical floor plan of Towers 3 and 4.

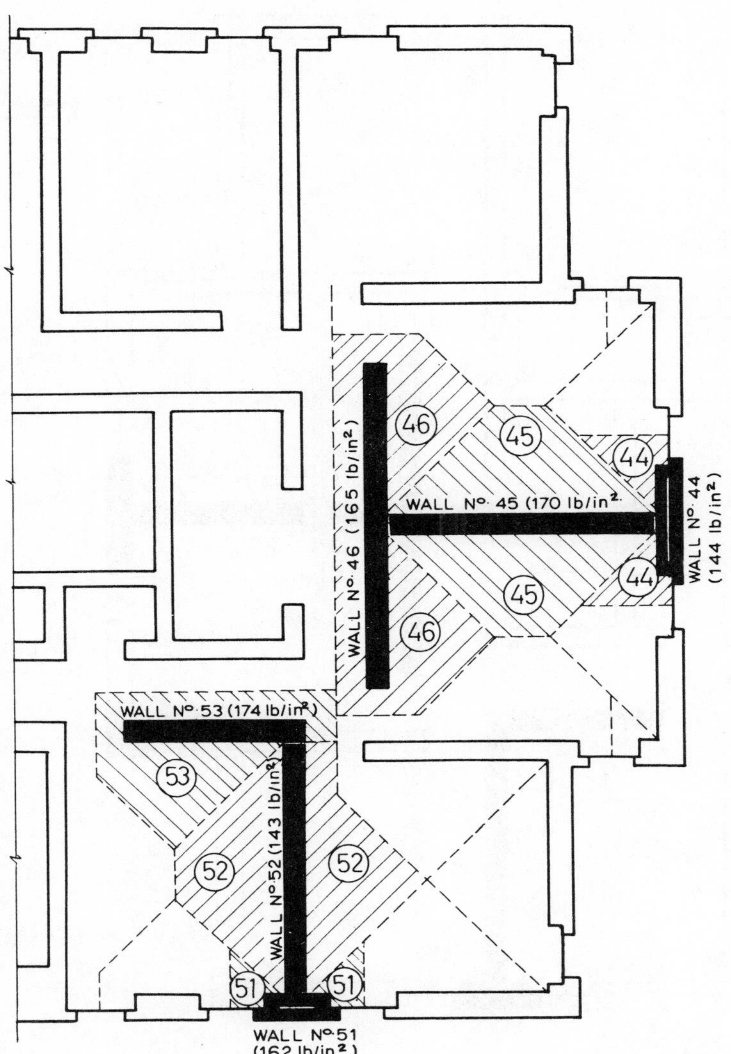

Figure 44-3. "Wall length" method of calculating stresses due to vertical load.

favour of brickwork, the extra cost of painting nearly always being much less than that of special formwork††. Prefabrication with concrete, though expected to be economical, still tends to cost more than traditional building.

These comparative costs not only make an economic case for brickwork but provide a foundation for my later remarks on structural design.

The economic argument for brickwork in Britain seems indisputable, and it was only by using bricks that we were able to build the first two Essex University Towers within cost limits set for low-rise buildings. Since then, we have had to refine our designs to meet rising cost by using fewer and cheaper bricks. Towers No. 3 and 4 could not have been built to the design used for the first two; if the 5th and 6th are to go ahead, we must make further structural savings.

†† Unpainted brick walls used internally are obviously less economical on tall buildings if, for appearances, the same brick must be used at all levels.

Design for Vertical Loads

With the same wall arrangement at all levels and a one-way floor spanning system (as between parallel cross-walls), wall stresses due to vertical loads present few design problems. However, with more complex two-way spanning layouts, as shown in Figure 44-2 (Towers No. 3 and 4 at Essex University), the calculation of wall stresses becomes not just tedious but virtually impossible to do accurately.

For the first four Towers, we divided the wall units into simple straight lengths and assumed that each supported a combination of mainly triangular floor areas, as one would when calculating beam loads in beam and slab construction. (Figure 44-3) Further, we assumed that the load on each wall length was uniformly distributed and that walls extending higher than the rest carried their full load right down to the foundations without spreading into those adjacent. Even with these simple assumptions, the calculation of stresses by this wall length method was a long-winded affair, and the resulting

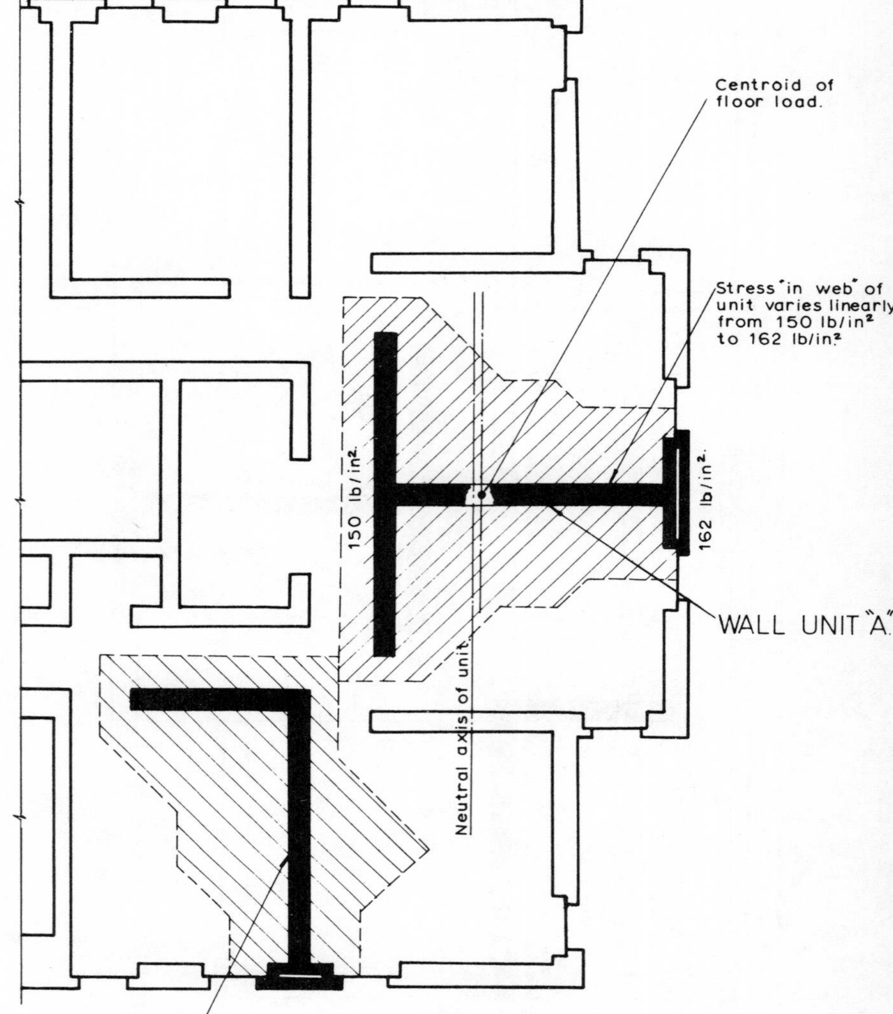

Figure 44-4. "Wall unit" method of calculating stresses due to vertical load.

stress distribution often quite illogical as can be seen in the samples in Figure 44-3.

A more exact but more complex assumption would be to consider complete wall units rather than wall lengths, to find the centroids of these and of the floor areas supported by them, and thus to calculate the stress distribution across the units.

An example of this is shown in Figure 44-4; Unit A, symmetrical about one axis, is fairly simple to check, but units like B, symmetrical about neither axis, far less so. The more uniform the wall stresses the better***. Those calculated by the wall unit method will generally be more constant than those derived from wall lengths, but the extra calculation can be quite considerable, and the results still far from correct. Arching tends to balance out uneven stresses still further.

With nearly symmetrical layouts of evenly spaced walls like the one in Figure 44-2, it would be tempting to assume the same stresses due to vertical loading in all the walls at any one level, but this, the greatest simplifying assumption of all, would be hard to justify, although by chance it may sometimes be correct enough for practical purposes. Although calculating vertical loads may at first seem simple, present methods are far from ideal for load-bearing walls.

Assessment of Wind Stresses

If vertical loads present problems, wind forces offer still more.

In Britain, the traditional way of calculating wind stresses in brickwork is to consider each wall unit as a separate

*** This is certainly true with vertical load stresses, although cases can occur where it is not so once wind stresses are added.

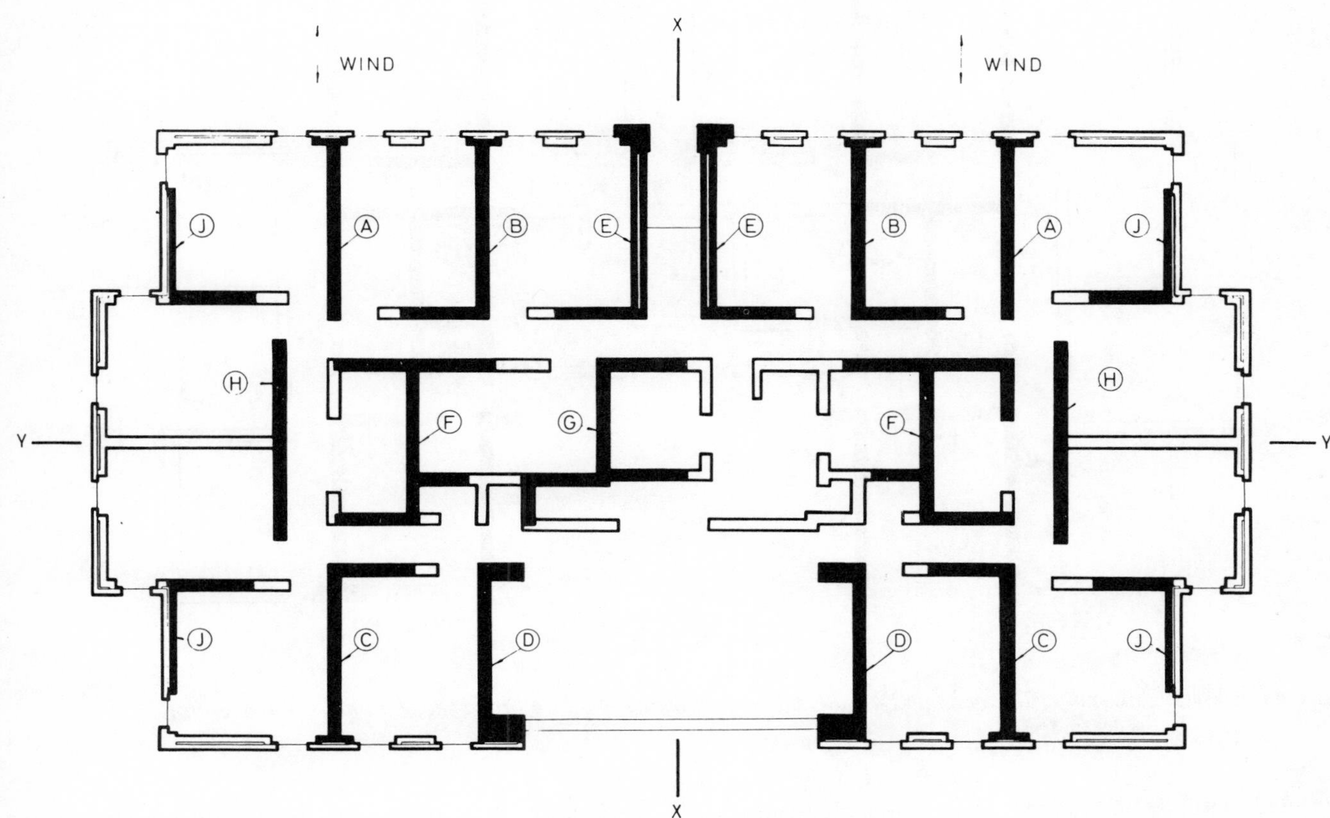

Figure 44-5. Essex University: Towers 3 and 4 walls taken as resisting wind on broad face (Independent Cantilever assumption). Notes: (a) Flange widths limited to 5 ft. in all cases. (b) This plan shows the final layout which differs slightly in central core area from that current when wind analysis was done; hence some apparent inconsistencies in assumptions on walls resisting wind.

cantilever, pin-jointed to the others at every floor level. The wind moment is then distributed between the units (whether straight T, L or I shaped—see Figure 44-5) in proportion to their stiffness. We used this method initially for the Essex towers because of the thin concrete floor slabs with no door lintels. Wind stresses were added to dead plus reduced live load stresses and subtracted from dead load ones only to give maximum and minimum total wall stresses.

This method ignores the frame action which undoubtedly takes place. Although seemingly simple, calculations with it can take a long time if the section properties of the wall units are very varied. Otherwise, the method is easily understood; it errs on the safe side and is thus suitable for general office use, at least until it shows unacceptable stresses in a seemingly stable structure. This is exactly what it did on our first towers.

It was not the magnitude of the compressive stresses in the walls which embarrassed us but the existence of large tensile ones. Even Professor Hendry could not wholly reassure us about these until he and Dr. Soane had done a model test and then backed this up with a computer analysis, a superb piece of work[2], but, alas, too late for the first towers†††. An unusual, valuable feature of this analysis is that it can be applied to irregular wall blocks connected by broad strips of slab instead of just to pierced plane walls.

After proving his analysis against the model results for the first two towers, Dr. Soane used the same programme on the revised layout for the third and fourth. Here, for simplicity, he considered only the two wall groups shown in Figure 44-6 for wind on the critical broad face.

It is interesting to compare wall stresses given by the cantilever and frame methods. Due to layout changes, the

††† For these we resorted to the clumsy expedient of thickening and vertically reinforcing some critical walls for the bottom four storeys.

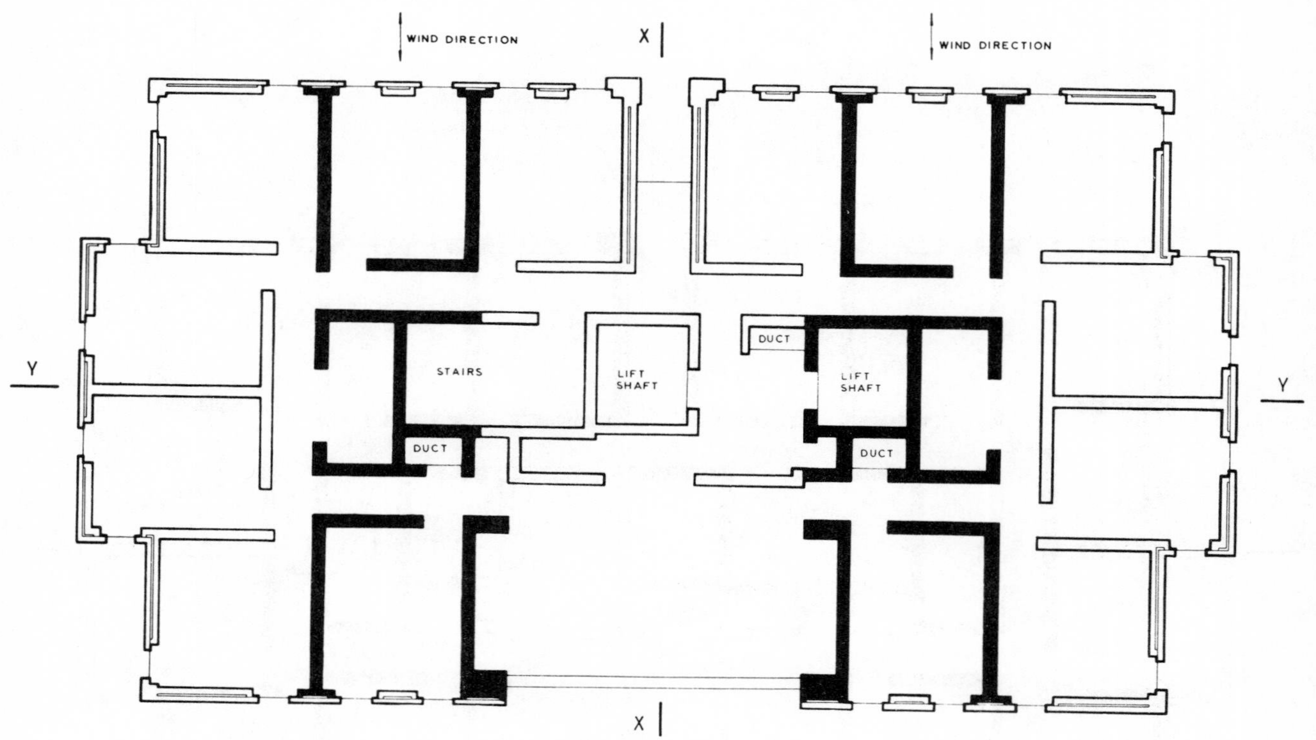

Figure 44-6. Essex University: Towers 3 and 4 walls taken as resisting wind on broad face (frame action assumption).

connected cantilever analysis gave more favourable results than it did on the first towers, although there were still zero stresses or tensions of up to 50 lb./in.^{2} under wind load. By modifying our conservative assumptions, it might not have been difficult to argue ourselves out of the tensions or into accepting them. However, such reasoning can be rash when the stresses in doubt are the small differences between appreciably larger ones. What if the wind exposure was underestimated? Should we have considered other lateral forces than wind?**** What about the accuracy of the stress calculations?

All these doubts pale into insignificance, when one considers the effect of frame action even using only part of the structure; with this the apparent tensions are replaced by substantial compressions at all points, and thus doubts on vertical load distribution immediately become less significant, wind forces could be increased by 50 percent (still with no tension), and there is also the consolation that the frame action must extend through more of the structure than it is convenient to assume in calculation. The frame analysis, which incidentally indicated a very small wind deflection, was the final justification for building the third and fourth Towers with 8-5/8″-thick inner walls and 11″-thick cavity outer ones for the full 14 storeys with no vertical reinforcement.

A slight snag with frame action of this type is that to make it work more reinforcement needs to be added to the floor slab than would be needed for simple vertical loads. This introduces an extra cost but not a very large one.

Perhaps too much trust should not be put on tests on glued plastic models. While doubtless reliable enough at working loads, the behaviour of such a plastic, with comparable strength in tension and compression, may give a misleading idea of how brickwork behaves under overload when the joints start to open up; most theoretical frame analyses also stop being applicable at this stage. The plastic model of the first Essex Tower showed that small semi-independent wall units attracted large bending stresses due to wind (see Figure 44-7) which was encouraging although this could lead to too great generosity in assessing the shapes assumed to act as one in the computer analysis.

We will know more of these relationships between theoretical, model, and full-scale action when Prof. Hendry's full-sized lateral load trials start at the Edinburgh University quarry test site. In the meantime, if, as on our towers, simple analysis shows a structure to develop only minor tensions while a frame analysis more than eliminates these, then I am reasonably happy about the safety of the final structure, but less so about the time spent in proving this!

**** Earthquakes are not allowed for in Britain, but there is a move, and a good case can be made for it, to include an arbitrary lateral stability force in our building codes (apart from wind). This has already been done in some European countries.

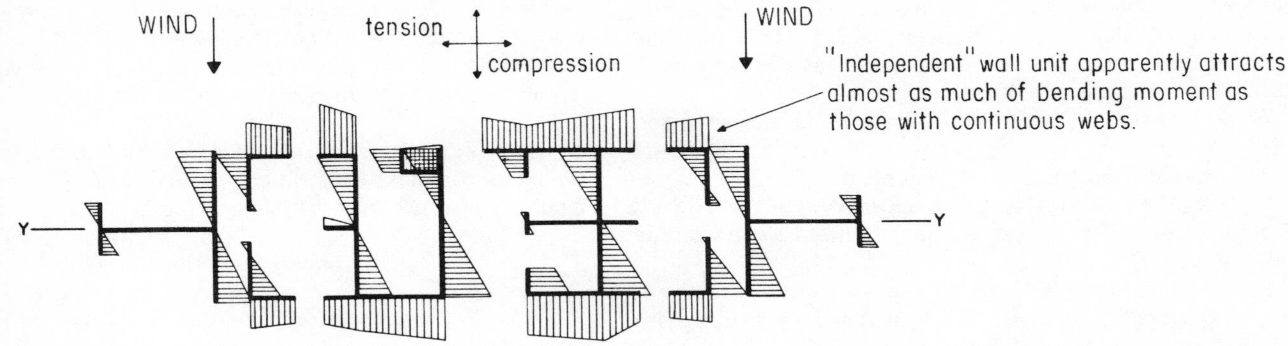
WIND
tension
compression
WIND
"Independent" wall unit apparently attracts almost as much of bending moment as those with continuous webs.
Y
Y

Figure 44-7. Plan of Perspex model of core area of Essex University Tower 1 showing wind stresses measured.

Assessment of Brick Strength Required

The method of stress analysis used on the Essex University Towers proved tricky and long-winded. This was partly due to the complex layouts, but these are just the arrangements on which brickwork shows most advantages. Further, if the architect or client cannot move a wall or a couple of doors without the engineer having to start almost from scratch, then high performance brickwork will not find much favour in any design office.

It is not that the engineering principles are different from those for other materials, but that brickwork's economy is so closely dependent on using the cheapest brick. Also with negligible tensile strength, stability can often be ensured only by analysing the structure as a whole instead of just adding a couple more reinforcing bars. These remarks may seem so obvious as not to be worth making, but structural designers nurtured on steel and concrete are often quite unaware of their significance. Those who claim that for high-rise structures, brick walls offer little or no saving over concrete ones have probably never tried to design for the cheapest wall for any position; with concrete the variation of cost with strength is small but with brickwork it is very considerable as has been shown in the section on economics.

If brickwork is to become more popular, the first design need is for a method of calculating stresses due to both vertical loads and wind which is quick, cheap, and accurate enough for assessing two or three preliminary schemes and, with little modification, for proving all details of the final one.

Much can be done by streamlining existing methods, but possibly the real solution is the fashionable one of making more use of computers and not just for frame analysis but also to help one to marshall the vertical loads and all the stresses more quickly. Definition of this overall problem for the computer would probably be quite a formidable task, but it should be no worse than many solved in the past. Perhaps such a programme exists; certainly some minor work has already been done in this direction.

In the first four Essex University Towers, we used a constant strength of brick at any one level for ease of control on the site. Changing one floor of one of these towers to a lower brick strength produces a saving of £400–£500 and, if this can be done several times, then quite an appreciable percentage of the wall costs will be saved. The strength needed at any storey tends to be dominated by the requirements at only one or two critical points. By using high strength bricks at these, it should be possible to down-grade the general run of brick on several storeys and save a large part of the wall cost.

We are carrying out studies on such a down-grading to make the savings needed for the proposed fifth and sixth Essex Tower Blocks, and these look promising. Given the same mortar at any level (mortar has little effect on cost) and bricks whose strength can be identified by their appearance, there should be little difficulty with site control. What we do need is quicker methods of assessing stresses at all levels.

The Cavity Wall and Related Problems

So far in considering wall stresses no mention has been made of the effects of slab deflection, thermal or moisture movements, nor of the uneven distribution of load due to differing elastic and creep properties. All these effects are known to exist, but there is surprisingly little information on them. Structural designers have no firm basis for deciding what allowance, if any, to make for each.

The effect of slab deflection on inner walls can usually be ignored, but at the building's perimeter it may well mean more if the wall is a cavity one, it will be joined by several other effects. In fact, differential loading and movement between the skins of the cavity wall is a real problem. The Swiss have demonstrated one way of handling it in tall buildings, or, more exactly, of avoiding it by taking all the floor loads down the inner skin and making the outer one independent except for flexible ties at each floor level. In Britain the Code (CP111) only allows this for a maximum of four storeys. The permitted alternative is to carry the outer skin at every floor, or at least at every fourth. Then, not only are the floor loads carried on the inner skin, but the weight of the outer skin is added as well. Both these arrangements tend to be especially uneconomic if the facing brick chosen is a strong one.

For the Essex Towers, with a blue engineering facing of at least 10,000 lb./in.^{2} strength, it seemed almost criminal not to use this structurally. Load sharing in cavity walls is not uncommon in medium rise buildings and the only question was whether it should be used for as many as 14 storeys with the strength of the inner skin reducing upwards.

We set out to calculate how the load would be shared and failed miserably because no one could tell us the basic properties of the materials we were using.

If you ask the average British brick maker for the Young's modulus of one of his bricks not only doesn't he know but he does not seem to want to know.††††

No one seems to be able to do more than guess the range of creep movement with masonry. It is small compared with concrete, or so the research man say. How small? They don't know.

Moisture movement is still the subject for research workers only and in spite of some interesting publications[3] there seems to be nothing for practical designers to use. Slab deflections can be calculated theoretically but creep will reduce their effect on the walls. With this paucity of information, it was obviously pointless to try to design on the basis of any definite proportional sharing of load in the cavity wall. The only thing to do was to find out what would happen under limiting conditions. We checked a typical independent section of wall as possibly the most critical (e.g. wall marked A on Figure 44-2). In this case the outer leaf could carry (within the Code stress limits) all the loads at any level, a very unlikely distribution. If, on the other hand, all the load went down the inner leaf (still more unlikely as most evidence pointed to more load on the outer than the inner), the code stresses would be exceeded by an amount which, while too great for use in design, was by no means ridiculous.

This check indicated that at least for the independent outer wall sections the actual load distribution was not too critical. However, just as a precaution and in particular to limit any tendency for the outer leaf to attract large loads from adjacent inner cross-walls, a thin layer of slightly compressible material***** was put in the outer leaf at each upper floor level where the disparity of brick quality was greatest. This was done for all upper wall sections in the first two Towers but is being confined to those adjacent to cross-walls (e.g. as wall B in Figure 44-2) in the case of Towers Nos. 3 and 4.

The first Tower has been complete for over two years, and the second one for more than one. So far we see no reason to regret the decision to save cost by assuming load sharing between the skins of an 11" cavity wall. However, in our attempt to justify this, we became well aware of two further major design needs, namely:

1. More information on the thermal, moisture, elastic and, in particular, creep behaviour of all clay materials.

2. More case histories of successes and troubles with load sharing between brick units of different quality under different conditions to exposure. There are quite a few reco cases of trouble with brick clad reinforced concrete fra (where the material disparities, are very real) but it is diff to find any with clay brickwork used on their own.

One does not want this extra information just to be abl do more complex sums, but to know which factors ca ignored and which must be taken seriously.

Sound Insulation

With its large mass, brickwork is excellent for so insulation, but wastefully thick walls are often called fo positions where openings and various forms of flank transmission limit the attenuation to that of a 4"-thick wal has been suggested that with the doors of adjacent ro opening onto a common corridor, as in the case of hotels hostels or within individual dwellings the attenuation betw the rooms will never exceed 40-45 decibels; if this is so the no point in using 8-or 9-inch-thick walls as is often d (although structurally not necessary) just on the ground better sound insulation.†††††

Too many of our ideas on sound insulation derive f laboratory tests on independent wall panels and not eno from tests in actual buildings or even user's reports. I n admit that our early 4-1/8" wall design for the Univer Grants Committee (see Economics) got a poor press f such tests but here the faults were shown to be mainly in detailing of service holes, etc. rather than in the wall thickn

As my fourth design need, I suggest more research on so insulation within actual buildings, and a comparision of insulating effects of walls of the same weight and typ different forms of construction. Present indications poin the same wall forming a more effective sound barrie load-bearing than when supported by a structural fra doubtless this is due to minor cracking the latter case.

Site Control of Quality

With the demand for increasingly high performance f brickwork, it becomes more and more essential to have s accepted method of site quality control equivalent to the cylinders and cubes used with concrete.

Checks on bricks alone are obviously not enough, opinion in England is divided on what further tests are n appropriate. Some think that mortar tests are good enou others that cubes and brickwork (generally 8-5/8" x 8-5/8 8-5/8") are best while there are those who would something nearer to the bending test used in Australi Mortar tests give no idea of bond but are easy to carry c brickwork cube tests give a closer approximation to act conditions but are most costly, while bending tests defini measure bond but nothing else.

With none of these methods can one yet be wholly sur the relationship between the test results and the performa

†††† An honourable exception is the London Brick Company who answered our questions by measuring the modulus not only of their bricks but also of the blue facings we intended to use with them.

***** This was done largely as a result of the London Brick Company's tests.

††††† These remarks do not necessarily apply to unpierced party w between buildings.

actual walls, but experience is growing. We have carried out ite extensive mortar and brickwork cube testing pro-mmes on the Essex University Towers (and elsewhere) and ot of work has been done to isolate the factors affecting the ength of brickwork cubes.[5,6,7,8,9,10] For the present, I our the testing of brickwork cubes for site control, but in future other methods may be proved superior.

Whatever it is, there must be some site test, as universally nowledged as concrete test cubes or cylinders, which can used with reasonable certainty as the basis for acceptance rejection. Perhaps this should be given as my fifth design d, although it is only indirectly connected with design.

One thing which our experience has shown is that any ular testing has a tonic effect on workmanship on the site.

Spanning Walls

One of the most obvious design limitations with conven-nal brickwork is the loss of the freedom of layout given by med buildings. What is more, large spans over entrance areas or the cantilevering of complete storeys, both of which are easy with R. C. box construction, have to be abandoned or carried out with framing which destroys the simplicity, and a large part of the economy, of the basic brickwork.

It occurred to us that by reinforcing the brick walls these could be made to act with concrete floor slabs as deep box beams with little increase in cost over simple brick walls and slabs. Thus, one of brickwork's greatest weaknesses would be largely eliminated.

The work of R. H. Wood[11] and others showed that the idea was sound, but we could find no evidence of previous use to justify its introduction, untested, on an actual job (especially in cantilever form). We were not sure how the reinforcement should best be arranged; after all reinforced brickwork is still very much a rarity in Britain.

Structural Clay Products Limited, an enterprising consortium of brick makers with an eye on the future, agreed to sponsor some full-scale loading tests on story-height walls cantilevering 10 feet. These tests have been fully described elsewhere[12] and all one need to say here is that the results

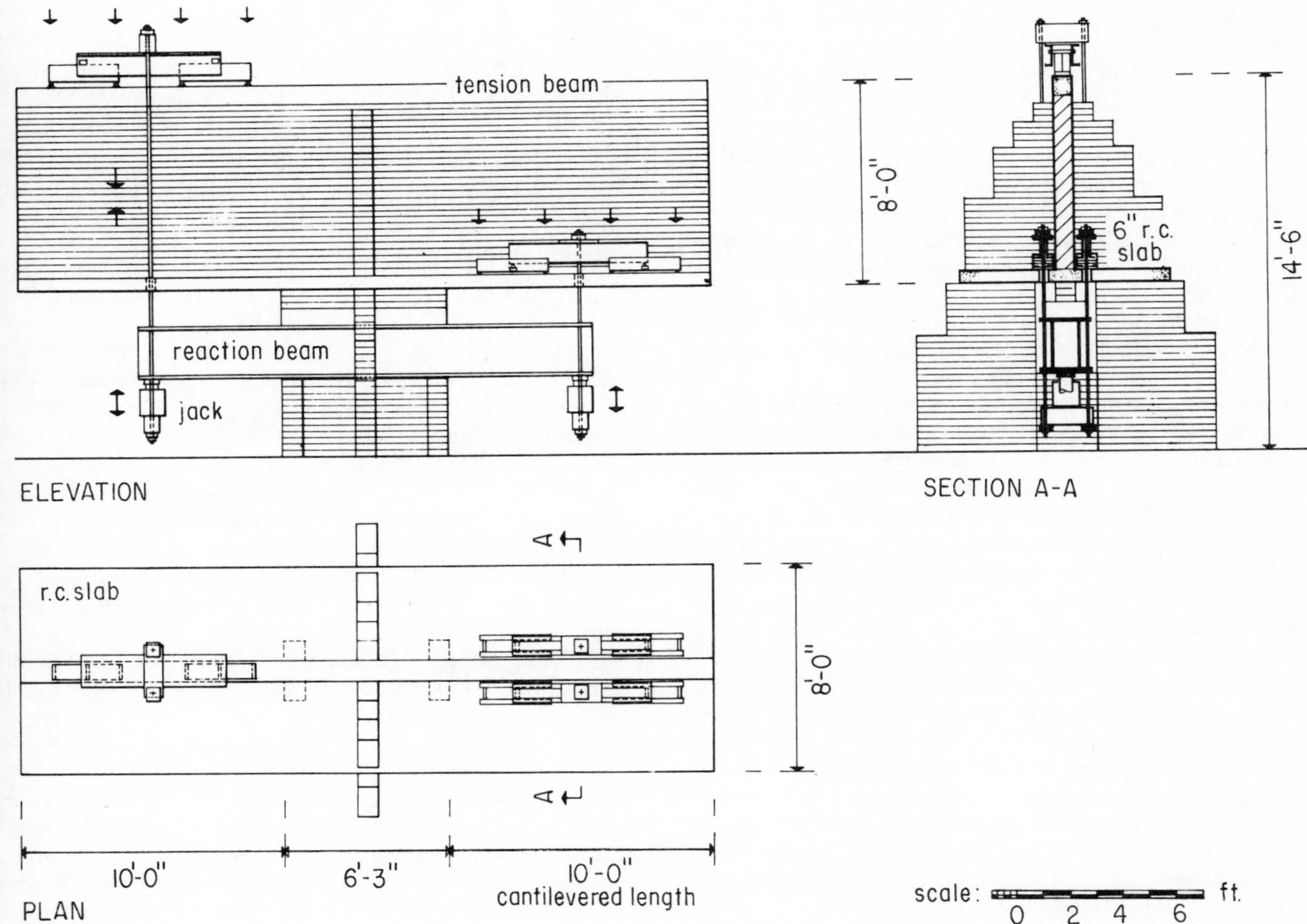

ure 44-8. Spanning wall test rig.

have been very encouraging, especially those on diagonally reinforced walls. Figure 44-8 shows the arrangement of the test rig.

Here is an obvious design need which has now been largely met by the sort of investigation which should be much commoner in the brickwork field.

Prefabrication

One big disadvantage which still offsets the economy of brick structures is the time taken to put them up. On the Essex Towers a cycle of three weeks per story for the structure is the best we have achieved with traditional methods, although with a tracked tower crane serving two adjacent towers, it has been possible to build the two in virtually the same time as one. Rates of 14 days per floor or less have been reported elsewhere but these still compare unfavourably with building speeds using concrete[13].

The only practicable way of reducing the building time seems to be by prefabricating the floor slabs or the walls or both.

With small rooms as here it would be relatively easy to make room-sized prefabricated floor panels which would still span two ways and be no thicker than the present in-situ ones. Soffit finishes would be better; there is no plaster on walls or ceilings in the Essex Towers and the horizontal plate action of the floors could be maintained with bars or mesh in the screed at the slab edges. The only new problem, not already solved by the concrete system builders, would be the maintenance of bending strength in the slabs if frame action is needed for stability. Even if in-situ concrete strips are essential in some places to get in the extra top and bottom steel, there could still be an appreciable time saving.

With essentially one way spanning floors (as between simple cross-walls in housing), there are a whole host of existing precast floor systems which can be used.

For the walls, there are grouting systems and mechanical brick-laying ones by which brickwork panels can be prefabricated. These may incorporate vertical lifting bars designed to be left in, or screwed out after erection for use over again. Structurally, the best vertical joints between panels would probably be narrow in-situ concrete ones, but toothed panels could doubtless be cobbled together with hand-laid bricks. In many circumstances, a vertical shear connection between wall units will be unnecessary.

High-bond mortars could hold the key to really successful prefabrication, but there has been virtually no experience yet with these in Britain and all information leads one to expect high costs.

The most annoying aspect of prefabrication is that it almost invariably costs more than traditional building. This is certainly the trouble with concrete systems, and there is little reason to expect brickwork to be immune from it. Prefabrication may well be justified in saving time or avoiding labour shortages, but at present these are likely to be the only gains.

More information is certainly needed here, especially on the cost of prefabrication. For instance how much would high bond mortar increase the wall costs given in Figure 44-1? Would it be reasonable to look forward to the day when large T, I or L shaped units say 4" thick can be made on the ground using high-bond mortar and then lifted into place without the need for propping or vertical jointing? If so an appreciable extra cost per square foot of wall might be justified.

Conclusion

Brickwork is cheap and, as long as it remains so, engineers should always consider using it, even sometimes when at first it looks only marginally appropriate.

Load-bearing walls limit freedom of layout but, by cooperation, client, architect, and engineer can often plan out any need for the flexibility of framed construction and thus build more cheaply.

Brickwork's limitations are less than they were a few years ago. By meeting the design needs outlined in this chapter, and others, its economy and range of application could be vastly extended in the future.

References

1. Thomas, K, Technical Note, Vol. 12, C.P.T.B., January 1967. (Describes Towers 1 and 2 only).
2. Soane, A. J. M., Research Note, Vol. 1, No. 1, C.P.T.B. January 1967.
3. For example see:

   Freeman, I. L. and Smith, R. G., "Moisture Expansion of Structural Ceramics," *Transactions, British Ceramic Society*, Vol. 66, No. 1, January 1967, pp. 13-35.

   or

   West, H. W. H., "Moisture Movement of Brick and Brickwork," *Transactions, British Ceramic Society*, Vol 66, No. 4, April 1967, pp. 137-160.
4. "Australian Standard Rules for Brickwork," Draft, Standards Association of Australia, July 1966.
5. Stedham, M. E. C., "Quality Control for Load-Bearing Brickwork," *Transactions, British Ceramic Society*, Vol. 64 No. 1, January 1965, pp. 1-17.
6. Stedham, M. E. C., "Quality Control for Load-Bearing Brickwork," *Proceedings, British Ceramic Society*, No. 4 July 1965.
7. Stedham, M. E. C., "Quality Control for Load-Bearing Brickwork," *Proceedings, British Ceramic Society*, No. 11 July 1968, pp. 83-100.
8. West, H. W. H., Everill, J. B., and Beech, D. G., "Development of Standard 9-Inch Cube Test for Brickwork," *Transactions, British Ceramic Society*, Vol. 65, 1966, p. 111.
9. West, H. W. H., Everill, J. B., and Beech, D. G., "Testing of Bricks and Blocks for Load-Bearing Brickwork," *Proceedings, 10th International Ceramic Conference*, June 1966, p. 559.
10. West, H. W. H., Everill, J. B., and Beech, D. G., "Experiment in Use of 9-Inch Brickwork Cube for Site Control

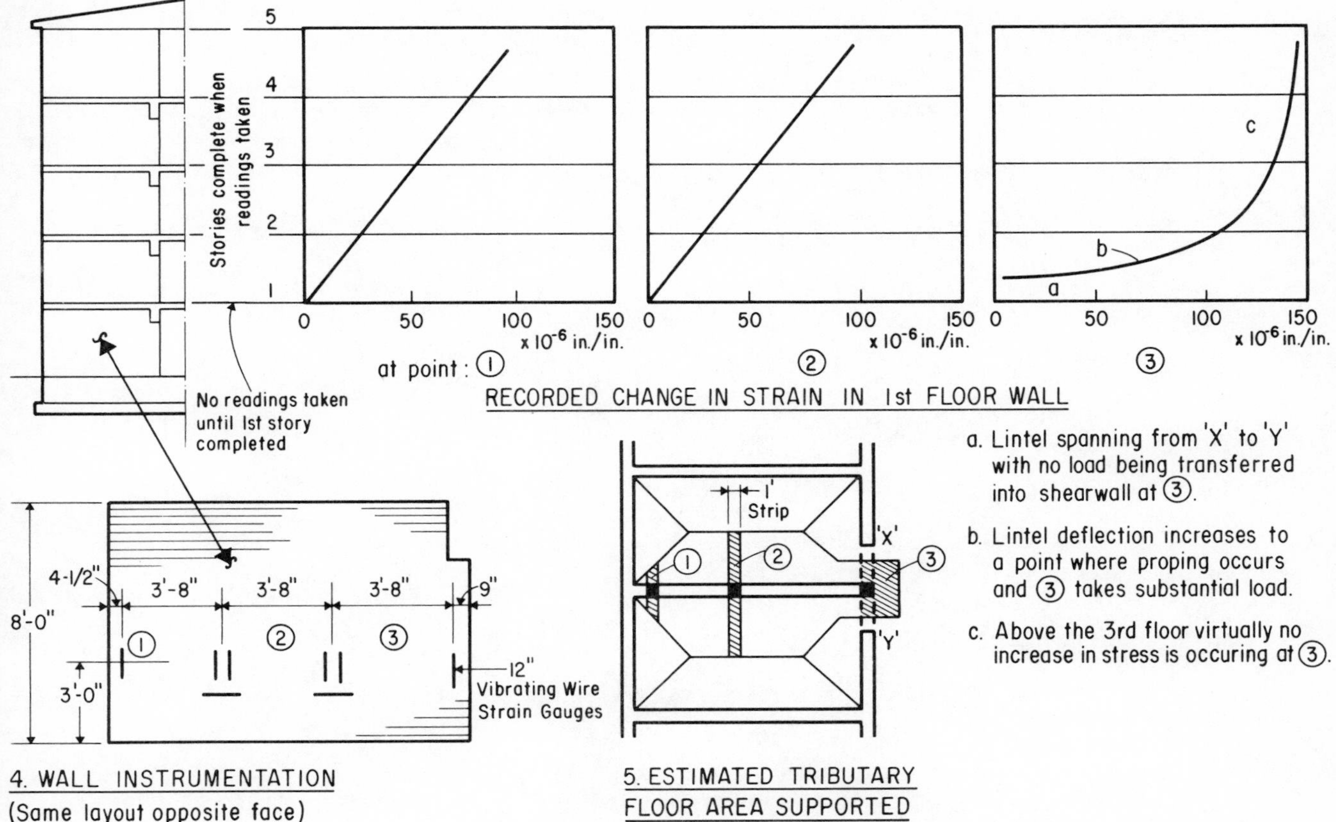

Figure 44-A.

Testing," *Proceedings, British Ceramic Society,* No. 11, pp. 135-141.

11. Wood, R. H., National Building Studies, Research Paper No. 13, H.M.S.O., 1962.
12. Plowman, J. M., Sutherland, R. J. M., and Couzens, M. L., Paper read at the Institution of Structural Engineers, November 9, 1967.
13. Stockbridge, J. C., and Hendry, A. W., "Cast Studies and Critical Evaluation of High-Rise Load-Bearing Brickwork in Britain," Chapter 51, *Designing, Engineering and Constructing with Masonry Products,* Gulf Publishing Company, Houston, 1969.

Remarks

By Jerry Stockbridge
Skidmore, Owings & Merrill, Chicago, Illinois

In part three of Mr. Sutherland's excellent paper he brings up the important point that the presently accepted methods for determining the distribution of vertical loads are far from ideal.

To develop some insight into this problem this writer, while at the University of Edinburgh, carried out a study to measure the distribution of vertical strains at the base of a crosswall in a 5-story brickwork building as it was being constructed.

Although the study was far from comprehensive, and much more work is required, the results do indicate that in the lower levels of a tall (10 stories plus) wall bearing high-rise all walls may well have approximately the same uniform stress due to vertical loading.

This appears to be due to arching action transferring the majority of stress to the most lightly loaded portions of wall as the relative deflection increases under the more heavily loaded portions. Two examples of this phenomenon are readily visual in Figure 44-A.

In Figure 44-A3 it can be seen that as the height of the crosswall increased above the 3rd floor most of the additional load was transferred by the less highly stressed areas of the wall, not by the already highly stressed end section, even though the largest loads were being applied directly above it.

If two more stories were constructed and the same stress distribution resulted as for the lower 5 stories, it appears reasonable to assume that a uniform state of stress would exist in the wall.

From Figure 44-A5 it can be seen that at the opposite end of the crosswall a lower than average stress occurs due to load distribution from the floor slab into the exterior wall, but this loading also was apparently evened out by arching action because the corner strains (Figure 44-A1) were found to be the same as those recorded over the center portion of the wall Figure 44-A2.

Part 6: Case studies

45. Hemispheric brick planetarium.

Orville G. Anderson, Wheeler and Lewis, Denver, Colorado

Introduction

Recognizing the need for future study of interplanetary travel and space science, the Board of Education for Lamar Public Schools determined that some facility should be provided at the high school level for an academic program of that kind in their community. Since they were planning an entirely new high school building to replace the archaic structure they had been using for the past 50 years, it seemed proper to include this space science center in the new school. This type of thinking is typical of that community and even though Lamar is a relatively small city, population 7,500, in southeastern Colorado, its educational program under the direction of Superintendent Alfred Young is vigorously progressive. Thus, the Board charged the architect with the responsibility of creating a contemporary structure which would house the equipment and excite the imagination of the community.

Design Considerations

As the requirements of the educational program were developed by the school superintendent and the architect, it became apparent that air conditioning, light and sound control, ample seating and lecture space, display and demonstration areas, and a 30'-diameter planetarium dome with elevator-type projection equipment and remote control consoles would be needed. There, of course, must be no restriction on future growth. With all this criteria for designing the planetarium and the new high school, we thought that a space science center as a separate structure divorced from the main building might offer more latitude in design and enable us to solve the problems more effectively. In searching for the proper structural system, we felt the shape had to be unusual, striking and attractive, and still be a logical choice. As we sketched and doodled, the dome shape kept reappearing, much to our dismay, because even though a 50'-diameter hemispheric dome was one solution, there are some obvious disadvantages such as acoustical control, ventilation, mechanical equipment, and additional construction costs. Since the appearance of the dome falls within the province of architectural license, and since it was our decision that any dome must present a uniform appearance of color and texture, it was obvious that if we pursued the dome idea we would be looking squarely at an unusual roofing and water protection problem. People who have never experienced the dry climate and large temperature changes of the Rocky Mountain area probably cannot fully appreciate the problems the roofing industry must solve in this region. Temperatures will range from -30 deg. F. to 110 deg. F. and the relative humidity is often as low as 3 percent. Acceptable, time-proven materials satisfactory for horizontal surfaces are just not acceptable for vertical or nearly vertical surfaces.

On the other hand, a dome does provide large floor area with a minimum cubage, particularly in reference to planetarium equipment. Its shape is simple and geometric, thus affording precise, refined structural analysis, and it is clean cut and striking in appearance. The space usually allotted for demonstration and lecture in planetariums accomodates about 80 people. With a dome over a dome concept of the outer hemispheric building shell over an interior planetarium equipment hemispheric shell, we can increase the seating to about 120 and still provide ample display space.

Foam Dome

About this time we became acquainted with Foam Domes, a product manufactured and erected by Dow Chemical Company. These spirally generated styrofoam domes are self-supporting. After contacting the Dow Chemical Company, we determined that we could spin a six-inch-thick foam dome capable of carrying a 40-pound-per-square-foot live load over a concrete foundation for a fairly moderate cost. Six inches of styrofoam affords thermal insulation and, being somewhat rough in texture, provides an excellent base for sprayed acoustical plaster, which in itself fireproofs the structure from the inside and provides a good degree of acoustical control.

What can we do now to the outside of the dome to make it watertight and vandalproof? After determining that 2-1/4'' of unreinforced brick masonry would be structurally self-supporting, we decided to use a covering of horizontally laid, running bond, 4''-nominal thickness masonry. The problem, of course, with any masonry wall is the possibility of leakage

Figure 45-1. Tension ring and bearing plate assembly.

through the joints, particularly in a dome where the surfaces are not vertical. Again, the Dow Chemical Company offered a solution with their material known as Sarabond. Sarabond is a mortar which contains a substance which Dow refers to as liquid Saran wrap. With this type of mortar in the joints, we decided to use a glazed brick, fired at a low temperature, thus providing a uniform surface which could shed water easily over the entire dome.

Although on paper we showed that no reinforcing was necessary in this masonry, we felt that we should provide temperature reinforcing as an additional measure to control the shrinkage cracks, especially since this was an unknown field. Assuming a 140 deg. temperature change for that area, we could almost anticipate a full 1″ movement in the perimeter of the building. To counteract this, we installed a 3 x 3 x 1/4″ continuous angle tension ring (Note Figure 45-1) at the base of the masonry and then reinforced the masonry with D-4 wires, 70,000 psi minimum yield strength, in the lower half of the dome. The spacing on the reinforcing is at every other course near the base of the dome and decreases to every fifth course up to a point approximately 40 degs. from the center point of the dome. From that point on up to the top there is no reinforcing. To allow the dome to move due to this temperature change, the brick was installed on the tension ring which in turn was welded to 12″ lengths of 12″ channels spaced 3′ apart and placed with the flanges pointing down to straddle the grade wall. Each channel acted as a bearing plate and rested on graphite paper which in turn rested on cast-in-place 10″ x 10″ steel plates in the concrete foundation. Caulking material was installed around each channel and bearing plate to prevent the entrance of moisture. Where openings occurred in the dome for doorways, a horizontal leg of tension ring angle was run through continuously and the wire reinforcing in the masonry was affectively gathered together by vertical reinforcement and carried on over the top of the doors.

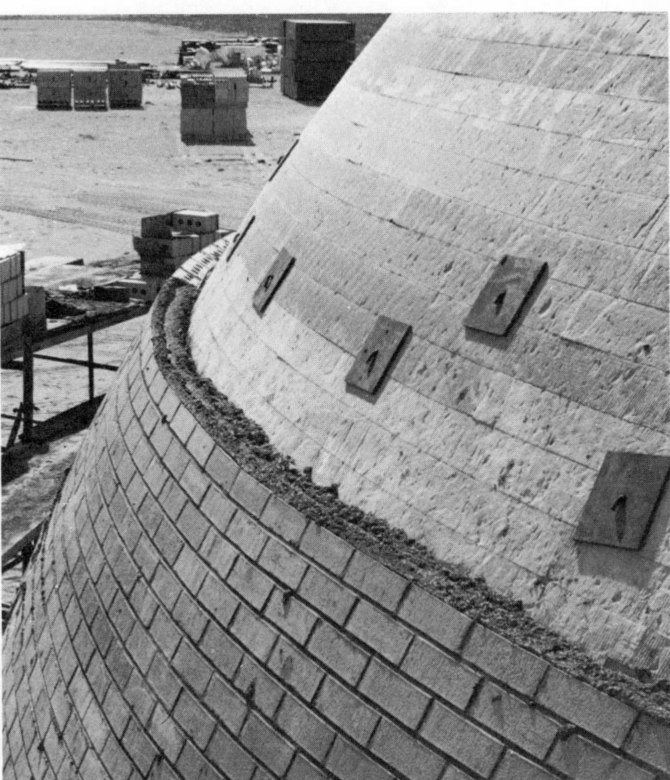

Figure 45-2. Masonry at mid-height.

Another problem was how to support hanging loads from inside the dome since styrofoam offers no strength in this regard. Hanger wires were forced down through the styrofoam and on the top of the dome they were welded to 6 x 6 plates. (Figures 45-2 and 45-3) To these 6 x 6 plates were attached other D-4 wires which could be bent into the coursing of the masonry and grouted into the Sarabond mortar, thus transferring all the load to the brick shell. The brick shell, as mentioned before,was laid with horizontal courses of masonry, each horizontal course being somewhat smaller in circumference, but tipped so that the glazed surface of the brick was always normal to the center of the hemispheric dome. Hence, as we approached the top of the dome, each course of masonry became smaller in radius and forced us to start cutting brick at a point 18′ in diameter. At this point, we used three-fourths brick. At a point 8′ in diameter we used one-half brick, and right at the apex of the dome we cut brick into several small pieces and fit them into place. At this point, the brick layers were working on a virtually horizontal surface.

To provide the number of exits required by the Building Code, it was necessary to put one pair of entry doors at the front of the dome and a single emergency exit door on the far side of the dome.To accommodate the doors and door frames, we put small projecting masonry walls out from the main dome and covered these small entries with precast reinforced brick slabs. Since we had one plumbing vent stack to accommodate, we elected to bring that vent up in these small

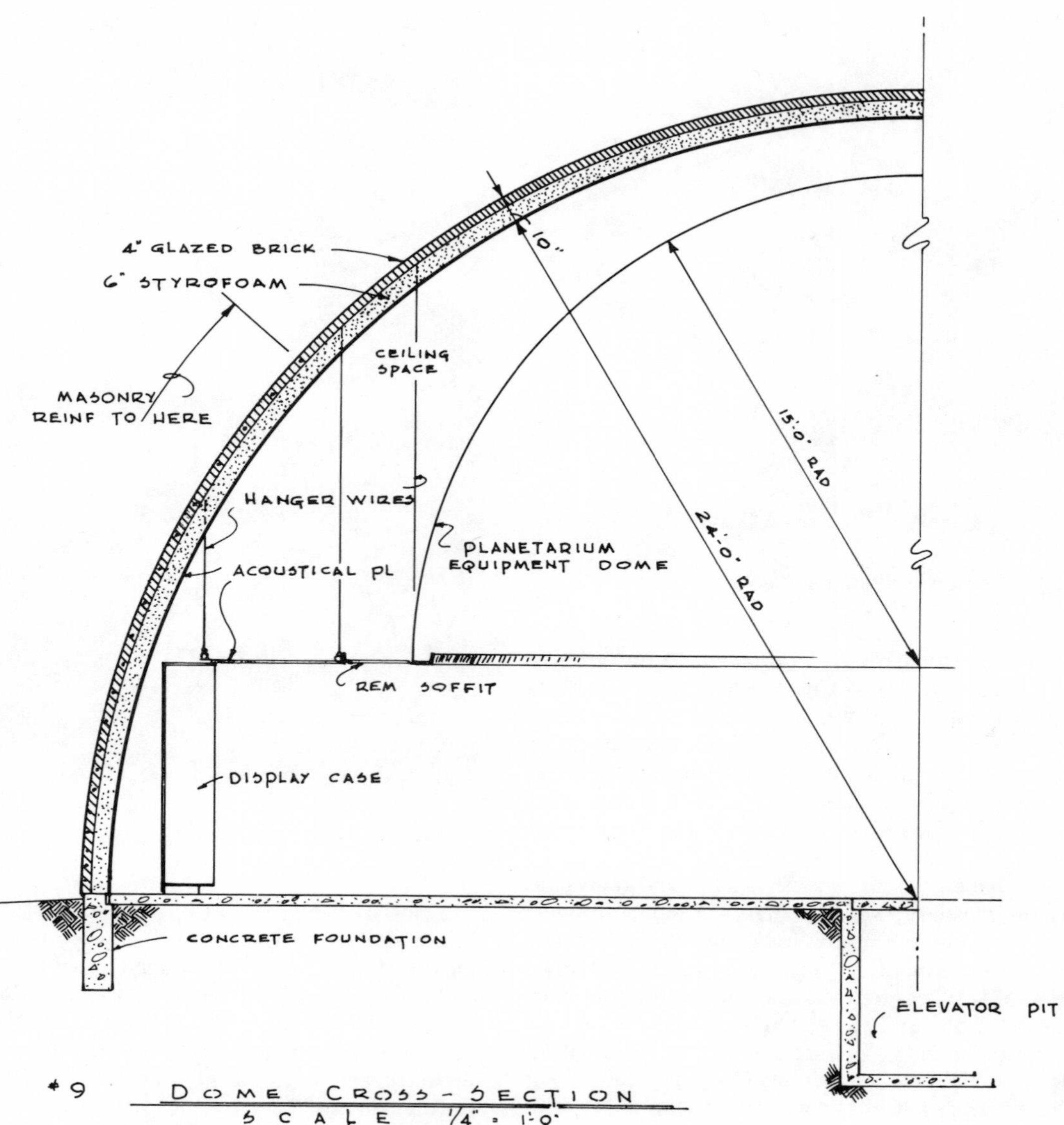

Figure 45-3. Cross section through dome.

brick walls to avoid puncturing the shell of the dome at a point where movement might cause a leakage problem. Another requirement of the Building Code was six air changes per hour for ventilation. Six air changes means moving a tremendous volume of air. To keep the velocity and accompanying noise to a very low level, we placed all of the mechanical equipment in the adjacent main building and delivered air conditioned or heated air in oversized ducts underground to the dome. The fresh air was delivered at the floor level around the perimeter of the dome and exhaust air was collected at the top of the dome in a system of ductwork located between the planetarium shell and the styrofoam dome and delivered to an underground duct and back to the air handling equipment.

Acoustical plaster sprayed on the interior of the styrofoam satisfied the Building Code requirements for fire protection.

Since this was an experimental project, the Dow Chemical Company provided an excellent staff to assist in designing and constructing this project and, in fact, provided a written warranty protecting the owner against undue cost in the event of water leakage for a five year period.

Construction

Economics

The costs involved were relatively moderate. For the excavation, foundations, floor slabs, styrofoam dome, and masonry work the cost was approximately $35,000.00 for about 2,000 square feet of floor area. The cost with all the heating and ventilation equipment, the lighting, display and demonstration areas, and other building amenities brought the total project to $65,000.00. If the project were to be repeated in the near future, the cost would likely remain the same even though the construction techniques might be improved.

Forms

During the design of this building, it was anticipated that perhaps no form work might be needed for the masonry work because after the masonry is up about half way it should be possible for the workmen to kneel on the foam and work backwards and upside down, so to speak. The foam is strong enough to support the weight of the workmen and the weight of their materials if properly located. However, in actual practice this did not happen. The contractor experimented with several types of form work including one mechanical system which could be erected on a curved rail at the base of the dome and travel around the foam. This idea was ultimately rejected because of excessive cost. The masonry contractor finally resolved the problem by using normal scaffolding up to about 12′. At this point, he cantilevered his scaffolding inwards and supported it or braced it against the dome. As the surface became more horizontal, he merely left out a few bricks at various locations, providing a toe hold of sorts, propped his formwork into the toe holds, and eventually formed across the top of the dome to the other side, so that the workmen were always on some kind of scaffolding.

Construction Problems

The masonry contractor had some difficulty training his men to lay the masonry on surfaces that were not plumb and square. They had some difficulty in keeping the coursing horizontal as it went around the dome. He tried to control it by measuring from the finished floor line up on all sides. It was very quickly apparent that too many masons really only got in each other's way so the crew was cut to six to construct the entire dome. As the masonry work increased in height, the workmen of lesser skills removed themselves from the work, and the dome was actually completed by one mason. His comment upon completion was that he hoped that he would never have to do another one. By that time his patience and concern for workmanship were exhausted.

This being a somewhat unusual and experimental structure, we encountered some unforeseen difficulties. The first had to do with the tension ring and base plate assembly which was installed over the concrete foundation walls. The tension ring of the 3 x 3 x 1/4″ angle rolled to a 50′-diameter shape and welded to channels just would not hold its shape. The entire assembly tended to twist and warp so that it would not fit properly to the cast-in-place bearing plates. The construction superintendent for the foam dome erection did not understand the scope of the project and took it upon himself to weld the entire assembly to the bearing plates. This was the correct thing to do from his view point because it enabled him to then erect the styrofoam on to a firm foundation. When we pointed out his error and explained to him why we needed this floating foundation, he burned all the welds loose, hoisted the entire dome up far enough to allow his men to grind all the welds smooth, and then reinstalled the dome onto the bearing plates. Since the bearing assembly was still twisted, Dow Chemical provided additional intermediate bearing plates grouted into place with Threadline mortar so that we could take up the difference in horizontal attitude between the channels and the cast-in-place bearing plates. Threadline mortar is an extremely high compressive strength mortar manufactured by Dow Chemical Company.

As testimony to the strength of the styrofoam dome, during the time the dome was lifted into the air there was a tornado and it moved the dome off the foundation. The workmen simply picked it up and carried it back to its proper place. The fact that this might happen again, until the dome was weighted down with the brick, was a consideration to hasten the erection of the brick masonry.

Another problem encountered was that the styrofoam dome was not a true hemispheric shape. Early in the erection of the styrofoam, there was a slight change in the radius and the dome had a small bulge at the base. This was corrected by shaving off about 1″ of styrofoam from the base of the dome up to a height of about 6′. Near the top of the dome, the styrofoam tended to flatten out.

This flat portion near the top presented a serious problem. Starting at the foundation, all of the brick was laid into a 3/8″ parge coat to bond the masonry to the styrofoam, and achieve something of a monolithic shell. As the surface became more horizontal in nature, the brick tended to slip down into the parge coat, even more so with Sarabond mortar than ordinary mortar. Where the flat portion occurred near the top of the dome, the parge coat actually became a 3-1/2″-thick mortar setting bed to keep the outside brick surface in a true hemispheric shape. The brick kept sliding down into the setting bed and, even though the mix of the mortar was changed so that it would set up more quickly, the bricks simply would not hold their positions. Hence, the dome has some slight flat areas near the top, however, they are almost undetectable except to a trained eye.

Shell Performance

At this writing, the masonry work on the dome shell is virtually completed. (Figure 45-4) The small walls on either side of the door openings have not yet been installed, but the work is finished enough to evaluate the result. The general appearance of the dome is highly satisfactory. The glazed surface provides a certain amount of light reflection and gives some depth to the dome shape. The contractor is having difficulty cleaning the Sarabond mortar off the glazed brick; however, we think this is a temporary problem. The workmen were very conscientious in placing the brick; header joints were deliberately placed so that they did not fall over a head joint on the course below; the coursing is nearly horizontal all the way up, certainly within limits of skilled workmen.

Our most drastic problem now is water. Our best laid plans notwithstanding, the dome leaks slightly. Minute scrutiniza-

Figure 45-4. Masonry nearly completed.

tion of the top surface fails to show any indication of a crack or pin hole yet enough water penetrates the surface to dampen the styrofoam on the top portion of the dome. The water does not drip or run, but there is enough to cause the plaster to lose its bond. The Dow Chemical Company is performing faithfully on its warranty, and we are presently starting corrective measures which are still in the experimental class. Our first effort will be to introduce some cementitious material into the joints near the top. If this fails, we might apply Dow silicones over the entire dome. As a last resort we will remove the top and rebuild it.

If we ever have occasion to do another dome of this nature, we would make some slight change in the foundation floating assembly, increase the tension angle to at least a 3-1/2" x 3-1/2" x 1/4" angle, and, when we reach the top of the dome, there would have to be some change in the method of installing the brickwork. The costs of the masonry work were much as the contractor anticipated them, until the surface became very nearly horizontal and the brick kept slipping into the mortar. At this point, his costs became excessive, and it would behoove the designer of the next project to make some correction in this regard. There may be some merit to precasting the brick cap to the exact size of the cap of the dome, and then merely lifting it in place and grouting it in place on top of the other brickwork.

The real key to the success of this type of construction is the mason. He must be a highly skilled, responsible craftsman with pride in his work. With some 35,000 brick on this size dome, there are some 35,000 opportunities for a leak, which means an exceptionally high proficiency level is required from the mason.

References

1. "Spiral Generation," Dow Chemical Company, Form No. 171-404A-10M-766
2. "High Bond Mortar Containing Sarabond," Dow Chemical Company, Form No. 171-361-5M-265.

46. Retaining wall for North Carolina's Death Valley.

M. R. Cochran, Brick & Tile Service, Inc., Greensboro, North Carolina

Design Considerations

Death Valley is the name newspapers have given a section of roadway on the southern edge of Greensboro, N. C., over which the merging traffic of I-85, I-40, U.S. 70, U.S. 29, travels with intersecting traffic to and from U.S. 421 and U.S. 220. The ominous title was earned by a mounting death toll which also prompted a crash program to increase the grossly inadequate four-lane system to a six-lane system.

The feat was accomplished under such handicaps as utilizing the same basic right-of-way and keeping it open to traffic with no deterrent other than reduced speed. But, the loss of 15 feet of sorely needed width posed one more obstacle which made possible this chapter about a reinforced brick masonry cantilever-type retaining wall.

The problem arose when the roadway passed a long-existent industry in the chemical field with large acid tanks directly in the path of the planned roadway. For all practical purposes, they could neither be moved nor by-passed; the only solution was to squeeze the right of way by "stealing" 15 feet away on one side and build an earth-retention structure to protect the foundations and to preserve structural integrity of the acid tanks.

Ordinarily, the selection of materials for a retaining wall would involve, other than engineering soundness, no more than two considerations: economy and/or aesthetics. But here the current problem deviates from the ordinary. Any aesthetic superiority which ordinarily might be claimed for brick never came into contention because of other serious implications.

First, there was the big problem of acid resistance; even the underground piping near the acid tanks had to be of clay, so inertness to chemical reaction pointed to brick here.

Next on the list of considerations was that of getting the job done under adverse conditions. Here brick construction seemed to have the edge because deliveries could be made in small increments or large, as desired, and at any time. On the other hand, it would have been awkward, to say the least, to schedule ready-mix concrete trucks; and there was almost no room for batching plant plus hoisting and pouring equipment. One last point favoring the decision for brick was that such

Table 46-1
Review of Projects Containing Alternate Bids

Project	Reinforced Brick Masonry	Reinforced Concrete Unit Bid Price
A	$ 50/C.Y.	$ 60/C.Y.
B	54/C.Y.	65/C.Y.
C	72/C.Y.	65/C.Y.
D	70/C.Y.	70/C.Y.
E	55/C.Y.	100/C.Y.
F	61/C.Y.	80/C.Y.
G	100/C.Y.	110/C.Y.

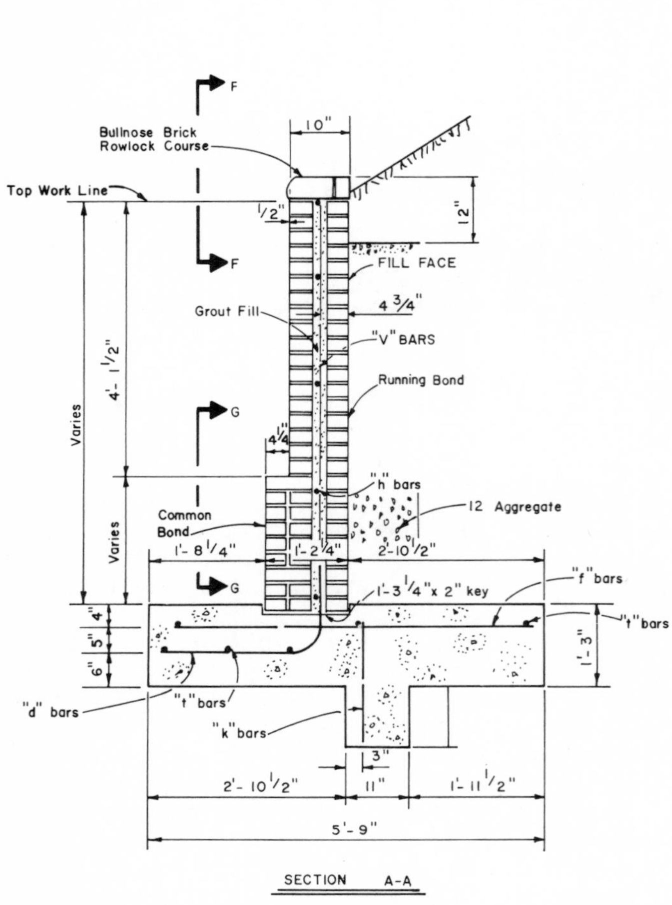

Figure 46-1. Typical wall section.

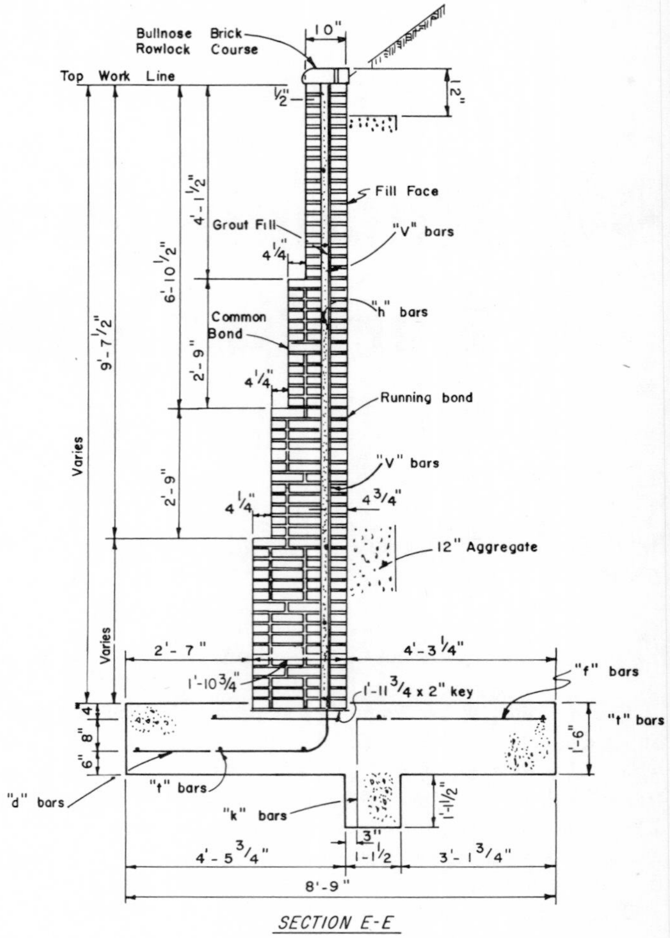

Figure 46-2. Typical wall section.

structures can be built practically on the property line with no space required for building, bracing, and stripping forms.

Economics

The last key point was economics. Cost of the structure is higher than would be expected under less strenuous circumstances. However, a review of many projects on which bids were taken on an alternate basis show that reinforced brick masonry structures are competitive with, if not cheaper than, similar items of reinforced concrete. Table 46-1 shows a sample of this study.

Having ascertained that reinforced brick masonry is competitive with other structural materials, highway engineers started their design with the system that satisfied all major project requirements.

Design

The decision to use a cantilever-type wall was readily agreed on since the restricted right-of-way area made it imperative to place the wall as close to the acid tanks as possible and to keep the stem to minimum thickness.

Our subject wall used basic principles incorporated in the Standard Design Sheets of the North Carolina Highway Commission but, since more stringent surcharge loadings were necessary to accomodate the acid tanks, a special design was prepared. Figures 46-1 and 46-2 show typical wall sections.

Price for reinforced brick masonry includes grout and grouting and approximately 120 cu. yds. of backfill aggregate, in place.

Masonry labor was handled under a subcontract for approximately $55 per M brick.

47. Seismic resistant reinforced masonry naval barracks.

Walter L. Dickey, Masonry Research, Los Angeles, California

Introduction

In 1962 the firm of Deems, Lewis, Martin & Associates-Architects, San Diego, were commissioned by the U.S. Navy to prepare studies for a 584 Enlisted Mens Barracks. The Navy design criteria required a permanent and sailor-proof construction with minimum maintenance and weathering, all to be within strict, preconceived, economic guidelines.

The architect is critically concerned with determining building materials and their suitability to solve a combination of specific design criteria. Generally, this design criteria will include normal structural properties; construction flexibility; wearing and maintenance characteristics; appearance factors such as color, texture, shape; and the all important economic reality.

Masonry was selected because masonry construction, with its many potential adaptations and variations, offers the architect the widest range of any of the basic materials for solution of a client's problem. Obviously, masonry will not solve all construction problems best, but with studied application and careful installation, masonry is a stimulating and satisfying design material that has historically challenged the architect's creativity and sensitivity.

This building project, designed for a specific masonry application, may partially illustrate this ancient material's wide design latitudes.

After studying various types and systems, the selection was the masonry bearing wall and precast concrete floor slab structural system, and no frame!

This structural system was chosen because of several advantages. First, by the repetitive use of similar and identical precast concrete floor slabs, in lieu of poured-in-place concrete slabs, there was a considerable savings in cost and a greatly improved appearance and tolerance obtained. This system required, for economy, that the walls of each four-man room provide structural support to the edges of the slabs above and that walls be used to house vertical and some horizontal chases for the electricity, T. V., and telephone, because of the difficulty of running these facilities within the precast slabs.

For the interior, 8″ walls were chosen of standard grouted concrete block. With the precast slabs bearing 2″ on each side, there was left in the center a 3-1/2″ clear space for reinforcing and for electrical and telephone conduit between floors. These interior block walls, painted eggshell enamel for housekeeping purposes and color accents, were otherwise left exposed. Some of the bearing walls consisted of a wythe of brick and a wythe of structural clay tile with a grout space to form a composite wall.[6]

The exterior walls were developed about Norman-sized clay structural brick units, which is one technique allowing a permanent, deep color selection. Color was critical because the Navy definitives leave all exterior concrete or masonry to weather. Concrete turns dark and splotchy next to the dampness of the ocean, and the overall effect of several of these existing buildings becomes rather drab and depressing.

The architects worked closely with Gladding McBean and Company in developing a deep, variegated blue glaze, which on close visual examination appears composed of small multihued crystalized particles. Being an unstable glaze, each brick unit automatically varied in tone and shading with a most distinctive and natural overall effect, both from a distance and from close scrutiny. The glazed unit also provides a self-cleaning quality, and after many years will still appear fresh and sparkling.

The exterior color pallet of this project thus becomes a multitone of blue masonry panels with dark grey mortar, light grey concrete, grey window glass, and aluminum sash.

The architects made a most interesting discovery in happening on a color photograph of the ancient Ishtar Gate which from 605 to 562 BC formed one of the principal entrances to Nebuchadnezzar II capital, Babylon. "The Ishtar Gate was the starting of processions, which assembled in front of it, marched through the triumphal arch and proceeded along the sacred way." The Ishtar gateway and walls were constructed of variegated blue glazed brick which appear to be identical with the glaze which was developed for this project 2500 years later.

In this structure, as in the older one, the finish is integrated into the construction as a portion of the structure, that is, it is performing a dual function, architectural finish and structural support as a homogeneous structural element.

The System

The system of construction was worked out carefully by close collaboration and cooperation between the architects and their structural engineer, Mr. Al Blaylock. Mr. Blaylock has designed several buildings in this system. He was one of the first in that area to recognize the inherent advantages of this system, particularly in an earthquake area. This recognition is in line with his earlier recognition of some dramatically shaped structures to solve unusual architectural problems. The system, which is a good example of masonry load-bearing multistory construction, consists essentially of the following:

1. The exterior walls, blue glazed brick for the exterior wythes and red clay brick for the interior wythes, form the two wythes of reinforced grouted walls, which are one story high. This makes a very efficient situation for use of the high-lift grout method, which increases the quality and economy of the system. With this method, the walls can be built a story height without reinforcing in the way, then the reinforcing can be put in, and the walls grouted.

2. Cross walls and corridor partitions were of concrete block to provide greater facility for mechanical installations, and also since the local prices for those walls were less in block than in brick. These also can be constructed economically by using the high-lift grouting method.[2,7,8]

One procedure is to build the walls the one story height, place the floor slabs in position, place the reinforcing steel, and then grout. This is an economical construction method since the walls can be built economically without the steel interfering with the mason's work. By placing the reinforcing after the slabs are placed, the bar provides in one piece the reinforcing and the dowel projecting above the floor. By installing these after the slabs are placed, they are not in the way to interfere with the positioning of the floor slabs. However, this requires that the crane operation be well controlled; the weight of a slab could knock over an ungrouted wall. Some constructors prefer to grout to near the top and add dowels after slab placement.

3. Slabs were designed to take advantage of the precasting technique. For example, as many as possible were made identical so that they could be cast in piles by just moving the side form up. Precasting in this manner saves costly deck forming and shoring, and merely requires perimeter or edge forms for the slabs. Then, by providing a smooth cement finish, the top of a slab also provides the ceiling finish for the next slab. These slabs were made to span one room so that there would be no joints in the rooms and so they would receive support all around the perimeter.

In general, as little as possible variation was made to the edges. There were keys put in the edges and, in a few instances, there were some bars projecting from the slabs. In general, this was for cases in which the lower bearing partition was to be eliminated from a certain area. The support for that slab edge at that line was provided by the wall above, and dowels were projected from the perimeter of the slab form at that edge and then upward to be developed by lap into the grout above. The wall above thus became a deep beam in function.[1]

4. Shear walls are provided by all the bearing walls. These walls will function as shear walls and hence are designed to resist the lateral loads. The total wall height will function as cantilevers above the foundation. Due to the low stresses involved, few critical design problems were introduced.

5. Deep Beam Design. Although deep beam calculations based on the Portland Cement Association bulletin[1] were used initially, simple and naive assumptions were used later because the stresses were so low this more refined and correct technique was not warranted.

The Portland Cement Association circular is a very good presentation of the stress considerations and is a good guide for study of this action.

Lateral Force Design

The scheme used was the basic assumption summarized as follows:

1. Vertical loads are carried by the slabs as flat plates to the bearing walls.

2. The lateral forces acting normal to the walls were assumed as carried to top and bottom slabs assuming their action as simple spans rather than as plates which is considerably on the safe side.

3. Floor slabs span as diaphragms laterally to shear walls.

4. Shear walls function as cantilever shear walls above the foundation.

The basic assumptions and procedures followed were as per the *Uniform Building Code*[2]. The *Uniform Building Code* Requirements are based primarily on the "Recommended Lateral Forces Requirements" of the Structural Engineers Association[3] which are, in turn based on the recommendations of the Lateral Force Committee and the ASCE Separate 66.[4]

This ASCE report was developed and adopted in the San Francisco area during the time the author was president of the Structural Engineers Association. Hence, he was quite aware of the compromises involved in developing and presenting the items that had to be based on good judgement, without any basic simple theory that could be presented. However, because of that judgment, the principles for the general run of construction are very good. They are based on studied consideration of damage, with compromises between economy, safety, and experience. This emphasizes that less attention is to be directed to precise calculation than to valid schemes and principles.

Prism Testing

Although it was recognized that stresses would not be high in this structure, it was desired that the actual f'_m, or 28-day ultimate strength of the composite materials be determined.

Therefore, the prism testing method, as outlined in the *Uniform Building Code,* was followed to determine the value of these composite materials working together. The prisms were made approximately in the two-to-one height-to-thickness ratio, so there was no need for the h/d correction. This ratio correction is, incidentally, subject to some question and is being tested by several agencies to establish the proper factors. The prisms showed that the masonry assemblages developed capacities far in excess of those permitted by code limits and very far in excess of the needs imposed by this structural system.

Wall Design

The walls were designed to resist lateral loads, such as wind or seismic forces, acting at right angles to the wall plane involved, considering the simultaneous vertical loads, that is, the problem of combining bending and direct stress.

Superficially this might be a complicated problem; however, we must recognize that the walls were designed with considerably more than minimum steel and were subject to compression stress. Also, they are relatively short in the vertical span of bending, from floor to floor. Therefore, the bending moment which might cause tension on one face and the necessary consequent assumption of a cracked section that would complicate the design will generally not occur and, of course, did not occur in this particular project.

A check was made of the upper story wall carrying roof only, to confirm that the tension effect caused by wind would not overcome the compressive value contributed by the P/A, the direct stress. It seems paradoxical the upper stories might need more reinforcing than the lower! The designers primary concern regarding bending and direct stress is essentially due to the function of the wall as a cantilever in the direction of its plane.

Details

The details in this scheme may have as great an impact on the cost and effectiveness of this system as would a design item and, therefore, must be carefully considered.

Many of the details and connections in this project were similar to conventional construction and would not warrant special discussion. However, some are discussed to indicate the general type of assembly and construction.

Slabs

In general, they were simply designed, precast slabs supported at the edges as plates. There was a minimum of deviation in size and a minimum of steel projecting from the slab edges so that the forms were simple and repetitively used.

Keys were provided at the edges. These were intermittent to transfer shear in the direction or line of the edge and to provide vertical support. In some instances, the line of bearing walls from roof to ground floor was interrupted. Here, the floor slab was supported by tension dowels developed in the wall above rather than by bearing support on a wall below.

Construction

Even in the early stages of design, the designer considered those details that would make for easier construction. Such planning should be particularly helpful in multi-story bearing wall construction with its repetitious character. As one contractor stated, "You merely build a simple room and do it a lot of times." This project benefited from mass production as compared to custom construction. Some items necessary to achieve full efficiency and economy with this system are that:

1. The layout was repetitious. Experience shows that by the time the crews reached the second or third floor they were working at double their initial efficiency. The construction sequence finally approached the assembly-line fitting together of parts.
2. The load-bearing concept of high-rise construction differed from earlier procedures for building high-rise facilities, which required various trades or crews working intermittently, that is pulling on and off. However, in this bearing-wall concept a continuous type of operation was followed. There is less confusion because fewer crews are required and because trades work in a sequential manner, one following behind the other very closely. Finish work was not only minimized, but it started closely behind the structural work and continued right on through to the end of the project. Avoiding on-and-off crews resulted in intangible but definite advantages in training and costs.
3. Efficiency and economy were gained because the crews worked immediately on clean, dry, level floors and high scaffolding was practically eliminated as the building completion proceeded in assembly-line fashion.
4. The newer techniques of scheduling and critical path studies enabled the general contractor to work quite effectively. Some of the scheduling methods used included the bar graph, and the PERT diagram. In this manufacturing process type of construction, scheduling of pre-bid conferences was a big factor in efficiently using the crane on the job.
5. The precast roomsize slab was the method chosen. Many other successful jobs have been built using this method of precast concrete floor and roof slabs of the lift-on type. There were other floor systems considered, such as use of Tee's, channels, and prestressed plank, but the use of the precast roomsize slab proved to be the most satisfactory for this project. The area of the site was large enough for precasting beds and was suitable for crane access, except for one portion. There were some power lines adjacent which prohibited the transport of the panels by the crane. Therefore, they were loaded on trucks and moved a short distance to the site. This, incidentally, made a very efficient crane operation.

Placing the floor slabs on the masonry wall can be achieved in several ways. One method is to use precut posts to accept the roof slab load until the mortar bed has set. The mortar bed was spread on the top course of the block wall just before the slabs were set in place. The slabs settled into position and provided a good mortar joint, squeezing out the excess. In some places, some dry pack was placed in the bed joint, in lieu of mortar, after the slab had been put into place. Another method considered was use of a series of small mortar pads placed on top of the masonry wall before the slabs are to be set. These pads can be set accurately to proper level by instrument and receive the slabs as they are lowered into place. They can accept the load until the mortar bed that has been placed between the pad along the length of the wall sets. The masonry contractor soon realized that the work was repetitious and that a minimum of scaffolding was required.

Material handling was a challenge in this type construction and required close coordination between the masonry contractor and the general contractor. Experience indicated that it is helpful to get an exact count of the number of each type of unit required for each room and then to assemble these in room increments for delivery to the job and movement to the building, either by lift truck or crane. This counting and planning ahead saves a great deal of moving and rehandling of brick from one area to another and also reduces waiting time.

The accompanying Figure 47-1 shows a slab being lifted from the truck into place. The exterior faces of the blue brick bearing walls were covered with film to keep them clean during construction.

Figure 47-2 shows the interior partitions, supporting some of the room-sized slabs and ready to receive others. In this figure, note the intermittent keys in the slabs, bars projecting as dowels, and conduit in the block work.

Figure 47-3 shows the exterior of the barracks.

Figure 47-1. Slab being lifted from truck into place.

Figure 47-2. Interior partitions.

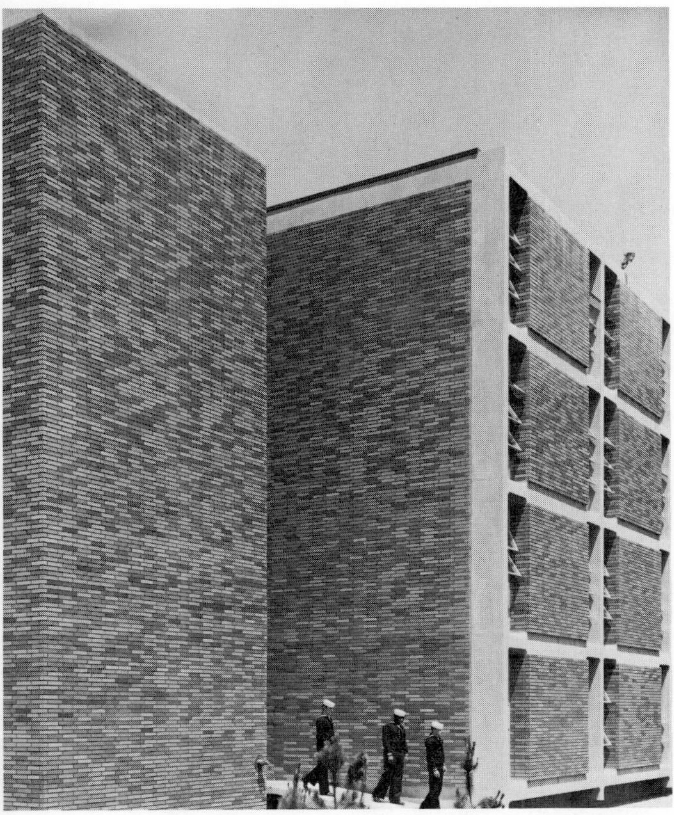

Figure 47-3. Exterior of barracks.

Conclusion

This project was chosen for discussion to emphasize that construction of smaller buildings, even in so-called earthquake areas, can be effective with the use of the masonry bearing-wall concept. Also this project utilized well, blue brick, red brick, concrete block, structural tile.

This project emphasized some advantages such as speed of construction, economy of construction, low maintenance factors, durability, versatility of masonry, and aesthetic attractiveness of masonry. The design, both vertical and horizontal is also advantageous because it is rather simple and conservative.

References

1. "Design of Deep Girders," ST66 Structural Bureau of Portland Cement Association, Nov. 1947.
2. *Uniform Building Code,* International Conference of Building Officials, 1967 Edition.
3. "Recommended Lateral Force Requirements," Structural Engineers Association of California, Revised 1966.
4. Joint Committee ASCE, SEAONC, "Lateral Forces of Earthquake and Wind," *ASCE Proceedings,* Separate No. 66, April 1951.
5. "Reinforced Load-Bearing Concrete Block Walls for Multistory Construction," Concrete Masonry Association of California.
6. ASTM designations C 126 and C 212.
7. Dickey, Walter L., "High Lift Grouting," *Masonry Industry Magazine,* March 1965.

Remarks

By Walter L. Dickey
Consulting Structural Engineer

There is another item that should have been emphasized more in the discussion of this paper (Chapter 47). Would you add the following to the discussion.

A comment is made "and that the trail to follow in the design of earthquake resistance structure was outlined." It must be emphasized again, as was stated in the paper (Chapter 47), that there are two basic specific fields in which earthquake consideration must be made. The first is in a general field which includes: considering the completeness of path of lateral force; recognizing that earthquakes induce forces due to inertia; recognizing that the forces of earthquake are much greater than two or five percent of gravity; proper consideration of tying together all of the elements; proper consideration of path distribution of force, and consideration of possible torsion.

These factors are probably the most important. However, the other field of considertion is that of assumptions and manipulations of numbers to arrive at the numerical values for economically compromised assumed forces for design.

Also, we must add a note of warning, even though we might suffer the torments of Cassandra in so doing. As you recall, she was blessed by the gods with a gift of being able to foretell events, however, she was cursed by the imposition of the condition that no one would believe her predictions.

In spite of this, we must emphasize that care should be exercised to make proper considerations in all buildings for the general factors of quakes, especially in high rise construction. This is primarily because the effects of failure of unreinforced masonry, i.e. brittle failures, in high rise construction could be so catastrophic, to the detriment of the image of the engineer throughout the whole world. Quakes can happen in almost any part of the world!

48. Park Mayfair East.

George C. Hanson, Sallada and Hanson, Denver, Colorado

The Park Mayfair East apartment building is one building in a three building complex using reinforced brick masonry bearing walls for the structural frame. The first apartment, Park Mayfair South, is 8 floors high, and the second, Park Mayfair North, is 9 floors high. The Park Mayfair East, the highest building in the complex, is 139 ft. 10 in. by 72 ft. 5 in. and has 17 floors, giving a total height of 164 ft. 6 in. This building contains 126 luxury-type apartments and has perimeter underground parking at the base of the tower.

Figure 48-1 is a view of the completed Park Mayfair East building. Main interior bearing walls are at center of building and at center of balconies.

Figure 48-1. Park Mayfair East.

Brick Masonry Assemblage Testing

Prior to designing Park Mayfair East, it was necessary to determine ultimate compressive strength of the brick masonry to be used in the design of the masonry walls. Due to the restrictive f'_m which is allowed to be assumed in most building codes, testing work was required to obtain the f'_m. Brick strength and absorbency vary from area to area, and it was necessary to perform prism tests on the brick masonry assemblage to determine the f'_m for the brick, mortar, and grout to be used in the building. The testing program for this project was sponsored by Region 12 of the Structural Clay Products Institute and was conducted by their staff under the direction of Mr. Donald Wakefield, Regional Director. To determine the strength of this assemblage, a test wall was built and allowed to cure. This wall was a double-wythe wall 12 in. wide, 2 ft. high, and 6 ft. long. The masonry for the test specimen was allowed to cure three days before the grout was poured. The grout was poured in two lifts with reconsolidation completed after about 45 minutes. After the wall was cured, prisms were cut from the wall by masonry saws. The dimensions of these prisms were approximately 4 in. wide by 12 in. long by 12 in. high. Additional prisms 8 in. high by 4 in. wide were cut in lengths of 12 in., 10 in. and 8 in. The average compressive strength of the brick was 12,600 psi. Ultimate compressive strength of the test assemblages varied from 4590 psi to 6200 psi. Although the minumum ultimate compressive break which occurred was 4590 psi, the maximum allowable f'_m which could be used and conform to the Uniform Building Code was 3500 psi.

Grout Composition Determination

The second test was to determine the proper cement content and slump to produce the best grout for the grout joint in the masonry wall. The 11-in. wall was built of two wythes 3 courses long stack bond and 13 courses high. The vertical mortar joints were raked deeply to within about one-half inch from the grout space to allow for easier cutting or breaking of the wall for inspection. These walls were built in two continuous rows of 14 prisms with wood dams placed between each prism.

Table 48-1

Cement Content	Slump	Ultimate Compressive Strength of Assemblage		Shear		Grout Test	
		No. of Prisms	Average	No. of Tests	Shear Value	No. of Prisms	Ultimate Compressive Strength
6	7½″			1	136 psi		
6	9″	4	6345 psi	2	402 psi		
6½	11″	16	6050 psi	4	210 psi	3	5130
7	7½″	5	6865 psi	3	280 psi	1	6400
7	9″	3	6950 psi	1	244 psi		
8	9″	4	6920 psi	3	556 psi		
8	9½″	5	6695 psi	2	463 psi	3	7045
8	10½″	3	6920 psi	4	282 psi	1	6830
8	11″	5	6235 psi	3	378 psi	1	5365

After the wall had cured, some units were broken to determine the bond of the grout to the brick and the percentage of voids in the grout. Visual inspection of the various prisms, comparing the grout in the grout void and the adherence to the masonry, did not indicate that a change in cement content or slump created very much difference in the knitting of the grout to the brick. The compression tests indicated that the 7-sack mix with about a 9 in. slump was as high in ultimate strength as any of the other mixes. The one closely approaching this one was an 8-sack mix, but it was not felt that the additional cement would be of any additional value in the grout.

The summary of tests on prisms cut from the walls for the grout test are tabulated in Table 48-1.

Testing During Construction

During construction, prisms were taken each 5,000 square feet of wall constructed. These prisms were then cured on the site and cut into units of such size that could be tested in a 300,000 pound compressive machine. The ultimate compressive strength of these prisms ranged from a low of about 4700 psi to a high of 6900 psi. Shear test conducted on the brick prisms varied in single shear from 246 psi to about 1150 psi; in double shear this varied from about 430 psi up to a value of 860 psi.

Design Loading

The design-floor live-load loadings for the building was 40 psf. live load for the apartment loading and upper floor corridors, 60 psf for balconies, 100 psf for first floor, and 30 psf for roof load. Horizontal loadings applied to the building were wind and seismic loading for Seismic Zone # 1. The wind loading was taken from the Uniform Building Code which requires 25 psf up to 30 ft., 30 psf from 30 ft. to 49 ft., 40 psf from 50 ft. to 99 ft. and 45 psf from 100 ft. to 499 ft. The seismic requirement was the requirement as specified in the Denver Building Code.

Foundation

The original foundation design was based on using the upper weathered bedrock above the Denver Formation for the bearing material to support the drilled-in caissons used to support this building. This weathered bedrock has a maximum end bearing pressure value of 15,000 psf and a side shear value of 1500 psf. The smallest diameter caisson used was a 12-in.-diameter caisson and the largest diameter was 48-in.-diameter caisson. These caissons had a variation in penetration, depending upon load, from the minimum penetration of 10 ft. to a maximum penetration of 28 ft. At the time of construction, the Denver Formation was found to be only a foot or two below the bottom of where the caissons would end, using the penetration for the caissons based upon the upper supporting value of the weathered shale. As a safety precaution, the caissons were then extended down to the blue shale of the Denver Formation. This formation has a capacity of a maximum end-bearing pressure of 120,000 psf and side shear of 6,000 psf. This then gave a much higher allowable bearing value for the caissons with only a few feet additional depth, and it was felt that this would be well worth the additional cost.

Reinforced concrete walls 12 in. thick extend from the top of the caisson just below the basement floor level, to the ground floor to support both the brick masonry bearing walls above the first floor level and the prestressed slab floor system of the first floor. These 12-in. concrete walls are reinforced to act as continuous beams spanning across the top of the caissons. In addition to the horizontal steel in these walls to give the beam action, vertical dowels are cast in the top of the wall at the same spacing as the vertical reinforcing steel which was placed in the reinforced brick masonry walls.

Reinforced Brick Masonry Bearing Walls

The main structural portion of Park Mayfair East, from the first floor to the roof, is composed of 11-in. reinforced brick

Figure 48-2. Laying masonry wall.

masonry bearing walls. These bearing walls support the twin-tee slabs of the floor system and resist the horizontal loading. The elevator walls and the stair walls are two different thicknesses of reinforced masonry bearing walls, one being 6-in. reinforced hollow-type utility brick and the other a combination of the 6-in. utility brick plus a standard brick, giving a 9-5/8-in-thick wall.

The 11-in. masonry wall was constructed of two wythes of brick with the center core filled with a high-slump grout. The horizontal reinforcing and the ties holding the two wythes together were laid with the masonry as the two wythes were laid up the full floor height. The horizontal steel consisted of two # 2 smooth rods which were laid in the horizontal mortar joints. These # 2 rods were placed each 5 courses or approximately 13 in. on centers. Additional horizontal reinforcing of two additional # 2 rods was placed in the first joint below the slab bearing. Ties consisting of # 2 rods bent in the shape of a U were laid in the joint directly above the joint which contained the # 2 horizontal rods. The U ties performed two functions. One function was to hold the two wythes of brick together to prevent bursting of the walls during the grout placement. The other purpose was to hold the vertical steel in alignment which was placed in the grout cavity prior to grouting the wall. The horizontal ties, which extend from wythe to wythe, were staggered horizontally so that alternate ties were on opposite sides of the vertical reinforcing. This placement of ties then provided vertical alignment for the main reinforcing.

Mortar and Grout

The mortar specified for the masonry walls was type S mortar and was mixed in the following ratio: 1:1/2:4-1/2. This would be one part Portland Cement, one-half part hydrated lime, and four and one-half parts sand. The grout mix for the grout space of the reinforced masonry bearing wall was 1:3:2. This would be one part Portland Cement, three parts sand and two parts pea gravel. Slump for this grout was approximately 7-1/2 to 9 in. No lime was allowed in the grout. This gave approximately a 6-1/2-sack-per-cubic-yard mix. High slump of the grout is required to allow the grout to more readily fill the grout void, to compensate for the absorbency of the brick bleeding water out of the grout mix, and to allow for easier pumping of the grout up to the working level.

Grout Space and Cleanouts

The void between the two wythes of brick, which is later to receive the concrete grout, must be kept free of mortar and droppings. One accepted practice for cleaning this void is to use a high-pressure water hose to wash the excess mortar off the brick before it sets up and to flush the droppings out of the bottom of the wall. In order to do this, it is necessary to provide cleanouts at the base of the wall which then will allow this excess mortar and the droppings to be washed down and flushed out through these cleanout holes. A second method, which was used extensively on this job, is a dry method. For this method, it is recommended that the masons lay the brick mortar joints with a 1/4-to 1/2-in. space back from the inside face of the brick and to clean the excess mortar off before it sets. In the dry method, cleanouts are also provided at the base of the wall; but, prior to starting the wall, a polyethelene sheet is placed in the void space to catch and to break the bond of any droppings which may fall to the base of the cleanout. An additional precaution to reduce the amount of droppings falling to the bottom of the wall is to place a board, the width

Figure 48-3. Cleanouts at base of exterior wall.

Figure 48-4. View from top showing slab leg bearing on masonry wall.

of the grout space, on the horizontal ties. This board will catch a great deal of the droppings and is raised to each successive placement of horizontal ties as the wall progresses upward. On completion of the wall and prior to pouring the grout, the base of the wall is cleaned by removing the polyethelene sheet and using compressed air to clean the remainder of droppings and foreign material out of the void space.

Figure 48-2 is a view of laying masonry wall. To the left of the picture on the far wythe is the mortar for the bed joint. Note the wedge shape of mortar bed. To insure full bed joints, the mortar bed must not be furrowed. The board between two wythes of brick catches most of the droppings and reduces the cleandown work.

Figure 48-3 shows the cleanouts at the base of an exterior wall. The cleanouts, as shown here, were raised to the sill of the window opening instead of being placed at the floor level. By placing the cleanouts at this level, it was possible to insure that the wall under the sill at the opening was completely full.

Prestressed Floor Slab Bearing

In the Park Mayfair East, the two wythes of brick were laid from the last completed floor level up to the bearing of the leg of the prestressed slabs. Neoprene bearing pads 1/8 in. thick were placed between the brick and the bottom of the slab leg to provide a uniform bearing on the masonry wall to prevent spalling due to point bearing of the slab leg on small variations of the bearing wall.

Figure 48-4 is a view from the top showing the slab leg bearing on the masonry wall before the wall is extended up to the floor slab level. Horizontal ties in the cavity are visible between the legs of the slab. Following the placement of the slab, the masons then continued with the two wythes of brick around the slab leg up to the top of the deck of the floor slabs on interior walls and to sill height on exterior walls. The grout space was then cleaned, and the vertical reinforcing placed.

Following this, the cleanouts at the base of the wall were closed, making the wall ready for the grouting operation.

Grouting of Wall

Grout was placed in the void between the two wythes of brick by using a grout pump. Placing the prestressed slabs and then bringing the wall up to the deck of the slabs gave the masons a surface on which to walk and work to perform the grouting operation. This was a distinct advantage over grouting the wall prior to placing the slabs. If the wall had been grouted prior to placing the slabs, it would have been necessary to build a scaffold, and the operator of the grout pump and the vibrators would have had to work off the scaffold. This would also have required the cleanouts for the next lift of wall to be placed below the floor instead of above the floor. It was estimated that working off the deck of the slabs probably cut the grouting operation by 50 percent. In the grouting operation, the first lift of grout was poured to a level about 4 ft. high in the wall and vibrated. Prior to placing the next lift of grout, the first lift was reconsolidated by a second vibration. The second lift of grout was placed and vibrated to consolidate with the first layer. The conditions of air temperature, humidity, and temperature of the brick at the time the grout was placed determined the waiting time between placement of the grout and the reconsolidation. On this building, the average time between placement and reconsolidation was from 20 to 30 minutes.

Figure 48-5 shows the grouting of the brick masonry walls. The grout hose is in the foreground with the 3/4-in. square head of the vibrator shown directly above the man's hand holding the grout hose. The reinforcing which ties the wall to the floor slab is shown on the top of the precast floor slab. Here it can be seen how the precast floor slabs provide a very good working surface for the grouting operation. This allows freedom of movement for the men performing the grouting operation and results in considerable saving in time and labor.

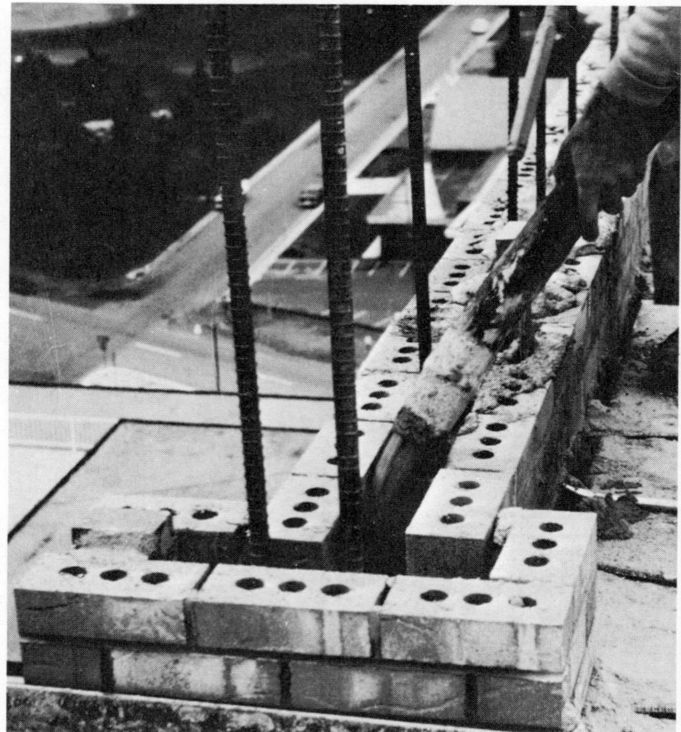

Figure 48-5. Grouting of brick masonry walls.

Winter Construction

Much of the construction was done during the winter; construction was discontinued for only two or three weeks due to a prolonged cold spell. Masonry was laid in temperature down to approximately 15 degrees above zero without any bad effects on the walls. The required curing temperature of the walls was maintained by using polyethelene covers and forced-air heaters and by heating the mortar ingredients prior to mixing and placing in the walls. During the colder weather, the walls had to be heated prior to placing the grout. This was done by using polyethelene sheets as covers and with heaters to force the warm air into the grout space and down through the wall to warm it to the proper temperature.

Floor Construction

The prestressed concrete slabs for the floor system of Park Mayfair East were 12-in. plus 2-in. double-tee slabs designed so that the 2-1/2-in. concrete topping would act composite with the slab for the live-load loading conditions. The rough finish given to the top of the prestressed slabs causes the topping to adhere to the slab and provides adequate bonding between slab and topping so that no separation occurs under applied load. To assure this action, the horizontal shearing forces are calculated to assure these stresses are not exceeded. The clear span of the floor slabs varied from 30 ft. 0 in. to 37 ft. 2 in. These spans allowed for large apartments without intermediate supporting partitions or bearing wall in the apartments. The twin-tee floor slab system served two purposes in this building: it developed a floor system to support vertical loads and transfer them to the walls, and it formed a diaphragm system which would transfer the horizontal wind loading and seismic loading to the wall system so the walls could act as a vertical cantilever beam to resist these horizontal loads.

The horizontal loads carried by the slabs were transmitted to the masonry bearing wall or shear wall through the action of the topping and also through the shear action developed by the legs of the slab anchored to the wall. The topping was anchored to the wall by #4 bars cast in the topping to give a transfer action from slab to wall. The legs of the slab were bricked into the wall so the vertical depth of the leg acted as a vertical bearing area bearing on the masonry walls to aid in the transmission of the horizontal loading to the wall. To obtain a better action of the horizontal shear steel which was placed in the topping, the bars were not placed at right angles to the wall but at a smaller angle to obtain anchorage in tension as well as bearing in the concrete topping. In the exterior walls, the bars were "L" bars bent down into the grout space and then extended out into the concrete topping. At the interior walls, where topping was on each side of the bearing wall, the bars were run through the wall and into the topping on either side of the wall to anchor the slabs and the topping to the wall. This anchorage of the wall to topping slab then gave continuity between the slab, the topping, and the reinforced brick masonry bearing wall. In this way, we had a very good composite action between the floor system and wall system.

Construction Time

Construction time on the lower floors of the building was six to seven days per floor. As the height of the building increased, the construction time also increased. The increase in time was occasioned by the additional time required to transport the construction materials to the upper floors and the additional time required to place the prestressed slabs at a higher level. Slab erection time on the lower floors was approximately one day; whereas on the upper floors this time increased to at least two days.

Definite Advantages and Savings

A distinct advantage of the reinforced brick masonry, in addition to those previously mentioned, is the sound control which can be developed by the walls. The walls in Park Mayfair East were planned so that they became the walls between apartments. The walls then practically eliminated all sound transmission between apartments and allowed for maximum privacy in the apartments.

The economy of this type of construction results from several advantages which are typical of masonry bearing wall. The structural frame of the building is also the closure walls for the building and is completed as the building progresses. In some areas, the masonry walls may be exposed without additional materials to give an attractive, maintenance-free wall with a minimum cost. If a dry-wall facing is desired, this may be placed by using a mastic adhesive in place of furring strips, which will save time and reduce cost. The rapid construction and ease of close-in of the building allows for more rapid completion and reduces cost by shorter construction loan time and more rapid occupancy.

Cost

The cost of Park Mayfair East was $12.25 per square ft. of floor area. This cost includes the entire building, the garage, appliances, drapes, furniture in public areas, and the landscaping of the grounds. The cost of the 11-in. bearing walls per square ft. of wall was as follows: unexposed wall $2.32 per square ft. and exposed face brick wall $2.82 per square ft. The cost of the structural system, which would include the masonry bearing walls, the prestressed T slabs, and the reinforcing and floor topping was $2.30 per square ft. of floor area of this building.

At the present writing, Park Mayfair East may be the tallest reinforced masonry bearing wall structure in the United States. However, I am sure that it will not keep this distinction very long. As the economies and advantages of this type of construction are recognized, an increase in this construction method will be noted.

Park Mayfair East was designed to resist stresses created in an area of classification of Seismic Zone 1. Since construction, many earth tremors of varying magnitude have occurred. On April 10, 1967, an earthquake occurred with a reading of 5.0 on the Richter Scale; on August 9, 1967 another shock with a reading of 5.5 on the Richter Scale shook the Denver area. These two were the most severe. Inspection of the building, following these tremors, did not show any damage or cracking in the structure.

49. Some load-bearing brick buildings in England.

B. A. Hazeltine, Jenkins, Potter, and Bingham, London, England

Load-bearing brickwork has been used in Great Britain for many years, but until recently its design has been based on rule of thumb methods. The resulting walls, usually using low-to-medium strength bricks, were heavy. In 1948, a Code of Practice was issued by the British Standards Institution setting out permissible stresses and rules of design, which enabled walls to be calculated and sized on the real loads coming down the building. In fact, very little advantage was taken of this code to design buildings for which brickwork was emminently suitable.

In the 1950's the favourite construction for multistorey blocks of flats was reinforced concrete, often clad in brickwork and with 9″ separating brick walls between dwellings. It was not realized at the time that, quite often, these walls alone were capable of carrying the building weight and the vertical reinforced concrete was unnecessary. Some calculated load-bearing structures were built, but these usually had 13-1/2″ walls, at least on the lower storeys, due to the relatively low stresses allowed under the 1948 code.

In the early 1960's, the Swiss were building high-rise calculated load-bearing structures, using very thin walls, made possible by an advanced Code of Practice, based on a considerable volume of storey-height wall testing carried out at the E.M.P.A. Laboratory. Engineers in England became interested in using brickwork and realized that cost savings could be made compared to reinforced concrete for flats and hostel types of buildings. At the same time the British Code of Practice was under review and the edition published in 1964[1] allowed considerably higher permissible stresses, and hence more slender walls than had previously been possible. Thus, the stage was set for a rapidly increasing awareness of the advantages of fully calculated load-bearing brickwork.

The author's firm, Jenkins and Potter, has been involved in numerous load-bearing brick schemes and has produced cost comparisons showing the economy of calculated load-bearing brickwork[2,3]. Two of the more interesting schemes are described in this chapter. They are:

1. Borough High Street, Southwark. Thirteen storeys plus lift motor room.
2. Hatfield Tower Block. Fifteen storeys.

New Bricks

The standard size brick generally available in Great Britain is 8-5/8″ x 4-1/8″ x 2-5/8″ (2-7/8″); this was used universally until four years ago. This standard brick is usually used in buildings to form two-skin, 11″ cavity external walls and 9″-solid internal load-bearing walls.

The range of brick strengths available is usually from 3,000 lb./sq. in. for the common fletton (a pressed brick made with a clay containing a high proportion of fuel) to 10,000 lb./sq.in. for a Class A engineering brick (using the crushing test specified in B.S. 3921[4]).With such a choice of brick strengths, the potential load-bearing capacity of a 9″-solid wall is greater than is normally required for the majority of high-rise blocks of flats or hostels, using the floor spans which are economical in this country.

One of the largest brick manufacturers in England recognised the need for a new brick size and, in conjunction with the author's firm, designed and marketed a 6-3/4″ wide x 8-5/8″ long x 2-5/8″ high brick in the range of strengths 5,000 lb./sq.in., 7,000 lb./sq.in., and 10,000 lb./sq.in. (the width has now been increased to 7″). These are shown in Figure 49-1. A stringent system of quality control is used in the works, and the product is aimed at the calculated load-bearing brickwork field, where it is used solely for single-leaf 7″ walls laid in stretcher bond. It is known as the Calculon.

Over a longer period, the Building Research Station, in conjunction with the same brick manufacturer, was developing a single brick for external use to replace the two-skin, 11″ cavity wall. This is known as the V-brick, Figure 49-2, and is used to form a 9″-wide hollow brick wall with a divided mortar bed. The external appearance of a V-brick wall is the same as that using regular, machine-made, sandfaced bricks. The V-brick has been fully described elsewhere[5]

Both of these new types of bricks have been used in the projects described in detail in this chapter.

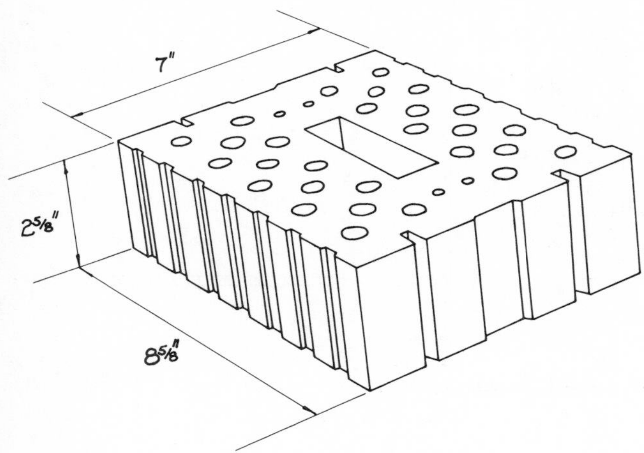

Figure 49-1. Calculon brick.

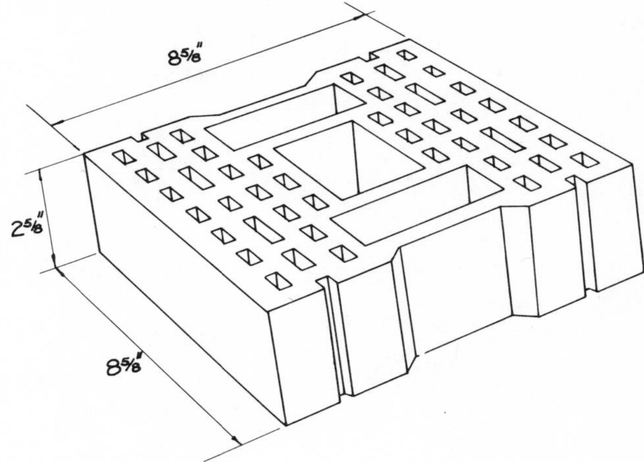

Figure 49-2. V-brick.

Borough High Street, Southwark

Client: Southwark Borough Council, now The London Borough of Southwark
Architect: Ronald Hardy Esq., M.B.E., B.Arch., A.R.I.B.A.
Consulting Engineers: Messrs. Jenkins and Potter
Contractor: William Willett (Contractors) Ltd.

The 2 acre site, which was mentioned in Dickensian stories, is in an old part of London just south of the River Thames. Part of the land was derelict after bomb damage, and the remainder was ready for redevelopment. There are 110 homes in the total scheme, and these are arranged in a long 5-storey block containing Old People's flats and maisonettes* and in the 13-storey block described herein. Unreinforced calculated load-bearing brickwork has been used throughout for the vertical structure. The client had previous experience of blocks of flats using a similar plan. One block had been built in reinforced concrete and another in load-bearing brickwork designed to the 1948 code, but some of the walls were 13-1/2" thick. Hopefully, when the final costs are available for all the schemes a sensible comparison of the economics of the different forms of construction can be made.

A plan of the Tall Block is shown in Figure 49-3. There are four 1-bedroom flats per floor, arranged symmetrically about the centre line. Access is from a common entrance hall served by twin lifts calling at alternate floors and there is a single staircase, mainly for escape purposes. Services rise in two main ducts from the basement boiler house to the lift motor room on the roof. The building is thus really 15-storeys high.

Structure

The foundations for the Tall Block bear on good Thames ballast 13 ft. below ground level. A 2 ft.-thick reinforced concrete raft spreads the load of the cross walls onto the ballast. All the walls in the basement are reinforced concrete, as the external ones are retaining 13 ft. of earth and the internal ones had to have large openings in them to accommodate boilers and heating plant.

The floors are 5"-thick in situ reinforced concrete flat slabs. It is not the author's practice to use precast floors for tall unreinforced load-bearing brickwork structures, as the plate action of an in situ floor is invaluable for stiffening the building against horizontal forces. When desired, a precast floor can probably be made to provide this plate action if an in situ topping is used, but in this case the layout would not have been economical for precasting.

A feature of this particular design is the slenderness of the load-bearing walls. Apart from two piers in the entrance hall area and a short length of external wall, all the internal structural walls are 6-3/4" thick, using Calculon bricks, and the external walls are 9"-wide sandfaced V-bricks laid in stretcher bond. The weatherproofing of the building is provided by the water resistance of these divided-joint, one-piece walls. The outcome of using such slender walls is that less than 8 percent of the gross floor area is taken up with structural walls, a very low proportion for such a building. A table of the strengths of brick used, together with the mortar mixes, is given in Table 49-1.

Design Basis

The purpose of a load-bearing wall is to

1. Transmit the live and dead loads vertically to the ground.
2. To provide sufficient stiffness to resist horizontal wind forces.

Thus, the method of design for the vertical load[1] is simply to calculate the total loads per foot run applied by the flooring and the self-weight of wall, and sum these for each floor level, in the same way as designing columns in reinforced concrete work. Walls carrying floors of unequal span, particularly external walls, can be said to be eccentrically loaded. However,

*A maisonette is a 2-storey apartment, just like a house, with lounge and kitchen on one floor and bedrooms on the next. It is stacked up to form a building of the height required.

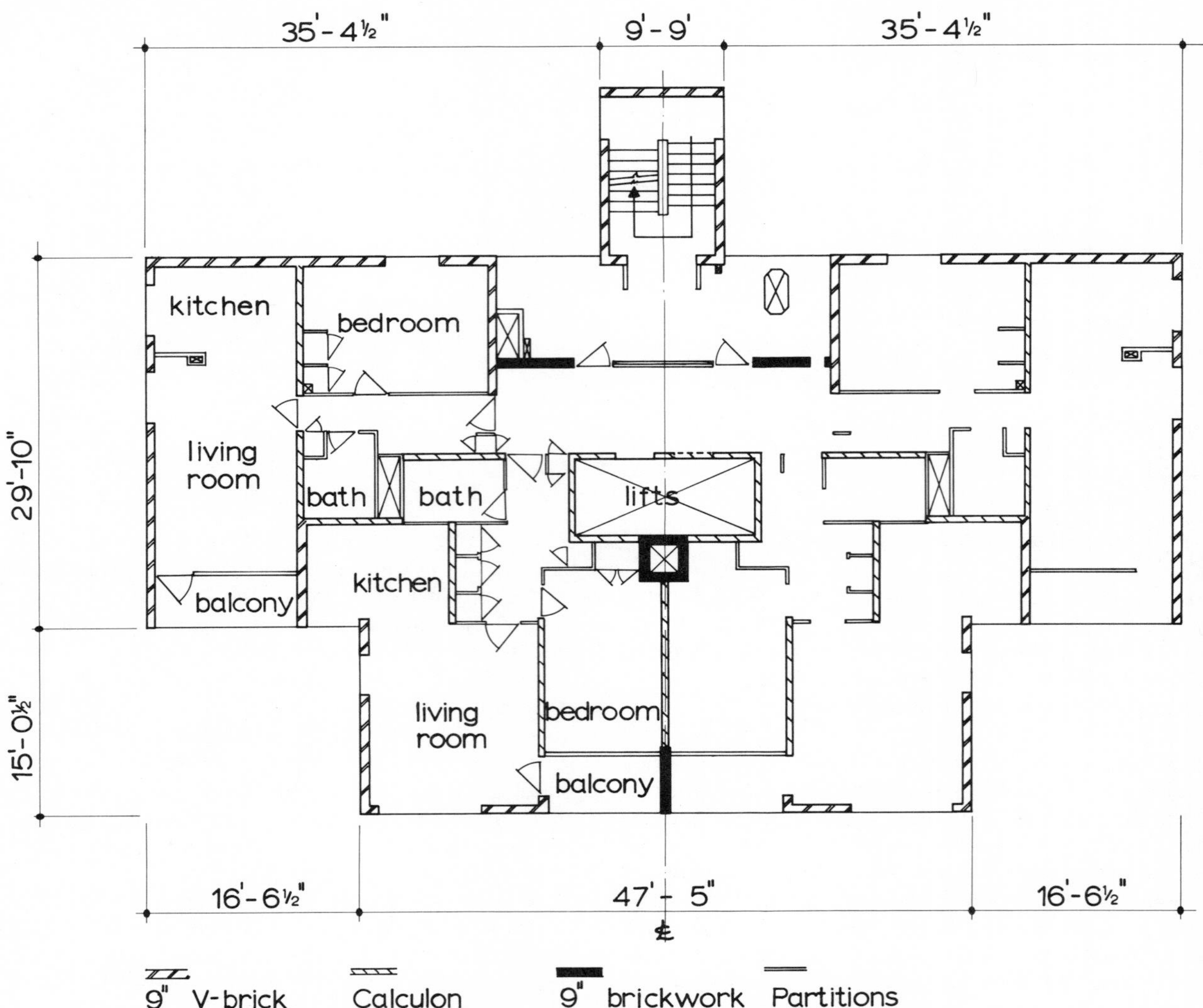

Figure 49-3. Plan of Borough High Street.

Table 49-1
Variation of Brick Strengths and Mortar Mix, Borough High Street

	Floor	Type of brick	Strength	Mortar
			lb./sq. in.	
External Walls	Ground-4th	V-Brick	6,000	1:¼:3
	4th-8th	V-Brick	5,000	1:¼:3
	8th-Roof	V-Brick	5,000	1:1:6
Internal Walls	Ground-3rd	6-3/4″ Calculon	10,000	1:¼:3
	3rd-6th	6-3/4″ Calculon	7,000	1:¼:3
	6th-8th	6-3/4″ Calculon	5,000	1:¼:3
	8th-Roof	6-3/4″ Calculon	5,000	1:1:6

if an effective eccentricity is calculated, making the usual assumption that eccentricities only apply on the floor being considered, then in the more critical lower parts of the building, the effect on the strength of brick required is negligible, especially as a 25 percent increase in permissible stress due solely to bending is allowed in the Code of Practice. Having arrived at a loading, it is simple to convert this into a brick strength and mortar mix by reference to the permissible stress and slenderness reduction factor tables in the Code of Practice, para. 3-4.

Wind Design.

The pressure to be used for the wind design, 14 lb./sq.ft. was obtained from the G.L.C. by-laws. This pressure is

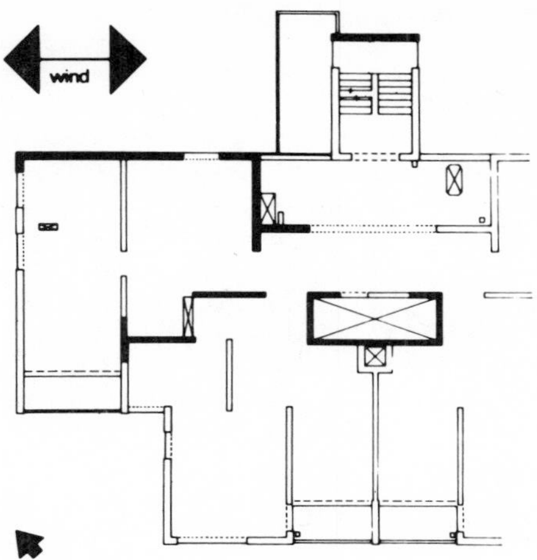

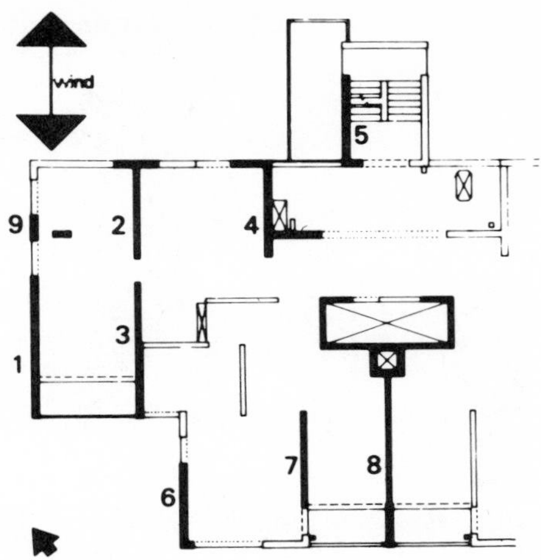

Figure 49-4. Wind wall layout, Borough High Street.

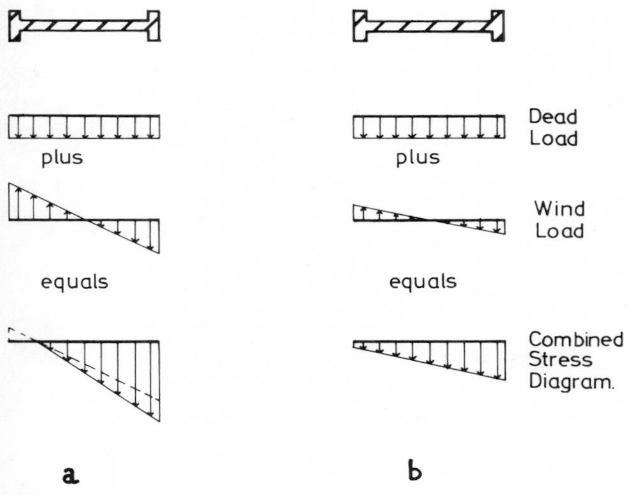

Figure 49-5. Stress diagram, with or without uplift.

assumed to act over the whole of the face being considered and is translated into a cantilever bending movement which must be resisted by the walls in the building. There are several ways of designing for this. The author prefers to calculate the second moments of areas (moments of inertia) of the walls or wall complexes assumed to resist wind, Figure 49-4, and to divide the total wind moment between the walls in proportion to their second moments of area. This is the normal method in England and assumes that the horizontal forces will distribute themselves to the stiffest members. Each individual wall is then designed to carry its share of the cantilever moment, together with the vertical load. It is clearly desirable, in an unreinforced wall, for the resultant stress diagram to have no tension (Figure 49-5b). However, in the East-West direction at Borough High Street, there was insufficient wall to prevent some theoretical uplift occurring at the end of some of the walls, so the stress block was adjusted to allow for the resulting increase in compression by ignoring the tensile triangle and making the area of the compression triangle equal to the total load on the wall. Only the end fifth of wall was allowed to have this theoretical uplift, to avoid difficulty under ultimate conditions (Figure 49-5a).

The 25 percent increase in stress due solely to wind or bending, mentioned earlier, is used in determining the final required brick strength shown in Table 49-1.

Typical Calculations

An extract of the calculations for wind moments on each wall or complex with wind blowing in one direction is given below, together with loads and a calculation for a typical wall (see Figure 49-4).

Live loads obtained from CP. 3, Chapter V[6] Design in accordance with CP 111 (1964)[1].

Roof Loads. 5 in. RC. slab + screed and finishes
Dead Load = 90 lb./sq.ft.
Live load, 30 lb./sq.ft. reduced by (up to) 40 percent
for building being over 5-storeys high = 20 lb./sq.ft.
Total roof load = 110 lb./sq.ft.

Floor Load. 5 in. RC. slab + 2 in screed and finishes
Dead Load = 90 lb./sq.ft.
Live load, 40 lb./sq.ft., allowing 40% reduction but
including partition allowance = 40 lb./sq.ft.
Total floor load = 130 lb./sq. ft.

Weight of Brickwork. The weight of the brickwork is:
Calculon wall (plastered both sides) = 75 lb./sq.ft.
V-brick wall (plastered one side) = 75 lb./sq.ft.

Load Capacity of Brickwork. The load capacity of the brickwork is:

V-brick (external walling): Storey height 8 ft. 8 in., effective thickness 9″ giving—Slenderness ratio =

$$\frac{(8.67 \times 12) \times 0.75}{9} = 8.67$$

Reduction factor for concentric loading (CP111 : 1964) = 0.89.

Permissible stresses:
6,000 lb./sq.in. bricks 1:1:6 mortar = 305 lb./sq.in.
6,000 lb./sq.in. bricks 1:1/4:3 mortar = 420 lb./sq.in.

Permissible loads per ft. run of V-brick wall with 6,000/lb./sq.in. bricks:

1:1:6 mortar = 305 x 12 x 9 x 0.89 = 29,300 lb./ft.rn.
1:1/4:3 mortar = 420 x 12 x 9 x 0.89 = 40,400 lb./ft.rn.

6-3/4 Calculon (internal walling): Storey height 8 ft. 8 in. effective thickness 6.75 giving–Slenderness ratio =

$$\frac{(8.67 \times 12) \times 0.75}{6.75} = 11.55$$

Reduction factor = 0.78

Permissible stresses (p) and permissible loads (P) calculated as above:

5,000 lb./sq.in. bricks
1:1:6 mortar p = 270 lb./sq.in. P = 16,800 lb./ft.rn.
1:¼:3 mortar p = 360 lb./sq.in. P = 22,500 lb./ft.rn.
7,000 lb./sq.in. bricks
1:¼:3 mortar p = 480 lb./sq.in. P = 30,000 lb./ft.rn.
10,000 lb./sq.in. bricks
1:¼:3 mortar p = 660 lb./sq.in. P = 41,000 lb./ft.rn.

Wind Calculations. The total height of the building is 113 ft. Using G.L.C. Regulations:

Table 49-3, wind pressure P = 14 lb./sq.ft.
Area of long face of building = 80 x 113 = 9,050 sq.ft.
Area of Tank Room = 50 x 9 = 450 sq.ft.
Cantilever wind moment with wind on the long face

$$= 14\left[\left(\frac{113}{2}\text{ft.}\right) \times 9050 + 117 \text{ ft.} \times 450\right] = 7{,}895{,}650 \text{ lb. ft.}$$

As described, the wind moment is distributed between the walls in proportion to their second moment of area. Where walls form complex sections that are stronger than a single wall, the additional strength is taken into account. Small walls having a low I are ignored as they will receive an insignificant proportion of the moment. The computation of the I's of all the shapes shown in the plan is too lengthy to be repeated here, but totals for the wind in the long direction (see plan) are provided in the following table, Table 49-2. In this direction, the building is symmetrical about the centre line.

Design of Calculon Wall No. 7. The design of this wall is:

Length of wall = 11.25 ft I = 69 ft.^{4}

Table 49-2

Wall No.	No. off	Total I (ft^4)	Moment proportional to Is (lb. ft.)	Moment on wall (lb. ft.)
1.	2	560	1.09×10^6	0.54×10^6
2.	2	260	0.50×10^6	0.25×10^6
3.	2	430	0.83×10^6	0.42×10^6
4.	2	429	0.83×10^6	0.42×10^6
5.	2	194	0.38×10^6	0.19×10^6
6.	2	123	0.24×10^6	0.12×10^6
7.	2	138	0.27×10^6	0.13×10^6
8.	1	1901	3.71×10^6	3.71×10^6
		4035	7.85×10^6	

Wind moment from table above = 0.13×10^6 lb. ft.
Span of floor on wall = 11.5 ft.
∴ load per foot run from each floor = 11.5 x 130 = 1,495 lb. (1,035 lb. ex live load)

Reactions from beams in slab bearing on end wall (see Figure 49-6) 28 sq. ft. of floor at leeward end = 46,700 lb. at just below 1st floor level. 17 sq. ft. of floor at windward end = 20,000 lb. at just below 1st floor level.

When taking into account wind on a wall, the uplift at one end can be as critical as the compression at the other. Therefore, one should take live load plus dead load at leeward end, but dead load only at the windward end. Then, uniform load at ground floor level:

with live load = 1,265 + 12 x 1,495 + 113 x 75
= 27,600 lb./ft.
without live load = 1,035 x 13 + 113 x 75
= 21,900 lb./ft.

Taking moments about centre of gravity of wall for loads on Figure 49-6:

$$46{,}700 \times \frac{11.25}{2} - 20{,}000 \times \frac{11.25}{2} + 27{,}600 \times \frac{11.25^2}{8}$$

$$- 21{,}900 \times \frac{11.25^2}{8} + 113{,}000 = 352{,}500 \text{ lb.ft.} = M.$$

Total vertical load

$$= 46{,}700 + 20{,}000 + 27{,}600 \times \frac{11.25}{2} + 21{,}900 \times \frac{11.25}{2}$$

= 345,200 lb = W.

Then stresses at ends of wall = $\frac{W}{A} \pm \frac{M}{Z}$ where $Z = \frac{I}{L/2}$

$$\text{Thus stress: } = \frac{345{,}200}{11.25 \times 0.58} \pm \frac{352{,}500}{69} \times \frac{11.25}{2}$$

= 53,000 ± 28,700

= 81,700 and 24,300 lb./sq.ft.

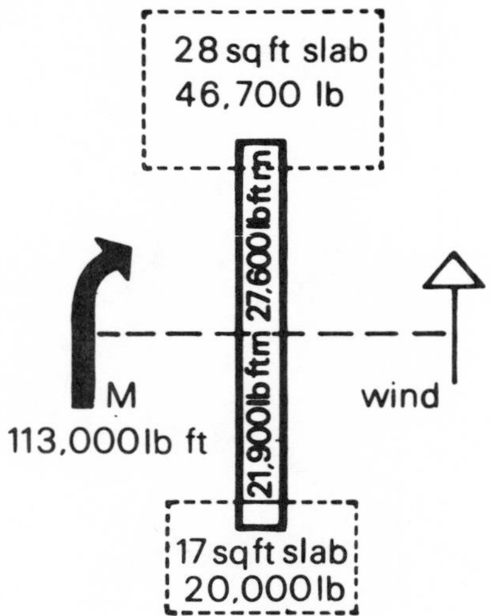

Figure 49-6. Loading diagram, wall 7.

or:

47,300 and 14,200 lb./ft.rn.

The permissible load on 10,000 lb./sq.in. Calculon bricks using 1:¼:3 mortar = 41,000 lb./ft.rn. + 10,250 lb./ft.rn. (25 percent wind allowance) = 51,250 lb./ft.rn. This is the strength to use carried to Table 49-1. By checking the stresses at other levels, and with reference to the permissible loads above, the brick strengths throughout the height of the building are obtained. With wind blowing on the short side, the resisting walls are not symmetrical about the centre line. In a building with in situ concrete floors, it is problematical what effect this has on stresses, but in this case no account has been taken of composite action and this was regarded as a sufficient safeguard of overstress due to possible torsion.

Site Work

The problems relating to work on site are common to both jobs described here, and the section, Specification and Site Work, is devoted to this. A photograph of the nearly completed structures is shown in Figure 49-7.

Figure 49-7. Borough High Street under construction.

Hatfield Tower Block

Client: Commission for New Towns, Hatfield Local Committee.
Architect: Messrs. Woodroffe, Buchanan & Coulter.
Consulting Engineers: Messrs. Jenkins and Potter.
Contractor: H. Fairweather Ltd.

Hatfield is one of the new towns being developed around London, and the site is an island area on the French Horn Lane housing estate. The surrounding development is two and three storey houses. Apart from 2-storey garages for tenants use, the contract is for the construction of one 15-storey block of flats. The vertical structure is entirely unreinforced calculated load-bearing brickwork.

A plan of the block is shown in Figure 49-8. There are three wings grouped around a central access and circulation area which contains two lifts and an escape staircase. On each floor, there is a one-bedroom flat and a bed-sitting room flat in each wing, except for the top two storeys where there are two maisonettes per wing. Thus there are 78 housing units in the block, the ground floor being taken up with tenants stores, electrical and water services. By having a maisonette on the top two storeys, the lift does not call above the 13th floor and the lift motor room is housed on the 14th floor, avoiding the need for a separate motor room on the roof.

Structure

The foundations consists of a 2 ft.-thick reinforced concrete raft bearing on very firm clay, containing stones and small pebbles, having a bearing capacity of 2-1/2T/sq.ft., at a depth of 4 ft.6in. The space between the load-bearing walls

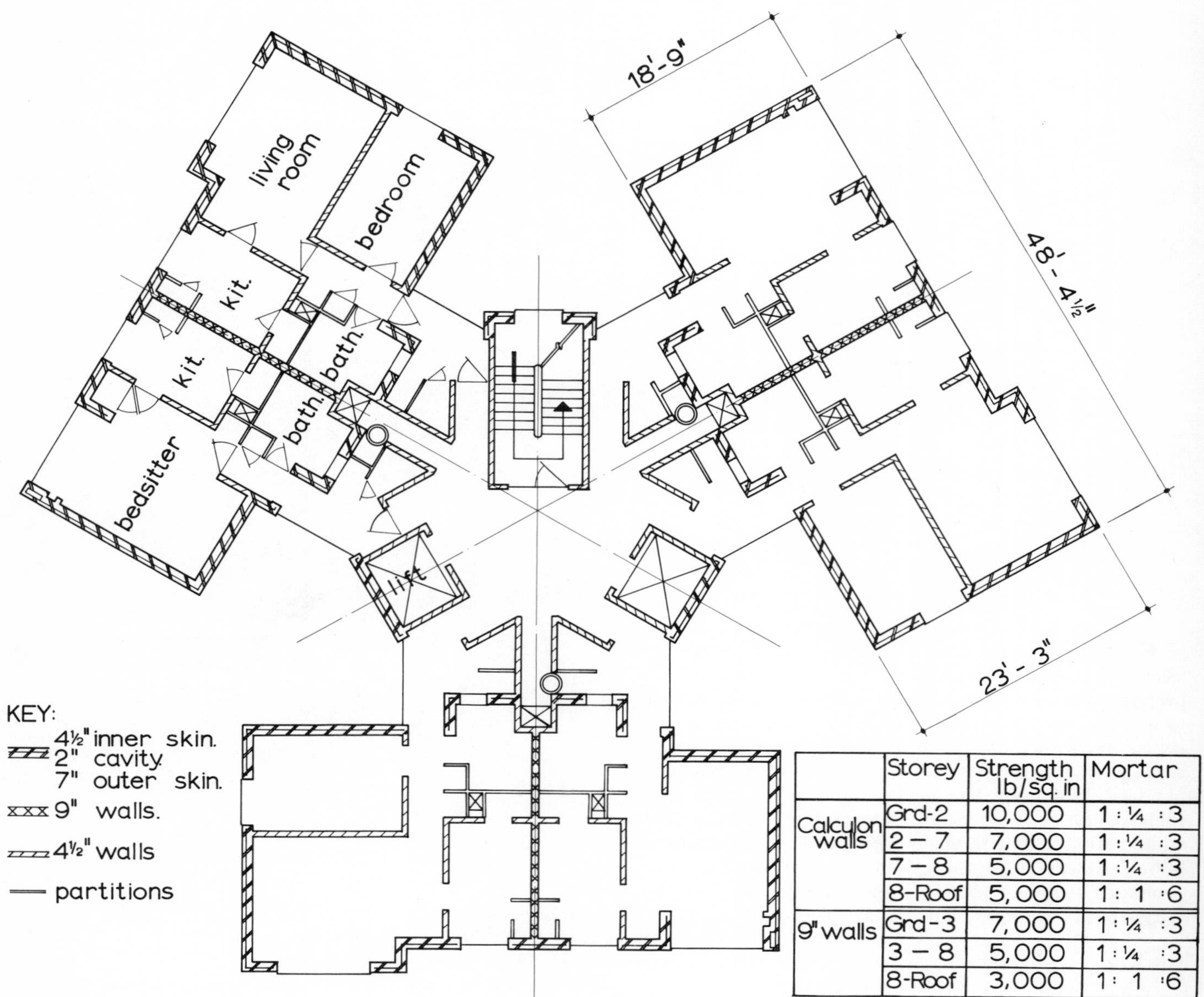

Figure 49-8. Plan of Hatfield block.

and from the raft top to ground floor slab was filled with surplus unconsolidated earth on which a reinforced ground floor slab was constructed.

The upper floors are 5-1/2"-thick in situ reinforced concrete slabs, spanning, in some cases, in two directions. As at Borough High Street, precast floors would not have been practicable even if they had been desirable structurally. However, some of the stiffening beams were precast and the contractor was allowed to precast edge segments of floor, Figure 49-9, bridging the outer cavity, to avoid the need for awkward edge shuttering, and to minimise concrete spillage down the face brickwork.

Table 49-3

	Floor	Strength lb./sq. in.	Mortar
Calculon Walls	Gd. to 2nd.	10,000	1:¼:3
	2nd to 7th	7,000	1:¼:3
	7th to 8th	5,000	1:¼:3
	8th to Roof	5,000	1:1:6
9 in. Walls	Gd. to 3rd	7,000	1:¼:3
	3rd to 8th	5,000	1:¼:3
	8th to Roof	3,000	1:1:6

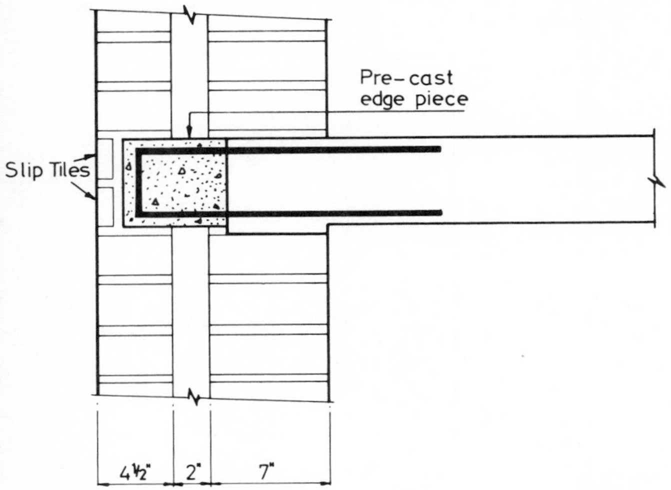

Figure 49-9. Precast edge segments.

The extra two storeys over the height of Borough High Street, together with the rather less sympathetic layout, ruled out the use of V-bricks for the external walls. Normal 11" cavity walls were also not strong enough. The external walls are, therefore, formed of 4-1/2" facing bricks, 2" cavity and 7" Calculon inner skins. The floors pass over the cavity onto the outer skin, but the outer skin has not been taken into account in calculating the strength of brick required. Brick slips are used to cover the edge of the concrete floor as the architect wanted a clear elevation of brickwork. The internal load-bearing walls are generally 7" Calculon, but the spine wall between flats is 9" thick to provide a greater wind stiffening effect. The strengths of bricks used together with the mortar mixes are shown in Table 49-3.

Design Basis

The basic method of design for this block follows that of Borough High Street (Design Basis), and the two design principles still apply. Concentrated loads arising from lintels and beams are assumed to spread out at about 60° to the horizontal until they become uniformly distributed loads on any given wall length. Most of the small eccentricities arising from loads coming onto piers at places other than the centroid can be assumed to be taken up by the stiffening walls at right angles helped by the plate action of floors.

Wind Design

The pressure to be used for the wind calculations was taken from the relevant Code of Practice CP.3. Chapter V[6] for a 1 minute mean wind speed of 63 m.p.h. giving a pressure over the whole face of the building of 20 lb./sq.ft. The overall cantilever moment on each individual wing acting as a whole was calculated. This is clearly on the safe side, for, taking the building as a whole, the other two wings will act together with the one being considered, although there will be a relatively small increase in elevational area and hence overturning moment.

The number of wind walls available in the building, Figure 49-10, gave rise to excessive uplift when distributing the wind moment between individual walls or wall complexes in proportion to their second moments of area, so consideration was given to making use of the composite interaction of sets of walls linked by beams and the floor slab. The overall moment was divided between the linked complexes in proportion to their overall second moments of area, and compression and tensile forces calculated in the usual way. The tension on the longer linked walls was always offset by dead loads, and it was not necessary to allow any uplift as had been the case for Borough High Street.

To calculate the forces in the linking beams the normal formula for horizontal shear in beams was used. The vertical shear obtained from this was applied to the beams ends and reinforcement provided accordingly. It was these linking beams, usually over small door openings, which were precast by the contractor.

Specification and Site Work

Building with bricks and mortar is a familiar trade, practised in Britain for hundreds of years. However, in the past, stresses in walls were always small, and the quality of workmanship was largely directed at producing attractive and permanent facework. Internal walls built in common bricks were usually laid very roughly in order to get a good plaster key. When brickwork was considered for highly stressed work, it was necessary to draw up a much more stringent specification than that previously used. The specification used for Borough High Street and Hatfield covered all the aspects of testing and workmanship, and was used as the basis for a model brickwork specification now published in England by the British Ceramic Research Association[7].

When Borough High Street was being designed it was usual to specify mortar by mix only, e.g. 1:¼:3. It was decided, for such an important job, to introduce a minimum strength as well. There was very little information available on what strengths were expected from the nominal mixes by those who drew up the Code of Practice, but in the end the strengths in Table 49-4 were adopted. There is now much more information available and considerably higher strengths (1:¼:3) are

Table 49-4
Laboratory Mortar Strength Specification

Mortar	1:¼:3 lb/sq. in.		1:1:6 lb/sq. in.	
	7 days	28 days	7 days	28 days
Borough High St. Hatfield	1200	1600	400	600
Model Specification	1600	2400	400	600

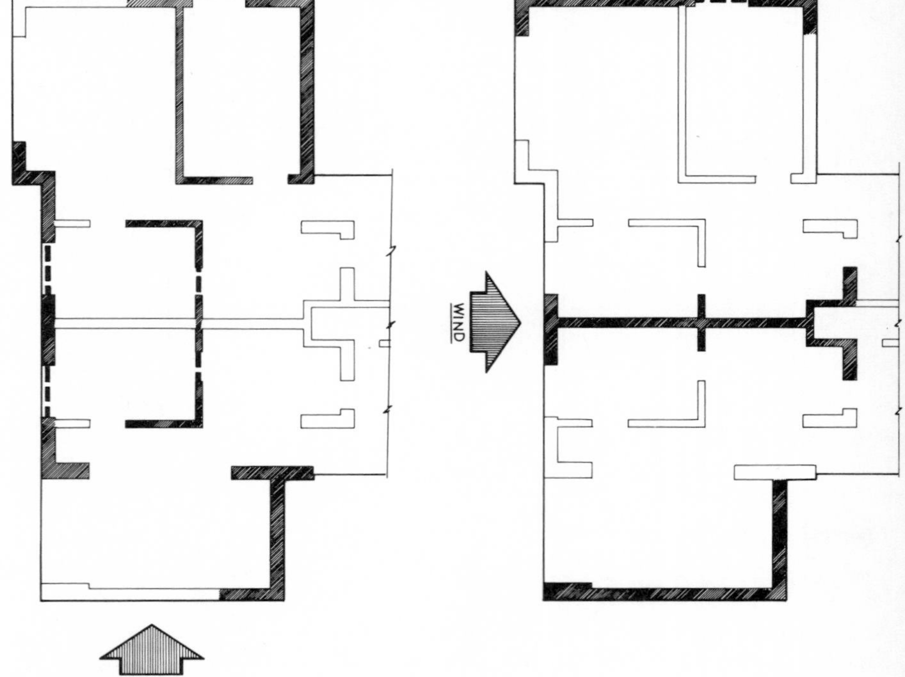

Figure 49-10. Wind wall layout, Hatfield.

required by the new model specification[7] which is believed to be in line with the projected revised CP.111.

The mortar sands available in this country are of a very variable nature and, in general, contain a lot of silty material. Mortar made with sands complying with B.S. 1200 Table 1[8] will frequently not attain the specified strength and contractors have to search for a suitable material. Once this is found, it is relatively easy to achieve a consistently high site strength. The best results have been obtained using premixed lime-sand coarse stuff, probably because the supplier is much more careful with his choice of sand.

Frequent sets of independent tests were carried out on bricks taken from stacks waiting to be delivered to the site. In this way, acceptance of loads on site was not dependent on subsequent tests, and no bricks had to be rejected from site. Table 49-5 gives the results of some of the tests carried out for Borough High Street and Hatfield. In general, the strengths achieved were outstandingly good.

As a means of controlling workmanship on site, several engineers decided to make use of 3 course high 9″ x 9″ cubes of brickwork made on the scaffold with the mortar and bricks used in the work. The cubes are tested between sheets of plywood at 7 and 28 days. As there was no information on the strengths to be expected from such cubes, it was part of the specification that preliminary cubes were to be made in the laboratory for all the combinations of brick type, strength, and mortar to be used in the job. These were tested at the same time as standard samples of bricks. The results, corrected to allow for the strength of the bricks used to make the cubes being greater than that specified, formed the control figures. Cubes made on site were expected to attain two thirds of the strength of the laboratory control figures.

Whilst such cubes and frequent mortar testing encourage the site to a higher standard of workmanship, the fact that bricks actually being used on site are often much stronger than those specified masks the variation of workmanship and even badly made cubes pass the test. The author's firm no longer uses this test and relies on mortar and brick testing coupled with adequate site supervision.

Further Projects

Limited space precludes the detailed description of several other interesting unreinforced load-bearing brick projects, but brief details are given below.

Hamilton Teacher's Training College Hostel, Scotland

16 storeys high and hexagonal on plan, most of the lower 2 storeys are in reinforced concrete, due to the omission of several walls. Slabs are 4 in.-thick in situ concrete with 4-1/2-in-and-9-in.-thick internal walls and 11-in.-thick external cavity walls. This building is complete.

Portsdown Hill Housing Development

A whole series of load-bearing brick buildings are arranged in this prize winning design to provide 523 homes. The tallest

Table 49-5
Brick Testing Results

Brick and specified strengths lb./sq. in.		Range of strengths lb./sq. in.	
		Borough High Street	Hatfield
Calculon	5,000	5,160 to 7,360	5,530 to 6,960
	7,000	10,430 to 11,570	11,350 to 11,880
	10,000	11,640 to 12,380	10,720 to 11,540
V-Brick	5,000	5,050 to 6,470	not used
	6,000	6,210 to 7,470	

blocks are 13, 15, and 17 storeys high and again make use of in situ reinforced concrete floor slabs, 7 in. thick. The walls are 9 in.-thick externally, with a nonload-bearing lightweight block inner skin for insulation and weather. Internal walls are both 9"-and 7"- (Calculon) thick unreinforced brickwork.

Work is due to start in early 1968.

Crosswall Blocks, Greenwich, London

The London Borough of Greenwich is using crosswall construction on three sites to provide 750 dwellings at a total cost of just under £5,000,000 ($14,000,000). The blocks are 6, 8, and 9 storeys high and contain mainly maisonettes, with a few flats. Seven-in. reinforced concrete floors span 17 ft. between 7-in.-thick Calculon crosswalls. Foundations are mass concrete strips bearing on good sand.

Work is in progress on site.

Conclusion

Calculated load-bearing brickwork is now an established form of construction for low, medium, and high-rise blocks of flats and has proved to be more economical than reinforced concrete frames and a lot cheaper than system built frames (prefabricated industrialised buildings).

The Ministry of Housing has now produced a new yardstick for costs for housing in Britain, and one authority has said that the only way to afford a reasonable standard of dwelling within the yardstick is to use calculated load-bearing brickwork for the structure. With improvements in design and an increase in knowledge, it is to be hoped that greater economies can be made.

References

1. "Structural Recommendation for Loadbearing Walls," CP 111 (1964), British Standards Institution, 1964.
2. "Calculated Loadbearing Brickwork," Lb 5, Sussex & Dorking Brick Company Limited.
3. "Practical Application of Calculated Loadbearing Brickwork," Lb 6, Sussex & Dorking Brick Company Limited.
4. "Bricks and Blocks of Fired Brickearth, Clay or Shale," B.S. 3921, British Standards Institution.
5. "The Use of V-brick," Note A.82, Building Research Station.
6. "Code of Functional Requirements of Buildings," Chapter V, Loading CP.3. British Standards Institution.
7. "Model Specification for Loadbearing Clay Brickwork," British Ceramic Research Association.
8. "Sands for Mortar and Reinforced Brickwork; Blockwalling and Masonry," B.S. 1200, British Standards Institution.

50. Special quality brick masonry multistory apartment houses built in Switzerland.

H. Lechner, Ziegelstrasse, Switzerland

Preparatory Planning

The building costs of multistory apartment houses are proportionately higher in Switzerland than those of two- to five-story houses. (Due to using high-grade bricks and mortar and to higher wages as compared to those for standard-grade masonry, the special-quality BS brickwork costs 15 percent more. The wages are higher because the laying must be done more carefully and consequently takes longer. An elevator for up to five stories is considerably cheaper in Switzerland than one for 8 to 20 stories. Sanitary installations, too, are more expensive–if only because the pipes have to be bigger than in lower houses. And so on . . .)

The project designer must therefore economize wherever feasible. Any engineer, on getting his first order to design a residential building, is likely to give preference to reinforced or steel concrete. On looking into the economic aspect, however, and on comparing high-grade, special-quality brick masonry with other materials, he will soon realize that brickwork offers the best for the price. Such a wall is simultaneously load-bearing and heat-insulating. Skeleton structures require an expensive load-bearing system and a filling of masonry between the supports, and each costs nearly as much as the load-bearing, special-quality masonry of a brickwork building. A cellular wall system using reinforced concrete is the most expensive way of building, since a reinforced concrete wall costs 30 percent more than a brick wall of the same thickness.

This only applies, however, to ground plans with small spans of 3 m. to 4.5 m. (9.84 ft. to 14.75 ft.) and provided all the walls assume the loads as cells do, as is generally the case in high-rise apartment buildings.

When developing the floor plan of an apartment, the architect must take pains to form cells with the living and

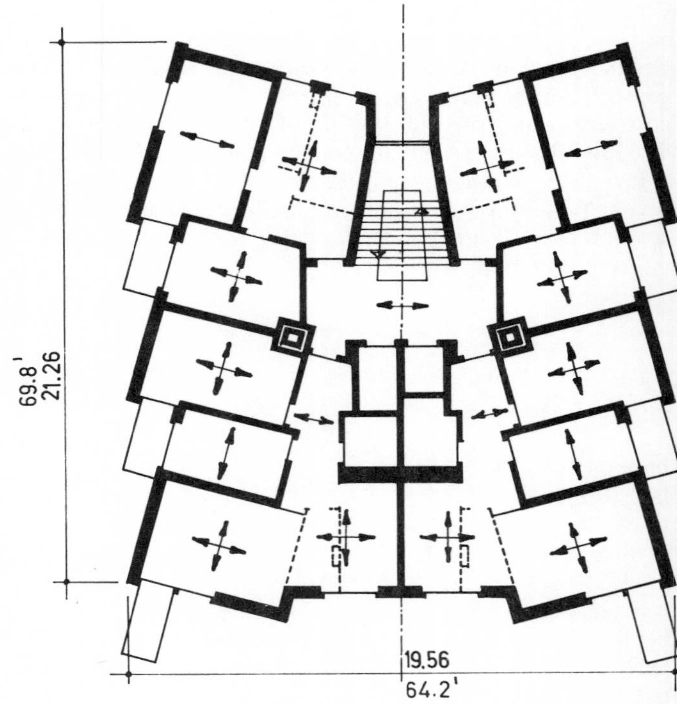

Figure 50-1. Ground plan of 18-storey "Hirzenback" building Zurich.

other rooms. As a result, the loads will be evenly distributed so that the walls may be relatively thin. For smaller spaces such as bathrooms and closets, nonload-bearing walls are quite adequate. (Note Figure 50-1).

In floor plans for parallel partitions, the maximum wall spacing must not exceed 4.5 m. or 5 m. (14.75 ft. or 16.4 ft.

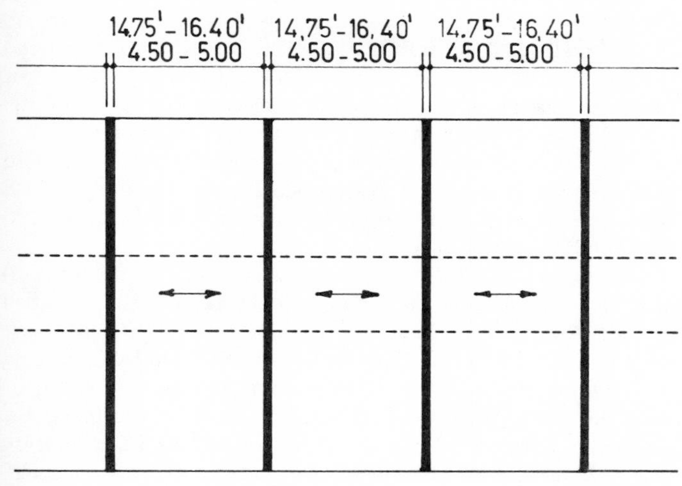

Figure 50-2. Diagram of plan for parallel partitions.

special form work of steel or plywood as large as whole walls, and since the concrete surface allows the wallpaper to be hung immediately, reinforced concrete is cheaper from the twentieth floor up, the expensive form work having been amortized by then.

Two years ago I had 22- to 25-story houses containing 416 apartments in all to build for the city of Zurich, using the type of construction with simple parallel partitioning walls. On comparing costs, the reinforced concrete structural system was given preference for the previously mentioned economic reasons.

Many years' research work by Professor Paul Haller of the Federal Material Testing Institute at Dubendorf–Zurich, with the cooperation of the Swiss brick industry, resulted in producing a special-quality brick (grade BS) which resists exceptionally heavy stresses.

The standard test of the special BS grade must arrive at the following values[2]:

s	Specific absorptive capacity g·/dm^2 x min.	$\leqq$ 17
Δ s	Scatter in g·/dm^2 x min.	±5

Figure 50-3. Example of interior wall details. 1/4, 1/2, 3/4, and 1/1 size bricks.

because here the stiffening effect of the intersecting walls is lacking, and the brickwork would otherwise have to be too thick. It goes without saying that the walls may be spaced further apart—but only at the expense of thicker walls. (See Figure 50-2.)

In elaborating the apartment floor plans, the architect must be guided by the brick dimensions when determining wall lengths and pillars. As a rule, the butt joints may be 1 to 1- 1.2 cm. (3/8" to 1/2") or maximum 1.5 cm. (5/8"). Bricks being produced in 1/4, 1/2, and 3/4 sizes, the architect has plenty of leeway. (Note Figure 50-3.)

Selection of Materials, Static Analysis, Dimensioning

The term "multistory" applies to buildings of at least eight floors. In Switzerland, the limit for brick masonry probably lies around 20 stories.

Obviously, it is not a technical problem to raise brickwork higher than 20 stories. It is rather for economy's sake. With

βs	Crushing strength in kg·/cm^2 (1.026 t. per sq. ft.)	= 400*
$\Delta\beta$s	Scatter in percent	± 15
Lo	Shape of perforation: round, triangular, rectangular, rhombic	
	Percentage of total area	15 to 35
AT	Dimensional allowances:	
AM	– maximum deviation of the single value from the mean value in percent	
	length and width	± 1
	height	± 1.5
AS	– maximum deviation of the mean value from the design value in mm. (0.039")	
	length	± 4
	width	± 2.5
	height	± 2

*The strength of the 18-cm. bricks must correspondingly be equal to 440/cm^2 (451 t. per sq.ft.)

EL	Planeness of bearing faces in mm. (average calipered height)	$\leqq$ 0.07 bs
R	Cracking	no cracks
KK	Expanding grains of quick lime (decrease in tensile strength and resistance to cracking in percent)	$\leqq$ 10

Mortar

Bonding agents (Portland cement) for preparing the brickwork mortar must meet the SIA (Swiss Association of Engineers and Architects) Standard 115 "Standards for Bonding Agents for Buildings".[3]

The natural sand used must not contain more than 5 percent of soft weathered grains.[4] Expanding or water-soluble component parts are harmful. The sulphate content must not exceed 0.1 percent by weight of SO_3. And to prevent metal corrosion, the chloride content must not exceed 0.05 percent by weight of Cl.

In a sedimentation test after the SIA method, brickwork subject to heavy stresses and/or exposure to the weather should deposit a fine layer of maximum 2 mm. (0.078 in.). Sand mixed according to the grain-size curves of SIA Standard 162, and screenings too, as a rule, make a good quality mortar. Sands lacking the finest grains (less than 0.12 mm.) but containing a lot of grains between 0.2 and 1 mm. (0.0078" and 0.039") in size, produce a porous mortar with little resistance to crushing. The largest grain size must not exceed one-half the joint thickness.

The mixing water should be above 8° C and must not contain any injurious substances, in particular none of an organic nature. (Oxidizability $<$ 100 mg. $KMnO_4$ per liter.)

The dose of bonding agents is specified in kg. per m^3 of prepared mortar. The dose for BS brickwork is 350 to 400 kg. per m^3 of ready-to-use mortar (0.30 to 0.34 t. per cu.yd.).

The mortar must be tested as to strength in advance as well as during construction at least once for every story. For BS brickwork the mortar strength must reach $\beta m_{28} = 200$ kg./cm^2 (205 t. per sq.ft.).

SIA Standards 160[6] and revised edition (in preparation) give the useful and the wind loads and also the assumed seismic stresses. For residential buildings, the useful loads are normally 200 kg/m^2 (0.02 t. per sq.ft.), the wind loads varying with the shape of the building. In extreme cases model tests must be made in a wind tunnel. As to seismic effects, the structures have to be calculated for a horizontal acceleration of g/50, as a rule. In regions particularly subject to earthquakes, the authorities may specify an allowance for an acceleration b equal to g/20. Wind and seismic stresses are not apt to occur simultaneously.

Static Analysis

General. The statical calculations must result in the safety of the whole structure and of its individual parts, as specified in SIA Standard 160 "for the assumed loads and for the putting into operation and the supervision of the structures".[7] They will be based on tried and proved methods of calculation and

Table 50-1
(a′ + b′) Specified Minimum Load Capacity of BS (Special-Quality) Brickwork in kg/cm^2 (1.026 t. per sq. ft.); Age 28 Days

Kind of brickwork	Thickness of wall d cm	Slenderness ratio lk/d	Cement bond PC 350 to 400 kg/m^3 m ≈ o	m = 1
One-brick masonry	12	8	250	135
		26	160	55
	15	8	210	135
		21	160	75
	18	8	190	135
		17.5	160	95
	25	8	200	135
		15	170	100
Bonded masonry	25	8	155	115
		15	135	90
	30, 32, 38	8	155	115

Table 50-2

Kind of Masonry	Thickness of wall, cm.	Thickness of wall, in.	Compressive stress and abscissae section	Special-quality BS masonry, m ≈ 0	m = 1/2	m = 1	m = 1½	m = 2
One-brick masonry	12	4.73	$\bar{\sigma}_5$	50	40	30	20	10
	12	4.73	A	55	45	36	28	16
	15	5.91	$\bar{\sigma}_5$	44	36	30	20	10
	15	5.91	A	55	45	36	28	16
	18 + 25	7.09 + 9.85	$\bar{\sigma}_5$	40	34	30	20	10
	18 + 25	7.09 + 9.85	A	55	45	36	28	16
Bonded masonry	25, 30	9.85, 12	$\bar{\sigma}_5$	34	29	25	16	6
	32, 38	12.6, 15	A	55	45	36	28	16

will allow for the actual performance of the buildings. The stress analyses must reveal the effects of each hypothetical load separately.

The stability of buildings and their component parts must be assured by ceilings, stiffening partitions, and other devices. When calculating and planning masonry, the inevitable secondary effects of temperature and the shrinkage of cement-bonded materials must be allowed for, in particular dynamic stresses from street traffic and other causes, as specified by SIA Standard 160.

Modulus of Elasticity. Should no values for the masonry used be available, the following approximative values of the moduli of elasticity may serve to determine deformations of artificial stone masonry due to temporary loads.

Brick masonry with Portland cement

$$E^8 = 360\,000 \frac{\beta M}{\beta M + 400} \qquad (50\text{-}1)$$

Vertical Load in the Wall Plane. The mean normal stress, calculated from the unfavorable overlapping of all the simultaneously acting factors, is determinative. Disregarding perforations and slots, the wall section is counted as cross-sectional surface.

The masonry must not be expected to resist any tensile stresses vertical to the bed joints.

The measure of eccentricity m of the axial force is to be calculated on the basis of the moduli of elasticity of the building materials, simplifying hypotheses being allowable. By no means must the eccentricity exceed double the kern width.

In lieu of the length subject to buckling, the story height is entered in the calculation. By allowing heavier compressive stresses for abutting brickwork walls and for T-shaped or cruciform parts of walls, their stiffening effect is accounted for. Concentrated loads may be distributed in undisturbed parts of the masonry under 60° to the horizontal. The load distribution must be judged according to the performance of the whole supporting structure.

Horizontal Loads Perpendicular to the Wall Plane.[9] Bending-tensile stresses may be borne parallel to the bed joints, provided the butt joints are adequately overlapped, and the load on the wall is vertical. Reinforced masonry with steel inserts in the bed joints is calculated like reinforced concrete, disregarding the tensile strength of the masonry.

The stresses in masonry and steel can be determined with the valence number:

$$n = \frac{Es}{EM} = 20 \qquad (50\text{-}2)$$

The specifications given in SIA Standard 162 "Calculation and execution of concrete and reinforced concrete work" are to be adhered to in the sense of the word.[10]

Calculation and Permissible Stresses[11]

Table 50-2 shows the stresses permissible for BS special-quality brick masonry with Portland cement mortar PC 350 to 400 kg. per m^3 (0.30 to 0.34 t. per cu.yd.).

In order to determine the eccentricity of the loads, all the expected static conditions must be taken into consideration, such as: torsions, unequal deformations, restraints, shifting of the supports, etc. The eccentricity of the points of application of normal forces in pillars and walls can be calculated from the moments at the top in the double cross (see Figure 50-4) with a flexible connection, assuming bilateral and alternate application of the useful load. Even if loads are applied more unfavorably, the permissible stress must not be exceeded. By halving the corner angles, the weight of the ceilings and the loads evenly applied thereto may be divided into three- or

$$\alpha_1 = \frac{h}{l_1}\xi \qquad \alpha_2 = \frac{h}{l_2}\xi \qquad \xi = \frac{J_r E_r}{J_S E_S}$$

$$e_1 = \frac{M_1}{P_1} \qquad \frac{e_1}{k} = m_1 \qquad e_2 = \frac{M_2}{P_2} \qquad \frac{e_2}{k} = m_2$$

$$1 + \alpha_1 + \alpha_2 = r$$

$$\frac{M_1}{M_2} = \frac{2l_1^2(1+r) - l_2^2 r}{2l_2^2(1+r) - l_1^2 r}$$

$$M_1 = \frac{p}{4}\,\frac{2l_1^2(1+r) - l_2^2 r}{4(1+r)^2 - r^2} \qquad M_2 = \frac{p}{4}\,\frac{2l_2^2(1+r) - l_1^2 r}{4(1+r) - r^2}$$

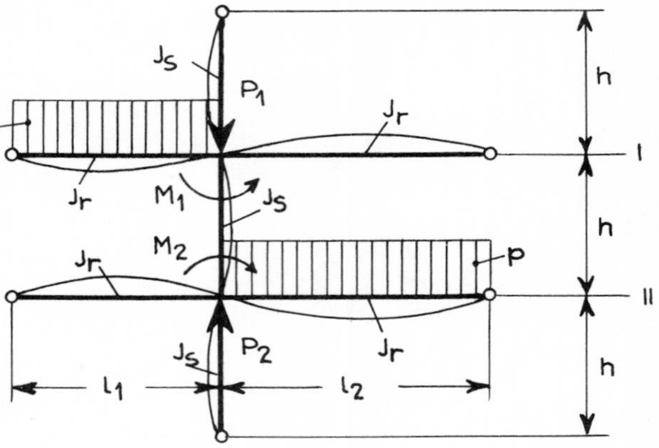

Figure 50-4. Calculation system for walls.[14]

four-cornered load parts and then reckoned with as a uniform load.

Compressive and Buckling Stresses

Structural masonry made of bricks meeting the specifications for special-quality BS brickwork (standard test[2] and the required minimum load-bearing capacity sub a′+b′[5]) may be dimensioned with the permissible mean stresses of the Table 50-2[11] (permissible stresses for special-quality BS brick masonry). (Margin of safety Y = approximately 5.) They are characterized by a linear diminution to the theoretical border-line slenderness A where the permissible stress becomes zero (see Figure 50-5).

In the Table 50-2[11] the basic values $\bar{\sigma}_5$ and A are given for near-concentric and for equilaterally eccentric loading (m=O, 1/2, 1, 1-1/2, 2). These values enable one to find the permissible mean normal stresses from the diagram above.

The classes of masonry corresponding to $\bar{\sigma}_5$ must not be exceeded under single load.

Unequally and Crossed Eccentric Attack of Load[16]

When the load attack on masonry of artificial stones is unequally and/or crossed eccentrical, the buckling stress $o^{\bar{\sigma}}k$ will be multiplied by the reduction factor a:

$$a = \frac{1}{2}\left[\frac{m^{\sigma}k}{o^{\bar{\sigma}}k}(1+\eta) + (1 - 0.1\,m)(1-\eta)\right] \qquad (50\text{-}4)$$

$m^{\sigma}k$ = permissible stress for a slenderness ratio of lk/d and an eccentricity ratio m:

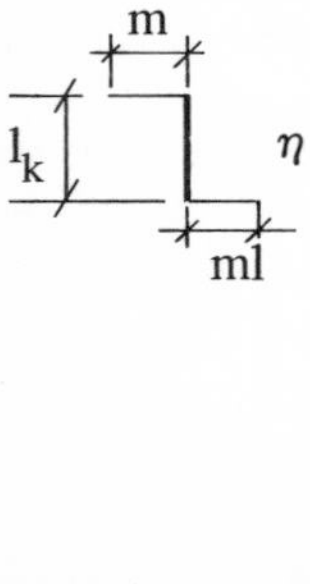

$$\eta = \frac{ml}{m} = +1 \text{ to } -1: \begin{array}{l}0 \text{ to } -1 \text{ crossed eccentricity}\\ 0 \text{ to } +1 \text{ equilateral eccentricity}\end{array}$$

$$|\,ml\,| \leqq |\,m\,| \qquad (50\text{-}5)$$

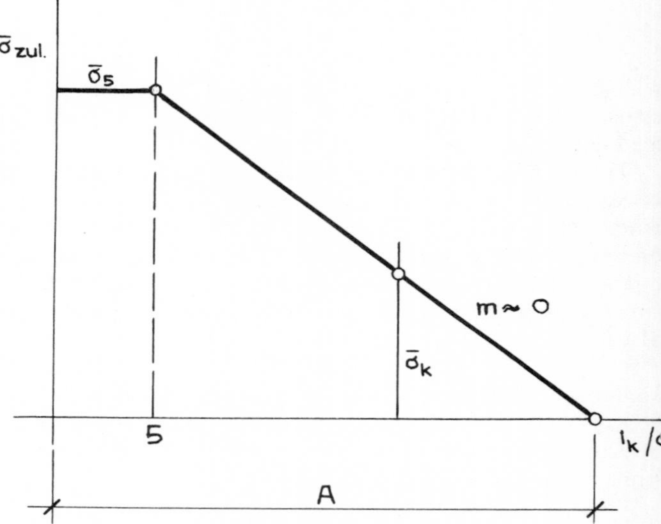

Figure 50-5. Diagram for finding the $\bar{\sigma}_{kzul}$ from the values $\bar{\sigma}$ and A after Table 50-2.[13]

L- or T-Shaped or Cruciform Wall Sections[17]

For L- or T-shaped wall sections and for sections placed crosswise the slenderness ratio lk/i is calculated from the minimum moment of inertia (main axis), for which purpose the permissible stress $\bar{\sigma}_{zul}$ is taken from the diagram[1] corresponding to the quality and strength of the masonry.

$$\frac{lk}{i} = \frac{lk}{d}\sqrt{12} \qquad (50\text{-}6)$$

At the distance 12d, measured from the inner line of intersection, the wall sections may only be loaded with the permissible stress $\bar{\sigma}_k$, i.e. irrespective of any stiffening effect of the angular wall sections. The reduction in the transition zone

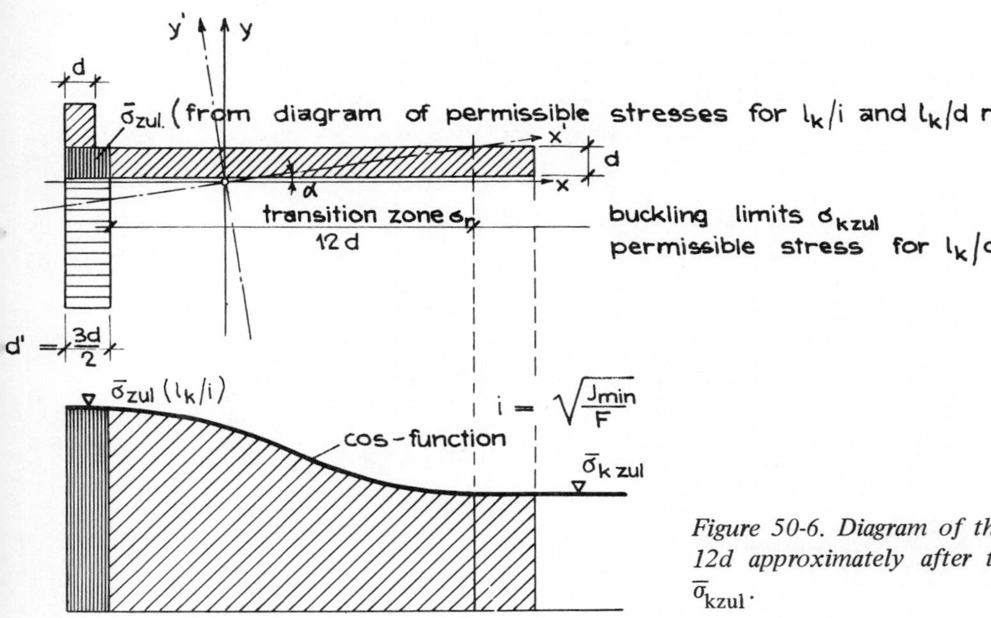

Figure 50-6. Diagram of the reduction in the transition zone of 12d approximately after the cos function between $\bar{\sigma}_{zul}$ and $\bar{\sigma}_{kzul}$.

Table 50-3

$\bar{\sigma}_k \,/\, \bar{\sigma}$	Length of wall section					
	2d	4d	6d	8d	10d	12d
1.0	1.00	1.00	1.00	1.00	1.00	1.00
0.8	0.99	0.98	0.96	0.94	0.92	0.90
0.6	0.99	0.97	0.93	0.88	0.84	0.80
0.4	0.98	0.95	0.89	0.82	0.76	0.70
0.2	0.98	0.93	0.85	0.76	0.68	0.60

12d is effected approximately after the cos function between $\bar{\sigma}_{zul}$ and $\bar{\sigma}_{kzul}$ (See Figure 50-6). Reduction value φ (= cos – area) may be taken from Table 50-3.

The reduced permissible stress to be entered into the calculation for one wall section:

$$\bar{\sigma}_r = \varphi \times \bar{\sigma} \tag{50-7}$$

The permissible stress $\bar{\sigma}_k$ governs the wall sections > 12d.

When verifying the capacity of the walls to resist seismic stresses, the permissible axial and buckling stresses may be raised by 50 percent.

Planning Data

For every story the architect will draw layer plans showing flawless brickwork bonds and depths of bonding-in recesses for plumbing, etc. Subsequent pointing is not admissible. Hard bricks like the special-quality ones are brittle and have more residual stresses than bricks of less compressive strength; they are apt to crack in odd places, thereby weakening the brickwork. Consequently, only bricks factory-made in 1/4, 1/2 or 3/4 lengths may be used besides full lengths. The layer plans must also give the bed and the butt joints, the former being 10 mm. thick, as a rule, the latter 12 mm. (0.47 in.) at the most.

To obviate cracks due to constraining stresses, the engineer will make a point of only using material having one and the same modulus of elasticity throughout a single ground plan. Should he, however, be forced to provide for a pillar of reinforced concrete, for example, he will dimension it in such a way as to ensure its deformability being analogous to that of the brick masonry. Attention must also be paid to having the existing compressive stresses in the masonry be approximately the same in all the walls.

Furthermore, the walls in each succeeding story are to rise concentrically above those below in order to avoid additional eccentricities.

Specifications regarding quality and execution covering bricks, mortar and quality of masonry, are to appear on each layer plan. (Note Figure 50-7)

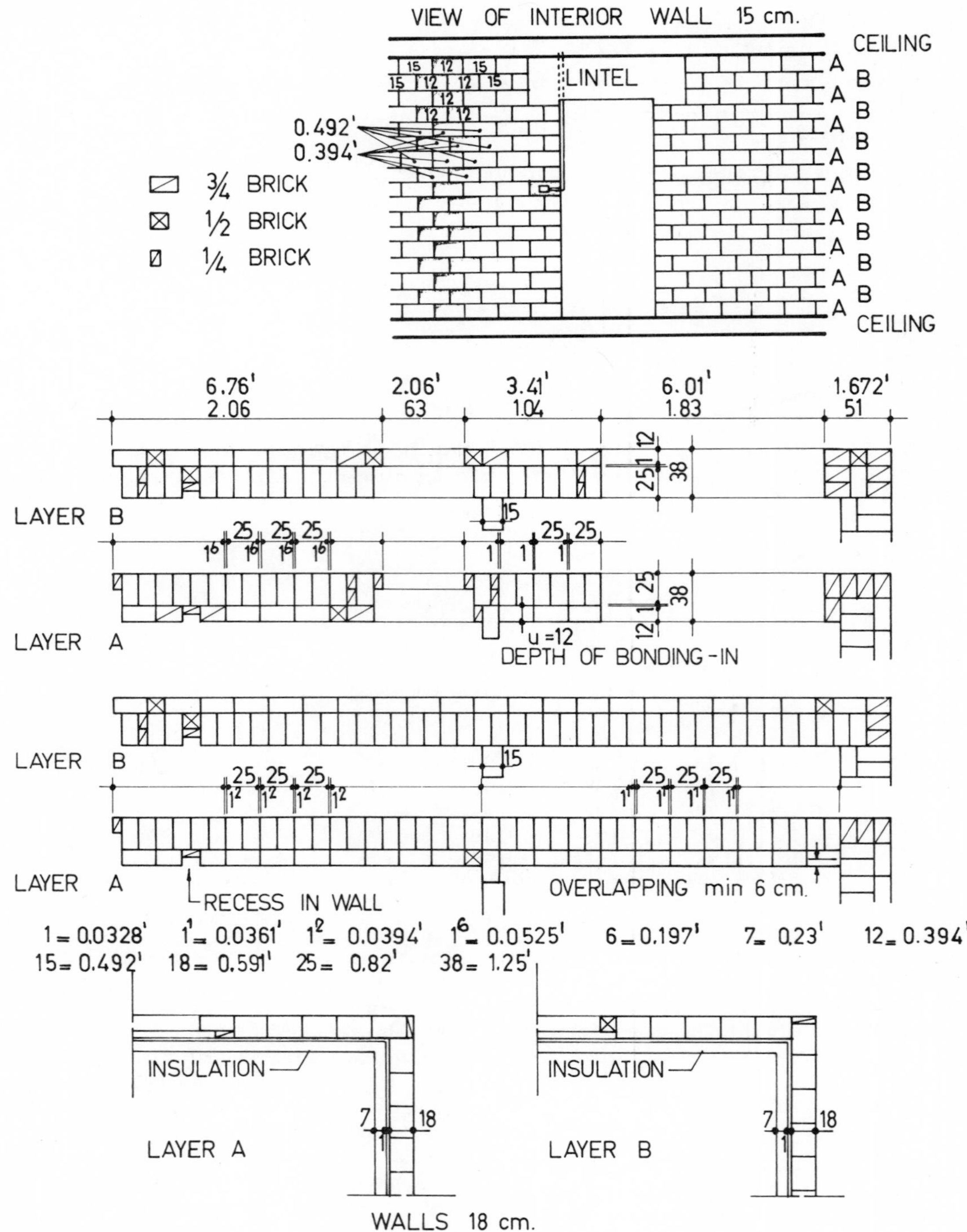

Figure 50-7. Layer plan.

Figure 50-8. "Hirzenback," Zurich, 18 stories. Constructed: 1956. Facades: 1.25 ft. Interior walls: 0.492 ft. – 0.82 ft.

Figure 50-9. "Zentrum," Wettingen, 19 stories. Constructed: 1963-1965. Façades: prefabricated concrete. Interior walls: 0.492 ft. – 0.591 ft. (brick).

Construction Superintendence

Supervision

Depending on the size of the structure, one of the engineer's responsible superintendents is to constantly check on the site whether the data of the layer plans are being observed. He also checks whether the demanded quality of the masonry meets the requirements specified, particularly in regard to the following values pertaining to BS masonry.

Permissible deviation from the straight line[12]	1/800
Deviation from the plumb in mm. per 2.5 m. of height (0.039 in. per 8.2 ft.)	3
Deviation of the bed joints from the horizontal in mm. per 2.5 m. of length	3.5
Thickness of the bed joints in mm. (0.39 in. to 0.47 in.) 10 to 12	

The masons will be provided with aligning poles with the accurate arrangement of the joints, and enjoined to lay each layer with the lead line. Dropped mortar must not be applied, and the mortar must have been used up by stopping time.

The superintendent will make sure that only skilled masons are put on BS jobs. It is a good idea to give them some preliminary training on a sample wall.

The contractor is responsible for the specified quality of the masonry.

Testing Bricks and Mortar Before and During Construction[13]

The mortar will be determined before hand by tests at the EMPA Research Institute. Three prisms 4 x 4 x 16 cm. (1.57 x 1.57 x 6.3 in.) each per story are tested after 28 days and must then show a minimum strength of 200 kg. per cm^2 (205 t. per sq. ft.).

At every second story at least ten bricks will be tested as to adherence to the standard.

Practical Experience

With the bricks available from Swiss brickworks, viz.:

sizes 12 x 25 x 13.5 cm., (4.73" x 9.85" x 5.32") 15 x 25 x 13.5 cm. (5.91" x 9.85" x 5.32") and

18 x 25 x 13.5 cm. (7.09" x 9.85" x 5.32") and

the corresponding fractional sizes 1/4, 1/2 and 3/4 which are 6 cm. (2.36 in.), 12 cm. (4.73 in.) and 18 cm. (7.09 in.), respectively, it is perfectly possible to construct walls of any length and pillars of any height.

In the 8-, 10-, 12-, 13-, 14-, 16-, 17-, and 18-story buildings I have constructed of special-quality bricks, I designed the façade walls 39, 32, 25 and 18 cm. (15.37, 12.6, 9.85 and 7.09 in.) thick, respectively, and the interior walls 12, 15 and 25 cm. (4.73, 5.9 and 9.85 in.) thick. (Note Figures 50-8 – 50-12) Of late I have changed over to even thinner walls: 18 or 25 cm. for façades with an extra insulating sheet, and 12 or 15 cm. for the inner walls. Facades being thick mainly for heat-insulating purposes, but too thick statically speaking, thinner walls plus insulation are actually more economical.

I have been occupied with multi-story brick buildings for 12 years now, but even in Switzerland, where there are extreme differences in meteorological conditions, I have thus far detected practically no cracks or other damages worth mentioning.

Future Improvements

What progress it would mean if research led to the production of an economical plastic mortar enabling a reduction of the joint thicknesses! Then glueing might even suffice. But the bricks' surfaces would have to be absolutely plane and smooth. It is conceivable that the strength of masonry could be increased this way. Prefabricated products like Preton, for instance, also have a promising future. But the bonding of the walls where they abut in the corners has not yet been solved satisfactorily.

Symbols

Bricks

B	Brick
ls	Length of brick in cm.

Figure 50-10. "Holzerhurd," Zurich, 18 stories. Constructed 1965-1966. Façades: reinforced Durisol, 0.656 ft. – 0.82 ft. Interior walls: 0.492 ft. – 0.591 ft. (brick).

Figure 50-11. "Sandacker," Neuenhof, 17 stories. Constructed: 1965-1966. Façades: 0.591 ft. + 0.23 ft. insulation – 1.05 ft. Interior walls: 0.492 ft.

Figure 50-12. Detail of interior wall (see Figure 50-3).

bs	Breadth of brick in cm.
hs	Height (thickness) of brick in cm.
ls/bs/hs	Format of brick in cm.
AT	Dimensional allowance
AM	Maximum deviation of the single value from the mean value in per cent
AS	Maximum deviation of the mean value from the design amount in mm.
s	Specific absorptive capacity after the EMPA method in g·/dm^2 x min.
Δs	Maximum deviation of the specific absorptive capacity from the mean value in g·/dm^2 x min.
Lo	Area of perforations in percent of total area
EL	Planeness of the bearing faces (mean of caliper checks taken at random in mm.)
R	Cracking
KK	Expanding grains of quick lime, effect on tensile strength, and resistance to cracking. Determination of these capacities in ten bricks after 24 hours' cooking.
t	Depth of brick in cm.
βs	Mean value of crushing strength of bricks taken from ten single values (breaking load divided by gross area)
Δβs	Greatest deviation of the single value from the mean value in per cent
nβs	Mean value of crushing strength of brick in kg/cm^2

Mortar for Wall

βm	Cubic crushing strength of the mortar prisms 4 x 4 x 16 cm.
PC 350/400	Dosage: 350/400 kg. of Portland cement per cubic meter of prepared mortar
nβm	Standard crushing strength of the mortar
vβm	Crushing strength of the mortar found by testing

Brickwork

BS	Special-quality brickwork
u	Overlapping of bricks in adjacent layers in cm.
d	Thickness of wall
dM	Thickness of part of wall in brickwork
βM	Strength of brickwork
nβM	Standard minimum load capacity of brickwork
vβM	Crushing strength of brickwork found by testing

Statical Symbols

N	Longitudinal force
i	Radius of gyration $i = \sqrt{J/F}$
J	Moment of inertia
F	Gross cross-sectional area (without deduction of perforations or slots)
lk	Length subject to buckling (distance between the joints, height of stories from axis to axis)
k	Kern width
e	Eccentricity of point of attack of load
m	Measure of eccentricity m = e/k
ϵ	Ratio of the eccentricity coefficients ml/m at both ends of the wall
EM	Modulus of elasticity of the brickwork
Es	Modulus of elasticity of the steel
n	Valence number n = Es/EM
A	Abscissae section of the straight line of buckling
v	Safety factor (breaking load divided by permissible load)
$o\bar{\sigma}5$	Permissible mean normal stress within the strength limits (lk/d $\leqq$ 5) with a near-concentric load
$m\bar{\sigma}5$	Permissible mean normal stress within the strength limits (lk/d $\leqq$ 5) with an eccentric load
$O\bar{\sigma}k$	Permissible mean normal stress within the buckling limits (lk/d $>$ 5) with a near-concentric load
$m\bar{\sigma}k$	Permissible mean normal stress within the buckling limits (lk/d $>$ 5) with an eccentric load
$\bar{\sigma}_g$	Mean normal stress from permanent load
σ_{bzul}	Permissible bending stress parallel to the bed joints
τ_{zul}	Permissible shearing stress
$\bar{\sigma}_{zul}$	Permissible stress for a given slenderness ratio and a measure of eccentricity taken from the diagram

References

1. "Standard for the Calculation and Execution of Masonry Using Artificial and Natural Stones." SIA Standard 113, Prof. P. Haller, Chairman of Standards Commission, 1965, p. 32.
2. *Ibid.*, Table V, p. 5.
3. "Standards for Bonding Agents Used In Building," SIA Standard 115, 1953, Art. 14, 15, pp. 10-12.
4. SIA Standard 113, pp. 1-2.
5. *Ibid.*, Table I, p. 3.
6. "Standards for the Assuming of Loads, the Putting into Operation and the Supervision of the Structures," SIA Standard 160, 1956, Art. 27, p. 20, Art. 20, p. 13-16, revision Art. 21, p. 13.
7. *Ibid.*, pp. 5-28.
8. SIA Standard 113, pp. 7-8.
9. *Ibid.*, p. 8.
10. "Standards for the Calculation and Execution of Concrete and Reinforced Concrete Structures," SIA Standard 162, 1956, pp. 4-48.
11. SIA Standard 113, Table X, p. 9.
12. *Ibid.*, Table XVI, p. 13.
13. *Ibid.*, p. 14.
14. *Ibid.*, p. 23.
15. *Ibid.*, p. 8.
16. *Ibid.*, p. 10.
17. *Ibid.*

51. Case studies and critical evaluation of high-rise load-bearing brickwork in Britain.

J. G. Stockbridge, Owings and Merrill, Chicago, Illinois, and Prof. A. W. Hendry, University of Edinburgh, Edinburgh, Scotland

Introduction

A 12-story tower block constructed at Elmwood Court, Birmingham, in 1961 marks the real acceptance of calculated high-rise load-bearing brickwork in Britain. Although other multi-story brick structures were constructed earlier, they were normally designed on a rule-of-thumb basis in accordance with local building codes.

Currently, more than a dozen blocks are either completed or under construction, each of which is 10-stories or higher. Although this is still a relatively small number of structures compared to those being constructed in concrete and steel, it is significant because, as far as can be determined, none of these buildings were designed with the intent of being brick structures. In most cases, economic considerations were cited as the influencing factor for selecting brickwork.

Basically, this economic advantage can be attributed to the vertical, structural elements preforming various functions which a frame, for example, would have to provide separately. Simultaneously, the brickwork provides structural support, subdivision of space, thermal and accoustic insulation, fire and weather protection.

PART I

Job Studies

Project A

The Elmwood Court Site, Birmingham encouraged using a high-rise structure because the client wished to save as many of the trees on the site as possible.

The architect was most anxious to consider several structural systems because he was not satisfied with the economy or construction time of a number of concrete frame high-rises he had just completed. Preliminary cost studies indicated that a brickwork structure would be the most economical system, especially because of some low-rise brick buildings also on the site.

In April 1962 when the 12-story apartment block was completed, it was the highest load-bearing structure to be constructed in Britain, and it allowed greater utilization of brick's inherent strength than previous buildings.

All wiring within the structure was run through conduit attached directly to the face of the brickwork and concealed in the 5/8" plaster.

Project B

At Alberta Street, Southwark, as in the previous structure and most of those to follow, brickwork was selected partly for economy. Cost studies carried out between a proposed brickwork and concrete frame solution indicated a saving of $13,400 in favor of the brickwork.

Construction began on the 12-story apartment in October 1962 and was completed in December 1964, a total of 27 months. There were also low-rise brickwork structures on the site which made it possible to set up a construction sequence between the two.

No provisions were made to allow work to continue in cold weather and an estimated six or seven weeks were lost.

Project C

The Baylis Road Scheme, London, consists of five linked towers of varying heights from 8 to 13 stories. All the apartments are contained in the four outer wings while the central tower is for the lobby and vertical circulation.

The staggered elements visually increase the building height and help to make it the point of punctuation and interest that the client encouraged.

The consulting engineer calculated that the exterior walls could have been constructed in 11" cavity wall for their entire height, but after consultations with the local building authority all but the upper three stories of each wall were increased to 15-1/2".

This increase in wall thickness eased the problem of handling services by making a certain amount of chasing acceptable.

In the 11" portion of the wall, some concern arose over the insulating properties of the walls and the 2" cavities were filled with foamed plastic insulation.

The project was completed in 18 months, one month behind schedule. Construction joints were located in the central tower which divided the building up into four quarters, allowing a sequence of trades to be set-up between the parts.

The contractor contributed his late completion to difficulties arising from working in these confined spaces and to using colored mortar required for the facade. In wet weather the colored mortar could not be made stiffer because this brought about a change in the color. Under these conditions, the bricks tended to float on the mortar, making laying difficult and slow.

Project D

The Dormitories at the University of Essex are composed of many small study room and study bedroom units, requiring good sound insulation and making the adaption of a wall-bearing system ideal. Preliminary cost studies bore this out and suggested the brickwork system which was eventually chosen.

Only the selection of the common bricks for the upper six stories was left to the contractor's discretion. The facing bricks and two strengths of engineering bricks were already ordered by the university, with the understanding that they be assigned to the successful contractor. This, however, in no way relieved the contractor of the responsibility of maintaining quality checks on the material.

A wind analysis carried out on the assumption that the walls acted as independent vertical cantilevers indicated that tension would develop in the core walls, thus requiring them to be reinforced.

The engineer felt, however, that the wind loading was a bit conservative and, therefore, financed a series of small scale-model tests at the University of Edinburgh which demonstrated that due to composite action the reinforcement was not structurally necessary.

Project E

The three tower blocks at the Market Square Redevelopment, Jarrow were originally designed to be constructed in a prefabricated system, but the considerably cheaper brickwork structure finally won out.

Generally, the layout was quite well-suited to brickwork except at ground level where it was supported on piers. There was considerable worry as to the effect of beam deflections on the supported brickwork walls. For this reason, the major second and third floor walls are reinforced in every other horizontal course to take any tension which might develop due to bending.

Some difficulty was found in achieving a completely filled collar joint so the engineer required that this particular joint be grouted.

While working in cold weather, reinforced polythene frames were fixed to the scaffolding, the water and sand were heated, and the finished work covered. To ensure the quality of the cold weather work, mortar cubes were made and tested after 3 days.

Project F

The Weston Rise Project, Islington, was also originally conceived as a precast concrete structure and, based on this, heavily sculptured precast concrete facing panels were designed to express the cellular nature of the building. At a later date, however, it was decided that the structure could be constructed more economically in brickwork.

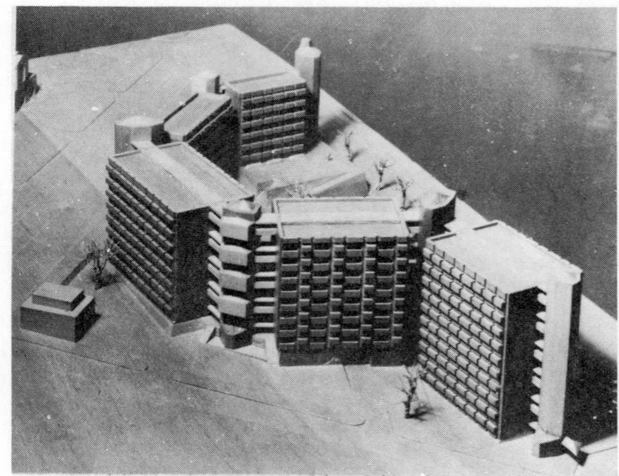

Figure 51-1. Weston Rise Project where brick buildings are faced with concrete.

Despite this structural change, the architect felt that facing a brick building with concrete was just as valid as facing a concrete building with brick, and the concrete cladding panels were retained. (Note Figure 51-1.)

Figure 51-2. Residential tower at the Beaconsfield Army School of Education.

Figure 51-3. Dormitory block, Teachers Training College, Hamilton, Scotland.

Project G

The residential tower at the Beaconsfield Army School of Education is a federal project being handled by the Ministry of Public Buildings and Works.

A very unusual feature for a wall-bearing structure is the introduction of quite large window openings at all of the exterior corners. Cantilevering a floor slab structurally can be done, but load concentrations develop in the supporting walls and occasionally economy can suffer.

The central core of the building was originally designed to be constructed in reinforced concrete, but the engineer felt that this would create problems due to differential shrinkage. Therefore, the core was later changed to brickwork, except at the roof and the base where it was aesthetically desired.

Early in the project, it was decided that a precast brickwork system would be used. A major brick manufacturer, in conjunction with the architect and engineer, developed and tested a single leaf wall built in a prototype prefabricating frame. Due to financial difficulties, however, the development was carried no further and standard layed-in-place brickwork was used. (Note Figure 51-2.)

Project H

For the dormitory block, Teachers Training College, Hamilton, Scotland, load-bearing brickwork was chosen because of the economy demonstrated by a series of material studies. Precast concrete panels were estimated to increase the superstructure cost by about $18,000 and poured-in-place concrete by $19,000. The architect also considered having special large-size bricks shipped from England where they had preformed very economically, but the shipping costs cancelled out any savings.

The exterior surfaces of the buildings are rendered, making it possible to use the same engineering brick for both the inner and outer leaves of the exterior cavity walls and eliminating concern over differencial settlement between them. (Note Figure 51-3.)

Project K

The three high-rise dormitories at the University of Liverpool were constructed of brickwork for economic reasons and to accent the difference in function between these and low-rise concrete structures with supporting facilities (catering, etc.).

A very interesting saw-tooth facade was developed to provide every room with some south light.

The structure possesses numerous shear walls, but they are especially short in the core. Over the area, therefore, the typical 4-1/2" one-way floor system was increased to a two-way 10" slab which sizeably increases the interaction of the core walls and considerably improved the buildings stiffness to lateral loads.

Although the following high-rise brickwork structures will not be discussed as job studies in this portion of the chapter, they are identified here because they contribute data to the figures and tables discussed in Part II.

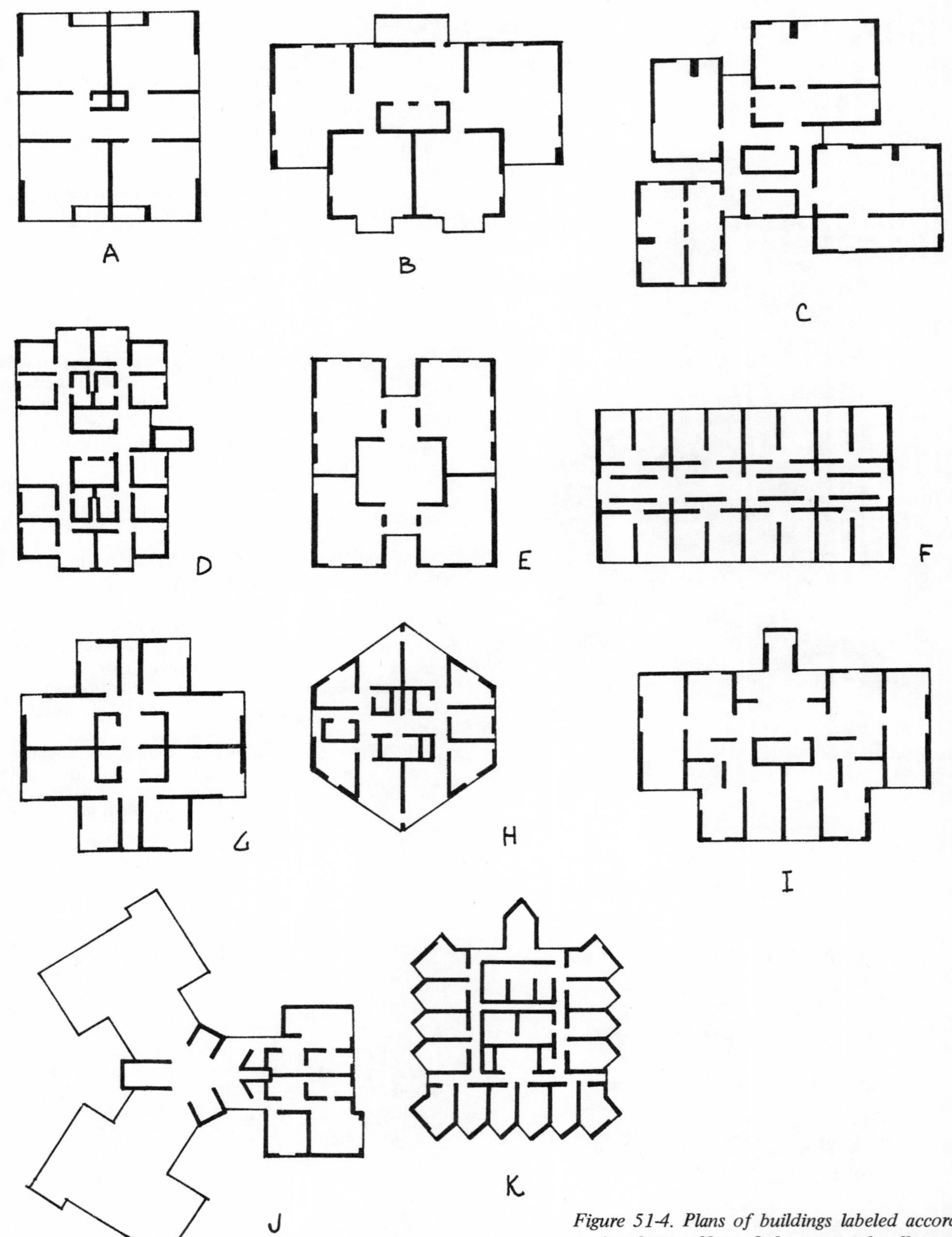

Figure 51-4. Plans of buildings labeled according to project letters. Note: Only structural walls are shown.

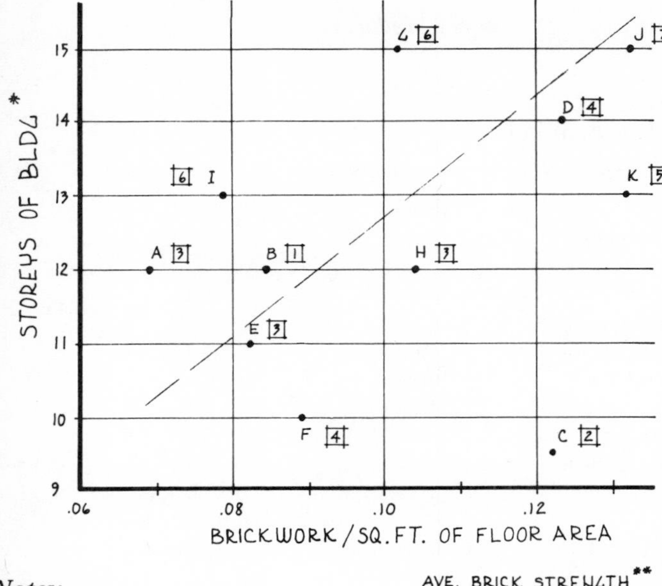

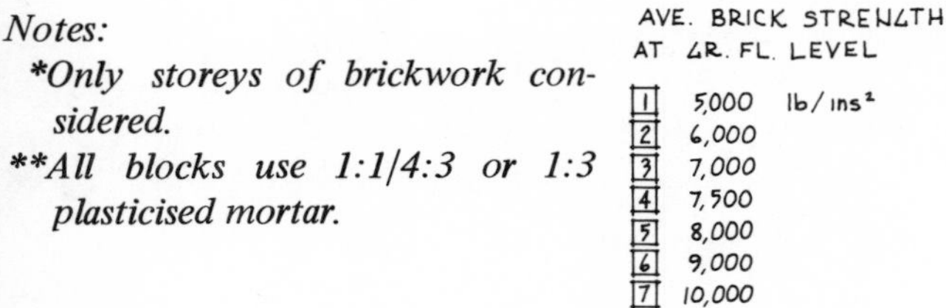
Notes:

*Only storeys of brickwork considered.

**All blocks use 1:1/4:3 or 1:3 plasticised mortar.

Figure 51-5. Relation of brickwork to building height.

Project I (Residential Housing at Borough High Street, Southwark, London) and Project J (Apartments at French Horn Lane, London) are discussed in some detail in the conference paper, "Some Loadbearing Brick Buildings in Britain"[1]. (Also, see Figure 51-4)

PART II

Critical Evaluation

Efficient Wall Distribution

The great flexibility of structural wall arrangement in brickwork structures can readily be seen in Figure 51-4. To efficiently use brickwork, floor areas should be subdivided into a relatively large number of small-to-medium sized rooms having repetitive floor plans for the entire building height. In addition, both the inner and outer walls must be oriented to provide lateral stability in both directions. The position of stairs, ducts, and elevators is also important to building stability and can be utilized to great advantage.

Each floor arrangement is unique and evolves as the solution to a particular set of functional requirements, but there are enough general similarties between blocks to make some group classifications discernible.

The most easily recognizable layout is the simple crosswall plan which has proved most efficient and has been the dominant wall arrangement used in low-rise brickwork structures for many years. Figure 51-4-F is an excellent example. In the crosswall layout, however, there is a limit to the depth of the building if the rooms are to have access to natural light. The simple crosswall structure in its slab block form is therefore not nearly as frequently used in higher buildings, but rather a somewhat more complex point block adaptation is used which oftentimes has crosswalls set parallel to both axis of the building, as in Figure 51-4G.

The cellular plan is one in which the interior and exterior walls ideally create closed units, which act as built up sections especially efficient in resisting lateral wind forces. See Figure 51-4C.

Other variations are possible, but they will almost invariably be a composite of the cellular and crosswall plans.

Partitions

When each habitable room in a building is an independent self-contained unit, as in a dormitory, hotel, or hospital, the heavy dividing walls required for sound insulation all lend themselves to be used as load-bearing elements.

In residential blocks, however, only the apartment separating walls need be heavy for sound insulation and fire protection, and those which subdivide the apartment into individual rooms have considerably less demanding rolls.

Light partitions rather than brickwork can often be used more economically for subdividing because they are less costly and the strength of the remaining structural walls will normally be more completely utilized. It is important to realize, however, that their use is economical only as long as they are not located in such a position that they sizeably affect the length of the controlling floor span.

For example, in structures with a floor area of approximately 3,000 sq. ft., it will usually be economical to provide an additional 30′ of 9″ wall if 1″ in slab thickness can be saved.

Percentage of Walls

For any specific building, as height increases, there will be an accompanying increase in plan area of brickwork per sq. ft. of floor area at ground level (brk. wk./sq.ft.) or, alternatively, an increase in brickwork strength, all else being equal. However, the layout and slenderness ratio of walls varies from structure to structure, as does the percentage of walls developing their capable strength.

Although considerable scatter is present in Figure 51-5, there appears some indication of an increase in the quantity of brickwork as height increases and a slightly less defined increase in brick strength.

Foundations

Although a brickwork building will normally be a relatively heavy structure compared to a frame, there is no evidence of any exceptional problems either structurally or economically being encountered in the structures constructed to date. A 2′-thick mat has most often been used (Table 51-1), but the wall-bearing system lends itself equally well to spread footings or pile foundations when soil conditions dictate them.

Table 51-1
Summary of Buildings Discussed in Part I

Project	No. of Stories	Floor Area/ Story Sq Ft	Function	Layout Type	Foundations Type
A	12	3,270	Apartments	Crosswall	Raft
B	12	3,135	Apartments	Cellular	Raft
C	8/13	3,400	Apartments	Cellular	Spread Footing
D	14	3,240	Dormitories	Composite	Piles
E	12	3,305	Apartments	Cellular	Raft
F	10	3,360	Apartments	Crosswall	Piles
G	16	2,595	Military Housing	Crosswall	Raft
H	15	2,015	Dormitories	Crosswall	Box Frame Basement Raft
I	13	3,300	Apartments	Composite	Box Frame Basement Raft
J	15	4,343	Apartments	Crosswall	Raft
K	13	31,150	Dormitories	Composite	Raft

Table 51-2
Some Construction Times

Project	Floor Area Per Story Sq Ft	Length of Contract Days	One-Story Brkwk + Slab Days	Brkwk Man/hours per Story *	Cu Ft of Brkwk Layed per Hour	Bricklayers	Laborers	Sequence of Construction
A	3,270	450	9	550	3.5	10	23	Between High-Rise Halves
B	3,135	1,008	27.5	1,056	2.0	8	4	Between High-Rise Halves
C	3,400	540	21	825	4.3	10	9	Between High-Rise Quarters
D	3,240	570	21	1,502	2.0	10	5	Between High-Rise Thirds
E	3,305	420	14	404	5.7	10	5	Between Adjacent High-Rises
F	3,360	Data not available						
G	2,595	Data not available						
H	2,015	236	11	432	3.8	6	3	Between High-Rise & Low-Rise
I	3,300	468	14			7	15	Between High-Rise & Low Rise
J	4,300	Data not available						
K	3,115	Work to start in 1968						

* Bricklayers time only.

Table 51-3
Recorded Site Costs*

Project	Stories	Floor Area per building	Brkwk Cost in place	Brkwk Cost per Sq ft of floor	Brkwk cost per cubic ft	Super-Structure cost		Total Building cost
	No	Sq ft	$	$/Sqft	$/Cu ft	$	$/Sq ft	$
A	Data not available							
B	12	37,000	28,100	.76	1.11	63,100	1.69	322,000
C	8/13	31,000	53,000	1.71	1.56	87,700	2.83	378,000
D	14	45,400	91,000	2.02	2.17	–	–	628,000
E	11	36,400	102,000	2.80	4.0	145,800	4.00	294,000
F	Data not available							
G	15	38,900	48,200	1.23	1.44	84,200	2.16	535,000
H	13	26,200	33.900	1.26	1.59	57,527	3.44	–
I	13	43,000	42,800	1.01	1.01	86,800	2.05	260,000
J	15	65,000	122,000	1.88	1.65	191,500	2.89	680,000
K	Work not to start until 1968							

* Stories of brickwork only.

In designing a mat foundation the walls stiffen the mat and encourage the development of uniform soil pressure. The amount of reinforcement required in the design of the mat is therefore dictated largely by the floor layout of the building it supports, thus making the previous discussion on good layout design even more important.

Construction

From Table 51-2, it can be seen that one story of brickwork can take as little as 9 days or as much as 27.5 days to complete, depending on variables which could only have been uncovered by a comprehensive time study.

It is interesting to note, however, that the number of cubic feet of brickwork layed per man-hour (2.0 – 5.7) is not too dissimilar to the values of from .9 to 3.75 recorded in a time-study at two job sites where low-rise brickwork structures were being constructed.

Economics

In considering the cost comparisons in Table 51-3, it must be remembered that site costs between various projects can easily vary up to 5 percent due to such factors as the accessibility and availability of labor and materials. There is bound to be a great amount of masking, making design evaluations based on construction costs questionable at best.

The cost figures are valuable however, in as much as they indicate the cost range which can be expected of the system. It is noteworthy that the cost of brickwork is remarkably stable at about $1.60 per cubic foot, irrespective of wall thickness.

Conclusion

High-rise load-bearing brickwork in Britain has competed quite successfully with other high-rise materials since its relatively recent acceptance as a sophisticated building material. Now that the codes of practice in America are being up-dated to allow the structural potential inherent in the material, there is no reason why it should not also compete equally well here.

Acknowledgements

Sincere thanks are due to all the architects and engineers of these projects for their help and generosity in supplying data.

References

1. Haseltine, B. A., "Some Load-Bearing Brick Buildings in England," *Designing Engineering and Constructing with Masonry Products,* Gulf Publishing Company, Houston, 1969.

52. Jayhawker Apartment Towers.

Thomas E. Woodward, AIA, Woodward, Cape & Associates, Dallas, Texas

Design Considerations

The project is a privately owned apartment complex in Lawrence, Kansas. The owners, who are University alumni, wanted an income-producing property which would contribute significantly to the campus. They wish to create an environment oriented to student living, which would accommodate approximately 1200 single and married residents in 300 apartments.

This program requirements include meeting rooms, recreation areas, laundry facilities, vending machine areas, administrative offices, swimming pool, and common areas. A major factor is for the project to be constructed in two phases, the first phase, consisting of 150 apartments, related offices, and common areas, was ready for occupancy by September 1968.

The project site is on the brow of a hill overlooking the campus. It is bounded on three sides by university owned property, and by a major street on the north. The site is in close proximity to all classrooms and existing university student housing. The heart of the campus lies to the east. A large open field bounds the site to the south, affording a view to the distant plains. The site slopes sharply from west to east, with grade variation of approximately 66 feet.

The solution was influenced largely by the sloping site, required phasing, and surrounding campus. Four, six-story towers are clustered in a semi-circle around a large plaza facing south (Figures 52-1 and 52-2). The university owned and operated student union building, scheduled to be built across the street, will face north and complete the enclosure of the plaza. The towers become walls which create outdoor spaces or rooms leading from this central plaza. These spaces step up and down the sloping site with the buildings, forming an ever changing spatial sequence for the pedestrian. The courts formed by these spaces serve as multi-purpose activity areas for the apartment dwellers. The towers are designed to appear as one building to the passerby and blend with the scale of the existing campus buildings. They will form a larger scale orientation of the project to the campus on the south and help define the campus from the residential area to the north.

The pool is integrated into the main public space adjacent to the central plaza at an intermediate level. Landscaping, paving patterns, concrete retaining wall textures, and exterior lighting are all designed as an integral part of the project. A two-story administration building, with an open arcade through the building, nestles between two of the towers and forms a gateway for the major pedestrian movement from the project's street side.

Project Solution

We used masonry load-bearing construction because of different conditions. While economic considerations are definite factors in our structural choice, of greatest interest to us in retrospect is the design freedom it gave us. Truly, the nature of the project influenced our choice of structure. On the other hand, the masonry load-bearing structure influenced our design concept.

Any dormitory or apartment complex is cellular in nature and lends itself to masonry bearing-wall construction. (See Figure 4-7, page 22.) The interior masonry walls are an excellent solution to the maintenance problem found in rental housing and will withstand the wear and tear for many years. This problem is very much a factor in student housing where actual destruction sometime arises.

This construction type is also a faster building process due to elimination of many building trades. Essentially, only two major trades are involved. By the time the brickwork and slabs are finished, the project is relatively complete.

Masonry load-bearing construction was in mind during the conceptual design phase and definitely influenced our thinking. We wanted to create a plan which departed from the traditional double loaded corridor concept found in so many housing projects. We wished to develop a housing complex which would give more of an individual identity to the inhabitants. With masonry load-bearing construction, the manipulation of the cellular spaces becomes entirely practical and allows a variable three-dimensional plan.

Figure 52-1. Jayhawker Apartment Towers. Four six-story towers clustered in a semi-circle around a large plaza facing south. (Also see Figure 4-8, page 23.)

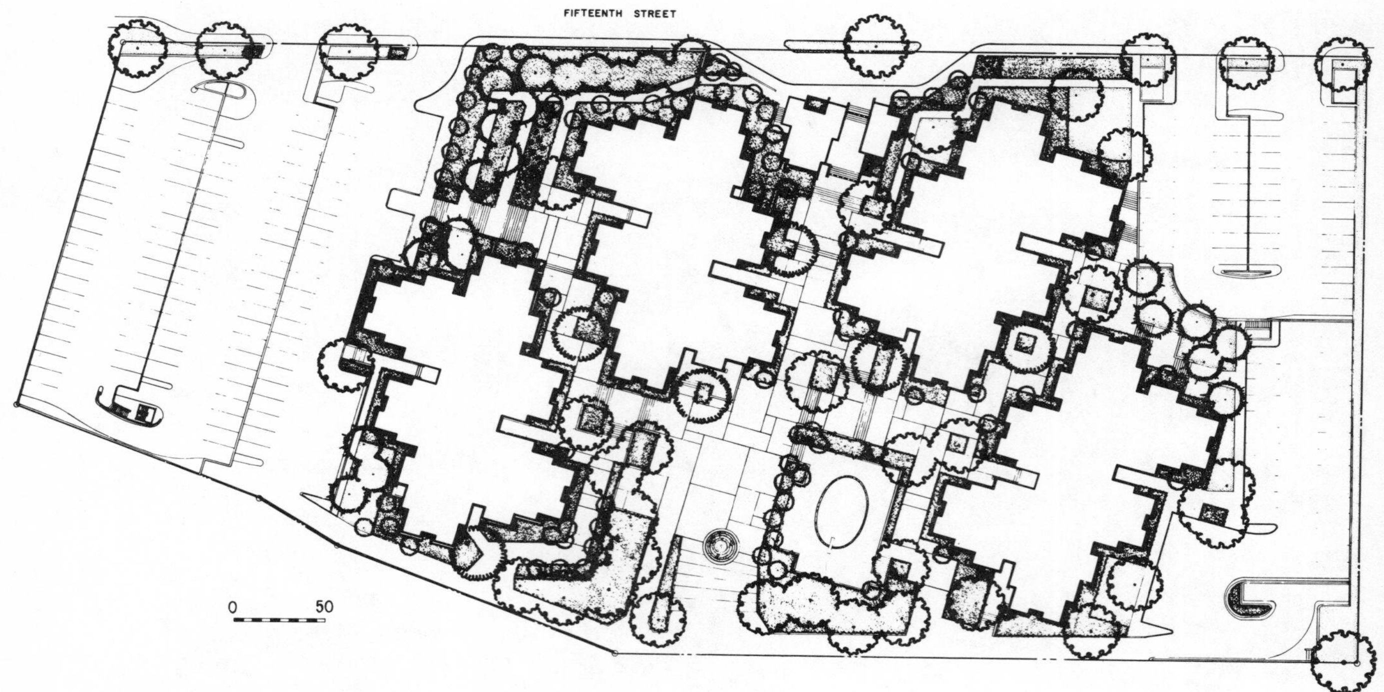

Figure 52-2. Site plan of the Jayhawker Apartment Towers.

Each tower contains six floors of apartments, plus a partial lower floor containing meeting rooms, laundry rooms, and mechanical rooms. A typical apartment tower floor is made up of six apartment clusters with two apartments forming a cluster. Each cluster is terminated by a foyer. A typical two-bedroom apartment is modified on the ground floor to accomodate a building manager and office. The parking is distributed at opposite ends of the site in parking structures, tucked into the slopes and conforming to the existing grades. The grouping of the buildings with the parking also facilitates the phasing of the project.

The six-story towers are constructed of 8″-thick bearing walls made up of two 3″ brick wythes, with 2″ mortar fill and 6″ concrete flat slab floors. This construction method affords an economic and expeditious means of creating a single frame which provides structure as well as the interior and exterior finishes. In addition, this system of construction lends itself to the cellular, short-year spatial requirements which provide a design flexibility for a variation of internal and external forms and spaces creating more intimate living experiences. The flat, concrete floor slab becomes the finished ceiling, and the acoustical plane is created by carpeting on floors throughout.

The construction schedule called for the two towers in the first phase to be topped out by December of this year, which is approximately four months from the time ground was broken. This was necessary to avoid laying brick in severe winter weather which would require special protection and laying procedures.

The staging of the project, together with construction techniques of masonry load-bearing construction, influenced the four, six-tower concept to some extent. Each phase includes two towers instead of one and enables the contractor to brick one story of one tower and move to the next while the concrete floor is poured on the first. This alternating of the two trades back and forth between the towers assures a continuous construction process.

The City of Lawrence adheres to the B.O.C.A. Code. When the City was presented with the plans for approval, the building inspector felt it necessary to rely on B.O.C.A. headquarters in Chicago for final engineering approval on the brick bearing-wall construction. They, in turn, accepted it as rational design by an engineer.

During the research for the design process, we found the ideal masonry load-bearing wall would be an 8″ wall consisting of one 3″ brick wythe, one 2″ void, and another 3″ brick wythe. This wall will provide the optimum waterproofed condition. However, the Code does not rate this wall as a 2-hour, fire-rated wall. Because we needed a 2-hour wall, it was necessary to grout the entire 2-inch void to obtain the required wall.

The brick color and texture becomes a very important design consideration in this project as it is the major exterior and interior material. It had to be selected with the understanding that it must be lived with day-in and day-out; it must have a human feeling and import a warmth to the apartment dwellers. A light brick was preferred over a dark due to the interior brick walls and the desire to keep the rooms light and fresh.

A handmade character, rather than a machine-like quality, was also looked for in the brick. The large exterior masses which can be viewed from good distances are vulnerable to a bland uninteresting cardboard effect if the right brick is not selected. These building masses had to read as a texture from a distance. This meant blending light and dark bricks, but not to such an extent that the walls would take on a salt and pepper effect when closely viewed. The final selection was made from those which had variation in color and texture within the individual bricks.

The many advantages to the masonry load-bearing system which affect the economics of a project both directly and indirectly might be summarized as follows:

1. Eliminated structural skeleton minimizes structural requirements and redundant construction procedures and applications.
2. Minimized floor to floor heights as floor construction creates the ceiling system eliminating added ceiling construction.
3. Structural system becomes finished building shell, and the structural walls become the completed interior finish.
4. Structural walls have inherent fire resistance ratings and acoustical properties.
5. Flat slab has inherent fire resistance rating, and when combined with carpet on the floor, it becomes acoustical phase.

Bids were taken on this project in September 1966. Because of the money market and various other reasons, the project was postponed and subsequently substantially revised. The final contract was negotiated with the contractor who had been the low bidder previously. The total cost of one of the four typical apartment towers was $928,000; this did not include any of the site work and landscaping, but it did include everything within the tower itself, such as year-round air-conditioning, carpeted floors, all of the toilets and their finishes, the built-in kitchens, and kitchenetts, two elevators, and generally everything within the tower except furnishings.

Of the $928,000, $703,000 was general construction. A typical apartment tower contains 76,130 square feet, which means the general construction was $9.19 per-square foot; the total cost, including air-conditioning, was $12.15 per-square foot.

Structural System

The load-bearing structural system used in this building utilizes load-bearing brick walls and a poured-in-place 6-inch-thick concrete slab diaphragm. Slabs were considered to have 100 percent bearing area on interior walls, and 50 percent on exterior walls. Bearing walls, resisting moment and shear due to wind, will act according to their relative stiffness.

The induced stresses due to wind and overturning were not critical due to the arrangement of bearing shear walls in both directions and the depth of the building.

Although the building is located in Seismic Zone 1, history indicates this area is not Seismic active, so earthquake forces were not considered.

The building consists of a lower level, six floors, and a roof. Typical 8-inch interior load-bearing brick walls were the supporting element from lower level to roof. The unreinforced brick walls consist of two wythes of brick, fully grouted collar joint, and minumum wall ties. Compressive strength of the brick is in excess of 10,000 psi and the mortar is ASTM Type "S". Actual compressive stresses on the walls were considerably less (200-300 psi) than the code allowable of 400 psi for grouted walls.

Part 7: Construction

53. Development of structural clay facing wall panels in Denmark.

Jørgen Brynup, Teglindustriens Tutniske Tjeneste, Copenhagen, Denmark

Background for Development of Brick Wall Panels

In Denmark several independent firms have each developed a brick wall panel system from their own background, and each of these systems competes with the others and with traditional masonry constructions alongside with concrete wall panels.

The development started in the early sixties, and now there are seven competing systems. The total production of brick wall panels is estimated to go up by 50 percent from 1966 to 1967.

Since the fifties, the demand in Denmark for all kinds of buildings has vastly exceeded the production capacity within the so-called traditional sector of the building industry. Consequently, the concrete panel industry has since rapidly developed in quality and capacity.

At present, the panel sector of the building activity covers about 20 percent of the total activity.

Since 1957 the mason contractors and the brick and tile industry have closely cooperated in advancing the traditional building sector, which in Denmark utilizes brickwork for all load-bearing walls. Our efforts on behalf of the masonry wall have aimed in the following directions:

1. Comparisons between economics of traditional and non-traditional constructions.
2. Rationalization of the bricklaying procedure.
3. Efforts to increase the number of bricklayers.
4. Efforts to teach the architect to combine brick walls with floor panels, carpentry panels, etc. in order to combine most of the advantages of the element building technique with the advantages of the load-bearing masonry wall.

Although these efforts are being continued, it has been natural for the Danish brick and tile industry to enter into the industrialization of the building activity by developing brick wall panels and generally promoting developments of such constructions.

After this background on the development of brick wall panels in Denmark, we are ready to discuss the different systems.

Figure 53-1. Part of a single family house with facing wall panels of the Thilo system. The facing bricks are 55 x 55 x 230 mm. (2-1/4 x 2-1/4 x 9-3/8 inches), which is half the thickness of the Danish normal size. The thickness of the layer of light-weight concrete depends upon the insulation value desired so that the total thickness of the panel may vary from 23 cm. to 30 cm. (9-3/8 inches to 12 inches).

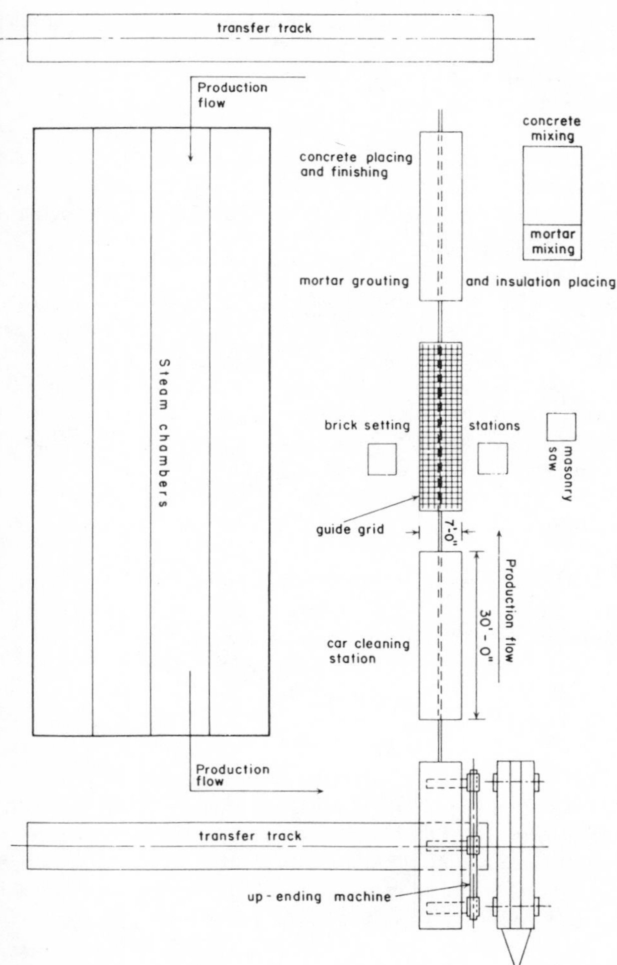

Figure 53-2. Production flowsheet and schematic layout of the Montage-Tegl plant.

Danish Systems of Brick Facing Wall Panels

The survey will be given in chronologic order.

The Thilo System

This was the first system on the market, and the first house to be built with these elements was erected in 1962.

The system was developed by the architect, Aage Emil Thilo. The panels are made on a horizontal grid of steel in which the facing bricks are fixed frontside down. A form frame of the desired dimensions is positioned in advance. Window or door frames may be installed if desired. Then, a cement mortar is poured out to fill all joints. Next, reinforcement is laid down, and light-weight concrete is added in the desired thickness. As aggregate for the concrete is used, lightweight expanded clay aggregates (Leca). The element is finished with a thin coat of plaster. After curing the panel is raised and stored until it goes to the building site.

It will be noticed that there is a traditional brick pattern in the wall, a pattern which continues from panel to panel only interrupted by the vertical joints which are finished on the building site with the same kind of mortar as used for the joints between the bricks.

So far, the system has been used only for single family houses (Figure 53-1).

A/S Montage-Tegl

In 1961, five Danish brick manufacturers on Zealand began work on designing and establishing a plant to produce brick wall facing panels. The first investigations were so successful that it was decided to start the company of A/S Montage-Tegl.

A plant was built and began producing panels in 1964. The first panels were used for single family houses, but later curtain wall panels were used for office buildings, plants, dormitories, etc.

Figure 53-3. Element from Montage-Tegl A/S for warehouse in Gothenburg. Size of element is 500 x 135 x 19 cm. (83 feet x 54 inches x 7-5/8 inches).

The production is highly mechanized; all the production takes place on cars running on tracks. The special bricks are laid frontside down on a steel table. They have a circular U-shaped groove in the back which serves as installation for ladder-type reinforcing wall ties that connect the facing bricks with a concrete wythe on the inner side. Stiff mineral wool bats are put in between, and over these the thin concrete wythe is poured. After curing in steam chambers, the elements are raised and cleaned on the front side. The panels spend four hours in the steam chamber at 100 percent relative humidity and at 140° Fahrenheit. The surface cleaning is facilitated by a special retarder. The productivity is indicated to be roughly 47 square feet of finished wall per man-hour (Figures 53-2 and 53-3).

Teglment System

This system was developed by Trøstrup Brick Works at Videbaek, Jutland. The design corresponds to that of the Thilo-system, but the production capacity is higher.

The present production covers elements for one-storey buildings of all kinds: single family houses, office buildings, factories, and farm buildings. In the lightweight concrete another type of light-weight clay named "Fibo" is used.

Although the plant is not highly mechanized, and therefore rather inexpensive in establishment, the productivity competes fairly well with that of A/S Montage-Tegl.

The element form is without grid, but the bricks are placed on T-irons, which ensures good horizontal placing of the bricks. Vertically the distance between the bricks is guided by small pins of sizes depending on the tolerances of the bricks. Thus, all lengths and all patterns of bricks may be used. And as the joints are finished after erection on the building site, all kinds of joints (as to form, color, and texture) may be used. Thus, except for the vertical joints between the elements, the panel wall looks like a well-made masonry wall (Figures 53-4 and 53-5).

The Kornerup System

This system may be characterized as a link between traditional brickwork and brick wall panels. The panels are constructed in a plant, but by traditional, although rationalized, bricklaying.

The elements consist of a 11 cm. (4-3/8 in.) brick wythe, a cavity filled with mineral wool bats of about 7.5 cm (3 in.) thickness, and an inner wythe of 4-3/8 in. common bricks or f. inst. sandlime bricks.

At the bottom, the element consists of a concrete beam which facilitates transportation as the element is not reinforced but is carried in a special angle bar. This beam also serves as part of the floor deck.

The first project where this system was used was a large children's hospital at Vangede near Copenhagen, erected in 1964.

The bricklaying process is facilitated by corner pole type jigs and by scaffold pallets which move vertically and maintain the mason's position to the work so that a minimum of bending and lifting is involved (Figure 53-6).

SHT Teglelement

SHT Teglelement is developed and produced by A/S Sander Hansens Traelasthandel (timber merchant). It does not in any way differ from the Teglment system, except that the joints between the elements are sawtoothed. The advantage of this is that theoretically it is not possible to distinguish a house built by this system from a traditional masonry house. Things, including houses, sell better when they do not look too industrialized. Architects do not consider this solution to be

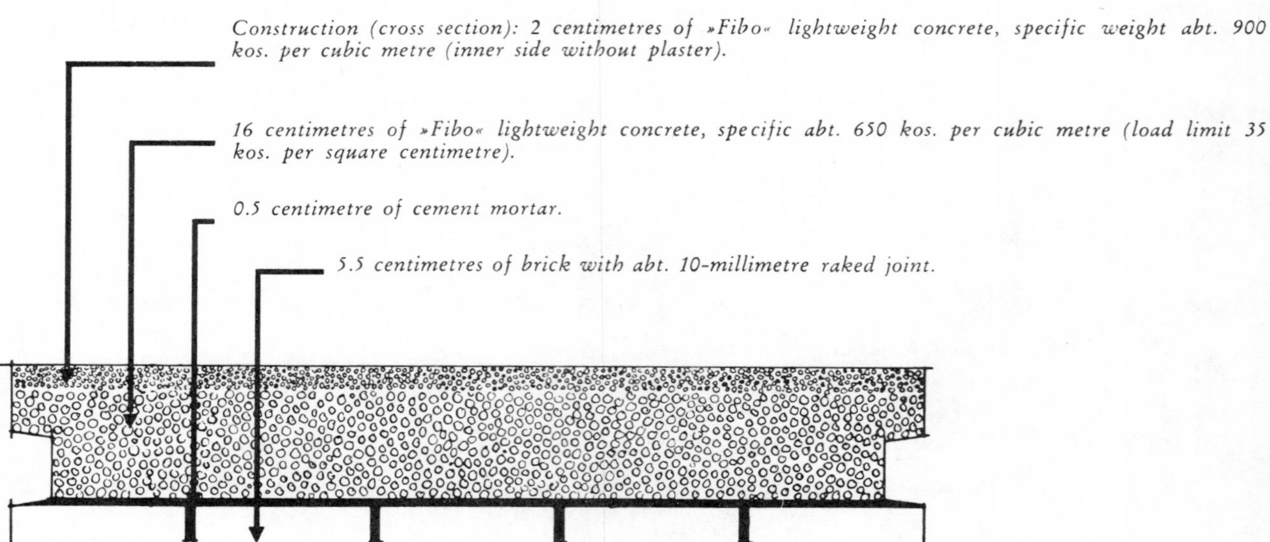
Construction (cross section): 2 centimetres of »Fibo« lightweight concrete, specific weight abt. 900 kos. per cubic metre (inner side without plaster).
16 centimetres of »Fibo« lightweight concrete, specific abt. 650 kos. per cubic metre (load limit 35 kos. per square centimetre).
0.5 centimetre of cement mortar.
5.5 centimetres of brick with abt. 10-millimetre raked joint.

Figure 53-4. Horizontal through-section of Teglment.

Figure 53-5. Teglment wall panel.

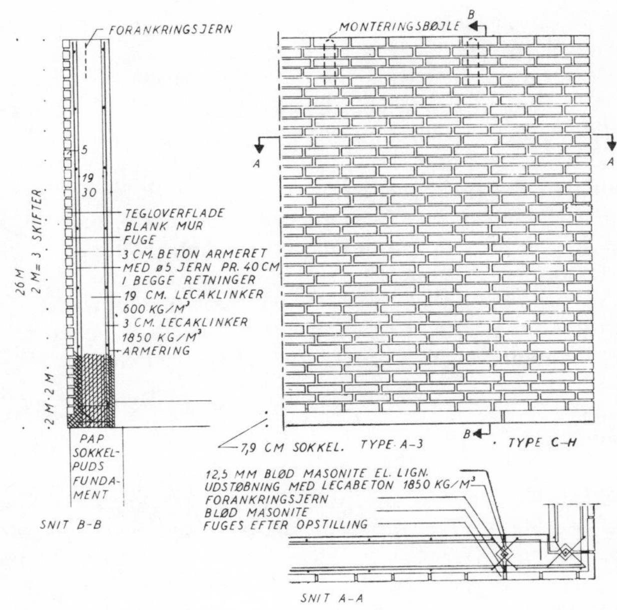

Figure 53-7. Through-section and front elevation of SHT Teglelement.

Figure 53-6. Glimpse of the Kornerup plant showing the equipment used. A considerable advantage in comparison with traditional brickwork is that production may go on independent of weather conditions and the building site in general.

quite honest, and they prefer some manifestation that wall elements are shown as such.

The disadvantage of this interlocking system is that the elements are somewhat more sensitive to transport and erection, and it has also proved to be difficult to make the joints made on site look like those made at the plant.

The plant is situated at Herning, Jutland, and the elements are especially used for single family houses. (Figure 53-7)

Arnborg Teglelement

Principally, this system does not differ from the SHT Teglelement, and therefore only a few details will be mentioned here. The bricks are only 3-1/4 in. thick, and the bonding between the elements is made by putting in locking bricks.

Prefanova

A/S Fyns Teglelementfabrik was started last year and is now delivering brick facing wall panels for some 4,600 apartments in four-storey blocks to the satelite town of Vollsmose near Odense. The satelite town was built by a joint effort of housing associations and is considered to have the highest degree of prefabrication yet realized.

The brick facing wall panels had to compete with panels of reinforced concrete with the normal grey surface and with more decorative concrete panels with exposed aggregates on the surface. The price for the brick elements was between those of the two competing elements, and it is significant for the evaluation of wall elements that the brick solution was preferred.

This is background for the start of the brick panel plant financed by the local brick and tile works and the biggest mason contractors in the area.

The elements are principally based on the Kornerup system, but with further developments in mechanization and design. Thus, the masons are placed at a fixed level, whereas the panels are lowered concurrently with the work speed.

The company has developed other similar elements which are to be used for a rather large plant and later for an agricultural high school.

It is the hope that these elements may be produced at least partly, by a bricklaying machine, which is under joint development in the Danish brick and tile industry (Figure 53-8).

Figure 53-8. Apartment building at Vollsmose under erection. (Prefanova facing wall panels.)

Lameltegl

A/S De forenede nordjyske Teglvaerker has developed a load-bearing wall element of hollow clay blocks in which mineral wool is placed. These elements stand for more advanced use of the burned clay material as the blocks themselves afford good heat insulation and represent the load-bearing quality in combination with slight reinforcement.

At the moment such elements are produced according to the Kornerup system, but due to the bigger size of the blocks, the bricklaying job runs faster, and the elements are not as heavy as the other types of elements (Figure 53-9).

Figure 53-9. Lameltegl facing wall element developed by A/S De forenede nordjyske Teglvaerker.

Broager Teglelementfabrik

A/S De forenede Teglvaerker ved Egernsund has erected a pilot plant for production of brick facing wall panels. The first panels from this plant have just been used for erection of three single family houses. These panels have bricks on the facing as well as on the inner side of the panel; the facing wall is made of bricks of normal size, and the inner wall is made of hollow clay blocks. The insulation between is a special kind of stiff, strong foam insulation, which not only gives the heat insulation desired but also a stiff connection between the facing wall and the inner panel. The facing and inner panels are made separately, frontside down, in a special grid like the Teglment system.

The pilot plant will continue as a pilot plant, but production of the panels developed will go on in buildings being erected in connection with the pilot plant (Figure 53-10).

Future of the Structural Clay Panel Industry in Denmark

It will be understood that there is a certain interest for using normal bricks in the brick facing wall elements. There are several reasons for this. Generally, the consumer prefers the normal brickwork with its Danish, traditional background of more than 800 years, and the brickworks obtain certain advantages from being able to run the same production both for elements and for normal brickwork. Further, the market gets the advantage that normal bricks are produced in a certain color range and with several surface treatments.

Figure 53-10. Newly developed brick facing wall element from A/S De forenede Teglvaerker ved Egernsund (Broager).

However, with future development within the wall panel industry it will become more economical to produce special bricks or blocks as components in the elements. This will result in a fertile interchange between the brick and tile industry and the market.

As to the further development of elements of burned clay it may be expected that one or more of the systems will turn out to be more successful than the others and thus invite a higher degree of industrialization. Within the concrete element industry, the evolution has moved to some extent from storey-high elements of about 4,000 pounds to elements of room-size with weights of up to 40,000 pounds for use in the so-called closed systems. A parallel development in burned clay elements is to be expected because such room-size elements will not be as heavy as the concrete elements of similar sizes.

As regards the mortars used in the elements, there is already some interest in using such advanced types as e.g. the Sarabond mortar. This opens new possibilities for developing some kind of glued, burned clay elements.

As mentioned, the development of the structural clay wall panels in Denmark is characterized by the several competing systems which have been developed and brought to market. Competition will show which of these systems will take the lead. This is not only a question of mechanizing production, but also a question of quality and appearance because bricks as such are sold mostly because of their appearance, in which word is also implied the ability to patinate well.

As it has been fairly easy to make concrete elements, the Danish concrete element industry has expanded rapidly. Now that the market wants a wider range of choice, the market for structural clay in facing wall panels seems very promising, and it is up to this industry to rationalize and expand the production to cover the demand.

References

1. Dawson, John A., "Report of the Canadian Technical Mission on the Use of Prefabricated Structural Ceramics in Industrialized Building in Europe," June 1966, pp. 1-124.
2. *Lerindustrien*, No. 3, Teglindustriens Tekniske Tjeneste, Special issue of the periodical on the occasion of the CIB Conference, Copenhagen, 1965, pp. 1-24.
3. *Tegl,* No. 3 1966,Teglindustriens Tekniske Tjeneste, Volume 14.000 pp. 1-36.
4. *Tegl,* No. 4, 1964, Teglindustriens Tekniske Tjeneste, Volume 14.000, pp. 1-34.
5. *Tegl,* No. 2, 1966, Teglindustriens Tekniske Tjeneste, Volume 14.000, pp. 1-36.
6. *Tegl,* No. 3, 1967, Teglindustriens Tekniske Tjeneste, Volume 14.000, pp. 1-32.

54. Bricklayer training in the U.S.

Don Halsell, Clay Products Association of the Southwest, Keene, Texas

This chapter reports various ways a young man can learn the bricklaying trade in the United States. Union apprenticeships, vocational bricklaying, building trades education, industrial cooperative training, institutional vocational training in the prison systems, and the chance method of learning the trade are the ways men learn bricklaying. Pertinent past and current events to stimulate the concern of the masonry industry for adequate bricklayer training are reviewed.

The local unions cannot put apprentices to work if there are not jobs for them. If contractors cannot provide on-the-job employment to train apprentices, unions cannot be expected to add to their apprentice rolls. Contracting brick work is extremely competitive. Contractors complain that the cost of training an apprentice is too great. Clearly, there are ways and means available for reducing this cost, which are discussed herein.

Obviously, the unions cannot expand if there is no place for their members to work. Most indicators show, however, that there is more work than there are available bricklayers at the present time, and this condition has prevailed for the last 100 years except in times of national economic depression. When training is not expanded, jobs for bricklayers decrease. In areas where there is an extreme shortage of craftsmen, the design professions substitute other building materials. For example, in 1883 the first skeleton frame steel building was built in Chicago, and load-bearing brick walls died for 83 years. What motivated the inventor of the steel frame? There is reason to believe that it may well have been a bricklayers' strike.[1]

The bricklayers' union, brick manufacturers, contractors, and individual homebuilders have a stake in seeing that craft training is provided. There has been a growing trend of togetherness among the major organizations concerned, which will undoubtedly expand future training opportunities.[2]

Shortage of Bricklayers

Number of Craftsmen.

The numbers of bricklayers in the United States is a concern to the entire building industry. Although it is difficult to determine the number of bricklayers in the U.S.A., a 1964 estimate of union and non-union craftsmen totaled 160,000.[3] An estimate developed by the Mason Contractors Association of America indicates this number to be nearer 200,000. The author believes there are definitely more non-union bricklayers laying brick than union.

It is interesting to note that in 1910, statistics compiled from the U.S. Census Bureau showed the number of masons in the country to be about 169,000.[4] During this period the annual physical volume of construction increased about 3-1/2 times.[5]

The national figures comparing numbers of journeyman completing apprenticeships to mortuary claims paid also indicate a current loss to the trade. From June 1, 1964 to June 1, 1965 there were 1,729 apprentices who became journeymen. The Bricklayers Masons and Plasterers International Union paid mortuary claims on 2,016 men. This is a national loss of 287 men.[6]

Union membership figures are available, but within the Bricklayers, Masons and Plasterers International Union there are tile setters, terrazo workers, cement finishers, plasterers, as well as bricklayers, marble setters and stone masons. In addition to these, there are pointers, caulkers and cleaners, refractory bricklayers, sewer bricklayers, and concrete block layers. As of February, 1967, Mr. Thomas F. Murphy, President of the Union stated the union membership was 151,000.[7] Although bricklayers make up the larger number of this membership, they do not make up the total. Also, no one knows how many union bricklayers are active at the trade. Many card-carrying members are engaged in other employment but have kept their membership active. The author knows of no local unions which keep records of active working members. The paying of dues determines membership.

Projected Future Need for Bricklayers

The United States is short of nearly all skilled trades craftsmen. The U.S. Department of Labor estimates that "an additional 100,000 brick and tile masons will be needed in the next decade. To meet this need, pre-apprentice courses and apprentice training must be greatly expanded."[8]

The President of the United States said in 1965 that to maintain and improve the standards of living for a growing population this country must double the number of buildings by the year 2000. This means that the U.S. must in 35 years construct as many buildings as were constructed in its previous 350 year history.[9]

In 1906 the retiring president of the National Brick Manufacturers' Association said, "The most serious menace to the consumption of brick in the future will be the lack of skilled workmen to put your output into brickwork."[10] This realistic prediction, made some 60 years ago, is probably the first recorded concern of the manufacturers, relating to bricklayer shortage.

Apprenticeship System of Training

Apprenticeship is the oldest method of producing craftsmen; even in Bible times the guilds perpetuated themselves by apprenticing young men to skilled artisans. However, the term and the process of learning by doing are probably the only remaining similarities today.

In 1640 the worker serves his master for an eight years period,or sometimes longer, and was compensated with "meat, drinke and clothing befitting an apprentice." He worked 60 or more hours a week and lived in the house of his master; the apprenticeship agreement dealt almost exclusively with his moral behavior.[11] Let us take a look at the modern apprenticeship system. (Note Figure 54-1.)

Joint Apprenticeship Committee

After World War I, the building boom and curtailment of immigration created a need for comprehensive apprentice training in this country. During the 1920's the effort to develop a national system of apprenticeship grew. By 1937 the Federal Bureau of Apprenticeship and Training was established under the Department of Labor.

> Since 1937 the Bureau of Apprenticeship and Training has cooperated closely with employer, labor, vocational schools and others concerned in setting up and conducting apprenticeship programs throughout American industry. In this undertaking industry has the assistance of field representatives of the bureau and state apprenticeship agencies which have been established in 30 states, the District of Columbia, Virgin Islands, and Puerto Rico.

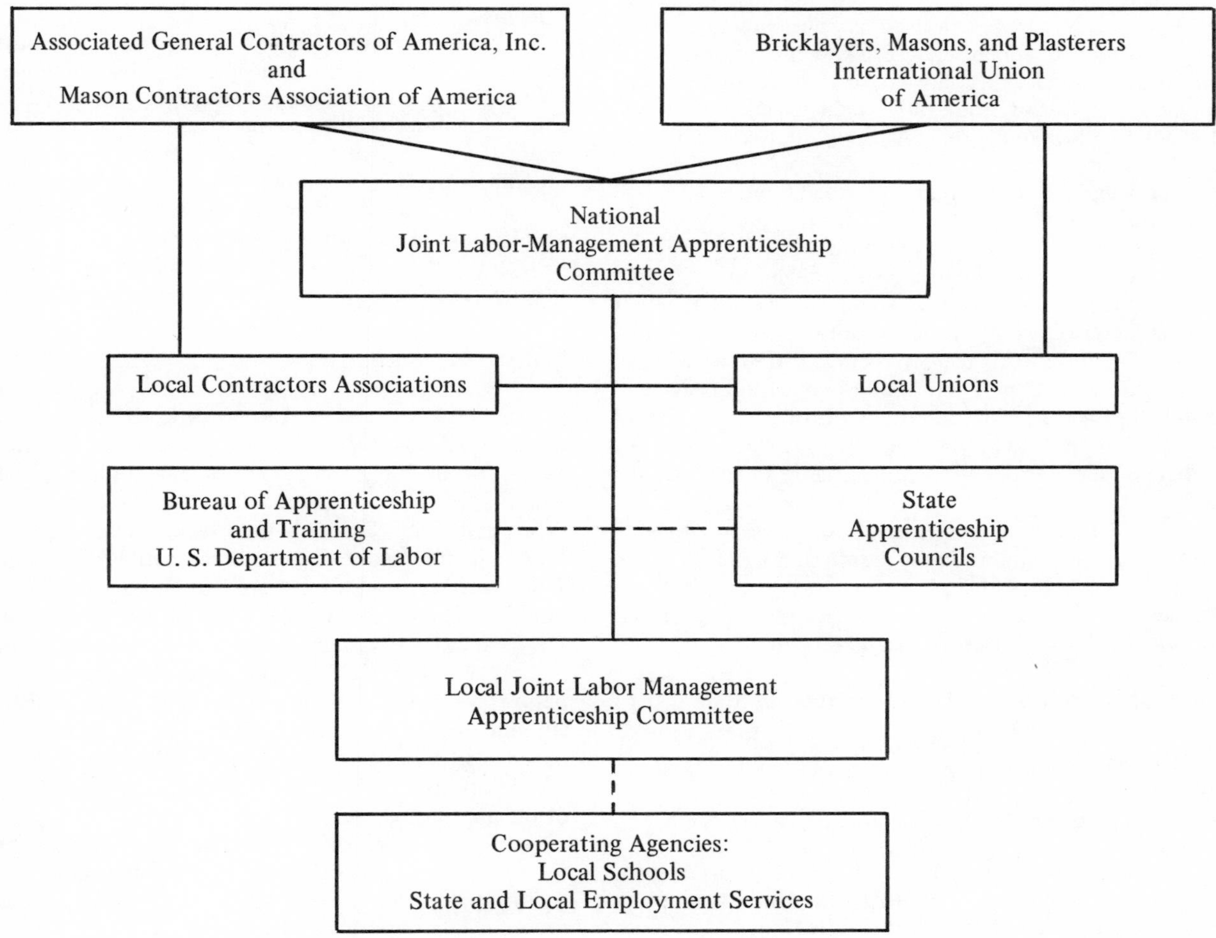

Figure 54-1. Apprenticeship system of the bricklaying trade.[12]

Programs, when established, as well as apprentices are registered with both the Bureau of Apprenticeship and Training and state apprenticeship agencies.[13]

In states where there is no apprentice council, the Bureau of Apprenticeship and Training usually does the coordination. Widespread dissemination and interchange of information on improved training is carried out through industrial periodicals, annual conventions, and conferences. Since 1945 multistate apprenticeship conferences have been held in the East, West and the South.[14]

Joint apprenticeship committees in local communities consists of an equal number of members from labor and management. This committee determines the numbers, standards, and controls of the local program, and submits their decisions to the Bureau of Apprenticeship and Training for approval.

Selection Procedures

The selection procedures for the apprentice are supposed to be set up on the basis of qualifications alone, without regard for race, creed, or color, in a completely non-discriminatory manner. This is not always followed as a fair practice. There are some states in which the Bricklayers, Masons, and Plasterers International Union has no, or few, Negro members. Many bricklayers do not want other men to learn the trade. They continue to feel that others learning the trade will make their jobs less secure.

The following are the minumum qualifications for all apprentice applicants:[15]

1. Age – The age requirements for those who have not had previous experience in the craft is 18 to 25 years. The upper age limit is determined by local conditions and individual circumstances. Allowance is usually made for military service.
2. Education – The minimum level of education is decided by the local program. The requirement of a high school diploma or equivalent is, in many instances, a device to limit the number of applicants and is unjustifiable in the author's opinion.
3. Physical Fitness – The necessity for physical fitness is obvious. If a medical examination is required, it is stated in the local program.
4. Citizenship – Applicants must be citizens of the United States of America or in process of naturalization.

Some local committees also give a written aptitude test to applicants. Such a test has been development by the Bureau of Employment Security.[16]

Apprenticeship Agreement

The apprentice must be covered by a written agreement, usually called an indenture, outlining the terms of employment and training. The agreement gives direction and purpose to the program and insures a satisfactory training experience if its terms are met. Standard agreement forms provide space for a brief statement of wages, hours, probationary period, and an outline of work processes and related study. All this is decided at the local level.

The apprenticeship term is a minimum of three years, as stated in the local standards. Provision is made for the appraisal of, and credit allowance for, previous experience of value. Each program may use its own method for appraising previous experience.

Every apprentice is supposed to be required to attend classes in related and supplemental instruction for a minimum of 144 hours per year. In small, isolated areas, this is not always accomplished. Hours spent on such instruction and study are not classed as hours worked, and wages are not paid.

Most local standards provide for a probationary period of three to six months; special attention is given throughout this time to determine the suitability of the apprentice for the job. During the probationary period, the agreement may be terminated by either party to the agreement upon request. After this period, the agreement is cancelled only after some formality, as provided by the standards. The purpose of the probationary provision is to encourage an effective evaluation of the situation before an apprenticeship is terminated and to do what is reasonable in carrying out the provisions of the agreement.

In setting up an apprenticeship wage schedule, the administrators of the program consider certain fundamentals. The starting wage is sufficient to attract applicants. Also, the wage scale provides for advancement at regular intervals, if satisfactory progress is being made. Toward the last six months of the apprenticeship, the wage of the apprentice approaches that of the journeyman. Apprentice wages usually are expressed as a percentage of the journeyman's wage.

Upon completion of the apprenticeship, a certificate is awarded and the graduate is recognized as a journeyman.

Federal Assistance

Since the passage of the Vocational Act of 1963, a few national MDTA–OJT (Manpower Development and Training Act – On the Job Training) contracts have been signed to train workers. Such was a national MDTA–OJT contract with the Structural Clay Products Institute, which represents some brick and tile manufacturers in the United States of America. This contract, signed in March of 1966, was to train 1,245 bricklayers and tile setters at a cost of $1,300,000. As of June 1967, some 214 bricklayers apprentices were in training.[17]

In brief, the MDTA–OJT programs provided a six-week period of preapprenticeship training. During this time the student receives a stipend. The student is indentured to a contractor, as any other apprentice. The contractor, however, is paid approximately $25.00 per week for the first 12 weeks of the apprenticeship.

The purpose of the government sponsorship is to increase the number of apprentices throughout the nation. The author doubts that the numbers will be appreciably increased. This program has not augmented the apprenticeship rolls in Texas thus far, because the admission of these apprentices is controlled.

The larger contractors, who normally indenture apprentices, are not particularly interested in the government subsidy, whereas the $25.00 per week per apprentice would perhaps be an incentive to smaller contractors.

Vocational Training

The Public School System

Vocational bricklaying in the public school system is a vehicle for contacting masses of young people. As early as 1908 the president of the Brick Manufacturers Association expressed the hope that before many years such courses would be a regular part of the public school system. "It is very important that this should be, for with the present opposition of the labor unions to the apprenticeship system, it is almost impossible for a young man to learn a trade."[18]

While opposition to training programs continues to be a problem in some areas, this is diminishing. The International Union gives this endorsement:

> Another important program that demonstrates our Government's activity and concern in the training field is the Vocational Act of 1963. This Act provides millions of dollars for vocational training and a great part of this money will be used for the establishment of area vocational schools. An attempt will be made to provide pre-employment training in most trades to high school students who desire such training. It is the B.M. & P.I.U's policy to cooperate with these programs, providing our local joint apprenticeship committees act as an advisory committee to the school officals responsible for the operation of vocational high school masonry courses, and providing a B.M. & P.I.U. member is instructing the course, and that the high school students, upon graduation, be given the opportunity of entering into apprenticeship whenever possible.[19]

Cooperation between labor and masonry contractors was evidenced in the establishment of a bricklaying class at Indianapolis Technical High School about 1920. The president of the local bricklayers' union was in charge of instruction. This is especially interesting in view of the fact that, in recent years, union men who accepted such teaching positions have often been criticized by their locals. At times, the local unions have attempted to revoke union membership of such teachers.

After a couple of years training in the vocational bricklaying shop, the student can enter apprenticeship whenever possible. If apprenticeship is not available, this student is certainly more employable as a result of the training received. Vocational bricklaying in the schools is a good way to cut training cost for the contractor, an important consideration if he is to provide on-the-job training.

This type of educational experience opens the door to more students who may want to learn the trade. It also cuts the drop-out rate in apprenticeship. Students usually know, after their experience in vocational education, if they want to pursue apprenticeship.

A year or two of bricklaying in high school has much to offer the student who has other career plans. Those who plan to be teachers face summers of unemployment at their profession. During the author's teaching years, summers and vacation found him working at the trade. Many teachers are forced by circumstances to seek any available employment during summer months, often unskilled and poorly paid. Summer is the peak employment period for the construction craftsmen, so fulltime bricklayers would not be displaced. Any young man who plans to attend college can be employed at bricklaying during summers, and often half days during the school year if he is employable.

As vocational field training representative for the Structural Clay Products Institute for 1965-66, it was the author's privilege to work with the state directors of vocational education in states east of the Rocky Mountains. As of June 1966, there were 28 states that taught vocational bricklaying in the public school system.[20] It is is difficult to determine vocational training from government statistics. The author found vocational schools teaching bricklaying and receiving federal money for operating, but these were not reported in government publications.

The three leading states in bricklayer training are North Carolina, South Carolina and Virginia. The total number for these three states in June of 1966 was 6,712 students. Nationally, there were 150 vocational bricklaying programs on which there is no student count, including the state and federal prison programs.

The Prison System

Bricklayer training in the federal and state penitentiaries has been in existence for many years. Not all institutions are involved in this type of training, but many manufacture their own brick. There was a total of 59 state and federal prisons teaching vocational bricklaying in 1966. These programs vary from a full 8 hours per day of construction to 3 hours per day of classroom instruction. Many of the prisons do their own construction within the walls.

The author believes that prison bricklaying instruction approaches the apprenticeship system in making men employable. For example, the Texas Prison system has one of the finest bricklayer training programs in the nation. This past year, the prison brick plant produced 5,152,000 brick. In addition, other masonry materials were purchased from commercial manufacturers. This material was put in place by prison bricklayers. Some 70 to 80 men are active the year round in laying brick. Bricklaying is especially attractive for men with prison records, because bricklayer craftsmen are hired to produce and no questions are asked about the past.

Building Trades Classes

A building trades program in public high schools usually incorporates the five basic building trades which are carpentry, electrical wiring, plumbing, painting, and masonry. The building trades class is a 3-hour work period each day. Usually, the class will build a house or some building project. Some classes work exclusively in a shop learning the various trades; this is not the best process for developing skill, but is the next best method to a project. The finished product of the training process is a boy who has some elementary knowledge and ability in several building trades. However, construction jobs of today are more specialized then a jack-of-all-trades can fill.

A given building trades class will, in reality, emphasize the area in which the teacher is most competent. Mississippi has some 2,000 students in the building trades program who spend one-fourth to one-half of their time learning the brick trade. For the first time, this year, in Texas, the promotion of bricklayer training has taken place in the building trades classes. Out of 59 building trades classes, bricklaying was taught, to some extent, in 22 classes, and this number will increase during the current school year.

Industrial Arts

Although industrial arts education has importance in the total educational program of a student, this concept usually does not attempt to make students employable. The philosophy is that of providing a general overview for numerous craft or skill areas rather than developing skill in a single field. The industrial arts programs have very little to contribute to bricklayer training. Very few industrial arts instructors have had the opportunity to learn a trade or work as a craftsman on a competitive basis. The educational requirement for the industrial arts teacher is usually a degree, Bachelor of Science in Education, with the major course of study being industrial arts education. The requirements for a vocational T. and I. (trade and industrial) instructor is a high school education, and from five to seven years as a fulltime craftsman. It is evident from this educational difference that the more employable student would come from the vocational school rather than the industrial arts shop.

Industrial Cooperative Training

Most all states participate in I.C.T. (Industrial Cooperative Training). In most states this training is called D.O. (Diversified Occupations). In the program, a student must spend 3 hours per day working in some industry, which does not involve the distribution of goods. D.O. or I.C.T. contribute little to the construction trades. The author has been employed as a coordinator of this type program in a public school. Insurance regulations for those under 18 years of age make it almost impossible for a contractor to hire high school students.

No Organized Program

In most areas of the nation, the open-shop bricklayer has not had the advantage of classroom instruction. This probably is not too surprising. However, one would assume that union bricklayers have enjoyed the more structured learning of apprenticeship. The acknowledgement by the National Building Trades Council and the Bureau of Apprenticeship and Training that about 50 percent of the card-carrying building trades craftsmen serve an apprenticeship or attend a vocational school indicates the lack of training for the other half. At the Southern States Apprenticeship Conference in Biloxi, Mississippi in July, 1967, it was reported that the percentage is 35 percent. In B.M. & P.I.U. Local # 5 of Dallas, Texas, three apprentices turned out this past year. The local took in 28 men from the open-shop field. These percentages are considerably less then even the 50 percent spoken of by the Bureau.

The majority of bricklayers learned their trade because they just happened to get a job working for a bricklayer, and he gave them the opportunity to learn the trade. The fact that some men have become top-notch craftsmen with no organized programs of instruction does not lend support to continuing this haphazard learning method.

Bricklayer Productivity

Many techniques,tools, and equipment make it possible for bricklaying production to be increased. A firm of industrial engineers, the A.B. Segur and Company of Oak Park, Illinois, in August 1950, made a motion-time analysis in exploring the possibility of reducing the bricklayer's cost for placing brick in the wall. After the completion of this study the A. B. Segur Company made this statement: "It is highly probable that the bricklaying cost on ordinary eight-inch or four-inch walls can be reduced by 67%."[21] The SCR (Structural Clay Research) Masonry Guide system is equipment used to build masonry corners. These guides eliminate the constant straightening, plumbing, and leveling and thereby substantially increase production.

A production time study was made on January 16, 1967 by the author using a Norman brick (2-2/3 x 4 x 12). The report states:

> " A comparison study was made today on bricklaying production at the double-wall-brick construction site in Dallas. This comparison was made by using SCR Masonry Guides on one wall versus the conventional method of laying brick (with level) on a comparable wall. With the SCR Masonry Guides there were 1,849 brick laid in 12 man hours, for an average of 154 brick laid per man hour. With the conventional method there were 1,828 brick laid in 22 man hours, for an average of 83 brick laid per man hour. This production increase was created by the elimination of lost motion and the competition created by using trig guides. For cost comparison, we figured the bricklayers at $4.50 per hour and labor at $2.40 per hour, then added one supervisory personnel at $4.75 plus 15% overhead. With the use of masonry guides the cost was $56.30 per thousand; with the conventional method, the cost was $93.00 per thousand."[22]

The non-union bricklayer does most of the residential building in Texas. He will probably be expected to lay more brick per day than the union bricklayer, constructing a commercial building. The author estimates the non-union bricklayer working on residences will average 900 to 1200 brick per 8-hour day, while the union bricklayer's production on commercial buildings would range from 600 to 800 brick, assuming a standard modular face brick is used. The author believes that the workmanship required on commercial building is generally superior to residential masonry.

From the author's experience, many residential bricklayers are not interested in building masonry structural systems because this type of construction is new to them. Working with two walls involves better workmanship than veneering a wooden structure.

The commercial bricklayer likes to build masonry structural systems. He usually is interested in doing good workmanship and would like to see all masonry structural systems of brick and clay tile.

The author believes most union bricklayers are against using tools and technics which will increase production. This is evident in the by-laws of many locals which outlaw using corner poles on commercial construction. Of course, the union masonry contractor can not use this equipment if the union does not permit its use. The author is convinced that bricklayers in general are against change. Usually, these technics and tools used to increase production seem to be a threat to job security.

The author believes that production can be increased 30 percent to 50 percent by using SCR masonry process which includes the use of the traditional trowel and level, corner poles, adjustable scaffolding, and a marked mason's line.[23] Most unions will not permit using corner poles on commercial jobs. All known technics, tools, and equipment to increase the production of bricklayers is promoted by the author in his educational activities.

Bricklayer Immigrants

Because of the opportunities for skilled bricklayers, many craftsmen came from Europe to the United States of America prior to 1920. In recent years, masonry contractors have gone to Europe on recruitment drives for bricklayers. For example, in 1966 24 bricklayers from England were recruited for Philip Evans, partner in a firm with 120 bricklayers at Springfield, Illinois. In 1965, this same firm recruited 15 bricklayers from northern Ireland. An American Embassy spokesman said that during the last eight months of 1966, two groups of about 30 to 40 each have gone to Massachusetts and Michigan.

The Swiss have requirements called "SIA – Standards 113 for the Calculation and Construction of Masonry" printed in 1964, which have certain specifications for workmanship at three levels of quality. When these are compared with the workmanship requirements by the U.S.A. standard, "Recommended Building Code Requirements for Engineered Brick Masonry, SCPI May 1966" comparisons can be drawn between minimal acceptable standards for workmanship in the U.S.A. and those in Switzerland. The following tables make such comparisons.

In all cases the U.S. minimum acceptable requirement for bricklayer craftsmanship in plumbing a wall is more stringent than the Swiss requirement for normal quality workmanship by factors ranging from 17 to 60 percent. The U.S. minimum requirement is more lax than the "Special Quality" Swiss requirement except for high walls, in which case the American requirement is more stringent.

In all cases, the mortar joint thickness permitted by U.S.A. standards is less then permitted by Swiss standards by factors ranging from 12 to 33 percent. Apparently, the normal bricklayers are better in the U.S.A. than in Switzerland. It is interesting that the Swiss recognize high-quality workmanship and U.S. standards make no provisions for existence of such a phenomenon.

Summary

Bricklayer training programs must be expanded if brick and tile is to obtain its present share of the building dollar. Because of the unwillingness of many labor unions and contractors to train men, the apprenticeship system of training is likely to rock along at about the same speed as it has in the past. In 1907 the B.M. & P.I.U. had nearly 10,000 apprentices,[24] and in June 1967 there were 9,556 apprentices on the B.M. & P.I.U. rolls.[25] During this time the annual physical volume of building construction more than tripled.

The MDTA–OJT grants are providing a better prepared apprentice, but will not appreciably increase the number.

The suggestions for increasing bricklayer training lie in the area of expansion in the public school system. The public, the industry, and all concerned must take steps to persuade the public schools of this nation to offer trade education as well as academic education.

Many people today are engaged in more than one type of yearly employment. Why not make vocational bricklaying classes available at night for adults who may wish to expand their base of employable skills?

Bricklaying has never been a craft where the demand is constant from month to month. If high school students with other career objectives study bricklaying as part-time employment, this also will help to meet the fluctuating market demands. They will be home from college in summer, and may possibly be available for part-time work during the school year.

State organizations should have full-time apprentice coordinators. The B.M. & P.I.U. of America should have an apprenticeship coordinator to help promote apprenticeship. The Negroes should be given a chance to learn the trade in all sections of our nation. Before the training problem is solved, industry will possibly have to set up training programs for men who want to be bricklayers.

I wish to express my sincere appreciation for the opportunity afforded me some 12 years ago to serve an apprenticeship in the bricklaying trade. The two organizations that made it possible for me to become a bricklayer are Local # 5, Dallas, Texas, of the B.M. & P.I.U., and Mr. George Connell of Connell Construction Company in Dallas. I enjoy having a part in making it possible for other young men to become bricklayers, if that is their choice.

References

1. Buchard, John and Bush, Albert, *The Architecture of America,* Little, Brown and Co., 1966, pp. 183-184.
2. Murphy, John J., "Special Circular N. 19," B.M. & P.I.U. of America, Washington, D.C., Nov. 30, 1965, pp. 2-4.

3. "Employment Outlook for Bricklayers," Occupational Outlook Report Series (Reprints from Bulletin #1450-12), U.S. Department of Labor, p. 10.
4. "A Chronological History of Trade Associations in the Brick Industry," *Objective Unity,* Structural Clay Products Institute, Washington, D.C., 1950.
5. *The Statistical History of the United States from Colonial Times to the Present,* Fairfield Publishing Co. Inc., 1965.
and
Statistical Abstracts of the United States, U.S. Gov. Printing Office, 1965, p. 742.
6. Murphy, *loc. cit.*
7. "Bricklayers' Murphy Blends the Old and New," *Engineered News-Record,* Feb. 23, 1967, p. 107.
8. "High School Career Days Speech," Structural Clay Products Institute, Washington, D.C., 1966.
9. *Ibid.*
10. *Objective Unity, op. cit.*, p. 1906.
11. Perry, Reginald, *Apprenticeship Past and Present,* Bureau of Apprenticeship and Training, Washington, D.C., Revised 1964, pp. 1-2.
12. *The National Apprenticeship Program,* Bureau of Apprenticeship and Training, U.S. Department of Labor, 1964.
13. Perry, *loc. cit.*
14. *Ibid.*
15. Perry, "Recommended Selected Standards and Procedure Prepared by the National Joint Apprenticeship and Trainin Committee for the Bricklaying Industry," Bureau o Apprenticeship and Training, Washington, D.C., 1964.
16. *Ibid.*
17. Perry, "Report of Mason Relations Committee," Structura Clay Products Institute, Washington, D.C., June 7, 1965 pp. 3-4.
18. *Objective Unity, op. cit.*, p. 1908.
19. Murphy, *loc. cit.*
20. Halsell, Don, "Vocational Bricklaying Report," Structura Clay Products Institute, Washington, D.C., June 1966, p. 7
21. "Motion Time Analysis," A.A. B. Segur Co., Industria Engineers, Oak Park, Illinois.
22. Halsell, Don, Comparison Study of Bricklaying Conducte on Double-Brick-Wall Village, Dallas, Texas, Jan. 16, 1967
23. "SCR Masonry Process," Structural Clay Products Institute Washington, D.C.
24. *Objective Unity, op. cit.*, p. 1907.
25. "Report of Mason Relations Committee," *loc. cit.*

55. Some investigations concerning design, technology, and test of cored brick panels.

Ilia Mitev and Rocen Malchev, Building Research Institute, Sofia, Bulgaria

Industry Development

In recent years, the ceramic industry has shown new trends in producing and applying structural ceramics. In the past the ceramic products were utilized predominantly as a structural material for building walls. Today, perfection of production indicates new possibilities for design and structure of other construction elements. The bricks with thin walls and high percent cavity are used successfully in constructing floor beams and panels, wall bearing or curtain wall panels, vaults, shells, and other structural elements with good technical and economic indicators. Resulting from this evolution, the cored bricks are used more and more in prefabricated construction as a material for the structure of large size construction elements.

In Bulgaria, there is a good background for the large scale application of various types of construction with cored bricks. The suitable climate conditions, the presence of good quality clay, and the modernization of the manufacturing industries are the prerequisites for using cored brick in production and using floor and wall panels in residential, industrial, and farming buildings.

Under these circumstances, during the past few years, the Building Research Institute investigated theoretically and experimentally the different types of large floor and wall elements for prefabricated construction in Bulgaria. Our task was to work out the necessary normative documents, standards, instruction, nomenclatures and typical designs, and to organize the experimental construction.

Available Brick

The design of the cored brick is an important factor in developing the constructive element. The economic factors depend on the type, form, and size of the elements, the manner of production, and their destination. The deciding factor, however, remains the destination of the bricks. This factor decides the cavity percent, the thickness of the walls and the place of the bricks in the cross section, e.g., the configuration of the brick.

Cored bricks of different sizes and forms for floor panels are being designed and tested. (Figures 55-1 and 55-2.) On Figure 55-1a a cored brick for floor panels is illustrated. It is 295 mm. wide, 120 mm. high and 297 mm. long. Typical of these bricks is the unsymmetrically cut shape 25 mm. high. For floor panel production, the cored bricks are turned 180° so that a continuous ceramic-concrete face is formed. The dimensions of these bricks correspond to a module of 30 cm., and they are used for floor panels with supporting distances of 300 to 510 cm. For prestressed floor elements, cored bricks are designed 200 mm. high, 243 mm. wide, and 295 mm. long, the cavity percent being 46 to 70 percent. These bricks are shown on Figure 55-1b and are destined for floor panels spanning 600 cm. and more.

According to their use, the cavity bricks for wall panels are applied in the production of load-bearing, self-bearing, and curtain walls.

With the load-bearing walls, the bricks have a relatively smaller percent of cavity and thicker walls, depending on the requirement for greater strength. With the curtain walls, this percent is considerably greater as the bricks are larger and lighter. The curtain walls are mostly exterior and brick design should be in accordance with the requirements for thermal insulation of the walls.

With load-bearing wall panels, the arrangement of the bricks can be done in the direction of the cavities and crossways. In the first case, the bricks are arranged next to each other forming vertical rows of bricks, while in the second, they form horizontal rows.

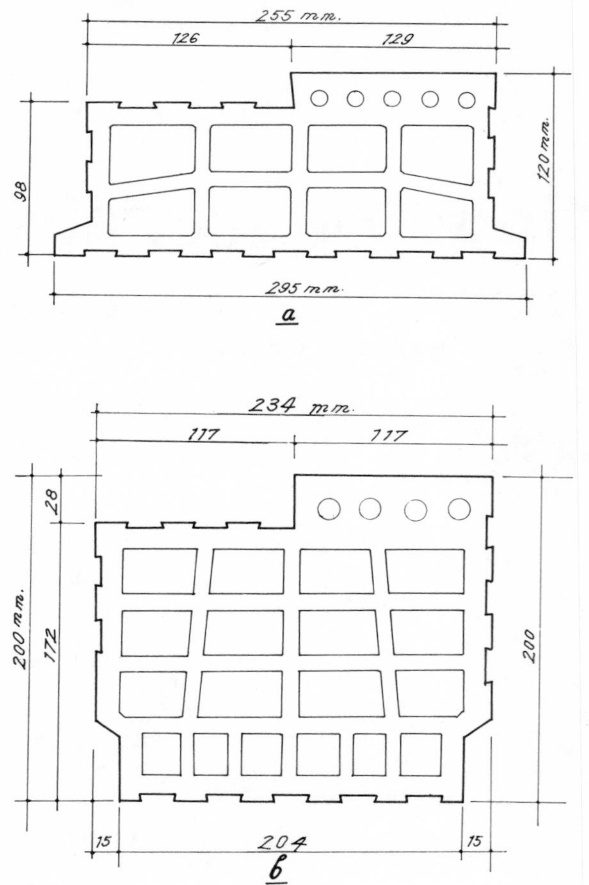

Figure 55-1. Ceramic cored bricks for: (a) floor panels and (b) pre-stressed floor panels.

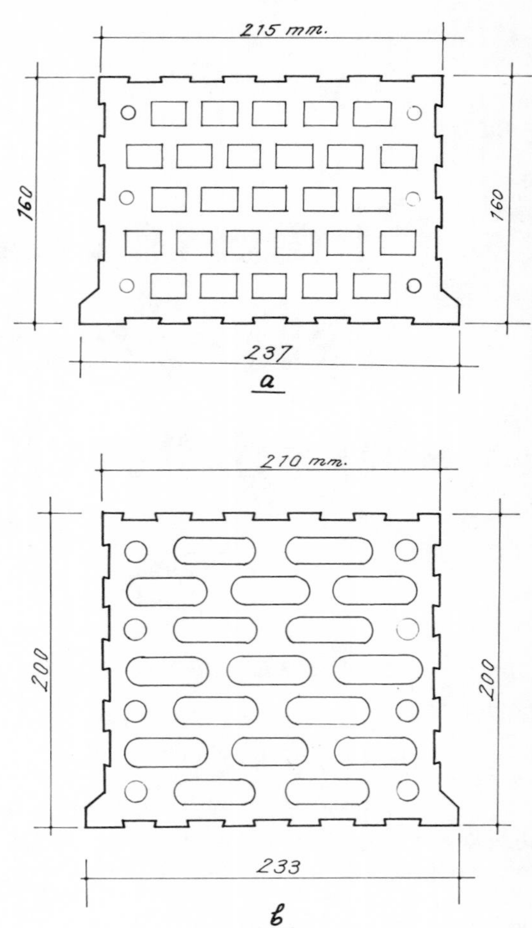

Figure 55-2. Brick for: (a) inside wall panels and (b) outside wall panels.

From the view point of fuller use of the carrying capacity of the bricks, the load transmission in the direction of the cavities is preferred, for in that direction the brick utilizes the whole crosssection. In loading in a perpendicular direction only those vertical walls of the brick which are directed towards the load take part in taking up the load, while the rest have a consolidating role.

Taking into consideration the method of panel production, the brick volume should be chosen so that the weight of a brick is not more than 10 to 15 kg.

The inner partition walls of the brick are usually parallel to the outer surface of the brick. The creation of diagonal walls and rhomboid cavities in our opinion is insufficient. These bricks have little strength when loaded in the perpendicular direction and should be used only in a vertical arrangement.

We must point out that with the production of the cored bricks for the production of bearing wall and panels, there are more stringent requirements in choosing the clay, as well as drying, baking, and transporting bricks. The well-designed brick can be compromised if the above processes are not taken in consideration.

In developing the designs for large sized ceramic panels, the idea that ceramics is a material only for the traditional monolithic building was refuted. The test made proved that panels made of cored bricks have the necessary strength and exploitation indicators and that possibilities even exist for the reduction of their value. This circumstance gives a new stimulus to the ceramic industry and offers great possibilities for utilizing thin wall ceramics.

Ceramic Floor Panels

In Bulgaria, ceramic floor panels are designed according to the module system with a basic module of 30 cm. For the supporting distances of 300 to 510 cm. and loadings corresponding to residential and social buildings, panels are 12, 16, and 18 cm. thick. The panel thickness is equal to the brick height. Brick height is accepted to be equal to about 1/30 of the supporting distance.

With larger loadings, it is advisable to use a thin reinforced concrete slab instead of thicker bricks in the pressure zone of the floor panel.

The width of the floor panels is accepted to be 90, 120 and 180 cm. to make them interchangeable with the reinforced concrete panels used in the practice.

To compute the pressure zone of the ceramic floor panels, it must be considered as a combined ceramic-concrete section with a computing characteristic equal to the arithmetical mean value of the characteristics of the concrete and the ceramics.

In determining the deformations, the stiffness of the section is multiplied by the coefficient 1.20, because of the presence of cavities in the cross section. The shear forces are taken up by the adjacent concrete in the ribs, but it is taken for granted that part of the thin walls of the bricks, which have solid cohesion with the concrete, have their influence on the concrete also. The floor ceramic panels are appropriate in building frameless large panel apartment buildings as well as for the traditional monolithic construction where the walls are monolithic only, while the floors are mode of prefabricated elements.

For covering spans more than 600 cm. and with heavier loading, prestressed ceramic floor panels are recommended. The length of such panels reaches about 7.20 m., the thickness about 25 cm., while the width is fixed at about 150 cm. In the assembly, these panels are reinforced in one direction and doubly supported. The bearing framework is built up of strong strings (rods) situated in the ribs between the longitudinal rows of bricks. The pressure zone is also ceramic concrete, but in view of greater safety statistically, the role of the concrete ribs is emphasized.

The prestressed panels are applied in floor construction of prefabricated apartment buildings on a large scale basis for some types of industrial and farming buildings.

Figure 55-3 shows a prestressed floor panel with a span of 6.0 m.

The construction of the industrial and farming buildings in Bulgaria is done industrially of prefabricated reinforced concrete elements. Parallel to these buildings, which are made of reinforced concrete wall panels with the necessary thermal insulation, wall panels of cored bricks are also designed and tested. These panels are hanging curtain or self-bearing walls and are made of cored bricks, arranged in horizontal rows with the necessary thermal insulation, fine concrete, and ordinary steel. Thus, single layer wall panels of low weight and reduced outlay of concrete and steel, when compared with the other wall panels and applied in practice, show good thermal insulating qualities.

The design calculations for these panels are made with respect to the loading which is obtained when erecting the panel from its horizontal position on the production landing at the time of assembly, and also for wind-loading with the panel in place.

The thermal insulation requirements for farming buildings are considerably greater than those for industrial buildings. Depending on the location of these walls, they should have thermal resistance R_o = 1.0; 1.25 and 1.60 $m^2h^oC/kcal$. This resistance is obtained by using cored bricks, with a cavity percent equal to 40 to 60 percent and a height of 22 to 25 cm.

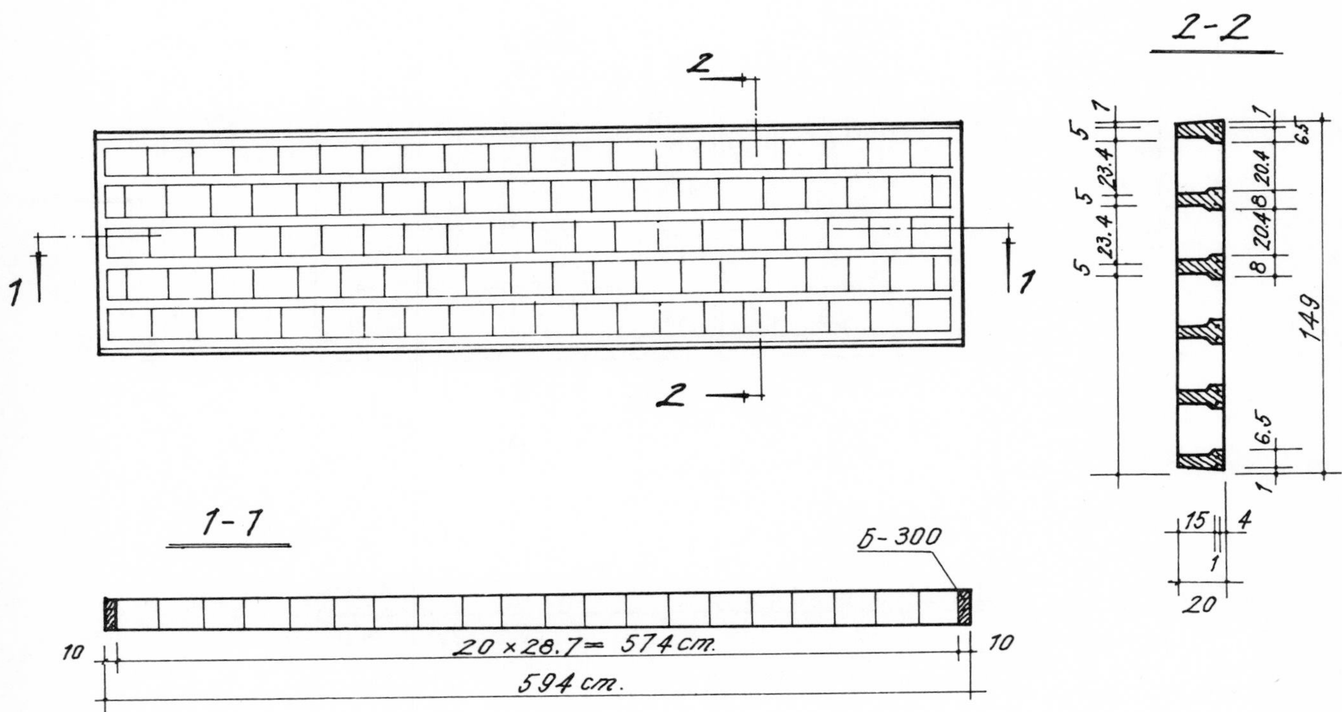

Figure 55-3. Prestressed floor panel.

The industrialized apartment building in Bulgaria was applied on a large scale after 1960. A popular application is in the frameless large panel apartment houses where all the panels are constructed of ordinary and light concrete.

Large Panel Apartment House

The investigations of the Building Research Institute for studying the application of the cored bricks in the panel production for the large panel apartment houses began in 1963. As a result of the initial studies, the authors of this chapter designed a large panel apartment house. The bearing wall floor panels were made out of cored bricks. The building was constructed in 1964.

The calculations of the wall panels were made for the loading, obtained from the horizontal roof and floor constructions and the walls above, and considering the eccentricity in the transmission of the load. Principally these calculations do not differ from the wall calculations when they are made for brick bearing masonry. With the wall panels, produced in a horizontal direction, calculations and measurements are made for the loads that occur during erection, transportation, and assembly.

The inside and outside wall panels for apartment houses are projected and carried out with the dimensions of a room. The arrangement of the bricks can be carried out in vertical or horizontal lines.

In arranging the cored bricks in horizontal lines, each panel with both vertical ends terminates with bricks. Where these cored bricks meet, vertical reinforced concrete columns are formed. The grout concrete of these columns penetrates into the brick cavities, creating small but numerous concrete dowels, which take the shear forces of cohesion. This method of joining provides the possibility for connecting the panels to one another and removes the vertical joint between the panels. At both horizontal ends, the panels are united with each other by a framework which is welded during assembly at the site. When the bricks are arranged vertically, the wall panels are framed with reinforced concrete girders which carry the framework of the panels connecting ties. In connecting these panels, the cross forces are taken up by vertical concrete dowels. In connecting the outside wall panels, vertical joints are formed, requiring packing materials. It should be noted in this case that the problem is solved more efficiently when the outside wall panels are made of cavity bricks. Each panel consists of separate bricks, between each of which numerous

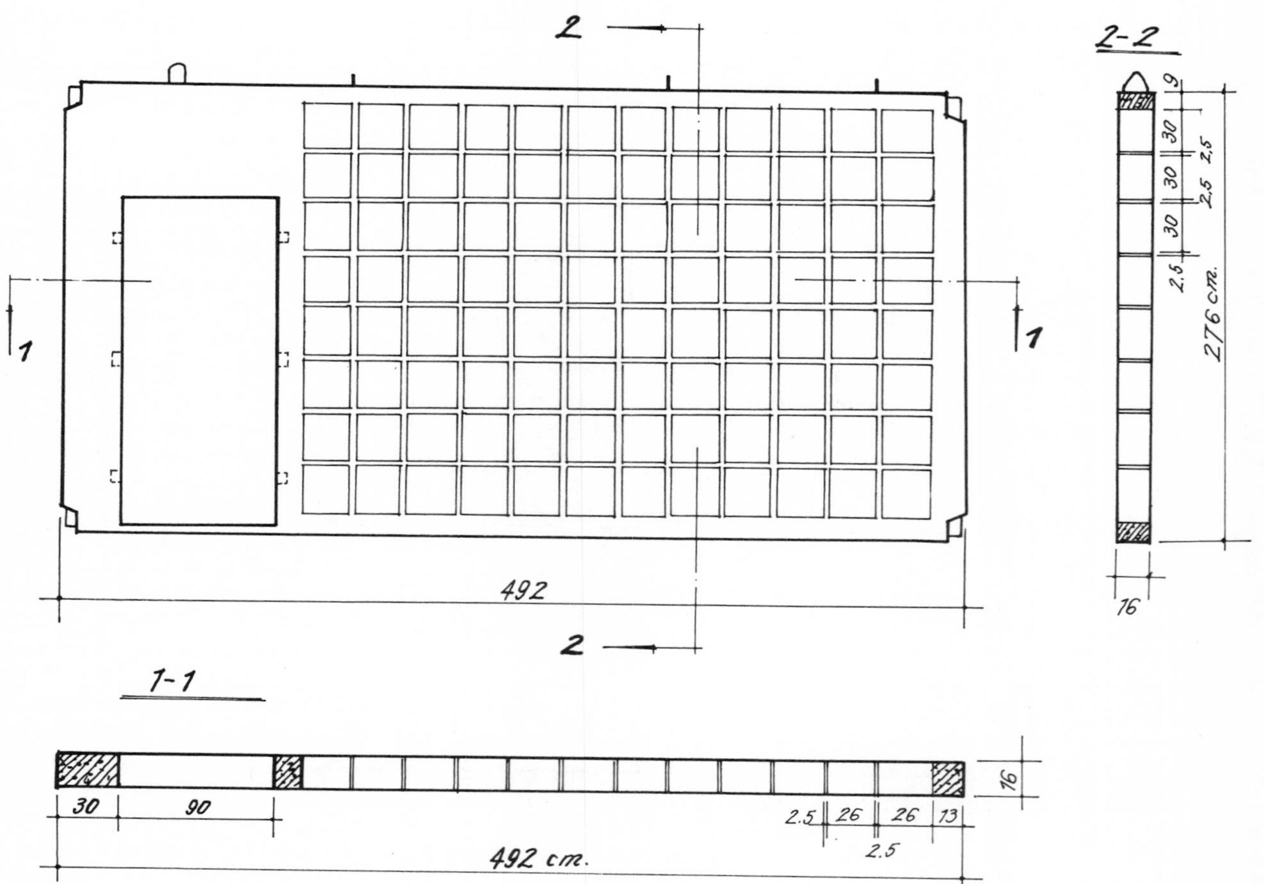

Figure 55-4. Inside wall panel.

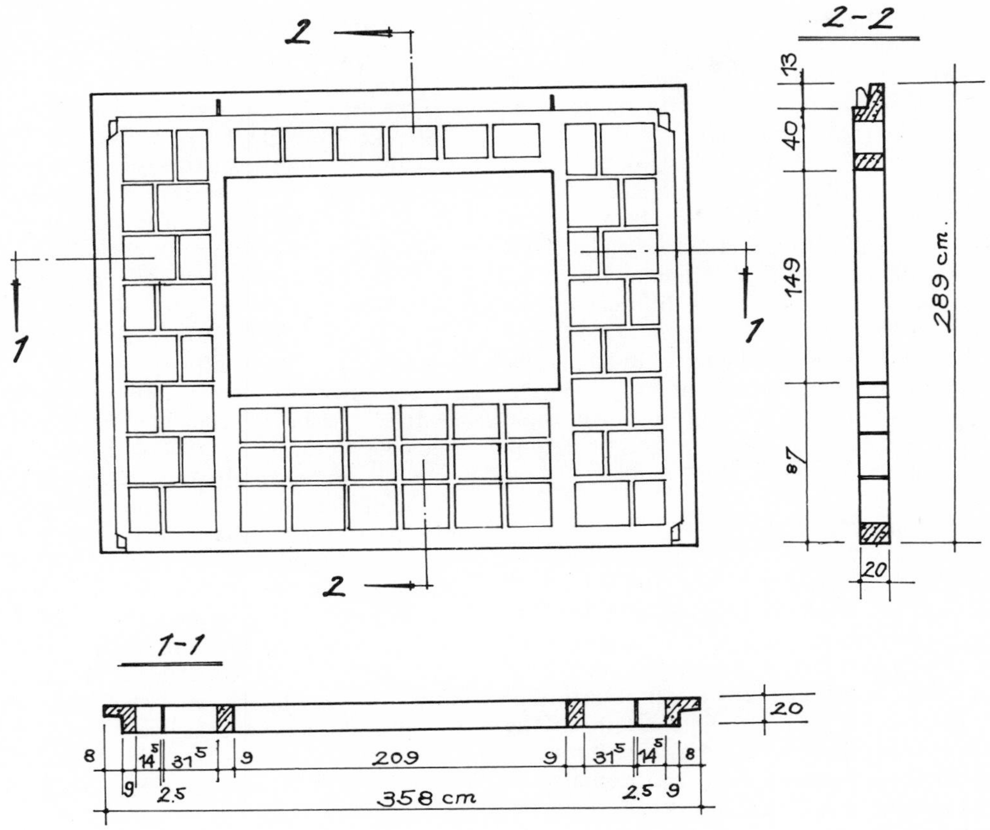

Figure 55-5. Outside wall panel.

small joints are formed taking up the temperature expansion of each brick separately. The joints between the panels have to take up the local building deformations and to compensate the tolerances made in assembling and producing the panels.

Figures 55-4 and 55-5 show the inside wall panel with a door opening and an outside wall panel with an opening for a window with a vertical arrangement of cored bricks.

Panel Manufacturing

The choice of technology in making the ceramic panel is a basic condition for successful implementation. The experience gained from previous investigations and the information from the building industry abroad provide grounds to believe new investigations are required to find the most appropriate methods for producing ceramic panels.

The production of ceramic panels is organized mainly on a grid for the production of reinforced concrete products, as is applied in the sandwich system.

The forms in this case are much lighter due to the decreased volume of the concrete and mortar for these panels.

The water saturated bricks are arranged by hand in the forms shown in the working project. The ribs between the lines of the bricks are covered with grout concrete. The application of the concrete can be done by hand, as is most frequently practiced, or it can be placed under pressure based on the principle of the air-placed concrete. The pressure method increases the labor productivity and the quality of the concrete work.

After the panels are concreted, the bricks are kept damp. Otherwise, especially in the warm summer days, the concrete drys and the grout concrete does not adhere to the bricks as they absorb all the water. The quicker bonding of the concrete and the grout of these panels is explained in that with the removal of the water at the time of bonding, a phenomenon occurs similar to that of vacuum-concrete. We consider using the pair useless as it could not be justified because the volume of the concrete and the grout taken together is too small in comparison with the whole volume (20 to 25 percent).

Comparing the expenditure of labor in producing cavity brick panels with concrete shows that it is 10 to 15 percent higher for panels of cored bricks. This parallel requires finding mechanized ways for laying bricks as well as for other construction processes.

Reinforcing panels consists of separate rods for the floor panels and welded framework for the wall panels. The fabrication of the panels can be done in the brick manufacturing plant. The problem of delivering bricks to the fabrication plant in the most direct way is solved, also the number of broken bricks is reduced. In the construction of a series of buildings of cored bricks,a grid could easily be established at the site which would facilitate transporting the panels from the fabrication point to the construction site.

Investigating the possibilities of using cavity bricks in panel construction began with the design and production of different types of brick. Every kind of brick was load-tested in the cavity direction as well as in cross section. A regular check is made of the brick's dimensions for determining the actual percent of the clay swelling. This percent is different for the different clays and varies between 5 and 8 percent. One should mention the considerable dispersion attaining 30 to 50 percent in the strength properties for the sample bricks tested. The causes for the dispersion are many, and our efforts are directed towards decreasing these values. We hope this will be accomplished with the new equipment now in construction.

Panel Research

To test the strength of the masonry using different kinds of cored bricks for outside and inside wall panels, with different strength of the cement mortar, and different directions of the brick cavities according the loading, a considerable number of test prisms were produced and tested. The effect of distortion was ignored with respect to loading-to-failure tests as the prisms have small dimensions. Each prism consists of 3 rows of bricks, with their cavities oriented either horizontally or vertically. The prism length is made of three bricks, with the size of the prism depending on the size of the tested bricks. During the loading, the deformation of the masonry was measured and data was obtained for determining the modulus E of the masonry. The testing prism showed the decisive factor for the masonry's strength to be the strength of the brick. The cement mortar or the gravel concrete which binds the bricks together must have strength equal to or greater than that of the bricks. An increase of the mortar's strength does not increase the strength of the masonry. This increase is important only in obtaining early strength in the erection of panels from a horizontal to a vertical position (70 percent of the projected strength.)

Observations

The tests are not sufficient to establish the interrelation between the strength of the bricks and the mortar and the effect of other factors. Investigations in this direction and for obtaining more exact data for the modulus E, are to be carried out in the near future.

The floor and wall panels of cored bricks were produced and tested to destruction in the Building Research Institute in Sofia to find out their actual ability to withstand transportation and their deformative aptitude.

The results of these tests served as a basis in the design of different types of panels for the housing, industrial and farming building.

The simply supported floor panels were loaded with different loads of cast iron, weighing 25 kg. and distributed equally on the panels. The degree of loading for the measurement of deformation was about 1/10 of the supposed destructive load. The dependence between the load ($q/t/m^2$) and the vertical deflection in the middle of a floor panel with a supporting distance, L = 360, is shown in Figure 55-6. The deflection with an applied load of q_h = 460 kg/m^2 is f = .660 cm. which is 1/550 of the span (L = 360 cm.). The failure load occurred at q = 800 kg/m^2.

The testing of bearing wall panels was carried out by two hydraulic jacks of 100 tons each and heavy cross beams allowing linear loading with different eccentricities.

While testing the bearing inside wall panels independent of the materials out of which they are made, it was determined that the distortion phenomenon does not appear even with the eccentricity loading amounting to 2 cm. Here also,the strength of the panels depends on the brick strength. The testing was for short-time loading and for an idealized loading scheme. This scheme is so much nearer the real condition if the test possibilities are bigger. Data for long-time loading of masonry with the cavity bricks, with which the influence of time can be established is not yet available.

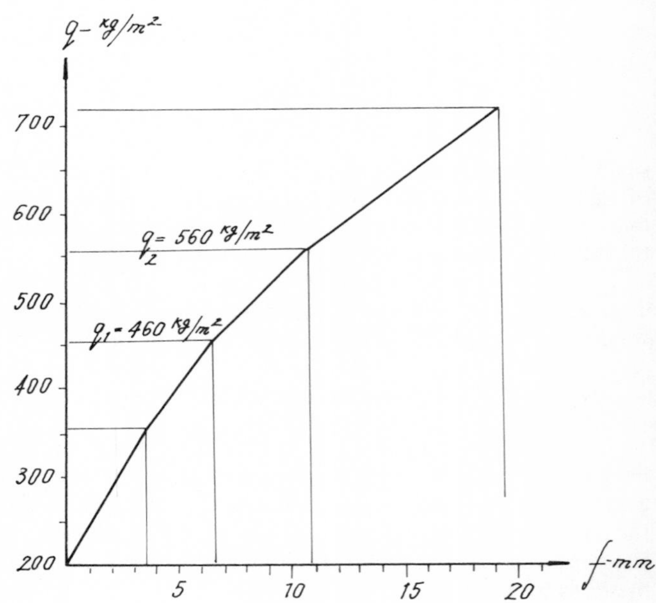

Figure 55-6. Dependence between the loading and the hanging of the floor panel.

Present Construction

Presently large panels 5-floor apartment buildings are under construction, designed by the authors of this chapter.

The bearing cross walls have a distance of 3.60 m., a distance between the longitudinal walls of 2 x 5.10 m., and the height of the floor is h = 2.90 m. The thickness of the walls without the plaster is 20 cm. for the outside and 16 cm. for the inside. The strength of the bricks the gravel concrete and the mortar is 150 kg/cm.^{2}

Table 55-1

Properties for 1m^2 walls

Properties Walls	Inside walls	Outside walls
Cement grout and concrete volume	0.0363 m^3/m^2	0.0478 m^3/m^2
Steel	3.04 kg/m^2	3.89 kg/m^2
Weight	201 kg/m^2	208 kg/m^2

The values in Table 55-1 are in connection with the general square surface of the wall panels, and the openings for doors and windows are not reduced. The floor panels are 12 cm. thick and weigh 176 kg/m^2 with steel in the amount of 6.60 kg/m^2.

After the construction is finished an actual analysis will be made with respect to all factors.

The ceramic industry in Bulgaria is now in a process of renovation. Conditions exists for producing new ceramic products of much better quality. In the future, we believe that we shall have cored bricks with forms, dimensions, and strength necessary for the production of all types of investigated panels.

The negative opinion toward the use of cored bricks in industrialized building is a notion of the past, and now ceramics offer new scopes for buildings.

Cored brick panels of different types and purposes will soon find full application in construction, thus a valuable building material will be put in use using the excellent properties indicated in research testing.

56. 14-story buildings in Switzerland with brick wall elements prefabricated by Preton process.

G. V. Zenobi and D. Szerdahelyi, Civil Engineers, Switzerland

The fact that burnt clay has proved itself and kept its position of importance in building for thousands of years is well-known. This is undoubtedly because this constructional material, with its constancy of volume and moderate density, exhibits not only respectable strength, but also other excellent constructional characterisitics: it stores heat and moisture well; it is not a good conductor of heat; it allows, thanks to its porosity, diffusion of gases and vapors; and, finally, it is almost indestructible by fire and by weather.

Obviously a constructional material with such characteristics is predestined for use in residential building. It is not a matter of chance, then, that burnt clay in the form of bricks, wall tiles, and roofing tiles has found its greatest distribution and application just there, where comfort and a feeling of ease were to be provided. The advantages of burnt clay still make it an unexcelled constructional material for farm buildings. Very likely it has been frequently used in industrial and administrative buildings and for sacral construction, thanks to, among other features, the durability and attractiveness of exposed brick masonry.

Prefabricated Elements Using Burnt Clay

The mentioned characteristics of burnt clay gave cause for its use in prefabricated building elements long before present prefabricated units came into use. Even if bricks, roofing tiles, and hollow earthenware blocks are not from current prefabricated elements, it should be recognized that the industrialization of manufacture of tiles soon led to that kind of standardization of formats that is believed today to be a prerequisite for economical production on a large scale.

As early as some dozens of years ago, prefabricated floor beams were made using clay elements which were cast with hollow clay blocks and cement to form load-bearing floors. Internationally, the prestressed Stahlton ceilings and lintels have become well-known. It is noteworthy that in prestressed ceramic beams the clay is used not only as an insulating substance and to balance or accomodate strains, but also as a fully functioning static element. This principle is the basis for especially the prestressed Stahlton ceiling, roof, and wall constructions.

Since the arising of true prefabrication, preponderantly pourable materials have been used for the production of

Figure 56-1. Room-sized Preton wall with window opening.

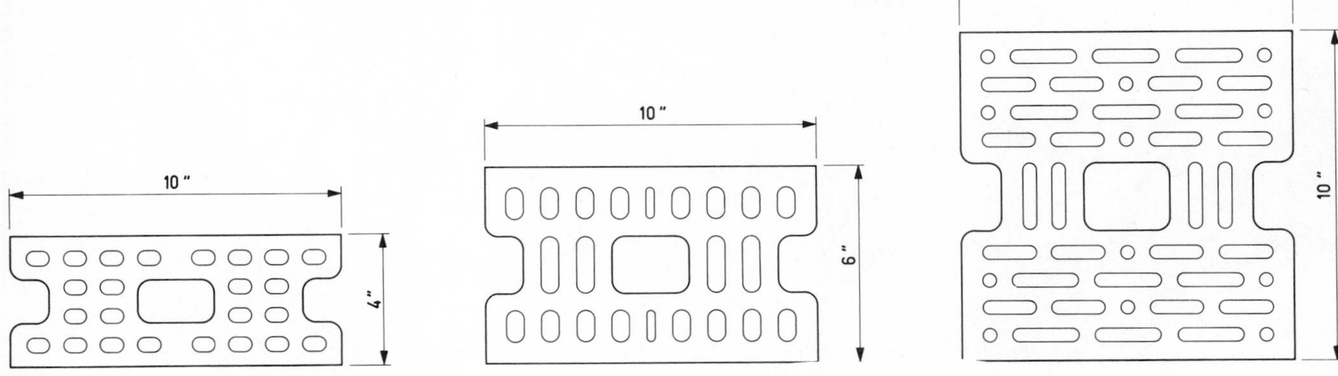

Figure 56-2. Typical Preton blocks.

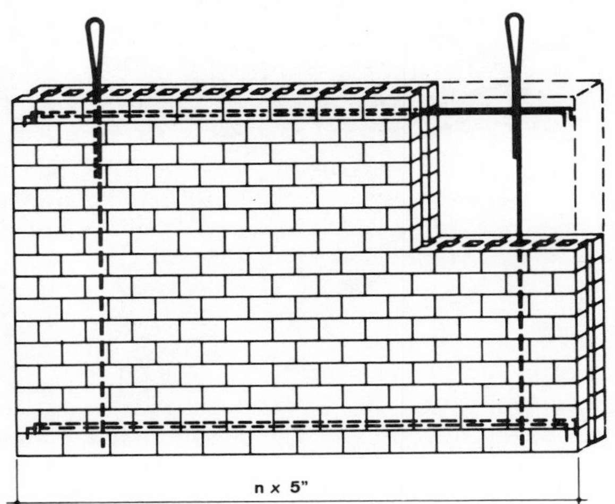

Figure 56-3. Perspective view of Preton wall with reinforcing.

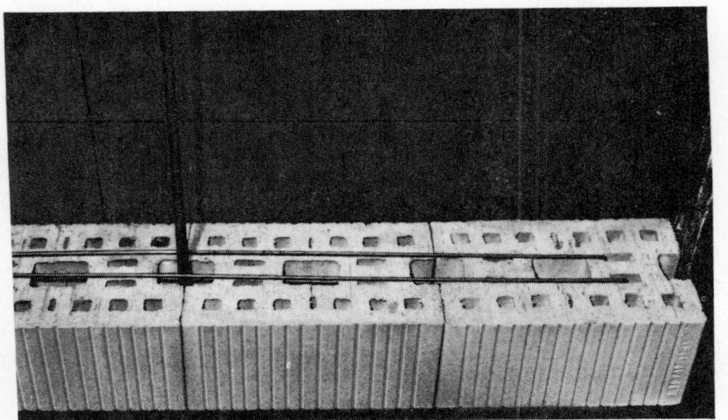

Figure 56-4. Bottom layer of Preton blocks on fabricating trestle.

plate-like elements of large format; this seemed to be a prerequisite for freedom in selection of form and for the industrialization of the process. In only a few of the processes of wall prefabrication does the proportion of special hollow bodies of clay play an essential role.

In the effort to develop an economical process for producing walls that would do justice to the specific properties of the material of tiles, Bureau BBR in Zurich, a study group of Misters M. Birkenmaier, A. Brandestini, and M. R. Ros, came upon the Preton Process, conceived in France by the engineer E. Schaeffer. This process utilizes simple means to efficiently fabricate high quality large brick walls in stationary workshops as well as at building sites. In 1963, Bureau BBR acquired the rights to use the patented Preton-Process, to develope it further, and to make it available to tile manufacturers and to the building trade (Figure 56-1).

The Preton-Process

The Preton-Process is distinguished by the following characteristics:

1. It uses Preton blocks, that is, appropriately sized blocks with vertical holes that, in assembly, form continuous vertical channels; these channels are filled with mortar and reinforcing is introduced into some of them, so that it is possible to make walls of practically any desired format that are not only readily transportable but also may be subjected to bending and tensile stresses (Figures 56-2 and 56-3).

2. Fabrication takes place in an upright position against slightly inclined fabricating trestles on which the wall edgings are affixed. The simple equipment allows fabrication of walls at building sites as well as in stationary workshops (Figure 56-4).

3. There exists unlimited freedom in choosing formats and weights of walls, in the disposition of inserts and openings, and in building conduits into the walls.

Figure 56-5. Stationary manufacture of Preton walls by Keller & Co. Ltd. at Pfungen, Switzerland.

4. The fabrication of small series of like elements is economical, since no molds are used and there is no module or norm of dimensions except that of half the length of a brick, that is, for example, 5 inches.

Preton walls are made by semi-skilled workmen under the supervision of a skilled craftsman; a better and, predominantly, a more uniform quality of masonry is achieved, without difficulty, than at the building-site, where it is possible then to employ qualified workers only. The fabrication of Preton-walls in closed factories or at the building-sites at least under a roof provides the independence from weather that is characteristic of prefabrication (Figures 56-5 and 56-6). Transportation and erection of Preton walls are exactly the same as with other wall-like building-elements.

It must be possible to reduce the labor expended per unit area of finished wall below that required for walls made at the building sites, for adjustment of dimensions and perpendicularity are obviated, flow of materials is mechanized, and the entire application and scheduling of labor are made more economical. Still, sober reflection will show that opposing these possibilities for saving are the costs of storage of the elements, transportation, and installation; just as with constructional elements of other materials, the savings made possible with Preton walls can be dissipated by the mentioned ancillary costs, especially when transport must take place over long distances or unfavorable conditions of mounting or installation. Nevertheless, it is true that with planning appropriate to the application of prefabricated constructional elements, there are advantages to their application that, in totality, lead to economies. With larger building projects, there additionally exists with the Preton Process the ready possibility of fabrication at the building site, so that at least part of the cost of storage and of transport may be averted.

The independence of fabrication time and of mounting allows the fabrication of Preton walls prior to when they are needed and at a desired rate and, additionally, the quick assembly of up to four dwelling-units daily by each mounting

Figure 56-6. Fabrication of Preton facing-walls at a building site in Berne, Switzerland.

Figure 56-7. Transportation of Preton walls on low-bed trailer from stacking yard of factory at Pfungen, Switzerland.

crew. The acceleration of construction realizable with exact planning of its use is, of course, one of the very conspicuous advantages of prefabrication; its full utility may be attained with the Preton Process. Additionally, the dwelling-units, apartments or other, maybe ready for occupancy sooner, especially when the walls are mounted with the finishing coats already applied and a minimum of moisture is brought into the building.

The ready adaptability of the Preton Process to many needs is evidenced by the absence of any module or norm of dimensions other than the unit, used in a dimensional grid, of half the length of a brick. The wall formats are limited only by transportation and mounting; ordinarily wall elements of room-size are made with a maximum width of about 25 feet and a maximum height of about 11 feet. Thanks to the relatively low density of about 87 pounds per cubic foot (1.4 metric tons per cubic meter), the costs of transport may be kept rather low and with the assembly cranes now available make possible placing of wall-elements of large area, so that costs of placing per unit area of wall are decreased and the number of joints is kept smaller; the structure is more rigid and the cost lower (Figures 56-7 and 56-8).

Preton walls can be delivered with nearly any conceivable wall finish, for example, "raw" "spattled", with a finishing coat on one or both sides, plaster-coated, or slurry-coated. Mosiac facings or rough cast are also possible. Especially interesting are the variants of Preton as exposed brick masonry in the various known and available colors and sizes of bricks. For facades too, there exist possibilities of using hollow walls.

Figure 56-8. Mounting of Preton bearing walls in multi-story building, designed by the Finnish architect Alvar Aalto.

Preton walls may be combined as desired with conventional masonry or concrete. It is particularly interesting that Preton walls with an additional vertical reinforcement of nearly any desired strength can withstand great stresses imposed by wind or earthquakes. With additional horizontal reinforcement the construction of self-supporting walls of large span or of true load-bearing panel walls becomes possible.

Although Preton walls may be used with any kind of ceiling-construction, rapid construction progress may be achieved most readily by using partially or completely prefabricated ceilings.

Since Preton Process came into being in 1961 and since the brickworks of Keller & Comp. Ltd. became general licensees in Switzerland, thousands of apartments, one-family houses, farm-buildings, administration buildings, and industrial structures in France and in Switzerland have been built using it (Figures 56-9 and 56-10). In addition to stationary fabrication of the Preton walls in permanent factories, fabrication at the sites of larger construction projects has been advantageously used so it offers the building contractor an additional possibility of expeditious construction.

The Preton Process is coming into use increasingly in numerous European countries and on other continents. The licenses for its use are granted by the Bureau BBR in Zurich, Switzerland. In the southern United States, a well-known brick manufacturer has decided to adopt the process.

Tall Buildings Built of Bricks

Tall buildings with load-bearing brick walls are not a rarity in Switzerland. Thanks to the efforts of the Swiss brick manufacturers, who are able to manufacture bricks of the requisite high quality, as well as to the experimental and theoretical findings of the Swiss Federal Institute for the Testing of Materials, brick now is used as a highly stressed bearing element.

Because of the need for industrialized construction, the mode of construction with large panels has in recent years gained greatly in importance in residential buildings. Most of the processes use concrete, with or without light aggregate, as the basic material, whereas the Preton process, in contrast, uses bricks, and these as a preponderantly bearing-element.

Figure 56-9. Preton facing-panels for industrial project at Elgg, Switzerland.

Until recently Preton walls were used in buildings of a few stories high only. In tall buildings Preton wall panels were used as load-bearing elements for the first time in the 14-story residential buildings built at Worblaufen, near Berne, in 1964 and 1965.

Description of the Building Project

About 300 apartments were erected in a project at Worblaufen, near Berne, more than half of them in the two tallest buildings 14 stories high. Distinctive for the project is that all the buildings are built in the same configuration. The basic type is a tandem unit with a three and one-half room and a four and one-half room apartment, the exception being that of the type at the ends of the two tallest buildings (Figure 56-11). The purpose of this ground-plan was to achieve, by way of large series, a most economical construction mode. After intensively comparing prices, the solution was to build the lower houses in conventional fashion and the tall ones with prefabricated Preton wall panels, while the floors were made at the site. Each of the tall buildings is divided by two expansion joints into three building units. All parapets and piers of the balconies consist of prefabricated concrete elements. At the sides with the balconies the rooms are closed off with walls of light construction and glass insulating-panes. Load-bearing parts of the facade received an external insulation of polystyrene and were then faced with concrete plates.

The essential engineering problems were those of constructing tall buildings, the special ones of building with bricks, of building with large panels, and of executing construction.

Engineering Problems in Construction of Tall Buildings

The problems that must be solved most importantly in the construction of tall buildings are those of (1) the transmission of the loads into the foundations and the soil upon which the buildings rest, (2) assumption of horizontal forces from wind and, as an eventuality, from earthquakes, and (3) the stresses and movements caused by variations and differences in temperature.

While the stresses from the weight of the structure itself and from the useful loads increase nearly linearly with increasing number of stories, as in Worblaufen, where the buildings were erected with a uniform thickness of wall, the stresses caused by wind increase parabolically with increasing height. Consequently, stiffening against the effect of wind becomes of central importance in tall buildings. With the present, usual mode of construction with partition-walls, as used in Worblaufen, there are as a rule enough wall-panels available that contribute to the stiffening in the transverse direction to take up the wind forces. To build economically, the engineer can utilize the concert of panels pierced by rows of openings. Effective methods of calculation were published by Rošmen[1] and Albigès-Goulet[2]. With the mentioned mode of construction, the requisite moments of resistance are generally more difficult to find in the longitudinal direction.

Figure 56-10. Dwelling units at Zuchwil, Switzerland, built with interior and exterior Preton walls.

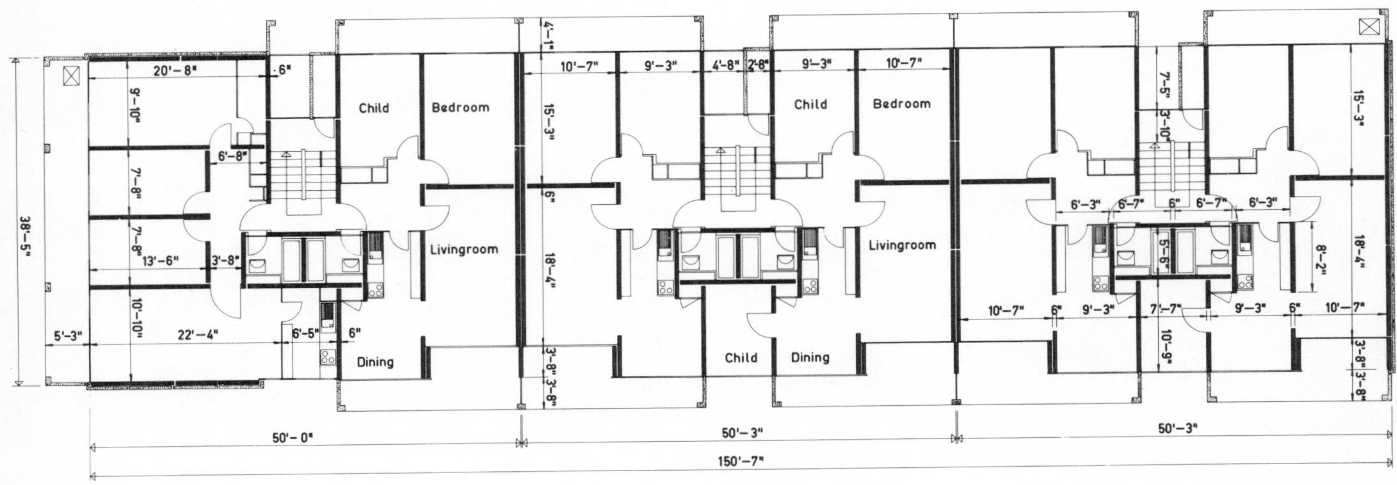

Figure 56-11. Ground plan of high-rise buildings at Worblaufen, near Berne, Switzerland.

Frequently, however, completed and enclosed cross sections, as stair wells, lavatory facilities, and such, may be included in calculating this direction, a prerequisite condition being that a shear-resistant connection between the individual cross-sectional parts is assured.

In planning tall buildings particular attention is to be paid to movements caused by variations and differences of temperature. The effort should be made to have all columns and similar structures of like function within the internal environment of the building to obviate different vertical movements caused by temperature variations. This demands external wall insulation, which is better also in relation to heating. If this condition can not be met, as may occur with balcony areas outlying stair wells, and such, the separation from one another of the various building elements subject to different movements should be planned carefully.

These aspects were taken into account in planning high-rise buildings at Worblaufen. All the external bearing walls were insulated externally and then faced with 3-in.-thick concrete plates about 8 ft. 6 in. by 5 ft. 5 in. in size. The outlying bearing separating-walls of the balcony floors are all separated throughout from the internal walls.

Dimensioning of the Bearing Brick Walls

Since at the time of planning, the new draft of norms, number 113,[3] of the Swiss Society of Engineers and Architects (SIA) was not yet complete, the dimensioning of the walls was done according to the directives of the Association of Swiss Brick and Tile Manufacturers[4], which already corresponded largely to the mentioned norms. These norms, which demand with high stresses permitted a high quality of material and execution, provide favorable conditions for prefabricated wall panels. The factory-produced wall panels of brick present the demanded high-dimensional accuracy. The strength of the bricks and of the walls may undergo regular control, whereby then, as it may be necessary, the permitted stresses can be increased by 25 percent, this reducing the factor of safety from 5 to 4. The Preton wall panels are executed exactly according to layer-plans, as the norms demand for the highest quality of wall.

The compressional strength of the Preton blocks was about 500 kg./cm.^{2} or 7100 p.s.i. Despite the large water absorption of the Preton bricks, the compressional strength of the masonry reached throughout and fully the values demanded.

The Mode of Construction with Brick Wall-Elements in the Form of Large Panels

Just as with construction with prefabricated parts of other materials, the greatest problem in construction with large panels made of bricks lies in the jointing of the elements to one another. This jointing should achieve (1) the air-tight and sound-proof enclosure of the rooms and (2) the transmission of the shear forces.

As a consequence of the form of the Preton blocks, a continuous groove is formed at the edge of each element; this groove can be filled readily with a fluid mortar. The mortar can be prevented from flowing out by using sheathing or by packing the joints. The joints to be filled with mortar can be reinforced with projecting hooks, and bars can be pushed through vertically. Later examination showed, however, that this way of jointing, which was undesirable in construction, was not necessary. The vertical shear forces could be transmitted through the floors, which received supplementary reinforcing above the wall-joints.

In the tall buildings at Worblaufen, the vertical tensile forces were, for the greater part, overweighed. In still taller buildings, however, a tensile reinforcement could become necessary. With Preton wall panels, as with those of concrete, this reinforcement could be prevented by passing through reinforcing bars, since the form of the Preton blocks enables this.

Execution of the Construction

The wall elements for Worblaufen were manufactured at the brickworks of the Keller group at Paradies and transported in vertical position on low-bed trailers to the building site. The

Figure 56-12. Front view during construction of the high-rise buildings at Worblaufen, near Berne, Switzerland.

Figure 56-13. General view of high-rise buildings at Worblaufen, near, Berne, Switzerland.

heaviest element weighed about 2.5 metric tons. Because of the relatively great transportation distance, about 150 kilometers (90 miles), needs for about a day were kept in an intermediate storage, from where mounting of the elements took place. Whereas a large building crane on rails was used for mounting and other construction work, a small fixedly mounted crane served for unloading the elements (Figure 56-12).

The brick wall elements, to the extent that they are delivered unfinished, should be protected from moisture during transportation, storage, and mounting; manipulation of the wall elements delivered with a rendering coat demands less caution in this respect. Despite this, in Worblaufen, delivery without a rendering coat was accepted; the dimensional accuracy of the wall panels made it necessary. The walls received as a finish only an economy coat of plaster about 3/16 in. thick, so that a significant saving was achieved. Experience has shown that an economy coat proves itself well where no moisture is met; walls of bathrooms and of kitchens should, however, receive special treatment.

The wall elements were set on a mortar bed; still somewhat plastic and moist mortar was levelled at somewhat above the final desired height between fixed and levelled gage points, the panel put on it and held with diagonal braces and screw clamps, and adjusted. The mortar bed was then stuffed from the side. Another way of installation consists of placing the elements on supports at a fixed height or on wedges and then, using transverse vibrators, vibrating the mortar into the gaps. With this method, a lath or other sheathing must be used to prevent the mortar from flowing out on the opposite side.

Summary

The project at Worblaufen is an example of the advantageous application of construction at the site combined with prefabrication. This was made possible by strict use of certain types of configurations of apartments and the close cooperation of architect, engineer, and building-owner. It was in Worblaufen that prefabricated Preton wall panels of brick were used for the first time as bearing walls in high-rise buildings (Figure 56-13).

References

1. Rošman, "Beitrag zur statischen Berechnung waagrecht belasteter Querwande bei Hochbauten," (I, II, III). *Der Bauingenieur,* 1960, S. 133, 1962, S. 24, 1962, S. 303.
2. Albiges-Goulet, "Contreventement des batiments," *Annales de l'Institut Technique du Batiment et des Travaux Publics,* Mai 1960.
3. Swiss Society of Engineers and Architects, S.I.A., Norm Nr. 113.
4. "Hochhausbau in Backstein," Verband Schweiz. Ziegel-und Steinfabrikanten, Society of Brick and Stone Fabrication, 1959.
5. Haller, P., "Warme-und Feuchtigkeitswanderung durch Aussenwande," *Schweizersche,* Bauzeitung, 1957, S. 741.
6. Haller, P. "Mauerwerk im Ingenieurbau," *Schweizerche,* Heft 7, Bauzeitung, 1965, S. 103.
7. "Diskussion Richtlinien fur Grosstafelbauten," Studiengemeinschaft fur Fertigbau, Darmstadt, 1965.
8. Amrein, E., "Der neuzeitliche Wohnungsbau und seine physikalischen Grundlagen," *Element* Nr. 12 and 13.

57. Prefabricated brick panels in Colorado.

Donald A. Wakefield, Structural Clay Products Institute, Denver, Colorado

Region 12 of Structural Clay Products Institute, a trade association for brick manufacturers in Colorado, based in Denver, Colorado, is resolute in its faith in the future of prefabricated brick and tile panels and the important effect they will have on the future of the brick industry.

In the Denver area, we have been working on prefabricated brick and tile panels for over five years. We have developed several different panel applications to answer several specific needs.

In 1966, our association formed a "Panel Research and Development Committee" made up of representatives of all the brick companies in this region to investigate, within its physical and economic limits, all facets of prefabricated brick and tile panels systems and applications. Up to that time, no systematic approach or study had been attempted on our part to ascertain what is the best type, the best size, the most ecónomical type or method. In fact, each new panel system has been investigated and developed only as each new need arose.

Until this committee makes a report of its findings or until the entire brick industry recognizes the vast potential of preassembled panels and does a proper research job, this report is presented as a resume of the progress of panels so far in the Rocky Mountain area of the USA.

We have gained much knowledge and experience from the large variety of projects in which we have participated, and there is still very much to be investigated. But, in the meantime, let me share some of our experiences.

First, I would like to discuss some of the reasons panels are needed. The reasons for using prefabricated brick and tile panels are just as varied as the panels themselves. The needs will also vary in different parts of the country and at different times of the year. For instance, winter construction is ideally suited for panelization. The need for more work for the bricklayers and the brick industry during the winter has long been a concern of the industry. Prelaid panels can be constructed in a factory and installed under almost any winter condition. This will then make brick and tile year-round materials. The ability to construct brick buildings in the winter will also alleviate a problem that may become more prevalent, and that is a shortage of bricklayers. If the increase in construction that we have been promised comes about, there will be a greater need for bricklayers.

Panels can help alleviate this possible shortage in several ways:

1. By making us a year-round industry and letting the available bricklayers work all year long.
2. The panelization method in a factory using ideal working conditions under cover and out of the weather, can allow the bricklayers to increase their productivity and, at the same time, increase their precision while expanding the same amount of energy and time.

Another cost item is speed of erection. Borrowing construction money is expensive, and the sooner the contractor can finish a building the more money he will save, and also, the sooner the building will be earning its income. Panelization of walls or entire units will cut down on the construction time. If a crane is already available on a job, it can be used efficiently to install the panels. If not, mobile cranes are readily and economically available. Also, there is a savings in cost by eliminating the need for large amounts of scaffolding.

We know that on a straight, running bond wall the bricklayer using conventional methods is, at this time, the most economical way of building a brick wall. But as soon as a pattern is introduced, the cost goes up. Many fancy patterns and intricate designs can be accomplished with panels at the same cost as regular patterns. Also, the architect can approve these patterns or the finished panel before it is erected in the structure.

Imaginative uses of brick can greatly enhance the appearance of a building, but sometimes increase the cost of the project. In many cases, prefabricated panels can accomplish the designers idea and save money at the same time. For instance, a horizontal brick surface such as a brick Soffit panel or a brick ceiling or a floor can be accomplished as a panel; beautifully, effectively and economically.

We have been talking primarily about panels, either straight, curved, or warped, but this same idea can be expanded into entire building units such as entire rooms in panelized form. This may be feasible after we have learned more about handling, connections, and erections of smaller panels.

Some of the more interesting projects we have accomplished will be described by the following discussion.

United Fund Building

The first major project we worked on was also one of the most spectacular. Any discussion of panels should rightfully start with this first project: the United Fund Building in downtown Denver.

One cold, snowing December morning in 1962 we moved into downtown Denver with a crane with a 200 foot boom and installed a mechanical pent house on the roof of the nine-story United Fund Building. In three days, we installed 56 four-foot-wide, fifteen-foot-high, four-inch-thick, load-bearing prefabricated panels made of brick, reinforcing steel and Sarabond mortar. Since the roof could only withstand a light load and the architect wanted a mechanical penthouse made of load-bearing brick in the winter time, four-inch-thick load-bearing brick panels were the answer. The cold and the snow did not stop the project and only two hours were lost due to high winds. As we were progressively installing panels, the roofers were installing and welding steel roof decking to the top of the panels and as we placed the last brick panel, they welded in the last of the roof decking to completely close in the structure three days after we started.

Since this was the first use of Sarabond Mortar in a panelized form that we knew of, the structural engineer, naturally being skeptical, insisted that a lightweight steel picture frame be installed around each of the panels. This helped greatly when the panels were welded together and when the roof decking was welded along the top of the panels, but this steel made the panels unnecessarily strong and greatly increased the cost. On all subsequent panel projects these steel picture frames were eliminated. Advantages of this includes the following: lightweight, wintertime construction, speed of erection, and load-bearing.

The largest panel on the United Fund Building Project in 1962 was twenty feet long, five feet high, and four inches thick with black coloring Sarabond mortar and steel picture frames (Figure 57-1). The majority of the panels were to be installed in a vertical position. A 200 foot boom on a mobile crane installed the 56 panels in three days on the roof of this nine story structure. The mechanical penthouse on top of the United Fund Building is made of four-inch-thick, fifteen-foot-high, four-foot-wide load-bearing brick panels. Openings in the upper section of the panels on the south wall are for louvers for the air-conditioning intake ports. A small enclosure on top of the elevator shafts and stairwell was also constructed of load-bearing pre-laid panels twenty feet by five feet by four inches.

Figure 57-1. Largest panel on United Fund Building project 1962.

Maxwell Falls Rest Area

Curved panels for this project were picked up when they were three days old, swung into position using four pick-up points, two opposite each other by means of a single bolt through the wall and hooking devises on either side (Figure 57-2). As an experiment, the panel was laid on the truck, the crane disconnected,and the panel rocked like a rocking horse.

In making the panels more economical, an aluminum curved wall template was used in conjunction with corner poles to allow the bricklayer to lay the wall for the same cost as straight walls would have been. Since the site for the out-house was about thirty miles from Denver up in a mountainous wooded area, the panels were combat loaded with the panels to come off first on the outside of the truck. The curved sections formed the outside walls. Two other curved sections made up the tank that is underground. The brick panel for this floor had an opening for the metal toilet. A two-sided, four-inch-thick, glazed tile panel was used as a divider panel between the men and women section and also acted as a vent stack for the gases from the tank.

The finished outhouse was a fine example of design and economy. The roof of this particular comfort station is of wood and was designed by the Forestry Service (Figure 57-3). Since then other models have been constructed using prefabricated brick roofs to carry out the vandalism and no maintenance theme.

Figure 57-2. Swinging curved panels into position.

Figure 57-3. Comfort station with wood roof.

Prospect Valley Elementary School, Jefferson County, Colorado

The architectural firm of Rogers, Nagel, and Langhart of Denver, when designing a futuristic school embodying some radical teaching ideas and environmental considerations, wished to create deeply recessed windows and doors in their school that would give the feeling of being outdoors with as little maintenance as possible. Their design included 92 recessed entries and windows,each having a brick pier between each opening and a brick soffit panel over the top. This was a perfect place to use prefabricated brick panels. The panels would be small, four foot square by four inches thick, and could be handled easily without a large crane. These panels were constructed in a factory building.

This panel project also served as a panel making school for union bricklayers and mason contractors. During construction of the panels, 17 mason contractors and 119 bricklayers helped lay the brick on different panels. When the panels were cured, they were brought to the project on pallets separated by styrofoam. The bricklayers had already constructed the columns and were waiting for arrival of the panels (Figure 57-4). The bricklayers left toothing in the vertical walls that were continued on across the top of the panels. The panels acted as lintles across the opening. Because they were small, they were easy to handle. They needed no pickup devises or connection devises; any ordinary forklift could handle them. The panels were installed by the regular mason contractors forklift operator. A bed of mortar was spread on the wall, then the panels were set and shimmed to the correct height, and the joints between were tuckpointed with mortar and tooled. On four large entrances to the gymnasium portion of the school much larger panels were called for. These panels varied from four feet wide by sixteen feet long by four inches thick down to four feet wide by ten feet long by four inches thick (Figure 57-5). These panels were also going to be horizontal Soffit panels, but because of the direction of their bed joints and the heavy air-conditioning equipment resting on them, they were supported by wood shoring and six inches of reinforced concrete was poured on top of the panels. In essence, these panels were going to be used as forms for the structural slab.

Figure 57-4. Prospect Valley Elementary School. Note toothing in the vertical walls.

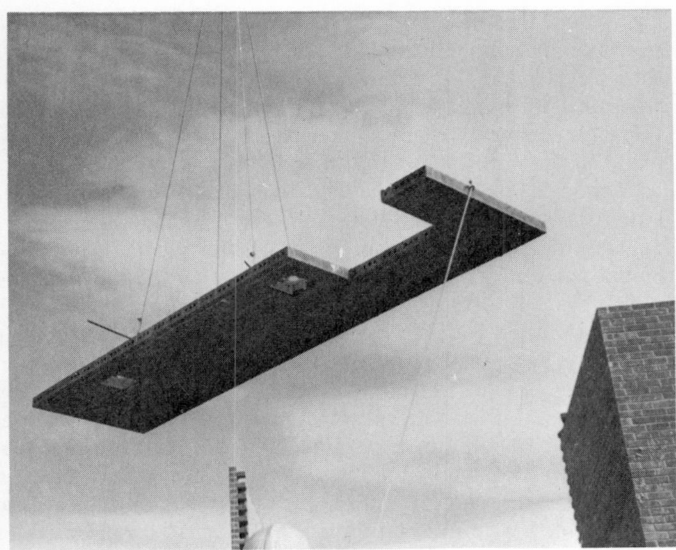

Figure 57-5. Panels for the gym portion of Prospect Valley Elementary School.

Figure 57-7. One of the larger brick panels constructed for the Fort Collins Interstate Highway Rest Area.

Therefore, shear connectors in the form of No. 9 gage wires were laid in the bed joints and left sticking out of the backside of the panels (Figure 57-6). Also, two light boxes were let into these panels. Quarter inch airplane cables were embedded in the mortar joints as pick-up devises. After the panels were in place, the bricklayers, in the conventional handlaid method, laid brick over the tops of the leading edge of the panel and over the back of the panel creating a hollow section above the

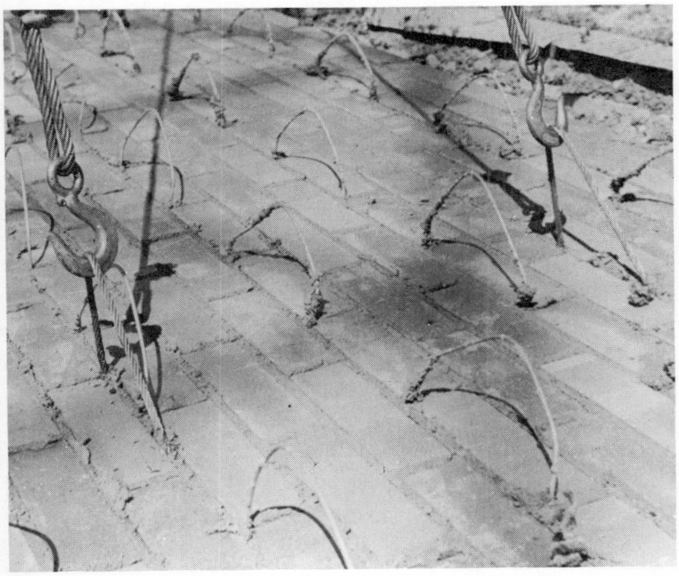

Figure 57-6. Shear connectors sticking out of the backside of the gymnasium panels.

Soffit panels. A large hole was left in each panel as part of an opening for the air-conditioning intake. A small L shaped return-end cantilevered out from the main panel creating a great strain on the mortar joints. The panels were made with standard brick, Sarabond mortar and quarter inch pencil rods. This school has been acclaimed for many innovations in construction, teaching technique, and educational philosophy.

Fort Collins Interstate Highway No. 25 Rest Area

The state highway department of Colorado wanted a spectacular rest area on Interstate 25 just south of Fort Collins. They wanted it to be beautiful, have low maintenance, be vandal proof, and designed for permanent construction. The brick panel system was selected. It was designed as an entire project of two outhouses and ten picnic shelters. The picnic shelters were also of prefabricated brick. The brick outhouses were bid against prefabricated procelain enamel outhouse packages and corrugated steel roofed ones on steel posts picnic shelters. The brick panel system was lower in cost. On each side of the comfort station are two compartments for toilets and one compartment for a lavatory. The panels were constructed by Russ Jones, a union mason contractor, in his storage yard. Since they were built in the summertime, we needed no cover or factory conditions. Some of the larger panels of the project were twenty-six feet by six feet by four inches both straight and curved (Figure 57-7). The project started out to be a tank type outdoor toilet with circular holes in the floor. Halfway through the project it was decided that this would be changed to a year-round facility so the holes were filled up and the flush-type toilets were installed with a heater, running hot and cold water and lighting. Since these panels were so large and only four inches thick, a six point pickup method was devised. The problem was to get the two center pickup points under the same lifting pressure as the two end ones. A turn-buckle was installed at one of the center lift points to adjust the tension. The panels were brought from Denver, 65 miles away, and laid out on the ground ready for assembly (Figure 57-8). Twenty-six foot by six foot by four inches thick curved panels formed the tanks for the outhouses. Side wall panels for the outhouse were also curved.

The twenty-six foot by six foot curved panels formed the outhouse tanks underground. Again we used the six point pickup with the turn buckle to adjust the tension on the center two points. Holes were drilled through the mortar joints of the panels for the pickup connections and were later tuck pointed with mortar and could not be detected.

With a brick panel floor already installed on a sand bed, the large curved sections of the tank were placed on a bed of Sarabond mortar and released from the crane (Figure 57-9). Because of the curved design, no shoring or bracing was needed (Figure 57-10). After the tank was caulked, further water-proofing protection was added on the outside in the form of asphalt water proofing membrane. The upper panels of the outhouse came to the project complete. They were cleaned, glazed tile sills in place and the glazing in place. Again, because of their curved shape, they needed no bracing and could be set into a bed of Sarabond mortar, and thus eliminated any need for anchor bolts or bracing during or after construction and thereby eliminating the inherent problems of alignment and rusting (Figure 57-11). The roof panels had six point pickups as the other panels, glass block inserts in the roof and stair stepped edges to follow the curve of the shelter and reduce the amount of cantilever overhang. A truck-mounted crane was used to install these panels. The biggest of the roof panels were installed by just two men and the crane. On this project, no problems whatsoever were encountered with any of the panels, even the large ones. The finished comfort station are ready for use for the thousands of people who travel between Cheyenne, Wyoming and Denver, Colorado. Since the outhouse has been completed, the area has been completely landscaped with grass and shruberies to be a showplace of the Colorado highway systems (Figure 57-12). In the same rest area are ten picnic shelters, five on either side of the dual highway. These shelters were bid against corrugated metal shelters and were accepted by the highway as a more economical alternate. The end panels are curved to give structural strength in the long direction. The larger panels have quarter inch pencil rods in some of the mortar joints and Sarabond mortar. The two 6-foot wide by 26-foot-high by 4-inch-thick floor sections were installed on top of a smooth bed of sand, no footings were installed. The roof panels of the same size were installed on top of the vertical walls without the aid of bracing. After the shelters were constructed, they were tested by loading the roof panels with 45 pounds per square foot of loose brick to similate a 50% overload of snow. These curved panels for the shelters were constructed in Denver at the yard of Russ Jones, Mason Contractor, and shipped up to the installation site on either the crane truck or a low-boy trailer. The curved shape allowed installation without bracing. The underside of the roof was the face side of the brick panel.

Samsonite Experimental Panels

The Samsonite Corporation in Denver, when designing a high complex north of the airport, wanted to have the flexibility of expanding their buildings by removing the walls at a later date and enlarging their buildings and then replacing the walls. The brick industry in Denver volunteered to experiment on making some panels, twenty-seven foot high, four to six foot wide by six inches thick (Figure 57-13). We constructed the panels in three small sections because of limited space in the factory and then assembled them together for one tall panel. We used both reinforcing and post-tensioning rods and both conventional and Sarabond mortar.

Figure 57-8. Fort Collins Interstate Highway Rest Area panels ready for assembly.

Figure 57-9. Large curved section of tank placed on a bed of Sarabond mortar.

Figure 57-10. Curved design eliminates necessity for bracing the tank.

Figure 57-11. No anchor bolts or bracing were needed during or after construction due to the curved design.

Figure 57-12. Since completion, the Fort Collins Interstate Highway Rest Area has become a showplace of the Colorado highway systems.

Figure 57-13. Experimental panel constructed for the Samsonite Corporation. The panel is 27 ft. high, 4 to 6 ft. wide, and 6 inches thick.

The panels were tested in a horizontal position with large plastic air bags and performed excellently. They were then stood up for visual inspection. Unfortunately, the Samsonite people could not wait until the investigation was complete so they designed the walls to be laid in place but in panel-form and panel-strength so they could, at a later date, take the wall sections out of the wall as a panel and reuse them again. Therefore, these panels were built in place to be moved later.

Longmont Downtown Renewal Project

In the city of Longmont, about 60 miles north of Denver, a downtown rejuvenation project has been started to tie all of the stores of the downtown area together with a single theme and a single material with a panelized system of beams and columns to form covered walkways from the parking areas to the main street and down along the front of the stores (Figure 57-14). The columns were laid in place and the beams were constructed of post-tensioned Sarabond brick panels and lifted onto the top of the columns by a crane. At certain intervals along the main street, openings or passages were made through the existing buildings from the main street to the street in back of the stores. Behind these stores will be large parking lots so that no parking will be allowed or needed on the main street. The complex will undoubtedly receive a lot of attention with this new mall type downtown renovation project. The

Figure 57-14. Panelized system of beams and columns to form covered walkways as part of a rejuvenation project in the city of Longmont, Colorado.

panels were picked up by sling methods to eliminate the need for pickup connections. Reinforcing rods were threaded and used as post-tensioning rods by tightening the end bolts to the proper design tension.

Safeway Store in Colorado Springs

The architect desired brick face on his store that had a new appearance. He wanted the joints to run vertically in a running bond pattern. It was proven by alternate bids that by building the panel on its side in a running bond pattern with conventional bricklaying methods and then turning them up on end in the wall would achieve the visual effect with the greatest economy.

Penn Square Apartment Project, Denver, Colorado

To date, the largest building with prefabricated brick panels in Colorado is the Penn Square Apartment project by Mike Lombardi, architect (Figure 57-15). It is a concrete frame structure with four inch thick Sarabond brick enclosing outside walls, styrofoam insulation and dry wall on the inside. On all of the balconies, there are five-foot-high, three-foot-wide railing panels for a total of 1008 such panels. These panels were constructed in a factory in the wintertime before the building was even started. The same contractor and the same bricklayers, after the panels were completed and stored (Figure 57-16), then proceeded to the actual building to do the conventional brickwork in the summer. These panels are light in appearance and yet give a feeling of structural strength that is not obtainable in metal grill-like balconies conventionally used.

More Outhouses

Another panel project was constructed at the brick contractors yard using straight walls (Figure 57-17). Many panels

Figure 57-15. Penn Square Apartment project is, to date, the largest building with prefabricated brick panels in Colorado.

Figure 57-16. 3 x 5 ft. balcony railing panels for Penn Square Apartment project.

Figure 57-17. Straight wall panel project.

Figure 57-18. Many straight wall panels can be built and stored in a small area.

Figure 57-19. Straight Creek Tunnel through the Continental Divide at Loveland Pass in central Colorado.

could be built and stored in a relatively small area (Figure 57-18). These panels were shipped 280 miles up into the mountainous areas of western Colorado. They were constructed in Denver and installed at Vega Reservoir by Grand Junction. Even at this distance, because of the shortage of bricklayers and high cost of material in this outlying area, the panels proved to be an economic saving. They were used to construct the largest of the rectangular type outhouses built so far. Each outhouse accommodates two toilets, a wash basin, and a shower per side in this year-round campsite and recreational area. Each roof was made of four-inch-thick panels with the end bricks turned down to give it a thicker appearance. These outhouses were installed in a snowstorm in November, 1966. Other similar but smaller outhouses were built in Colorado at the Green Mountain Reservoir Recreation area–a four holer tank type, all year, all weather rest area.

The Straight Creek Tunnel to be built through the Continental Divide at Loveland Pass in central Colorado will take Interstate Highway 70, 9900 feet through the Continental Divide at 11,000 feet elevation (Figure 57-19). The highway engineers, because of the possible shortage of bricklayers, the unknown production at 11,000 feet and the fantastic temperature changes from 80 degrees Fahrenheit in the summer to 40 degrees below zero Fahrenheit in the winter, called for some type of panelization. Region 12, Structural Clay Products Institute, did an extensive testing program for the highway engineers of Tibbett, Abbot, McCarthy and Stratton and the highway department of the state of Colorado. The panels, ten foot by six foot and seventeen feet long by six foot wide, were made of structural glazed facing tile laid by hand by union bricklayers using Sarabond mortar and high tensile steel quarter inch reinforcing rods. The panels were laid in a vertical position and were stood up vertically with the bed joints running vertically. Before the highway department would approve their use, the panels were tested by placing 185 pounds per square foot of loose brick on the panel without serious damage (Figure 57-20). Each panel spanned ten feet horizontally. This load is about five times greater than the design load. Ceiling panels for this same project were also designed both as all tile panels and concrete panels faced with two inch glazed tile soaps. A six-inch-thick glazed tile post-tensioned ceiling panel spanning seventeen feet was loaded with loose stacked brick to 365 pounds per square foot live load before it broke. Another group of ceiling panels with concrete backing both prestressed and reinforced were flexed 17,000 times in a fatigue test and satisfied all requirements excellently. The final bid for the tunnel calls for panels in both the side walls and the ceiling. There will be over 6600 such panels in the two twin bores.

To create these different panel systems, we have used several different construction methods. There are undoubtedly many other methods of panel construction around the world. I will attempt to describe and evaluate those I have seen or used.

1. The hand-laid system. Using a yard or a factory building, protected from the elements and employing union bricklayers, using conventional bricklaying techniques to lay the panels has been, to date, our most successful system. It has many advantages: (a) low initial tool-up costs, (b) great versatility and flexibility of design and size, (c) the ability of reducing your overhead and labor force when work is slack, (d) a better reception by the construction industry, etc.

Figure 57-20. Panels for the Straight Creek Tunnel were tested for strength by supporting 135 lbs. per square foot of loose brick.

Its greatest disadvantages are its (a) higher cost per square foot (hand-laid brickwork plus installation costs), (b) dependence on availability of bricklayers, (c) the reluctance of bricklayers to work under factory conditions, and (d) difficulty of producing intricate patterns.

The other method usually involves some type of mechanical means of manufacturing panels:

2. A "cookie-pan" method uses a large (10′ × 10′) steel pan into which the bricks are placed face down. The faces of the units are protected from smearing of the mortar by a material previously placed in the bottom of the pan. This material also forms the joint and alignes the units properly. The bricks are then placed face down into this protective material and held in proper alignment. Reinforcing rods are placed in the joints and in the holes and the grout is applied from the back side. After the panel has cured, it is stood up and cleaned on both sides. The time required to cure depends on the type and strength of grout. We have tried at least four different types of this method using both brick and glazed tile with excellent results. A variation of this method will be used on the ceiling panels of the 9900 foot long Straight Creek Tunnel thru Loveland Pass here in Colorado.

3. A third method involves holding the bricks in proper postion, clamped between two sponge covered vertical steel walls. After the reinforcing steel has been placed, grout is pumped down into the holes and joints from above and depends on gravity and flow to fill out all of the voids. The sponge surface of the form, forms a "tooled" appearing joint while it is holding in the grout. One such system was designed and used several years ago by a firm in Texas. This year (May

1967) I was fortunate to visit the Redlands Brick Company in England. They have developed and are using an excellent panel making machine that is very similar to the Vertical Press Jigs used here in the United States.

The advantage of the mechanical panel making machine are (a) lower cost of the panels per square foot (after machines are paid for) (b) ability to make a standardized panel rapidly, uniformly and economically; (c) use of unskilled plant labor and (d) it makes intricate patterns at the same cost as "running bond".

The disadvantages are: (a) high initial investment in creating a plant, the handling equipment and machinery themselves, that must be amortized over many panel projects, (b) resistance from the unions, (c) limited in the design, shape and size of panels that can be accommodated, (d) after training your personnel you have to support them or find them other jobs during slack periods.

The big question that has to be faced in creating a panel factory is do you spend a lot of money to tool-up first and create the ability to produce panels and then create the market for panels; or do you create the market before you have the ability to produce the panels? We chose a middle road! We found structures that needed panels, created a system of building the panels at the least tool-up cost, used union bricklayers and worked with union contractors who had the necessary handling equipment. Each panel project created interest and caught the attention of the architects and engineers. These then lead to other projects by other architects who have utilized the panelized concept to answer their needs.

Summary

Our panels have varied in size from six feet wide by twenty-six feet long to four feet wide by twenty-seven feet high and down to four feet by four feet square, all four inches thick, some curved and some straight, from outhouses to skyscrapers. One factor that is best to remember is that each project answered a need. Some of these needs were shortage of bricklayers, speed of erection, winter construction, lower costs by saving construction time, scaffolding, travel cost for labor when project is away from a large city, savings in interest money on construction loans, use of available cranes, year round construction, protected and mechanized factory conditions, short building seasons, intricate patterns normally considered expensive, and horizontal surfaces and other hard to construct shapes.

The number of new projects being designed using panels or projects that should be changed to prefabricated panels is growing rapidly day by day. We are preparing for this interesting, profitable and exciting new construction era and we hope the rest of the brick industry will do likewise.

Acknowledgements

We were helped greatly by many professional members of the Building Industry of Denver. Therefore, the brick manufacturers of Colorado would like to publicly extend to them our sincere gratitude. The are George Hanson of Sallada and Hanson, P. E. for work on Straight Creek Tunnel, Ft. Collins Rest Area, Samsonite panel investigation, construction and testing and others; Mike Lombardi, Architect, for Penn Square Apartments, Denver, Colorado, USA; Robert Morris, Architect, for Samsonite Corporation; George Thorson of Smith and Thorson Architects and Ketchum, Konkel, Ryan and Hastings, Engineers for the United Fund Building, Denver, Colorado; Vic Langhart of Rogers, Nagel and Langhart Architects for Prospect Valley School, Jefferson County, Colorado; Keith Ames, Architect for the Heart of Longmont Rejuvenation Project, Longmont, Colorado; Gil Bonforte of Tippets, Abbett, McCarthy and Stratton Engineers and Adolph Zulian of the Colorado State Highway Department for Straight Creek Tunnel thru Loveland Pass on Interstate 70, Colorado; Russ Jones of J.C.R. Masonry for work on all other outhouses and some of the other projects; and Robert Taylor and Clar Monk of the Structural Clay Products Research Foundation, Geneva, Illinois, USA for their assistance and investigation on the original panels for the United Fund Building, Denver, Colorado, USA.

Index

D

E

F

U-V

W-Z